RECORD Albums 1948-1978

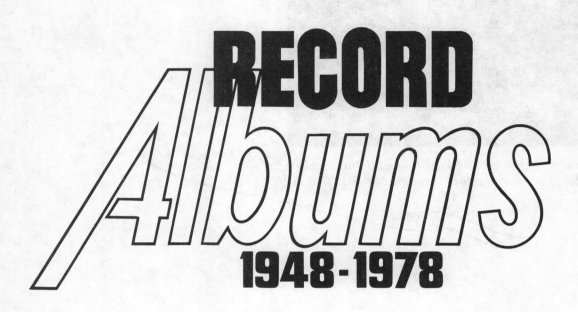

by Jerry Osborne

Bruce Hamilton
Editor

Distributed by

O'SULLIVAN WOODSIDE & CO.
Phoenix, Arizona

This book is dedicated to Skip Rose and Jim Harkey.
Thanks, fellas, for your support through our first five books!

Published in the United States of America

Second Edition.
Second Printing
Manufactured in the United States of America.

ISBN: 0-89019-066-6

Table of Contents

Acknowledgements

This book is the output of Jellyroll Productions, a corporation comprising the combined efforts of author Jerry Osborne, editor Bruce Hamilton, and business manager Victoria Erickson.

This book would not be the masterpiece we feel it is without the incredible dedication, hours of work, and amazing memory and expertise of Tom Koehler. We would like to thank the following people for their suggestions, corrections and additions to this book. We couldn't have done it without their help. There were several people who didn't write their names legibly, or didn't include it at all, who aren't on this list, so we'd like to thank our unknown contributors...only you know who you are!

Alex Aberbon
Jerry Abraham
D. Acker
George A. Barr
Charles Berger
Derek Bill
Frank Black
Rick Bolger
Ski Bowser
Howard Caine
Bob Cattaneo
Stevan Challenger
James Chapman
Tony Colao
Chris Creamer
Robin Cunningham
Geri Anne Dotson
Paul Dowling
Thomas Ebken
Roger Emery
Ed Engel
Warren Erickson
Don R. Fox
Roger Gentile
Sid Goldstein
Bill Griggs
Tanguy Le Guyader
Jim Harkey
John P. Hermes
George Hiatt

Jeff Hobbard
Dave Hummel
Rich Irwin
Mark Jacobs
Wayne M. Jancik
Paul Janscik
Peter A. Jensen
Randall Jones
Les Kasten
Paul A. Kattelman
Tom Kelly
John Kershaw
Rip Lay
Don Lego
Rob Lythall
Leonard Major
Henry Mariano
Harold D. Mathews
Barry Mayor
Jon McAuliffe
Ken McDonald
Mitch McGeary
M.H. McGuiness
Scott McKay
Thomas Meenach III
Lon Melton
Mike Michel
Richard Minor
Scott Moseley
Rory Musil
Nay Nassar

High Nelson
Richard Ochoa
Diane Otis
Terry A. Parkening
Mark Plummer
Gareth Powlowski
Lynn Pulsipher
Vince Redman
Peter Reum
Skip Rose
Mr. Rymarzick
Rick Salierno
Dvoyy Sayers
David Schlosh
Bill Schwartz
Greg Shaw
Jack Shadoian
Ed Smith
Peter Soldat
Steven Swenson
Rick Tello
Gay Triphahn
Michael J. Vaughan
Vince Waldron
Jim Weaver
Dennis W. West
Bob Westfall
Clinton C. Whitmer
Dean Wood
Frank Wright

A Preface and Introduction

By Jerry Osborne and Bruce Hamilton

This is our fifth book and our second update and a significantly improved work. We think we are justly proud of what we've done. The paradox is that this second time around we know even better, and see more clearly where the directions of expansion and perfection are leading us than we envisioned with our first edition.

It is **truly** a monumental, endless task. At times thankless.

With all the experience we've had over a decade and a half in dealing with collectors and collectibles, this record-collecting business is unique. We find authentication and release dates of early works in some cases that we are not absolutely sure were really put out, or merely announced. We have stereo records that are labelled and advertised as such, but are not. We have a solidly established 20-year old item that is worth so much and then have the market killed on it when a warehouse turns up with 10,000 mint copies.

The good part about record collecting—but, conversely, the nemesis of it all, if you want to look at it another way—is the fact that a record isn't basically a throw-away item. People don't buy one, play it once and then pitch it in the trash. Sure, a large number of records **do** get worn out and eventually discarded, but it's a tough decision for people to make. After all, isn't a record always good for at least one more play, if it's unbroken? Rather than throw them away, people would prefer to box them up for a garage sale and let somebody "get some enjoyment out of them." That's good. Makes for great hunting, great collecting, and some gold mine discoveries. But it sure means there's a lot of it out there.

We believe that record collecting actually has the potential to become the largest hobby of its kind in the world. But that, admittedly, is thinking ahead. In any case, it's a good time for buying. Though the hits of the past are the least likely to be valuable collectors items today, and the ones that didn't make it, the rarer, and more expensive, we believe that a person should not let that be a deterrant to what you collect. Collect what you **like**. If you collect what you **like**, and not what's "in," chances are it's because it was **good**. If that sounds like an over simplification, consider: if it was good enough to become a hit the first time around and is a record of only minimal value today, it's only because it sold so **well** the first time around that it's still readily available today. The demand hasn't exceeded the supply. But every year that goes by is one year further away from 1954. And that 1954 hit that sold a million copies back then will grow fewer and fewer in number. **Some**day it could be worth its weight in gold.

This is the main reason why we've listed a lot of albums in this book that are still in print. They are records that we've attached a minimal value to **at this time** because they're in print and can be bought at most record stores. But they're records that, for the most part, will be out-of-print soon and have the potential to be sought-after in years to come. The time to document them is obviously now.

A far more serious problem from our standpoint is the attempt to standardize the spread of value from good or very good to near mint. This is not easy, because most of the experts only think they have clear opinions. We have found that when we put them on the "witness stand," so to speak, their answers aren't so clear after all.

The pattern that has slowly emerged, however, generally is that the older a record is, the wider the spread seems to be between the value of an average, used copy and the ever-elusive mint. Most collectors and all dealers equate values as measured by "mint," even though there may be none in existence. Therein lies the trap and the confusion.

The old 45s and 78s present their own unique problems, which we won't go into here. As to the long play album, it has been in existence roughly thirty years. The collectors of recent records—in this case, ones that we'll label as being from the '70's—tend to be less discriminating than the "serious" collectors of older material. The albums are usually not priced very highly, and the saleability seems to vary more from dealer to dealer. These records are usually in the guide with a spread of twice, or double, from "good" to "near mint."

We've listed the 1960s records with a spread of three times the value, and 1940s and 1950s albums with the spread quadruple. One of our problems has been dating. When we didn't know the date—whether, for instance, a record came out in the 1950s or the 1960s— we didn't know which spread to use. We know there are some cases where we've chosen wrong.

In the case of the major section of Original Casts and Soundtracks, there are an enormous number of releases—especially re-issues, or what we call studio cast recordings—that we can't date. What made this a particularly annoying problem from a price-spread-structure standpoint, was the grouping. If we have twelve records listed under one show heading and we don't know the release date of four, would it be better to have eight correctly structured and guess on the other four, assuming that some would be wrong? Or would it be better to standardize the whole section this time around at the "safe" double spread with the ex-

planation that you should expect to pay more than the listed "near mint" price for a 1950 album if you're able to get one in that condition of that vintage. If the spread is listed as $30 to $60, for instance, you might correctly assume that in reality it might be $20 to $80.

The "trap and confusion" that dealers have lead themselves into is the assumption that "general knowledge" is correct. An example: let us say that a rare 10" LP from 1950 is generally agreed to be worth $50 in mint, according to the experts. We find, when we query the "experts," that you never **see** a mint copy. In fact, because of that, they say, a collector will pay more for a "very good" copy because that is the best condition he'll likely ever find. So the expert says a vg-condition copy is worth $35. He falls prey to the locked-in-to-thinking-in-mint syndrome and prices his vg copy accordingly, even though he has no first-hand experience with mint. We have never seen a collectible in **any** field—not just records—that would command a set price in very good condition because it is unavailable in mint that wouldn't command two or three times as much if it ever did show up in mint.

The bottom line of this is that even though it is "agreed" that the example we've given is a $50 record in mint, the fact that it is a **proven** $35 record in very good, means—invariably—that the agreed mint price is wrong. It would probably go for $70 with no trouble if priced that high set sale. Maybe more. A structure is meaningless when it comes to mint. There are mint collectors who will pay any price to get the condition they seek, even if it's ten times as much. That's why we regret that our sources will so often only give us information on what something is worth in mint, even if they don't really know.

But such is the life of collectors and collecting. And that's also why this good book is only a "guide." All of these abberations-in-thinking are what makes the hobby fun.

Speaking of the 10" albums mentioned earlier, we're particularly desirous to get more input from our friends and fellow collectors on collectible 10 inchers that we don't have listed in this second edition. We're actively soliciting help of any nature that will make the third edition a better and more comprehensive book than the one you're holding.

The time is coming when just more additional information, or listings, is not what we want. No matter how many different price guides we eventually get going in our series, we'll never be able to come close to listing all of the records that have ever been put out. The product of this industry has been absolutely staggering.

At the present time, we're in the process of gathering together the last of the information that's needed for inclusion in our forthcoming **Blues, Rhythm and Blues, and Soul** Price Guide. One of our sources alone, has listed 1,000 pages of blues 78s prior to World War II. For us to list complete discographies of more than the most collectible of the artists that put out material from those early days is unthinkable and would make the cost of our book prohibitive. So, it's clear, we will only list one or two "representative" songs by most artists and leave the reader with the understanding that other 78s of that period are worth approximately the same by the same artists.

By the time the third edition of this book comes off the press, we'll integrate the country albums in our **Country/Western** second edition. The **Rhythm and Blues** guide will have its appropriate albums. This book will, then, become essentially the long play equivalent to our **Pop and Rock** singles book, i.e., a popular and rock album guide, with a special section for Original Casts and Soundtracks.

Another ambitious project that's hopefully going to see presstime in 1979 will be our forthcoming price guide on **Jazz and the Big Bands**. As they say in the salt mines, it's going to be a lot of work, but as with war, famine and pestilence, there will be more price guides, so we figure we might as well be the ones to do it, with the momentum we've already got going. So why not give us a hand? Any listing or input for corrections will be muchly appreciated. Be **sure**, however, to list everything **exactly** as it appears on the record, the exact title, including punctuation, if any, and the complete record number. In the case of particularly rare or valuable items, if a clear, black and white photo is sent us, we'll reimburse the sender up to $2 for a print. We suggest you write us first, before sending any photos, though.

Thanks again, and let us hear from you. We'd like to acknowledge **your** name in our third edition.

Jerry and Bruce

Jellyroll Productions, Inc.
Box 3017
Scottsdale, Arizona 85257

P.S.

Whatever you do, don't forget to send in your name for our next Collector's Directory. A lot of people have been unhappy the second time around to find their names not listed. You **must** send in your name each year to be included in each Directory!

Scarcity, Demand and Grading

The two main ingredients to be considered in determining the asking price of a record, or any collectible, are scarcity and demand. Just because a record is old does not necessarily make it valuable. There *has* to be a demand for it. For the value to continue to rise, the demand must always be greater than the supply. There are a great number of records that, only a few years old, are more in demand and carry a greater value than many old records. All of the so-called "money records" (usually referring to those worth $25.00 and up) are both rare and in demand. The third factor is condition. Once the value of the item has been agreed upon, the only other variable would be its grade. The most accurate grading system and the easiest one to explain and understand is as follows:

M - MINT

MINT means the record must be in perfect condition, like new, showing no signs of wear or usage whatsoever. There can be no compromise with mint by definition. It is quite possible for a record to be unplayed, or just as it came from the factory, and still not be mint. If you have two mint records, but can tell a slight difference between the two, one is not mint. It should be more accurately graded "near mint." It is for this reason that the term "near mint" appears as the highest grade listed. We have never known a collector who wouldn't accept something slightly less than perfect (near mint) to fill a hole in his want list. Though the playing surface is the most important consideration, label defects—such as stickers, writing, rubbing, fading, or warping and wrinkling—will detract from its value. If a record is, indeed, perfect in every way, it will bring somewhat more than the near mint listing.

VG - VERY GOOD

This is the halfway mark between good and near mint. A very good record has been played and you can tell it, but it shouldn't bother you. The disc should have only a minimum amount of foreign, or surface noise and it should not detract at all from the recorded sound. A VG record may show some label wear, but as with the audio, it would be minimal. Most collectors will accept a very good record, *if* it is priced accordingly. A synonym: fine.

G - GOOD

The most misunderstood of all grades. No dealer likes to sell a record for a half to a fourth the near mint price, but most collectors won't *pay* more than that unless the condition is misrepresented to them. It's important that we get standardized once and for all on these terms. Good should not mean bad! A record in good condition will show signs of wear, an audible amount of foreign noises. There may be scratches and it may be obvious it was never properly cared for (such as being stacked with other records not in sleeves). Nevertheless, it still plays "good" enough to enjoy, and may still bring a high price. Many of the bargains you'll run across in thrift and junk stores will fall into the "good" category.

F - FAIR

Fair is the beginning of bad. A fair record will play all the way through without skips, but will contain a distracting amount of noises and will not be a pleasure to listen to. It may suffice until a better copy comes along, but it shouldn't sell for more than half a good-conditioned copy.

P - POOR

Stepped on by an elephant and it sells for peanuts.

The more this system is used, the more widespread the satisfaction between buyers and sellers. More and more, dealers are subscribing to it, but, regardless, all will define their standards when you receive a list from them. When you receive orders from them, then *you'll* be able to define *their* standards. Various meaningless terms, synonyms, for mint, that you'll find: pristine mint, stone mint, store stock, virgin, new.

The *very* specific dealer—or more commonly, the collector-dealer—will use a plus (+) or a minus (-) at times to indicate that a grade is just slightly better or worse than a certain grade.

All reputable dealers offer a money-back guarantee if the record is not in the condition described.

Glossary of Terms

ALBUM—See **LONG PLAY ALBUM.**

BLUEGRASS—A steady, driving country rhythm with emphasis on the banjo and fiddles. Bluegrass may be performed with or without vocal and is invariably upbeat. Notable artists in this field include: Bill Monroe, Flatt & Scruggs, Mac Wiseman and the Osborne Bros.

BLUES—A song of lament, trouble or low spirits. The blues originated among Blacks and is usually performed in a slow rhythm. The Father of the Blues, W.C. Handy, describes it this way, "The Blues began with Blacks, it involves our history, where we came from and what we experienced. The Blues came from the man farthest down, from want and desire."

BOOTLEG—A Bootleg (Boot) is any unauthorized issuance of previously unreleased material. Also see **REPRODUCTION.**

BOX SET—Custom, box-style holder for two or more discs.

C&W—See **COUNTRY & WESTERN MUSIC.**

COLORED PLASTIC—Colored plastic, or wax, records which have the playing surface of the disc made of some color other than black, usually red, green, blue or gold.

COUNTRY & WESTERN MUSIC—Through the years Country & Western has become the label applied to both Country music and Western music—meaning either or both. In recent years these two art forms are almost exclusively refered to as "Country Music."

COUNTRY MUSIC—Quite simply, Country Music is the music of the American people—their down-to-earth struggles, accomplishments and attempts to get by as best they can. Country Music deals with the cold, hard facts of life.

DISCO—A product of last few years designed to give the disco music clubs an endless supply of funky, dancin' music. Basically soul music with a hard, driving beat.

DJ (DISC JOCKEY) COPY—See **PROMOTIONAL COPY.**

DOO WOP—A fiftie's-style Rhythm & Blues group sound. Mainly a product of the Black groups. Can be either a ballad or a fast-paced song. A bass man delivering such nonsensical lyrics as "Bom bom, doo wop, diddy wah wah" and a wailing high voice are essential "doo wop" ingredients.

DOUBLE POCKET—Special jacket made to hold two LP's. Usually opens up book style. Although less common, some triple pockets have been issued.

EP—See **EXTENDED PLAY.**

EXTENDED PLAY—The Extended Play (EP) is a seven inch 45 rpm disc containg four or more songs. Usually 45 rpm, but many were made at 33 1/3 and some in stereo, accompanied by album-type cardboard jacket. Very few EP's were made in 1965.

FOLK—The music of the "Folk" expressing a message. History set to music—from the early revolutionary songs to the 19th century tunes about either slavery or the westward movement right up to this century's folk songs about good times, bad times, hootnannies, political unrest and mans desire for freedom.

GOSPEL—The expression of worship through song—usually performed by a group of four or five members. These "Quartets" were noted for their fine tenor and bass singers.

GROUP SOUND—Basically any vocal group with a rhythm & blues sound. Normally, but not limited to, a Black group, from the 50's, with a "doo wop" sound.

JACKET—The heavy cardboard-type sleeve that LP's and EP's are sold in.

JAZZ—A southern (New Orleans) music form, based on blues chords, that has also included some ragtime, boogie-woogie and big band jazz.

LONG PLAY ALBUM—The long play album (LP) is a twelve inch disc containing from twelve to thirty minutes per side. Not to be confused with the binder-type folders that contained several singles (45 or 78). At the time these were also called albums thus the term long play was introduced to describe the twelve inch album as we now know it.

LP—See **LONG PLAY ALBUM.**

ORIGINAL CAST—The music from the "Broadway" stage production of a play.

PICTURE SLEEVE—Picture sleeve or picture cover for singles—usually offering a photo of the artist.

PROMOTIONAL COPY—A copy of a record specifically issued for radio station air play. Normally identified as such and marked "Not for Sale."

PUNK ROCK—Unlike some of the spring-off forms of pop music that are easily understood by their name, such as Surf, Hot Rod and British music, Punk Rock does require some explanation. Though not so named at the time, the music of a great number of white, American groups of the mid-to-late-sixties is now known as Punk Rock. Many of these groups emerged with a noteworthy British influence in their music. Some of the more successful of these were: The Kingsmen, Paul Revere & The Raiders, Standells, Seeds and the Leaves.

R&B—See **RHYTHM & BLUES.**

R&R—See **ROCK & ROLL.**

RECORD GRADING—See page 3 for complete explanation of proper record grading.

REISSUE—The later issue of a previously available item. Not necessarily reissued by the same label that had the original.

REPACKAGE—The rerelease of an item utilizing more timely merchandising techniques such as a new jacket, updated photos, etc., occasionally combined with other material in a double pocket set.

REPRODUCTION—Although unauthorized, like a bootleg, the reproduction is a duplication of the original record, often reproducing the original label with suprising exactness. Some reproductions have the date or some indication of its reproduction on the disc. This prevents the reproduction from being passed off as an original.

RHYTHM & BLUES—From the urbanization of the Blues in the late 40's by solo acts like Fats Domino, Joe Turner, Ray Charles, a market evolved for the Black vocal group. The Colvers, Drifters, Midnighters and thousands of others gave us a sound that became known as Rhythm & Blues. Essentially these groups added Rhythm to the Blues.

ROCKABILLY—A particular music form utilizing an upbeat country/rock sound by a White, Southern-sounding, solo male singer. Other important rockabilly ingredients are a rockin' lead guitar, slappin' bass fiddle and some piano, depending on the overall arrangement. Male backup vocals are generally undesirable, but female voices are a no-no! Rockabilly, in it's purest form, can be heard on many of the recordings made by Elvis on the *Sun* label.

ROCK & ROLL—This is the hit music of the fifties—though not limited to the fifties as far as recording and release dates—but instead, the sound of the fifties. Best represented by such hits as "Shake, Rattle & Roll," "Rock & Roll is Here to Stay," "At the Hop" and "Buzz, Buzz, Buzz."

ROCK MUSIC—"Pop" music has worn such labels as "Tin Pan Alley," "The Hit Parade," "Top 40" and "Rock & Roll." During the mid-sixties this mainstream of popular, best sellers became known as "Rock" music and carries that label to the present.

SACRED—Music of faith and inspiration.

SEALED—Meaning the shrink-wrap (cellophane) covering the album jacket has not been removed or broken.

SINGLE—Either a 45 or 78 rpm featuring one song on each side.

SOUNDTRACK—Music taken directly from the audio track of a motion picture.

WESTERN MUSIC—This is the music of the West or the move to the West—from Jimmie Rodger's railroad songs and "Goin' to California," Gene Autry's "Back in the Saddle Again" to the story of the plight of a young Texas cowboy from "El Paso." The songs & stories of the West, the prairies, the "Tumbling Tumbleweeds" and the "Cool Water."

TITLE	LABEL & NO.	GOOD	VERY GOOD	NEAR MINT
ABBA				
ALBUM	Atlantic (S) SD 19164	2.00	3.00	4.00
ARRIVAL	Atlantic (S) SD 18207	2.50	3.75	5.00
GREATEST HITS	Atlantic (S) SD 18189	2.50	3.75	5.00
ABBA	Atlantic (S) SD 18146	2.50	3.75	5.00
WATERLOO	Atlantic (S) SD 18101	3.00	4.50	6.00
ABDNOR, John Howard, Involvement				
INTRO TO CHANGE	Abnak (S) ABST 2072	3.00	4.50	6.00
A.B. SKHY				
A.B. SKHY	MGM (S) SE 4628	2.50	3.75	5.00
RAMBLIN ON	MGM (S) SE 4676	2.50	3.75	5.00
ABSTRACTS				
ABSTRACTS, THE	Pompeii (S) SD6002	3.00	4.50	6.00
ACE				
FIVE-A-SIDE	Anchor (S) 2001	3.00	4.50	6.00
TIME FOR ANOTHER	Anchor (S) 2013	3.00	4.50	6.00
ACE, Johnny				
JOHNNY ACE	Duke (EP) 80	5.00	12.50	20.00
JOHNNY ACE	Duke (EP) 81	5.00	12.50	20.00
JOHNNY ACE MEMORIAL ALBUM	Duke (M) DLP 71	8.00	20.00	32.00
JOHNNY ACE MEMORIAL ALBUM	Duke (S) X-71	4.00	6.00	8.00
ACKLIN, Barbara				
LOVE MAKES A WOMAN	Brunswick (S) BL 754137	3.50	5.25	7.00
PLACE IN THE SUN	Capitol (S) ST-11377	2.50	3.75	5.00
ACUFF, Roy Jr.				
BEST OF ROY ACUFF	Capitol (M) T 1870	2.50	3.75	5.00
BEST OF ROY ACUFF	Capitol (S) ST 1870	2.50	3.75	5.00
CALIFORNIA LADY	Hickory (S) H3G-4514	2.00	3.00	4.00
FAVORITE HYMNS	MGM (M) E 3707	2.50	3.75	5.00
GREAT ROY ACUFF	Capitol (M) T-2103	2.00	3.00	4.00
GREAT ROY ACUFF	Capitol (S) ST-2103	2.00	3.00	4.00
HYMN TIME	MGM (S) SE-4044	2.00	3.00	4.00
REVIVAL TIME	Columbia (EP) H-1514	1.00	1.50	2.00
ROY ACUFF	Columbia (EP) B-2825	1.00	1.50	2.00
SONGS OF THE SMOKY MOUNTAINS	Capitol (M) 617	4.00	6.00	8.00
SONGS OF THE SMOKY MOUNTAINS	Capitol (EP) EAP 1-617	1.00	2.00	3.00
SONGS OF THE SMOKY MOUNTAINS	Capitol (EP) EAP 2-617	1.00	2.00	3.00
SONGS OF THE SMOKY MOUNTAINS	Capitol (EP) EAP 3-617	1.00	2.00	3.00
VOICE OF COUNTRY MUSIC	Capitol (M) T 2276	2.00	3.00	4.00
VOICE OF COUNTRY MUSIC	Capitol (S) ST 2276	2.00	3.00	4.00
ADAMS, Don				
GET SMART	United Artists (M) 3533	3.00	6.00	9.00
GET SMART	United Artists (M) 6533	4.00	8.00	12.00
ON HIS WAY	Atlantic (S) 7280	2.50	3.75	5.00
ADAMS, Edie				
MUSIC TO LISTEN TO RECORDS TO	MGM (M) E-3751	2.50	5.00	7.50
MUSIC TO LISTEN TO RECORDS TO	MGM (S) SE-3751	3.00	6.00	9.00
ADAMS, Faye				
SHAKE A HAND	Warwick (M) 2031	8.00	20.00	32.00
ADAMS, Johnny				
HEART AND SOUL	SSS (S) 5	2.50	3.75	5.00
ADAMS, Mike & The Red Jackets				
SURFERS BEAT	Crown (S) CST 312	3.00	6.00	9.00
ADDRISI BROTHERS				
WE'VE GOT TO GET IT ON AGAIN	Columbia (S) KC 31296	2.50	3.75	5.00
ADRIAN & THE SUNSETS				
BREAKTHROUGH	Sunset (M) SE 63-601	6.00	12.00	18.00
AEROSMITH				
AEROSMITH	Columbia (S) KC-32005	3.00	4.50	6.00
DRAW THE LINE	Columbia (S) JC 34856	2.00	3.00	4.00
GET YOUR WINGS	Columbia (S) KC-32847	2.50	3.75	5.00
GET YOUR WINGS	Columbia (Q) KCQ-32847	2.50	3.75	5.00
ROCKS	Columbia (S) 34165	2.00	3.00	4.00
TOYS IN THE ATTIC	Columbia (S) PC-33479	2.50	3.75	5.00
TOYS IN THE ATTIC	Columbia (Q) PCQ-33479	2.50	3.75	5.00

(M) Mono (S) Stereo (EP) Extended Play (Q) Quad (RI) Re-issued

TITLE	LABEL & NO.	GOOD	VERY GOOD	NEAR MINT
AESOPS FABLES				
IN DUE TIME	Cadet Concept (S) LPS 323	3.50	5.25	7.00
AFDEM, Jeff & The Springfield Flute				
JEFF AFDEM AND THE SPRINGFIELD FLUTE	Burdette (S) ST 5162	2.50	3.75	5..00
AFFINITY				
AFFINITY	Paramount (S) PAS 5027	2.50	3.75	5.00
AFO EXECUTIVES With Tami Lynn				
A COMPENDIUM	AFO (M) LP 0002	8.00	20.00	32.00

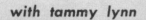

TITLE	LABEL & NO.	GOOD	VERY GOOD	NEAR MINT
AFTERGLOW				
AFTERGLOW	MTA (M) 5010	6.00	9.00	12.00
AJAYE, Franklin				
COMEDIAN	A&M (S) 4405	2.50	3.75	5.00
I'M A COMEDIAN, SERIOUSLY	A&M (S) 3642	3.00	4.50	6.00
AKENS, Jewel				
BIRDS & THE BEES	ERA (M) EL-110	2.00	4.00	6.00
BIRDS & THE BEES	ERA (S) ES-110	3.00	6.00	9.00
ALAIMO, Steve				
EVERY DAY I HAVE TO CRY	Checker (M) LP 2986	3.00	6.00	9.00
MASHED POTATOES	Checker (M) LP 2983	3.00	6.00	9.00
STARRING STEVE ALAIMO	ABC/Paramount (M) ABC 501	2.00	4.00	6.00
STARRING STEVE ALAIMO	ABC/Paramount (S) ABCS 501	3.00	6.00	9.00
STEVE ALAIMO	Crown (M) CLP 5382	3.00	4.50	6.00
STEVE ALAIMO	Checker (EP) 5135	3.00	6.00	9.00
STEVE ALAIMO SINGS AND SWINGS	ABC/Paramount (M) ABC 551	2.00	4.00	6.00
STEVE ALAIMO SINGS AND SWINGS	ABC/Paramount (S) ABCS 551	3.00	6.00	9.00
TWIST WITH STEVE ALAIMO	Checker (M) LP 2981	3.00	6.00	9.00
WHERE THE ACTION IS	ABC/Paramount (M) ABC 531	3.00	6.00	9.00
WHERE THE ACTION IS	ABC/Paramount (S) ABCS 531	4.00	8.00	12.00
ALAN, Buddy				
CHAINS/ANOTHER SATURDAY NIGHT	Capitol (S) ST-11400	2.00	3.00	4.00
ALBERGHETTI, Anna Maria				
SONGS BY ANNA MARIA ALBERGHETTI	Wing (M) MGW-12135	3.00	6.00	9.00
ALBERT, Eddie				
HIGH UPON A MOUNTAIN	Dot (M) DLP 3109	2.50	3.75	5.00
NINA, PINTA & THE SANTA MARIA (WITH JOHNNY GILBERT)	Dot (M) DLP 9009	2.50	5.00	7.50
NINA, PINTA & THE SANTA MARIA (WITH JOHNNY GILBERT)	Dot (S) DLP 29009	3.00	6.00	9.00
OH, WHAT A BEAUTIFUL MORNIN	Hamilton (S) H-12103	2.50	3.75	5.00
ALBERT, Morris				
FEELINGS	RCA (S) APL1-1018	3.50	5.25	7.00

STEVE ALAIMO

TITLE	LABEL & NO.	GOOD	VERY GOOD	NEAR MINT
ALBERTS, Al				
MAN HAS GOT TO SING	Coral (M) CRL-57259	2.00	3.00	4.00
MAN HAS GOT TO SING	Coral (S) CRL-757259	2.00	3.00	4.00
ALBRIGHT, Lola				
DREAMSVILLE	Columbia (M) CL-1327	2.00	4.00	6.00
DREAMSVILLE	Columbia (S) CS-8133	3.00	6.00	9.00
DREAMSVILLE	Columbia (EP) B-13271	1.50	3.00	4.50
ALEONG, Aki & The Nobles				
COME SURF WITH ME	Vee Jay (M) LP 1060	3.00	4.50	6.00
ALESSI				
ALESSI	A&M (S) SP 4608	2.00	3.00	4.00
ALL FOR A REASON	A&M (S) SP 4657	2.00	3.00	4.00
ALEXANDER, Arthur				
YOU BETTER MOVE ON	Dot (M) DLP-3434	3.00	6.00	9.00
YOU BETTER MOVE ON	Dot (S) DLP-25434	4.00	8.00	12.00
ALEXANDER, Gordon				
GORDON'S BUSTER	Columbia (S) CS 9693	4.00	6.00	8.00
ALEXANDER, Jeff				
TAKIN' IT EASY	FH (M) 102	3.50	4.25	7.00
NAPPIN'	FH (M) 104	3.50	4.25	7.00
ALEXANDERS TIMELESS BLOOZBAND				
ALEXANDERS TIMELESS BLOOZBAND	Smack (M) 1001	5.00	7.50	10.00
FOR SALE	UNI (S) 73021	3.00	4.50	6.00
ALICE COOPER				
ALICE COOPER'S GREATEST HITS	Warner Bros. (S) BS 2803	3.00	4.50	6.00
BILLION DOLLAR BABIES	Warner Bros. (S) BS 2685	2.50	3.75	5.00
BILLION DOLLAR BABIES	Warner Bros. (Q) BS4-2685	2.50	3.75	5.00
KILLER	Warner Bros. (S) BS 2567	3.00	4.50	6.00
LOVE IT TO DEATH	Warner Bros. (S) WS 1883	3.50	5.25	7.00
MUSCLE OF LOVE	Warner Bros. (S) BS 2748	2.50	3.75	5.00
PRETTIES FOR YOU	Straight (S) STS1051	4.00	6.00	8.00
RAPED AND FREEZIN'	Warner Brothers (EP) 208	3.00	4.50	6.00
SCHOOL'S OUT	Warner Bros. (S) BS 2623	3.00	4.50	6.00
WELCOME TO MY NIGHTMARE	Atlantic (S) 18130	3.00	4.50	6.00
ALIVE 'N KICKIN'				
ALIVE N' KICKIN'	Roulette (S) SR 42052	2.00	4.50	6.00
ALL STARS				
BOOGIE WOOGIE	Gramophone (M) 20192	9.00	21.50	36.00
ALLAN, Johnnie				
DEDICATED TO YOU	Jin (M) 9006	4.50	7.00	9.00
JOHNNIE ALLAN SINGS	Jin (M) 9002	4.50	7.00	9.00
SOUTH TO LOUISIANNA AND OTHER HITS	Jin (M) 4001	4.50	9.00	13.50
SOUTH TO LOUISIANA AND OTHER HITS	Jin (S) LP 4001	4.00	6.00	8.00
ALLEN, Bernie & His Stereo Mad Men				
MUSICALLY MAD	RCA (S) LSP 1929	6.00	15.00	24.00

(M) Mono   (S) Stereo   (EP) Extended Play   (Q) Quad   (RI) Re-issued

TITLE	LABEL & NO.	GOOD	VERY GOOD	NEAR MINT
ALLEN, Dave				
COLOR BLIND	International Artists (M) 1A LP 11	8.00	20.00	32.00
ALLEN, Davie & The Arrows				
APACHE '65	Tower (M) T 5002	5.00	7.50	10.00
APACHE '65	Tower (S) DT 5002	6.00	9.00	12.00
BLUES THEME	Tower (M) T 5078	4.00	6.00	8.00
BLUES THEME	Tower (S) DT 5078	5.00	7.50	10.00
THE CYCLE-DELIC SOUNDS OF DAVIE ALLAN AND THE ARROWS	Tower (M) T 5094	4.00	6.00	8.00
THE CYCLE-DELIC SOUNDS OF DAVIE ALLAN AND THE ARROWS	Tower (S) DT 5094	5.00	7.50	10.00
ALLEN, Lee				
WALKIN' WITH MR. LEE (1st Pressing, red)	Ember (M) ELP 200	11.00	27.50	44.00
WALKIN' WITH MR. LEE (2nd Pressing, black)	Ember (M) ELP 200	5.00	12.50	20.00
WALKIN' WITH MR. LEE	Ember (EP) 103	4.00	10.00	16.00
ALLEN, Peter				
CONTINENTAL AMERICAN	A&M (S) SP 3643	2.00	3.00	4.00
TAUGHT BY EXPERTS	A&M (S) SP 4584	2.00	3.00	4.00
ALLEN, Ray & The Upbeats				
TRIBUTE TO 6	Blast (M) BLP 6804	9.00	22.50	36.00
ALLEN, Rex				
ALLEN SINGS	Mercury (EP) 1-3209	1.00	1.50	2.00
ALLEN SINGS	Mercury (EP) 1-3111	1.00	1.50	2.00
ALLEN SINGS	Mercury (EP) 1-3113	1.00	1.50	2.00
FAITH OF A MAN	Mercury (M) MG-20719	2.00	3.00	4.00
FAITH OF A MAN	Mercury (S) SR-60719	2.00	3.00	4.00
MISTER COWBOY	Decca (S) DL-78776	2.50	3.75	5.00
PATTI PAGE AND REX SING	Mercury (EP) 1-3114	1.00	1.50	2.00
REX ALLEN SINGS & TELLS TALES	Mercury (M) MG-20752	2.00	3.00	4.00
REX ALLEN SINGS & TELLS TALES	Mercury (S) SR-60752	2.00	3.00	4.00
SAY ONE FOR ME	Vista (M) BV 1302	2.00	3.00	4.00
SMOOTH COUNTRY SOUND OF REX ALLEN	Decca (M) 5011	2.50	3.75	5.00
SMOOTH COUNTRY SOUND OF REX ALLEN	Decca (S) 75011	2.50	3.75	5.00
SONG TALES	Mercury (EP) 1-3193	1.00	1.50	2.00
WESTERN STYLE	Mercury (EP) EP1-3198	1.00	1.50	2.00
WESTWARD HO THE WAGONS	Decca (EP) ED-2448	1.00	1.50	2.00
ALLEN, Rex, Jr.				
ANOTHER GOODBYE SONG	Warner Bros. (S) BS-2821	2.00	3.00	4.00
ALLEN, Richie & The Pacific Surfers				
RISING SURF, THE	Imperial (M) LP 9229	3.00	4.50	6.00
SURFERS SLIDE	Imperial (M) LP 9243	3.00	4.50	6.00
ALLEN, Steve				
GREAT RAGTIME HITS	Dot (M) DLP 3560	2.00	3.00	4.00
GREAT RAGTIME HITS	Dot (S) DLP 25560	2.00	3.00	4.00
SONGS FROM THE STEVE ALLEN TV SHOW	Dot (M) DLP 3587	2.00	3.00	4.00
SONGS FROM THE STEVE ALLEN TV SHOW	Dot (S) DLP 25587	2.00	3.00	4.00
STEVE ALLEN, MORE FUNNY FONE CALLS	Dot (M) DLP-3517	3.00	4.50	6.00
STEVE ALLEN PLAYS BOSSA NOVA JAZZ	Dot (M) DLP-3480	2.00	3.00	4.00
STEVE ALLEN PLAYS BOSSA NOVA JAZZ	Dot (S) DLP-25480	2.00	3.00	4.00
STEVE ALLEN PLAYS THE PIANO GREATS	Dot (M) DLP-3519	2.00	3.00	4.00
STEVE ALLEN PLAYS THE PIANO GREATS	Dot (S) DLP-25519	2.00	3.00	4.00
STEVE ALLEN PRESENTS 12 GOLDEN HITS	Dot (M) DLP-3473	2.00	3.00	4.00
STEVE ALLEN PRESENTS 12 GOLDEN HITS	Dot (S) DLP-25473	2.00	3.00	4.00
STEVE ALLEN'S FUNNY FONE CALLS	Dot (M) DLP-3472	3.00	4.50	6.00
STEVE ALLEN SINGS	Dot (M) DLP 3530	2.00	3.00	4.00
STEVE ALLEN SINGS	Dot (S) DLP-25530	2.00	3.00	4.00
ALLEN, Tony & The Night Owls				
ROCK AND ROLL WITH TONY ALLEN AND THE NIGHT OWLS	Crown (M) CLP 5231	8.00	20.00	32.00
ALLEN, Woody				
NIGHT CLUB YEARS 1964-1968	United Artists (S) 9968	3.00	4.50	6.00
STAND UP COMIC 1964-1968	United Artists (S) UA-LA849	2.50	3.75	5.00
THIRD WOODY ALLEN ALBUM	Capitol (S) ST-2986	3.00	4.50	6.00
WONDERFUL WACKY WORLD	Bell (S) 6008	5.00	10.00	15.00
WOODY ALLEN	Colpix (M) CP-488	5.00	10.00	15.00
WOODY ALLEN	Colpix (S) SCP-488, black	6.00	12.00	18.00
WOODY ALLEN	Colpix (M) CP-518	5.00	10.00	15.00
WOODY ALLEN	Colpix (S) SCP-518	6.00	12.00	18.00
ALLISON, Fran				
KUKLA, FRAN & OLLIE	Camden (S) 2582	2.50	3.75	5.00
ALLISON, Gene				
GENE ALLISON	Vee Jay (M) LP 1009	6.00	15.00	24.00
ALLISON, Keith				
IN ACTION	Columbia (M) CL 2641	5.00	10.00	15.00
IN ACTION	Columbia (S) CS 9441	6.00	12.00	18.00

2

ALLISON, Luther

TITLE	LABEL & NO.	GOOD	VERY GOOD	NEAR MINT
BAD NEWS IS COMING	Gordy (S) 964	3.00	4.50	6.00
LUTHER'S BLUES	Gordy (S) 967	3.00	4.50	6.00

ALLMAN BROTHERS BAND

TITLE	LABEL & NO.	GOOD	VERY GOOD	NEAR MINT
ALLMAN BROTHERS BAND AT FILLMORE EAST	Capricorn (S) SD2-802	8.00	12.00	16.00
ALLMAN BROHERS BAND AT FILLMORE EAST	Capricorn (S) 2CX-0131	5.00	7.50	10.00
ALLMAN BROTHERS BAND AT FILLMORE EAST	Capricorn (Q) CX4-0131	4.00	6.00	8.00
ALLMAN BROTHERS, THE	Atco (M) SD 33-308	7.00	10.50	14.00
BEGINNINGS	Capricorn (S) 2CX-0132	5.00	7.50	10.00
BEGINNINGS	Atco (S) SD2-805	8.00	12.00	16.00
BROTHERS & SISTERS	Capricorn (S) CP 0111	4.00	6.00	8.00
EAT A PEACH	Capricorn (S) 2CP-0102	5.00	7.50	10.00
EAT A PEACH	Capricorn (Q) 2S4-0102	4.00	6.00	8.00
FANTASTIC ALLMAN BROTHERS ORIGINAL HITS	K-Tel (M) NI-471	4.00	6.00	8.00
IDLEWILD SOUTH	Atco (S) SD 33-342	7.00	10.50	14.00
ROAD GOES ON FOREVER	Capricorn (S) 2CP-0164	4.00	6.00	8.00
WIN, LOSE OR DRAW	Capricorn (S) CP 0156	3.50	5.25	7.00
WIPE THE WINDOWS, CHECK THE OIL, DOLLAR GAS	Capricorn (S) 2CX-0177	4.00	6.00	8.00

Also see HOUR GLASS

ALLMAN, Duane & Gregg

TITLE	LABEL & NO.	GOOD	VERY GOOD	NEAR MINT
DUANE AND GREGG ALLMAN	Bold (M) 33 301	5.00	7.50	10.00

ALLMAN, Gregg

TITLE	LABEL & NO.	GOOD	VERY GOOD	NEAR MINT
GREGG ALLMAN TOUR	Capricorn (S) 2CP-0141	4.00	6.00	8.00
LAID BACK	Capricorn (S) CP 0116	4.50	6.75	9.00
PLAYIN' UP A STORM	Capricorn (S) CP 0181	3.00	4.50	6.00

ALLMAN, Sheldon

TITLE	LABEL & NO.	GOOD	VERY GOOD	NEAR MINT
SING ALONG WITH DRAC	Del Fi (S) DFST 1213	6.00	12.00	18.00

ALLSUP, Tommy

TITLE	LABEL & NO.	GOOD	VERY GOOD	NEAR MINT
BUDDY HOLLY SONG BOOK, THE	Reprise (S) RS 6182	5.00	10.00	15.00

ALPERT, Herb

TITLE	LABEL & NO.	GOOD	VERY GOOD	NEAR MINT
HERB ALPERT/HUGH MASEKELA (And Hugh Masekela)	Horizon (S) SP 728	2.00	3.00	4.00
JUST YOU AND ME	A&M (S) SP 4591	2.00	3.00	4.00

ALPERT, Herb, & The Tiajuana Brass

TITLE	LABEL & NO.	GOOD	VERY GOOD	NEAR MINT
BEAT OF THE BRASS	A&M (S) SP 4146	2.00	3.00	4.00
BRASS ARE COMIN'	A&M (S) SP 4228	2.50	3.75	5.00
CONEY ISLAND	A&M (S) SP 4521	2.00	3.00	4.00
GOING PLACES	A&M (M) LP 112	3.00	4.50	6.00
GOING PLACES	A&M (S) SP 4112	2.00	3.00	4.00
GREATEST HITS	A&M (S) SP 4245	2.50	3.75	5.00
GREATEST HITS	A&M (Q) QU 54245	3.00	4.50	6.00
GREATEST HITS VOLUME II	A&M (S) SP 4627	2.00	3.00	4.00
HERB ALPERT & THE TIAJUANA BRASS FOUR SIDER	A&M (S) SP 3521	2.50	3.75	5.00
HERB ALPERT'S NINTH	A&M (M) LP 134	2.50	3.75	5.00
HERB ALPERT'S NINTH	A&M (S) SP 4134	3.00	4.50	6.00
HERB ALPERT'S TIAJUANA BRASS, Vol. 2	A&M (M) LP 103	3.00	6.00	9.00
HERB ALPERT'S TIAJUANA BRASS, Vol. 2	A&M (S) SP 103	4.00	8.00	12.00
LONELY BULL	A&M (M) LP 101	3.00	6.00	9.00
LONELY BULL (Orig.)	A&M (S) SP 101	4.00	8.00	12.00
SOLID BRASS	A&M (S) SP 4341	2.00	3.00	4.00
SOUNDS LIKE	A&M (M) LP 124	2.50	3.75	5.00
SOUNDS LIKE	A&M (S) SP 4124	3.00	4.50	6.00
SOUTH OF THE BORDER	A&M (M) LP 108	2.50	5.00	7.50
SOUTH OF THE BORDER	A&M (S) SP 108	3.00	6.00	9.00
SUMMERTIME	A&M (S) SP 4314	2.50	3.75	5.00
WARM	A&M (S) SP 4190	2.50	3.75	5.00
WHAT NOW MY LOVE	A&M (M) LP 114	3.00	4.50	6.00
WHAT NOW MY LOVE	A&M (S) SP 4114	2.00	3.00	4.00
WHIPPED CREAM & OTHER DELIGHTS	A&M (M) LP 110	3.00	4.50	6.00
WHIPPED CREAM & OTHER DELIGHTS	A&M (S) SP 4110	2.00	3.00	4.00
WHIPPED CREAM & OTHER DELIGHTS	A&M (Q) QU 54110	3.00	4.50	6.00
YOU SMILE—THE SONG BEGINS	A&M (S) SP 3620	2.00	3.00	4.00

AMAZING BLONDEL

TITLE	LABEL & NO.	GOOD	VERY GOOD	NEAR MINT
EVENSONG	Island (S) SMAS 9302	3.00	4.50	6.00
FANTASIA LINDUM	Island (S) SW 9310	3.00	4.50	6.00

AMAZING RHYTHM ACES

TITLE	LABEL & NO.	GOOD	VERY GOOD	NEAR MINT
BURNING THE BALLROOM DOWN	ABC (S) 1063	2.00	3.00	4.00
STACKED DECK	ABC (S) 913	2.50	3.75	5.00
TOO STUFFED TO JUMP	ABC (S) 940	2.00	3.00	4.00
YOU CAN DO IT TOO	ABC (S) 1005	2.00	3.00	4.00

AMBASSADORS

TITLE	LABEL & NO.	GOOD	VERY GOOD	NEAR MINT
SOUL SUMMIT	Arctic (M) ALPS 1005	4.00	6.00	8.00

AMBOY DUKES

TITLE	LABEL & NO.	GOOD	VERY GOOD	NEAR MINT
AMBOY DUKES, THE	Mainstream (M) 56104	4.00	6.00	8.00
AMBOY DUKES, THE	Mainstream (S) 6104	5.00	7.50	10.00

(M) Mono   (S) Stereo   (EP) Extended Play   (Q) Quad   (RI) Re-issued

---

TITLE	LABEL & NO.	GOOD	VERY GOOD	NEAR MINT
BEST OF THE ORIGINAL AMBOY DUKES, THE	Mainstream (S) 6125	4.00	6.00	8.00
JOURNEYS AND MIGRATIONS	Mainstream (S) 801	5.00	7.50	10.00
JOURNEY TO THE CENTER OF THE MIND	Mainstream (S) 6112	4.00	6.00	8.00
MARRIAGE OF THE ROCKS/ROCK BOTTOM	Polydor (S) 24-4012	4.00	6.00	8.00
MIGRATION	Mainstream (S) 6118	4.00	6.00	8.00
SURVIVAL OF THE FITTEST/LIVE	Polydor (S) 24-4035	4.00	6.00	8.00
(Listed as "Ted Nugent & The Amboy Dukes")				
TOOTH FANG & CLAW	DiscReet (S) 2203	3.50	5.25	7.00

Also see TED NUGENT

AMBROSE, Amanda

TITLE	LABEL & NO.	GOOD	VERY GOOD	NEAR MINT
AMANDA	Dunwich (M) 668	3.00	4.50	6.00
AMANDA	Dunwich (S) S 668	4.00	6.00	8.00

AMECHE, Don and Frances Langford

TITLE	LABEL & NO.	GOOD	VERY GOOD	NEAR MINT
BICKERSONS, THE	Columbia (M) CL-1692	3.00	4.50	6.00
BICKERSONS, THE	Columbia (S) CS-8692	3.00	4.50	6.00
BICKERSONS FIGHT BACK	Columbia (M) CL-1883	3.00	4.50	6.00
BICKERSONS FIGHT BACK	Columbia (S) CS-8683	3.00	4.50	6.00

AMERICA

TITLE	LABEL & NO.	GOOD	VERY GOOD	NEAR MINT
AMERICA	Warner Bros. (S) B-2576	3.50	5.25	7.00
HAT TRICK	Warner Bros. (S) B-2728	3.00	4.50	6.00
HEARTS	Warner Bros. (S) B-2852	2.50	3.75	5.00
HEARTS	Warner Bros. (Q) BS4-2852	2.50	3.75	5.00
HISTORY (AMERICA'S GREATEST HITS)	Warner Bros. (S) B-2894	2.50	3.75	5.00
HOLIDAY	Warner Bros. (S) W 2808	2.50	3.75	5.00
HOLIDAY	Warner Bros. (Q) W4-2808	2.50	3.75	5.00
HOMECOMING	Warner Bros. (S) B-2655	3.00	4.50	6.00

AMERICAN BLUES

TITLE	LABEL & NO.	GOOD	VERY GOOD	NEAR MINT
DO THEIR THING	UNI (S) 73044	6.00	12.00	18.00
IS HERE	Karma (M) KLP 1001	10.00	20.00	30.00

AMERICAN BREED

TITLE	LABEL & NO.	GOOD	VERY GOOD	NEAR MINT
AMERICAN BREED	Acta (M) A 8002	2.50	3.75	5.00
AMERICAN BREED, THE	Acta (S) A 38002	3.00	4.50	6.00
LONELY SIDE OF THE CITY	Acta (S) A 38008	3.00	4.50	6.00
PUMPKIN, POWDER, SCARLET AND GREEN	Acta (S) A 38006	3.00	4.50	6.00

AMERICAN DREAM

TITLE	LABEL & NO.	GOOD	VERY GOOD	NEAR MINT
AMERICAN DREAM, THE	Ampex (S) A 10101	2.50	3.75	5.00

AMERICAN EAGLE

TITLE	LABEL & NO.	GOOD	VERY GOOD	NEAR MINT
AMERICAN EAGLE	Decca (S) DH 75258	2.00	3.00	4.00

AMERICAN REVOLUTION

TITLE	LABEL & NO.	GOOD	VERY GOOD	NEAR MINT
AMERICAN REVOLUTION, THE	Flick Disc (S) FLS 45,002	3.50	5.25	7.00

AMES BROTHERS

TITLE	LABEL & NO.	GOOD	VERY GOOD	NEAR MINT
AMES BROTHERS	RCA (EP) EPA 5020	1.00	1.50	2.00
AMES BROTHERS, THE	Vocalion (M) VL 3617	2.00	3.00	4.00
AMES BROTHERS, THE	RCA (M) LPM 1228	2.50	3.75	5.00
AMES BROTHERS, THE	RCA (EP) EPA 790	1.00	1.50	2.00
AMES BROTHERS CONCERT	Coral (M) 57031	3.00	4.50	6.00
AMES BROTHERS SING FAMOUS HITS OF FAMOUS QUARTETS	RCA (M) LPM 1954	2.50	3.75	5.00
AMES BROTHERS SING FAMOUS HITS OF FAMOUS QUARTETS	RCA (S) LSP 1954	2.50	3.75	5.00
AMES BROTHERS SING THE BEST IN THE COUNTRY	RCA (M) LPM 1998	2.50	3.75	5.00
AMES BROTHERS SING THE BEST IN THE COUNTRY	RCA (S) LSP-1998	2.50	3.75	5.00
AMES BROTHERS SING THE BEST OF THE BANDS	RCA (M) LPM-2273	2.00	3.00	4.00
AMES BROTHERS SING THE BEST OF THE BANDS	RCA (S) LSP-2273	2.00	3.00	4.00
AMES BROTHERS SING THE BEST OF THE BANDS	RCA (S) LPC-112	1.00	1.50	2.00
AMES BROTHERS-SWEET & SWING	Camden (M) CAL-571	2.00	3.00	4.00
BEST OF THE AMES, THE	RCA (M) LPM 1859	2.50	3.75	5.00
BEST OF THE AMES	RCA (S) LSP-1859	2.50	3.75	5.00
BEST OF THE AMES, THE	RCA (EP) EPA 4320	1.00	1.50	2.00
BLEND & THE BEAT	RCA (M) LPM-2182	2.00	3.00	4.00
BLEND & THE BEAT	RCA (S) LSP-2182	2.00	3.00	4.00
CHRISTMAS HARMONY	Vocalion (M) 3788	2.00	3.00	4.00
CHRISTMAS HARMONY	Vocalion (S) 7-3788	2.00	3.00	4.00
DESTINATION MOON	RCA (M) LPM 1680	2.50	3.75	5.00
DESTINATION MOON	RCA (EP) EPA-4227	1.00	1.50	2.00
DESTINATION MOON	RCA (S) ESP 1680	2.50	3.75	5.00
DOWN MEMORY LANE WITH THE AMES BROTHERS	RCA (M) LPM 2981	2.00	3.00	4.00
DOWN MEMORY LANE WITH THE AMES BROTHERS	RCA (S) LSP 2981	2.00	3.00	4.00
EXACTLY LIKE YOU	RCA (M) LPM 1142	2.50	3.75	5.00
EXACTLY LIKE YOU	RCA (EP) EPA 680	1.00	1.50	2.00
FOR SENTIMENTAL REASONS	RCA (M) LPM-2876	2.00	3.00	4.00
FOR SENTIMENTAL REASONS	RCA (S) LSP-2876	2.00	3.00	4.00
FOUR BROTHERS	RCA (M) LPM 1157	2.50	3.75	5.00
FOUR BROTHERS	RCA (EP) EPA 819	1.00	1.50	2.00
FOUR BROTHERS	RCA (EP) EPA 820	1.00	1.50	2.00
HELLO, AMIGOS	RCA (M) LPM-2100	2.00	3.00	4.00
MAN WITH THE BANJO	RCA (EP) EPA 571	1.00	1.50	2.00
MELODLE D'AMOUR	RCA (EP) EPA 4173	1.00	1.50	2.00
OUR GOLDEN FAVORITES	Coral (M) CRL-57338	3.00	4.50	6.00
SENTIMENTAL MOOD	RCA (EP) EPA 4213	1.00	1.50	2.00
SWEET SEVENTEEN	RCA (M) LSPA 1487	2.50	3.75	5.00
TAMMY	RCA (EP) EPA 4096	1.00	1.50	2.00
THERE'LL ALWAYS BE A CHRISTMAS	RCA (M) LPM 1541	2.50	3.75	5.00
THERE'LL ALWAYS BE A CHRISTMAS	RCA (EP) EPA 1-1541	1.00	1.50	2.00
THERE'LL ALWAYS BE A CHRISTMAS	RCA (EP) EPA 2-1541	1.00	1.50	2.00
THERE'LL ALWAYS BE A CHRISTMAS	RCA (EP) EPA 3-1541	1.00	1.50	2.00

TITLE	LABEL & NO.	GOOD	VERY GOOD	NEAR MINT
AMESBURY, Bill				
JUS' A TASTE OF THE KID	Casablanca (S) 9005	2.50	3.75	5.00
AMES, Ed				
DO YOU HEAR WHAT I HEAR	Camden (S) ACL1-0244	2.00	3.00	4.00
SOMEWHERE MY LOVE	Camden (S) 2598	2.00	3.00	4.00
SONGS FROM "LOST HORIZON"	RCA (S) LSP-4808	2.00	3.00	4.00
TRY TO REMEMBER	Camden (S) ACL1-1467	2.00	3.00	4.00
AMON DUUL II				
AMON DUUL	Prophesy (S) PRS 1003	8.00	12.00	16.00
DANCE OF THE LEMMINGS	United Artists (S) UAS9954	7.00	10.50	14.00
VIVE LA TRANCE	United Artists (S) UA\LA198	3.00	4.50	6.00
ANDERS AND PONCIA				
ANDERS AND PONCIA ALBUM, THE	Warner Bros. (S) WS 1778	2.50	3.75	5.00
ANDERSEN, Eric				
AVALANCHE	Warner Brothers (S) WS1748	2.50	3.75	5.00
BE TRUE TO YOU	Arista (S) 4033	2.00	3.00	4.00
'BOUT CHANGES AND THINGS	Vanguard (M)	6.00	9.00	12.00
'BOUT CHANGES AND THINGS, TAKE 2	Vanguard (M) VRS 9236	4.00	6.00	8.00
'BOUT CHANGES AND THINGS, TAKE 2	Vanguard (S) VSD 79236	5.00	7.50	10.00
TODAY IS THE HIGHWAY	Vanguard (S) VRS 9157	2.50	3.75	5.00
TODAY IS THE HIGHWAY	Vanguard (S) VSD 79157	3.00	4.50	6.00
ANDERSON, Bill				
ALWAYS REMEMBER (RI)	MCA (S) 29	2.00	3.00	4.00
BILL	MCA (S) 320	2.00	3.00	4.00
BILL ANDERSON'S GREATEST HITS (RI)	MCA (S) 13	2.00	3.00	4.00
BILL ANDERSON'S GREATEST HITS, Vol. 2 (RI)	MCA (S) 40	2.00	3.00	4.00
BILL ANDERSON SINGS FOR ALL THE LONELY WOMEN IN THE WORLD (RI)	MCA (S) 48	2.00	3.00	4.00
DON'T SHE LOOK GOOD	Decca (S) 75383	2.00	3.00	4.00
DON'T SHE LOOK GOOD (RI)	MCA (S) 59	2.00	3.00	4.00
EVERYTIME I TURN THE RADIO ON/ TALK TO ME OHIO	MCA (S) 454	2.00	3.00	4.00
WHISPERING BILL ANDERSON	MCA (S) 416	2.00	3.00	4.00
ANDERSON, Casey				
BLUES IS A WOMAN GONE	Atco (M) 33-176	2.50	3.75	5.00
ANDERSON, Liz				
LIZ ANDERSON SINGS HER FAVORITES	RCA (M) LPM 3908	2.00	3.00	4.00
LIZ ANDERSON SINGS HER FAVORITES	RCA (S) LPS 3908	2.00	3.00	4.00
ANDERSON, Lynn				
BIG GIRLS DON'T CRY	Chart (M) 1008	2.00	3.00	4.00
I'VE NEVER LOVED ANYONE MORE	Columbia (S) KC-33691	2.00	3.00	4.00
KEEP ME IN MIND	Columbia (S) KC-32078	2.00	3.00	4.00
LYNN ANDERSON	Chart (M) 1050	2.00	3.00	4.00
PROMISES PROMISES	Chart (M) 1004	2.00	3.00	4.00
PROMISES PROMISES	Chart (S) 1004	2.00	3.00	4.00
QUEEN'S OF COUNTRY	Columbia (S) KC-32719	2.00	3.00	4.00
ROSE GARDEN/HOW CAN I UNLOVE YOU	Columbia (S) CG-33636	2.00	3.00	4.00
SINGING MY SONG	Harmony (S) KH-32433	2.00	3.00	4.00
SMILE FOR ME	Columbia (S) KC-32941	2.00	3.00	4.00
TOP OF THE WORLD	Columbia (S) KC-32429	2.00	3.00	4.00
WHAT A MAN MY MAN IS	Columbia (S) KC-33293	2.00	3.00	4.00
ANDREWS, Julie				
TV'S FAIR JULIE	Harmony (S) KH-31958	2.50	3.75	5.00
WORLD OF JULIE ANDREWS	Columbia (S) KG-31970	2.00	3.00	4.00
ANDREWS SISTERS				
ANDREWS SISTERS	Decca (M) DL 5120	3.00	4.50	6.00
ANDREWS SISTERS IN HI-FI	Capitol (M) 790	2.00	3.00	4.00
ANDREWS SISTERS SING	Decca (EP) A660	1.50	2.25	3.00
BERLIN SONGS	Decca (M) DL 5264	2.50	3.75	5.00
BERLIN SONGS	Decca (EP) A656	1.00	1.50	2.00
BY POPULAR DEMAND	Decca (M) DL 8360	2.00	3.00	4.00
CLUB 15	Decca (M) DL 5155	2.50	3.75	5.00
CLUB 15	Decca (EP) A744	2.50	3.75	5.00
CURTAIN CALL	Decca (M) DL 7019	2.00	3.00	4.00
DANCING TWENTIES	Capitol (M) T 973	2.50	3.75	5.00
DANCING TWENTIES	Capitol (EP) EAP 1-973	1.50	2.25	3.00
FRESH AND FANCY FREE	Capitol (M) T 860	2.50	3.75	5.00
FRESH AND FANCY FREE	Capitol (EP) EAP 1-860	1.00	2.00	3.00
FRESH AND FANCY FREE	Capitol (EP) EAP 2-860	1.50	2.25	3.00
FRESH AND FANCY FREE	Capitol (EP) EAP 3-860	1.50	2.25	3.00
HITS OF THE ANDREWS SISTERS	Capitol (M) T-1924	2.00	3.00	4.00
HITS OF THE ANDREWS SISTERS	Capitol (S) ST-1924	2.00	3.00	4.00
IN THE MOOD	Paramount (S) 2-1023	3.00	4.50	6.00
JINGLE BELLS	Decca (M) DL 8354	2.00	3.00	4.00
16 GREATEST HITS	ABC (S) DP-4003	3.00	4.50	6.00
TROPICAL SONGS	Decca (M) DL 5065	3.00	4.50	6.00
TROPICAL SONGS	Decca (EP) A551	1.50	2.25	3.00
ANDREWS, Lee & The Hearts				
BIGGEST HITS	Lost Nite (M) LP 101	3.50	5.25	7.00
DEAN TYLER PRESENTS LEE ANDREWS AND THE HEARTS	Lost Nite (M) LP 113	3.50	5.25	7.00
ANDWELLA				
PEOPLE'S PEOPLE	Dunhill (S) 50105	3.00	4.50	6.00
ANGEL				
ANGEL	Casablanca (S) NBLP 7021	2.00	3.00	4.00
WHITE HOT	Casablanca (S) NBLP 7085	2.00	3.00	4.00
ANGELS				
AND THE ANGELS SING	Caprice (M) LP 1001	6.00	12.00	18.00
AND THE ANGELS SING	Caprice (S) SLP 1001	7.00	14.00	21.00
ANGELS SING 12 OF THEIR GREATEST HITS	Ascot (M) AM 13009	5.00	7.50	10.00
A HALO TO YOU	Smash (M) MGS 27048	5.00	7.50	10.00
A HALO TO YOU	Smash (S) SRS 67048	6.00	9.00	12.00
MY BOYFRIEND'S BACK	Smash (M) MGS 27039	5.00	7.50	10.00
MY BOYFRIEND'S BACK	Smash (S) SRS 67039	6.00	9.00	12.00

MY Till Someday My Prince Will Come
He's So Fine A Night Has A Thousand Eyes The Guy With The Black Eye Has Anybody Seen My Boyfriend
Love Me (Now) Why Don't The Boy Leave Me Alone The Hurdy-Gurdy Man Thank You And Good Night
World Without Love
BOYFRIEND'S by The Angels BACK
SMASH RECORDS
MONAURAL 7039

TITLE	LABEL & NO.	GOOD	VERY GOOD	NEAR MINT
ANIMALS				
ANIMALISM	MGM (M) E-4414	2.50	3.75	5.00
ANIMALISM	MGM (S) SE-4414	3.00	4.50	6.00
ANIMALIZATION	MGM (M) E-4384	2.50	3.75	5.00
ANIMALIZATION	MGM (S) SE-4384	3.00	4.50	6.00
ANIMALS, THE	MGM (M) E-4264	7.50	3.75	5.00
ANIMALS, THE	MGM (S) SE-4264	3.00	4.50	6.00
ANIMALS ON TOUR, THE	MGM (M) E-4281	2.50	3.75	5.00
ANIMALS ON TOUR, THE	MGM (S) SE-4281	3.00	4.50	6.00
ANIMAL TRACKS	MGM (M) E-4305	2.50	3.75	5.00
ANIMAL TRACKS	MGM (S) SE-4305	3.00	4.50	6.00
BEFORE WE WERE SO RUDELY INTERRUPTED	Jet (S) JT-LA790	2.50	3.75	5.00
BEST OF ERIC BURDON AND THE ANIMALS, Vol. II	MGM (M) E-4454	2.50	3.75	5.00
BEST OF ERIC BURDON AND THE ANIMALS, Vol. II	MGM (S) SE-4454	3.00	4.50	6.00
BEST OF THE ANIMALS,	MGM (M) E-4324	2.50	3.75	5.00
BEST OF THE ANIMALS,	MGM (S) SE-4324	3.00	4.50	6.00
BEST OF THE ANIMALS	ABKCO (S) AB 4226	3.00	4.50	6.00
EARLY ANIMALS WITH ERIC BURDON, THE	Pickwick (M) SPC-3330	2.50	3.75	5.00
ERIC IS HERE	MGM (M) E-4433	2.50	3.75	5.00
ERIC IS HERE	MGM (S) SE-4433	3.00	4.50	6.00
EVERY ONE OF US	MGM (M) E-4553	3.00	4.50	6.00
EVERY ONE OF US	MGM (S) SE-4553	4.00	6.00	8.00
GREATEST HITS OF ERIC BURDON, THE AND THE ANIMALS	MGM (S) SE-4602	3.00	4.50	6.00
IN THE BEGINNING	Wand (S) WDS 690	4.00	6.00	8.00
LOVE IS	MGM (S) SE-4591-2	4.00	6.00	8.00
TWAIN SHALL MEET, THE	MGM (M) E-4537	2.50	3.75	5.00
TWAIN SHALL MEET, THE	MGM (S) SE-4537	3.00	4.50	6.00
WINDS OF CHANGE	MGM (M) E-4484	3.00	4.50	6.00
WINDS OF CHANGE	MGM (S) SE-4484	4.00	6.00	8.00
ANKA, Paul				
ANKA	United Artists (S) UA-LA314	3.00	4.50	6.00
ANKA AT THE COPA	ABC/Paramount (M) ABC-353	2.00	4.00	6.00
ANKA AT THE COPA	ABC/Paramount (S) ABCS-353	3.00	6.00	9.00
DIANA	ABC/Paramount (M) ABC 420	5.00	10.00	15.00
DIANA	ABC/Paramount (S) ABCS 420	6.00	12.00	18.00
ESSENTIAL PAUL ANKA	Buddah (S) 2-5667	3.50	5.25	7.00
EXCITEMENT ON PARK AVENUE (LIVE AT THE RCA WALDORF-ASTORIA)	RCA (M) LPM-2966	3.00	6.00	9.00
EXCITEMENT ON PARK AVENUE (LIVE AT THE RCA WALDORF-ASTORIA)	RCA (S) LSP-2966	4.00	8.00	12.00

(M) Mono (S) Stereo (EP) Extended Play (Q) Quad (RI) Re-issued

PAUL ANKA

ORCHESTRA CONDUCTED BY DON COSTA

TITLE	LABEL & NO.	GOOD	VERY GOOD	NEAR MINT
ITALIANNETTE	Buena Vista (M) BV3304	3.00	6.00	9.00
LONELY GUITAR + 3	Buena Vista (EP) 3301A	3.00	4.50	6.00
MICKEY MOUSE CLUB — ANNETTE	Disneyland (EP) 69	3.00	4.50	6.00
MUSCLE BEACH PARTY	Buena Vista (M) BV 3314	3.00	6.00	9.00
PAJAMA PARTY	Buena Vista (M) BV 3325	3.00	6.00	9.00
(With Dorothy Lamour)				
PAJAMA PARTY	Buena Vista (S) STER 3325	6.00	12.00	18.00
(With Dorothy Lamour)				
SNOW WHITE & THE SEVEN DWARFS	Disneyland (M) 3906	5.00	10.00	15.00
SOMETHING BORROWED SOMETHING BLUE	Buena Vista (M) 3328	3.00	6.00	9.00
SONGS FROM ANNETTE AND OTHER WALT DISNEY SERIALS	Mickey Mouse (M) MM24	5.00	10.00	15.00
STORY OF MY TEENS, THE	Buena Vista (M) BV 3312	5.00	10.00	15.00
TEEN STREET	Buena Vista (M) BV 3313	4.00	8.00	12.00
TUBBY THE TUBA & OTHER SONGS ABOUT MUSIC	Disneyland (M) 1287	5.00	10.00	15.00
(With Jimmie Dodd)				

ANN-MARGRET

TITLE	LABEL & NO.	GOOD	VERY GOOD	NEAR MINT
AND HERE SHE IS	RCA (M) LPM-2399	4.50	6.75	9.00
AND HERE SHE IS	RCA (S) LSP-2399	6.00	9.00	12.00
BACHELORS' PARADISE	RCA (M) LPM-2659	2.50	3.75	5.00
BACHELORS' PARADISE	RCA (S) LSP-2659	2.50	3.75	5.00
BEAUTY AND THE BEARD (WITH AL HIRT)	RCA (M) LPM 2690	2.00	3.00	4.00
BEAUTY AND THE BEARD (WITH AL HIRT)	RCA (S) LSP-2690	2.00	3.00	4.00
IT'S THE MOST HAPPY SOUND	Warner Bros. (M) W-1285	3.50	5.25	7.00
IT'S THE MOST HAPPY SOUND	Warner Bros. (S) WS 1285	4.00	6.00	8.00
ON THE WAY UP	RCA (M) LPM-2453	3.00	4.50	6.00
ON THE WAY UP	RCA (S) LPS-2453	3.50	5.25	7.00
SWINGER	RCA (M) LPM-3710	2.50	3.75	5.00
SWINGER	RCA (S) LSP-3710	2.50	3.75	5.00
VIVACIOUS ONE	RCA (M) LPM-2551	2.50	3.75	5.00
VIVACIOUS ONE	RCA (S) LSP-2551	2.50	3.75	5.00

ON THE WAY UP ANN-MARGRET

TITLE	LABEL & NO.	GOOD	VERY GOOD	NEAR MINT
FABULOUS PAUL ANKA & OTHERS	Rivera (M) R 0047	6.00	15.00	24.00
FEELINGS	United Artists (S) UA-LA367	3.00	4.50	6.00
GOODNIGHT MY LOVE	RCA (S) LSP 4142	4.00	6.00	8.00
IT'S CHRISTMAS EVERYWHERE	ABC/Paramount (M) ABC 360	4.00	10.00	16.00
IT'S CHRISTMAS EVERYWHERE	ABC/Paramount (S) ABCS 360	5.00	12.50	20.00
JUBILATION	Buddah (S) 5114	4.50	6.75	9.00
LET'S SIT THIS ONE OUT	RCA (M) LPM-2575	3.00	6.00	9.00
LET'S SIT THIS ONE OUT	RCA (S) LSP-2575	4.00	8.00	12.00
LIFE GOES ON	RCA (S) LSP 4250	4.00	6.00	8.00
MUSIC MAN	United Artists (S) UA-LA746	2.00	3.00	4.00
MY HEART SINGS	ABC/Paramount (M) ABC 296	5.00	10.00	15.00
MY HEART SINGS	ABC/Paramount (S) ABCS 296	8.00	20.00	32.00
MY HEART SINGS	ABC/Paramount (EP) 296-1	3.00	6.00	9.00
MY HEART SINGS	ABC/Paramount (EP) 296-2	3.00	6.00	9.00
MY HEART SINGS	ABC/Paramount (EP) 296-3	3.00	6.00	9.00
MY WAY	Camden (M) ACL1-0616	3.50	5.25	7.00
OUR MAN AROUND THE WORLD	RCA (M) LPM-2614	3.00	6.00	9.00
OUR MAN AROUND THE WORLD	RCA (S) LSP-2614	4.00	8.00	12.00
PAUL ANKA	ABC/Paramount (M) ABC 240	4.00	10.00	16.00
PAUL ANKA	ABC/Paramount (S) ABCS 240	8.00	20.00	32.00
PAUL ANKA	Buddah (S) 5093	4.50	6.75	9.00
PAUL ANKA GOLD	Sire (S) 3704	4.00	6.00	8.00
PAUL ANKA SINGS HIS BIG 15	ABC/Paramount (M) ABC 323	4.00	8.00	12.00
PAUL ANKA SINGS HIS BIG 15	ABC/Paramount (S) ABCS 323	8.00	20.00	32.00
PAUL ANKA SINGS HIS BIG 15 VOL. 2	ABC/Paramount (M) ABC 390	4.00	8.00	12.00
PAUL ANKA SINGS HIS BIG 15 VOL. 2	ABC/Paramount (S) ABCS 390	5.00	10.00	15.00
PAUL ANKA SINGS HIS BIG 15 VOL. 3	ABC/Paramount (M) ABC 409	3.00	6.00	9.00
PAUL ANKA SINGS HIS BIG 15 VOL. 3	ABC/Paramount (S) ABCS 409	4.00	8.00	12.00
PAUL ANKA SINGS HIS FAVORITES	RCA (S) ANL1-1584	2.50	3.75	5.00
SONGS I WISH I'D WRITTEN	RCA (M) LPM 2744	3.00	6.00	9.00
SONGS I WISH I'D WRITTEN	RCA (S) LSP 2744	3.00	6.00	9.00
SONGS I WISH I'D WRITTEN (RI)	RCA (S) ANL1-2482	2.50	3.75	5.00
STRICKLY NASHVILLE	RCA (M) LPM-3580	3.00	6.00	9.00
STRICKLY NASHVILLE	RCA (S) LSP-3580	4.00	8.00	12.00
STRICTLY INSTRUMENTAL	ABC/Paramount (M) ABC 371	5.00	16.00	24.00
STRICTLY INSTRUMENTAL	ABC/Paramount (S) ABCS 371	9.00	18.00	27.00
SWINGS FOR YOUNG LOVERS	ABC/Paramount (M) ABC 347	3.00	6.00	9.00
SWINGS FOR YOUNG LOVERS	ABC/Paramount (S) ABCS 347	4.00	8.00	12.00
TIMES OF YOUR LIFE	United Artists (S) UA-LA569	3.00	4.50	6.00
(With Odia Coates)				
21 GOLDEN HITS	RCA (M) LPM 2691	4.00	8.00	12.00
21 GOLDEN HITS	RCA (S) LPS 2691	5.00	10.00	15.00
VINTAGE YEARS 1957-1961	Sire (S) K-6043	2.50	3.75	5.00
YOUNG, ALIVE AND IN LOVE	RCA (M) LPM 2502	3.00	6.00	9.00
YOUNG, ALIVE AND IN LOVE	RCA (S) LPS 2502	3.00	6.00	9.00

ANNETTE

TITLE	LABEL & NO.	GOOD	VERY GOOD	NEAR MINT
ANNETTE	Buena Vista (M) BV3301	4.00	8.00	12.00
ANNETTE AT BIKINI BEACH	Buena Vista (M) BV 3324	3.00	6.00	9.00
ANNETTE FUNICELLO	Buena Vista (M) BV 4037	4.00	6.00	8.00
ANNETTE ON CAMPUS	Buena Vista (M) BV 3320	3.00	6.00	9.00
ANNETTE'S BEACH PARTY	Buena Vista (M) BV 3316	3.00	6.00	9.00
ANNETTE SING ANKA	Buena Vista (M) BV3302	3.00	6.00	9.00
ANNETTE SINGS GOLDEN SURFIN' HITS	Buena Vista (M) BV 3327	4.00	8.00	12.00
DANCE ANNETTE	Buena Vista (M) BV3305	3.00	6.00	9.00
HAWAIIANNETTE	Buena Vista (M) BV3303	3.00	6.00	9.00

ANTRELL, Dave

TITLE	LABEL & NO.	GOOD	VERY GOOD	NEAR MINT
DAVE ANTRELL	Amaret 5007	2.50	3.75	5.00

AORTA

TITLE	LABEL & NO.	GOOD	VERY GOOD	NEAR MINT
AORTA	Columbia (S) CS9785	3.00	4.50	6.00
AORTA 2	Happy Tiger (M) HT1010	4.00	6.00	8.00

APHRODITE'S CHILD

TITLE	LABEL & NO.	GOOD	VERY GOOD	NEAR MINT
666	Vertigo (S) 2500	3.00	4.50	6.00

APOLLO 100

TITLE	LABEL & NO.	GOOD	VERY GOOD	NEAR MINT
MASTER PIECES	Mega (S) 5005	3.00	4.50	6.00

APPELL, Dave

TITLE	LABEL & NO.	GOOD	VERY GOOD	NEAR MINT
ALONE TOGETHER	Cameo (M) C 1004	5.00	10.00	15.00

(M) Mono (S) Stereo (EP) Extended Play (Q) Quad (RI) Re-issued

5

TITLE	LABEL & NO.	GOOD	VERY GOOD	NEAR MINT
APPLE PIE MOTHERHOOD BAND				
APPLE PIE	Atlantic (S) SD 8233	2.50	3.75	5.00
THE APPLE PIE MOTHERHOOD BAND	Atlantic (S) SD8189	2.50	3.75	5.00
APPLETREE THEATRE				
PLAYBACK	Verve/Forecast (S) FTS3042	2.50	3.75	5.00
AQUATONES				
AQUATONES SING, THE	Fargo (M) FLP3001	10.00	25.00	40.00

FLP-3001

TITLE	LABEL & NO.	GOOD	VERY GOOD	NEAR MINT
ARBORS				
ARBORS, FEATURING, I CAN'T QUIT HER AND THE LETTER,	Date (S) TES4017	2.50	3.75	5.00
ARBORS SING VALLEY OF THE DOLLS,	Date (M) TEM3011	2.00	3.00	4.00
ARBORS SING VALLEY OF THE DOLLS,	Date (S) TES4011	2.50	3.75	5.00
SYMPHONY FOR SUSAN	Date (M) TEM3003	2.00	3.00	4.00
SYMPHONY FOR SUSAN	Date (S) TES4003	2.50	3.75	5.00
ARCHIES				
ARCHIES, THE	Calendar (S) KES101	4.00	6.00	8.00
ARCHIES GREATEST HITS	Kirshner (S) KES109	3.00	4.50	6.00
EVERYTHINGS ARCHIE	Calendar (S) KES103	4.00	6.00	8.00
JINGLE JANGLE	Calendar (S) KES105	4.00	6.00	8.00
SUNSHINE	Calendar (S) KES107	4.00	6.00	8.00
THIS IS LOVE	Kirshner (S) KES110	4.00	6.00	8.00
ARDEN, Toni				
BESAME	Decca (M) DL-8875	1.50	3.00	4.50
BESAME	Decca (S) DL178875	2.00	4.00	6.00
EXCITING TONI ARDEN	Harmony (EP) HL-7212	1.00	1.50	2.00
GIRL FRIENDS	Harmony (EP) HL-7148	1.00	1.50	2.00
MISS TONI ARDEN	Decca (M) DL 8651	1.50	3.00	4.50
ARGENT				
ALL TOGETHER NOW	Epic (S) KE-31556	3.00	4.50	6.00
CIRCUS	Epic (S) PE-33422	3.50	5.25	7.00
ENCORE	Epic (S) PEG-33079	3.00	4.50	6.00
IN DEEP	Epic (S) KE-32195	3.50	5.25	7.00
IN DEEP	Epic (Q) EQ-32195	3.00	4.50	6.00
NEXUS	Epic (S) KE-32573	3.50	5.25	7.00
ARISTOCATS				
BOOGIE AND BLUES	HiFi (M) R610	8.00	20.00	32.00
ARKANSAS BLUES				
ARKANSAS BLUES	Kent (M) 9007	2.00	3.00	4.00
ARMAGEDDON				
ARMAGEDDON	A&M (S) SP 4513	2.00	3.00	4.00
ARMATRADING, Joan				
BACK TO THE NIGHT	A&M (S) SP 4525	2.00	3.00	4.00
JOAN ARMATRADING	A&M (S) SP 4588	2.00	3.00	4.00
WHATEVER'S FOR US	A&M (S) SP 4382	2.00	3.00	4.00

(M) Mono (S) Stereo (EP) Extended Play (Q) Quad (RI) Re-issued

TITLE	LABEL & NO.	GOOD	VERY GOOD	NEAR MINT
ARNELL, Ginny				
MEET GINNY ARNELL	MGM (M) E4228	3.00	6.00	9.00
MEET GINNY ARNELL	MGM (S) SE4228	4.00	8.00	12.00
ARNOLD, Billy Boy				
BLUES ON THE SOUTH SIDE	Prestige (M) 7389	5.00	7.50	10.00
ARNOLD, P.P.				
KAFUNTA	Immediate (S) Z12 52 016	5.00	7.50	10.00
ARRIVAL				
ARRIVAL	London (S) PS 576	3.50	5.25	7.00
ARS NOVA				
ARS NOVA	Elektra (S) EKS 74020	3.00	4.50	6.00
SUNSHINE AND SHADOWS	Atlantic (S) SD 8221	3.00	4.50	6.00
ARTFUL DODGER				
ARTFUL DODGER	Columbia (S) PC-33811	2.00	3.00	4.00
ARTHUR, HURLEY & GOTTLIEB				
SUNLIGHT SHININ'	A&M (S) SP 4503	2.00	3.00	4.00
ARTISTICS				
LOOK OUT	Brunswick (S) 754195	3.00	4.50	6.00
WHAT HAPPENED	Brunswick (S) BL 754153	3.00	4.50	6.00
ARZACHEL				
ARZACHEL	Roulette (S) SR 42036	8.00	12.00	16.00
ASHER, Jane				
ALICE IN WONDERLAND	London (M) OSA-1206	5.00	10.00	15.00
ASHES (Featuring Pat Taylor)				
ASHES	Vault (M) 125	4.00	6.00	8.00
ASHFORD & SIMPSON				
GIMME SOMETHING REAL	Warner Bros. (S) BS-2739	2.00	3.00	4.00
I WANNA BE SELFISH	Warner Bros. (S) BS-2789	2.00	3.00	4.00
ASHKAN				
IN FROM THE COLD	Sire (S) SES 97017	3.00	4.50	6.00
ASHLEY, Leon				
MENTAL JOURNEY	Ashley (S) 3700	2.00	3.00	4.00
NEW BRAND OF COUNTRY	Ashley (S) 3695	2.00	3.00	4.00
ASHTON, GARDNER & DYKE				
ASHTON, GARDNER, AND DYKE	Capitol (S) ST-563	2.50	3.75	5.00
WHAT A BLOODY LONG DAY IT'S BEEN	Capitol (S) SMAS-862	2.50	3.75	5.00
ASHWORTH, Ernie				
BEST OF ERNIE ASHWORTH	Hickory (S) 146	2.00	3.00	4.00
HITS OF TODAY & TOMORROW	Hickory (M) MH-118	2.00	3.00	4.00
ASLEEP AT THE WHEEL				
ASLEEP AT THE WHEEL	Epic (S) KE-33097	2.00	3.00	4.00
COMIN' RIGHT AT YA	United Artists (S) UA-LA038-F	2.50	3.75	5.00
FATHERS & SONS (WITH BOB WILLS & TEXAS PLAYBOYS)	Epic (S) BG 33782	2.00	3.00	4.00
TEXAS GOLD	Capitol (S) ST-11441	2.00	3.00	4.00
ASSOCIATION				
AND THEN ALONG COMES THE ASSOCIATION	Valiant (M) VLM 5002	4.00	6.00	8.00
AND THEN ALONG COMES THE ASSOCIATION	Valiant (S) VLS 25002	5.00	7.50	10.00
AND THEN ALONG COMES THE ASSOCIATION (RI of Valiant LP)	Warner Bros. (S) WS 1702	3.00	4.50	6.00
BIRTHDAY	Warner Brothers (M) W 1733	2.50	3.75	5.00
BIRTHDAY	Warner Brothers (S) WS 1733	3.00	4.50	6.00
1800	Warner Bros. (S) WS 1800	3.00	4.50	6.00
GOODBYE COLUMBUS	Warner Brothers (S) WS 1786	3.00	4.50	6.00
GREATEST HITS	Warner Brothers (S) WS 1767	3.00	4.50	6.00
INSIGHT OUT	Warner Bsothers (M) WS 1696	3.00	4.50	6.00
LIVE	Warner Bros. (S) WS 1868	4.00	6.00	8.00
RENAISSANCE	Valiant (M) VLM 5004	4.00	6.00	8.00
RENAISSANCE	Valiant (S) VLS 25004	5.00	7.50	10.00
STOP YOUR MOTOR	Warner Brothers (S) WS 1927	3.50	5.25	7.00
WATERBEDS IN TRINIDAD	Columbia (S) 31348	3.00	4.50	6.00
ASTRONAUTS				
ASTRONAUTS ORBIT CAMPUS	RCA (M) LPM 2903	5.00	7.50	10.00
ASTRONAUTS ORBIT CAMPUS	RCA (S) LSP 2903	6.00	7.50	12.00
COMPETITION COUPE	RCA (M) LPM 2858	5.00	7.50	10.00
COMPETITION COUPE	RCA (S) LSP 2858	6.00	9.00	12.00
DOWN THE LINE	RCA (M) LPM 3454	4.00	6.00	8.00
DOWN THE LINE	RCA (S) LSP 3454	5.00	7.50	10.00
EVERYTHING IS A-OK	RCA (M) LPM2782	5.00	7.50	10.00

TITLE	LABEL & NO.	GOOD	VERY GOOD	NEAR MINT
EVERYTHING IS A-OK	RCA (S) LSP 2782	6.00	9.00	12.00
FAVORITES FOR YOU, OUR FANS, FROM US	RCA (M) LPM 3359	4.00	6.00	8.00
FAVORITES FOR YOU, OUR FANS, FROM US	RCA (S) LSP 3359	5.00	7.50	10.00
GO GO GO	RCA (M) LPM 3307	4.00	6.00	8.00
GO GO GO	RCA (S) LSP 3307	5.00	7.50	10.00
ROCKIN' WITH THE ASTRONAUTS	RCA (M) PRM 183	6.00	12.00	18.00
SURFIN' WITH THE ASTRONAUTS	RCA (M) LPM 2760	4.00	6.00	8.00
SURFIN' WITH THE ASTRONAUTS	RCA (S) LSP 2760	5.00	7.50	10.00
TRAVELIN' MEN	RCA (M) LPM 3733	4.00	6.00	8.00
TRAVELIN' MEN	RCA (S) LSP 3733	5.00	7.50	10.00

ATKINS, Chet

TITLE	LABEL & NO.	GOOD	VERY GOOD	NEAR MINT
ALONE	RCA (S) APL1-0159	2.00	3.00	4.00
BEST OF CHET ATKINS	RCA (M) LPM-2887	2.00	3.00	4.00
BEST OF CHET ATKINS	RCA (S) LSP-2887	2.00	3.00	4.00
CARIBBEAN GUITAR	RCA (M) LPM-2549	2.00	3.00	4.00
CARIBBEAN GUITAR	RCA (S) LSP-2549	2.00	3.00	4.00
CHET ATKINS AND HIS GUITAR	RCA (EP) EPA 588	2.00	3.00	4.00
CHET ATKINS AT HOME	RCA (M) LPM 1544	2.50	3.75	5.00
CHET ATKINS AT HOME	RCA (EP) EPA 4194	1.00	2.00	3.00
CHET ATKINS FAVORITES	RCA (EP) EPA-5154	1.00	2.00	3.00
CHET ATKINS GOES TO THE MOVIES	RCA (S) APL1-0845	2.00	3.00	4.00
CHET ATKINS' GUITAR	RCA (EP) EPA-5125	1.00	2.00	3.00
CHET ATKINS IN HOLLYWOOD	RCA (M) LPM-1933	2.00	3.00	4.00
CHET ATKINS IN HOLLYWOOD	RCA (S) LSP-1933	2.50	3.75	5.00
CHET ATKINS IN 3 DIMENSIONS	RCA (M) LPM 1197	3.00	4.50	6.00
CHET ATKINS IN 3 DIMENSIONS	RCA (EP) EPA 685	1.00	2.00	3.00
CHET ATKINS PICKS ON THE BEATLES	RCA (M) LPM-3531	3.00	4.50	6.00
CHET ATKINS PICKS ON THE BEATLES	RCA (S) LSP-3531	2.50	3.75	5.00
CHET ATKINS TEENSVILLE	RCA (M) LPM-2161	2.50	3.75	5.00
CHET ATKINS' TEENSVILLE	RCA (S) LSP-2161	2.50	3.75	5.00
CHET ATKINS WORKSHOP	RCA (M) LPM-2232	2.00	3.00	4.00
CHET ATKINS WORKSHOP	RCA (S) LSP-2232	2.50	3.75	5.00
CHRISTMAS WITH CHET ATKINS	RCA (M) LPM-2423	2.00	3.00	4.00
CHRISTMAS WITH CHET ATKINS	RCA (S) LSP-2423	2.00	3.00	4.00
DOWN HOME	RCA (M) LPM-2450	2.00	3.00	4.00
DOWN HOME	RCA (S) LSP-2450	2.00	3.00	4.00
FINGER PICKIN' GOOD	Camden (S) 2600	2.00	3.00	4.00
FINGER STYLE GUITAR	RCA (M) LPM 1383	3.00	4.50	6.00
GUITAR COUNTRY	RCA (M) LPM-2783	2.00	3.00	4.00
GUITAR COUNTRY	RCA (S) LSP-2783	2.00	3.00	4.00
HI FI IN FOCUS	RCA (M) LPM 1577	2.50	3.75	5.00
HUM & STRUM ALONG WITH CHET ATKINS	RCA (M) LPM-2025	2.00	3.00	4.00
HUM & STRUM ALONG WITH CHET ATKINS	RCA (S) LSP-2025	2.50	3.75	5.00
HUM & STRUM ALONG WITH CHET ATKINS	RCA (EP) EPA-4343	1.00	2.00	3.00
MISTER GUITAR	RCA (M) LPM-2103	2.00	3.00	4.00
MISTER GUITAR	RCA (S) LSP-2103	2.50	3.75	5.00
MOST POPULAR GUITAR	RCA (M) LPM-2346	2.00	3.00	4.00
MOST POPULAR GUITAR	RCA (S) LSP-2346	2.00	3.00	4.00
NOW & THEN	RCA (S) VPSX-6079	3.00	4.50	6.00
ONE MINT JULEP	RCA (EP) EPA-4356	1.00	2.00	3.00
OTHER CHET ATKINS	RCA (M) LPM-2175	2.00	3.00	4.00
OTHER CHET ATKINS	RCA (S) LSP-2175	2.50	3.75	5.00
PICKIN' THE HITS	RCA (EP) EPA 594	1.00	2.00	3.00
SESSION WITH CHET ATKINS	RCA (M) LPM 1090	3.50	5.25	7.00
STRINGIN' ALONG WITH CHET ATKINS	RCA (M) LPM 1236	2.50	3.75	5.00
STRINGIN' ALONG WITH CHET ATKINS	RCA (EP) EPA 796	1.00	2.00	3.00
SUPERPICKERS	RCA (S) APD1-0329	2.00	3.00	4.00
TEEN SCENE	RCA (M) LPM-2719	2.00	3.00	4.00
TEEN SCENE	RCA (S) LSP-2719	2.00	3.00	4.00

ATKINS, Chet & Hank Snow

TITLE	LABEL & NO.	GOOD	VERY GOOD	NEAR MINT
REMINISCING	RCA (M) LPM-2952	2.00	3.00	4.00
REMINISCING	RCA (S) LSP-2952	2.00	3.00	4.00

ATKINS, Chet/Jerry Reed

TITLE	LABEL & NO.	GOOD	VERY GOOD	NEAR MINT
CHET ATKINS PICKS ON JERRY REED	RCA (S) APL1-0545	2.50	3.75	5.00

ATLANTA DISCO BAND

TITLE	LABEL & NO.	GOOD	VERY GOOD	NEAR MINT
BAD LUCK	Ariola America (S) ST 50004	3.00	4.50	6.00

ATLANTA RHYTHM SECTION

TITLE	LABEL & NO.	GOOD	VERY GOOD	NEAR MINT
CHAMPAGNE JAM	Polydor (S) PD-1-6134	2.00	3.00	4.00
DOG DAYS	Polydor (S) 6041	3.00	4.50	6.00
THIRD ANNUAL PIPE DREAM	Polydor (S) 6027	3.00	4.50	6.00

ATOMIC ROOSTER

TITLE	LABEL & NO.	GOOD	VERY GOOD	NEAR MINT
ATOMIC ROOSTER	Elektra (S) 75074	4.00	6.00	8.00
DEATH WALKS BEHIND YOU	Elektra (S) 74094	3.50	5.25	7.00
IN HEARING OF	Elektra (S) 74109	3.00	4.50	6.00
MADE IN ENGLAND	Elektra (S) 75039	3.00	4.50	6.00

AUGER, BRIAN/TRINITY

TITLE	LABEL & NO.	GOOD	VERY GOOD	NEAR MINT
BEFOUR	RCA (S) LSP 4342	3.50	5.25	7.00
GENESIS	Polydor (S) 6505	3.00	4.50	6.00

AUGER'S, BRIAN, OBLIVION EXPRESS

TITLE	LABEL & NO.	GOOD	VERY GOOD	NEAR MINT
CLOSER TO IT	RCA (S) APL1-0140	2.50	3.75	5.00
LIVE OBLIVION, VOL. 1	RCA (S) CPL1-0645	2.50	3.75	5.00
SECOND WIND	RCA (S) LSP 4703	3.50	5.25	7.00

AU GO GO SINGERS

TITLE	LABEL & NO.	GOOD	VERY GOOD	NEAR MINT
THEY CALL US AU GO-GO SINGERS	Roulette (S) SR 25280	10.00	20.00	30.00

(M) Mono (S) Stereo (EP) Extended Play (Q) Quad (RI) Re-issued

AUM

TITLE	LABEL & NO.	GOOD	VERY GOOD	NEAR MINT
BLUESVIBES	Sire (S) SES 97007	3.00	4.50	6.00
RESURRECTION	Fillmore (M) F 30002	3.00	4.50	6.00

AURACLE

TITLE	LABEL & NO.	GOOD	VERY GOOD	NEAR MINT
GLIDER	Chrysalis (S) CHR 1172	2.00	3.00	4.00

AUSTIN, Gene

TITLE	LABEL & NO.	GOOD	VERY GOOD	NEAR MINT
GENE AUSTIN GREAT HITS	Dot (M) DLP-3300	2.50	3.75	5.00
GENE AUSTIN GREAT HITS	Dot (S) DLP-25300	2.50	3.75	5.00
GENE AUSTIN SINGS ALL-TIME FAVORITES	X (M) LVA 1007	3.00	4.50	6.00
MY BLUE HEAVEN	RCA (M) LPM 3200	2.00	3.00	4.00

AUSTIN, Sil

TITLE	LABEL & NO.	GOOD	VERY GOOD	NEAR MINT
EVERYTHINGS SHAKIN'	Mercury (M) MG 20320	2.00	5.00	8.00
GOLDEN SAXOPHONE HITS	Mercury (M) MG-20663	3.00	6.00	9.00
GOLDEN SAXOPHONE HITS	Mercury (S) SR-60663	4.00	8.00	12.00
SLOW WALK ROCK	Mercury (M) MG 20237	2.00	5.00	8.00

AUTOSALVAGE

TITLE	LABEL & NO.	GOOD	VERY GOOD	NEAR MINT
AUTOSALVAGE	RCA (S) LSP 3940	3.50	5.25	7.00

AUTRY, Gene

TITLE	LABEL & NO.	GOOD	VERY GOOD	NEAR MINT
EASTERN FAVORITES	Columbia (M) CL2568	1.00	2.00	3.00
GENE AUTRY GREATEST HITS	Columbia (M) CL-1575	2.50	3.75	5.00
GENE AUTRY SELECTIONS	Columbia (EP) H 1663	1.00	2.00	3.00
GENE AUTRY SELECTIONS	Columbia (EP) H1721	1.00	2.00	3.00
GENE AUTRY'S GOLDEN HITS	RCA (M) LPM-2623	2.50	3.75	5.00
GENE AUTRY'S GOLDEN HITS	RCA (S) LSP-2623	2.00	3.00	4.00
GENE AUTRY'S GREAT WESTERN HITS	Harmony (M) HL-7332	1.00	2.00	3.00

AVALANCHES

TITLE	LABEL & NO.	GOOD	VERY GOOD	NEAR MINT
SKI SURFIN' WITH THE AVALANCHES	Warner Bros. (M) W 1525	2.50	5.00	7.50
SKI SURFIN' WITH THE AVALANCHES	Warner Brothers (S) WS 1525	3.00	6.00	9.00

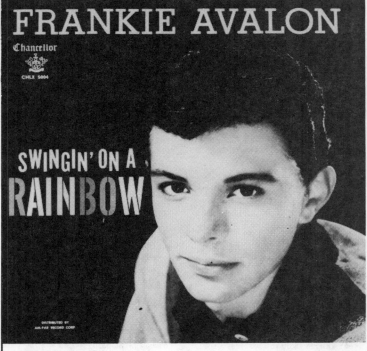

AVALON, Frankie

TITLE	LABEL & NO.	GOOD	VERY GOOD	NEAR MINT
AND NOW ABOUT MR. AVALON	Chancellor (M) CHL 5022	3.00	6.00	9.00
AND NOW ABOUT MR. AVALON	Chancellor (S) CHLS 5022	3.00	6.00	9.00
BALLAD OF THE ALAMO	Chancellor (EP) 303	4.00	6.00	8.00
(With complete kit)		8.00	20.00	32.00
15 GREATEST HITS	United Artists (M) UAL 3382	3.00	6.00	9.00
FRANKIE AVALON	Chancellor (M) CHL 5001	6.00	12.00	18.00
FRANKIE AVALON	Sunset (S) SUS 5244	3.00	6.00	9.00
FRANKIE AVALON, Vol. 1	Chancellor (EP) A-5001	2.00	3.00	4.00
FRANKIE AVALONS CHRISTMAS ALBUM	Chancellor (M) CHL 5031	3.00	7.50	12.00
FRANKIE AVALONS CHRISTMAS ALBUM	Chancellor (S) CHLS 5031	4.00	10.00	16.00
FRANKIE AVALON SINGS CLEOPATRA PLUS 13 OTHER GREAT HITS	Chancellor (M) CHL 5032	3.00	7.50	12.00
FRANKIE AVALON SINGS CLEOPATRA PLUS 13 OTHER GREAT HITS	Chancellor (S) CHLS 5032	4.00	10.00	16.00
GOOD OLD SUMMERTIME, VOL. 2	Chancellor (EP) B-5012	2.00	3.00	4.00
GUNS OF THE TIMBERLAND	Chancellor (EP) CHLA-302	3.00	4.50	6.00
ITALIANO	Chancellor (M) CHL 5025	3.00	6.00	9.00

7

TITLE	LABEL & NO.	GOOD	VERY GOOD	NEAR MINT
ITALIANO	Chancellor (S) CHLS 5025	4.00	8.00	12.00
MUSCLE BEACH PARTY	United Artists (M) UAL 3371	3.00	6.00	9.00
MUSCLE BEACH PARTY	United Artists (S) UAS 6371	7.00	14.00	21.00
16 GREATEST HITS	ABC (M) ABCX 805	3.00	4.50	6.00
SUMMER SCENE	Chancellor (M) CHL 5011	3.00	7.50	12.00
SUMMER SCENE, Vol. 1	Chancellor (EP) A-5011	2.00	3.00	4.00
SUMMER SCENE, Vol. 2	Chancellor (EP) B-5011	2.00	3.00	4.00
SUMMER SCENE, Vol. 3	Chancellor (EP) C-5011	2.00	3.00	4.00
SWINGIN ON A RAINBOW	Chancellor (M) CHLX 5004	3.00	7.50	12.00
SWINGIN' ON A RAINBOW, Vol. 1	Chancellor (EP) A-5004	2.00	3.00	4.00
SWINGIN' ON A RAINBOW, Vol. 2	Chancellor (EP) B-5004	2.00	3.00	4.00
SWINGIN' ON A RAINBOW, Vol 3	chancellor (EP) C-5004	2.00	3.00	4.00
VENUS	De-Lite (S) 2020	3.00	4.50	6.00
VERY BEST OF FRANKIE AVALON, THE	United Artists (M) UALA450	2.50	3.75	5.00
A WHOLE LOTTA FRANKIE	Chancellor (M) CHL 5018	3.00	7.50	12.00
YOU ARE MINE	Chancellor (M) CHL 5027	3.00	7.50	12.00
YOU ARE MINE	Chancellor (S) CHLS 5027	4.00	10.00	16.00
YOUNG AND IN LOVE	Chancellor (M) CHL 69801	4.00	10.00	16.00

(This LP was also sold in a special box containing photos
and a 3D relief portrait of Frankie suitable for wall hanging).

YOUNG FRANKIE AVALON	Chancellor (M) CHL 5002	3.00	7.50	12.00
YOUNG FRANKIE AVALON, Vol. 1	Chancellor (EP) A-5002	2.00	3.00	4.00
YOUNG FRANKIE AVALON, Vol. 2	Chancellor (EP) B-5002	2.00	3.00	4.00

AVANT SLANT
ONE PLUS ONE = II	Decca (S) 75018	2.00	3.00	4.00

AVERAGE WHITE BAND
AVERAGE WHITE BAND	MCA (S) 345	4.00	6.00	8.00
AVERAGE WHITE BAND	Atlantic (S) 7308	3.00	4.50	6.00
AVERAGE WHITE BAND	Atlantic (Q) QD-7308	2.50	3.75	5.00
CUT THE CAKE	Atlantic (S) 18140	2.50	3.75	5.00
PUT IT WHERE YOU WANT IT	MCA (S) 475	3.00	4.50	6.00
WARMER COMMUNICATIONS	Atlantic (S) SD 19162	2.00	3.00	4.00

AVONS
AVONS, THE	Hull (M) HLP 1000	12.50	31.25	50.00

AXTON, Hoyt
FEARLESS	A&M (S) SP 4571	2.00	3.00	4.00
FREE SAILIN'	MCA (S) 2319	2.00	3.00	4.00
HOYT AXTON EXPLODES!	Vee Jay (M) LP 1098	5.00	10.00	15.00
LESS THAN THE SONG	A&M (S) SP 4376	2.00	3.00	4.00
LIFE MACHINE	A&M (S) SP 4422	2.00	3.00	4.00
MY GRIFFIN IS GONE	Columbia (S) KC-33103	2.50	3.75	5.00
ROAD SONGS	A&M (S) SP 4669	2.00	3.00	4.00
SOUTHBOUND	A&M (S) SP 4510	2.00	3.00	4.00

AYERS ROCK
BEYOND	A&M (S) SP 4565	2.00	3.00	4.00
BIG RED ROCK	A&M (S) SP 4523	2.00	3.00	4.00

AZTECS
LIVE AT THE AD-LIB CLUB OF LONDON	World Artists (M) WAM 2001	4.00	8.00	12.00

(M) Mono (S) Stereo (EP) Extended Play (Q) Quad (RI) Re-issued

TITLE	LABEL & NO.	GOOD	VERY GOOD	NEAR MINT
BABE RUTH				
AMAR CABALLERO	Harvest (S) ST-11275	3.50	5.25	7.00
BABE RUTH	Harvest (S) ST-11367	3.00	4.50	6.00
FIRST BASE	Harvest (S) SW-11151	3.50	5.25	7.00
STEALIN' HOME	Harvest (S) ST-11451	3.00	4.50	6.00
BABY				
BABY	Mercury (S) SRM-1-1062	2.50	3.75	5.00
WHERE DID ALL THE MONEY GO?	Chelsea (S) CHL 517	3.00	4.50	6.00
BABY RAY				
WHERE SOUL LIVES	Imperial (M) LP 9335	3.00	4.50	6.00
WHERE SOUL LIVES	Imperial (S) LP 12335	4.00	6.00	8.00
BACHARACH, Burt				
BURT BACHARACH	A&M (S) SP 3501	2.50	3.75	5.00
BUTCH CASSIDY & THE SUNDANCE KID	A&M (S) SP4227	3.00	4.50	6.00
(Soundtrack)				
FUTURES	A&M (S) SP 4622	2.00	3.00	4.00
GREATEST HITS	A&M (S) 3661	2.50	3.75	5.00
GREATEST HITS	A&M (Q) QU 53661	3.00	4.50	6.00
HITS OF BURT BACHARACH (RI)	MCA (S) 65	2.50	3.75	5.00
LIVING TOGETHER	A&M (S) 3527	2.00	3.00	4.00
MAKE IT EASY ON YOURSELF	A&M (S) SP 4188	2.50	3.75	5.00
MAKE IT EASY ON YOURSELF	A&M (Q) QU 54188	3.00	4.50	6.00
REACH OUT	A&M (S) SP 4131	2.50	3.75	5.00
REACH OUT	A&M (Q) QU 54131	2.50	3.75	5.00
BACHELORS				
BACHELORS GIRLS	London (S) 491	4.00	6.00	8.00
BACK AGAIN	London (M) LL 3393	4.00	6.00	8.00
BACK AGAIN	London (S) PS 393	5.00	7.50	10.00
GOLDEN ALL TIME HITS	London (M) LL 3518	3.00	4.50	6.00
GOLDEN ALL TIME HITS	London (S) PS 518	4.00	6.00	8.00
HITS OF THE 60's	London (M) LL 3460	3.00	4.50	6.00
HITS OF THE 60's	London (S) PS 460	4.00	6.00	8.00
MARIE	London (M) LL 3435	4.00	6.00	8.00
MARIE	London (S) PS 435	5.00	7.50	10.00
NO ARMS CAN EVER HOLD YOU	London (M) LL 3418	4.00	6.00	8.00
NO ARMS CAN EVER HOLD YOU	London (S) PS 418	5.00	7.50	10.00
PRESENTING THE BACHELORS	London (M) LL 3353	4.00	6.00	8.00
PRESENTING THE BACHELORS	London (S) PS 353	5.00	7.50	10.00
'68	London (S) 528	4.00	6.00	8.00
UNDER AND OVER	London (S) XPS 611	4.00	6.00	8.00
BACHMAN, Randy				
SURVIVOR	Polydor (S) PD-1-6141	2.00	3.00	4.00
Also see BACHMAN-TURNER OVERDRIVE, GUESS WHO				
BACHMAN-TURNER OVERDRIVE				
BACHMAN-TURNER OVERDRIVE 2	Mercury (S) SRM-1-696	3.50	5.25	7.00
BEST OF B.T.O. (SO FAR)	Mercury (S) SRM-1-1011	3.00	4.50	6.00
FOUR WHEEL DRIVE	Mercury (S) SRM-1-1027	3.00	4.50	6.00
FREEWAYS	Mercury (S) SRM-1-3700	3.00	4.50	6.00
HEAD ON	Mercury (S) SRM-1-1067	3.00	4.50	6.00
NOT FRAGILE	Mercury (S) SRM-1-1004	3.50	5.25	7.00
STREET ACTION	Mercury (S) SRM-1-3713	2.00	3.00	4.00
Also see BACHMAN, Randy, GUESS WHO				
BACKUS, Jim				
DIRTY OLD MAN	Dore (S) 332	2.00	3.00	4.00
BACKWATER				
BACKWATER	Bongwater (S) 0001	3.00	4.50	6.00
BACON FAT				
GREASE ONE FOR ME	Blue Horizon (M) BH 4807	3.00	4.50	6.00
BAD COMPANY				
BAD COMPANY	Swan Song (S) SS 8410	2.50	3.75	5.00
BURNIN' SKY	Swan Song (S) SS 8500	2.00	3.00	4.00
RUN WITH THE PACK	Swan Song (S) SS 8415	2.50	3.75	5.00
STRAIGHT SHOOTER	Swan Song (S) SS 8413	2.50	3.75	5.00
BADFINGER				
ASS	Apple (S) SW 3411	3.00	4.50	6.00
BADFINGER	Warner Brothers (S) BS 2762	2.50	3.75	5.00
MAGIC CHRISTIAN MUSIC	Apple (S) ST 3364	6.00	9.00	12.00
MAGIC CHRISTIAN				
Soundtrack	Commonwealth United (S) CU 6004	5.00	7.50	10.00
NO DICE	Apple (S) ST 3367	3.00	4.50	6.00
STRAIGHT UP	Apple (S) SW 3387	3.00	4.50	6.00
WISH YOU WERE HERE	Warner Brothers (S) BS 2827	3.00	4.50	6.00

TITLE	LABEL & NO.	GOOD	VERY GOOD	NEAR MINT

BAEZ, Joan

TITLE	LABEL & NO.	GOOD	VERY GOOD	NEAR MINT
BEST OF JOAN BAEZ	A&M (S) 4668	2.00	3.00	4.00
BLOWIN' AWAY	Portrait (S) PR 34697	2.00	3.00	4.00
BLOWIN' AWAY	Portrait (Q) PRQ 34697	2.00	3.00	4.00
COME FROM THE SHADOWS	A&M (S) SP 4339	2.00	3.00	4.00
COME FROM THE SHADOWS	A&M (Q) QU 54339	2.00	3.00	4.00
CONTEMPORARY BALLAD BOOK	Vanguard (S) VSD-49/50	3.50	5.25	7.00
DIAMONDS & RUST	A&M (S) 4527	3.00	4.50	6.00
DIAMONDS & RUST	A&M (Q) QU-54527	2.50	3.75	5.00
FAREWELL ANGELINA	Vanguard (M) VRS-9200	2.00	3.00	4.00
FAREWELL ANGELINA	Vanguard (S) VSD7-9200	2.50	3.75	5.00
FROM EVERY STAGE	A&M (S) SP 3704	3.00	4.50	6.00
GRACIAS A LA VIDA	A&M (S) SP 3614	3.00	4.50	6.00
GULF WINDS	A&M (S) SP 4603	2.00	3.00	4.00
HITS/GREATEST & OTHERS	Vanguard (S) 79332	2.50	3.75	5.00
HITS/GREATEST & OTHERS	Vanguard (Q) 40032	2.50	3.75	5.00
JOAN BAEZ BALLAD BOOK	Vanguard (S) VSD-41/42	3.50	5.25	7.00
JOAN BAEZ IN SAN FRANCISCO	Fantasy (M) 5015	6.00	9.00	12.00
JOAN BAEZ IN SAN FRANCISCO	Vanguard (M) VRS-9160	2.00	3.00	4.00
JOAN BAEZ IN SAN FRANCISCO	Vanguard (S) VSD7-9160	2.50	3.75	5.00
MILAN	Vanguard (S) 79320	2.50	3.75	5.00
NOEL	Vanguard (M) 9230	2.00	3.00	4.00
NOEL	Vanguard (S) 7-9230	2.50	3.75	5.00
WHERE ARE YOU NOW, MY SON	A&M (S) SP 4390	2.50	3.75	5.00

BAGDASARIAN, Ross

TITLE	LABEL & NO.	GOOD	VERY GOOD	NEAR MINT
BAGDASARIAN	Liberty (M) LRP 3451	4.00	8.00	12.00
BAGDASARIAN	Liberty (S) LST 7451	5.00	10.00	15.00

BAILEY, Buster

TITLE	LABEL & NO.	GOOD	VERY GOOD	NEAR MINT
ALL ABOUT MEMPHIS	Felsted (M) FAJ-7003	2.50	5.00	7.50
ALL ABOUT MEMPHIS	Felsted (S) SJA-2003	3.00	6.00	9.00

BAILEY, J.R.

TITLE	LABEL & NO.	GOOD	VERY GOOD	NEAR MINT
JUST ME 'N' YOU	Mam (S) 9	3.50	5.25	7.00

BAILEY, Pearl

TITLE	LABEL & NO.	GOOD	VERY GOOD	NEAR MINT
FOR ADULT LISTENING	Wing (M) MGW-12132	2.00	3.00	4.00
MORE SONGS FOR ADULTS ONLY	Roulette (M) R-25101	2.00	3.00	4.00
MORE SONGS FOR ADULTS ONLY	Roulette (S) SR-25101	2.00	3.00	4.00
NAUGHTY BUT NICE	Roulette (M) R-25125	2.00	3.00	4.00
NAUGHTY BUT NICE	Roulette (S) SR-25125	2.00	3.00	4.00
PEARL BAILEY SINGS	Harmony (M) HL-7184	2.00	3.00	4.00
PEARL BAILEY SINGS FOR ADULTS ONLY	Roulette (M) R25063	2.00	4.00	6.00
PEARL BAILEY SINGS PORGY & BESS	Roulette (M) R25063	2.00	4.00	6.00
PEARL BAILEY SINGS PORGY & BESS	Roulette (S) SR-25063	2.00	4.00	6.00
SONGS OF THE BAD OLD DAYS	Roulette (M) R-25116	2.00	3.00	4.00
SONGS OF THE BAD OLD DAYS	Roulette (S) SR-25116	2.00	3.00	4.00

BAJA MARIMBA BAND

TITLE	LABEL & NO.	GOOD	VERY GOOD	NEAR MINT
BAJA MARIMBA BAND	A&M (M) LP 104	2.50	5.00	7.50
BAJA MARIMBA BAND	A&M (S) SP 104	3.00	6.00	9.00
BAJA MARIMBA BAND RIDES AGAIN	A&M (M) LP 109	2.50	5.00	7.50
BAJA MARIMBA BAND RIDES AGAIN	A&M (S) SP 109	3.00	6.00	9.00
BAJA MARIMBA BAND'S BACK	Bell (S) 1124	2.50	3.75	5.00
DO YOU KNOW THE WAY TO SAN JOSE?	A&M (S) SP 4150	2.50	3.75	5.00
FOR ANIMALS ONLY	A&M (M) LP 113	2.50	3.75	5.00
FOR ANIMALS ONLY	A&M (S) SP 4113	3.00	4.50	6.00
FOWL PLAY	A&M (M) LP 136	2.50	3.75	5.00
FOWL PLAY	A&M (S) SP 4136	3.00	4.50	6.00
FRESH AIR	A&M (S) SP 4200	2.50	3.75	5.00
GREATEST HITS	A&M (S) SP 4248	2.00	3.00	4.00
HEADS UP!	A&M (M) LP 123	2.50	3.75	5.00
HEADS UP!	A&M (S) SP 4123	3.00	4.50	6.00
JULIUS WECHTER AND THE BAJA MARIMBA BAND FOUR SIDER	A&M (S) SP 3523	2.00	3.00	4.00
THOSE WERE THE DAYS	A&M (S) SP 4167	2.50	3.75	5.00
WATCH OUT	A&M (M) LP 118	2.50	3.75	5.00
WATCH OUT	A&M (S) SP 4118	3.00	4.50	6.00

(Shown as "Julius Wechter & The Baja Marimba Band" beginning with A&M 136)

BAKER, Bonnie

TITLE	LABEL & NO.	GOOD	VERY GOOD	NEAR MINT
OH JOHNNY	Warner Brothers (M) B 1212	2.50	3.75	5.00

BAKER, Ginger

TITLE	LABEL & NO.	GOOD	VERY GOOD	NEAR MINT
GINGER BAKER AT HIS BEST	Polydor (S) 24-3504	3.00	4.50	6.00
GINGER BAKER'S AIR FORCE	Atco (S) 703	4.00	6.00	8.00

Also see CREAM & BAKER-GURVITZ ARMY

BAKER-GURVITZ ARMY

TITLE	LABEL & NO.	GOOD	VERY GOOD	NEAR MINT
BAKER-GURVITZ ARMY	Janus (S) 7015	3.50	5.25	7.00
ELYSIAN ENCOUNTER	Atco (S) 36-123	3.00	4.50	6.00

Also see BAKER, GINGER & CREAM

BAKER, La Vern

TITLE	LABEL & NO.	GOOD	VERY GOOD	NEAR MINT
BEST OF LA VERN BAKER	Atalntic (M) 8078	3.00	7.50	12.00
BEST OF LA VERN BAKER	Atlantic (SD) 8078	2.00	5.00	8.00
BLUES BALLADS	Atlantic (M) 8030	4.00	10.00	16.00
BLUES BALLADS	Atlantic (S) SD 8030	3.00	7.50	12.00
HER GREATEST RECORDINGS	Atco (M) 372	3.00	4.50	6.00
LA VERN	Atlantic (M) 8002	6.00	15.00	24.00
LA VERN	Atlantic (S) SD 8002	2.00	5.00	8.00
LA VERN BAKER	Atlantic (M) 8007	4.00	10.00	16.00
LA VERN BAKER SINGS BESSIE SMITH	Atlantic (M) 1281	3.00	7.50	12.00
LA VERN BAKER SINGS BESSIE SMITH	Atlantic (SD) 1281	3.00	7.50	12.00
LET ME BELONG TO YOU	Brunswick (S) BL 754160	3.50	5.25	7.00
PRECIOUS MEMORIES	Atlantic (M) 8036	3.00	7.50	12.00
PRECIOUS MEMORIES	Atlantic (SD) 8036	2.00	5.00	8.00
SAVED	Atlantic (M) 8050	3.00	7.50	12.00
SAVED	Atlantic (S) SD 8050	2.00	5.00	8.00
SEE SEE RIDER	Atlantic (M) 8071	3.00	7.50	12.00
SEE SEE RIDER	Atlantic (S) SD 8071	2.00	5.00	8.00
TWEEDLE DEE-SOUL ON FIRE	Atlantic (EP) EP 566	3.00	6.00	9.00
TWEEDLE DEE-SOUL ON FIRE	Atlantic (EP) EP 588	3.00	6.00	9.00

BAKER, Mickey

TITLE	LABEL & NO.	GOOD	VERY GOOD	NEAR MINT
WILDEST GUITAR	Atlantic (S) SD 8035	4.00	10.00	16.00

Also see MICKEY & SYLVIA

BAKER, Robert

TITLE	LABEL & NO.	GOOD	VERY GOOD	NEAR MINT
PARDON ME FOR BEING SO FRIENDLY BUT THIS IS MY FIRST LSD TRIP	GNP/Crescendo (M) GNP 2027	3.00	6.00	9.00

BALDRY, Long John

TITLE	LABEL & NO.	GOOD	VERY GOOD	NEAR MINT
EVERYTHING STOPS FOR TEA	Warner Bros. (S) BS 2614	3.00	4.50	6.00
GOOD TO BE ALIVE	Casablanca (S) 7012	2.50	3.75	5.00
IT AIN'T EASY	Warner Bros. (S) WS 1921	3.00	4.50	6.00
LONG JOHN'S BLUES	Ascot (M) ALM 13022	4.00	8.00	12.00

BALLADEERS

TITLE	LABEL & NO.	GOOD	VERY GOOD	NEAR MINT
ALIVE-O	Del Fi (M) DF-1204	3.00	6.00	9.00

BALLARD, Frank

TITLE	LABEL & NO.	GOOD	VERY GOOD	NEAR MINT
RHYTHM AND BLUES PARTY	Phillips (M) PILP 1985	15.00	37.50	60.00

BALLARD, Hank & The Midnighters

TITLE	LABEL & NO.	GOOD	VERY GOOD	NEAR MINT
BIGGEST HITS	King (M) 867	5.00	10.00	15.00
DANCE ALONG	King (M) 759	6.00	12.00	18.00
GLAD SONGS, SAD SONGS	King (M) 927	4.00	8.00	12.00
GREATEST HITS	Federal (EP) EP-333	4.00	10.00	16.00
HANK BALLARD AND THE MIDNIGHTERS	King (M) 581	8.00	20.00	32.00
HANK BALLARD SINGS 24 GREAT SONGS	King (M) 981	4.00	8.00	12.00
JUMPIN'	King (EP) EP 793	2.00	4.00	6.00
JUMPIN' HANK BALLARD AND THE MIDNIGHTERS	King (M) 793	6.00	12.00	18.00
LET'S GO AGAIN	King (M) 748	6.00	15.00	24.00
MR. RHYTHM AND BLUES	King (M) 700	6.00	15.00	24.00
1963 SOUND OF HANK BALLARD AND THE MIDNIGHTERS	King (M) 815	5.00	10.00	15.00
ONE AND ONLY, THE	King (M) 674	7.00	17.50	28.00
SINGIN' AND SWINGIN'	King (M) 618	7.00	17.50	28.00
SINGIN' AND SWINGIN', VOL. I	King (EP) EP 435	3.00	7.50	12.00
SINGIN' AND SWINGIN' VOL. II	King (EP) EP 451	3.00	7.50	12.00
SPOTLIGHT OF HANK BALLARD	King (M) 740	6.00	15.00	24.00
A STAR IN YOUR EYES	King (M) 896	6.00	12.00	18.00
THEIR GREATEST JUKE BOX HITS	King (M) 541	9.00	22.50	36.00
THOSE LAZY, LAZY, DAYS	King (M) 913	5.00	10.00	15.00
24 HIT TUNES	King (M) 950	4.00	8.00	12.00
TWISTIN' FOOLS, THE	King (M) 781	6.00	12.00	18.00
YOU CAN'T KEEP A GOOD MAN DOWN	King (S) KSD 1052	4.00	8.00	12.00

Note: many King LPs by Hank Ballard & the Midnighters were later re-pressed with the same catalog numbers but "in electronically re-channelled stereo." The value of these is about 25% of the originals.

BALLIN' JACK

TITLE	LABEL & NO.	GOOD	VERY GOOD	NEAR MINT
BALLIN' JACK	Columbia (S) 30344	3.00	4.50	6.00
BALLIN' JACK LIVE & IN COLOR	Mercury (S) SRM-1-700	2.50	3.75	5.00
SPECIAL PRIDE	Mercury (S) SRM-1-672	2.50	3.75	5.00

BANANA & THE BUNCH

TITLE	LABEL & NO.	GOOD	VERY GOOD	NEAR MINT
MID MOUNTAIN RANCH	Warner Brothers (S) BS 2626	2.50	3.75	5.00

BAND

TITLE	LABEL & NO.	GOOD	VERY GOOD	NEAR MINT
BAND	Capitol (S) ST 132	4.50	6.75	9.00
CAHOOTS	Capitol (S) ST 651	3.50	5.25	7.00
LAST WALTZ	Warner Bros. (S) 3WS 3146	3.50	5.25	7.00
MOONDOG MATINEE	Capitol (M) 11214	3.00	4.50	6.00
MUSIC FROM BIG PINK	Capitol (S) SKAO 2955	4.50	6.75	9.00
NORTHERN LIGHTS, SOUTHERN LIGHTS	Capitol (S) ST 11440	3.00	4.50	6.00
ROCK OF AGES	Capitol (S) SABB 11045	3.00	4.50	6.00
STAGE FRIGHT	Capitol (S) ST 425	3.50	5.25	7.00

Also see DYLAN, Bob

BANDY, Moe

TITLE	LABEL & NO.	GOOD	VERY GOOD	NEAR MINT
BANDY THE RODEO CLOWN	GRC (S) 10016	3.50	5.25	7.00
I JUST STARTED HATIN' CHEATIN' SONGS TODAY	GRC (S) 10005	3.00	4.50	6.00
IT WAS ALWAYS SO EASY	GRC (S) 10007	3.00	4.50	6.00

BANGOR FLYING CIRCUS

TITLE	LABEL & NO.	GOOD	VERY GOOD	NEAR MINT
BANGOR FLYING CIRCUS	Dunhill (S) DS 50069	2.50	3.75	5.00

BANKS, Darrell

TITLE	LABEL & NO.	GOOD	VERY GOOD	NEAR MINT
DARRELL BANKS IS HERE	Atco (M) 33-216	2.00	3.00	4.00
HERE TO STAY	Volt (M) VOS 6002	2.50	3.75	5.00

(M) Mono (S) Stereo (EP) Extended Play (Q) Quad (RI) Re-issued

TITLE	LABEL & NO.	GOOD	VERY GOOD	NEAR MINT

BANTAMS
BEWARE	Warner Broshers (M) WS 1625	3.00	4.50	6.00

BARBARIANS
ARE YOU A BOY OR A GIRL	Laurie (M) LLP 2033	8.00	20.00	32.00
ARE YOU A BOY OR A GIRL	Laurie (S) SLP 2033	10.00	25.00	40.00

BARBOUR, Keith
ECHO PARK	Epic (S) BN 26485	2.50	3.75	5.00

BARDENS, Peter
ANSWER	Verve/Forecast (S) FTS 3088	3.00	4.50	6.00
WRITE MY NAME IN DUST	Verve/Forecast (S) FTS 3091	3.50	5.25	7.00

BARDOT, Brigitte
BRIGITTE BARDOT	Philips (M) PCC-204	2.50	3.75	5.00
BRIGITTE BARDOT	Philips (S) PCC-604	2.00	3.00	4.00

BARE, Bobby
BARE	Columbia (S) KC 35314	2.00	3.00	4.00
BEST OF BOBBY BARE	RCA (M) LPM-3479	2.50	3.75	5.00
BEST OF BOBBY BARE	RCA (S) LSP-3479	2.50	3.75	5.00
BEST OF BOBBY BARE	RCA (M) LPM-3994	2.00	3.00	4.00
BEST OF BOBBY BARE	RCA (S) LSP-3994	2.00	3.00	4.00
A BIRD NAMED YESTERDAY	RCA (M) LPM-3831	2.50	3.75	5.00
A BIRD NAMED YESTERDAY	RCA (S) LPS-3831	2.50	3.75	5.00
BOBBY BARE	RCA (S) APL1-0040	2.00	3.00	4.00
BOBBY BARE (Sings Lullabys, Legends & Lies)	RCA (S) CPL2-0290	2.50	3.75	5.00
CONSTANT SORROW	RCA (M) LPM-3395	2.50	3.75	5.00
CONSTANT SORROW	RCA (S) LPS-3395	2.50	3.75	5.00
COWBOYS & DADDYS	RCA (S) APL1-1222	2.00	3.00	4.00
DETROIT CITY & OTHER HITS	RCA (M) LPM-2776	2.50	3.75	5.00
DETROIT CITY & OTHER HITS	RCA (S) LSP-2776	2.50	3.75	5.00
500 MILES AWAY FROM HOME	RCA (M) LPM-2835	2.50	3.75	5.00
500 MILES AWAY FROM HOME	RCA (S) LSP-2835	2.50	3.75	5.00
FOLSOM PRISON BLUES	Camden (M) 2290	2.00	3.00	4.00
FOLSOM PRISON BLUES	Camden (S) 2290	2.00	3.00	4.00
HARD TIME HUNGRYS	RCA (S) APL1-0906	2.00	3.00	4.00
ME & McDILL	RCA (S) APL1-2179	2.00	3.00	4.00
MEMPHIS, TENNESSEE	Camden (M) ACL1-0150	2.00	3.00	4.00
SINGIN' IN THE KITCHEN (& Family)	RCA (S) APL1-0700	2.00	3.00	4.00
STREETS OF BALTIMORE	RCA (M) LPM-3618	2.00	3.00	4.00
STREETS OF BALTIMORE	RCA (S) LSP-3618	2.00	3.00	4.00
TALK ME SOME SENSE	RCA (M) LPM-3515	2.00	3.00	4.00
TALK ME SOME SENSE	RCA (S) LSP-3515	2.00	3.00	4.00
THIS IS BOBBY BARE	RCA (S) VPS 6090	2.50	3.75	5.00
THIS IS BARE COUNTRY	United Artists (S) UA-LA621	2.00	3.00	4.00
TRAVELIN' BARE	RCA (M) LPM-2955	2.50	3.75	5.00
TRAVELIN' BARE	RCA (S) LSP-2955	2.50	3.75	5.00
VERY BEST OF BOBBY BARE	United Artists (S) UA-LA427	2.50	3.75	5.00

BARE, Bobby & Skeeter Davis
TUNES FOR TWO	RCA (M) LPM-3336	2.00	3.00	4.00
TUNES FOR TWO	RCA (S) LSP-3336	2.00	3.00	4.00

BAREFOOT JERRY
BAREFOOT JERRY	Warner Bros. (S) BS2641	2.00	3.00	4.00

(M) Mono (S) Stereo (EP) Extended Play (Q) Quad (RI) Re-issued

TITLE	LABEL & NO.	GOOD	VERY GOOD	NEAR MINT
BAREFOOT JERRY'S GROCERY	Monument (S) PZG 33909	2.00	3.00	4.00
YOU CAN'T GET OFF WITH YOUR SHOES ON	Monument (S) KZ-33381	2.00	3.00	4.00
WATCHIN' TV	Monument (S) KZ-32926	2.00	3.00	4.00

BARGE, Gene
DANCE WITH DADDY G	Checker (M) 2994	4.00	10.00	16.00

BAR-KAYS
BLACK ROCK	Volt (S) 6011	3.00	4.50	6.00
COLD BLOODED	Volt (S) 6023	3.00	4.50	6.00
SOUL FINGER	Volt (M) 417	3.50	5.25	7.00
SOUL FINGER	Volt (S) S 417	4.00	6.00	8.00

BARKER, Warren
77 SUNSET STRIP	Warner Brothers (M) W-1289	2.00	4.00	6.00
77 SUNSET STRIP	Warner Brothers (S) WS-1289	3.00	6.00	9.00
77 SUNSET STRIP	Warner Brothers (EP) EA 1289	1.00	2.00	3.00
77 SUNSET STRIP	Warner Bros. (EP) ESA 1289	3.00	6.00	9.00
(Rare Stereo Version)				

BARLOW, Jack
I LIVE THE COUNTRY SONGS I SING	Antique (S) 6004	2.50	3.75	5.00

BARNES, JJ & Steve Mancha
RARE STAMPS	Volt (S) VOS 6001	4.00	6.00	8.00

BARNUM, H.B.
BIG HITS OF DETROIT	Capitol (M) T-2289	2.00	3.00	4.00
BIG HITS OF DETROIT	Capitol (S) ST-2289	3.00	4.50	6.00
GOLDEN BOY	Capitol (M) T-2278	2.00	3.00	4.00
GOLDEN BOY	Capitol (S) ST-2278	3.00	4.50	6.00
LEARN TO DANCE THE CHA CHA CHA	Tropic Isle (M) TR-1001	3.00	4.50	6.00

BARONS
BARONS, THE	Decca (EP) 2400	3.00	7.50	12.00

BAROQUES
BAROQUES, THE	Chess (M) LP 1516	4.00	6.00	8.00
BAROQUES, THE	Chess (S) LPS 1516	5.00	7.50	10.00

BAROQUE ENSEMBLE OF MERSEYSIDE KAMMERMUSIKGESELLSCHAFT
BAROQUE BEATLES BOOK	Elektra (M) EKL-306	2.00	3.00	4.00
BAROQUE BEATLES BOOK	Elektra (S) EKS7-306	3.00	4.50	6.00

BARRABAS
BARRABAS	RCA (S) APL1-0219	2.50	3.75	5.00
WILD SAFARI	RCA (S) LSP-4861	3.00	4.50	6.00

BARRACUDAS
A PLANE VIEW	Justice (M) 143	8.00	16.00	24.00

BARRA, Rocky
DON'T KNOCK THE ROCK	Barratone (M) BSL 1003	3.50	5.25	7.00
GOOD ROCKIN' TONIGHT	Barratone (M) BSL 1002	3.50	5.25	7.00

BARRETT, Rona
MISS RONA SINGS HOLLYWOOD'S GREATEST HITS	Miss Rona (S) 1001	4.00	6.00	8.00

BARRETT, Syd
MADCAP LAUGHS/BARRETT, THE	Harvest (S) SABB-11314	4.00	6.00	8.00

BARRON, Ronnie
REVEREND ETHER	Decca (S) DL 75303	3.00	4.50	6.00

BARRY & TAMERLANES
I WONDER WHAT SHE'S DOING TONIGHT	Valiant (M) W-406	5.00	10.00	15.00

BARRY, Jeff
WALKIN' IN THE SUN	A&M (S) SP 4393	3.00	4.50	6.00
Also see RAINDROPS				

BARRY, Len
LEN BARRY SINGS WITH THE DOVELLS	Cameo (M) C 1082	4.00	8.00	12.00
MY KIND OF SOUL	RCA (M) LPM 3823	2.00	4.00	6.00
MY KIND OF SOUL	RCA (S) LSP 3823	3.00	6.00	9.00
1-2-3	Decca (M) DL-4720	3.00	6.00	9.00
1-2-3	Decca (S) DL 74720	4.00	8.00	12.00
UPS AND DOWNS	Buddah (M) BDS 5105	2.50	3.75	5.00
Also see DOVELLS				

BARRY SISTERS
AT HOME WITH THE BARRY SISTERS	Roulette (M) R-25060	3.00	7.50	12.00
AT HOME WITH THE BARRY SISTERS	Roulette (S) SR-25060	4.00	10.00	16.00

BARTHOLOMEW, Dave
FATS DOMINO PRESENTS DAVE BARTHOLOMEW & HIS GREAT BIG BAND	Imperial (M) 9162	4.00	10.00	16.00

FATS DOMINO PRESENTS DAVE BARTHOLOMEW

TITLE	LABEL & NO.	GOOD	VERY GOOD	NEAR MINT
& HIS GREAT BIG BAND	Imperial (S) 12076	5.00	12.50	20.00
NEW ORLEANS HOUSE PARTY	Imperial (M) 9217	4.00	10.00	16.00
NEW ORLEANS HOUSE PARTY	Imperial (S) S 12217	5.00	12.50	20.00

BARTLEY, Chris

TITLE	LABEL & NO.	GOOD	VERY GOOD	NEAR MINT
SWEETEST THING THIS SIDE OF HEAVEN, THE	Vando (M) VA 60,000	3.00	4.50	6.00
SWEETEST THING THIS SIDE OF HEAVEN, THE	Vando (S) VAS 60,000	3.00	4.50	6.00

BASKERVILLE HOUNDS

TITLE	LABEL & NO.	GOOD	VERY GOOD	NEAR MINT
THE BASKERVILLE HOUNDS, FEATURING SPACE ROCK, PART 2	Dot (M) DLP 3823	4.00	6.00	8.00
THE BASKERVILLE HOUNDS, FEATURING SPACE ROCK, PART 2	Dot (S) DLP 25823	5.00	7.50	10.00

BASS, Fontella

TITLE	LABEL & NO.	GOOD	VERY GOOD	NEAR MINT
FREE	Paula (S) LPS 2203	3.00	4.50	6.00
NEW LOOK, THE	Checker (M) LP 2997	3.50	5.25	7.00

BASSEY, Shirley

TITLE	LABEL & NO.	GOOD	VERY GOOD	NEAR MINT
AND I LOVE YOU SO	United Artists (S) UAS 5643	3.00	4.50	6.00
FABULOUS SHIRLEY BASSEY	MGM (M) E 3862	2.50	5.00	7.50
FABULOUS SHIRLEY BASSEY	MGM (S) SE 3862	3.00	6.00	9.00
GOOD, BAD BUT BEAUTIFUL	United Artists (S) UA-LA542	2.50	3.75	5.00
I CAPRICORN	United Artists (S) UAS 5565	3.00	4.50	6.00
LIVE AT CARNEGIE HALL	United Artists (S) UA-LA111	2.50	3.75	5.00
NEVER, NEVER, NEVER	United Artists (S) UA-LA055	2.50	3.75	5.00
SHIRLEY BASSEY BELTS THE BEST!	United Artists (M) UAL 3419	2.50	3.75	5.00
SHIRLEY BASSEY BELTS THE BEST!	United Artists (S) UAS 6419	3.00	4.50	6.00
SHIRLEY BASSEY IS REALLY "SOMETHING"	United Artists (S) UAS 6765	3.00	4.50	6.00
SOMETHING ELSE	United Artists (S) UAS 6797	3.00	4.50	6.00
YESTERDAYS	United Artists (S) UA-LA847	2.00	3.00	4.00

BATAAN

TITLE	LABEL & NO.	GOOD	VERY GOOD	NEAR MINT
AFROFILIPINO	Epic (S) KE-33471	2.00	3.00	4.00
AFROFILIPINO (RI)	Salsoul (S) 4101	3.00	6.00	9.00

BATDORF & RODNEY

TITLE	LABEL & NO.	GOOD	VERY GOOD	NEAR MINT
BATDORF & RODNEY	Asylum (S) 5056	2.50	3.75	5.00
LIFE IS YOU	Arista (S) 4041	2.00	3.00	4.00

BATTERED ORNAMENTS

TITLE	LABEL & NO.	GOOD	VERY GOOD	NEAR MINT
BATTERED ORNAMENTS	Harvest (S) 422	7.00	10.50	14.00

BATTIN, Skip

TITLE	LABEL & NO.	GOOD	VERY GOOD	NEAR MINT
SKIP BATTIN	Signpost (S) SP 8408	3.00	4.50	6.00

BAY CITY ROLERS

TITLE	LABEL & NO.	GOOD	VERY GOOD	NEAR MINT
BAY CITY ROLLERS	Arista (S) AL 4049	2.50	3.75	5.00
DEDICATION	Arista (S) AL 4093	2.50	3.75	5.00
GREATEST HITS	Arista (S) AB 4158	2.50	3.75	5.00
ROCK N' ROLL LOVE LETTER	Arista (S) AL 4071	2.50	3.75	5.00

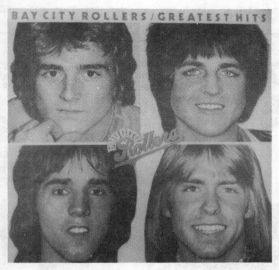

BAYSIDERS

TITLE	LABEL & NO.	GOOD	VERY GOOD	NEAR MINT
OVER THE RAINBOW	Everest (M) LPBR 5124	7.00	17.50	28.00

BAZUKA

TITLE	LABEL & NO.	GOOD	VERY GOOD	NEAR MINT
DYNOMITE	A&M (S) SP 3406	2.50	3.75	5.00

B.B. BLUNDER

TITLE	LABEL & NO.	GOOD	VERY GOOD	NEAR MINT
WORKERS PLAYTIME	Polydor (S) 24-4060	3.00	4.50	6.00

(M) Mono   (S) Stereo   (EP) Extended Play   (Q) Quad   (RI) Re-issued

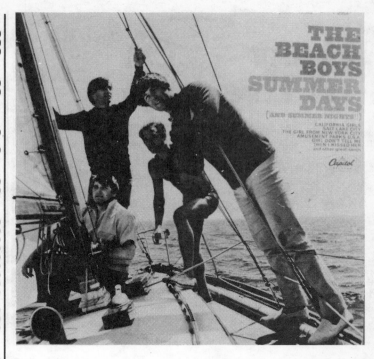

TITLE	LABEL & NO.	GOOD	VERY GOOD	NEAR MINT

BEACH BOYS

TITLE	LABEL & NO.	GOOD	VERY GOOD	NEAR MINT
ALL SUMMER LONG	Capitol (M) T 2110	4.00	8.00	12.00
ALL SUMMER LONG	Capitol (S) ST 2110	3.00	6.00	9.00
AMERICAN SUMMER (From RCA Record Club)	Capitol (S) R-233593	15.00	22.50	30.00
(A combination of "Spirit of America" and "Endless Summer.")				
BEACH BOYS, THE	Pickwick (S) SPC 3221	1.50	2.25	3.00
BEACH BOYS CHRISTMAS ALBUM	Capitol (M) T 2164	4.00	8.00	12.00
BEACH BOYS CHRISTMAS ALBUM	Capitol (S) ST 2164	3.00	6.00	9.00
BEACH BOYS' CHRISTMAS ALBUM (RI of ST2164)	Capitol (S) SM 2164	2.00	3.00	4.00
BEACH BOYS CONCERT	Capitol (M) TAO 2198	4.00	8.00	12.00
BEACH BOYS CONCERT	Capitol (S) STAO 2198	3.00	6.00	9.00
BEACH BOYS DELUXE SET	Capitol (M) TCL 2813	35.00	70.00	105.00
BEACH BOYS DELUXE SET	Capitol (S) DTCL 2813	111.00	22.00	33.00
BEACH BOYS GREATEST HITS, 1961-1963, THE	Orbit (S) OR 688	2.50	3.75	5.00
BEACH BOYS IN CONCERT (2 records)	Reprise (S) 6484	3.00	4.50	6.00
BEACH BOYS PARTY	Capitol (M) MAS 2398	5.00	10.00	15.00
BEACH BOYS PARTY	Capitol (S) DMAS 2398	5.00	10.00	15.00
BEACH BOYS PARTY	Capitol (EP) 2993/2994	18.00	36.00	54.00
(Promotional release only; red label)				
BEACH BOYS TODAY	Capitol (M) T 2269	4.00	8.00	12.00
BEACH BOYS TODAY	Capitol (S) DT 2269	4.00	8.00	12.00
BEST OF THE BEACH BOYS, THE	Scepter (S) CRN 18004	2.00	3.00	4.00
BEST OF THE BEACH BOYS (Compact 33)	Capitol (S) DT 2545	20.00	30.00	40.00
BEST OF THE BEACH BOYS: GOOD VIBRATIONS (RI of Reprise 2223)	Reprise (S) K 2280	2.00	3.00	4.00
BEST OF THE BEACH BOYS VOL. 1	Capitol (M) T 2545	3.00	4.50	6.00
BEST OF THE BEACH BOYS VOL. 2	Capitol (M) T 2706	3.00	4.50	6.00
BEST OF THE BEACH BOYS VOL. 3	Capitol (S) DKAO 2945	7.50	11.25	15.00
BRIAN WILSON INTRODUCES SELECTIONS FROM "BEACH BOYS CONCERT))	Capitol (EP) PRO 2754/2755	70.00	140.00	210.00
(Flip side is "Brian Wilson Introduces Selections From "Beach Boys Songbook." This EP contains "Little Old Lady," "Johnny B. Goode," "I Get Around," "The Warmth Of The Sun.")				
CARL AND THE PASSIONS SO TOUGH/PET SOUNDS (2 records)	Reprise (S) 2083	3.00	4.50	6.00
CLOSE UP	Capitol (S) SWBB 253	4.00	8.00	12.00
ENDLESS SUMMER	Capitol (S) SVBB 11307	2.25	3.75	4.50
15 BIG ONES	Reprise (S) MS 2251	2.00	3.00	4.00
4-BY THE BEACH BOYS	Capitol (EP) R 5267	7.50	11.25	15.00
FRIENDS	Capitol (S) ST 2895	5.00	7.50	10.00
FRIENDS/SMILEY SMILE (RI of Capitol 2895 & 2891 (2 records)	Reprise (S) 2MS 2167	3.00	4.50	6.00
GOLDEN YEARS OF THE BEACH BOYS (Candlelight TV sampler)	Capitol (S) SLB 6994	8.00	16.00	24.00
GOOD VIBRATIONS (Green Label is Original)	Capitol (S) 422	10.00	15.00	20.00
GOOD VIBRATIONS	Reprise (S) 2223	2.00	3.00	4.00
GOOD VIBRATIONS	Pickwick (S) SPC 3269	1.50	2.25	3.00
HIGHWATER	Pickwick (S) PTP 2059	2.00	3.00	4.00
HOLLAND (With compact 33)	Reprise (S) 2118	5.00	7.50	10.00
HOLLAND (German issue)	Reprise (S) 54008	70.00	140.00	210.00
(Contains a studio version of "We Got Love" which has not appeared on any other Beach Boys release.)				
LITTLE DEUCE COUPE	Capitol (M) T 1998	4.00	8.00	12.00
LITTLE DEUCE COUPE	Capitol (S) ST 1998	3.00	6.00	9.00

TITLE	LABEL & NO.	GOOD	VERY GOOD	NEAR MINT
PET SOUNDS	Capitol (M) T 2458	3.00	6.00	9.00
PET SOUNDS	Capitol (S) DT 2458	3.00	6.00	9.00
PET SOUNDS (RI of Capitol 2458)	Reprise (S) MS 2197	2.00	3.00	4.00
SHUT DOWN VOL. 2	Capitol (M) T 2027	4.00	8.00	12.00
SHUT DOWN VOL. 2	Capitol (S) ST 2027	3.00	6.00	9.00
SHUT DOWN VOL. 2 (Compact 33)	Capitol (S) SXA 2027	25.00	37.50	50.00
SMILEY SMILE (Capitol Record Club issue)	Capitol (S) ST8 2891	34.00	68.00	102.00
SMILEY SMILE	Brother (M) DT 9001	3.00	6.00	9.00
SPIRIT OF AMERICA	Capitol (S) SVBB 11384	2.25	3.75	4.50
STACK-O-TRACKS (With Book)	Capitol (S) DKAO 2893	25.00	50.00	75.00
STACK-O-TRACKS (Without Book)	Capitol (S) DKAO 2893	17.00	25.50	51.00
SUMMER DAYS AND SUMMER NIGHTS	Capitol (M) T 2354	4.00	8.00	12.00
SUMMER DAYS AND SUMMER NIGHTS	Capitol (S) DT 2354	4.00	8.00	12.00
SUNFLOWER	Reprise (S) 6382	2.00	3.00	4.00
SUPER GIRL (Compact 33)	Capitol (S) SXA 1981	25.00	50.00	75.00
SURFER GIRL	Capitol (M) T 1981	4.00	8.00	12.00
SURFER GIRL	Capitol (S) ST 1981	3.00	6.00	9.00
SURFER GIRL	Pickwick (S) SPC 3351	1.50	2.25	3.00
SURFIN' SAFARI	Capitol (M) T 1808	4.00	8.00	12.00
SURFIN' SAFARI	Capitol (S) DT 1808	3.00	6.00	9.00
SURFIN' USA	Capitol (M) T 1890	4.00	8.00	12.00
SURFIN' USA	Capitol (S) ST 1890	3.00	6.00	9.00
SURF'S UP	Reprise (S) 6453	3.00	4.50	6.00
10 LITTLE INDIANS	Capitol (EP) PRO 2186	70.00	140.00	210.00

(The Beach Boys sing "10 Little Indians," and "Little Miss America" on one side, and Ray Anthony sings two songs on the flip side.)

20/20	Capitol (S) SKAO 133	6.00	9.00	12.00
20/20 - WILD HONEY (RI of Capitol 133 & 2859) (2 records)	Reprise (S) 2MS 2166	7.50	11.25	15.00
WILD HONEY	Capitol (M) T 2859	5.00	7.50	10.00
WILD HONEY	Capitol (S) ST 2859	5.00	7.50	10.00
WOW! GREAT CONCERT	Pickwick (S) SPC 3309	2.00	3.00	4.00

(Many of the Capitol LP's have been reissued. These prices apply to original, black label, first issues)

BEACON STREET UNION

CLOWN DIED IN MARVIN GARDENS, THE	MGM (M) SE 4568	2.50	3.75	5.00
EYES OF THE BEACON STREET UNION, THE	MGM (M) SE 4517	2.50	3.75	5.00

BEAN, Arnold

COSMIC BEAM	SSS (S) SSS21	2.50	3.75	5.00

BEARCATS

BEATLEMANIA	Somerset (M) 20800	4.00	8.00	12.00
RAMA LAMA DING DONG	Bravo (EP) 70-2	2.00	4.00	6.00

BEASLEY, Jimmy

FABULOUS	Crown (M) CLP 5014	5.00	12.50	20.00
TWIST WITH JIMMY BEASLEY	Crown (M) CLP 5247	3.00	7.50	12.00

BEAST

BEAST	Cotillion (S) 9012	2.50	3.75	5.00

BEATLE BUDDIES

BEATLE BUDDIES	Diplomat (M) 2313	4.00	8.00	12.00

(M) Mono (S) Stereo (EP) Extended Play (Q) Quad (RI) Re-issued

TITLE	LABEL & NO.	GOOD	VERY GOOD	NEAR MINT

BEATLES

ABBEY ROAD	Apple (S) SO 383	1.50	3.00	4.50
AMERICAN TOUR WITH ED RUDY (#2)	Radio Pulsebeat News	8.00	16.00	24.00

Beatle Interviews.

AMERICAN TOUR WITH ED RUDY (#3)	Radio Pulsebeat News	10.00	20.00	30.00

Beatle Interviews.

BEATLES	Apple (S) SWBO 101	4.00	8.00	12.00

Also known as the "White Album" a two record set.
With number on cover.

BEATLES	Apple (S) SWBO 101	3.00	6.00	9.00

Without number on cover.

BEATLES AGAIN	Apple (S) SW 385	3.50	5.25	7.00

(Original title of "Hey Jude")

BEATLES AND FRANK IFIELD (On Stage)	Vee Jay (M) LP 1085	80.00	160.00	240.00

Has a drawing of the four Beatles on cover-Mono.

BEATLES AND FRANK IFIELD (On Stage)	Vee Jay (S) LPS 1085	170.00	340.00	510.00

Same-but Stereo.

BEATLES—THE CHRISTMAS FAN CLUB ALBUM	Apple (S) SBC 100	18.00	36.00	54.00

Released only to Beatle fan club members . . . containing Christmas messages from the Beatles to their fans.
  (Beware of a very convincing bootleg. The cover photos are slightly out of focus and less detailed.)

BEATLES 1962-1966	Apple (S) SKBO 3403	4.00	8.00	12.00

Two record set-originals were with a red cover.

BEATLES 1962-1966	Apple (S) SKBO 3403	3.00	6.00	9.00

With orange/Red cover.

BEATLES 1967-1970	Apple (S) SKBO 3404	3.00	6.00	9.00
BEATLES SECOND ALBUM	Capitol (M) T 2080	3.00	6.00	9.00
BEATLES SECOND ALBUM	Capitol (S) ST 2080	3.00	6.00	9.00

Black label.

BEATLES SECOND ALBUM	Capitol (S) ST 2080	5.00	10.00	15.00

Green label.

BEATLES SECOND ALBUM	Apple (S) ST 2080	3.00	6.00	9.00

With Capitol logo.

BEATLES SECOND ALBUM	Apple (S) ST 2080	1.50	3.00	4.50

Without Capitol logo.

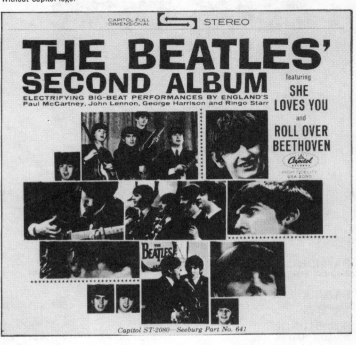

Capitol ST-2080—Seeburg Part No. 641

TITLE	LABEL & NO.	GOOD	VERY GOOD	NEAR MINT
BEATLES VI	Capitol (M) T 2358	3.00	6.00	9.00
BEATLES VI	Capitol (S) ST 2358	3.00	6.00	9.00
Cover reads "See label for correct playing order" with black label.				
BEATLES VI	Capitol (M) T 2358	2.00	5.00	6.00
BEATLES VI	Capitol (S) ST 2358	2.00	4.00	6.00
Black label (with correct playing order given).				
BEATLES VI	Capitol (S) ST 2358	4.00	8.00	12.00
Green label.				
BEATLES VI	Apple (S) ST 2358	1.50	3.00	4.50
With or without Capitol logo.				
BEATLES '65	Capitol (M) T 2228	2.00	4.00	6.00
BEATLES '65	Capitol (S) ST 2228	2.00	4.00	6.00
Black label.				
BEATLES '65	Capitol (S) ST 2228	3.00	6.00	9.00
Green label.				
BEATLES '65	Apple (S) ST 2228	1.50	3.00	4.50
With or without Capitol logo.				
BEATLES STORY	Capitol (M) T BO 2222	3.00	6.00	9.00
BEATLES STORY	Capitol (S) ST BO 2222	3.00	6.00	9.00
Black label.				
BEATLES STORY	Capitol (S) ST BO 2222	5.00	10.00	15.00
Green label.				
BEATLES STORY	Apple (S) ST BO 2222	2.00	4.00	6.00
With or without Capitol logo.				
BEATLES VS, THE FOUR SEASONS	Vee Jay (M) DX 30	18.00	36.00	54.00
Another repackage of "Introducing the Beatles" along with a four Seasons LP, in a double album set—Mono. (With Poster)				
BEATLES VS, THE FOUR SEASONS	Vee Jay (S) DXS 30	30.00	60.00	90.00
Stereo issue. (With Poster)				
EARLY BEATLES	Capitol (M) T 2309	2.00	4.00	6.00
EARLY BEATLES	Capitol (S) ST 2309	2.00	4.00	6.00
Black label.				
EARLY BEATLES	Capitol (S) ST 2309	3.00	6.00	9.00
Green Label.				
EARLY BEATLES	Apple (S) ST 2309	1.50	3.00	4.50
With or without Capitol logo.				
HARD DAYS NIGHT, A	United Artists (M) UAL 6366	3.00	4.50	6.00
HARD DAYS NIGHT, A	United Artists (S) UAS 6366	3.00	4.50	6.00
(Black label)				
HARD DAYS NIGHT, A	United Artists (S) UAS 6366	3.00	4.50	6.00
(Pink/orange label)				
HARD DAYS NIGHT, A	United Artists (S) UAS 6366	3.00	4.50	6.00
(Tan label)				
HEAR THE BEATLES TELL ALL	Vee Jay (M) PRO 202	10.00	20.00	30.00
Beatle interviews Mono only.				
HELP!	Capitol (M) MAS 2368	2.00	4.00	6.00
HELP!	Capitol (S) SMAS 2368	2.00	4.00	6.00
Black label.				
HELP!	Capitol (S) SMAS 2368	4.00	8.00	12.00
Green label.				
HELP!	Apple (S) SMAS 2368	1.50	3.00	4.50
With or without Capitol logo.				

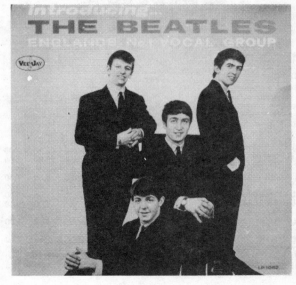

(M) Mono   (S) Stereo   (EP) Extended Play   (Q) Quad   (RI) Re-issued

TITLE	LABEL & NO.	GOOD	VERY GOOD	NEAR MINT
HEY JUDE	Apple (S) SW 385	1.50	3.00	4.50

(Original issues had "Beatles Again" as the title instead of "Hey Jude".)

IN THE BEGINNING	Polydor (S) 24-4504	5.00	7.50	10.00

INTRODUCING THE BEATLES
This album came in two versions: Version 1 has Love Me Do/
P.S. I Love You; Version 2 has Please Please Me/Ask Me Why.

First issue, pictures of 25 lp's on back, version 1 oval or brackets label	Vee Jay (M) 1062	30.00	60.00	90.00
Second issue, same as above, except has 'stereophonic' white banner on the cover	Vee Jay (S) 1062	45.00	90.00	135.00
Third issue song titles in columns on back version 1	Vee Jay (M) 1062	7.00	15.00	21.00
version 2 oval or brackets label	Vee Jay (M) 1062	5.00	10.00	15.00
Fourth issue song titles in columns on back 'stereophonic' banner on cover, oval or brackets label version 1	Vee Jay (S) 1062	50.00	100.00	150.00

Not enough copies of this fourth issue version 1 have been sold
to substantiate an accurate price. It's considered very rare, but
prices may vary widely.
Numerous counterfeit copies have surfaced and may be distinguished
from originals by a smaller off-center label with the color band
partly cut off.

version 2	Vee Jay (S) 1062	35.00	70.00	105.00
Fifth issue, issued on black label only, songs titles in columns on back, version 2	Vee Jay (M) 1062	1.50	3.00	4.50
Sixth issue same as above Version 2	Vee Jay (S) 1062	18.00	36.00	54.00

Please Note: some stereo copies do not have the white banner on
the front, but instead have a sticker or an embossed stamp,
stating that the disc was a stereo. This was done by Vee Jay
when they ran short of stereo jackets, and substituted mono
jackets—adding the 'stereo'.

Version 1   Version 2

First Issue Back Cover for "Introducing the Beatles"

Beware of bootleg issues, with the 'stereophonic' white banner
on the front cover. The most common way to distinguish them is
by checking the clarity of the front cover—the originals are very
clear, the boots are somewhat blurry.
   The discs are made of thin plastic, and the labels
are off-center, making the multicolor band on the label of varying widths.
There are numerous minor label variations in addition to those listed
here. However, these make no difference in price.

LET IT BE	Apple (S) AR 34001	1.50	3.00	4.50
LIVE AT THE HOLLYWOOD BOWL	Capitol (S) SMAS 11638	2.00	3.00	4.00
LIVE (AT THE STAR CLUB IN HAMBURG, GERMANY)	Lingasong 2-7001	5.00	7.50	10.00
LOVE SONGS	Capitol (S) SKBL 11711	4.00	6.00	8.00
MAGICAL MYSTERY TOUR	Capitol (M) MAL 2835	4.00	8.00	12.00
MAGICAL MYSTERY TOUR	Capitol (S) SMAL 2835	3.00	6.00	9.00
(Black label)				
MAGICAL MYSTERY TOUR	Capitol (S) SMAL 2835	3.00	6.00	9.00
Green label.				
MAGICAL MYSTERY TOUR	Apple (S) SMAL 2835	1.50	3.00	4.50
With or without Capitol logo.				
MEET THE BEATLES	Capitol (M) T 2047	4.00	8.00	12.00
MEET THE BEATLES	Capitol (S) ST 2047	4.00	8.00	12.00

"Beatles" is in a light tan color-black label.

(M) Mono (S) Stereo (EP) Extended Play (Q) Quad (RI) Re-issued

TITLE	LABEL & NO.	GOOD	VERY GOOD	NEAR MINT
MEET THE BEATLES	Capitol (M) T 2047	3.00	6.00	9.00
MEET THE BEATLES	Capitol (S) ST 2047	3.00	6.00	9.00
"Beatles" is in light green-black label.				
MEET THE BEATLES	Capitol (S) ST 2047	3.00	6.00	9.00
"Beatles" is in light green-green label.				
MEET THE BEATLES	Apple (S) ST 2047	1.50	3.00	4.50
Beatles is in light green-Apple label.				
MEET THE BEATLES	Capitol (S) ST 2047	1.50	3.00	4.50
"Beatles" is in dark green-black label.				
MEET THE BEATLES	Capitol (M) T 2047	3.00	6.00	9.00
MEET THE BEATLES	Capitol (S) ST 2047	3.00	6.00	9.00
"Beatles" is in dark green-green label.				
MEET THE BEATLES	Apple (S) ST 2047	1.50	3.00	4.50
With Capitol Logo.				
MEET THE BEATLES	Apple (S) ST 2047	1.50	3.00	4.50
Without Capitol Logo.				
REVOLVER	Capitol (M) T 2576	1.50	3.00	4.50
REVOLVER	Capitol (S) ST 2576	1.50	3.00	4.50
Black label.				
REVOLVER	Capitol (S) ST 2576	3.00	6.00	9.00
Green label.				
REVOLVER	Apple (S) ST 2576	1.50	3.00	4.50
With or without Capitol logo.				
ROCK AND ROLL MUSIC	Capitol (S) SKBO 11537	4.00	6.00	8.00
RUBBER SOUL	Capitol (M) T 2442	1.50	3.00	4.50
RUBBER SOUL	Capitol (S) ST 2442	1.50	3.00	4.50
Black label.				
RUBBER SOUL	Capitol (S) ST 2442	3.00	6.00	9.00
Green label.				
RUBBER SOUL	Apple (S) ST 2442	1.50	3.00	4.50
With or without Capitol logo.				
SAVAGE YOUNG BEATLES	Savage (M) BM 69	7.00	10.50	14.00

Issued in Mono only-covers that say stereo are bootlegs .
SGT. PEPPER'S LONELY

HEARTS CLUB BAND	Capitol (M) MAS 2653	2.00	4.00	6.00

14

TITLE	LABEL & NO.	GOOD	VERY GOOD	NEAR MINT
SGT. PEPPER'S LONELY HEARTS CLUB BAND	Capitol (S) SMAS 2653	2.00	4.00	6.00
Black label.				
SGT. PEPPER'S LONELY HEARTS CLUB BAND	Capitol (S) SMAS 2652	3.00	6.00	9.00
Green label.				
SGT. PEPPER'S LONELY HEARTS CLUB BAND	Apple (S) SMAS 2652	1.50	3.00	4.50
With or without Capitol logo.				
SOMETHING NEW	Capitol (M) T 2094	3.00	4.50	6.00
SOMETHING NEW	Capitol (S) ST 2094	3.00	4.50	6.00
Black label.				
SOMETHING NEW	Capitol (S) ST 2094	3.00	6.00	9.00
Green label.				
SOMETHING NEW	Apple (S) ST 2094	1.50	3.00	4.50
With or without Capitol logo.				
SONGS, PICTURES AND STORIES OF THE FABULOUS BEATLES	Vee Jay (M) LP 1092	10.00	20.00	30.00
Contains the same songs as "Introducing the Beatles" but a different-fold open cover—Mono.				
YELLOW SUBMARINE	Apple (S) SW 153	1.50	3.00	4.50
YESTERDAY . . . AND TODAY (Original issue)	Capitol (M) T 2553	80.00	160.00	240.00
YESTERDAY . . . AND TODAY (Original issue)	Capitol (S) ST 2553	100.00	200.00	300.00

This album was first issued with a devastatingly controversial jacket photo showing the Beatles in butcher smocks sitting among pieces of meat and cut up toy dolls. Capitol shortly removed the now famous "Butcher Cover" from the record stores.

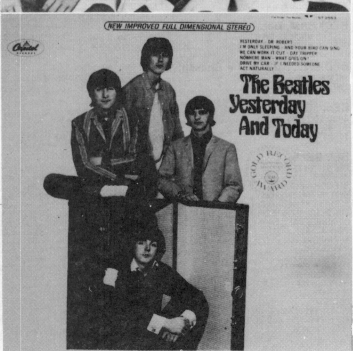

TITLE	LABEL & NO.	GOOD	VERY GOOD	NEAR MINT
YESTERDAY . . . AND TODAY	Capitol (M) T 2553	30.00	60.00	80.00
YESTERDAY . . . AND TODAY	Capitol (S) ST 2553	70.00	140.00	210.00

Shortly after the first issue was taken off the shelves, Capitol released the same jackets with a new cover-photo pasted over the original "Butcher Cover". The value of this issue is because of the photo that has been covered up. The prices listed are for the second cover as it was released with the paste-over still intact. The value of the LP and jacket with the second cover removed is hightly negotiable and could be higher or much lower, depending on the success in removing the top cover. It is not recommended that a novice attempt to peel back a corner, even "to see what's under it." The second, or "Trunk Cover," can be held under a good light to determine if it is covering the original "Butcher Cover." The black v-neck of Ringo's sweater (right center) faintly shows through the thin paper paste-over of the "Trunk Cover." See the two photos for comparison to judge approximately where to look for the black v.

TITLE	LABEL & NO.	GOOD	VERY GOOD	NEAR MINT
YESTERDAY . . . AND TODAY	Capitol (M) T 2553	3.00	6.00	9.00
YESTERDAY . . . AND TODAY	Capitol (S) ST 2553	2.00	4.00	6.00
Black label.				
YESTERDAY . . . AND TODAY	Capitol (M) T 2553	2.00	4.00	6.00
YESTERDAY . . . AND TODAY	Capitol (S) ST 2553	3.00	6.00	9.00
Green label.				
YESTERDAY . . . AND TODAY	Apple (S) ST 2553	1.50	3.00	4.50
With Capitol Logo.				
YESTERDAY AND TODAY	Apple (S) ST 2553	1.50	3.00	4.50
Without Capitol Logo				
YESTERDAY AND TODAY	Capitol (S) ST 8-2553	10.00	20.00	30.00
Capitol record club issue offers all songs on LP in true stereo whereas other issues have 3 songs in simulated stereo.—Black label.				
YESTERDAY AND TODAY	Capitol (S) ST8-2553	8.50	12.75	25.00
Same. Green Label				
YEATERDAY AND TODAY	Apple (S) ST8-2553	5.00	10.00	15.00
Same. Capitol Logo				
YESTERDAY AND TODAY	Apple (S) ST 8-2553	3.00	6.00	9.00
Same, without Capitol Logo.				
YESTERDAY . . . AND TODAY	Capitol (S) ST 2553	7.00	14.00	21.00
Green label.				
YESTERDAY . . . AND TODAY	Apple (S) ST 2553	5.00	10.00	15.00
With Capitol logo.				
YESTERDAY . . . AND TODAY	Apple (S) ST 2553	2.00	4.00	6.00
Without Capitol logo.				

Capitol LP's 2047, 2080, 2094, 2222, 2228, 2358, 2309, 2368, 2442, 2576, 2652, 2653, 2553, and 2835 were issued with four different labels—originally were black, early seventies reissues were green, then they were on Apple with the Capitol logo and finally they were on Apple, without the Capitol logo. Except for the Magical Mystery Tour and Yesterday and Today LP's, numbers 2835 and 2553, these Capitol LP's are given just one price for both mono and stereo issues. It seems that, while there is more demand for the mono release, the stereo is scarcer.

These are Compact 33 1/3's.

TITLE	LABEL & NO.	GOOD	VERY GOOD	NEAR MINT
BEATLES SECOND ALBUM	Capitol SXA 2080	18.00	36.00	54.00
MEET THE BEATLES	Capitol SXA 2047	30.00	60.00	90.00
SOMETHING NEW	Capitol SXA 2108	35.00	70.00	105.00

These were regular EP issues.

TITLE	LABEL & NO.	GOOD	VERY GOOD	NEAR MINT
FOUR BY THE BEATLES	Capitol EAP 2121	18.00	36.00	54.00

TITLE	LABEL & NO.	GOOD	VERY GOOD	NEAR MINT
"4" BY THE BEATLES	Capitol EPR 5365	8.50	12.75	25.00
SOUVENIR OF THEIR VISIT TO AMERICA	Vee Jay EP 18901	8.50	12.75	25.00
SOUVENIR OF THEIR VISIT TO AMERICA	Vee Jay EP 18901	20.00	40.00	60.00
Black label, silver letters.				

(M) Mono (S) Stereo (EP) Extended Play (Q) Quad (RI) Re-issued

All Apple LP's have been reissued on Capitol, orange label. Same approximate prices as Apple LP's.

BEATLES AND OTHERS

TITLE	LABEL & NO.	GOOD	VERY GOOD	NEAR MINT
AIN'T SHE SWEET (4 BEATLE SONGS)	Atco (M) M169	14.00	28.00	42.00
AIN'T SHE SWEET (4 BEATLE SONGS)	Atco (S) MS 169	17.00	34.00	51.00

TITLE	LABEL & NO.	GOOD	VERY GOOD	NEAR MINT
ALPHA OMEGA VOL 1	Audio Tape Atrbh 1-8	4.00	8.00	12.00
ALPHA OMEGA VOL 2	Audio Tape Atrbh 1-8	4.00	8.00	12.00
ALPHA OMEGA VOL 3	Audio Tape Atrbh 1-4	7.00	14.00	21.00
AMAZING BEATLES AND OTHER GREAT GROUP SOUNDS	Clarion (M) M 601	7.00	14.00	21.00

Repackage of Atco 169 Beatle drawing on front/small LP ad on back same as front—Mono.

TITLE	LABEL & NO.	GOOD	VERY GOOD	NEAR MINT
AMAZING BEATLES AND OTHER GREAT GROUP SOUNDS	Clarion (S) MS 601	10.00	20.00	30.00

Stereo issue.

TITLE	LABEL & NO.	GOOD	VERY GOOD	NEAR MINT
AMAZING BEATLES AND OTHER GREAT GROUP SOUNDS	Clarion (M) M 601	12.00	24.00	36.00

Same as above-except small LP ad on back pictures different LP cover with flag—Mono.

TITLE	LABEL & NO.	GOOD	VERY GOOD	NEAR MINT
AMAZING BEATLES AND OTHER GREAT GROUP SOUNDS	Clarion (S) MS 601	13.00	26.00	39.00

Stereo issue.

TITLE	LABEL & NO.	GOOD	VERY GOOD	NEAR MINT
BEATLES WITH TONY SHERIDAN AND GUESTS (4 Beatle Songs)	MGM (M) E 4215	7.00	14.00	21.00

Mono.

TITLE	LABEL & NO.	GOOD	VERY GOOD	NEAR MINT
BEATLES WITH TONY SHERIDAN AND GUESTS (4 Beatle Songs)	MGM (S) SE 4215	12.00	24.00	36.00

Stereo.

TITLE	LABEL & NO.	GOOD	VERY GOOD	NEAR MINT
BIG HITS FROM ENGLAND AND THE U.S.A.	Capitol T 2125	8.50	12.75	25.00

TITLE	LABEL & NO.	GOOD	VERY GOOD	NEAR MINT
BIG HITS FROM ENGLAND AND THE U.S.A.	Capitol ST 2125	10.00	20.00	30.00
Contains 2 Beatle songs.				
CHARTBUSTERS VOL IV	Capitol T 2094	7.00	14.00	21.00
Contains 2 Beatle songs.				
CHARTBUSTERS VOL IV	Capitol ST 2094	7.00	14.00	21.00
Contains 2 Beatle songs.				
DISCOTEQUE IN ASTROSOUND	Clarion M 609	10.00	20.00	30.00
DISCOTEQUE IN ASTROSOUND	Clarion MS 609	17.00	34.00	51.00
2 Beatle songs.				
DO IT NOW! 20 GIANT HITS	Ronco LP 1001	3.00	6.00	9.00
Contains 1 Beatle song.				
DO IT NOW! 20 GIANT HITS	First Vibration 1001	7.00	14.00	21.00
Contains 1 Beatle song.				
GREAT AMERICAN TOUR	Ins Radio News L 1001/1002	14.00	28.00	42.00
HISTORY OF BRITISH ROCK	Sire 2p 6547	5.00	7.50	10.00
(Columbia Record Club Release, 1 beatle cut)				
HISTORY OF BRITISH ROCK VOL II	Sash 3705-2	2.00	4.00	6.00
1 Beatle song.				

TITLE	LABEL & NO.	GOOD	VERY GOOD	NEAR MINT
HISTORY OF BRITISH ROCK VOL III	Sash 3712-2	2.00	4.00	6.00
1 Beatle song.				
JOLLY WHAT! BEATLES AND FRANK IFIELD (On Stage)	Vee Jay (M) LP 1085	5.00	10.00	15.00
Blue and Red cover with drawing of an older man-Mono				
60 FLASHBACK GREATS OF THE SIXTIES	K-Tel 229	3.00	6.00	9.00
Contains 1 Beatle song.				
THIS IS WHERE IT STARTED	Metro (M) M 563	10.00	15.00	20.00
Reissue of above MGM LP—Mono.				
THIS IS WHERE IT STARTED	Metro (S) MS 563	12.50	18.75	25.00
Stereo issue.				

BEATS

TITLE	LABEL & NO.	GOOD	VERY GOOD	NEAR MINT
THE MERSEY SOUND	Design (M) 170	4.00	8.00	12.00

(Same as the Liverpool Beats "New Merseyside Sound" Sound Rondo 2026)

BEAU BRUMMELS

TITLE	LABEL & NO.	GOOD	VERY GOOD	NEAR MINT
BEAU BRUMMELS	Warner Bros. (S) BS 2842	3.00	4.50	6.00
BEAU BRUMMELS SING	Post (M) 6000	2.50	3.75	5.00
BEAU BRUMMELS 66	Warner Bros. (M) W1644	4.00	8.00	12.00
BEAU BRUMMELS '66	Warner Bros. (S) WS 1644	5.00	10.00	15.00
BEAU BRUMMELS VOL. 2	Autumn (M) LP104	5.00	10.00	15.00
BEAU BRUMMELS, Vol. 2	Autumn (S) 104	6.00	12.00	18.00
BEAU BRUMMELS VOL. 44	Vault (S) 121	5.00	10.00	15.00
BEST OF BEAU BRUMMELS	Vault (M) 114	10.00	20.00	30.00
BEST OF BEAU BRUMMELS	Vault (S) 114	11.00	22.00	33.00
BRADLEY'S BARN	Warner Brothers (S) WS1760	4.00	8.00	12.00
INTRODUCING THE BEAU BRUMMELS	Autumn (M) LP103	5.00	10.00	15.00
INTRODUCING THE BEAU BRUMMELS	Autumn (S) 103	6.00	12.00	18.00
TRIANGLE	Warner Brothers (M) W1692	4.00	8.00	12.00
TRIANGLE	Warner Bros. (S) WS 1692	5.00	10.00	15.00

BEAUREGARDE

TITLE	LABEL & NO.	GOOD	VERY GOOD	NEAR MINT
BEAUREGARDE	F-Empire (M)	5.00	10.00	15.00

BE BOP DELUXE

TITLE	LABEL & NO.	GOOD	VERY GOOD	NEAR MINT
AXE VICTIM	Harvest (S) 11689	3.00	4.50	6.00
DRASTIC PLASTIC	Harvest (S) SW 11750	2.50	3.75	5.00
FUTURAMA	Harvest (S) ST-11432	3.50	5.25	7.00
LIVE! IN THE AIR AGE (WHITE VINYL)	Harvest (S) SKB 11666	5.00	7.50	10.00
MODERN MUSIC	Harvest (S) ST 11575	3.00	4.50	6.00
SUNBURST FINISH	Harvest (S) ST 11478	2.00	3.00	4.00

BECK, BOGART, & APPICE

TITLE	LABEL & NO.	GOOD	VERY GOOD	NEAR MINT
BECK, BOGERT & APPICE	Epic (Q) EQ-32140	2.50	3.75	5.00
BECK, BOGART & APPICE	Epic (S) KE-32140	2.00	3.00	4.00

BECK, Jeff

TITLE	LABEL & NO.	GOOD	VERY GOOD	NEAR MINT
BECK-OLA	Epic (S) BN 26478	3.00	4.50	6.00
BLOW BY BLOW	Epic (S) PE 33409	2.50	3.75	5.00
BLOW BY BLOW	Epic (Q) PEQ 33409	2.50	3.75	5.00
JEFF BECK GROUP	Epic (S) KE 31331	2.50	3.75	5.00
ROUGH AND READY	Epic (S) KE 30973	2.50	3.75	5.00
TRUTH	Epic (S) BN 26413	3.00	4.50	6.00
TRUTH/BECK-OLA	Epic (S) BG 33779	3.50	5.25	7.00
WIRED	Epic (S) PE 33849	2.50	3.75	5.00
WIRED	Epic (Q) PEQ 33849	2.50	3.75	5.00

BECKHAM, Bob

TITLE	LABEL & NO.	GOOD	VERY GOOD	NEAR MINT
JUST AS MUCH AS EVER	Decca (M) DL-8967	2.50	3.15	5.00
JUST AS MUCH AS EVER	Decca (S) DL7-8967	3.00	4.50	6.00

BEDIENT, Jack & The Chessmen

TITLE	LABEL & NO.	GOOD	VERY GOOD	NEAR MINT
JACK BEDIENT	Executive Productions (M)	7.00	14.00	21.00
LIVE AT HARVEY'S	Fantasy (M) 3365	6.00	12.00	18.00

BEE, Molly

TITLE	LABEL & NO.	GOOD	VERY GOOD	NEAR MINT
GOOD GOLLY MS. MOLLY	Granite (S) 1002	2.50	3.75	5.00
YOUNG ROMANCE	Capitol (S) T1097	3.50	5.25	7.00
YOUNG ROMANCE	Capitol (EP) EAP1-1097	2.00	3.00	4.00

BEE GEES

TITLE	LABEL & NO.	GOOD	VERY GOOD	NEAR MINT
BEE GEE'S 1ST	Atco (M) 33-223	4.50	6.75	9.00
BEE GEES' 1ST	Atco (S) 33-223	4.00	6.00	8.00
BEE GEES GOLD, Vol. 1	RSO (S) 3006	3.00	4.50	6.00
BEST OF THE BEE GEES	Atco (S) 33-292	4.00	6.00	8.00
BEST OF THE BEE GEES, Vol. 2	RSO (S) 875	3.50	5.25	7.00
CHILDREN OF THE WORLD	RSO (S) 3003	3.00	4.50	6.00
CUCUMBER CASTLE	Atco (S) 33-327	4.00	6.00	8.00
HERE AT LAST . . . LIVE	RSO (S) 2-3901	3.50	5.25	7.00
HORIZONTAL	Atco (M) 33-233	3.00	4.50	6.00
HORIZONTAL	Atco (S) 33-233	4.00	6.00	8.00
IDEA	Atco (S) 33-253	4.00	6.00	8.00
LIFE IN A TIN CAN	RSO (S) 870	3.50	5.25	7.00
MAIN COURSE	RSO (S) 4807	3.50	5.25	7.00
MAIN COURSE (RI of RSO 4807)	RSO (S) 3024	2.50	3.75	5.00
MR. NATURAL	RSO (S) 4800	3.50	5.25	7.00
ODESSA	Atco (S) 2-702	4.50	6.75	9.00
ODESSA (RI of Atco 2-702)	RSO (S) 3007	2.50	3.75	5.00
RARE, PRECIOUS AND BEAUTIFUL	Atco (S) 33-264	4.00	6.00	8.00

(M) Mono   (S) Stereo   (EP) Extended Play   (Q) Quad   (RI) Re-issued

TITLE	LABEL & NO.	GOOD	VERY GOOD	NEAR MINT
RARE, PRECIOUS & BEAUTIFUL - Vol. 2	Atco (S) 33-321	3.50	5.25	7.00
TO WHOM IT MAY CONCERN	Atco (S) 7012	3.50	5.25	7.00
TRAFALGAR	Atco (S) 7003	3.25	5.25	7.00
2 YEARS ON	Atco (S) 33-353	4.00	6.00	8.00

BEETHOVEN SOUL
TITLE	LABEL & NO.	GOOD	VERY GOOD	NEAR MINT
THE BEETHOVEN SOUL	Dot (M) DLP 3821	2.00	3.00	4.00
THE BEETHOVEN SOUL	Dot (S) DLP 25821	2.50	3.75	5.00

BEGGARS OPERA
TITLE	LABEL & NO.	GOOD	VERY GOOD	NEAR MINT
ACT ONE	Verve (M) 65080	2.50	3.75	5.00

BEGINNING OF THE END
TITLE	LABEL & NO.	GOOD	VERY GOOD	NEAR MINT
FUNKY NASSAU	Alston (S) SD 33-379	3.00	4.50	6.00

BELAFONTE, Harry
TITLE	LABEL & NO.	GOOD	VERY GOOD	NEAR MINT
ABRAHAM, MARTIN & JOHN	Camden (S) ACL1-0502	2.00	3.00	4.00
BALLADS BY BELAFONTE	RCA (EP) EPA4217	1.00	3.00	2.00
BALLADS BY BELAFONTE	Jubilee (EP) EP5006	1.50	2.25	3.00
BALLADS, BLUES & BOASTERS	RCA (M) LPM2953	2.00	3.00	4.00
BALLADS, BLUES & BOASTERS	RCA (S) LSP2953	2.00	3.00	4.00
BELAFONTE	RCA (M) LPM1150	3.00	4.50	6.00

TITLE	LABEL & NO.	GOOD	VERY GOOD	NEAR MINT
BELAFONTE AT CARNEGIE HALL	RCA (M) LOC6006	4.00	6.00	8.00
BELAFONTE AT CARNEGIE HALL	RCA (S) LSO6006	4.00	6.00	8.00
BELAFONTE AT HOME & ABROAD	RCA (M) LPM2309	2.00	3.00	4.00
BELAFONTE AT HOME & ABROAD	RCA (M) LSP2309	2.00	3.00	4.00
BELAFONTE AT THE GREEK THEATRE	RCA (M) LOC6009	4.00	6.00	8.00
BELAFONTE AT THE GREEK THEATRE	RCA (S) LSO6009	4.00	6.00	8.00
BELAFONTE RETURNS TO CARNEGIE HALL	RCA (M) LOC6007	4.00	6.00	8.00
BELAFONTE SINGS OF THE CARIBBEAN	RCA (M) LPM1505	3.00	4.50	6.00
BELAFONTE SINGS SPIRITUALS	RCA (EP) EPA4354	1.00	2.00	2.00
BELAFONTE SINGS THE BLUES	RCA (M) LOP 1006	4.00	6.00	8.00
CALYPSO	RCA (M) LPM1248	3.00	4.50	6.00
CALYPSO	RCA (EP) EPA-768	1.00	2.00	3.00
CLOSE YOUR EYES	Capitol (M) EAP1-619	1.50	2.25	3.00
DAY-O	RCA (EP) EPA5138	1.00	3.00	2.00
EVENING WITH BELAFONTE	RCA (M) LPM1402	3.00	4.50	6.00
EVENING WITH BELAFONTE	RCA (EP) EPA 1402-1	1.50	2.25	3.00
EVENING WITH BELAFONTE	RCA (EP) EPA1402-2	1.50	2.25	3.00
EVENING WITH BELAFONTE	RCA (EP) EPA1402-3	1.50	2.25	3.00
HARRY BELAFONTE	Camden (S) 2599	2.00	3.00	4.00
HARRY BELAFONTE	RCA (EP) EPA5031	1.00	3.00	2.00
JUMP UP CALYPSO	RCA (M) LPM2388	2.50	3.75	5.00
JUMP UP CALYPSO	RCA (S) LSP2388	2.50	3.75	5.00
LOVE IS A GENTLE THING	RCA (M) LPM1927	2.50	3.75	5.00
LOVE IS A GENTLE THING	RCA (S) LSP1927	2.50	3.75	5.00
MAN SMART AND OTHER FOLK SONGS	RCA (EP) EPA412	1.00	1.50	2.00
MARK TWAIN & OTHER FOLK FAVORITES	RCA (M) LPM1022	3.50	5.25	7.00
MIDNIGHT SPECIAL	RCA (M) LPM2449	2.00	3.00	4.00
MIDNIGHT SPECIAL	RCA (S) LSP2449	2.00	3.00	4.00
PLAY ME	RCA (M) APL1-0094	2.00	3.00	4.00
PORGY & BESS	RCA (S) LOP1507	2.50	3.75	5.00
PORGY & BESS	RCA (S) LSO1507	2.50	3.75	5.00
STREETS I HAVE WALKED	RCA (M) LPM2695	2.00	3.00	4.00
STREETS I HAVE WALKED	RCA (S) LSP2695	2.00	3.00	4.00
SWING DAT HAMMER	RCA (M) LPM2194	2.50	3.75	5.00
SWING DAT HAMMER	RCA (S) LSP2194	2.50	3.75	5.00
TO WISH YOU A MERRY CHRISTMAS	RCA (M) LPM1887	2.50	3.75	5.00
TO WISH YOU A MERRY CHRISTMAS	RCA (M) LPM2626	2.00	3.00	4.00
TO WISH YOU A MERRY CHRISTMAS	RCA (S) LSP2626	2.00	3.00	4.00

BELEW, Carl
TITLE	LABEL & NO.	GOOD	VERY GOOD	NEAR MINT
HELLO OUT THERE	RCA (M) LPM-2848	2.50	3.75	5.00
HELLO OUT THERE	RCA (S) LSP-2848	2.50	3.75	5.00
TWELVE SHADES OF BELEW	RCA (M) LPM-3919	2.00	3.00	4.00
TWELVE SHADES OF BELEW	RCA (S) LSP-3919	2.00	3.00	4.00

BELL AND ARC
TITLE	LABEL & NO.	GOOD	VERY GOOD	NEAR MINT
BELL AND ARC	Columbia (S) C 31142	2.50	3.75	5.00

BELL, Archie & Drells
TITLE	LABEL & NO.	GOOD	VERY GOOD	NEAR MINT
ARCHIE BELL & THE DRELLS	Philadelphia Intl (S) PZ-33844	2.00	3.00	4.00
THERE'S GONNA BE A SHOWDOWN	Atlantic (S) SD 8226	3.00	4.50	6.00
TIGHTEN UP	Atlantic (S) SD 8181	3.00	4.50	6.00

BELL, Benny
TITLE	LABEL & NO.	GOOD	VERY GOOD	NEAR MINT
SHAVING CREAM	Vanguard (S) 79357	3.50	5.25	7.00

BELL, Carey
TITLE	LABEL & NO.	GOOD	VERY GOOD	NEAR MINT
LAST NIGHT	Bluesway (S) 6079	2.00	3.00	4.00

BELL, Freddie & The Bellboys
TITLE	LABEL & NO.	GOOD	VERY GOOD	NEAR MINT
BELLS ARE SWINGING	20th Century (M) TFS 4146	3.00	6.00	9.00
ROCK AND ROLL . . . ALL FLAVORS	Mercury (M) MG 20289	6.00	15.00	24.00

BELLINE, Denny & The Rich Kids
TITLE	LABEL & NO.	GOOD	VERY GOOD	NEAR MINT
DENNY BELLINE AND THE RICH KIDS	RCA (M) LPM 3655	3.00	4.50	6.00
DENNY BELLINE AND THE RICH KIDS	RCA (S) LSP 3655	4.00	6.00	8.00

BELL, Madeline
TITLE	LABEL & NO.	GOOD	VERY GOOD	NEAR MINT
I'M GONNA MAKE YOU LOVE ME	Philips (S) 600271	5.00	10.00	15.00

BELL, Maggie
TITLE	LABEL & NO.	GOOD	VERY GOOD	NEAR MINT
QUEEN OF THE NIGHT	Atlantic (S) SD 7293	2.50	3.75	5.00

BELLUS, Tony
TITLE	LABEL & NO.	GOOD	VERY GOOD	NEAR MINT
ROBBIN' THE CRADLE	NRC (M) LPA 8	6.00	15.00	24.00

BELL, William
TITLE	LABEL & NO.	GOOD	VERY GOOD	NEAR MINT
BOUND TO HAPPEN	Stax (S) STS 2014	3.00	4.50	6.00
PHASES TO REALITY	Stax (S) STS 3005	3.00	4.50	6.00
RELATING	Stax (S) 5502	2.50	3.75	5.00
WOW	Stax (S) STS 2037	3.00	4.50	6.00

BELL NOTES
TITLE	LABEL & NO.	GOOD	VERY GOOD	NEAR MINT
I'VE HAD IT	Time (EP) TEP 100	3.00	6.00	9.00

BELMONTS
TITLE	LABEL & NO.	GOOD	VERY GOOD	NEAR MINT
BELMONTS	Buddah (S) 5123	5.00	7.50	10.00
CARNIVAL OF HITS	Sabina (M) SALP 5001	5.00	10.00	15.00
CIGARS, ACAPPELLA, AND CANDY	Buddah (S) BDS 5123	3.00	4.50	6.00
SUMMER LOVE	Dot (S) DLP 25949	3.00	6.00	9.00

Also see Dion & Belmonts

(M) Mono   (S) Stereo   (EP) Extended Play   (Q) Quad   (RI) Re-issued

THE BELL NOTES

Robbin' the Cradle with Tony Bellus

TITLE	LABEL & NO.	GOOD	VERY GOOD	NEAR MINT
BELVIN, Jesse				
BUT NOT FORGOTTEN	Custom (M) CS 1058	4.00	8.00	12.00
CASUAL JESSE BELVIN, THE	Crown (M) CLP 5145	4.00	8.00	12.00
JESSE BELVIN'S BEST	Camden (M) CAM 960	4.00	8.00	12.00
JESSE BELVIN'S BEST	Camden (S) CAS 960	3.00	6.00	9.00
JUST JESSE BELVIN	RCA (M) LPM-2089	4.00	8.00	12.00
JUST JESSE BELVIN	RCA (S) LSP-2089	5.00	10.00	15.00
MR. EASY	RCA (M) LPM-2105	4.00	8.00	12.00
MR. EASY	RCA (S) LSP-2105	5.00	10.00	15.00
UNFORGETTABLE JESSE BELVIN, THE	Crown (M) CLP 5187	4.00	8.00	12.00
YESTERDAYS	RCA (S) APLI-0966	5.00	10.00	15.00
BENNETT, Boyd				
BOYD BENNETT	King (M) LP 594	20.00	50.00	80.00
ROCK AND ROLL	King (EP) EP 377	4.00	10.00	16.00
ROCK AND ROLL	King (EP) EP 383	4.00	10.00	16.00
BENNETT, Duster				
JUSTA DUSTER	Blue Horizon (M) BH 4804	2.50	3.75	5.00
12 DB'S	Blue Horizon (M) BH 4812	2.50	3.75	5.00
BENNETT, Tony				
ALONE TOGETHER	Columbia (M) CL-1471	3.00	4.50	6.00
ALONE TOGETHER	Columbia (S) CS-8262	3.00	4.50	6.00
BECAUSE OF YOU	Columbia (M) CL 2550	2.00	3.00	4.00
BENNETT SPOTLITE	Columbia (EP) B 1842	1.00	1.50	2.00
BEST OF MY HEART, THE	Columbia (M) CL 1079	3.00	4.50	6.00
BEST OF MY HEART, THE	Columbia (EP) B 0791	1.50	2.25	3.00
BLUE VELVET	Columbia (M) CL-1292	2.50	3.75	5.00
CLOUD 7	Columbia (M) CL 621	4.00	6.00	8.00
CLOUD 7	Columbia (EP) B 1960	1.50	2.25	3.00
FLOWER DRUM SONG (HITS)	Columbia (EP) B-2151	1.50	2.25	3.00
GOOD THINGS IN LOFE	Verve (M) V-5088	2.50	3.75	5.00
GREAT HITS OF TODAY	Columbia (M) CG-33612	2.00	3.00	4.00
HOMETOWN, MY HOMETOWN	Columbia (EP) B-13011	1.50	2.25	3.00
HOMETOWN, MY HOMETOWN	Columbia (M) CL-1301	2.50	3.75	5.00
HOMETOWN, MY HOMETOWN	Columbia (S) CS-8107	2.50	3.75	5.00
IF I RULED THE WORLD	Columbia (M) CL-2343	2.00	3.00	4.00
I LEFT MY HEART IN SAN FRANCISCO	Columbia (M) CL-1869	2.00	3.00	4.00
I LEFT MY HEART IN SAN FRANCISCO	Columbia (S) CS-8669	2.00	3.00	4.00
I LEFT MY HEART IN SAN FRANCISCO ... GREAT HITS OF TODAY	Columbia (S) CG-33612	2.00	3.00	4.00
IN PERSON	Columbia (M) CL-1294	2.50	3.75	5.00
IN PERSON	Columbia (EP) B-12941	1.50	2.25	3.00
IN PERSON	Columbia (S) CS-8104	2.50	3.75	5.00
I WANNA BE AROUND	Columbia (M) CL-2000	2.00	3.00	4.00
I WANNA BE AROUND	Columbia (S) CS-8800	2.00	3.00	4.00
LET'S FALL IN LOVE	Columbia (S) KG-33376	2.00	3.00	4.00
LIFE IS BEAUTIFUL	Improv (S) 7112	2.00	3.00	4.00
LISTEN EASY	Verve (M) V-5094	2.50	3.75	5.00
LONG AGO AND FAR AWAY	Columbia (M) CL 1186	2.50	3.75	5.00

TITLE	LABEL & NO.	GOOD	VERY GOOD	NEAR MINT
LONG AGO AND FAR AWAY	Columbia (EP) B 11861	1.50	2.25	3.00
MR. BROADWAY (TONY'S GREATEST BROADWAY HITS)	Columbia (M) CL-1763	2.50	3.75	5.00
MR. BROADWAY (TONY'S GREATEST BROADWAY HITS)	Columbia (S) CS-8563	2.50	3.75	5.00
MANY MOODS OF TONY	Columbia (M) CL-2141	2.00	3.00	4.00
MANY MOODS OF TONY	Columbia (S) CS-8941	2.00	3.00	4.00
MORE TONY'S GREATEST HITS	Columbia (M) CL-1535	2.50	3.75	5.00
MORE TONY'S GREATEST HITS	Columbia (S) CS-8335	2.50	3.75	5.00
MOVIE SONG ALBUM	Columbia (M) CL-2472	2.00	3.00	4.00
MOVIE SONG ALBUM	Columbia (S) CS-9272	2.00	3.00	4.00
MY HEART SINGS	Columbia (M) CL-1658	2.50	3.75	5.00
MY HEART SINGS	Columbia (S) CS-8458	2.50	3.75	5.00
THIS IS ALL I ASK	Columbia (M) CL-2056	2.00	3.00	4.00
THIS IS ALL I ASK	Columbia (S) CS-8856	2.00	3.00	4.00
TO MY WONDERFUL ONE	Columbia (M) CL-1429	3.00	4.50	6.00
TO MY WONDERFUL ONE	Columbia (S) SC-8226	3.00	4.50	6.00
TONY	Columbia (M) CL 938	3.50	5.25	7.00
TONY	Columbia (EP) B 9381	1.50	2.25	3.00
TONY	Columbia (EP) B 9382	1.50	2.25	3.00
TONY	Columbia (EP) B 9383	1.50	2.25	3.00
TONY	Harmony (S) KH-32171	2.00	3.00	4.00
TONY BENNETT	Columbia (EP) B 2518	1.50	2.25	3.00
TONY BENNETT	Columbia (EP) B-2620	1.50	2.25	3.00
TONY BENNETT AT CARNEGIE HALL	Columbia (M) CSL-23	4.00	6.00	8.00
TONY BENNETT AT CARNEGIE HALL	Columbia (S) C2S-823	4.00	6.00	8.00
TONY BENNETT'S GREATEST HITS	MGM (S) 4929	2.50	3.75	5.00
TONY BENNETT SINGS A STRING OF HAROLD ARLEN	Columbia (M) CL-1559	3.00	4.50	6.00
TONY BENNETT SINGS A STRING OF HAROLD ARLEN	Columbia (S) CS-8359	3.00	4.50	6.00
TONY'S GREATEST HITS	Columbia (M) CL 1229	3.00	4.50	6.00
TONY'S GREATEST HITS	Columbia (M) CL 1852	2.00	3.00	4.00
TONY'S GREATEST HITS	Columbia (S) CS 8652	2.00	3.00	4.00
TONY SINGS FOR TWO	Columbia (M) CL-1446	3.00	4.50	6.00
TONY SINGS FOR TWO	Columbia (S) CS-8242	3.00	4.50	6.00
TREASURE CHEST OF SONG HITS	Columbia (M) CL 613	4.00	6.00	8.00
WHEN LIGHTS ARE LOW	Columbia (M) CL-2185	2.00	3.00	4.00
WHEN LIGHTS ARE LOW	Columbia (S) CS-8975	2.00	3.00	4.00
WHO CAN I TURN TO	Columbia (M) CL 2285	2.00	3.00	4.00
WHO CAN I TURN TO	Columbia (S) CS 9085	2.00	3.00	4.00
BENNETT, Tony & Count Basie				
BENNETT & BASIE STRIKE UP THE BAND	Roulette (M) R-25231	2.00	3.00	4.00
BENNETT & BASIE STRIKE UP THE BAND	Roulette (S) SR-25231	2.00	3.00	4.00
BENSON, George				
BENSON BURNER	Columbia (S) CG 33569	2.00	3.00	4.00
BLUE BENSON	Polydor (S) PD 6084	2.00	3.00	4.00
BREEZIN'	Warner Bros. (S) BS-2919	2.50	3.75	5.00
BREEZIN' (RI of WB 2919)	Warner Bros. (S) BSK 3111	2.00	3.00	4.00
GOOD KING BAD	CTI (S) 6062	2.00	3.00	4.00
IN CONCERT — CARNEGIE HALL	CTI (S) 6072	2.00	3.00	4.00
IN FLIGHT	Warner Bros. (S) BS-2983	2.00	3.00	4.00
OTHER SIDE OF ABBEY ROAD	A&M (S) SP 3028	2.50	3.75	5.00
SHAPE OF THINGS TO COME	A&M (S) SP 3014	2.50	3.75	5.00
TELL IT LIKE IT IS	A&M (S) SP 3020	2.50	3.75	5.00
WEEKEND IN L.A.	Warner Bros. (S) 2BS-3139	3.00	4.50	6.00
BENTON, Barbi				
BARBI BENTON	Playboy (S) 406	2.50	3.75	5.00
BARBI DOLL	Playboy (S) 404	2.50	3.75	5.00
BENTON, Brook				
BOLL WEEVIL SONG (& 11 OTHER GREAT HITS)	Mercury (M) MG-20641	2.50	3.75	5.00
BOLL WEEVIL SONG (& 11 OTHER GREAT HITS)	Mercury (S) SR-60641	2.50	3.75	5.00
BOLL WEEVIL SONG (& 11 OTHER GREAT HITS)	Mercury (EP) 1-4046	1.00	2.25	3.00
BORN TO SING THE BLUES	Mercury (M) MG-20886	2.00	3.00	4.00
BORN TO SING THE BLUES	Mercury (S) SR-60886	2.00	3.00	4.00
BROOK BENTON	Mercury (M) MG-20464	3.00	4.50	6.00
BROOK BENTON	Mercury (S) SR-60146	3.00	4.50	6.00
BROOK BENTON	Mercury (EP) 1-3394	1.50	2.25	3.00
BROOK BENTON AT HIS BEST	Epic (M) LN-3573	5.00	7.50	10.00
BROOK BENTON GOLDEN HITS	Mercury (M) MG-20607	2.50	3.75	5.00
BROOK BENTON GOLDEN HITS	Mercury (S) SR-60607	2.50	3.75	5.00
GOLDEN HITS VOL. 2	Mercury (M) MG-20774	2.50	3.75	5.00
GOLDEN HITS VOL. 2	Mercury (S) SR-60774	2.50	3.75	5.00
IT'S JUST A MATTER OF TIME	Mercury (M) MG-20421	4.00	6.00	8.00
MAKIN' LOVE IS GOOD FOR YOU	Olde World (S) 7700	2.00	3.00	4.00
SINGS A LOVE STORY	RCA (S) APL1-1044	2.00	3.00	4.00
SO MANY WAYS	Mercury (M) MG-20565	2.50	3.75	5.00
SO MANY WAYS	Mercury (S) SR-60217	2.50	3.75	5.00
SOMETHING FOR EVERYONE	MGM (S) 4874	2.50	3.75	5.00
SONGS I LOVE TO SING	Mercury (M) MG-20602	2.50	3.75	5.00
SONGS I LOVE TO SING	Mercury (S) SR-60602	2.50	3.75	5.00
THERE GOES THAT SONG AGAIN	Mercury (M) MG-20673	2.50	3.75	5.00
THERE GOES THAT SONG AGAIN	Mercury (S) SR-60673	2.50	3.75	5.00
TWO OF US-WITH DINAH WASHINGTON	Mercury (M) MG 20588	2.50	3.75	5.00
TWO OF US-WITH DINAH WASHINGTON	Mercury (S) SR60244	2.50	3.75	5.00
BENTON, Brook & Jesse Belvin				
BROOK BENTON AND JESSE BELVIN	Crown (M) CST 350	3.00	6.00	9.00

(M) Mono (S) Stereo (EP) Extended Play (Q) Quad (RI) Re-issued

IT'S JUST A MATTER OF TIME
BROOK BENTON
HIGH Custom FIDELITY

TITLE	LABEL & NO.	GOOD	VERY GOOD	NEAR MINT
BERGEN, Polly				
ALL ALONE BY THE TELEPHONE	Columbia (M) CL-1300	2.00	4.00	6.00
ALL ALONE BY THE TELEPHONE	Columbia (S) CS-8100	2.00	4.00	6.00
ALL ALONE BY THE TELEPHONE	Columbia (EP) B-13001	1.50	2.25	3.00
BERGEN SINGS MORGAN	Columbia (M) CL 994	3.00	6.00	9.00
FOUR SEASONS OF LOVE	Columbia (M) CL-1451	2.00	3.00	4.00
FOUR SEASONS OF LOVE	Columbia (S) CS-8246	2.00	3.00	4.00
GIRLS, THE	RKO (M) ULP-136	2.00	4.00	6.00
MY HEART SINGS	Columbia (S) CS-8018	2.00	4.00	6.00
POLLY BERGEN, COUNTRY GIRL	Harmony (M) HL-7256	2.00	3.00	4.00
BERMAN, Shelley				
GREAT MOMENTS OF COMEDY	Metro (M) M-546	2.50	3.75	5.00
GREAT MOMENTS OF COMEDY WITH SHELLEY BERMAN	Verve (M) V-15048	2.50	3.75	5.00
NEW SIDES	Verve (M) V-15036	2.50	3.75	5.00
SEX LIFE OF THE PRIMATE (& OTHER BITS OF GOSSIP)	Verve (M) V-15043	2.50	3.75	5.00
SEX LIFE OF THE PRIMATE (& OTHER BITS OF GOSSIP)	Verve (S) V6-15043	2.50	3.75	5.00
BERNARD, Rod				
ROD BERNARD	Jin (M) LP 4007	7.50	11.25	15.00
BERRY, Brooks				
BROOKS BERRY	Blueville (M) 1074	7.50	11.25	15.00
BERRY, Chuck				
AFTER SCHOOL SESSION	Chess (M) LP 1426	7.00	14.00	21.00
BACK HOME	Chess (S) LPS 1550	4.00	6.00	8.00
BIO	Chess (M) CH 50043	2.50	3.75	5.00
BIO	Chess (M) CH 60032	2.50	3.75	5.00
CHUCK BERRY	Chess (M) LP 1495	6.00	12.00	18.00
CHUCK BERRY IN LONDON	Chess (M) LP 1495	6.00	12.00	18.00
CHUCK BERRY IS ON TOP	Chess (M) LP 1435	7.00	14.00	21.00
CHUCK BERRY'S GOLDEN DECADE	Chess (S) LPS 1514	3.00	6.00	9.00
CHUCK BERRY'S GREATEST HITS	Chess (M) LP 1485	6.00	12.00	18.00
CONCERTO IN B. GOODE	Mercury (S) SR 61223	3.50	5.25	7.00
FRESH BERRY'S	Chess (M) LP 1498	6.00	12.00	18.00
FROM ST. LOUIS TO FRISCO	Mercury (M) SR 61176	3.50	5.25	7.00
GOLDEN DECADE (2nd Press)	Chess (S) 2 CH 1514	3.00	6.00	9.00
GOLDEN DECADE VOL. 2	Chess (S) 2CH 60023	4.00	6.00	8.00
GOLDEN HITS	Mercury (M) MG 21103	3.00	4.50	6.00
GOLDEN HITS	Mercury (S) SR 61103	4.00	6.00	8.00
HEAD OVER HEELS	Chess (EP) EP 5118	5.00	12.50	20.00
IN MEMPHIS	Mercury (M) MG 21123	3.00	4.50	6.00
IN MEMPHIS	Merucyr (S) SR 61123	4.00	6.00	8.00
LIVE AT FILLMORE AUDITORIUM	Mercury (M) MG 21138	3.00	4.50	6.00
LIVE AT FILLMORE AUDITORIUM	Mercury (S) SR 61138	4.00	6.00	8.00
LONDON SESSIONS	Chess (S) CH 60020	3.50	5.25	7.00
MORE CHUCK BERRY	Chess (M) LP 1465	7.00	14.00	21.00
NEW JUKE BOX HITS	Chess (M) LP 1456	7.00	14.00	21.00
ONE DOZEN BERRYS	Chess (M) LP 1432	7.00	14.00	21.00
PICKIN' BERRIES	Chess (EP) EP 5124	5.00	12.50	20.00
ROCK AND ROLL MUSIC	Chess (EP) EP 5119	5.00	12.50	20.00
ROCKIN' AT THE HOPS	Chess (M) LP 1448	7.00	14.00	21.00
ST. LOUIE TO FRISCO TO MEMPHIS	Mercury (M) SRM-2-6501	3.50	5.25	7.00
ST. LOUIS TO LIVERPOOL	Chess (M) LP 1488	6.00	12.00	18.00
SAN FRANCISCO DUES	Chess (S) CH 50008	3.50	5.25	7.00
SWEET LITTLE 16	Chess (EP) EP 5121	5.00	12.50	20.00
TWIST	Chess (M) 1465	7.00	14.00	21.00

Note: Most LPs in 1400 series were later issued in re-channelled stereo with the same catalog numbers. These are worth about one third as much as the mono originals

(M) Mono (S) Stereo (EP) Extended Play (Q) Quad (RI) Re-issued

TITLE	LABEL & NO.	GOOD	VERY GOOD	NEAR MINT
BERRY, Chuck & Howlin Wolf				
POP ORIGINS	Chess (M) 1544	4.00	8.00	12.00
BERRY, Richard				
LIVE AT THE CENTURY CLUB	Pam (M) 1001	7.00	14.00	21.00
(& The Soul Searchers)				
RICHARD BERRY AND THE DREAMERS	Crown (M) CLP5371	3.00	7.50	12.00
WILD BERRY	Pam (M) 1002	7.00	14.00	21.00
(& The Soul Searchers)				
BEST, Peter				
BEST OF THE BEATLES	Savage (M) BM 71	10.00	20.00	30.00
Mono only.—Note: The bootleg's jacket has a bluish tint over the whole cover. On the original all whites are pure. Also see BEATLES				
BETHLEHEM ASYLUM				
BETHLEHEM ASYLUM	Ampex (S) 10124	2.75	4.00	5.50
COMMIT YOURSELF	Ampex (S) A 10106	2.50	3.75	5.00
BETTS, Richard				
HIGHWAY CALL	Capricorn (S) GP 0123	2.50	3.75	5.00
BIDDU ORCHESTRA				
BIDDU ORCHESTRA	Epic (S) PE 33903	2.00	3.00	4.00
EASTERN MAN	Epic (S) PE 34723	2.00	3.00	4.00
RAIN FOREST	Epic (S) PE 34230	2.00	3.00	4.00
BIG BEATS				
BIG BEATS LIVE, THE	Liberty (M) LRP 3407	2.50	3.75	5.00
BIG BEATS LIVE, THE	Liberty (S) LST 7407	3.00	4.50	6.00
BIG BEN				
BIG BEN SINGS SCATMAN CROTHERS	Motown (¾) M 777	3.50	5.25	7.00
BIG BOPPER				
CHANTILLY LACE	Mercury (M) MG-20402	15.00	37.50	60.00
CHANTILLY LACE	Pickwick (M) 3365	3.00	4.50	6.00
BIG BROTHER				
BIG BROTHER FEATURING ERNIE JOSEPH	All American (M) AA 5770	5.00	10.00	15.00
BIG BROTHER & THE HOLDING COMPANY				
BE A BROTHER	Columbia (S) C 30222	3.00	4.50	6.00
BIG BROTHER AND THE HOLDING COMPANY	Columbia (S) C 30631	4.00	6.00	8.00
BIG BROTHER & THE HOLDING COMPANY	Mainstream (M) 56099	6.00	7.50	10.00
BIG BROTHER & THE HOLDING COMPANY	Mainstream (S) S 6099	6.00	9.00	12.00
CHEAP THRILLS	Columbia (S) KCS 9700	3.50	5.25	7.00
HOW HARD IT IS	Columbia (S) C 30738	4.00	6.00	8.00
Also see JOPLIN, Janis				
BIG DADDY				
BIG DADDY'S BLUES	Gee (M) G 704	5.00	12.50	20.00
TWIST PARTY	Regent (M) 6106	4.00	10.00	16.00
BIG MAYBELLE				
BIG MAYBELLE SINGS	Savoy (M) MG 14005	4.00	10.00	16.00
BIG MAYBELLE SINGS THE BLUES	Epic (M)	5.00	10.00	15.00
BIG MAYBELLE SINGS THE BLUES	Epic (EP) EG 7071	3.00	6.00	9.00
BLUES, CANDY AND BIG MAYBELLE	Savoy (M) MG 14011	4.00	10.00	16.00
GOT A BRAND NEW BAG	Rojac (M) RO 122	2.50	3.75	5.00
SOUL OF BIG MAYBELLE	Scepter (M) S-522	3.00	6.00	9.00
SOUL OF BIG MAYBELLE	Scepter (S) SS-522	4.00	8.00	12.00
WHAT MORE CAN A WOMAN DO	Brunswick (M) BL 54107	3.00	6.00	9.00
WHAT MORE CAN A WOMAN DO	Brunswick (S) BL7 54107	4.00	8.00	12.00
BIG MOE & THE PANICS				
BIG MOE & THE PANICS	Audio Lab (EP) 1	6.00	15.00	24.00
BIG ROSS AND THE MEMPHIS SOUND				
ELVIS PRESLEY'S GOLDEN HITS SUNG BY BIG ROSS AND THE MEMPHIS SOUND	Pickwick (M) SPC 3292	3.00	4.50	6.00
BIG STAR				
RADIO CITY	Ardent (M) ADS 1501	3.00	4.50	6.00
#1 RECORD	Ardent (M) ADS 2803	3.00	4.50	6.00
BIG THREE				
BIG THREE, THE	FM (M) 307	4.00	8.00	12.00
LIVE AT THE RECORDING STUDIO	FM (M) 311	4.00	8.00	12.00
LIVE AT THE RECORDING STUDIO	FM (S) SFM 311	5.00	10.00	15.00
BIG WHEELIE & The Hubcaps				
SOLID GREASE	Bandstand (M) NO 1001	4.00	6.00	8.00
BIKEL, Theodore				
YIDDISH THEATRE & FOLK SONGS	Legacy (S) 121	2.00	3.00	4.00

TITLE	LABEL & NO.	GOOD	VERY GOOD	NEAR MINT
BILK, Mr. Acker				
ABOVE THE STARS	Atco (M) 33-144	3.00	6.00	9.00
ABOVE THE STARS	Atco (S) SD 33-144	4.00	8.00	12.00
CALL ME MISTER	Atco (M) 33-158	2.50	3.75	5.00
CALL ME MISTER	Atco (S) SD 33-158	3.00	4.50	6.00
ONLY YOU	Atco (M) 33-150	2.50	3.75	5.00
ONLY YOU	Atco (S) SD 33-150	3.00	4.50	6.00
STRANGER ON THE SHORE	Atco (M) 33-129	4.00	8.00	12.00
STRANGER ON THE SHORE	Atco (S) SD 33-129	5.00	10.00	15.00

TITLE	LABEL & NO.	GOOD	VERY GOOD	NEAR MINT
THEMES FROM FOREIGN FILMS	Atco (M) 33-170	2.50	3.75	5.00
THEMES FROM FOREIGN FILMS	Atco (S) SD 33-170	3.00	4.50	6.00
A TOUCH OF LATIN	Atco (M) 33-168	2.50	3.75	5.00
A TOUCH OF ATIN	Atco (S) SD 33-168	3.00	4.50	6.00
BIRKIN, Jane & Serge Gainsbourg				
JE T'AIME	Fontana (S) SRF-67610	5.00	7.50	10.00
BISHOP, Elvin				
BEST OF ELVIN BISHOP/ CRABSHAW RISING	Epic (S) PE 33693	2.00	3.00	4.00
HOMETOWN BOY MAKES GOOD	Capricorn (S) CP 0176	3.00	4.50	6.00
JUKE JOINT JUMP	Capricorn (S) CP 0151	3.00	4.50	6.00
LET IT FLOW	Capricorn (S) CP 0134	3.00	4.50	6.00
ROCK MY SOUL	Epic (S) KE-31563	2.00	3.00	4.00
BIT A SWEET				
HYPNOTIC	ABC (S) ABCS 640	2.50	3.75	5.00
BLACK ACE				
BLACK ACE	Arhoolie (M) 1003	2.50	4.00	5.00
BLACK, Bill Combo				
ALL TIMERS	Hi (M) 12032	3.00	6.00	9.00
ALL TIMERS	Hi (S) 32032	4.00	8.00	12.00
AWARD WINNERS	Hi (S) HLP 6005	2.00	3.00	4.00
BILL BLACK COMBO GOES BIG BAND	Hi (M) H-12020	3.00	6.00	9.00
BILL BLACK COMBO GOES BIG BAND	Hi (S) S-32020	4.00	8.00	12.00
BILL BLACK COMBO GOES WEST	Hi (M) HL-12013	3.00	6.00	9.00
BILL BLACK COMBO GOES WEST	Hi (S) SHL-32013	4.00	8.00	12.00
BILL BLACK COMBO (PLAYS TUNES BY CHUCK BERRY)	Hi (M) H-12017	3.00	6.00	9.00
BILL BLACK COMBO (PLAYS TUNES BY CHUCK BERRY)	Hi (S) S-32017	4.00	8.00	12.00
BILL BLACK'S BEAT GOES ON	Hi (M) 12041	3.00	6.00	9.00
BILL BLACK'S BEAT GOES ON	Hi (S) 32041	4.00	8.00	12.00
BILL BLACK'S GREATEST HITS	Hi (M) HL-12012	3.00	6.00	9.00
BILL BLACK'S GREATEST HITS	Hi (S) SHL-32012	4.00	8.00	12.00
BILL BLACK GREATEST HITS VOL. 2	Hi (S) X-32078	2.50	3.75	5.00
BILL BLACK'S RECORD HOP	Hi (M) HL-12006	9.00	18.00	27.00
BILL BLACK'S RECORD HOP	Hi (S) SHL 32006	10.00	20.00	30.00
BLACK BILL IS BACK	Mega (S) 600	3.00	4.50	6.00
BLACK WITH SUGAR	Columbia (S) CS 9848	4.00	6.00	8.00
LET'S TWIST HER ("Bill Black's Record Hop" Retitled)	Hi (M) HL 12006	4.00	8.00	12.00
LET'S TWIST HER ("Bill Black's Record Hop" Retitled)	Hi (S) SHL 32006	5.00	10.00	15.00
MR. BEAT	Hi (M) H-12027	3.00	6.00	9.00
MR. BEAT	Hi (S) S-32027	4.00	8.00	12.00
MORE SOLID & RAUNCHY	Hi (M) H-12023	3.00	6.00	9.00
MORE SOLID & RAUNCHY	Hi (S) 32023	4.00	8.00	12.00
MOVIN'	Hi (M) HL-12005	4.00	8.00	12.00
MOVIN'	Hi (S) SHL-32005	5.00	10.00	15.00
ROCK & ROLL FOREVER	Mega (S) 5008	3.00	4.50	6.00
SAXY JAZZ	Hi (M) HL 12002	6.00	12.00	18.00
SMOKIE	Hi (M) HL-12001	6.00	12.00	18.00

TITLE	LABEL & NO.	GOOD	VERY GOOD	NEAR MINT
SOLID & COUNTRY	Hi (S) 32088	2.50	3.75	5.00
SOLID & RAUNCHY	Hi (M) HL-12003	6.00	12.00	18.00
SOLID & RAUNCHY	Hi (EP) EP-22002	2.50	5.00	7.50
SOLID & RAUNCHY, Vol. 3	Hi (S) SHL 32052	3.50	5.25	7.00
THAT WONDERFUL FEELING	Hi (M) HL-12004	4.00	8.00	12.00
THAT WONDERFUL FEELING	Hi (S) SHL-32004	5.00	10.00	15.00
THAT WONDERFUL FEELING	Hi (EP) HE-22003	2.50	5.00	7.50
UNTOUCHABLE SOUND, THE	Hi (M) HL-12009	3.00	6.00	9.00
UNTOUCHABLE SOUND, THE	Hi (S) SHL-32009	4.00	8.00	12.00

TITLE	LABEL & NO.	GOOD	VERY GOOD	NEAR MINT
BLACKBYRDS				
CITY LIFE	Fantasy (S) F 9490	2.50	3.75	5.00
FLYING START	Fantasy (S) F 9472	2.50	3.75	5.00
FLYING START	F/P/M (Q) FPM 4004	2.50	3.75	5.00
BLACK, Cilla				
IS IT LOVE?	Capitol (M) T 2308	5.00	7.50	10.00
BLACK, Jeanne				
LITTLE BIT LONELY	Capitol (M) T-1513	5.00	10.00	15.00
LITTLE BIT LONELY	Capitol (S) ST-1513	6.00	12.00	18.00
BLACK MERDA				
BLACK MERDA	Chess (S) LPS 1551	3.00	4.50	6.00
BLACKMORE, Ritchie				
RAINBOW	Polydor (S) 6049	3.00	4.50	6.00
Also see DEEP PURPLE, RAINBOW				
BLACK OAK ARKANSAS				
AIN'T LIFE GRAND	Atco (S) 36-111	3.00	4.50	6.00
BLACK OAK ARKANSAS	Atco (S) SD 33-354	3.50	5.25	7.00
EARLY TIMES	Stax (S) 5504	3.50	5.25	6.00
HIGH ON THE HOG	Atco (S) SD 7035	3.00	4.50	6.00
IF AN ANGEL CAME TO YOU, WOULD YOU MAKE HER FEEL AT HOME?	Atco (S) SD 7008	3.00	4.50	6.00
KEEP THE FAITH	Atco (S) SD 33-381	3.50	5.25	7.00
LIVE, MUTHA	Atco (S) 36-128	3.00	4.50	6.00
RAUNCH & ROLL	Atco (S) SD 7019	3.00	4.50	6.00
RAUNCH & ROLL	Atco (Q) QD 7019	2.50	3.75	5.00
STREET PARTY	Atco (S) 36-101	3.00	4.50	6.00
X-RATED	MCA (S) 2155	2.50	3.75	6.00
BLACK PEARL				
BLACK PEARL	Aslantic (M) SD 8220	3.50	5.25	7.00
BLACK PEARL LIVE	Prophesy (S) PR S 1001	3.50	5.25	7.00
BLACK SABBATH				
BLACK SABBATH	Warner Bros. (S) WS 1871	3.50	5.25	7.00
BLACK SABBATH - Vol. 4	Warner Bros. (S) BS 2602	3.00	4.50	6.00
MASTER OF REALITY	Warner Bros. (S) BS 2562	3.00	4.50	6.00
PARANOID	Warner Bros. (S) WS 1887	3.50	5.25	7.00
PARANOID (RI)	Warner Bros. (S) BSK 3104	2.00	3.00	4.00
PARANOID	Warner Bros. (Q) WS4-1887	2.50	3.75	5.00
SABOTAGE	Warner Bros. (S) BS 2822	2.50	3.75	5.00
BLACK SHEEP				
BLACK SHEEP	Capitol (S) ST-11369	2.50	3.75	5.00
ENCOURAGING WORDS	Capitol (S) ST-11447	2.50	3.75	5.00
BLACKWELL, Otis				
SINGIN' THE BLUES	Davis (M) 109	6.00	15.00	24.00
BLACKWOOD APOLOGY				
HOUSE OF LEATHER	Fontana (S) SRF 67591	3.50	5.25	7.00
BLADES OF GRASS				
NUT FOR SMOKING	Jubilee (M)	4.00	6.00	8.00
BLAINE, Hal				
PSYCHEDELIC PERCUSSION	Dunhill (M) D 50019	2.50	3.75	5.00

(M) Mono (S) Stereo (EP) Extended Play (Q) Quad (RI) Re-issued

BLAKE, Barbara & The Uniques
BARBARA BLAKE & THE UNIQUES .... 20th Century (S) 462		2.50	3.75	5.00

BLAND, Bobby Blue
AIN'T NOTHING YOU CAN DO .... Duke (M) DLP 78	5.00	10.00	15.00
AIN'T NOTHING YOU CAN DO .... Duke (S) DLPS 78	3.00	4.50	6.00
BEST OF BOBBY BLAND, THE .... Duke (M) DLP 84	4.00	8.00	12.00
BEST OF BOBBY BLAND, THE .... Duke (S) DLPS 84	3.00	4.50	6.00
BEST OF BOBBY BLAND VOL. 2 .... Duke (M) DLP 86	4.00	8.00	12.00
BEST OF BOBBY BLAND VOL. 2 .... Duke (S) DLPS 86	3.00	4.50	6.00
CALL ON ME .... Duke (M) DLP 77	5.00	10.00	15.00
CALL ON ME .... Blues Way (M) BLS 6065	2.50	3.75	5.00
DREAMER .... Dunhill (S) DSX 50169	2.50	3.75	5.00
GET ON DOWN .... ABC (S) ABCD 895	2.50	3.75	5.00
HERE'S THE MAN .... Duke (S) DLP 75	5.00	10.00	15.00
HERE'S THE MAN .... Duke (S) DLP 7s	3.00	4.50	6.00
HIS CALIFORNIA ALBUM .... Dunhill (M) DSX 50163	2.50	3.75	5.00
IF LOVING YOU IS WRONG .... Duke (S) X-90	3.00	4.50	6.00
INTROSPECTIVE OF THE EARLY YEARS ...... Duke (S) DLPD 92-2	4.00	6.00	8.00
SOUL OF THE MAN, THE .... Duke (M) DLP 79	5.00	10.50	15.00
SOUL OF THE MAN, THE .... Duke (S) DLPS 79	3.00	4.50	6.00
SPOTLIGTING THE MAN .... Duke (S) DLP 89	4.00	8.00	12.00
TOUCH OF THE BLUES .... Duke (S) DLP 88	4.00	8.00	12.00
TWO STEPS FROM THE BLUES .... Duke (M) DLP 74	5.00	10.00	15.00
TWO STEPS FROM THE BLUES .... Duke (S) DLPS 74	3.00	4.50	6.00

BLAND, Bobby Blue & Johnny Guitar Watson
2 IN BLUES .... Crown (M) CLP 5358	5.00	12.50	20.00

BLASTERS
SOUNDS OF THE DRAGS .... Crown (M) CST 392	3.50	5.25	7.00

BLATTNER, Jules, Group
CALL ME MAN .... Buddah (S) BDS 5080	3.00	4.50	6.00

BLESSITT, Arthur (Minister to Sunset Strip)
SOUL SESSION .... Creative Sound (S) CSS 1530	3.00	4.50	6.00

BLIND FAITH
BLIND FAITH (WITH GROUP ON COVER) ... Atco (S) SD 33-304	3.00	4.50	6.00
BLIND FAITH (WITH GIRL ON COVER) .... Atco (S) SD 33-304	4.50	6.75	9.00

BLOCKER, Dan
TALES FOR YOUNG 'UNS .... Trey (M) T-903	2.00	3.00	4.00

BLOCKER, Dan & John Mitchum
OUR LAND-OUR HERITAGE .... RCA (M) LPM-2896	2.50	3.75	5.00
OUR LAND-OUR HERITAGE .... RCA (S) LSP-2896	2.50	3.75	5.00

BLODWYN PIG
GETTING TO THIS .... A&M (S) SP 4243	3.50	5.25	7.00
A HEAD RINGS OUT .... A&M (S) SP 4210	3.00	4.50	6.00

BLONDIE
BLONDIE .... Private Stock (S) PS 2023	2.50	3.75	5.00
PLASTIC LETTERS .... Chrysalis (S) CHR 1166	2.00	3.00	4.00

BLOOD, SWEAT & TEARS
BLOOD, SWEAT & TEARS .... Columbia (S) CS 9720	3.00	4.50	6.00
BLOOD, SWEAT & TEARS .... Columbia (Q) 30994	2.50	3.75	5.00
BLOOD, SWEAT & TEARS .... Columbia (S) CS30090	3.00	4.50	6.00
BRAND NEW DAY .... ABC (S) 1015	2.00	3.00	4.00
B, S & T; 4 .... Columbia (S) KC 30590	3.00	4.50	6.00
CHILD IS FATHER TO THE MAN .... Columbia (S) CS 9619	3.00	4.50	6.00
GREATEST HITS .... Columbia (S) KC 31170	2.50	3.75	5.00
GREATEST HITS .... Columbia (Q) CQ 31170	2.50	3.75	5.00
NEW BLOOD .... Columbia (S) KC 31780	2.50	3.75	5.00
NO SWEAT .... Columbia (S) KC 32180	2.00	3.00	4.00

BLOODROCK
BLOODROCK .... Capitol (S) ST 435	5.00	7.50	10.00
BLOODROCK N' ROLL .... Capitol (S) SM 11417	3.00	4.50	6.00
BLOODROCK PASSAGE .... Capitol (S) SW 11109	5.00	7.50	10.00
BLOODROCK 3 .... Capitol (S) ST 765	4.00	6.00	8.00
BLOODROCK 2 .... Capitol (S) ST 491	4.00	6.00	8.00
LIVE .... Capitol (S) SVBB 11038	3.50	5.25	7.00
U.S.A. .... Capitol (S) SMAS 645	3.50	5.25	7.00
WHIRLWINDS TONGUES .... Capitol (S) SMAS 11259	3.50	5.25	7.00

BLOOMFIELD, Mike
ANALINE (LISTED AS "MICHAEL BLOOMFIELD") .... Takoma (S) 1059	3.50	5.25	7.00
IT'S NOT KILLING ME				
(LISTED AS "MICHAEL BLOOMFIELD") ...... Columbia (S) CS 9883	3.50	5.25	7.00
TRIUMVIRATE (WITH JOHN HAMMOND				
& DR. JOHN) .... Columbia (S) KC-32172	2.50	3.75	5.00
TRY IT BEFORE YOU BUY IT .... Columbia (S) PC-33173	3.00	4.50	6.00

BLOSSOM DEARIE
BLOSSOM DEARIE .... Fontana (S) SRF 67562	6.00	8.00	12.00

BLOSSOMS
SHOCKWAVE .... Lion (M) LN 1007	2.25	3.50	4.50

BLOSSOM TOES
IF ONLY FOR A MOMENT .... Marmalade (S) 608 010	6.00	9.00	12.00

BLUE
BLUE .... RSO (S) 873	2.50	3.75	5.00

BLUE ASH
NO MORE, NO LESS .... Mercury (M) SRM-1-666	3.50	5.25	7.00

BLUE BARONS
TWIST TO THE GREAT BLUES HITS .... Philips (M) PHM-200017	3.00	6.00	9.00
TWIST TO THE GREAT BLUES HITS .... Philips (S) PHS-600017	4.00	8.00	12.00

BLUE BEATS
BEATLE BEAT, THE .... A.A. (M) 133	5.00	10.00	15.00

BLUE BOYS
WE REMEMBER JIM REEVES .... RCA (M) LPM 3331	2.50	3.75	5.00
WE REMEMBER JIM REEVES .... RCA (S) LSP 3331	2.50	3.75	5.00

BLUE CHEER
BLUE CHEER .... Philips (S) PHS 600-333	5.00	7.50	10.00
NEW! IMPOVED! .... Philips (S) PHS 600-305	5.00	7.50	10.00
OH! PLEASANT HOPE .... Philips (S) PHS 600-350	6.00	8.00	12.00
ORIGINAL HUMAN BEING, THE .... Philips (S) PHS 600-347	6.00	8.00	12.00
OUTSIDEINSIDE .... Philips (S) PHS 600-278	5.00	7.50	10.00
VINCEBUS ERUPTUM .... Philips (M) PHM 200-264	4.00	6.00	8.00
VINCEBUS ERUPTUM .... Philips (S) PHS 600-264	5.00	7.50	10.00

BLUE, David
COMIN' BACK FOR MORE .... Asylum (S) 7E-1043	2.50	3.75	5.00
DAVID BLUE .... Elektra (S) EKS 74003	3.00	4.50	6.00
NICE BABY & THE ANGEL .... Asylum (S) 5066	3.00	4.50	6.00
THESE 23 DAYS IN SEPTEMBER .... Reprise (S) RS 6296	2.50	3.75	5.00

BLUE DIAMONDS
BLUE DIAMONDS, FEATURING RAMONA .... London (M) LL 3235	5.00	10.00	15.00

BLUE MAGIC
BLUE MAGIC .... Atco (S) 7038	3.00	4.50	6.00
MAGIC OF THE BLUE .... Atco (S) 36-103	2.50	3.75	5.00

BLUE MINK
BLUE MINK .... MCA (S) 332	2.00	3.00	4.00
MELTING POT .... Philips (S) 600-323	3.00	4.50	6.00
REAL MINK .... Philips (S) 600-339	3.00	4.50	6.00

BLUE OYSTER CULT
AGENTS OF FORTUNE .... Columbia (S) PC 34164	2.00	3.00	4.00
BLUE OYSTER CULT .... Columbia (S) KC 31063	3.00	4.50	6.00
IN MY MOUTH OR ON THE GROUND (10 inch LP) ...... IMP (M) 1106	4.00	6.00	8.00
ON YOUR FEET OR ON YOUR KNEES ...... Columbia (S) KG 33371	2.50	3.75	5.00
SECRET TREATIES .... Columbia (S) KC 32858	2.50	3.75	5.00
SECRET TREATIES .... Columbia (Q) PCQ 32858	2.50	3.75	5.00
SPECTRES .... Columbia (S) JC 35019	2.00	3.00	4.00
TYRANNY & MUTATION .... Columbia (S) KC 32017	3.00	4.50	6.00
TYRANNY & MUTATION .... Columbia (Q) PCQ 32017	2.50	3.75	5.00

BLUES CLIMAX
BLUES CLIMAX, THE .... Horn (M) JC 888	5.00	10.00	15.00

BLUES MAGOOS
BASIC BLUES MAGOOS .... Mercury (M) SR 61167	4.00	6.00	8.00
ELECTRIC COMIC BOOK .... Mercury (M) MG 21104	5.00	7.50	10.00
ELECTRIC COMIC BOOK .... Mercury (S) SR 61104	6.00	8.00	12.00
GULF COAST BOUND .... ABC (M) ABCS 710	4.00	6.00	8.00
NEVER GOIN' BACK TO GEORGIA .... ABC (M) ABCS 697	4.00	6.00	8.00
PSYCHEDELIC LOLLIPOP .... Mercury (M) MG 21096	5.00	7.50	10.00
PSYCHEDELIC LOLLIPOP .... Mercury (S) SR 61096	6.00	8.00	12.00

BLUES PROJECT
BEST OF THE BLUES PROJECT ...... Verve Forecast (S) FTS 3077	3.00	4.50	6.00
BLUES PROJECT .... Capitol (S) SMAS 11017	2.50	3.75	5.00
BLUES PROJECT LIVE AT				
TOWN HALL, THE .... Verve/Forecast (M) FT 3025	2.00	3.00	4.00
BLUES PROJECT LIVE AT				
TOWN HALL, THE .... Verve/Forecast (S) FTS 3025	3.00	4.50	6.00
LIVE AT THE CAFE AU GO GO ...... Verve/Folkways (M) FV 9024	2.00	3.00	4.00
LIVE AT THE CAFE AU GO GO ...... Verve/Folkways (S) FVS 9024	3.00	4.50	6.00
PLANNED OBSOLESCENCE .... Verve Forecast (S) FTS 3046	3.00	4.50	6.00
PROJECTIONS .... Verve/Folkways (M) FT 3008	2.50	3.75	5.00
PROJECTIONS .... Verve/Folkways (S) FTS 3008	3.50	5.25	7.00
REUNION IN CENTRAL PARK .... MCA (S) 2-8003	3.00	4.50	6.00

BLUE SWEDE
HOOKED ON A FEELING .... EMI (S) ST-11286	3.50	5.25	7.00
OUT OF THE BLUE .... EMI (S) ST-11346	3.50	5.25	7.00

BLUE THINGS
BLUE THINGS .... RCA (M) LPM 3603	3.00	4.50	6.00
BLUE THINGS .... RCA (S) LSP 3603	4.00	6.00	8.00

(M) Mono (S) Stereo (EP) Extended Play (Q) Quad (RI) Re-issued

TITLE	LABEL & NO.	GOOD	VERY GOOD	NEAR MINT

BLUE VELVET BAND
SWEET MOMENTS WITH . . . . *Warner Bros. (S) WS 1802* — 2.00 3.00 4.00

BOB AND EARL
BOB AND EARL . . . . *Crestview (M) CRS 3055*	3.00	6.00	9.00
HARLEM SHUFFLE . . . . *TIP (M) TLP 1011*	2.00	4.00	6.00
HARLEM SHUFFLE . . . . *TIP (S) TLS 9011*	3.00	6.00	9.00

BODINE, Rita Jean
| RITA JEAN BODINE . . . . *20th Century (S) 455* | 2.00 | 3.00 | 4.00 |
| SITTING ON TOP OF MY WORLD . . . . *20th Century (S) 431* | 2.00 | 3.00 | 4.00 |

BODY AND SOUL
BODY AND SOUL . . . . *National General (M) NG 2002* — 4.00 6.00 8.00

BOETCHER, Curt
THERE'S AN INNOCENT FACE . . . . *Elektra (S) EKS 75037* — 3.00 4.50 6.00

BOHANNON
INSIDE OUT . . . . *Dakar (S) 76916*	2.50	3.75	5.00
KEEP ON DANCIN' . . . . *Dakar (S) 76910*	2.50	3.75	5.00
MIGHTY BOHANNON . . . . *Dakar (S) 76917*	2.50	3.75	5.00
STOP & GO . . . . *Dakar (S) 76903*	2.50	3.75	5.00

BOHEMIAN VENDETTA
| BOHEMIAN VENDETTA . . . . *Mainstream (M) 56106* | 4.00 | 6.00 | 8.00 |
| BOHEMIAN VENDETTA . . . . *Mainstream (S) S/6106* | 5.00 | 7.50 | 10.00 |

BOLD
BOLD . . . . *ABC (S) ABCS-705* — 2.50 3.75 5.00

BONADUCE, Danny (Of the Partridge Family)
DANNY BONADUCE . . . . *Lion (S) 1015* — 2.50 3.75 5.00

BOND, Grahame
LOVE IS THE LAW . . . . *Pulson (M) 10604*	3.50	5.25	7.00
MIGHTY GRAHAME BOND . . . . *Pulson (M) 10606*	3.50	5.25	7.00
SOLID . . . . *Warner Bros. (S) LS 2555*	3.00	4.50	6.00
WE PUT OUR MAGIC ON YOU . . . . *Mercury (S) SRM1-612*	4.00	6.00	8.00

BOND, Johnny
JOHNNY BOND AND HIS RED RIVER VALLEY BOYS . . . . . . *Columbia (EP) B 2820*	1.00	1.50	2.00
SONGS THAT MADE HIM FAMOUS . . . . *Starday (M) 227*	2.00	3.00	4.00
TEN LITTLE BOTTLES . . . . *Starday (S) S-333*	2.00	3.00	4.00
THREE SHEETS IN THE WIND . . . . *Starday (S) S 298*	2.00	3.00	4.00

BONDS, Gary U.S.
DANCE 'TILL QUARTER TO THREE . . . *Legrand (M) LLP 3001*	6.00	12.00	18.00
GREATEST HITS OF GARY U.S. BONDS . *Legrand (M) LLP 3003*	6.00	12.00	18.00
TWIST UP CALYPSO . . . . *Legrand (M) LLP 3002*	6.00	12.00	18.00

BONFIRE, Mars
| FASTER THAN THE SPEED OF LIFE . . . *Columbia (S) CS 9834* | 3.00 | 4.50 | 6.00 |
| MARS BONFIRE . . . . *UNI (S) 73027* | 3.00 | 4.50 | 6.00 |

BONNEVILLES
MEET THE BONNEVILLES . . . . *Drum Boy (M) DBLM 1001* — 3.00 6.00 9.00

BONNIE LOU
BONNIE LOU SINGS . . . . *King (EP) EP 335* — 3.00 6.00 9.00

BONNIWELL MUSIC MACHINE
BONNIWELL MUSIC MACHINE, THE . . . . . *Warner Brothers (M) 1732* — 4.00 6.00 8.00

BONNIWELL, T.S.
CLOSE . . . . *Capitol (S) ST 277* — 3.00 4.50 6.00

BONOFF, Karla
KARLA BONOFF . . . . *Columbia (S) PC 34672* — 2.00 3.00 4.00

BONZO DOG BAND
BEAST OF THE BONZOS . . . . *United Artists (S) UAS 5517*	2.50	3.75	5.00
GORILLA . . . . *Imperial (S) 12370*	5.00	7.50	10.00
HISTORY OF THE BONZOS . . . . *United Artists (S) UA-LA321*	2.50	3.75	5.00
KEYNSHAM . . . . *Imperial (S) 12457*	4.00	6.00	8.00
LET'S MAKE UP AND BE FRIENDLY . . *United Artists (S) UAS 5584*	2.50	3.75	5.00
TADPOLES . . . . *Imperial (S) 12445*	5.00	7.50	10.00
URBAN SPACE MAN . . . . *Imperial (S) 12432*	4.00	6.00	8.00

BOOGIE KINGS
| BLUE-EYED SOUL . . . . *Montel-Michelle (M) LP 109* | 6.00 | 12.00 | 18.00 |
| BOOGIE KINGS, THE . . . . *Montel-,michelle (M) MLP 104* | 6.00 | 12.00 | 18.00 |

BOOGIE WOOGIE PIONEERS
| BOOGIE WOOGIE PIONEERS VOL. 1 . . . *Riverside (M) RLP 1034* | 4.00 | 6.00 | 8.00 |
| BOOGIE WOOGIE PIONEERS VOL. 2 . . . *Riverside (M) RLP 1009* | 4.00 | 6.00 | 8.00 |

BOOKBINDER, Roy
TRAVELIN' MAN . . . . *Adelphi (M) AD 1017* — 3.50 5.25 7.00

TITLE	LABEL & NO.	GOOD	VERY GOOD	NEAR MINT

BOOKER T & THE M.G.'s
AND NOW . . . . *Stax (M) 711*	2.50	3.75	5.00
AND NOW . . . . *Stax (S) 711*	3.50	5.25	7.00
BEST OF BOOKER T AND THE MG'S . . . . . *Atlantic (M) 8202*	3.00	4.50	6.00
BOOKER T SET, THE . . . . *Stax (S) STS 2009*	3.00	4.50	6.00
DOIN OUR THING . . . . *Stax (M) 724*	2.50	3.75	5.00
DOIN OUR THING . . . . *Stax (S) 724*	3.50	5.25	7.00
GREATEST HITS . . . . *Stax (S) STS 2033*	3.00	4.50	6.00
GREEN ONIONS . . . . *Stax (M) 701*	4.00	6.50	8.00
HIP HUG-HER . . . . *Stax (M) 717*	2.50	3.75	5.00
HIP HUG-HER . . . . *Stax (S) 717*	3.50	5.25	7.00
IN THE CHRISTMAS SPIRIT . . . . *Stax (M) 713*	2.50	3.75	5.00
IN THE CHRISTMAS SPIRIT . . . . *Stax (S) 713*	3.50	5.25	7.00
MCLEMORE AVE . . . . *Stax (S) 2027*	3.00	4.50	6.00
MELTING POT . . . . *Stax (S) STS 2035*	3.00	4.50	6.00
SOUL DRESSING . . . . *Stax (M) 705*	2.50	3.75	5.00
SOUL DRESSING . . . . *Stax (S) 705*	3.50	5.25	7.00
SOUL LIMBO . . . . *Stax (S) STS 2001*	3.00	4.50	6.00
UPTIGHT . . . . *Stax (S) STS 2006*	3.00	4.50	6.00

BOOM, Memphis Willie
MEMPHIS WILLIE BOOM . . . . *Bluesway (M) 1034* — 5.00 7.50 10.00

BOONE, Daniel
| DANIEL BOONE . . . . *Mercury (S) SRM-1-649* | 2.50 | 3.75 | 5.00 |
| RUN TELL THE PEOPLE . . . . *Pye (S) 12105* | 3.00 | 4.50 | 6.00 |

BOONE, Debby
YOU LIGHT UP MY LIFE . . . . *Warner/Curb (S) BS 3118* — 2.00 3.00 4.00

BOONE, Pat
AIN'T THAT A SHAME . . . . *Dot (M) DLP-3573*	2.00	3.00	4.00
AIN'T THAT A SHAME . . . . *Dot (S) DLP-25573*	2.00	3.00	4.00
APRIL LOVE (Soundtrack) . . . . *Dot (M) DLP 9000*	3.00	4.50	6.00
BEYOND THE SUNSET . . . . *Dot (EP) DEP-1090*	1.00	1.50	2.00
DATE WITH PAT BOONE . . . . *Dot (EP) DEP 1055*	1.00	1.50	2.00
FRIENDLY PERSUASION . . . . *Dot (EP) DEP 1054*	1.50	2.25	3.00
FOUR BY PAT . . . . *Dot (EP) DEP 1057*	1.50	2.25	3.00
GREAT, GREAT, GREAT . . . . *Dot (M) DLP-3346*	2.00	3.00	4.00
GREAT, GREAT, GREAT . . . . *Dot (S) DLP-25346*	2.00	3.00	4.00
GREAT MILLIONS . . . . *Dot (M) DLP-3181*	2.50	3.75	5.00
HOWDY . . . . *Dot (M) DLP 3030*	3.00	4.50	6.00
I LOVE YOU MORE & MORE EVERY DAY . . . *MGM (S) 4899*	2.50	3.75	5.00
I'LL SEE YOU IN MY DREAMS . . . . *Dot (M) DLP-3399*	2.50	3.75	5.00
I'LL SEE YOU IN MY DREAMS . . . . *Dot (S) DLP-25399*	2.50	3.75	5.00
I'M IN THE MOOD FOR LOVE . . . . *Dot (EP) DEP-1086*	1.00	1.50	2.00
JOURNEY TO THE CENTER OF THE EARTH . . . *Dot (EP) DEP-1091*	1.50	2.25	3.00
MARDI GRAS . . . . *Dot (EP) DEP 1075*	1.00	1.50	2.00
MERRY CHRISTMAS . . . . *Dot (EP) DEP 1062*	1.00	1.50	2.00
MOONGLOW . . . . *Dot (M) DLP-3270*	2.50	3.75	5.00
MOONGLOW . . . . *Dot (S) DLP-25270*	2.50	3.75	5.00
MOONGLOW . . . . *Dot (EP) DEP-1096*	1.00	1.50	2.00
PAT . . . . *Dot (M) DLP 3050*	3.00	4.50	6.00
PAT BOONE . . . . *Dot (M) DLP 3012*	3.50	5.25	7.00
PAT BOONE . . . . *Dot (EP) DEP 1049*	1.50	2.25	3.00
PAT BOONE GOLDEN HITS . . . . *Dot (M) DLP-3455*	2.00	3.00	4.00
PAT BOONE GOLDEN HITS . . . . *Dot (S) DLP-25455*	2.00	3.00	4.00
PAT BOONE GUESS WHO (Elvis Tribute) . . . *Dot (M) DLP 3501*	6.00	9.00	12.00
PAT BOONE GUESS WHO (Elvis Tribute) . . . *Dot (S) DLP-25501*	9.00	13.50	18.00
PAT BOONE SINGS . . . . *Dot (M) DLP-3158*	2.50	3.75	5.00
PAT BOONE SINGS . . . . *Dot (S) DLP-25158*	2.50	3.75	5.00
PAT BOONE SINGS . . . . *Dot (M) DLP-3667*	2.00	3.00	4.00
PAT BOONE SINGS . . . . *Dot (S) DLP-25667*	2.00	3.00	4.00
PAT BOONE SINGS IRVING BERLIN . . . . . . *Dot (M) DLP 3077*	2.00	3.00	4.00
PAT BOONE SINGS IRVING BERLIN . . . . . . *Dot (S) DLP 25077*	2.00	3.00	4.00
PAT ON MIKE . . . . *Dot (EP) DEP 1053*	1.00	1.50	2.00
PAT'S GREATEST HITS . . . . *Dot (M) LDP 3071*	3.00	4.50	6.00
PAT'S GREATEST HITS . . . . *Dot (S) DLP-25071*	2.00	3.00	4.00
PAT'S GREATEST HITS . . . . *Dot (EP) DEP-1083*	1.00	1.50	2.00
PAT'S GREATEST HITS, VOL. 2 . . . . *Dot (M) DLP-3261*	2.00	3.00	4.00
PAT'S GREATEST HITS, VOL. 2 . . . . *Dot (S) DLP-25261*	2.00	3.00	4.00
STAR DUST . . . . *Dot (M) DLP 3118*	2.50	3.75	5.00
STAR DUST . . . . *Dot (S) DLP 25118*	2.50	3.75	5.00
STAR DUST . . . . *Dot (EP) DEP 1069*	1.00	1.50	2.00
TENDERLY . . . . *Dot (M) DLP-3180*	2.50	3.75	5.00
TENDERLY . . . . *Dot (S) DLP-25180*	2.50	3.75	5.00
TENDERLY . . . . *Dot (EP) DEP 1082*	1.00	1.50	2.00

(M) Mono   (S) Stereo   (EP) Extended Play   (Q) Quad   (RI) Re-issued

STAR DUST
PAT BOONE

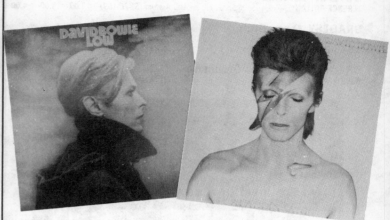

TITLE	LABEL & NO.	GOOD	VERY GOOD	NEAR MINT
TEXAS WOMAN	Hitsville (S) 405	2.00	3.00	4.00
THIS & THAT	Dot (M) DLP-3285	2.00	3.00	4.00
THIS & THAT	Dot (S) DLP-25285	2.00	3.00	4.00
TUTTI FRUTTI	Dot (EP) DEP 1064	1.50	2.25	3.00
WHITE CHRISTMAS	Dot (M) DLP-3222	2.00	3.00	4.00
WHITE CHRISTMAS	Dot (S) DLP-25222	2.00	3.00	4.00
YES INDEED	Dot (M) DLP 3121	2.50	3.75	5.00

BOONE, Pat & Shirley
TITLE	LABEL & NO.	GOOD	VERY GOOD	NEAR MINT
BESIDE ME	Dot (EP) DEP-1088	1.00	1.50	2.00
SIDE BY SIDE	Dot (M) DLP-3199	2.00	3.00	4.00
SIDE BY SIDE	Dot (S) DLP-25199	2.00	3.00	4.00
SIDE BY SIDE	Dot (EP) DEP-1076	1.00	1.50	2.00

BOOT
TITLE	LABEL & NO.	GOOD	VERY GOOD	NEAR MINT
BOOT	Agape (M) 2601	5.00	7.50	10.00

BOOTH, Tony
TITLE	LABEL & NO.	GOOD	VERY GOOD	NEAR MINT
HAPPY HOUR	Capitol (S) ST-11270	2.00	3.00	4.00
LONESOME 7-7203	Capitol (S) ST-11126	2.00	3.00	4.00
THIS IS TONY BOOTH	Capitol (S) ST-11210	2.00	3.00	4.00
WHEN A MAN LOVES A WOMAN	Capitol (S) ST-11160	2.00	3.00	4.00
WORKIN' AT THE CAR WASH BLUES	Capitol (S) ST-11352	2.00	3.00	4.00

BOSTIC, Earl
TITLE	LABEL & NO.	GOOD	VERY GOOD	NEAR MINT
ALTO-TUDE	King (M) LP 515	5.00	12.50	20.00
BEST OF BOSTIC	King (M) 560	6.00	15.00	24.00
BEST OF EARL BOSTIC	King (M) 881	3.00	6.00	9.00
BOSTIC BLOWS	King (EP) KEP 381	2.00	5.00	8.00
BOSTIC FOR YOU	King (M) 503	6.00	15.00	24.00
BOSTIC ROCKS	King (M) LP 571	5.00	12.50	20.00
BOSTIC ROCKS	King (EP) KEP 414	2.00	5.00	8.00
BOSTIC ROCKS, Vol. 1	King (EP) KEP 414	2.00	5.00	8.00
BOSTIC ROCKS, Vol. 2	King (EP) KEP 414	2.00	5.00	8.00
BY POPULAR DEMAND	King (M) 786	4.00	10.00	16.00
BY POPULAR DEMAND	King (S) 786	3.00	7.50	12.00
DANCE TIME	King (M) LP 525	5.00	12.50	20.00
EARL BOSTIC	King (EP) KEP 207	3.00	7.50	12.00
EARL BOSTIC AND HIS ALTO SAX	King (EP) KEP 284	2.00	5.00	8.00
EARL BOSTIC PLAYS BOSSA NOVA	King (M) 827	4.00	8.00	12.00
EARL BOSTIC PLAYS BOSSA NOVA	King (S) 827	3.00	6.00	9.00
EARL BOSTIC WITH STRINGS	King (EP) KEP 375	2.00	5.00	8.00
JAZZ AS I FEEL IT	King (M) 846	4.00	8.00	12.00
JAZZ AS I FEEL IT	King (S) 846	3.00	6.00	9.00
LET'S DANCE WITH EARL BOSTIC	King (M) LP 529	5.00	12.50	20.00
NEW SOUND	King (M) 900	3.00	6.00	9.00
SWEET TUNES OF THE FANTASTIC FIFTIES	King (M) LP 602	4.00	10.00	16.00
SWEET TUNES OF THE FANTASTIC FIFTIES	King (EP) KEP 427	5.00	10.00	15.00
25 YEARS OF RHYTHM & BLUES HITS	King (M) 725	4.00	10.00	16.00

BOSTON
TITLE	LABEL & NO.	GOOD	VERY GOOD	NEAR MINT
BOSTON	Epic (S) PE 34188	2.00	3.00	4.00

BOSTON TEA PARTY
TITLE	LABEL & NO.	GOOD	VERY GOOD	NEAR MINT
BOSTON TEA PARTY, THE	Flick Disc (S) FLS 45,000	4.00	6.00	8.00

(M) Mono (S) Stereo (EP) Extended Play (Q) Quad (RI) Re-issued

TITLE	LABEL & NO.	GOOD	VERY GOOD	NEAR MINT
BOWEN, Jimmy				
JIMMY BOWEN	Roulette (M) R 25004	12.50	31.25	50.00
JIMMY BOWEN	Roulette (EP) EPR 1 302	3.00	7.50	12.00
SUNDAY MORNING WITH THE COMICS	Reprise (M) R-6210	2.00	4.00	6.00
SUNDAY MORNING WITH THE COMICS	Reprise (S) RS-6210	3.00	6.00	9.00

BOWIE, David
TITLE	LABEL & NO.	GOOD	VERY GOOD	NEAR MINT
ALADDIN SANE	RCA (S) LSP-4852	4.00	6.00	8.00
CHANGESONE BOWIE	RCA (S) APL1-1732	2.50	3.75	5.00
DAVID BOWIE	Deram (M) DE 16003	7.00	10.50	14.00
DAVID BOWIE	Deram (S) DES 18003	8.00	12.00	16.00
DAVID BOWIE	RCA (EP) 103	2.50	3.75	5.00
DAVID LIVE	RCA (S) CPL2-0771	3.00	4.50	6.00
DIAMOND DOGS	RCA (S) CPL1-0576	3.00	4.50	6.00
HEROES	RCA (S) AFL1-2522	2.00	3.00	4.00
HUNKY DORY	RCA (S) LSP 4623	5.00	7.50	10.00
IMAGES	London (S) BP-628/9	3.50	5.25	7.00
LOW	RCA (S) CPL1-2030	2.50	3.75	5.00
MAN OF WORDS/MAN OF MUSIC	Mercury (S) SR 61246	10.00	15.00	20.00
MAN WHO SOLD THE WORLD, THE	Mercury (S) SR 61325	5.00	7.50	10.00
MAN WHO SOLD THE WORLD (Original 'drag' cover)	Mercury (S) SR 61246	125.00	187.50	250.00
MAN WHO SOLD THE WORLD	RCA (S) LSP-4816	3.00	4.50	6.00
PINUPS	RCA (S) APL1-0291	3.00	4.50	6.00
RISE & FALL OF ZIGGY STARDUST & THE SPIDERS FROM MARS	RCA (S) LSP 4702	4.50	6.75	9.00
SPACE ODDITY	RCA (S) LSP-4813	3.00	4.50	6.00
STARTING POINT	London (S) LC-50007	2.00	3.00	4.00
STATION TO STATION	RCA (S) APL1-1327	2.50	3.75	5.00
YOUNG AMERICANS	RCA (S) APL1-0998	3.00	4.50	6.00

BOWMAN, Don
TITLE	LABEL & NO.	GOOD	VERY GOOD	NEAR MINT
FRESH FROM THE FUNNY FARM	RCA (M) LPM-3345	2.00	3.00	4.00
FRESH FROM THE FUNNY FARM	RCA (S) LSP-3345	2.00	3.00	4.00
FUNNY FOLK FLOPS	RCA (M) LPM-3920	2.00	3.00	4.00
FUNNY FOLK FLOPS	RCA (S) LSP-3920	2.00	3.00	4.00
FUNNY WAY TO MAKE AN ALBUM	RCA (M) LPM-3495	2.00	3.00	4.00
FUNNY WAY TO MAKE AN ALBUM	RCA (S) LSP-3495	2.00	3.00	4.00
OUR MAN IN TROUBLE	RCA (M) LPM-2831	2.00	3.00	4.00
OUR MAN IN TROUBLE	RCA (S) LSP-2831	2.00	3.00	4.00

BOWN, Alan
TITLE	LABEL & NO.	GOOD	VERY GOOD	NEAR MINT
ALAN BOWN	Deram (S) DES 18032	4.00	6.00	8.00
ALAN BOWN	Verve Forecast (S) FTS3062	4.50	6.75	9.00
LISTEN	Iland (S) SW 9308	4.00	6.00	8.00

BOWN, Andy
TITLE	LABEL & NO.	GOOD	VERY GOOD	NEAR MINT
GONE TO MY HEAD	Mercury (S) SRM 1-625	2.50	3.75	5.00
SWEET WILLIAM	Mercury (S) SRM 1-656	2.50	3.75	5.00

BOW STREET RUNNERS
TITLE	LABEL & NO.	GOOD	VERY GOOD	NEAR MINT
BOW STREET RUNNERS	B.T. Puppy (M) 1026	8.00	12.00	16.00

BOX TOPS
TITLE	LABEL & NO.	GOOD	VERY GOOD	NEAR MINT
CRY LIKE A BABY	Bell (S) 6017	2.50	3.75	5.00
DIMENSIONS	Bell (S) 6032	4.00	6.00	8.00
LETTER, THE/NEON RAINBOW	Bell (S) 6011	3.00	4.50	6.00
LETTER, THE/NEON RAINBOW	Bell (S) 6011	4.00	6.00	8.00
NONSTOP	Bell (S) 6023	4.00	6.00	8.00
SUPER HITS	Bell (S) 6025	4.00	6.00	8.00

BOYCE, Tommy
TITLE	LABEL & NO.	GOOD	VERY GOOD	NEAR MINT
A TWOFOLD TALENT	RCA/Camden (M) CAL 2202	4.00	6.00	8.00
A TWOFOLD TALENT	RCA/Camden (S) CAS 2202	3.00	4.50	6.00

BOYCE, Tommy & Bobby Hart
TITLE	LABEL & NO.	GOOD	VERY GOOD	NEAR MINT
IT'S ALL HAPPENING ON THE INSIDE	A&M (S) SP 4162	3.00	4.50	6.00
I WONDER WHAT SHE'S DOING TONIGHT	A&M (S) SP 4143	3.00	4.50	6.00
WHICH ONE'S BOYCE & WHICH ONE'S HART	A&M (S) SP 4162	3.00	4.50	6.00

TITLE	LABEL & NO.	GOOD	VERY GOOD	NEAR MINT
BOYD, Jimmy				
CHILDREN'S CHRISTMAS	Columbia (EP) B 2611	1.00	2.00	3.00
COUNTRY CHOIR BOY	Columbia (M) CL 2589	4.00	6.00	8.00
XMAS WITH BOYD	Columbia (M) CL 6270	4.00	6.00	8.00
XMAS WITH BOYD	Columbia (EP) B343	1.00	2.00	3.00
BOYLAN, Terence				
TERENCE BOYLAN	Asylum (S) 7E-1091	2.00	3.00	4.00
BRADLEY, Owen Orch.				
BIG GUITAR	Decca (M) DL-8868	3.00	4.50	6.00
BIG GUITAR	Decca (S) DL7-8868	3.50	5.25	7.00
BRADLEY, Will & His Orchestra				
BOOGIE WOOGIE	Epic (M) LN 3115	8.00	20.00	32.00

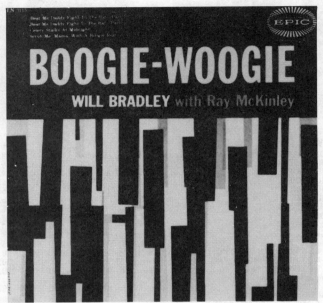

TITLE	LABEL & NO.	GOOD	VERY GOOD	NEAR MINT
BRADSHAW, Tiny				
GREAT COMPOSER	King (M) 653	8.00	20.00	32.00
LIGHT AND CHOICE VOL. 5	King (EP) EP 351	3.00	7.50	12.00
OFF AND ON	King (M) LP 295-74	8.00	20.00	32.00
SELECTIONS	King (M) LP 501	10.00	25.00	40.00
STOMPING ROOM ONLY	King (EP) EP 360	3.00	7.50	12.00
TINY BRADSHAW	King (EP) EP-208	3.00	7.50	12.00
TINY BRADSHAW (10")	King (M) 295 74	9.00	22.50	35.00
24 GREAT SONGS	King (M) 953	3.00	7.50	12.00
BRADY BUNCH				
BRADY BUNCH PHONOGRAPHIS ALBUM	Paramount (S) 6058	2.00	3.00	4.00
KIDS FROM THE BRADY BUNCH	Paramount (S) 6037	2.00	3.00	4.00
BRAINBOX				
BRAINBOX	Capitol (S) ST 596	4.00	6.00	8.00
BRAMLETT, Bonnie (Of Delaney & Bonnie)				
IT'S TIME	Capricorn (S) CP 0148	3.00	4.50	6.00
SWEET BONNIE BRAMLETT	Columbia (S) KC-31786	2.50	3.75	5.00
BRAMLETT, Delaney (Of Delaney & Bonnie)				
GIVING BIRTH TO A SONG (AND BLUE DIAMOND)	MGM (S) M3G-5011	3.00	4.50	6.00
MOBIUS STRIP	Columbia (S) KC-32420	3.00	4.50	6.00
SOME THINGS COMING	Columbia (S) KC-31631	3.00	4.50	6.00
BRASSELLE, Keefe				
MINSTREL MAN	Coral (M) CRL-57295	2.00	3.00	4.00
MINSTREL MAN	Coral (S) CRL 757295	2.50	3.75	5.00
BRAUN, Bob				
BOB BRAUN	Decca (EP) EP-2735	1.00	1.50	2.00
BREAD				
BABY I'M - A WANT YOU	Elektra (S) EKS 75015	3.00	4.50	6.00
BABY I'M - A WANT YOU	Elektra (Q) EQ 5015	2.50	3.75	5.00
BEST OF BREAD	Elektra (S) EKS 75056	3.00	4.50	6.00
BEST OF BREAD	Elektra (Q) EQ 5056	2.50	3.75	5.00
BEST OF BREAD, Vol. 2	Elektra (S) 7E-1005	2.30	3.75	5.00
BREAD	Elektra (S) EKS 74044	4.50	6.75	9.00
GUITAR MAN	Elektra (S) EKS 75047	3.00	4.50	6.00

(M) Mono (S) Stereo (EP) Extended Play (Q) Quad (RI) Re-issued

TITLE	LABEL & NO.	GOOD	VERY GOOD	NEAR MINT
LOST WITHOUT YOUR LOVE	Elektra (S) 7E-1094	2.00	3.00	4.00
MANNA	Elektra (S) EKS 74086	3.50	5.25	7.00
ON THE WATERS	Elektra (S) EKS 74076	3.50	5.25	7.00
Also see GATES, David				
BRECKER BROS.				
BRECKER BROS.	Arista (S) 4037	2.50	3.75	5.00
BREMERS, Beverly				
I'LL MAKE YOU MUSIC	Scepter (S) SPS 5102	3.00	4.50	6.00
BRENDA & The Tabulations				
DRY YOUR EYES	Dionn (M) LPM 2000	4.00	6.00	8.00
BRENNAN, Walter				
DUTCHMAN'S GOLD	Dot (M) DLP-3309	2.50	3.75	5.00
DUTCHMAN'S GOLD	Dot (S) DLP-25309	3.00	4.50	6.00
GUNFIGHT AT THE O.K. CORRAL	Liberty (M) LRP-3372	2.00	3.00	4.00
GUNFIGHT AT THE O.K. CORRAL	Liberty (S) LST-7372	2.00	3.00	4.00
MAMA SANG A SONG	Liberty (M) LRP-3266	2.00	3.00	4.00
MAMA SANG A SONG	Liberty (S) LST-7266	2.00	3.00	4.00
OLD RIVERS	Liberty (M) LRP-3233	2.50	3.75	5.00
OLD RIVERS	Liberty (S) LST-7233	2.50	3.75	5.00
PRESIDENT, THE	Liberty (M) LRP-3241	2.00	3.00	4.00
PRESIDENT, THE	Liberty (S) LST-7241	2.00	3.00	4.00
TALKIN' FROM THE HEART	Liberty (M) LRP-3317	2.00	3.00	4.00
TALKIN' FROM THE HEART	Liberty (S) LST-7317	2.00	3.00	4.00
'TWAS THE NIGHT BEFORE CHRISTMAS BACK HOME	Liberty (M) LRP-3257	2.00	3.00	4.00
'TWAS THE NIGHT BEFORE CHRISTMAS BACK HOME	Liberty (S) LST-7257	2.00	3.00	4.00
VERY BEST OF WALTER BRENNAN	United Artists (S) UA-LA438	2.00	3.00	4.00
WORLD OF MIRACLES	Everest (S) BR-5103	2.00	3.00	4.00
WORLD OF MIRACLES	Everest (S) SDBR-1103	2.00	3.00	4.00
WORLD OF MIRACLES	Liberty (M) LRP-3244	2.00	3.00	4.00
WORLD OF MIRACLES	Liberty (S) LST-7244	2.00	3.00	4.00
BRETHREN				
BRETHREN	Tiffany (S) TFS 0013	2.50	3.75	5.00

TITLE	LABEL & NO.	GOOD	VERY GOOD	NEAR MINT
BREWER, Teresa				
AT CHRISTMAS TIME	Coral (M) CRL 57144	2.00	3.00	4.00
BOUQUET OF HITS FROM TERESA BREWER	Coral (M) CRL 56072	3.50	5.25	7.00
DON CORNELL & TERESA BREWER	Coral (EP) EC 81073	1.00	1.50	2.00
FAVORITES	Coral (EP) EC 81108	1.00	1.50	2.00
FOR TEENAGERS IN LOVE	Coral (M) CRL 57135	2.00	3.00	4.00
GOOD NEWS	Signature (S) BSL1-0577	2.00	3.00	4.00
HEAVENLY LOVER	Coral (M) CRL-57297	2.50	3.75	5.00
HEAVENLY LOVER	Coral (S) CRL7-57297	2.50	3.75	5.00
HITSVILLE	Coral (M) CRL 57269	2.50	3.75	5.00
HITSVILLE	Coral (S) CRL7-57269	2.50	3.75	5.00
IT DON'T MEAN A THING (WITH DUKE ELLINGTON)	Flying Dutchman (S) FD-10166	2.00	3.00	4.00
KISS ME	Coral (EP) EC-81178	1.00	1.50	2.00
MISS MUSIC	Coral (M) CRL 57179	2.00	3.00	4.00
MISS MUSIC	Coral (EP) EC 81162	1.00	1.50	2.00
MUSIC, MUSIC, MUSIC	Coral (M) CRL 57027	4.00	6.00	8.00
MUSIC, MUSIC, MUSIC	Amsterdam (S) 10213	2.50	3.75	5.00
MY GOLDEN FAVORITES	Coral (M) CRL-57351	5.00	7.50	10.00

TITLE	LABEL & NO.	GOOD	VERY GOOD	NEAR MINT
RIDIN' HIGH	Coral (M) CRL-57315	2.50	3.75	5.00
RIDIN' HIGH	Coral (S) CRL7-57315	2.50	3.75	5.00
ROCK LOVE	Coral (EP) 81115	1.50	2.25	3.00
SING, SING, SING	Coral (EP) EC 81008	1.00	1.50	2.00
SONGS OF BESSIE SMITH	Flying Dutchman (S) 10161	3.00	4.50	6.00
TERESA	Coral (M) CRL 57053	3.00	4.50	6.00
TERESA BREWER	Coral (EP) EC 81072	1.00	1.50	2.00
TERESA BREWER	London (M) AB 1006	4.00	6.00	8.00
TERESA BREWER	London (EP) BEP 6039	1.50	2.25	3.00
TERESA BREWER AND THE DIXIELAND BAND	Coral (M) CRL-757245	2.50	3.75	5.00
TERESA BREWER AND THE DIXIELAND BAND	Coral (S) CRL7-245	2.50	3.75	5.00
TERESA BREWER AND THE DIXIELAND BAND	Coral (EP) EC-81176	1.00	1.50	2.00
TERESA BREWER AND THE DIXIELAND BAND	Coral (SEP) EC-781176	2.00	3.00	4.00
TERESA BREWER IN LONDON	Amsterdam (S) AM-12015	3.00	4.50	6.00
TERESA BREWER VOL. 2	London (EP) BEP 6041	1.50	2.25	3.00
TILL I WALTZ AGAIN WITH YOU	Coral (M) CRL 56093	3.50	5.25	7.00
TIME FOR TERESA	Coral (M) CRL 57232	2.00	3.00	4.00
UNLIBERATED WOMAN	Signature (S) BSL1-0935	2.00	3.00	4.00
WHEN YOUR LOVER HAS GONE	Coral (SEP) EC-781175	2.00	3.00	4.00

BREWER & SHIPLEY

DOWN IN L.A.	A&M (S) SP 4154	2.00	3.00	4.00
RURAL SPACE	Kama Sutra (S) 2058	2.50	3.75	5.00
WELCOME TO RIDDLE BRIDGE	Capitol (S) ST-11402	2.50	3.75	5.00

BRIGGS, Lillian

LILLIAN BRIGGS	Epic (EP) EG 7163	1.50	2.25	3.00
PLEASE SAY YOU WANT ME	Epic (M) LN-3702	3.00	4.50	6.00

BRILLIANT, Ashleigh

ASHLEIGH BRILLIANT IN THE HAIGHT ASHBURY	Dorash (M) 1001	9.00	18.00	27.00

BRILL, Marty

MISSING TAPES, THE	Laurie (S) 5002	2.50	3.75	5.00

BRISTOL, Johnny

FEELING THE MAGIC	MGM (S) M3G-4983	2.50	3.75	5.00
HANG ON IN THERE BABY	MGM (S) M3G-4959	2.50	3.75	5.00

BRITISH CASUALS

HOUR WORLD	Mainstream (S) S/6124	3.50	5.25	7.00

BRITISH LIONS

BRITISH LIONS	RSO (S) RS-1-3032	2.00	3.00	4.00

BRITT, Elton

BEST OF BRITT	RCA (M) LPM-2669	2.50	3.75	5.00
BEYOND THE SUNSET	ABC (M) ABC-322	2.50	3.75	5.00
BEYOND THE SUNSET	ABC (S) ABCS-322	3.00	4.50	6.00
DUETS	RCA (EP) EPA 505	1.50	2.25	3.00
ELTON BRITT IN COUNTRY SONG HITS	RCA (M) P 221	4.00	6.00	8.00
ELTON BRITT YODEL SONGS	RCA (M) LPM 1288	4.00	6.00	8.00
ELTON BRITT YODEL SONGS	RCA (EP) EPA 817	1.50	2.25	3.00
GREAT COUNTRY SONGS	RCA (EP) EPA 425	2.00	3.00	4.00

BROCK, B. & The Sultans

DO THE BEETLE	Crown (M) 399	4.00	8.00	12.00

BROMBERG, David

DAVID BROMBERG (2nd Press)	Columbia (S) C-31753	2.00	3.00	4.00
DEMON IN DISGUISE	Columbia (S) KC-31753	2.50	3.75	5.00
WANTED/DEAD OR ALIVE	Columbia (S) KC-32717	2.50	3.75	5.00

BROOKLYN BRIDGE (Featuring Johnny Maestro)

BRIDGE IN BLUE	Buddah (S) 5107	4.50	6.75	9.00
BROOKLYN BRIDGE	Buddah (S) BDS 5034	7.50	11.25	15.00
BROOKLYN BRIDGE	Buddah (S) 50659.00	13.50	18.00	
SECOND	Buddah (S) 5042	6.00	9.00	12.00

BROOKLYN DREAMS

BROOKLYN DREAMS	Millennium (S) 8002	2.50	3.75	5.00

BROOKS, Bobby

TEENAGERS DANCE TO BOBBY BROOKS	RCA (EP) EPA 4273	2.50	6.25	10.00

BROOKS, Donnie

HAPPIEST, THE	Era (M) EL 105	4.00	8.00	12.00

BROOKS, Elkie

RICH MAN'S WOMAN	A&M (S) SP 4554	2.00	3.00	4.00
TWO DAYS AWAY	A&M (S) SP 4631	2.00	3.00	4.00

BROOKS, Foster

LOVABLE LUSH	Decca (S) DL 75395	3.00	4.50	6.00

BROOKS, Hadda

FEMME FATALS	Crown (M) CLP 5010	4.00	10.00	16.00
SINGS AND SWINGS	Crown (M) CLP 5374	4.00	10.00	16.00

(M) Mono (S) Stereo (EP) Extended Play (Q) Quad (RI) Re-issued

---

BROOKS, Hadda & Pete Johnson

SWINGS THE BOOGIE	Crown (M) 5058	5.00	12.50	20.00

BROOKS, Hadda, Trio

BOOGIE	Modern (EP) EP 45X115	3.00	7.50	12.00

BROOKS, Mel & Carl Reiner

2000 & THIRTEEN	Warner Bros. (S) B-2741	4.00	6.00	8.00
2000 YEARS WITH CARL REINER & MEL BROOKS	Warner Bros. (S) 3XX-2744	5.00	7.50	10.00

BROTHERHOOD

BROTHERHOOD	RCA (M) LSP 4092	4.00	6.00	8.00
BROTHERHOOD	RCA (M) LSP 4228	4.00	6.00	8.00

BROTHERHOOD OF MAN

UNITED WE STAND	Deram (M) DES 18046	2.50	3.75	5.00

BROTHERS FOUR

BEATLES' SONGBOOK	Columbia (M) CL-2502	2.00	3.00	4.00
BEATLES' SONGBOOK	Columbia (S) CS-9302	2.00	3.00	4.00
B.M.O.C. (BEST MUSIC ON/OFF CAMPUS)	Columbia (M) CL-1578	2.00	3.00	4.00
B.M.O.C. (BEST MUSIC ON/OFF CAMPUS)	Columbia (S) CS-8378	2.00	3.00	4.00
BROTHERS FOUR	Columbia (M) CL-1402	2.50	3.75	5.00
BROTHERS FOUR	Columbia (S) CS-8197	2.50	3.75	5.00
BROTHERS FOUR GREATEST HITS	Columbia (M) CL-1803	2.50	3.75	5.00
BROTHERS FOUR GREATEST HITS	Columbia (S) CS-8603	2.50	3.75	5.00
IN PERSON	Columbia (M) CL-1828	2.00	3.00	4.00
IN PERSON	Columbia (S) CS-8628	2.00	3.00	4.00
MERRY CHRISTMAS	Columbia (M) CL-2568	2.00	3.00	4.00
MERRY CHRISTMAS	Columbia (S) CS-9368	2.00	3.00	4.00
MORE BIG FOLK HITS	Columbia (M) CL-2213	2.00	3.00	4.00
MORE BIG FOLK HITS	Columbia (S) CS-9013	2.00	3.00	4.00
RALLY ROUND	Columbia (M) CL-1479	2.00	3.00	4.00
RALLY ROUND	Columbia (S) CS-8270	2.00	3.00	4.00

BROTHERS JOHNSON

LOOK OUT FOR #1	A&M (S) SP 4567	2.50	3.75	5.00
RIGHT ON TIME	A&M (S) SP 4644	2.50	3.75	5.00

BROTHER TO BROTHER

IN THE BOTTLE	Turbo (S) 7013	2.50	3.75	5.00

BROWN, Arthur

CRAZY WORLD OF ARTHUR BROWN, THE	Track (S) SD 8198	3.00	4.50	6.00
DANCE WITH ARTHUR BROWN	Gull (S) GU-405	3.00	4.50	6.00

BROWN, Duncan

GIVE ME TAKE YOU	Immediate (M) Z12 52 012	5.00	7.50	10.00

BROWN, Boots

ROCK THAT BEAT	RCA (M) LG 1000	3.00	4.50	6.00
ROCK THAT BEAT	RCA (EP) EGB 1000	1.50	2.25	3.00

vol 114 hadda brooks trio — BOOGIE

BUSTER BROWN — THE NEW KING OF THE BLUES

BROWN, Buster

GET DOWN WITH BUSTER BROWN	Souffle (M) 2014	2.00	3.00	4.00
NEW KING OF THE BLUES, THE	Fire (M) FLP 102	12.00	30.00	48.00

BROWN, Charles

BALLADS MY WAY	Mainstream (M) 6035	4.00	8.00	12.00
BALLADS MY WAY	Mainstream (S) 56035	4.00	8.00	12.00
BEST OF THE BLUES	Imperial (M) 9257	8.00	16.00	24.00
CHARLES BROWN SINGS HIS CHRISTMAS SONGS	King (M) 775	9.00	18.00	27.00
DRIFTING BLUES	Score (M) SLP 4011	20.00	50.00	80.00
GREAT CHARLES BROWN, THE	King (M) 878	9.00	18.00	27.00
LEGEND	Blues Way (M) BLS 6039	4.00	8.00	12.00
MILLION SELLERS	Imperial (M) A-9178	8.00	16.00	24.00
MOOD MUSIC	Aladdin (M) 809	10.00	25.00	40.00
MOOD MUSIC	Aladdin (M) 702	20.00	50.00	80.00
MOOD MUSIC (10") (Red vinyl)	Aladdin (M) 702	40.00	100.00	160.00
MOOD MUSIC (10") (Black vinyl)	Aladdin (M) 702	30.00	75.00	120.00

(With Johnny Moore's Three Blazers)

TITLE	LABEL & NO.	GOOD	VERY GOOD	NEAR MINT
BROWN, Hash & His Ignunt Strings				
HASH BROWN SOUNDS, THE	Philips (M) PHM 200 018	2.50	3.75	5.00
HASH BROWN SOUNDS, THE	Philips (S) PHS 600-018	3.00	4.50	6.00
BROWNE, Jackson				
FOR EVERY MAN	Asylum (S) 5067	3.00	4.50	6.00
LATE FOR THE SKY	Asylum (S) 7E-1017	2.50	3.75	5.00
PRETENDER, THE	Asylum (S) 7E-1079	3.00	4.50	6.00
RUNNING ON EMPTY	Asylum (S) 6E-113	2.50	3.75	5.00
BROWN, James & The Famous Flames				
AIN'T IT FUNKY	King (S) KS1092	2.50	3.75	5.00

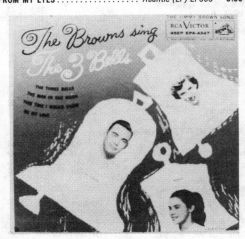

TITLE	LABEL & NO.	GOOD	VERY GOOD	NEAR MINT
AMAZING JAMES BROWN AND THE FAMOUS FLAMES, THE	King (M) 743	8.00	20.00	32.00
BLACK CAESAR	Polydor (S) 6014	2.00	3.00	4.00
CHRISTMAS SONGS	King (M) 1010	4.00	8.00	12.00
GET ON THE GOOD FOOT	Polydor (M) (D23004	2.00	3.00	4.00
GRITS AND SOUL	Smash(M) MGS27057	2.00	3.00	4.00
GRITS AND SOUL	Smash (S) SRS67057	3.00	4.50	6.00
HANDFUL OF SOUL	Smash (M) MGS27084	2.00	3.00	4.00
HANDFUL OF SOUL	Smash (S) SRS67084	3.00	4.50	6.00
I GOT THE FEELIN'	King (S) 1031	3.00	6.00	9.00
I GOT YOU, I FEEL GOOD	King (M) KS946	4.00	8.00	12.00
IT'S A MAN'S, MAN'S, MAN'S WORLD	King (M) KS985	4.00	8.00	12.00
IT'S A MOTHER	King (M) KSD1063	2.50	3.75	5.00
JAMES BROWN TODAY AND YESTERDAY	Smash (M) MGS27072	2.00	3.00	4.00
JAMES BROWN TODAY AND YESTERDAY	Smash (S) SRS 67072	3.00	4.50	6.00
JAMES BROWN AND FAMOUS FLAMES TOUR THE U.S.A.	King (M) 804	4.00	8.00	12.00
JAMES BROWN HELL	Polydor (S) D2-9001	2.00	3.00	4.00
JAMES BROWN PLAYS NEW BREED	Smash (M) MGS27080	2.00	3.00	4.00
JAMES BROWN PLAYS NEW BREED	Smash (S) SRS67080	3.00	4.50	6.00
JAMES BROWN SHOW, THE	King (M) KS 826	5.00	10.00	15.00
JAMES BROWN SHOW, THE	Smash (M) MGS27087	2.00	3.00	4.00
JAMES BROWN SINGS OUT OF SIGHT	Smash (S) 67109	3.00	4.50	6.00
JUMP AROUND	King (M) KS 771	5.00	10.50	15.00
LIVE AT THE APOLLO	King (EP) E(826	2.00	5.00	8.00
LIVE AT THE APOLLO VOL. 2	King (S) KS1022	3.00	6.00	9.00
NOTHING BUT SOUL	King (S) 1054	3.00	6.00	9.00
PAPA'S GOT A BRAND NEW BAG	King (S) KSD938	4.00	8.00	12.00
PAYBACK	Polydor (S) 2-3907	2.00	3.00	4.00
PLEASE PLEASE PLEASE	King (M) 610	6.00	12.00	18.00
PLEASE PLEASE PLEASE	King (M) KS909	4.00	8.00	12.00
PLEASE, PLEASE, PLEASE	King (EP) EP430	2.00	4.00	6.00
PRISONER OF LOVE	King (S) KS 851	5.00	10.00	15.00
PURE DYNAMITE	King (M) KS 883	4.00	8.00	12.00
RAW SOUL	King (S) KS1016	3.00	6.00	9.00
REALITY	Polydor (S) 6039	2.00	3.00	4.00
REVOLUTION OF THE MIND	Polydor (S) 25-3003	2.00	3.00	4.00
SEX MACHINE TODAY	Polydor (S) 6042	2.00	3.00	4.00
SHOWTIME	Smash(M) MGS27054	2.00	3.00	4.00
SHOWTIME	Smash (S) STS67054	3.00	4.50	6.00
SLAUGHTER'S BIG RIP OFF	Polydor (S) 6015	2.00	3.00	4.00
SOUL CLASSICS VOL. 2	Polydor (S) SC5402	2.00	3.00	4.00
THERE IT IS	Polydor (S) 24-5028	2.00	3.00	4.00
THERE WAS A TIME	King (EP) EP1	2.00	4.00	6.00
THINK	King (M) KS 683	6.00	12.00	18.00
THINKING ABOUT (LITTLE WILLIE JOHN & A NEW NICE THING)	King (S) 1038	3.00	6.00	9.00

TITLE	LABEL & NO.	GOOD	VERY GOOD	NEAR MINT
TRY ME	King (M) 635	6.00	12.00	18.00
UNBEATABLE 16 HITS, THE	King (M) KS919	4.00	8.00	12.00

NOTE: Many King LPs by James Brown were later re-issued with the same catalog numbers but in "electronically re-channelled stereo". The value of these is about 15 - 25% of that of the originals

TITLE	LABEL & NO.	GOOD	VERY GOOD	NEAR MINT
BROWN, Jim 'ED'				
ALONE WITH YOU	RCA (M) LPM3569	2.00	3.00	4.00
ALONE WITH YOU	RCA (S) LSP3569	2.00	3.00	4.00
BARROOMS & POP-A-TOPS	RCA (S) APL1-0172	2.00	3.00	4.00
BOTTLE, BOTTLE	RCA (M) LPM3942	2.00	3.00	4.00
BOTTLE, BOTTLE	RCA (S) LSP3942	2.00	3.00	4.00
COUNTRY'S BEST ON RECORD	RCA (M) LPM4011	2.00	3.00	4.00
COUNTRY'S BEST ON RECORD	RCA (S) LSP4011	2.00	3.00	4.00
IT'S THAT TIME OF NIGHT	RCA (S) APL1-0572	2.00	3.00	4.00

Also See Browns

TITLE	LABEL & NO.	GOOD	VERY GOOD	NEAR MINT
BROWN, Maxine				
FABULOUS SOUND OF MAXINE BROWN	Wand (M) 656	3.00	4.50	6.00
GREATEST HITS	Wand (M)684	3.00	4.50	6.00
MAXINE BROWN	Guest Star (M) 1911	3.00	6.00	9.00
MAXINE BROWN & IRMA THOMAS	Grand Prix (S) KS 426	2.50	3.75	5.00
WE'LL CRY TOGETHER	Commonwealth-United (S CU-6001	2.50	3.75	5.00
BROWN, Nappy				
NAPPY BROWN SINGS	Savoy (M) MG14002	6.00	15.00	24.00
RIGHT TIME	Savoy (M) MG14025	5.00	12.50	20.00
BROWN, Roy				
BLUES ARE ALL BROWN	Bluesway (S) 6019	5.00	7.50	10.00
BLUES BOOGIE	King (EP) EP254	4.00	10.00	16.00
HARD LUCK BLUES	King (S) KS1130	5.00	7.50	10.00
HARD TIMES	Bluesway (S) 6056	5.00	7.50	10.00
ROY BROWN AND WYNONIE HARRIS	King (M) 607	12.00	30.00	48.00
ROY BROWN SINGS 24 HITS	King (M) 956	9.00	22.50	36.00
BROWN, Ruth				
ALONG COMES RUTH	Philips (M) PHM200028	4.00	8.00	12.00
ALONG COMES RUTH	Philips (EP) SR623	2.50	5.00	7.50
BEST OF RUTH BROWN	Atlantic (M) 8080	5.00	10.00	15.00
BEST OF RUTH BROWN	Atlantic (S) SD8080	4.00	8.00	12.00
JIM DANDY	Philips (EP) EP028	2.50	5.00	7.50
LATE DATE WITH RUTH BROWN	Atlantic (M) 1308	4.00	8.00	12.00
LATE DATE WITH RUTH BROWN	Atlantic (S) SD1308	5.00	10.00	15.00
MISS RHYTHM	Atlantic (M) 8026	7.00	17.50	28.00
REAL RUTH BROWN	Cobblestone (M) 9007	3.00	4.50	6.00
RUTH BROWN	Atlantic (EP) EP585	3.00	7.50	12.00
RUTH BROWN SINGS (10")	Atlantic (M) 115	25.00	62.50	100.00
RUTH BROWN SINGS	Atlantic (M) 8004	7.00	17.50	28.00
RUTH BROWN SINGS	Atlantic (S) SD8004	5.00	10.00	15.00
SINGS	Atlantic (EP) EP535	3.00	7.50	12.00
TEARDROPS FROM MY EYES	Atlantic (EP) EP505	3.00	7.50	12.00

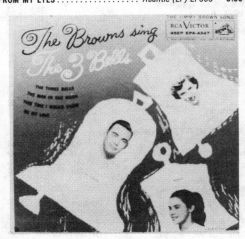

TITLE	LABEL & NO.	GOOD	VERY GOOD	NEAR MINT
BROWNS				
BEST OF THE BROWNS	RCA (M) LPM3561	2.50	3.75	5.00
BEST OF THE BROWNS	RCA (S) LSP3561	2.00	3.00	4.00
BROWNS	RCA (EP) EPA5089	1.00	1.50	2.00
BROWNS SING THEIR HITS	RCA (M) LPM2260	2.00	3.00	4.00
BROWNS SING THEIR HITS	RCA (S) LSP2260	2.50	3.75	5.00
BROWNS SING THE 3 BELLS	RCA (EP) EPA4347	1.50	2.25	3.00
GRAND OLE OPRY FAVORITES	RCA (M) LPM2784	2.00	2.25	4.00
GRAND OLE OPRY FAVORITES	RCA (S) LSP2784	2.00	2.25	4.00
JIM EDWARD, MAXINE AND BONNIE BROWN	RCA (M) LPM1433	4.00	6.00	8.00
JIM EDWARD; MAXINE AND BONNIE BROWN	RCA (EP) EPA1-1433	1.50	2.25	3.00
OLD LAMPLIGHTER	RCA (EP) EPA4364	1.50	2.25	3.00
OUR KIND OF COUNTRY	RCA (M) LPM3668	2.00	3.00	4.00
OUR KIND OF COUNTRY	RCA (S) LSP3668	2.00	3.00	4.00
SCARLET RIBBONS	RCA (EP) EPA4352	1.50	2.25	3.00

(M) Mono (S) Stereo (EP) Extended Play (Q) Quad (RI) Re-issued

TITLE	LABEL & NO.	GOOD	VERY GOOD	NEAR MINT
SWEET SOUND BY THE BROWNS	RCA (M) LPM2144	2.50	3.75	5.00
SWEET SOUND BY THE BROWNS	RCA (S) LSP2144	3.00	4.50	6.00
THIS YOUNG LAND	RCA (M) LPM2860	2.00	3.00	4.00
THIS YOUNG LAND	RCA (S) LSP2860	2.00	3.00	4.00
TOWN AND COUNTRY	RCA (M) LPM2174	2.00	3.00	4.00
TOWN AND COUNTRY	RCA (S) LSP2174	2.50	3.75	5.00

Also see BROWN, Jim 'Ed'

BROWN'S, ARTHUR, KINGDOM COME
TITLE	LABEL & NO.	GOOD	VERY GOOD	NEAR MINT
JOURNEY	Passport (S) 98003	2.50	3.75	5.00

BROWN, Shirley
TITLE	LABEL & NO.	GOOD	VERY GOOD	NEAR MINT
WOMAN TO WOMAN	Truth (S) 4206	3.00	4.50	6.00

BROWNSVILLE STATION
TITLE	LABEL & NO.	GOOD	VERY GOOD	NEAR MINT
MOTOR CITY CONNECTION	Big Tree (S) 89510	2.50	3.75	5.00
SCHOOL PUNKS	Big Tree (S) 89500	2.50	3.75	5.00
YEAH	Big Tree (S) 2102	3.00	4.50	6.00

BRUCE, Jack
TITLE	LABEL & NO.	GOOD	VERY GOOD	NEAR MINT
JACK BRUCE AT HIS BEST	Polydor (S) 24-3505	3.00	4.50	6.00
OUT OF THE STORM	RSO (S) 4805	3.50	5.25	7.00

Also see CREAM

BRUCE, Lenny
TITLE	LABEL & NO.	GOOD	VERY GOOD	NEAR MINT
AMERICAN	Fantasy (M) LP7011	6.00	12.00	18.00
CARNEGIE HALL	United Artists (S) UAS9800	3.00	4.50	6.00
ESSENTIAL LENNY BRUCE	Douglas (M) 785	4.00	6.00	8.00
LENNY BRUCE	Warner/Spector (S) 9101	3.00	4.50	6.00
LENNY BRUCE IS OUT AGAIN	Philles (M) PHLP 4010	10.00	20.00	30.00
LIVE AT CURRAN THEATRE	Fantasy (S) 34201	4.00	8.00	12.00
MIDNIGHT CONCERT	United Artists (S) UAS6794	3.00	4.50	6.00
REAL LENNY BRUCE	Fantasy (S) 79003	4.00	8.00	12.00
THE SICK HUMOR OF LENNY BRUCE	Fantasy (M) LP7001	6.00	12.00	18.00
THANK YOU MASKED MAN	Fantasy (S) 7017	6.00	12.00	18.00

BRUSH ARBOR
TITLE	LABEL & NO.	GOOD	VERY GOOD	NEAR MINT
BRUSH ARBOR	Capitol (S) ST-11158	2.50	3.75	5.00
BRUSH ARBOR/2	Capitol (S) ST-11209	2.50	3.75	5.00

BRUTE FORCE
TITLE	LABEL & NO.	GOOD	VERY GOOD	NEAR MINT
I, BRUTE FORCE	Columbia (M) CL2615	3.00	4.50	6.00

BRYANT, Anita
TITLE	LABEL & NO.	GOOD	VERY GOOD	NEAR MINT
ANITA BRYANT	Carlton (M) 118	2.50	3.75	5.00
ANITA BRYANT	Carlton (S) ST118	3.00	4.50	6.00
HEAR ANITA BRYANT IN YOUR HOME TONIGHT	Carlton (M) 127	2.00	3.00	4.00
HEAR ANITA BRYANT IN YOUR HOME TONIGHT	Carlton (S) S127	2.50	3.75	5.00
IN MY LITTLE CORNER OF THE WORLD	Carlton (M) 132	2.00	3.00	4.00
IN MY LITTLE CORNER OF THE WORLD	Carlton (S) S132	2.50	3.75	5.00

BRYANT, Boudleaux
TITLE	LABEL & NO.	GOOD	VERY GOOD	NEAR MINT
BOUDLEAUX'S BEST SELLERS	Monument (M) M8007	4.00	8.00	12.00
I, BRUTE FORCE	Columbia (S) CS9415	4.00	6.00	8.00
BOUDLEAUX'S BEST SELLERS	Monument (S) SM18007	5.00	10.00	15.00

BRYANT, Browning
TITLE	LABEL & NO.	GOOD	VERY GOOD	NEAR MINT
BROWNING BRYANT	Reprise (S) MS 2191	2.00	3.00	4.00

BRYANT, Ray, Combo
TITLE	LABEL & NO.	GOOD	VERY GOOD	NEAR MINT
ALONE WITH THE BLUES	New Jazz (M) NJLP8213	4.00	8.00	12.00
DANCING THE BIG TWIST	Columbia (M) CL1746	3.00	7.50	12.00
DANCING THE BIG TWIST	Columbia (S) CS8546	4.00	10.00	16.00
GROOVE HOUSE	Sue (M) 1016	3.00	7.50	12.00
LITTLE SUSIE	Columbia (M) CL1449	4.00	10.00	16.00
LITTLE SUSIE	Columbia (S) CS8244	5.00	12.50	20.00
MADISON TIME	Columbia (M) CL1476	4.00	10.00	16.00
MADISON TIME	Columbia (S) CS8267	5.00	12.50	20.00
RAY BRYANT COMBO PLAYS	Signature (M) SM 6008	3.00	6.00	9.00

BRYANT, Rusty
TITLE	LABEL & NO.	GOOD	VERY GOOD	NEAR MINT
ALL NITE LONG	Dot (M) DLP 3006	4.00	10.00	16.00

BRYCE, Sherry
TITLE	LABEL & NO.	GOOD	VERY GOOD	NEAR MINT
THIS SONG'S FOR YOU	MGM (S) M3G-5000	2.00	3.00	4.00
TREAT ME LIKE A LADY	MGM (S) M3G-4967	2.00	3.00	4.00

BUBBLE PUPPY
TITLE	LABEL & NO.	GOOD	VERY GOOD	NEAR MINT
A GATHERING OF PROMISES	International Artists (M) 1A LP 10	8.00	16.00	24.00

BUCHANAN & GOODMAN
TITLE	LABEL & NO.	GOOD	VERY GOOD	NEAR MINT
FLYING SAUCER STORY VOL. 1	Buchanan and Goodman (M) BG716	8.00	20.00	32.00

Also see GOODMAN, Dickie

BUCHANAN BROTHERS
TITLE	LABEL & NO.	GOOD	VERY GOOD	NEAR MINT
MEDICINE MAN	Event (M) ES101	5.00	7.50	10.00

(M) Mono   (S) Stereo   (EP) Extended Play   (Q) Quad   (RI) Re-issued

BUCKAROOS
TITLE	LABEL & NO.	GOOD	VERY GOOD	NEAR MINT
BUCK OWENS SONG BOOK	Capitol (M) T2436	2.00	3.00	4.00

Also see OWENS, Buck

BUCKINGHAM NICKS
TITLE	LABEL & NO.	GOOD	VERY GOOD	NEAR MINT
BUCKINGHAM NICKS	Polydor (S) PD5058	2.50	3.75	5.00

Also see FLEETWOOD MAC

BUCKINGHAMS
TITLE	LABEL & NO.	GOOD	VERY GOOD	NEAR MINT
IN ONE EAR AND OUT THE OTHER	Columbia (S) CS9703	3.00	4.50	6.00
KIND OF A DRAG	USA (M) USA107	4.50	6.75	9.00
KIND OF A DRAG (With extra track)	USA (M) USA 107	8.00	10.00	16.00
MADE IN CHICAGO	Columbia (S) KG-33333	2.50	3.75	5.00
PORTRAITS	Columbia (M) CL2798	3.00	4.50	6.00
PORTRAITS	Columbia (S) CS9598	3.00	4.50	6.00
TIME AND CHARGES	Columbia (M) CL2669	3.00	4.50	6.00
TIME AND CHARGES	Columbia (S) CS9469	3.00	4.50	6.00

BUCKLEY, Lord
TITLE	LABEL & NO.	GOOD	VERY GOOD	NEAR MINT
BEST OF LORD BUCKLEY	Elektra (S) EKS 74047	4.00	6.00	8.00
BUCKLEY'S BEST	World Pacific (S) WPS 21879	5.00	7.50	10.00

BUCKLEY, Tim
TITLE	LABEL & NO.	GOOD	VERY GOOD	NEAR MINT
LOOK AT THE FOOL	Disc Reet (S) 2201	2.50	3.75	5.00
SEFRONIA	Disc Reet (S) 2157	2.50	3.75	5.00

BUCKWHEAT
TITLE	LABEL & NO.	GOOD	VERY GOOD	NEAR MINT
CHARADE	London (S) XPS-621	2.00	3.00	4.00
HOT TRACKS	London (S) XPS-635	2.00	3.00	4.00

BUD & TRAVIS
TITLE	LABEL & NO.	GOOD	VERY GOOD	NEAR MINT
BUD & TRAVIS	Liberty (M) LRP 3125	2.50	3.75	5.00
BUD & TRAVIS	Liberty (S) LST 7125	2.50	3.75	5.00
BUD & TRAVIS LATIN ALBUM	Liberty (M) LRP 3398	2.50	3.75	5.00
BUD & TRAVIS LATIN ALBUM	Liberty (S) LST 7398	2.50	3.75	5.00
IN CONCERT	Liberty (M) LDM 11001	3.00	4.50	6.00
IN CONCERT	Liberty (S) LDS 12001	3.00	4.50	6.00
IN PERSON	Liberty (M) LRP 3386	2.50	3.75	5.00
IN PERSON	Liberty (S) LST 7386	2.50	3.75	5.00
PERSPECTIVE ON BUD & TRAVIS	Liberty (M) LRP 3341	2.50	3.75	5.00
PERSPECTIVE ON BUD & TRAVIS	Liberty (S) LST 7341	2.50	3.75	5.00
SPOTLIGHT ON BUD & TRAVIS	Liberty (M) LRP 3138	2.50	3.75	5.00
SPOTLIGHT ON BUD & TRAVIS	Liberty (S) LST 7138	2.50	3.75	5.00

BUDD, Julie
TITLE	LABEL & NO.	GOOD	VERY GOOD	NEAR MINT
CHILD OF PLENTY	MGM (S) SE 4545	2.50	3.75	5.00

BUDDIES
TITLE	LABEL & NO.	GOOD	VERY GOOD	NEAR MINT
GO GO WITH THE BUDDIES	Wing (M) MGW12306	3.00	6.00	9.00
GO GO WITH THE BUDDIES	Wing (S) SRW16306	4.00	8.00	12.00

BUDDIES & THE COMPACTS
TITLE	LABEL & NO.	GOOD	VERY GOOD	NEAR MINT
THE BUDDIES AND THE COMPACTS	Wing (S) SRW16293	4.00	8.00	12.00

BUFFALO SPRINGFIELD
TITLE	LABEL & NO.	GOOD	VERY GOOD	NEAR MINT
AGAIN	Atco (M) 33-226	1.50	2.25	3.00
AGAIN	Atco (S) SD 33-226	2.00	3.00	4.00
BUFFALO SPRINGFIELD	Atco (S) 2-806	2.00	3.00	4.00
BUFFALO SPRINGFIELD	Atco (M) 33-200	1.50	2.25	3.00
BUFFALO SPRINGFIELD	Atco (S) SD33-200	2.00	3.00	4.00
BUFFALO SPRINGFIELD (Without "For What it's Worth")	Atco (S) SD33-200	8.00	10.00	16.00
LAST TIME AROUND	Atco (S) SD33-256	2.00	3.00	4.00
RETROSPECTIVE	Atco (S) SD 33-283	3.00	4.50	6.00

Also see CROSBY, STILLS, NASH & YOUNG

BUFFETT, Jimmy
TITLE	LABEL & NO.	GOOD	VERY GOOD	NEAR MINT
A-1-A	Dunhill (S) D-50183	3.00	4.50	6.00
CHANGES IN LATITUDES, CHANGES IN ATTITUDES	ABC (S) 990	2.00	3.00	4.00
HAVANA DAYDREAMIN'	ABC (S) 914	3.00	4.50	6.00
HIGH CUMBERLAND JUBILEE	Barnaby (S) 6014	2.50	3.75	5.00
LIVING & DYING IN 3/4 TIME	Dunhill (S) 50132	3.00	4.50	6.00
SON OF A SON OF A SAILOR	ABC (S) AA 1046	2.00	3.00	4.00
WHITE SPORT COAT & A PINK CRUSTACEAN	Dunhill (S) X-50150	3.50	5.25	7.00

BUGGS
TITLE	LABEL & NO.	GOOD	VERY GOOD	NEAR MINT
THE BEETLE BEAT	Coronet (M) 212	4.00	8.00	12.00

BULLDOG
TITLE	LABEL & NO.	GOOD	VERY GOOD	NEAR MINT
BULLDOG	Decca (S) PL 75340	3.50	5.25	7.00
SMASHER	Buddah (S) 5600	3.00	4.50	6.00

Also see RASCALS

BULL, Sandy
TITLE	LABEL & NO.	GOOD	VERY GOOD	NEAR MINT
DEMOLITION DERBY	Vanguard (S) 6578	2.00	3.00	4.00
E PLURIBUS UNUM	Vanguard (S) 6513	2.00	3.00	4.00
ESSENTIAL SANDY BULL	Vanguard (S) 59/60	2.50	3.75	5.00
FANTASIAS FOR GUITAR AND BANJO	Vanguard (M) VRS 9119	2.00	3.00	4.00
FANTASIAS FOR GUITAR AND BANJO	Vanguard (S) VSD 79119	2.25	3.50	4.50
INVENTIONS	Vanguard (S) 79191	2.00	3.00	4.00

TITLE	LABEL & NO.	GOOD	VERY GOOD	NEAR MINT
BUMP				
BUMP	Pioneer (S) PRSD 2150	5.00	7.50	10.00
BUNKERS				
ALL IN THE FAMILY-2nd ALBUM	Atlantic (S) 7232	2.50	3.75	5.00
ARCHIE & EDITH-SIDE BY SIDE	RCA (S) APL1-0102	2.50	3.75	5.00
BUOYS				
TIMOTHY	Scepter (S) SPS24001	2.50	3.75	5.00
BURDON, Eric, Band				
STOP	Capitol (S) SMAS-11426	3.00	4.50	6.00
SUN SECRETS	Capitol (S) ST-11359	3.00	4.50	6.00
Also see ANIMALS				
BURDON, Eric & Jimmy Witherspoon				
GUILTY	MGM (S) 4791	3.00	4.50	6.00
Also See ANIMALS				
BURKE, Jerry				
PRESENTING JERRY BURKE	Brunswick (M) BL54052	2.00	3.00	4.00
PRESENTING JERRY BURKE	Brunswick (S) BL754052	2.00	3.00	4.00
BURKE, Solomon				
BEST OF SOLOMON BURKE	Atlantic (M) 8109	3.00	6.00	9.00
ELECTRONIC MAGNETISM	MGM (S) SE 4767	2.50	3.75	5.00
GREATEST HITS	Atlantic (S) SD8067	3.00	6.00	9.00
HISTORY OF SOLOMON BURKE	Pride (S) 0011	2.50	3.75	5.00
IF YOU NEED ME	Atlantic (S) SD8085	3.00	6.00	9.00
I HAVE A DREAM	Dunhill (S) X-50161	2.50	3.75	5.00
I WISH I KNEW	Atlantic (S) SD 8185	3.00	6.00	9.00
KING SOLOMON	Atlantic (S) SD8158	4.00	8.00	12.00
MUSIC TO MAKE LOVE BY	Chess (S) 60042	3.00	4.50	6.00
PROUD MARY	Bell (S) 6033	3.00	4.50	6.00
ROCK 'N SOUL	Atlantic (S) SD 8096	3.00	6.00	9.00
SOLOMON BURKE	Apollo (M) ALP498	9.00	22.50	36.00
BURNETTE, Dorsey				
DORSEY BURNETTE	Capitol (S) ST-11219	3.00	4.50	6.00
DORSEY BURNETTE	Dot (M) DLP 3456	4.00	8.00	12.00
DORSEY BURNETTE	Dot (S) DLP 25456	5.00	10.00	15.00
GREATEST HITS	Era (M) ES 800	4.00	8.00	12.00
TALL OAK TREE	Era (M) EL 102	4.00	8.00	12.00
TALL OAK TREE	Era (S) ES-700	5.00	10.00	15.00
BURNETTE, Johnny & The Rock And Roll Trio				
JOHNNY BURNETTE AND THE ROCK AND ROLL TRIO (10")	Coral (M) CRL 57080	30.00	75.00	120.00

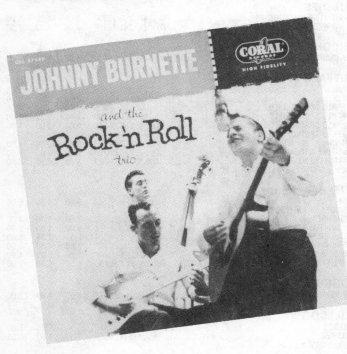

TITLE	LABEL & NO.	GOOD	VERY GOOD	NEAR MINT
BURNETTE, Johnny				
DREAMIN'	Sunset (M) SUM 1179	3.00	6.00	9.00
DREAMIN'	Sunset (S) SUS 5179	4.00	8.00	12.00
DREAMIN'	Liberty (M) LRP 3179	7.00	17.50	28.00
DREAMIN'	Liberty (S) LST 7179	8.00	20.00	32.00

TITLE	LABEL & NO.	GOOD	VERY GOOD	NEAR MINT
DREAMIN'	Liberty (EP) LSX-1004	3.00	6.00	9.00
DREAMIN'	Liberty (EP) LSX 1011	3.00	6.00	9.00
HITS	Liberty (M) LRP 3206	7.00	17.50	28.00
HITS AND OTHER FAVORITES	Liberty (M) LRP 3206	7.00	17.50	28.00
HITS AND OTHER FAVORITES	Liberty (S) LST 7206	8.00	20.00	32.00
JOHNNY BURNETTE	Liberty (M) LRP3183	7.00	17.50	28.00
JOHNNY BURNETTE	Liberty (S) LST 7183	8.00	20.00	32.00
JOHNNY BURNETTE SINGS	Liberty (M) LRP 3190	7.00	17.50	28.00
JOHNNY BURNETTE SINGS	Liberty (S) LST 7190	8.00	20.00	32.00
JOHNNY BURNETTE STORY	Liberty (M) LRP 3389	5.00	12.50	20.00
JOHNNY BURNETTE STORY	Liberty (S) LST 7389	6.00	15.00	24.00
ROSES ARE RED	Liberty (M) LRP 3255	6.00	15.00	24.00
ROSES ARE RED	Liberty (S) LST7255	7.00	17.50	28.00
VERY BEST OF JOHNNY BURNETTE	United Artists (M) UA LA 432	2.00	3.00	4.00
BURNS & SCHREIBER				
BURNS & SCHREIBER'S PURE B.S.	Little David (S) 1006	3.50	5.25	7.00
IN ONE HEAD & OUT THE OTHER	Columbia (S) 32442	2.50	3.75	5.00
BURNS, George				
EVENING WITH GEORGE BURNS	Pride (S) 00011	2.00	3.00	4.00
MUSICAL TRIP	Buddah (S) 5127	2.50	3.75	5.00
BURROUGHS, William				
CALL ME BURROUGHS	ESP (M) 1050	5.00	7.50	10.00
BURTON, Lori				
BREAKOUT	Mercury (S) SR 61136	6.00	12.00	18.00
BUSH, Johnny				
BEST OF JOHNNY BUSH	Million (M) 1001	2.00	3.00	4.00
HERE COMES THE WORLD AGAIN	RCA (S) APL1-0216	2.00	3.00	4.00
SOUND OF A HEARTACHE	Stop (M) LP 10002	2.50	3.75	5.00
SOUND OF A HEARTACHE	Stop (S) SLP 10002	2.50	3.75	5.00
TEXAS DANCE HALL GIRL	RCA (S) APL1-0369	2.00	3.00	4.00
UNDO THE RIGHT	Stop (M) LP 10005	2.00	3.00	4.00
UNDO THE RIGHT	Stop (S) SLP 10005	2.00	3.00	4.00
WHISKEY RIVER/ THERE STANDS THE GLASS	RCA (S) LSP-4817	2.00	3.00	4.00
YOU GAVE ME A MOUNTAIN	Stop (M) LP 10008	2.00	3.00	4.00
YOU GAVE ME A MOUNTAIN	Stop (S) SLP 10008	2.00	3.00	4.00
BUTLER, Billy				
RIGHT TRACK	Okeh (M) OKM 12115	4.00	8.00	12.00
BUTLER, Carl				
DON'T LET ME CROSS OVER	Columbia (M) CL-2002	2.00	3.00	4.00
DON'T LET ME CROSS OVER	Columbia (S) CS-8802	2.00	3.00	4.00
BUTLER, Freddy				
WITH A DAB OF SOUL	Kapp (M) KL 1519	2.00	3.00	4.00
WITH A DAB OF SOUL	Kapp (S) KS 3519	3.00	4.50	6.00
BUTLER, George "Wild Child"				
FUNKY BUTT LOVER	Roots (M) R 1003	3.00	4.50	6.00
BUTLER, Jerry				
ALL TIME HITS	Up Front (M) 124	1.50	2.25	3.00
ALL TIME HITS	Trip (M) 8011-2	1.50	2.25	3.00
AWARE OF LOVE	Vee Jay (M) 1038	4.00	8.00	12.00
AWARE OF LOVE	Vee Jay (S) 1038	5.00	10.00	15.00
BEST OF JERRY BUTLER	Mercury (S) SR 61281	2.50	3.75	5.00
BEST OF JERRY BUTLER	Vee Jay (M) 1048	4.00	8.00	12.00
BEST OF JERRY BUTLER	Vee Jay (S) 1048	4.50	9.00	13.00
FOLK SONGS	Vee Jay (M) LP 1057	4.00	8.00	12.00
FOLK SONGS	Vee Jay (S) SR 1057	4.50	9.00	13.50
GIFT OF LOVE	Sunset (S) 5216	2.00	3.00	4.00
HE WILL BREAK YOUR HEART	Vee Jay (S) 1029	5.00	10.00	15.00
ICE MAN COMETH, THE	Mercury (S) 61198	3.00	4.50	6.00
ICE ON ICE	Mercury (S) SR 61234	2.50	3.75	5.00
JERRY BUTLER ESQUIRE	Vee Jay (M) 1027	5.00	10.00	15.00
JERRY BUTLER ESQUIRE	Abner (M) 2001	6.00	12.00	18.00
JERRY BUTLER SINGS	Post (M) 7000	3.00	4.50	6.00
JERRY BUTLER'S GOLDEN HITS (LIVE)	Mercury (M) 21151	2.00	3.00	4.00
LOVE ME	Vee Jay (M) 1034	4.00	8.00	12.00
MELINDA	Pride (S) 0006	2.50	3.75	5.00
MR. DREAM MERCHANT	Mercury (S) 61146	3.00	4.50	6.00
MOON RIVER	Vee Jay (M) SR 1046	4.00	8.00	12.00
MORE OF THE BEST OF	Vee Jay (M) 1119	4.00	8.00	12.00
MORE OF THE BEST OF	Vee Jay (S) 1119	5.00	10.00	15.00
POWER OF LOVE	Mercury (S) SRM 1-689	2.00	3.00	4.00
SAGITTARIUS MOVEMENT	Mercury (S) 61347	2.50	3.75	5.00
SINGS ASSORTED SONGS	Mercury (S) SR 61320	2.50	3.75	5.00
SOULED OUT	Up Front (M) 100	1.50	2.25	3.00
SOUL GOES ON, THE	Mercury (S) 61171	3.00	4.50	6.00
SPICE OF LIVE	Mercury (S) 2-7502	3.00	4.50	6.00
SWEET SIXTEEN	Mercury (S) SRM 1-006	2.00	3.00	4.00
VERY BEST OF JERRY BUTLER	United Artists (S) S UA-LA-498-E	1.50	2.25	3.00
YOU & ME	Mercury (S) SR 61269	2.50	3.75	5.00
Also See IMPRESSIONS				
BUTLER, Jerry & Betty Everett				
DELICIOUS TOGETHER	Vee Jay (M) 1099	3.00	6.00	9.00
DELICIOUS TOGETHER	Vee Jay (S) 1099	3.00	6.00	9.00

TITLE	LABEL & NO.	GOOD	VERY GOOD	NEAR MINT
BUTLER, Jerry & Brenda Lee Eager				
LOVE WE HAVE, LOVE WE HAD	Mercury (S) SRM-1-660	2.50	3.75	5.00
BUTLER, Wild Child				
KEEP ON DOING WHAT YOU'RE DOING	Mercury (S) SR 61293	2.50	3.75	5.00
BUTTERWORTH, Mary				
MARY BUTTERWORTH	Custom Fidelity (M)	4.00	6.00	8.00
BUZZOS BANDITS AND FRIENDS				
TAKE A CHANCE	United Sound (M) USR 4933	4.00	6.00	8.00
BYRD, Jerry				
BYRD OF PARADISE	Monument (M) M4003	2.00	3.00	4.00
BYRD OF PARADISE	Monument (S) SM 14003	2.50	3.75	5.00
MEMORIES OF MARIA (& OTHER GREAT HITS) . . .	Monument (M) M-4008	2.00	3.00	4.00
MEMORIES OF MARIA (& OTHER GREAT HITS) . . .	Monument (S) SM-14008	2.50	3.75	5.00
BYRD, Joe & The Field Hippies				
AMERICAN METAPHYSICAL CIRCUS, THE	Columbia (M) MS 7317	4.50	6.75	9.00
BYRDS				
BALLAD OF EASY RIDER	Columbia (S) CS 9942	3.00	4.50	6.00
BEST OF THE BYRDS - Vol. 2	Columbia (S) KC 31795	3.00	4.50	6.00
BYRDMANIAX	Columbia (S) KC 30640	3.00	4.50	6.00
BYRDS	Asylum (S) SP 5058	4.00	6.00	8.00
BYRDS GREATEST HITS, THE	Columbia (M) CL 2716	4.00	6.00	8.00
BYRDS GREATEST HITS, THE	Columbia (S) CS 9516	4.00	6.00	8.00
CANDY (SOUND TRACK)	ABC (S) ABCS-OC-9	6.00	8.00	12.00
DR. BYRDS & MR. HYDE	Columbia (S) CS 9755	3.00	4.50	6.00
DON'T MAKE WAVES (SOUND TRACK)	MGM (M) E-4483	5.00	7.50	10.00
DON'T MAKE WAVES (SOUND TRACK)	MGM (S) SE 4483	6.00	8.00	12.00
FARTHER ALONG	Columbia (S) KC 31050	3.00	4.50	6.00
FIFTH DIMENSION	Columbia (S) CL 2549	3.00	4.50	6.00
FIFTH DIMENSION	Columbia (S) CS 9349	3.00	4.50	6.00
MR. TAMBOURINE MAN	Columbia (M) CL 2372	4.00	6.00	8.00
MR. TAMBOURINE MAN	Columbia (S) CS 9172	4.00	6.00	8.00
MR. TAMBOURINE MAN / TURN, TURN, TURN	Columbia (S) CG 33645	3.50	5.25	7.00
NOTORIOUS BYRD BROTHERS, THE	Columbia (M) CL 2775	3.00	4.50	6.00
NOTORIOUS BYRD BROTHERS, THE	Columbia (S) CS 9575	3.00	4.50	6.00
PREFLYTE	Columbia (S) KC 32183	3.00	4.50	6.00
PREFLYTE	Together (S) ST-T-1001	5.00	7.50	10.00
SWEETHEART OF THE RODEO	Columbia (S) CS 9670	3.00	4.50	6.00
TURN, TURN, TURN	Columbia (M) CL 2454	4.00	6.00	8.00
TURN, TURN, TURN	Columbia (S) CS 9254	4.00	6.00	8.00
(UNTITLED)	Columbia (S) G 30127	3.00	4.50	6.00
YOUNGER THAN YESTERDAY	Columbia (M) CL 2642	3.00	4.50	6.00
YOUNGER THAN YESTERDAY	Columbia (S) CS 9442	3.00	4.50	6.00
BYRNES, Edd				
EDD "KOOKIE" BYRNES	Warner Brothers (EP) EA 1309	2.50	6.25	10.00
KOOKIE	Warner Brothers (M) W-1309	2.00	5.00	8.00
KOOKIE	Warner Brothers (S) WS-1309	3.00	7.50	12.00

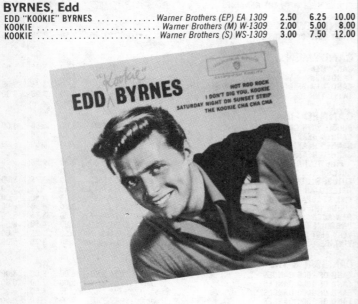

C

TITLE	LABEL & NO.	GOOD	VERY GOOD	NEAR MINT
CABOOSE				
CABOOSE	Enterprise (S) ENS 1015	2.00	3.00	4.00
CACTUS				
SON OF CACTUS	Atco (S) 7017	2.50	3.75	5.00
CADETS				
CADETS	Relic (M) 5025	4.00	6.00	8.00
CADETS, THE	Crown (S) CST 370	5.00	12.50	20.00
ROCKIN' AND REELIN'	Crown (M) CLP 5015	6.00	15.00	24.00

CADILLACS				
CRAZY CADILLACS, THE . . . . (Black label)	Jubilee (M) 1089	9.00	22.50	36.00
CRAZY CADILLACS, THE . . . . (Multi-color label)	Jubilee (M) 1089	4.00	10.00	16.00
CRUISIN' WITH THE CADILLACS	Harlem Hitparade (M) HHP 5009	4.00	6.00	8.00
FABULOUS CADILLACS, THE . . . . (Blue label)	Jubilee (M) JGM 1045	15.00	37.50	60.00
FABULOUS CADILLACS, THE . . . . (Black label)	Jubilee (M) JGM 1045	10.00	25.00	40.00
FABULOUS CADILLACS, THE . . . . (Multi-color label)	Jubilee (M) JGM 1045	5.00	12.50	20.00
TWISTING WITH THE CADILLACS	Jubilee (M) JGM 5009	5.00	12.50	20.00

CAIN, Jeffrey

TITLE	LABEL & NO.	GOOD	VERY GOOD	NEAR MINT
WHISPERING THUNDER	Warner Brothers (S) BS 2613	2.50	3.75	5.00

CAIOLA, Al

TITLE	LABEL & NO.	GOOD	VERY GOOD	NEAR MINT
AMERICANS	Camden (S) ACL1-0478	2.00	3.00	4.00
BEST OF AL CAIOLA	United Artists (M) UAL 3310	3.50	5.25	7.00
BEST OF AL CAIOLA	United Artists (S) UAS 6310	4.00	6.00	8.00
GERSHWIN & GUITARS	Time (M) 52010	2.00	4.00	6.00
GERSHWIN & GUITARS	Time (S) S/2010	2.50	5.00	7.50
GREAT PICKIN'	Chancellor (M) CHL 5008	4.00	8.00	12.00
GREAT PICKIN'	Chancellor (S) CHS 5008	5.00	10.00	15.00
GUITARS, GUITARS, GUITARS	United Artists (M) UAL 3077	3.50	5.25	7.00
GUITARS, GUITARS, GUITARS	United Artists (S) UAS 6077	4.00	6.00	8.00
HIGH STRUNG	RCA (M) LPM 2031	2.00	4.00	6.00
HIGH STRUNG	RCA (S) LPS 2031	2.50	5.00	7.50
MIDNIGHT DANCE PARTY	United Artists (M) UAL 3228	2.50	3.75	5.00
MIDNIGHT DANCE PARTY	United Artists (S) UAS 6228	3.00	4.50	6.00
MUSIC FOR SPACE SQUIRRELS	Atco (M) 33-117	3.00	6.00	9.00
MUSIC FOR SPACE SQUIRRELS	Atco (S) SD 33-117	4.00	8.00	12.00
OPEN FIRE, TWO GUITARS	Columbia (M) CL 1270	2.00	4.00	6.00
OPEN FIRE, TWO GUITARS	Columbia (S) CS 8056	2.50	5.00	7.50
PERCUSSION ESPANOL	Time (M) 52006	2.00	4.00	6.00
PERCUSSION ESPANOL	Time (S) S/2006	2.50	5.00	7.50
SALUTE ITALIA	Roulette (M) R-25108	2.00	4.00	6.00
SALUTE ITALIA	Roulette (S) SR-25108	2.50	5.00	7.50
THEME FROM "THE MAGNIFICENT 7 RIDE" '73	Avalanche (S) AV-LA058-F	2.50	3.75	5.00
TUFF GUITAR	United Artists (M) UAL 3389	2.50	3.75	5.00
TUFF GUITAR	United Artists (S) UAS 6389	3.00	4.50	6.00

CAKE

TITLE	LABEL & NO.	GOOD	VERY GOOD	NEAR MINT
CAKE	Decca (M) DL 4927	4.00	8.00	12.00
CAKE	Decca (S) DL 74927	5.00	10.00	15.00
A SLICE OF THE CAKE	Decca (S) DL 75039	5.00	10.00	15.00

CALDWELL, Louise Harrison

TITLE	LABEL & NO.	GOOD	VERY GOOD	NEAR MINT
ALL ABOUT THE BEATLES	Recar (M) 2012	10.00	25.00	40.00

CALE, J.J.

TITLE	LABEL & NO.	GOOD	VERY GOOD	NEAR MINT
NATURALLY ... J.J. CALE	Shelter (S) SW 8908	3.50	5.25	7.00
NATURALLY ... J.J. CALE (1st RI)	Shelter (S) 2122	3.00	4.50	6.00
NATURALLY ... J.J. CALE (2nd RI)	Shelter (S) 52009	2.00	3.00	4.00
OKIE	Shelter (S) 2107	3.00	4.50	6.00
REALLY J.J. CALE	Shelter (S) SW 8912	3.50	5.25	7.00
REALLY J.J. CALE (1st RI)	Shelter (S) 2123	3.00	4.50	6.00
REALLY J.J. CALE (2nd RI)	Shelter (S) 52012	2.00	3.00	4.00
TROUBADOUR	Shelter (S) 52002	2.50	3.75	5.00

CALE, John

TITLE	LABEL & NO.	GOOD	VERY GOOD	NEAR MINT
ACADEMY IN PERIL	Reprise (M) 2079	3.00	4.50	6.00
FEAR	Island (S) 9301	2.00	3.00	4.00
GUTS	Island (S) 9459	2.00	3.00	4.00
PARIS 1919	Reprise (S) MS 2131	4.00	6.00	8.00
SLOW DAZZLE	Island (S) 9317	2.00	3.00	4.00
VINTAGE VIOLENCE	Columbia (S) CS 1037	5.00	7.50	10.00

CALE, John and Terry Riley

TITLE	LABEL & NO.	GOOD	VERY GOOD	NEAR MINT
CHURCH OF ANTHRAX	Columbia (S) C 30131	4.00	6.00	8.00

CALIFORNIA, Randy

TITLE	LABEL & NO.	GOOD	VERY GOOD	NEAR MINT
KAPT. KOPTER AND THE (FABULOUS) TWIRLY BIRDS	Epic (S) KE 31755	5.00	7.50	10.00

CALLICOAT, Mississippi Joe

TITLE	LABEL & NO.	GOOD	VERY GOOD	NEAR MINT
BLUES MASTERS VOL. 6	Blue Horizon (M) BM 4606	4.00	6.00	8.00

CAMEL

TITLE	LABEL & NO.	GOOD	VERY GOOD	NEAR MINT
MIRAGE	Janus (S) 7009	2.50	3.75	5.00
MOONMADNESS	Janus (S) 7024	2.50	3.75	5.00
RAIN DANCES	Janus (S) 7035	2.00	3.00	4.00
SNOW GOOSE	Janus (S) 7016	2.50	3.75	5.00

CAMP, Hamilton

TITLE	LABEL & NO.	GOOD	VERY GOOD	NEAR MINT
HERE'S TO YOU	Warner Bros. (M) W 1737	3.00	4.50	6.00
HERE'S TO YOU	Warner Bros. (S) WS 1737	3.50	5.25	7.00

CAMP, Hamilton

TITLE	LABEL & NO.	GOOD	VERY GOOD	NEAR MINT
WELCOME TO HAMILTON CAMP	Warner Brothers (S) WS 1753	2.50	4.25	5.00

CAMPBELL, Dick

TITLE	LABEL & NO.	GOOD	VERY GOOD	NEAR MINT
DICK CAMPBELL SINGS WHERE IT'S AT	Mercury (M) MG 21060	4.00	6.00	8.00
DICK CAMPBELL SINGS WHERE IT'S AT	Mercury (S) SR 61060	5.00	7.50	10.00

CAMPBELL, Glen

TITLE	LABEL & NO.	GOOD	VERY GOOD	NEAR MINT
ARKANSAS	Capitol (S) SW 11407	2.50	3.75	5.00
ASTOUNDING 12 STRING GUITAR OF GLEN CAMPBELL	Capitol (M) T-2023	2.00	3.00	4.00
ASTOUNDING 12 STRING GUITAR OF GLEN CAMPBELL	Capitol (S) ST-2023	2.00	3.00	4.00
ASTOUNDING 12-STRING GUITAR OF GLEN CAMPBELL (RI)	Capitol (S) SM 2023	2.00	3.00	4.00
BEST OF GLEN CAMPBELL	Capitol (S) ST 11577	2.00	3.00	4.00

TITLE	LABEL & NO.	GOOD	VERY GOOD	NEAR MINT
BIG BLUE GRASS SPECIAL (WITH THE GREEN RIVER BOYS)	Capitol (M) T-1810	2.00	5.00	8.00
BIG BLUE GRASS SPECIAL (WITH THE GREEN RIVER BOYS)	Capitol (S) ST-1810	2.00	5.00	8.00
BLOODLINE	Capitol (S) SW 11516	2.00	3.00	4.00
BY THE TIME I GET TO PHOENIX	Capitol (M) T 2851	3.50	5.25	7.00
BY THE TIME I GET TO PHOENIX	Capitol (S) ST 2851	4.00	6.00	8.00
COUNTRY SHINDIG	Surrey (M) S-1007	2.50	3.75	5.00
COUNTRY SHINDIG	Surrey (S) SS-1007	2.50	3.75	5.00
COUNTRY SOUL	Starday (M) 424	2.00	3.00	4.00
ERNIE SINGS & GLEN PICKS	Capitol (S) ST-11389	2.00	3.00	4.00
GALVESTON	Capitol (S) ST 210	3.00	4.50	6.00
GENTLE ON MY MIND	Capitol (M) T 2809	3.50	5.25	7.00
GENTLE ON MY MIND	Capitol (S) ST 2809	4.00	6.00	8.00
GLEN CAMPBELL - LIVE	Capitol (S) STBO-268	3.50	5.25	7.00
GLEN TRAVIS CAMPBELL	Capitol (S) SW 11117	3.00	4.50	6.00
GOODTIME ALBUM	Capitol (S) SW 493	3.00	4.50	6.00
GREATEST HITS	Capitol (S) SW 752	3.00	4.50	6.00
HEY LITTLE ONE	Capitol (S) ST 2878	3.50	5.25	7.00
I KNEW JESUS	Capitol (S) SW 11185	2.50	3.75	5.00
LAST TIME I SAW HER	Capitol (S) SW 733	3.00	4.50	6.00
LIVE AT THE ROYAL FESTIVAL HALL	Capitol (S) SWBC 11707	2.00	3.00	4.00
A NEW PLACE IN THE SUN	Capitol (S) ST 2907	3.50	5.25	7.00
OH HAPPY DAY	Capitol (S) ST 443	3.00	4.50	6.00
REUNION	Capitol (S) SW 11336	2.50	3.75	5.00
RHINESTONE COWBOY	Capitol (S) SW 11430	2.00	3.00	4.00
SOUTHERN NIGHTS	Capitol (S) SO 11601	2.00	3.00	4.00
TOO LATE TO WORRY-TOO BLUE TO CRY	Capitol (M) T-1881	3.00	4.50	6.00
TOO LATE TO WORRY-TOO BLUE TO CRY	Capitol (S) ST-1881	3.00	4.50	6.00
TRY A LITTLE KINDNESS	Capitol (S) SW 389	3.00	4.50	6.00
WICHITA LINEMAN	Capitol (S) ST 103	3.00	4.50	6.00

CAMPBELL, Jimmy

TITLE	LABEL & NO.	GOOD	VERY GOOD	NEAR MINT
HALF BAKED	Vertigo (M) Vel 1000	3.00	4.50	6.00

CAMPBELL, Jo Ann

TITLE	LABEL & NO.	GOOD	VERY GOOD	NEAR MINT
ALL THE HITS BY JO ANN CAMPBELL	Cameo (M) C 1026	5.00	9.00	14.00
ALL THE HITS BY JO ANN CAMPBELL	Cameo (S) SC 1026	3.00	6.00	9.00
I'M NOBODY'S BABY	End (M) LP 306	6.00	12.50	20.00
STARRING JO ANN CAMPBELL	Coronet (M) CXS 199	4.00	10.00	16.00
TWISTIN AND LISTENIN	ABC Paramount (M) 393	5.00	12.50	20.00

CAMPI, Ray

TITLE	LABEL & NO.	GOOD	VERY GOOD	NEAR MINT
IT AIN'T ME, IT'S RAY CAMPI, THE EAGER BEAVER BOY	Rollin Rock (M) LP 008	4.00	6.00	8.00
ROCKABILLY	Rollin Rock (M) LP 001	4.00	6.00	8.00
ROCKABILLY LIVES	Rollin Rock (M) LP 104	4.00	6.00	8.00
ROCKABILLY REBEL	Rollin Rock (M) LP 006	4.00	6.00	8.00

CANADIAN BEADLES

TITLE	LABEL & NO.	GOOD	VERY GOOD	NEAR MINT
THREE FACES NORTH	Tide (M) 2005	8.00	16.00	24.00

CANARIES

TITLE	LABEL & NO.	GOOD	VERY GOOD	NEAR MINT
FLYING HIGH WITH THE CANARIES	BT Puppy (S) BTPS 1007	5.00	10.00	15.00

CANDLEWICK GREEN

TITLE	LABEL & NO.	GOOD	VERY GOOD	NEAR MINT
WHAT KIND OF SONGS	BASF (M) BC 29229	2.50	3.75	5.00

CANDYMEN

TITLE	LABEL & NO.	GOOD	VERY GOOD	NEAR MINT
CANDYMEN	ABC (M) 616	2.50	3.75	5.00
CANDYMEN	ABC (S) 616	3.00	4.50	6.00
CANDYMEN BRING YOU CANDY POWER, THE	ABC (S) ABCS 633	2.50	3.75	5.00
TWIST, THE	Diplomat (M) FM 100	2.00	3.00	4.00

CANNED HEAT

TITLE	LABEL & NO.	GOOD	VERY GOOD	NEAR MINT
BOOGIE WITH CANNED HEAT	Liberty (S) LST 7541	3.00	4.50	6.00
CANNED HEAT	Liberty (M) LRP 3526	2.50	3.75	5.00
CANNED HEAT	Liberty (S) LST 7526	3.00	4.50	6.00
CANNED HEAT COOKBOOK (THE BEST OF CANNED HEAT)	Liberty (S) LST 11000	3.00	4.50	6.00
COLLAGE	Sunset (S) SUS 5298	2.50	3.75	5.00
FUTURE BLUES	Liberty (S) 11002	2.50	3.75	5.00
HALLELUJAH	Liberty (S) 7618	2.50	3.75	5.00
LIVE AT TOPANGO CANYON	Wand (S) WDS 693	3.00	4.50	6.00
LIVING THE BLUES	Liberty (S) LSTY 27200	3.00	4.50	6.00
NEW AGE	United Artists (S) UA-LA049-F	2.50	3.75	5.00
ONE MORE RIVER TO CROSS	Atlantic (S) SD 7239	3.00	4.50	6.00
VERY BEST OF CANNED HEAT	United Artists (S) UA-LA431-E	2.50	3.75	5.00
VINTAGE	Janus (S) JLS 3009	2.50	3.75	5.00

CANNIBAL & THE HEADHUNTERS

TITLE	LABEL & NO.	GOOD	VERY GOOD	NEAR MINT
LAND OF 1000 DANCES	Date (M) TEM 3001	4.00	6.00	8.00
LAND OF 1000 DANCES	Date (S) TES 3001	5.00	7.50	10.00
LAND OF 1000 DANCES	Rampart (M) RM 3302	3.00	4.50	6.00
LAND OF 1000 DANCES	Rampart (S) RS 3302	4.00	6.00	8.00

CANNON, Ace

TITLE	LABEL & NO.	GOOD	VERY GOOD	NEAR MINT
ACE CANNON LIVE	Hi (M) HL 12025	2.00	3.00	4.00
ACE CANNON LIVE	Hi (S) SHL 32025	2.50	3.75	5.00
ACES BACK TO BACK	Hi (S) SHL 32072/73	3.50	5.25	7.00
ACES HI	Hi (M) HL 12016	2.25	4.50	6.75
ACES HI	Hi (S) SHL 32016	2.50	5.00	7.50
BABY DON'T GET HOOKED ON ME	Hi (S) SHL 32076	2.50	3.75	5.00

(M) Mono (S) Stereo (EP) Extended Play (Q) Quad (RI) Re-issued

TITLE	LABEL & NO.	GOOD	VERY GOOD	NEAR MINT
COUNTRY COMFORT	Hi (S) SHL 32080	2.50	3.75	5.00
LOOKING BACK	Hi (M) HL 12008	3.00	6.00	9.00
MOANIN' SAX	Hi (M) HL 12014	2.50	5.00	7.50
NASHVILLE HITS	Hi (M) HL 12028	2.00	3.00	4.00
SUPER SAX COUNTRY STYLE	Hi (S) SHL 32090	2.50	3.75	5.00
THAT MUSIC CITY FEELING	Hi (S) SHL 32086	2.50	3.75	5.00
"TUFF" SAX	Hi (M) HL 12007	3.00	6.00	9.00

CANNON, Freddy

ACTION!	Warner Bros. (M) W 1612	5.00	10.00	15.00
ACTION!	Warner Bros. (S) WS 1612	4.00	8.00	12.00
BIG 22 CANNON (Malaysian Import)	Wanderer (M) 1002	10.00	15.00	20.00
EXPLOSIVE FREDDY CANNON, THE	Swan (S) LP 502	8.00	20.00	32.00
FREDDIE CANNON	Warner Brothers (S) WS 1544	3.00	6.00	8.00
FREDDY CANNON SINGS HAPPY SHADES OF BLUE	Swan (M) LP 504	5.00	12.50	20.00
FREDDY CANNON STEPS OUT	Swan (M) LP 511	4.00	10.00	16.00
FREDDY CANNON STEPS OUT	Swan (S) LPS 511	5.00	12.50	20.00
GREATEST HITS	Warner Bros. (M) W 1628	5.00	10.00	15.00
GREATEST HITS	Warner Brothers (S) WS 1628	5.00	10.00	15.00
PALISADES PARK	Swan (M) LP 507	5.00	12.50	20.00
SOLID GOLD HITS	Swan (M) LP 505	5.00	12.00	20.00

CANNON, Gus

WALK RIGHT IN	Stax (M) 702	10.00	15.00	20.00

CANTELON, Willard

LSD BATTLE FOR THE MIND	Bible Voice (M) M 113	2.50	3.75	5.00

CANTOR, Eddie

BEST OF EDDIE CANTOR	Camden (M) CAL-531	2.00	3.00	4.00
BEST OF EDDIE CANTOR	Camden (S) CAS-531	2.00	3.00	4.00
CANTOR SINGS (SONGS IN CANTOR STORY)	Decca (M) 5504	6.00	9.00	12.00
CANTOR SINGS (SONGS IN CANTOR STORY)	Decca (EP) ED 592	2.00	3.00	4.00
CURTAIN CALL	Decca (M) DL 7018	5.00	7.50	10.00
EDDIE CANTOR (SONGS HE MADE FAMOUS)	Decca (M) DL-4431	6.00	9.00	12.00
EDDIE CANTOR STORY	Capitol (M) L467	5.00	7.50	10.00

CAPABILITY BROWN

FROM SCRATCH	Charisma (S) CAS 1056	3.00	4.50	6.00
VOICE	Passport (S) PPSD 98004	2.00	3.00	4.00

CAPALDI, Jim

OH, HOW WE DANCED	Island (S) 9187	2.50	3.75	5.00
WHALE MEAT AGAIN	Island (S) 9252	2.50	3.75	5.00

CAPITAL CITY ROCKETS

CAPITAL CITY ROCKETS	Elektra (S) EKS 75059	4.00	6.00	8.00

(Members from this Columbus, Ohio group were killed shortly after this release.
Surviving members now called the *Godz*, punk rock group)
Also see GODZ

CAPITOLS

DANCE THE COOL JERK	Atco (M) 190	2.00	3.00	4.00
DANCE THE COOL JERK	Atco (S) 190	2.50	3.75	5.00
WE GOT A THING	Atco (M) 201	2.00	3.00	4.00
WE GOT A THING	Atco (S) 201	2.50	3.75	5.00

CAPTAIN & TENNILLE

CAPTAIN & TENNILLE'S GREATEST HITS	A&M (S) SP 4667	2.00	3.00	4.00
COME IN FROM THE RAIN	A&M (S) SP 4700	2.00	3.00	4.00
LOVE WILL KEEP US TOGETHER	A&M (S) SP 4552	2.50	3.75	5.00
LOVE WILL KEEP US TOGETHER	A&M (Q) QU 54552	2.50	3.75	5.00
POR AMOR VIVIREMOS (Spanish Version of "Love Will Keep Us Together")	A&M (M) SP 4561	2.50	3.75	5.00
SONG OF JOY	A&M (S) SP 4570	2.00	3.00	4.00

CAPTAIN BEEFHEART

BLUEJEANS & MOONBEAMS	Mercury (S) SRM-1-1018	3.00	4.50	6.00
CLEAR SPOT	Reprise (S) MS 2115	3.50	5.25	7.00
LICK MY DECALS OFF, BABY	Straight (S) RS 6420	4.00	6.00	8.00
MIRROR MAN	Buddah (S) BDS 5077	4.00	6.00	8.00
SAFE AS MILK	Buddah (S) BDS 5001	4.00	6.00	8.00
SPOTLIGHT KID	Reprise (S) MS 2050	3.50	5.25	7.00

TITLE	LABEL & NO.	GOOD	VERY GOOD	NEAR MINT
STRICTLY PERSONAL	Blue Thumb (S) BTS 1	5.00	7.50	10.00
TROUT MASK REPLICA	Straight (S) STS 1053	5.00	7.50	10.00
UNCONDITIONALLY GUARANTEED	Mercury (S) SRM-1-709	3.00	4.50	6.00

C.A. QUINTET

TRIP THROUGH HELL	Candy Floss (M)	8.00	16.00	24.00

CARAVAN

CARAVAN	Verve/Forecast (S) FTS 3066	5.00	7.50	10.00
CARAVAN & THE NEW SYMPHONIA	London (S) PS-650	2.00	3.00	4.00
CUNNING STUNTS	BTM (S) 5000	3.00	4.50	6.00
FOR GIRLS WHO GROW PLUMP IN THE NIGHT	London (S) XPS-637	2.50	3.75	5.00
IF I COULD DO IT ALL OVER AGAIN, I'D DO IT ALL OVER YOU	London (S) PS 582	3.50	5.25	7.00
IN THE LAND OF GREY AND PINK	London (S) PS 593	3.50	5.25	7.00
SOUL OF THE CARAVANS	Trip (S) 7038	2.00	3.00	4.00
WATERLOO LILY	London (S) XPS 615	3.50	5.25	7.00

CARAVELLES

YOU DON'T HAVE TO BE A BABY TO CRY	Smash (M) MGS 27044	4.00	8.00	12.00
YOU DON'T HAVE TO BE A BABY TO CRY	Smash (S) SRS 67044	5.00	10.00	15.00

CAREFREES

CAREFREES, THE	London (M) LL 3379	6.00	12.00	18.00
CAREFREES, THE	London (S) PS 379	7.00	14.00	21.00

CARGILL, Henson

THIS IS HENSON CARGILL COUNTRY	Atlantic (S) SD 7279	2.00	3.00	4.00

CARGOE

CARGOE	Ardent (S) ADS 2802	3.50	5.25	7.00

CARLIN, George

CLASS CLOWN	Little David (S) 1004	3.50	5.25	7.00
EVENING WITH WALLY LONDO	Little David (S) 1008	3.00	4.50	6.00
GEORGE CARLIN, OCCUPATION: FOOLE	Little David (S) 1005	3.50	5.25	7.00
TOLEDO WINDOW BOX	Little David (S) 3003	3.50	5.25	7.00

CARMEN, Eric

BOATS AGAINST THE CURRENT	Arista (S) AL 4124	2.00	3.00	4.00
ERIC CARMEN	Arista (S) AL 4057	2.50	3.75	5.00
ERIC CARMEN	Arista (Q) AQ 4057	2.50	3.75	5.00

Also see RASPBERRIES & CHOIR

CARNES, Kim

KIM CARNES	A&M (S) SP 4548	2.00	3.00	4.00
SAILIN'	A&M (S) SP 4606	2.00	3.00	4.00

CARNEY, Art

ART CARNEY	Columbia (EP) B 2034	1.00	1.50	2.00

CARPENTERS

CARPENTERS	A&M (S) SP 3502	2.00	3.00	4.00
CARPENTERS	A&M (Q) QU 53502	3.00	4.50	6.00
CLOSE TO YOU	A&M (S) SP 4271	2.50	3.75	5.00
CLOSE TO YOU	A&M (Q) QU 54271	3.00	4.50	6.00
HORIZON	A&M (S) SP 4530	2.00	3.00	4.00
HORIZON	A&M (Q) QU 54530	2.50	3.75	5.00
A KIND OF A HUSH	A&M (S) SP 4581	2.00	3.00	4.00
NOW & THEN	A&M (S) SP 3519	2.00	3.00	4.00
NOW & THEN	A&M (Q) QU 53519	2.50	3.75	5.00
PASSAGE	A&M (S) SP 4703	2.50	3.75	5.00
SINGLES 1969-1973	A&M (S) SP 3601	2.00	3.00	4.00
SINGLES 1969-1973	A&M (Q) QU 53601	2.50	3.75	5.00
A SONG FOR YOU	A&M (S) SP 3511	2.00	3.00	4.00
A SONG FOR YOU	A&M (Q) QU 53511	3.00	4.50	6.00
TICKET TO RIDE	A&M (S) SP 4205	3.00	4.50	6.00

CARR, Cathy

CATHY CARR	Brunswick (EP) EB 71033	2.00	4.00	6.00
IVORY TOWER	Dot (M) DLP-3674	4.00	8.00	12.00
IVORY TOWER	Dot (S) DLP-25674	5.00	10.00	15.00
IVORY TOWER	Fraternity (M) F1005	4.00	10.00	16.00
SHY	Roulette (M) R-25077	4.00	8.00	12.00
SHY	Roulette (S) SR-25077	5.00	10.00	15.00

CARR, James

MAN NEEDS A WOMAN, A	Goldwax (S) 3002	5.00	7.50	10.00

CARR, Joe "Fingers"

HITS OF JOE "FINGERS" CARR (RI)	Capitol (S) SM-2019	2.00	3.00	4.00

CARR, Leroy

BLUES BEFORE SUNRISE	Columbia (M) C 30496	4.00	6.00	8.00

CARR, Vikki

ANATOMY OF LOVE	Liberty (M) LRP 3420	2.50	3.75	5.00
ANATOMY OF LOVE	Liberty (S) LSP 7420	2.50	3.75	5.00
DISCOVERY!	Liberty (M) LRP 3354	2.50	3.75	5.00
DISCOVERY!	Liberty (S) LST 7354	2.50	3.75	5.00
DISCOVERY - VOL. II	Liberty (M) LRP 3383	2.50	3.75	5.00

(M) Mono   (S) Stereo   (EP) Extended Play   (Q) Quad   (RI) Re-issued

DISCOVERY - VOL. II	Liberty (S) LST 7383	2.50	3.75	5.00
EN ESPANOL	Columbia (S) 31470	2.00	3.00	4.00
FIRST TIME EVER	Columbia (S) 31453	2.00	3.00	4.00
FOR ONCE IN MY LIFE	Liberty (S) LST 7604	2.50	3.75	5.00
GOLDEN SONGBOOK	United Artists (S) UA-LA089	2.00	3.00	4.00
HOY	Columbia (S) PC 33340	2.00	3.00	4.00
INTIMATE EXCITEMENT	Liberty (M) LRP 3506	2.50	3.75	5.00
INTIMATE EXCITEMENT	Liberty (S) LST 7506	2.50	3.75	5.00
IT MUST BE HIM	Liberty (M) LRP 3533	3.00	4.50	6.00
IT MUST BE HIM	Liberty (S) LST 7533	3.00	4.50	6.00
LIVE AT THE GREEK THEATRE	Columbia (S) KG 32656	2.50	3.75	5.00
LOVE STORY/FIRST TIME EVER	Columbia (S) CG 33609	2.50	3.75	5.00
MS. AMERICA	Columbia (S) KC 32251	2.00	3.00	4.00
NASHVILLE BY CARR	Liberty (S) 11001	2.50	3.75	5.00
ONE HELL OF A WOMAN	Columbia (S) KC 32860	2.00	3.00	4.00
SUPERSTAR	Columbia (S) 31040	2.00	3.00	4.00
VERY BEST OF VIKKI CARR	United Artists (S) UA-LA244	2.00	3.00	4.00
VERY BEST OF VIKKI CARR (RI of UA 244)	United Artists (S) UA-LA385	2.00	3.00	4.00
VERY BEST OF VIKKI CARR	United Artists (S) UA-LA516	2.00	3.00	4.00
VIKKI!	Liberty (S) LST 7548	3.00	4.50	6.00
VIKKI CARR'S LOVE STORY	Columbia (S) 30662	2.00	3.00	4.00

CARROLL BROTHERS

| COLLEGE TWIST PARTY | Cameo (M) C-1015 | 2.00 | 4.00 | 6.00 |
| COLLEGE TWIST PARTY | Cameo (S) CS-1015 | 3.00 | 6.00 | 9.00 |

CARROLL, David

CONTRASTS	Wing (M) MGW-12146	2.00	3.00	4.00
CONTRASTS	Wing (S) SRW-12508	2.00	3.00	4.00
DANCE & STAY YOUNG	Mercury (S) SR-60027	2.00	3.00	4.00
DAVID CARROLL	Mercury (EP) EPS-1-6000	1.00	1.50	2.00
FEATHERY FEELING	Mercury (S) SR-60026	2.00	3.00	4.00
SHOW STOPPERS FROM THE FABULOUS 50's	Mercury (M) MG-20411	2.00	3.00	4.00
SHOW STOPPERS FROM THE FABULOUS 50's	Mercury (S) SR-60060	2.00	3.00	4.00

CARROLL, Diahann

DIAHANN CARROLL AT THE PERSIAN ROOM	United Artists (M) UAL 3080	2.00	3.00	4.00
DIAHANN CARROLL AT THE PERSIAN ROOM	United Artists (S) UAS 6080	2.00	3.00	4.00
PORGY & BESS	United Artists (M) UAL-4021	2.00	3.00	4.00
PORGY & BESS	United Artists (S) UAS-5021	2.50	3.75	5.00

CARTER, Calvin

| TWIST ALONG | Vee Jay (M) 1041 | 3.00 | 6.00 | 9.00 |
| TWIST ALONG | Vee Jay (S) 1041 | 4.00 | 8.00 | 12.00 |

CARTER, Mel

EASY LISTENING	Imperial (M) 9319	2.00	4.00	6.00
HOLD ME, THRILL ME, KISS ME	Imperial (M) LP 9289	2.00	4.00	6.00
HOLD ME, THRILL ME, KISS ME	Imperial (S) LP 12289	3.00	6.00	9.00
MEL CARTER	Sunset (S) 5227	2.00	3.00	4.00
MY HEART SINGS	Imperial (M) 9300	2.00	4.00	6.00
MY HEART SINGS	Imperial (S) 12300	3.00	6.00	9.00
WHEN A BOY FALLS IN LOVE	Derby (M) 702	5.00	10.00	15.00

CARTOONE

| CARTOONE | Atlantic (S) SD 8219 | 4.00 | 6.00 | 8.00 |

CARVER, Johnny

DON'T TELL	ABC (S) D-843	2.00	3.00	4.00
DOUBLE EXPOSURE	ABC (S) X-612	2.00	3.00	4.00
I START THINKING ABOUT YOU	Harmony (S) KH-32476	2.00	3.00	4.00
LINES & CIRCLES & TRIANGLES	United Artists (S) UA-LA268-G	2.00	3.00	4.00
STRINGS	ABC (S) D-864	2.00	3.00	4.00
YELLOW RIBBON	ABC (S) X-792	2.00	3.00	4.00

CASCADES

MAYBE THE RAIN WILL FALL	UNI (S) 73069	4.00	6.00	8.00
RHYTHM OF THE RAIN	Valiant (M) 405	6.00	12.00	18.00
WHAT GOES ON INSIDE THE CASCADES	Cascades (M) AD 6820	5.00	7.50	10.00

CASH, Johnny

ALL ABOARD THE BLUE TRAIN	Sun (M) 1270	4.00	8.00	12.00
AMERICA: A 200-YEAR SALUTE IN STORY AND SONG	Columbia (S) 31645	2.50	3.75	5.00
ANY OLD WIND THAT BLOWS	Columbia (S) KC 32091	2.00	3.00	4.00
BALLADS OF THE AMERICAN INDIAN	Harmony (S) KH 32388	2.00	3.00	4.00
BITTER TEARS	Columbia (M) CL-2248	2.00	3.00	4.00
BITTER TEARS	Columbia (S) CS-9048	2.00	3.00	4.00
BLOOD, SWEAT & TEARS	Columbia (M) CL 1930	2.50	3.75	5.00
BLOOD, SWEAT & TEARS	Columbia (S) CS 8730	2.50	3.75	5.00
CARRYIN' ON (RI as "Jackson")	Columbia (M) CL 2728	3.50	5.25	7.00
CARRYIN' ON (RI as "Jackson")	Columbia (S) CS 9528	4.00	6.00	8.00
CHILDREN'S ALBUM	Columbia (S) C 32898	2.00	3.00	4.00
CHRISTMAS SPIRIT	Columbia (M) CL-2117	2.50	3.75	5.00
CHRISTMAS SPIRIT	Columbia (S) CS-8917	2.50	3.75	5.00
COLLECTION: HIS GREATEST HITS, VOL. 2	Columbia (S) 30887	2.00	3.00	4.00
COUNTRY BOY	Sun (EP) SPA 112	2.00	4.00	6.00
EVERYBODY LOVES A NUT	Columbia (M) CL-2492	2.00	3.00	4.00
EVERYBODY LOVES A NUT	Columbia (S) CS-9292	2.00	3.00	4.00

FABULOUS JOHNNY CASH	Columbia (M) CL 1253	2.50	3.75	5.00
FABULOUS JOHNNY CASH	Columbia (S) CS-8122	2.50	3.75	5.00
FIVE FEET HIGH & RISING	Columbia (S) C 32951	2.00	3.00	4.00
FROM SEA TO SHINING SEA	Columbia (M) CL-2647	2.00	3.00	4.00
FROM SEA TO SHINING SEA	Columbia (S) CS-9447	2.00	3.00	4.00
GREATEST	Sun (M) SLP-1240	4.00	8.00	12.00
GREATEST HITS, VOL. 1	Columbia (M) CL 2678	2.00	3.00	4.00
GREATEST HITS, VOL. 1	Columbia (S) CS 9478	2.00	3.00	4.00
HELLO, I'M JOHNNY CASH	Columbia (S) CS 9943	2.00	3.00	4.00
HOLY LAND	Columbia (S) CS 9766	2.00	3.00	4.00
HOME OF THE BLUES	Sun (EP) SEP 116	2.00	4.00	6.00
HOT & BLUE GUITAR	Sun (M)	4.00	8.00	12.00
HYMNS BY JOHNNY CASH	Columbia (M) CL-1284	2.00	3.00	4.00
HYMNS BY JOHNNY CASH	Columbia (S) CS-8125	2.00	3.00	4.00
I WALK THE LINE	Columbia (M) CL-2190	2.00	3.00	4.00
I WALK THE LINE	Columbia (S) CS-8990	2.00	3.00	4.00
I WALK THE LINE	Sun (EP) EP 113	2.00	4.00	6.00
I WOULD LIKE TO SEE YOU AGAIN	Columbia (S) KC 35313	2.00	3.00	4.00
JOHNNY CASH	Sun (M) 1220	4.00	8.00	12.00
JOHNNY CASH	Everest (S) 276	2.50	3.75	5.00
JOHNNY CASH	Harmony (S) 11342	2.00	3.00	4.00
JOHNNY CASH AND THE TENNESSEE TWO	Sun (EP) EP 114	2.00	4.00	6.00
JOHNNY CASH AT FOLSOM PRISON	Columbia (S) CS 9639	2.00	3.00	4.00
JOHNNY CASH AT FOLSOM PRISON & SAN QUENTIN	Columbia (S) CG 33639	2.00	3.00	4.00
JOHNNY CASH AT SAN QUENTIN	Columbia (S) CS 9827	2.00	3.00	4.00
JOHNNY CASH SHOW	Columbia (S) C 30100	2.00	3.00	4.00
JOHNNY CASH SINGS HANK WILLIAMS	Sun (M) 1245	4.00	8.00	12.00
JOHNNY CASH SINGS HANK WILLIAMS	Sun (EP) EPA 111	2.00	4.00	6.00
JOHNNY CASH SINGS HANK WILLIAMS (WITH JERRY LEE LEWIS-5 SONGS BY EACH)	Sun (M) 125	3.00	4.50	6.00
JOHNNY CASH SINGS PRECIOUS MEMORIES	Columbia (S) C 33087	2.00	3.00	4.00
JOHNNY CASH SINGS THE REBEL— JOHNNY YUMA	Columbia (EP) B-2155	2.00	4.00	6.00
(With picture of Nick Adams)				
JOHNNY CASH SUNDAY DOWN SOUTH (WITH JERRY LEE LEWIS-5 SONGS BY EACH)	Sun (M) 119	3.00	4.50	6.00
JOHN R. CASH	Columbia (S) KC 33370	2.00	3.00	4.00
LOOK AT THEM BEANS	Columbia (S) KC 33814	2.00	3.00	4.00

(M) Mono (S) Stereo (EP) Extended Play (Q) Quad (RI) Re-issued

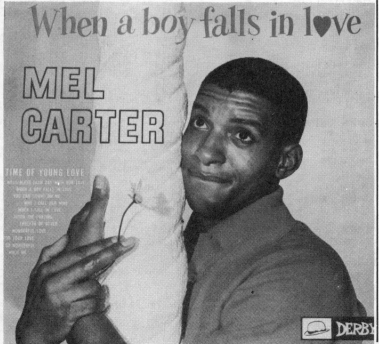

TITLE	LABEL & NO.	GOOD	VERY GOOD	NEAR MINT
LURE OF THE GRAND CANYON				
(NARRATION BY J. CASH)	Columbia (M) CL 1622	5.00	12.50	20.00
MAN IN BLACK	Columbia (S) KC 30440	2.00	3.00	4.00
MEAN AS HELL	Columbia (M) CL-2446	2.00	3.00	4.00
MEAN AS HELL	Columbia (S) CS-9246	2.00	3.00	4.00
NOW HERE'S JOHNNY CASH	Sun (M) 1255	4.00	8.00	12.00
NOW, THERE WAS A SONG	Columbia (M) CL-1463	2.50	3.75	5.00
NOW, THERE WAS A SONG	Columbia (S) CS-8254	2.50	3.75	5.00
NOW, THERE WAS A SONG	Columbia (EP) B 14631	1.00	1.50	2.00
NOW, THERE WAS A SONG	Columbia (EP) B 14632	1.00	1.50	2.00
NOW, THERE WAS A SONG	Columbia (EP) B 14633	1.00	1.50	2.00
ORANGE BLOSSOM SPECIAL	Columbia (M) CL-2309	2.00	3.00	4.00
ORANGE BLOSSOM SPECIAL	Columbia (S) CS-9109	2.00	3.00	4.00
ORIGINAL SUN SOUND OF JOHNNY CASH	Sun (M) S-1275	4.00	8.00	12.00
RAGGED OLD FLAG	Columbia (S) KC 32917	2.00	3.00	4.00
RIDE THIS TRAIN	Columbia (M) CL 1464	2.50	3.75	5.00
RIDE THIS TRAIN	Columbia (S) CS 8255	2.50	3.75	5.00
RING OF FIRE	Columbia (M) CL 2053	2.00	3.00	4.00
RING OF FIRE	Columbia (S) CS 8853	2.00	3.00	4.00
SO DOGGONE LONESOME	Sun (EP) SEP 117	2.00	4.00	6.00
SONGS OF OUR SOIL	Columbia (M) CL-1339	2.50	3.75	5.00
SONGS OF OUR SOIL	Columbia (S) CS-8148	2.50	3.75	5.00
SONGS OF OUR SOIL	Columbia (EP) B-13391	1.00	1.50	2.00
SONGS OF OUR SOIL	Columbia (EP) B 13392	1.00	1.50	2.00
SONGS OF OUR SOIL	Columbia (EP) B 13393	1.00	1.50	2.00
SONGS THAT MADE HIM FAMOUS	Sun (M) 1235	4.00	8.00	12.00
SOUND OF JOHNNY CASH	Columbia (M) CL-1802	2.50	3.75	5.00
SOUND OF JOHNNY CASH	Columbia (S) CS-8602	2.00	3.00	4.00
SUNDAY MORNING COMING DOWN	Columbia (S) C 32240	2.00	3.00	4.00
THAT'S WHAT YOU GET FOR LOVIN' ME	Columbia (M) CL-2537	2.00	3.00	4.00
THAT'S WHAT YOU GET FOR LOVIN' ME	Columbia (S) CS-9337	2.00	3.00	4.00
A THING CALLED LOVE	Columbia (S) 31332	2.00	3.00	4.00
WORLD OF JOHNNY CASH	Columbia (S) GP 29	3.00	4.50	6.00

CASH, June Carter

TITLE	LABEL & NO.	GOOD	VERY GOOD	NEAR MINT
APPALACHIAN PRIDE	Columbia (S) KC-33686	2.00	3.00	4.00

CASHMAN AND WEST

TITLE	LABEL & NO.	GOOD	VERY GOOD	NEAR MINT
BOUND TO HAPPEN	ABC (S) ABCS-629	3.00	4.50	6.00
LIFESONG	Dunhill (S) DSX 50179	2.00	3.00	4.00
MOONDOG SERENADE	Dunhill (S) DSX 50141	2.00	3.00	4.00

A TALE OF TWO CITIES/NY '45 and '72
Manhattan Tower composed by Gordon Jenkins through the courtesy
of Decca Records. American City Suite composed by Terry Cashman and
T.P. West from their Album, "A Song Or Two".

TITLE	LABEL & NO.	GOOD	VERY GOOD	NEAR MINT
(DSX 50126)	Dunhill (S) SPDJ 17	4.00	6.00	8.00

CASH, Tommy

TITLE	LABEL & NO.	GOOD	VERY GOOD	NEAR MINT
BEST OF TOMMY CASH	Epic (S) KE-31995	2.50	3.75	5.00
THAT CERTAIN ONE	Epic (S) KE-31747	2.50	3.75	5.00

CASINOS

TITLE	LABEL & NO.	GOOD	VERY GOOD	NEAR MINT
THEN YOU CAN TELL ME GOODBYE	Fraternity (M) 1019	4.00	8.00	12.00

CASSIDY, David (Of the Partridge Family)

TITLE	LABEL & NO.	GOOD	VERY GOOD	NEAR MINT
CASSIDY LIVE	Bell (S) 1312	2.50	3.75	5.00
CHERISH	Bell (S) 6070	3.00	4.50	6.00
DREAMS ARE NUTTIN' MORE THAN WISHES	Bell (S) 1132	2.50	3.75	5.00
GETTIN' IT IN THE STREET	RCA (S) APL1-1852	2.50	3.75	5.00
GREATEST HITS	Bell (S) 1321	3.00	4.50	6.00
HIGHER THEY CLIMB (THE HARDER THEY FALL)	RCA (S) APL1-1066	2.50	3.75	5.00
HOME IS WHERE THE HEART IS	RCA (S) APL1-1309	2.50	3.75	5.00
ROCK ME BABY	Bell (S) 1109	3.00	4.50	6.00

CASSIDY, Shaun

TITLE	LABEL & NO.	GOOD	VERY GOOD	NEAR MINT
BORN LATE	Warner Bros./Curb (S) BSK 3126	2.00	3.00	4.00
SHAUN CASSIDY	Warner Bros./Curb (S) BS 3067	2.00	3.00	4.00

CASTELLS

TITLE	LABEL & NO.	GOOD	VERY GOOD	NEAR MINT
SO THIS IS LOVE	Era (M) EL 109	4.00	8.00	12.00
SO THIS IS LOVE	Era (S) ES 109	5.00	10.00	15.00

CASTOR, Jimmy, Bunch

TITLE	LABEL & NO.	GOOD	VERY GOOD	NEAR MINT
BUTT OF COURSE	Atlantic (S) SD 18124	2.00	3.00	4.00
DIMENSION III	RCA (S) APD1-0103	2.50	3.75	5.00
EVERYTHING MAN	RCA (S) APL1-0313	2.50	3.75	5.00
EVERYTHING MAN	Atlantic (S) SD 7305	2.50	3.75	5.00
SUPERSOUND	Atlantic (S) SD 18150	2.00	3.00	4.00

CASUALS

TITLE	LABEL & NO.	GOOD	VERY GOOD	NEAR MINT
ORIGINAL CASUALS, THE/THREE KISSES PAST MIDNIGHT	Back Beat (EP) EP 40	4.00	10.00	16.00

CATALINAS

TITLE	LABEL & NO.	GOOD	VERY GOOD	NEAR MINT
FUN, FUN, FUN	RIC (M) M 1006	4.00	8.00	12.00

CATHY JEAN and The Roomates

TITLE	LABEL & NO.	GOOD	VERY GOOD	NEAR MINT
AT THE HOP	Valmor (M) LP 789	11.00	27.50	44.00
CATE BROS	Asylum (S) 7E-1050	3.00	4.50	6.00

CAT MOTHER AND THE ALL NIGHT NEWS BOYS

TITLE	LABEL & NO.	GOOD	VERY GOOD	NEAR MINT
ALBION DOO-WAH	Polydor (S) 24-4023	2.50	3.75	5.00
CAT MOTHER	Polydor (S) 5017	2.50	3.75	5.00
LAST CHANCE DANCE	Polydor (S) 5042	2.50	3.75	5.00
STREET GIVETH AND THE STREET TAKETH AWAY, THE	Polydor (S) 24-4001	2.50	3.75	5.00

CATS

TITLE	LABEL & NO.	GOOD	VERY GOOD	NEAR MINT
45 LIVES	Rare Earth (S) RS 521	3.00	4.50	6.00
LOVE IN YOUR EYES, THE	Fantasy (S) F-9449	2.00	3.00	4.00

CAVALIERE, Felix (Ex-Rascals Member)

TITLE	LABEL & NO.	GOOD	VERY GOOD	NEAR MINT
DESTINY	Bearsville (S) 6958	3.00	4.50	6.00
FELIX CAVALIERE	Bearsville (S) 6955	3.00	4.50	6.00

Also see RASCALS

C COMPANY (Featuring Terry Nelson)

TITLE	LABEL & NO.	GOOD	VERY GOOD	NEAR MINT
WAKE UP AMERICA	Plantation (M) PLP 15	5.00	7.50	10.00

CENTRAL NERVOUS SYSTEM

TITLE	LABEL & NO.	GOOD	VERY GOOD	NEAR MINT
I COULD HAVE DANCED ALL NIGHT	Music Factory (S) MFS 12003	3.00	4.50	6.00

CENTURIANS

TITLE	LABEL & NO.	GOOD	VERY GOOD	NEAR MINT
SURFERS PAJAMA PARTY	Del Fi (M) DFLP 1228	5.00	10.00	15.00
SURFERS PAJAMA PARTY	Del Fi (S) DFST 1228	6.00	12.00	18.00

CHAD AND JEREMY

TITLE	LABEL & NO.	GOOD	VERY GOOD	NEAR MINT
ARK, THE	Columbia (S) CS 9699	5.00	10.00	15.00
BEFORE AND AFTER	Columbia (M) CL 2374	5.00	10.00	15.00
BEST OF CHAD AND JEREMY, THE	Capitol (M) T 2470	3.00	6.00	9.00
BEST OF CHAD AND JEREMY, THE	Capitol (S) ST2470	4.00	8.00	12.00
BRITISH FOLK ARTIST CONCERT FEATURING CHAD AND JEREMY	Tradition Rest (M) 2062	3.00	6.00	9.00
CHAD AND JEREMY	Harmony (S) HS 11357	3.00	6.00	9.00
CHAD AND JEREMY SING FOR YOU	World Artists (M) WAM 2005	3.00	6.00	9.00
CHAD AND JEREMY SING FOR YOU	World Artists (S) WAS 3005	2.00	4.00	6.00
DISTANT SHORES	Columbia (M) CL 2564	3.00	6.00	9.00
DISTANT SHORES	Columbia (S) CS 9364	4.00	8.00	12.00
5 PLUS 10 EQUALS 15 FABULOUS HITS	Fidu (M) 101	3.00	6.00	9.00
I DON'T WANT TO LOSE YOU BABY	Columbia (M) CL 2398	3.00	6.00	9.00
MORE CHAD AND JEREMY	Capitol (M) TT 2546	4.00	8.00	12.00
MORE CHAD AND JEREMY	Capitol (S) ST 2546	5.00	10.00	15.00
OF CABBAGES AND KINGS	Columbia (M) CL 2657	3.00	6.00	9.00
OF CABBAGES AND KINGS	Columbia (S) CS 9471	4.00	8.00	12.00
YESTERDAYS GONE	World Artists (M) WAM 2002	3.00	6.00	9.00
YESTERDAYS GONE	World Artists (S) WAS 3002	2.00	4.00	6.00

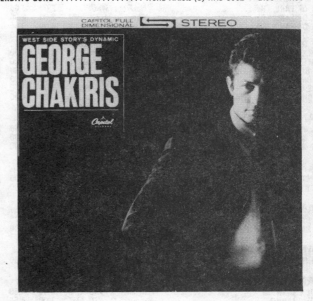

CHAKIRIS, George

TITLE	LABEL & NO.	GOOD	VERY GOOD	NEAR MINT
GEORGE CHAKIRIS	Capitol (M) T 1750	3.00	6.00	9.00
GEORGE CHAKIRIS	Capitol (S) ST 1750	4.00	8.00	12.00

(M) Mono   (S) Stereo   (EP) Extended Play   (Q) Quad   (RI) Re-issued

TITLE	LABEL & NO.	GOOD	VERY GOOD	NEAR MINT
CHALLENGERS				
CALIFORNIA KICKS	GNP/Crescendo (M) GNP 2025	3.00	6.00	9.00
CHALLENGERS A GO GO, THE	Vault (M) VS 110	3.00	6.00	9.00
CHALLENGERS AT THE TEEN-AGE FAIR, THE	GNP/Crescendo (M) GNP 2010	3.00	6.00	9.00
CHALLENGERS GO SIDEWALK SURFING, THE	Triumph (M) 100	7.00	14.00	21.00
CHALLENGERS ON THE MOVE, THE	Vault (M) LP 102	3.00	6.00	9.00
K-39	Vault (M) 107	4.00	8.00	12.00
LIGHT MY FIRE	GNP/Crescendo (M) 2045	3.00	6.00	9.00
MAN FROM UNCLE, THE	GNP/Crescendo (M) GNP 2018	2.50	5.00	7.50
SURFBEAT	Vault (M) LP 100	3.00	6.00	9.00
SURFBEAT, VOL. II	Vault (M) LP 105	3.00	6.00	9.00
SURFING WITH THE CHALLENGERS	Vault (M) 101A	4.00	8.00	12.00
SURF'S UP	Vault (M) 109	3.00	6.00	9.00
25 GREATEST INSTRUMENTAL HITS	GNP/Crescendo (M) GNP 609	3.00	6.00	9.00
VANILLA FUNK	GNP/Crescendo (M) 2056	3.00	6.00	9.00
WHERE WERE YOU IN THE SUMMER OF '62	Fantasy (S) 9443	3.50	5.25	7.00
CHALLENGERS and Billy Strange				
BILLY STRANGE AND THE CHALLENGERS	GNP/Crescendo (M) GNP 2030	2.50	5.00	7.50
CHAMAELEON CHURCH				
CHAMAELEON CHURCH	MGM (S) SE 4574	2.50	3.75	5.00
CHAMBERLAIN, Richard				
JOY IN THE MORNING	MGM (M) E-4287	2.00	3.00	4.00
JOY IN THE MORNING	MGM (S) SE-4287	2.00	3.00	4.00
RICHARD CHAMBERLAIN SINGS	MGM (M) E-4088	2.50	3.75	5.00
RICHARD CHAMBERLAIN SINGS	MGM (S) SE-4088	2.50	3.75	5.00
CHAMBERS BROTHERS				
LOVE, PEACE, AND HAPPINESS	Columbia (S) 20	2.50	3.75	5.00
NEW GENERATION	Columbia (S) 30032	2.50	3.75	5.00
A NEW TIME/A NEW DAY	Columbia (S) 9671	3.00	4.50	6.00
PEOPLE GET READY	Vault (M) 9003	2.50	3.75	5.00
PEOPLE GET READY	Vault (S) 9003	3.50	5.25	7.00
RIGHT MOVE	Avco (S) 69003	3.00	4.50	6.00
TIME HAS COME, THE	Columbia (M) 2722	3.00	4.50	6.00
TIME HAS COME/ A NEW TIME, A NEW DAY	Columbia (S) CG-33642	2.50	3.75	5.00
UNBONDED	Avco (S) 11013	3.00	4.50	6.00
CHAMPS				
ALL AMERICAN (MUSIC FROM)	Challenge (M) 614	4.00	8.00	12.00
ALL AMERICAN (MUSIC FROM)	Challenge (S) CHS 614	5.00	10.00	15.00
CARAMBA	Challenge (EP) EP 7101	2.00	4.00	6.00
CHAMPS AND THE FAMOUS CYCLONES	International award (M) AK223	3.00	6.00	9.00
EVERYBODY'S ROCKIN' WITH THE CHAMPS	Challenge (M) CHL 605	5.00	10.00	15.00
EVERYBODY'S ROCKIN' WITH THE CHAMPS	Challenge (S) CHS 605	8.00	16.00	24.00
GO CHAMPS GO	Challenge (M) CHL 601	7.00	14.00	21.00
GREAT DANCE HITS	Challenge (M) 613	4.00	8.00	12.00
GREAT DANCE HITS	Challenge (S) CHS 613	5.00	10.00	15.00
TEQUILA	Challenge (EP) EP 7100	2.00	4.00	6.00
CHANDLER, Gene				
DUKE OF EARL, THE	Up Front (M) UPF105	2.00	3.00	4.00
DUKE OF EARL, THE	Checker (M) LP 3003	3.00	6.00	9.00
DUKE OF EARL, THE	Checker (S) LPS 3003	3.00	6.00	9.00
DUKE OF EARL, THE	VeeJay (M) MR1040	3.00	7.50	12.00
DUKE OF EARL, THE	Vee Jay (S) SR 1040	4.00	10.00	16.00
GIRL DONT CARE, THE	Brunswick (M) BL 54124	3.00	4.50	6.00
GREATEST HITS BY GENE CHANDLER	Constellation (M) M-1421	4.00	8.00	12.00
JUST BE TRUE	Constellation (M) LP 1423	4.00	8.00	12.00
LIVE ON STAGE IN '65	Constellation (M) 1425	4.00	8.00	12.00
THERE WAS A TIME	Brunswick (S) 754131	3.00	4.50	6.00
TWO SIDES OF GENE CHANDLER, THE	Brunswick (S) BL 754149	3.00	4.50	6.00
CHANDLER, Karen				
DEAR MR. GABLE	Strand (M) L-1028	3.00	7.50	12.00
DEAR MR. GABLE	Strand (S) SLS-1028	4.00	10.00	16.00
HOLD ME, THRILL ME, KISS ME	Coral (EP) EC 81075	2.00	5.00	8.00
CHANGO				
CHANGO	ABC (S) 872	2.00	3.00	4.00
HONEY IS SWEETER THAN BLOOD	Mercury (S) SRM-1-1103	2.00	3.00	4.00
CHANNEL, Bruce				
HEY! BABY	Smash (M) MGS 27008	4.50	6.75	9.00
HEY! BABY	Smash (S) SRS 67008	6.00	9.00	12.00
CHANNELS				
ALL THEIR HITS	Channel 1001	4.00	6.00	8.00
CHANNING, Carol				
CAROL CHANNING	Vanguard (M) VRS-9056	3.00	4.50	6.00
CAROL CHANNING	Vanguard (S) VSD-2041	3.00	4.50	6.00
CHANTAYS				
PIPELINE	Dot (M) DLP 3516	4.00	8.00	12.00
PIPELINE	Dot (S) DLP 25516	5.00	10.00	15.00
TWO SIDES OF THE CHANTAYS	Dot (M) DLP 3771	6.00	12.00	18.00
TWO SIDES OF THE CHANTAYS	Dot (S) DLP 25771	7.00	14.00	21.00

TITLE	LABEL & NO.	GOOD	VERY GOOD	NEAR MINT
CHANTELS				
C'EST SI BON	End (EP) EP-202	3.00	6.00	9.00
CHANTELS, THE (Juke Box Cover)	End (M) LP 301	6.00	12.00	18.00
CHANTELS, THE (Juke Box Cover)	End (M) LP 301	2.50	3.75	5.00
CHANTELS ON TOUR, THE	Carlton (S) STLP 144	8.00	16.00	24.00
LOOK IN MY EYES	Carlton (M)	8.00	16.00	24.00
SING THEIR FAVORITES	Forum (M) 9104	6.00	12.00	18.00
THERE'S OUR SONG AGAIN	End (M) LP 312	8.00	16.00	24.00
WE ARE THE CHANTELS (Group Photo cover)	End (M) LP 301	30.00	75.00	120.00
CHAPIN BROTHERS				
CHAPIN MUSIC	Rockland (M) 66	6.00	8.00	12.00
CHAPIN, Harry				
DANCE BAND ON THE TITANIC	Elektra (S) 9E-301	3.00	4.50	6.00
GREATEST STORIES - LIVE	Elektra (S) 7E-2009	2.50	3.75	5.00
HEADS & TALES	Elektra (S) EKS 75023	3.00	4.50	6.00
ON THE ROAD TO KINGDOM	Elektra (S) 7E-1082	2.00	3.00	4.00
PORTRAIT GALLERY	Elektra (S) 7E-1041	2.00	3.00	4.00
SHORT STORIES	Elektra (S) EKS 75065	3.00	4.50	6.00
SNIPER AND OTHER LOVE SONGS	Elektra (S) EKS 75042	3.00	4.50	6.00
VERITIES & BALDERDASH	Elektra (S) 7E-1012	2.00	3.00	4.00
CHAPMAN, Michael				
FULLY QUALIFIED SURVIVOR	Harvest (S) SW 816	3.00	4.50	6.00
CHARIOTEERS				
CHARIOTEERS WITH BILLY WILLIAMS	Harmony (M) HL 7089	6.00	9.00	12.00
CHARISMA				
CHARISMA	Roulette (S) SR 42037	3.00	4.50	6.00
CHARLATANS				
CHARLATANS, THE	Philips (S) PHS 600-309	4.00	6.00	8.00
CHARIOTEERS				
SWEET AND LOW (10") (Canadian pressing; blue cover)	Columbia (M) 6014	6.00	15.00	24.00
SWEET AND LOW (10") (U.S. pressing; pink soft cover)	Columbia (M) 6014	13.00	32.50	52.00
CHARLES, Ray				
ALL TIME GREAT COUNTRY & WESTERN HITS	ABC (S) X-781	2.00	3.00	4.00
ARTISTRY OF RAY CHARLES	Baronet (M) BM-111	2.00	3.00	4.00
ARTISTRY OF RAY CHARLES	Baronet (S) BS-111	2.00	3.00	4.00
COME LIVE WITH ME	Crossover (S) 9000	2.00	3.00	4.00
CRYING TIME	ABC/Paramount (M) ABC 544	2.00	3.00	4.00
CRYING TIME	ABC/Paramount (S) ABCS 544	2.00	3.00	4.00
DO THE TWIST WITH RAY CHARLES	Atlantic (M) 8054	3.00	7.50	12.00
FABULOUS	Hollywood (M) 505	5.00	12.50	20.00
GENIUS AFTER HOURS	Atlantic (M) 1369	2.50	3.75	5.00
GENIUS HITS THE ROAD	ABC/Paramount (M) ABC335	2.00	3.00	4.00
GENIUS HITS THE ROAD	ABC/Paramount (S) ABCS-335	2.00	3.00	4.00
GENIUS LIVE IN CONCERT	Bluesway (S) Q-6052	2.00	3.00	4.00
GENIUS OF RAY CHARLES	Atlantic (M) 1312	2.50	3.75	5.00
GENIUS OF RAY CHARLES	Atlantic (S) SD 1312	2.50	3.75	5.00
GENIUS PLUS SOUL EQUALS JAZZ	Impulse (M) A 2	2.50	3.75	5.00
GENIUS PLUS SOUL EQUALS JAZZ	Impulse (S) AS 2	2.50	3.75	5.00
GENIUS SINGS THE BLUES	Atlantic (M) 8052	3.00	7.00	12.00
THE GREAT RAY CHARLES	Atlantic (M) LP1256	4.00	6.00	8.00
THE GREAT RAY CHARLES	Atlantic (EP) EPS597	1.50	2.25	3.00
HALLELUJAH I LOVE HER SO!	Atlantic (M) LP 8006	5.00	12.50	20.00
HAVE A SMILE WITH ME	ABC/Paramount (M) ABC495	2.00	3.00	4.00
HAVE A SMILE WITH ME	ABC/Paramount (S) ABCS 495	2.00	3.00	4.00
INCOMPARABLE RAY CHARLES, THE	Strand (M) SL 1076	2.00	3.00	4.00
INGREDIENTS IN A RECIPE FOR SOUL	ABC Paramount (M) ABC465	2.00	3.00	4.00
INGREDIENTS IN A RECIPE FOR SOUL	ABC Paramount (S) ABCS465	2.00	3.00	4.00
LIVE	Atlantic (S) 2-503	4.00	6.00	8.00
LIVE IN CONCERT	ABC/Paramount (M) ABC500	2.50	3.75	5.00
LIVE IN CONCERT	ABC/Paramount (S) ABCS500	2.50	3.75	5.00
MEMORIES OF A MIDDLE-AGED MAN	Atco (S) 263	2.00	3.00	4.00
MODERN SOUNDS IN COUNTRY & WESTERN MUSIC	ABC/Paramount (M) ABC410	2.00	3.00	4.00

(M) Mono (S) Stereo (EP) Extended Play (Q) Quad (RI) Re-issued

TITLE	LABEL & NO.	GOOD	VERY GOOD	NEAR MINT
MODERN SOUNDS IN COUNTRY & WESTERN MUSIC	ABC/Paramount (S) ABCS 410	2.00	3.00	4.00
MOODS OF LOVE	ABC/Tangerine (S) ABCX-772	2.00	3.00	4.00
MORE MODERN SOUNDS IN COUNTRY & WESTERN MUSIC	ABC Paramount (M) ABC435	2.00	3.00	4.00
MORE MODERN SOUNDS IN COUNTRY & WESTERN MUSIC	ABC Paramount (S) ABCS435	2.00	3.00	4.00
MY KIND OF JAZZ PART 3	Crossover (S) 9007	2.00	3.00	4.00
RAY CHARLES	Hollywood (M) 504	5.00	12.50	20.00
RAY CHARLES	Atlantic (EP) EP587	1.50	2.25	4.00
RAY CHARLES AT NEWPORT	Atlantic (M) LP1289	2.50	3.75	5.00
RAY CHARLES DEDICATED TO YOU	ABC Paramount (M) ABC355	2.00	3.00	4.00
RAY CHARLES DEDICATED TO YOU	ABC Paramount (S) ABCS355	2.00	3.00	4.00
RAY CHARLES GREATEST HITS	ABC Paramount (M) ABC415	2.00	3.00	4.00
RAY CHARLES GREATEST HITS	ABC Paramount (S) ABCS415	2.00	3.00	4.00
RAY CHARLES IN PERSON	Atlantic (M) 8039	3.00	7.50	20.00
RAY CHARLES LIVE IN CONCERT	ABC/Paramount (M) ABC500	2.00	3.00	4.00
RAY CHARLES LIVE IN CONCERT	ABC/Paramount (S) ABCS500	2.00	3.00	4.00
RAY CHARLES STORY, VOL. 1	Atlantic (M) 8063	3.00	6.00	9.00
RAY CHARLES STORY, VOL. 2	Atlantic (M) 8064	3.00	6.00	9.00
RAY CHARLES STORY, VOLS. 1 & 2	Atlantic (S) 2-900	4.00	6.00	8.00
RAY CHARLES STORY, Vol. 4	Atlantic (M) 8094	3.00	6.00	9.00
RAY CHARLES STORY, Vol. 4	Atlantic (S) 8094	3.00	6.00	9.00
RAY'S MOODS	ABC (M) 550	2.00	3.00	4.00
RAY'S MOODS	ABC (S) 550	2.00	3.00	4.00
RENAISSANCE	Crossover (S) 9005	2.00	3.00	4.00
ROCK AND ROLL	Atlantic (M) 8006	5.00	12.50	20.00
ROCK WITH RAY CHARLES	Atlantic (EP) EPS607	1.50	2.25	3.00
SINGING THROUGH THE SEASONS	MGM (M) E-3797	3.00	4.50	6.00
SOUL BROTHERS (With Milt Jackson)	Atlantic (M) LP1279	4.00	6.00	8.00
SOUL BROTHERS (With Milt Jackson)	Atlantic (M) 1360	2.50	3.75	5.00
SOUL MEETING (With Milt Jackson)	Atlantic (S) 1360	2.50	3.75	5.00
SWEET AND SOUR TEARS	ABC/Paramount (M) ABC480	2.00	3.00	4.00
SWEET AND SOUR TEARS	ABC/Paramount (S) ABCS 480	2.00	3.00	4.00
THROUGH THE EYES OF LOVE	ABC (S) 765	2.00	3.00	4.00
A 25TH ANNIVERSARY IN SHOW BUSINESS SALUTE TO RAY CHARLES	ABC (S) ABCH731	3.00	4.00	6.00
WHAT'D I SAY	Atlantic (M) 8029	4.00	10.00	16.00
YES INDEED!	Atlantic (M) 8025	4.00	10.00	16.00

CHARLES RIVER VALLEY BOYS

TITLE	LABEL & NO.	GOOD	VERY GOOD	NEAR MINT
BEATLE COUNTRY	Elektra (S) 74006	4.00	8.00	12.00

CHARLES, Tina

TITLE	LABEL & NO.	GOOD	VERY GOOD	NEAR MINT
I LOVE TO LOVE	Columbia (S) PC 34424	2.00	3.00	4.00
RENDEZVOUS	Columbia (S) PC 34807	2.00	3.00	4.00

CHARLIE

TITLE	LABEL & NO.	GOOD	VERY GOOD	NEAR MINT
FANTASY GIRLS	Columbia (S) PC 34081	2.00	3.00	4.00
LINES	Janus (S) JXS 7036	2.00	3.00	4.00
NO SECOND CHANCE	Janus (S) JXS 7032	2.00	3.00	4.00

CHARMS, Featuring Otis Williams

TITLE	LABEL & NO.	GOOD	VERY GOOD	NEAR MINT
CHARMS VOL 2, THE	King (EP) EP364	3.00	7.50	12.00
HITS	King (EP) EP385	3.00	7.50	12.00
HITS BY THE CHARMS	King (EP) EP357	3.00	7.50	12.00
OTIS WILLIAMS & THE CHARMS	King LP 570	17.00	34.00	51.00
(The bootleg of this album has a dark red cover)				
THIS IS OTIS WILLIAMS & THE CHARMS	King (M) LP614	9.00	22.50	36.00
Also see WILLIAMS, Otis				

CHARTS

TITLE	LABEL & NO.	GOOD	VERY GOOD	NEAR MINT
GREATEST HITS	Lost Nite (M) LNLP 138	4.00	6.00	8.00

CHASE

TITLE	LABEL & NO.	GOOD	VERY GOOD	NEAR MINT
CHASE/ENNEA	Epic (S) BG-33737	2.50	3.75	5.00
PURE MUSIC	Epic (S) KE-32572	2.50	3.75	5.00
PURE MUSIC	Epic (Q) EQ-32572	2.50	3.75	5.00

CHASE, Lincoln

TITLE	LABEL & NO.	GOOD	VERY GOOD	NEAR MINT
THE EXPLOSIVE LINCOLN CHASE	Liberty (M) LRP3076	5.00	12.50	20.00

CHECKER, Chubby

TITLE	LABEL & NO.	GOOD	VERY GOOD	NEAR MINT
ALL THE HITS	Parkway (M) P7014	3.00	6.00	9.00
BEACH PARTY	Parkway (M) P7030	2.00	4.00	6.00
BEACH PARTY	Parkway (S) SP7030	3.00	6.00	9.00
BIGGEST HITS	Parkway (M) P7022	2.00	4.00	6.00
BIGGEST HITS	Parkway (S) SP7022	3.00	6.00	9.00
CHUBBY'S FOLK ALBUM	Parkway (M) P7040	2.00	4.00	6.00
CHUBBY'S FOLK ALBUM	Parkway (S) SP7040	3.00	6.00	9.00
CHUBBY CHECKER	Parkway (M) 5001	4.00	8.00	12.00
CHUBBY CHECKER DISCOTEQUE	Parkway (M) P7045	2.00	4.00	6.00
CHUBBY CHECKER DISCOTEQUE	Parkway (S) SP7045	3.00	6.00	9.00
CHUBBY CHECKER GREATEST HITS	Abkco (S) 4219	3.00	4.50	6.00
DON'T KNOCK THE TWIST (Soundtrack)	Parkway (M) P7011	3.00	6.00	9.00
FOR TEEN TWISTERS ONLY	Parkway (M) P 7009	3.00	6.00	9.00
FOR TWISTERS ONLY	Parkway (M) P 7002	4.00	8.00	12.00
IN PERSON	Parkway (M) P7026	3.00	6.00	9.00
IN PERSON	Parkway (S) SP7026	3.00	6.00	9.00
IT'S PONY TIME	Parkway (M) P 7003	4.00	8.00	12.00
LET'S LIMBO SOME MORE	Parkway (M) P 7027	2.00	4.00	6.00
LET'S LIMBO SOME MORE	Parkway (S) SP7027	3.00	6.00	9.00
LET'S TWIST AGAIN	Parkway (M) P 7004	4.00	8.00	12.00

(M) Mono (S) Stereo (EP) Extended Play (Q) Quad (RI) Re-issued

TITLE	LABEL & NO.	GOOD	VERY GOOD	NEAR MINT
LIMBO PARTY	Parkway (M) P7020	2.00	4.00	6.00
LIMBO PARTY	Parkway (S) SP7020	3.00	6.00	9.00
TWIST WITH CHUBBY CHECKER	Parkway (M) P7001	4.00	8.00	12.00
TWISTIN' ROUND THE WORLD	Parkway (M) P 7008	4.00	8.00	12.00
YOUR TWIST PARTY	Parkway (M) P 7007	4.00	8.00	12.00

CHECKER, Chubby & Bobby Rydell

TITLE	LABEL & NO.	GOOD	VERY GOOD	NEAR MINT
CHUBBY CHECKER & BOBBY RYDELL	Cameo (M) C1013	2.50	5.00	7.50
GOLDEN HITS	Cameo (M) C1063	4.00	6.00	

CHECKER, Chubby & Dee Dee Sharp

TITLE	LABEL & NO.	GOOD	VERY GOOD	NEAR MINT
DOWN TO EARTH	Cameo (M) C1029	2.50	5.00	7.50
DOWN TO EARTH	Cameo (S) SC1029	3.00	6.50	10.00

CHECKMATES LTD.

TITLE	LABEL & NO.	GOOD	VERY GOOD	NEAR MINT
F/S/O	Rustic (M) RR2004	2.50	3.75	5.00
LIVE AT CAESAR'S PALACE	Capitol (M) T2840	2.50	3.75	5.00
LIVE AT CAESAR'S PALACE	Capitol (S) ST2840	3.50	5.25	7.00
LIVE AT HARVEY'S TOO MUCH	Ikon (M) IER121	2.50	3.75	5.00
LOVE IS ALL I HAVE TO GIVE	A&M (S) SP 4183	4.00	6.00	8.00

CHEECH & CHONG

TITLE	LABEL & NO.	GOOD	VERY GOOD	NEAR MINT
BIG BAMBU	Ode (S) SP 77014	2.50	3.75	5.00
CHEECH & CHONG (RI)	Epic/Ode (S) PE 34947	2.00	3.00	4.00
CHEECH & CHONG	Ode (S) SP 77010	2.50	3.75	5.00
CHEECH & CHONG'S WEDDING ALBUM (RI)	Epic/Ode (S) PE 34954	2.00	3.00	4.00
CHEECH & CHONG'S WEDDING ALBUM	Ode (S) SP 77025	2.50	3.75	5.00
LOS COCHINOS (RI)	Epic/Ode (S) PE 34951	2.00	3.00	4.00
LOS COCHINOS	Ode (S) SP 77019	2.50	3.75	5.00
SLEEPING BEAUTY (RI)	Epic/Ode (S) PE 34960	2.00	3.00	4.00
SLEEPING BEAUTY	Ode (S) SP 77040	2.50	3.75	5.00

CHEERS

TITLE	LABEL & NO.	GOOD	VERY GOOD	NEAR MINT
BAZOOM	Capitol (EP) 1-584	2.00	5.00	8.00

CHENIER, Clifton

TITLE	LABEL & NO.	GOOD	VERY GOOD	NEAR MINT
BAYOU BLUES	Specialty (S) 2139	5.00	7.50	10.00
BON TON ROULET	Arhoolie (M) F1031	3.50	5.25	7.00
CLIFTON CHENIER LIVE	Arhoolie (M) 1059	3.50	5.00	7.00
CLIFTON'S CAJUN BLUES	Phophesy (S) PRS1004	3.00	4.50	6.00
LOUISIANA BLUES AND ZYDECO	Arhoolie (M) F1024	3.50	5.25	7.00
VERY BEST OF	Blue Thumb (S) BTS 15	3.00	4.50	6.00

CHER

TITLE	LABEL & NO.	GOOD	VERY GOOD	NEAR MINT
ALL I REALLY WANT TO DO	Imperial (M) LP9292	3.00	4.50	6.00
ALL I REALLY WANT TO DO	Imperial (S) LP 12292	4.00	6.00	8.00
BACKSTAGE	Imperial (S) LP12373	3.00	4.50	6.00
BITTERSWEET WHITE LIGHT	MCA (S) 2101	2.50	3.75	5.00
CHER	Imperial (M) 9320	3.00	4.50	6.00
CHER	Imperial (S) 12320	3.00	4.50	6.00
CHER	Kapp (S) KS 3649	3.00	4.50	6.00
CHER	United Artists (S) UXS 88	3.50	5.25	7.00
CHER, VOL. 2	United Artists (S) UXS 94	3.50	5.25	7.00
CHERISHED	Warner Bros. (S) BS 3046	2.00	3.00	4.00
DARK LADY	MCA (S) 2113	2.50	3.75	5.00
FOXY LADY	Kapp (S) KS 5514	3.00	4.50	6.00
GOLDEN GREATS	Imperial (S) LP12406	3.00	4.50	6.00
GREATEST HITS	MCA (S) 2127	2.50	3.75	5.00
HALF BREED	MCA (S) 2104	3.00	4.50	6.00
THE SONNY SIDE OF CHER	Imperial (M) LP9301	3.00	4.50	6.00
THE SONNY SIDE OF CHER	Imperial (S) LP12301	4.00	6.00	8.00
3614 JACKSON HIGHWAY	Atco (S) SD33-298	2.50	3.75	5.00
VERY BEST OF CHER	United Artists (S) UA-LA237	3.00	4.50	6.00
VERY BEST OF CHER (RI OF UA 237)	United Artists (S) UA-LA377	2.50	3.75	5.00
VERY BEST OF CHER, VOL. 2	United Artists (S) UA-LA435	2.50	3.75	5.00
WITH LOVE	Imperial (M) LP 9358	3.00	4.50	6.00
WITH LOVE	Imperial (S) LP 12358	3.00	4.50	6.00
Also see SONNY & CHER				

CHEROKEE

TITLE	LABEL & NO.	GOOD	VERY GOOD	NEAR MINT
CHEROKEE	ABC (S) ABCS719	4.00	6.00	8.00

TITLE	LABEL & NO.	GOOD	VERY GOOD	NEAR MINT
CHERRY PEOPLE				
CHERRY PEOPLE	Heritage (S) HTS35,000	2.50	3.75	5.00
CHESS, Tubby and his Candy Stripe Twisters				
DO THE TWIST	Grand Prix (M)K187	2.50	5.00	7.50
CHEVRONS				
SING A LONG ROCK AND ROLL	Time (M) T10008	3.00	6.00	9.00
CHIC				
CHIC	Atlantic (S) SD 19153	2.00	3.00	4.00
CHICAGO				
CHICAGO	Columbia (S) KGP 24	3.00	4.50	6.00
CHICAGO	Columbia (Q) GQ 33258	3.50	5.25	7.00
CHICAGO AT CARNEGIE HALL	Columbia (S) C4X 30865	5.00	7.50	10.00
CHICAGO AT CARNEGIE HALL	Columbia (Q) CQ 30865	6.00	9.00	12.00
CHICAGO TRANSIT AUTHORITY	Columbia (S) GP 8	3.00	4.50	6.00
CHICAGO TRANSIT AUTHORITY	Columbia (Q) GQ 33255	3.50	5.25	7.00
CHICAGO III	Columbia (S) C2 30110	3.00	4.50	6.00
CHICAGO III	Columbia (Q) C2Q 30110	3.50	5.25	7.00
CHICAGO V	Columbia (S) KC 31102	2.50	3.75	5.00
CHICAGO V	Columbia (Q) CQ 31102	3.00	4.50	6.00
CHICAGO VI	Columbia (S) KC 32400	2.00	3.00	4.00
CHICAGO VI	Columbia (Q) CQ 32400	2.50	3.75	5.00
CHICAGO VII	Columbia (S) C2 32810	2.50	3.75	5.00
CHICAGO VII	Columbia (Q) C2Q 32810	3.00	4.50	6.00
CHICAGO VIII	Columbia (S) PC 33100	2.00	3.00	4.00
CHICAGO VIII	Columbia (Q) PCQ 33100	2.50	3.75	5.00
CHICAGO X	Columbia (S) PC 34200	2.00	3.00	4.00
CHICAGO X	Columbia (Q) PCQ 34200	2.50	3.75	5.00
CHICAGO XI	Columbia (S) JC 34860	2.00	3.00	4.00
GREATEST HITS	Columbia (S) PC 33900	2.00	3.00	4.00
GREATEST HITS	Columbia (Q) PCQ 33900	2.50	3.75	5.00
CHICAGO BLUES ALLSTARS				
LOADED WITH THE BLUES	BASF (M) 20707	4.00	6.00	8.00
CHICKEN SHACK				
ACCEPT CHICKEN SHACK	Blue Horizon (M) BH4809	3.50	5.25	7.00
FORTY BLUE FINGERS, FRESHLY PACKED AND READY TO SERVE	Epic (S) BN26414	3.50	5.25	7.00
O.K. KEN?	Blue Horizon (M) BH7705	3.50	5.25	7.00
100 TON CHICKEN	Blue Horizon (M) BH 7706	3.50	5.25	7.00
CHICORY				
SON OF MY FATHER	Epic (S) 31374	2.50	3.75	5.00
CHIFFONS				
EVERYTHING YOU ALWAYS WANTED TO HEAR BY THE CHIFFONS	Laurie (S) LES4001	3.00	4.50	6.00
HE'S SO FINE	Laurie (M) LLP2018	5.00	10.00	15.00
MY SECRET LOVE	BT Puppy (S) BTPS 1011	6.00	12.00	18.00
ONE FINE DAY	Laurie (M) LLP 2020	5.00	10.00	15.00
SWEET TALKIN' GUY	Laurie (M) LLP 2036	4.00	8.00	12.00
SWEET TALKIN' GUY	Laurie (S) SLP 2036	5.00	10.00	15.00
CHILDREN				
REBIRTH	Cinema (M) CLP. #1	5.00	7.50	10.00
REBIRTH	Atco (S) SD33-271	3.50	5.25	7.00
CHILDREN OF THE NIGHT				
DINNER WITH DRAC	Pip (M) 6 822	8.00	12.00	16.00
CHI-LITES				
CHI-LITES	Brunswick (S) 754197	2.50	3.75	5.00
GIVE MORE POWER TO THE PEOPLE	Brunswick (S) 754170	2.50	3.75	5.00
GREATEST HITS	Brunswick (S) 754184	2.50	3.75	5.00
HALF A LOVE	Brunswick (S) 754204	2.50	3.75	5.00
I LIKE YOUR LOVIN	Brunswick (S) 754165	2.50	3.75	5.00
LETTER TO MYSELF	Brunswick (S) 754188	2.50	3.75	5.00
TOBY	Brunswick (S) 754200	2.50	3.75	5.00
CHILLIWACK				
ALL OVER YOU	A&M (S) 4375	2.00	3.00	4.00
DREAMS, DREAMS, DREAMS	Mushroom (S) MRS 5006	2.50	3.75	5.00
ROCKERBOX	Sire (S) D-7511	2.50	3.75	5.00
CHIPMUNKS (Featuring David Seville)				
ALVIN'S HARMONICA	Liberty (EP) 1007	2.00	4.00	6.00
ALVIN SHOW	Liberty (M) LRP3209	4.00	8.00	12.00
ALVIN SHOW	Liberty (M) LRP3209	5.00	10.00	15.00
CHIPMUNKS A-GO-GO	Liberty (M) LRP3424	4.00	8.00	12.00
CHIPMUNKS A-GO-GO	Liberty (S) LST7424	5.00	10.00	15.00
CHIPMUNKS SING THE BEATLES	Liberty (M) LRP3388	4.00	8.00	12.00
CHIPMUNKS SING THE BEATLES	Liberty (S) LST7388	5.00	10.00	15.00
CHIPMUNKS SING WITH CHILDREN	Liberty (M) LRP3405	4.00	8.00	12.00
CHIPMUNKS SING WITH CHILDREN	Liberty (S) LST7405	5.00	10.00	15.00
CHIPMUNK SONGBOOK	Liberty (M) LRP3229	4.00	8.00	12.00
CHIPMUNK SONGBOOK	Liberty (S) LST7229	5.00	10.00	15.00
CHIPMUNK SONGBOOK	Liberty (EP) 1015	2.00	4.00	6.00
CHRISTMAS TIME	Liberty (EP) 1017	2.00	4.00	6.00

TITLE	LABEL & NO.	GOOD	VERY GOOD	NEAR MINT
CHRISTMAS WITH THE CHIPMUNKS	Liberty (M) LRP3334	4.00	8.00	12.00
CHRISTMAS WITH THE CHIPMUNKS	Liberty (S) LST7334	5.00	10.00	15.00
CHRISTMAS WITH THE CHIPMUNKS	Liberty (M) LRP3256	4.00	8.00	12.00
CHRISTMAS WITH THE CHIPMUNKS	Liberty (S) LST7256	5.00	10.00	12.00
CHRISTMAS WITH THE CHIPMUNKS	Liberty (EP) 1016	2.00	4.00	6.00
CHRISTMAS WITH THE CHIPMUNKS	United Artists (S) UA-LA 352	2.00	3.00	4.00
DOCTOR DOOLITTLE	Sunset (M) 1300	4.00	6.00	9.00
DOCTOR DOOLITTLE	Sunset (S) 5300	3.00	6.00	9.00
LET'S ALL SING WITH THE CHIPMUNKS	Liberty (M) LRP3132	5.00	10.00	15.00
LET'S ALL SING WITH THE CHIPMUNKS (Red Plastic)	Liberty (M) LRP3132	10.00	15.00	20.00
LET'S ALL SING WITH THE CHIPMUNKS	Liberty (S) LST7132	6.00	12.00	18.00
SING ALONG WITH THE CHIPMUNKS	Liberty (M) LRP3159	4.00	8.00	12.00
SING ALONG WITH THE CHIPMUNKS	Liberty (S) LST7159	5.00	10.00	15.00
VERY BEST OF THE CHIPMUNKS	United Artists (S) UA-LA 570	2.00	3.00	`4.00

Also see SEVILLE, David

CHOCOLATE WATCH BAND				
THE INNER MYSTIQUE	Tower (S) ST 5106	12.00	24.00	36.00
NO WAY OUT	Tower (M) T5096	5.00	10.00	15.00
NO WAY OUT	Tower (S) ST 5096	6.00	12.00	18.00
ONE STEP BEYOND	Tower (S) ST5153	6.00	12.00	18.00

CHOIR				
THE CHOIR	Bomp (M) EP104	1.50	2.25	3.00

Also see RASPBERRIES

(M) Mono (S) Stereo (EP) Extended Play (Q) Quad (RI) Re-issued

CHORDETTES

		GOOD	VERY GOOD	NEAR MINT
ALL THE VERY BEST OF THE CHORDETTES	Barnaby (M) BR4003	3.00	4.50	6.00
CHORDETTES, THE	Cadence (M) LP3001	4.00	8.00	12.00
CHORDETTES, THE	Cadence (EP) EP101	2.00	4.00	6.00
CHORDETTES, THE	Cadence (EP) CEP102	2.00	4.00	6.00
CHORDETTES	Cadence (EP) CEP-115	2.00	4.00	6.00
CHORDETTES, THE	Columbia (M) CL2519	3.00	6.00	9.00
CHORDETTES	Harmony (M) HL-7164	2.00	4.00	6.00
CHORDETTES SING NEVER ON SUNDAY	Cadence (M) 3056	3.00	6.00	9.00
CHORDETTES SING NEVER ON SUNDAY	Cadence (S) 25056	4.00	8.00	12.00
CLOSE HARMONY	Cadence (M) CLP1002	3.00	6.00	9.00
HARMONY ENCORES	Columbia (M) CL6218	3.00	6.00	9.00
HARMONY ENCORES	Columbia (EP) B309	2.00	4.00	6.00
HARMONY TIME	Columbia (M) CL6111	3.00	6.00	9.00
HARMONY TIME	Columbia (EP) B201	2.00	4.00	6.00
HARMONY TIME VOL 2	Columbia (M) CL6170	3.00	6.00	9.00
HARMONY TIME VOL 2	Columbia (EP) B241	2.00	4.00	6.00
LISTEN	Columbia (M) CL956	3.00	6.00	9.00
YOUR REQUESTS	Columbia (M) CL6285	3.00	6.00	9.00
YOUR REQUESTS	Columbia (EP) B401	2.00	4.00	6.00

CHOSEN FEW

CHOSEN FEW	RCA (S) LSP4242	3.00	4.50	6.00
TAKIN ALL THE LOVE I CAN	Maple (M) 6000	5.00	10.00	15.00

CHRISTIE, Lou

LIGHTNIN' STRIKES	MGM (M) E4360	2.00	3.00	4.00
LIGHTNING STRIKES	MGM (S) E4360	3.00	4.50	6.00
LOU CHRISTIE	Roulette (M) R25208	4.00	8.00	12.00
LOU CHRISTIE	Roulette (S) SR25208	5.00	10.00	15.00
LOU CHRISTIE PAINTER OF HITS	MGM (M) E4394	2.00	3.00	4.00
LOU CHRISTIE PAINTER OF HITS	MGM (S) SE4394	3.00	4.50	6.00
LOU CHRISTIE STRIKES AGAIN	Colpix (M) CP 4001	3.00	4.50	6.00
LOU CHRISTIE STRIKES AGAIN	Colpix (CPS 4001	4.00	6.00	8.00
LOU CHRISTIE STRIKES BACK	CO & CE (M) LP1231	3.00	4.50	6.00
LOU CHRISTIE STRIKES BACK	CO & CE (S) LP1231	4.00	6.00	8.00
STARRING LOU CHRISTIE AND THE CLASSICS	Spinorama (M) M173	2.00	3.00	4.00
STARRING LOU CHRISTIE AND THE CLASSICS	Spinorama (S) S173	2.00	3.00	4.00

CHRISTIE

YELLOW RIVER	Epic (S) E30403	2.50	3.75	5.00

CHRISTMAS, Keith

BRIGHTER DAY	Manticore (S) MA6-503S1	2.50	3.75	5.00
KEITH CHRISTMAS	Polydor (S) PD24-2511	3.50	5.25	7.00

CHRISTOPHER CLOUD (Tommy Boyd)

BLOWIN' AWAY	Chelsea (S) BCL-10234	3.00	4.50	6.00

CHRISTOPHER MILK

CHRISTOPHER MILK	United Artists (EP) SP66	2.50	3.75	5.00
SOME PEOPLE WILL DRINK ANYTHING	Reprise (S)(MS2111	3.00	4.50	6.00

CHRISTY, June

COOL SCHOOL	Capitol (M) T 1398	2.00	4.00	6.00
JUNE'S GOT RHYTHM	Capitol (M) T 1076	2.00	4.00	6.00
SOMETHING COOL	Capitol (M) T 516	4.00	6.00	8.00

CHRYSALIS

CHRYSALIS	MGM (S) SE4547	2.50	3.75	5.00

CHUNKY, NOVI & ERNIE

CHUNKY, NOVI & ERNIE	Reprise (S) MS 2146	2.50	3.75	5.00
CHUNKY, NOVI & ERNIE	Warner Bros. (S) BS 3030	2.00	3.00	4.00

CHURLS

CHURCHILL	Attarack (M) AT5003	2.50	3.75	5.00
SEND ME NO FLOWERS	A & M (S) SP4233	3.00	4.50	6.00
CHURLS, THE	A & M (S) SP4169	3.00	4.50	6.00

CIRCUS

CIRCUS	Metromedia (S) LPS7401	6.00	9.00	12.00

CIRCUS MAXIMUS

TITLE	LABEL & NO.	GOOD	VERY GOOD	NEAR MINT
CIRCUS MAXIMUS	Vanguard (S) VSD79260	3.00	4.50	6.00
NEVER LAND REVISITED	Vanguard (S) VSD 79274	3.50	5.25	7.00

CITY

NOW THAT EVERYTHINGS BEEN SAID	Ode (M) Z1244012	10.00	20.00	30.00

CLANTON, Jimmy

BEST OF JIMMY CLANTON	Philips (M) PHM 200-154	4.00	8.00	12.00
BEST OF JIMMY CLANTON	Philips (S) PHS 600-154	5.00	10.00	15.00
I'M ALWAYS CHASING RAINBOWS	Ace (EP) 103EP	2.00	5.00	8.00
JIMMY CLANTON AND BRISTOW HOPPER	Design (M) DLP176	4.00	6.00	8.00
JIMMY'S BIG FOUR	Top Rank (EP) 10087	3.00	7.50	12.00
JIMMY'S BLUE	Ace (M) M1008	7.00	17.50	28.00
JIMMY'S HAPPY	Ace (M) 1007	7.00	17.50	28.00
JIMMY'S HAPPY/JIMMY'S BLUE	Ace (M) DLP100	9.00	22.50	36.00
JUST A DREAM	Ace (M) 1001	8.00	20.00	32.00
JUST A DREAM	Ace (EP) 101EP	2.00	5.00	8.00
MY BEST TO YOU	Ace (M) 1011	7.00	17.50	28.00
TEENAGE MILLIONAIRE	Ace (M) 1014	8.00	20.00	32.00
TEENAGE MILLIONAIRE	Ace (EP) 642	2.00	5.00	8.00
THINKING OF YOU	Ace (EP) 102EP	2.00	5.00	8.00
VENUS IN BLUE JEANS	Ace (M) 1026	7.00	17.50	28.00

CLAPTON, Eric

CLAPTON	Polydor (S) 24-5526	3.00	4.50	6.00
E.C. WAS HERE	RSO (S) 4809	3.50	5.25	7.00
ERIC CLAPTON	Atco (S) SD33-329	3.00	4.50	6.00
ERIC CLAPTON	RSO (S) 3008	2.50	3.75	5.00
ERIC CLAPTON AT HIS BEST	Polydor (S) 24-3503	3.00	4.50	6.00
461 OCEAN BOULEVARD	RSO (S) 4801	3.50	5.25	7.00
461 OCEAN BOULEVARD	RSO (Q) QD-4801	3.00	4.50	6.00
461 OCEAN BOULEVARD (RI)	RSO (S) 3023	2.50	3.75	5.00
HISTORY OF ERIC CLAPTON	Atco (S) 803	4.00	6.00	8.00
NO REASON TO CRY	RSO (S) 3004	3.00	4.50	6.00
RAINBOW CONCERT	RSO (S) S0877	3.00	4.50	6.00
SLOWHAND	RSO (S) 3030	3.00	4.50	6.00
THERE'S ONE IN EVERY CROWD	RSO (S) 4806	3.50	5.25	7.00
THERE'S ONE IN EVERY CROWD	RSO (Q) QD-4806	3.00	4.50	6.00

Also see CREAM, DEREK & THE DOMINOES

CLARK, Chris

CC RIDES AGAIN	Weed (M) 801	3.00	4.50	6.00
SOUL SOUNDS	Motown (M) 664	3.00	6.00	9.00

CLARK, Claudine

PARTY LIGHTS	Chancellor (M) CHL5029	5.00	10.00	15.00

CLARK, Dave, Five

AMERICAN TOUR	Epic (M) LN24117	4.00	6.00	8.00
AMERICAN TOUR	Epic (S) BN26117	3.00	4.50	6.00
BEAT BATTLE OF THE WORLD (DC5 Versus N. Sedaka, Dick Dale, The Tottenhammers)	Groovemaster (M) BR140	5.00	10.00	15.00
CHAQUITA IN YOUR HEART	Crown (S) CST473	4.00	8.00	12.00

(M) Mono (S) Stereo (EP) Extended Play (Q) Quad (RI) Re-issued

TITLE	LABEL & NO.	GOOD	VERY GOOD	NEAR MINT
CHAQUITA IN YOUR HEART	Cortleigh (M) 1073	5.00	10.00	15.00
COAST TO COAST	Epic (M) LN24128	4.00	6.00	8.00
COAST TO COAST	Epic (S) BN26128	3.00	4.50	6.00
DAVE CLARK FIVE RETURN	Epic (M) LN24104	4.00	6.00	8.00
DAVE CLARK FIVE RETURN	Epic (S) BN26104	3.00	4.50	6.00
DAVE CLARK FIVE'S GREATEST HITS	Epic (M) LN24185	4.00	6.00	8.00
DAVE CLARK FIVE'S GREATEST HITS	Epic (S) BN26185	3.00	4.50	6.00
THE DC5 PLAYBACKS	Crown (M) CLP5400	4.00	8.00	12.00
EVERYBODY KNOWS	Epic (M) LN24354	4.00	6.00	8.00
EVERYBODY KNOWS	Epic (S) BN26354	3.00	4.50	6.00
5 BY 5	Epic (M) LN24236	4.00	6.00	8.00
5 BY 5	Epic (S) BN26236	3.00	4.50	6.00
GLAD ALL OVER (Cover with Instruments)	Epic (M) LN24093	4.00	6.00	8.00
GLAD ALL OVER (Cover with Instruments)	Epic (S) BN26093	3.00	4.50	6.00
GLAD ALL OVER (Cover without Instruments)	Epic (M) LN24093	5.00	7.50	10.00
GLAD ALL OVER (Cover without Instruments)	Epic (S) BN26093	4.00	6.00	8.00
HAVING A WILD WEEKEND (Soundtrack)	Epic (M) LN24162	4.00	6.00	8.00
HAVING A WILD WEEKEND (Soundtrack)	Epic (S) BN26162	3.00	4.50	6.00
I LIKE IT LIKE THAT	Epic (M) LN24178	4.00	6.00	8.00
I LIKE IT LIKE THAT	Epic (S) BN26178	3.00	4.50	6.00
IT'S HAPPENING	Custom (S) CS1098	3.00	6.00	9.00
IT'S HERE LUV (Ed Rudy Interview Lp)	INS Radio News (M) LL1006	6.00	12.00	18.00
MORE GREATEST HITS	Epic (M) LN24221	4.00	6.00	8.00
MORE GREATEST HITS	Epic (S) BN26221	3.00	4.50	6.00
SATISFIED WITH YOU	Epic (M) LN24212	4.00	6.00	8.00
SATISFIED WITH YOU	Epic (S) BN26212	3.00	4.50	6.00
TRY TOO HARD	Epic (M) LN24198	4.00	6.00	8.00
TRY TOO HARD	Epic (S) BN26198	3.00	4.50	6.00
WEEKEND IN LONDON	Epic (M) LN24139	4.00	6.00	8.00
WEEKEND IN LONDON	Epic (S) BN26139	3.00	4.50	6.00
YOU GOT WHAT IT TAKES	Epic (M) LN24312	4.00	6.00	8.00
YOU GOT WHAT IT TAKES	Epic (S) BN26312	3.00	4.50	6.00

CLARK, Dee

BEST OF DEE CLARK	Vee Jay (M) 1047	5.00	12.50	20.00
DEE CLARK	Abner (M) LP2000	6.00	15.00	24.00
DEE CLARK	Abner (S) 2000	7.00	17.50	28.00
DEE CLARK	Vee Jay(M) 1028	5.00	12.50	20.00
HOLD ON, IT'S DEE CLARK	Vee Jay (M) 1037	5.00	12.50	20.00
HOW ABOUT THAT	Abner (M) LP2002	6.00	15.00	24.00
WONDERING	Sunset (S) SUS5217	2.00	4.00	6.00
YOURE LOOKING GOOD	Vee Jay (M) 1019	5.00	12.50	20.00

CLARK, Dick

ALL TIME HITS VOL 2	No Label (EP) No S	1.50	3.75	6.00
ALL TIME HITS VOL 3	No Label (EP) No S	1.50	3.75	6.00
ALL TIME HITS VOL 4	Dr. Pepper Presents (EP)	2.00	5.00	8.00
DANCE WITH DICK CLARK VOL 1	ABC/Paramount (M) ABC258	3.00	7.50	12.00
DANCE WITH DICK CLARK VOL 1	ABC/Paramount (EP) A258	2.00	5.00	8.00
DANCE WITH DICK CLARK VOL 2	ABC/Paramount (M) ABC288	3.00	7.50	12.00
DANCE WITH DICK CLARK VOL 2	ABC/Paramount (EP) B258	2.00	5.00	8.00
DANCE WITH DICK CLARK VOL 3	ABC/Paramount (EP) C258	2.00	5.00	8.00
20 YEARS OF ROCK N'ROLL	Buddah (S) BDS5133-2	2.00	3.00	4.00

CLARK, Doug, and The Hot Nuts

FREAK OUT	Gross (M) GR108	4.00	6.00	8.00
FREAK OUT	Gross (S) LP108	6.00	9.00	12.00
HELL NIGHT	Gross (M) GR107	4.00	6.00	8.00
HOMECOMING	Gross (M) GR103	4.00	6.00	8.00
NUTS TO YOU	Gross (M) GR101	4.00	6.00	8.00

(M) Mono (S) Stereo (EP) Extended Play (Q) Quad (RI) Re-issued

ON CAMPUS	Gross (M) GR102	4.00	6.00	8.00
PANTY RAID	Gross (M) GR105	4.00	6.00	8.00
RUSH WEEK	Gross (M) GR104	4.00	6.00	8.00
SUMMER SESSION	Gross (M) GR106	4.00	6.00	8.00

CLARK, Gene

EARLY L. A. SESSIONS	Columbia (S) KC31123	3.00	4.50	6.00
GENE CLARK WITH THE GOSDIN BROTHERS	Columbia (M) CL2618	4.00	6.00	8.00
GENE CLARK WITH THE GOSDIN BROTHERS	Columbia (S) CS9418	5.00	7.50	10.00
NO OTHER	Asylum (S) 7E-1016	2.00	3.00	4.00
TWO SIDES TO EVERY STORY	RSO (S) RS-1-3011	2.00	3.00	4.00
WHITE LIGHT	A&M (S) SP 4292	2.50	3.75	5.00

Also see BYRDS

CLARK, Petula

COLOR MY WORLD/WHO AM I	Warner Bros. (M) W 1673	2.00	3.00	4.00
COLOR MY WORLD/WHO AM I	Warner Bros. (S) WS 1673	3.00	4.50	6.00
DOWNTOWN	Warner Brothers (M) W1590	2.00	3.00	4.00
DOWNTOWN	Warner Brothers (S) WS1590	3.00	4.50	6.00
ENGLISH SOUND STARRING PETULA CLARK	Premier (M) PM 9016	2.50	5.00	7.50
ENGLISH SOUND STARRING PETULA CLARK	Premier (S) PS 9016	2.00	4.00	6.00
FINIAN'S RAINBOW (Soundtrack)	Warner Bros. (S) B2550	3.00	4.50	6.00
GREATEST HITS VOL 1	Warner Brothers (S) WS1765	3.00	4.50	6.00
I COULDNT LIVE WITHOUT YOUR LOVE	Warner Brothers (M) W1645	2.00	3.00	4.00
I COULDN'T LIVE WITHOUT YOUR LOVE	Warner Brothers (S) WS1645	3.00	4.50	6.00

TITLE	LABEL & NO.	GOOD	VERY GOOD	NEAR MINT
I KNOW A PLACE	Warner Brothers (M) W 1598	2.00	5.00	7.00
I KNOW A PLACE	Warner Brothers (S) WS1598	3.00	4.50	6.00
IN LOVE	Laurie (M) LLP2032	4.00	8.00	12.00
JUST PET	Warner Bros. (S) WS 1823	3.00	4.50	6.00
MEMPHIS	Warner Bros. (S) WS 1862	3.00	4.50	6.00
MY LOVE	Warner Brothers (M) W1630	2.00	3.00	4.00
MY LOVE	Warner Brothers (S) WS1630	3.00	4.50	6.00
NOW	MGM (S) SE 4859	2.50	3.75	5.00
THE OTHER MAN'S GRASS IS ALWAYS GREENER	Warner Brothers (M) W1719	2.00	3.00	4.00
THE OTHER MAN'S GRASS IS ALWAYS GREENER	Warner Brothers (S) WS1719	3.00	4.50	6.00
PETULA	Warner Brothers (S) WS1743	3.00	4.50	6.00
PETULA CLARK	GNP/Crescendo (S) 2069	4.00	6.00	8.00
PORTRAIT OF PETULA	Warner Bros. (S) WS 1789	3.00	4.50	6.00
THESE ARE MY SONGS	Warner Brothers (M) W1698	2.00	3.00	4.00
THESE ARE MY SONGS	Warner Brothers (S) WS1698	3.00	4.50	6.00
THIS IS PETULA CLARK	Sunset (M) SUM 1101	3.00	4.50	6.00
THIS IS PETULA CLARK	Sunset (S) SUS 5101	4.00	6.00	8.00
UPTOWN WITH PETULA CLARK	Imperial (M) LP9281	4.00	8.00	12.00
UPTOWN WITH PETULA CLARK	Imperial (S) LP12281	5.00	10.00	15.00
WARM & TENDER	Warner Bros. (S) WS 1885	3.00	4.50	6.00
WORLD'S GREATEST INTERNATIONAL HITS	Warner Brothers (M) W 1608	2.00	3.00	4.00
WORLD'S GREATEST INTERNATIONAL HITS	Warner Brothers (S) WS1608	3.00	4.50	6.00

CLARK, Roy

TITLE	LABEL & NO.	GOOD	VERY GOOD	NEAR MINT
COME LIVE WITH ME	Dot (S) 26010	2.50	3.75	5.00
ENTERTAINER, THE	Dot (S) 2001	2.50	3.75	5.00
HEART TO HEART	Dot (S) DOSD-2041	2.00	3.00	4.00
PAIR OF FIVES	Dot (S) DOSD-2015	2.00	3.00	4.00
ROY CLARK	Dot (S) 2-1040	3.00	4.50	6.00
ROY CLARK, LIVE	Dot (S) 26005	2.50	3.75	5.00
ROY CLARK'S FAMILY ALBUM	Dot (S) 26018	2.00	3.00	4.00
ROY CLARK'S GREATEST HITS	Dot (S) DOSD2030	2.00	3.00	4.00
SO MUCH TO REMEMBER	Capitol (S) SM-11412	2.00	3.00	4.00
SUPERPICKER	Dot (S) 26008	2.50	3.75	5.00

CLARKE, Allan

TITLE	LABEL & NO.	GOOD	VERY GOOD	NEAR MINT
MY REAL NAME IS 'ARNOLD	Epic (S) KE-31757	2.50	3.75	5.00

Also see HOLLIES

CLASSICS IV

TITLE	LABEL & NO.	GOOD	VERY GOOD	NEAR MINT
DENNIS YOST & THE CLASSICS IV	MGM South (S) MSH702	3.00	4.50	6.00
GOLDEN GREATS VOL 1	Imperial (S) LP16000	3.50	5.25	7.00
MAMAS AND PAPAS/SOUL TRAIN	Imperial (S) 12407	4.00	6.00	8.00
SPOOKY	Imperial (S) LP12371	4.00	6.00	8.00
TRACES	Imperial (S) LP12429	4.00	6.00	8.00
VERY BEST OF THE CLASSICS IV	United Artists (S) UA-LA446	2.50	3.75	5.00

CLAY, Cassius Marcellos Jr.

TITLE	LABEL & NO.	GOOD	VERY GOOD	NEAR MINT
I AM THE GREATEST	Columbia (M) CL2093	10.00	15.00	20.00
I AM THE GREATEST	Columbia (S) CS8893	12.00	18.00	24.00

CLAY, Judy and Billy Vera

TITLE	LABEL & NO.	GOOD	VERY GOOD	NEAR MINT
STORYBOOK CHILDREN	Atlantic (M) 8174	2.50	3.75	5.00
STORYBOOK CHILDREN	Atlantic (S) 8174	3.50	5.25	7.00

CLAYTON, Merry

TITLE	LABEL & NO.	GOOD	VERY GOOD	NEAR MINT
GIMME SHELTER	Ode (S) SP 77001	3.50	5.25	7.00
KEEP YOUR EYE ON THE SPARROW (RI)	Epic/Ode (S) PE 34957	2.00	3.00	4.00
KEEP YOUR EYE ON THE SPARROW	Ode (S) SP 77030	3.00	4.50	6.00
MERRY CLAYTON (RI)	Epic/Ode (S) PE 34948	2.00	3.00	4.00
MERRY CLAYTON	Ode (S) SP 77012	3.00	4.50	6.00

CLAYTON-THOMAS, David

TITLE	LABEL & NO.	GOOD	VERY GOOD	NEAR MINT
DAVID CLAYTON-THOMAS	RCA (S) APL1-0173	3.00	4.50	6.00

Also see BLOOD, SWEAT & TEARS

CLEANLINESS AND GODLINESS SKIFFLE BAND

TITLE	LABEL & NO.	GOOD	VERY GOOD	NEAR MINT
GREATEST HITS	Vanguard (S) VSD79285	4.50	6.75	9.00

CLEAR LIGHT

TITLE	LABEL & NO.	GOOD	VERY GOOD	NEAR MINT
CLEAR LIGHT	Elektra (S) EKS 74011	4.00	6.00	8.00

CLEFTONES

TITLE	LABEL & NO.	GOOD	VERY GOOD	NEAR MINT
FOR SENTIMENTAL REASONS	Gee (M) GLP707	5.00	12.50	20.00
HEART AND SOUL	Gee (S) SGLP705	5.00	12.50	20.00

CLIFF, Jimmy

TITLE	LABEL & NO.	GOOD	VERY GOOD	NEAR MINT
CAN'T GET ENOUGH OF IT	Veep (S) VPS16536	4.00	8.00	12.00
IN CONCERT	Reprise (S) MS 2256	3.00	4.50	6.00
SENSE OF DIRECTION	Sire (S) 7501	2.50	3.75	5.00
STRUGGLING MAN	Island (S) 9235	2.50	3.75	5.00
WONDERFUL WORLD, BEAUTIFUL PEOPLE	A & M (S) SP4251	3.00	4.50	6.00

CLIFFORD, Buzz

TITLE	LABEL & NO.	GOOD	VERY GOOD	NEAR MINT
BABY SITTIN' WITH BUZZ	Columbia (M) CL1616	5.00	10.00	15.00
BABY SITTIN' WITH BUZZ	Columbia (S) CS8416	6.00	12.00	18.00
SEE YOUR WAY CLEAR	Dot (S) DLP 25965	3.50	5.25	7.00

(M) Mono   (S) Stereo   (EP) Extended Play   (Q) Quad   (RI) Re-issued

CLIFFORD, Mike

TITLE	LABEL & NO.	GOOD	VERY GOOD	NEAR MINT
FOR THE LOVE OF MIKE	United Artists (M) UAL3409	3.00	6.00	9.00
FOR THE LOVE OF MIKE	United Artists (S) UAS6409	4.00	8.00	12.00

CLIMAX BLUES BAND

TITLE	LABEL & NO.	GOOD	VERY GOOD	NEAR MINT
FM/LIVE	Sire (S) 7411	4.00	6.00	8.00
FM/LIVE (RI)	Sire (S) 6013	3.00	4.50	6.00
GOLD PLATED	Sire (S) SASD 7523	3.00	4.50	6.00
LOT OF BOTTLE	Sire (S) 6004	2.50	3.75	5.00
#3	Sire (S) SI4901	3.00	4.50	6.00
PLAYS ON	Sire (S) 97023	3.00	4.50	6.00
RICH MAN	Sire (S) 7402	3.50	5.25	7.00
SHINE ON	Sire (S) SRK 6056	2.00	3.00	4.00
STAMP ALBUM (RI)	Sire (S) 6016	2.50	3.75	5.00
STAMP ALBUM	Sire (S) 7507	3.50	5.25	7.00
TIGHTLY KNIT	Sire (S) SI5903	3.00	4.50	6.00
TIGHTLY KNIT (RI)	Sire (S) 6008	2.50	3.75	5.00

CLIMAX CHICAGO BLUES BAND

TITLE	LABEL & NO.	GOOD	VERY GOOD	NEAR MINT
CLIMAX CHICAGO BLUES BAND (Climax Blues Band)	Sire (S) SES97013	3.50	5.25	7.00

CLINE, Patsy

TITLE	LABEL & NO.	GOOD	VERY GOOD	NEAR MINT
IN MEMORIAM	Everest (M) 5217	2.50	3.75	5.00
IN MEMORIAM	Everest (S) 1217	2.50	3.75	5.00
PATSY CLINE	Everest (S) 302	2.50	3.75	5.00
PATSY CLINE	Decca (M) DL8611	5.00	10.00	15.00
PATSY CLINE	Decca (EP) ED2542	1.00	1.50	2.00
PATSY CLINE	Decca (EP) ED2703	1.00	1.50	2.00
PATSY CLINE	Decca (EP) ED2707	1.00	1.50	2.00
PATSY CLINE	Decca (EP) ED2719	1.00	1.50	2.00
PATSY CLINE	Decca (EP) 2757	1.00	1.50	2.00
PATSY CLINE	Decca (EP) 2759	1.00	1.50	2.00
PATSY CLINE	Decca (EP) ED2768	1.00	1.50	2.00
PATSY CLINE	Decca (EP) 2802	1.00	1.50	2.00
PATSY CLINE, ENCORES	Everest (M) BR5204	2.50	3.75	5.00
PATSY CLINE, ENCORES	Everest (S) SD1204	2.50	3.75	5.00
PATSY CLINE (SENTIMENTALLY YOURS)	Decca (M) DL4282	2.50	3.75	5.00
PATSY CLINE (SENTIMENTALLY YOURS)	Decca (S) SL74282	2.50	3.75	5.00
PATSY CLINE SHOWCASE	Decca (M) DL4202	3.00	4.50	6.00
PATSY CLINE SHOWCASE	Decca (S) DL7-4202	3.00	4.50	6.00
PATSY CLINE (THAT'S HOW A HEARTACHE BEGINS)	Decca (M) DL4586	2.00	3.00	4.00
PATSY CLINE (THAT'S HOW A HEARTACHE BEGINS)	Decca (S) DL74586	2.00	3.00	4.00
PORTRAIT OF PATSY CLINE	Decca (M) DL4508	2.00	3.00	4.00
PORTRAIT OF PATSY CLINE	Decca (S) DL74508	2.00	3.00	4.00
PORTRAIT OF PATSY CLINE	Decca (EP) ED2794	1.00	1.50	2.00
REFLECTIONS	Everest (M) 5229	2.50	3.75	5.00
REFLECTIONS	Everest (S) 1229	2.50	3.75	5.00
SOMEDAY YOU'LL WANT ME TO WANT YOU	Decca (EP) ED2770	1.00	1.50	2.00

CLIQUE

TITLE	LABEL & NO.	GOOD	VERY GOOD	NEAR MINT
THE CLIQUE	White Whale (S) WW7126	4.00	6.00	8.00

CLOCKWORK

TITLE	LABEL & NO.	GOOD	VERY GOOD	NEAR MINT
CLOCKWORK	Green Bottle (S) 1013	2.00	3.00	4.00

CLOONEY, Rosemary

TITLE	LABEL & NO.	GOOD	VERY GOOD	NEAR MINT
BLUE ROSE	Columbia (M) CL872	3.00	4.50	6.00
CLOONEY TUNES	Columbia (M) CL969	3.00	4.50	6.00
HEY THERE	Columbia (EP) B1952	1.00	1.50	2.00
MOOD INDIGO	Columbia (M) CL872	3.00	4.50	6.00
RING AROUND ROSIE	Columbia (M) CL1006	3.00	4.50	6.00
RING AROUND ROSIE	Columbia (EP) B10061	1.00	1.50	2.00
RING AROUND ROSIE	Columbia (EP) 10062	1.00	1.50	2.00
RING AROUND ROSIE	Columbia (EP) 10063	1.00	1.50	2.00
ROSIE'S GREATEST HITS	Columbia (M) CL1230	4.00	6.00	8.00
SOPHISTICATED LADY	Columbia (M) CL872	3.00	4.50	6.00
TENDERLY	Columbia (M) CL2525	2.50	3.75	5.00

CLOSE, Del and John Brent

TITLE	LABEL & NO.	GOOD	VERY GOOD	NEAR MINT
HOW TO SPEAK HIP	Mercury (S) SR61245	4.00	6.00	8.00

CLOUDS

TITLE	LABEL & NO.	GOOD	VERY GOOD	NEAR MINT
UP ABOVE OUR HEADS	Deram (S) DES18044	3.00	4.50	6.00
WATERCOLOUR DAYS	Deram (S) DES18058	3.00	4.50	6.00

CLOVER

TITLE	LABEL & NO.	GOOD	VERY GOOD	NEAR MINT
CLOVER	Fantasy (S) 8395	3.00	4.50	6.00

CLOVERS

TITLE	LABEL & NO.	GOOD	VERY GOOD	NEAR MINT
THE CLOVERS	Atlantic (M) 1248	12.00	30.00	48.00
THE CLOVERS	Atlantic (M) 8009	8.00	20.00	32.00
THE CLOVERS	Atlantic (EP) EP590	3.00	7.50	12.00
CLOVER'S DANCE PARTY	Atlantic (S) 8034	9.00	22.50	36.00
IN CLOVER	United Artists (M) UAL3033	6.00	18.00	24.00
IN CLOVER	Poplar (M) 1001	8.00	20.00	32.00
LOVE POTION NUMBER NINE	United Artists (M) UAL3099	5.00	12.50	20.00
LOVE POTION NUMBER NINE	United Artists (S) UAS 6099	6.00	15.00	24.00
THE ORIGINAL LOVE POTION NUMBER NINE	Grand Prix (M) K428	3.00	6.00	9.00
SING GOOD LOVIN'	Atlantic (EP) EP537	3.00	7.50	12.00
SING ONE MINT JULEP	Atlantic (EP) EP504	3.00	7.50	12.00
THEIR GREATEST RECORDINGS	Atco (S) SD33374	3.00	4.50	6.00

TITLE	LABEL & NO.	GOOD	VERY GOOD	NEAR MINT
COASTERS				
COAST ALONG WITH THE COASTERS	Atco (M) 135	3.00	7.50	12.00
COAST ALONG WITH THE COASTERS	Atco (S) 135	4.00	10.00	16.00
COASTERS	Atco (M) 101	5.00	12.50	20.00
COASTERS, THE	Atco (EP) EP4506	3.00	7.50	12.00
COASTERS GREATEST HITS	Atco (M) 111	5.00	12.50	20.00
IT AIN'T SANITARY	Trip (M) TLP8028	3.00	4.50	6.00
KEEP ROCKIN WITH	Atco (EP) EP4502	3.00	7.50	12.00
ON BROADWAY	King (S) 1146	5.00	7.50	10.00
ONE BY ONE	Atco (M) 123	3.00	7.50	12.00
ONE BY ONE	Atco (S) 123	4.00	10.00	16.00
ROCK AND ROLL WITH	Atco (EP) EP4501	3.00	7.50	12.00
THAT'S ROCK AND ROLL	Clarion (M) 605	4.00	6.00	8.00
THEIR GREATEST RECORDINGS (EARLY YEARS)	Atco (M) 371	3.00	4.50	6.00
TOP HITS	Atco (EP) EP4507	3.00	7.50	12.00
COCHISE				
SWALLOW TALES	United Artists (S) UAS5518	4.00	6.00	8.00
SWALLOW TALES	United Artists (EP) SP50	4.00	6.00	8.00
COCHRAN, Eddie				
EDDIE COCHRAN	Liberty (M) LRP3172	9.00	22.50	36.00
EDDIE COCHRAN	Liberty (S) LST-7172	15.00	37.50	60.00
EDDIE COCHRAN LEGENDARY MASTERS SERIES	United Artists (S) UAS9959	5.00	7.50	10.00
NEVER TO BE FORGOTTEN	Liberty (M) LRP3220	3.00	7.50	12.00
SINGIN' TO MY BABY	Liberty (M) LRP3061	15.00	37.50	60.00
SUMMER TIME BLUES	Sunset (M) SUM 1123	4.00	6.00	8.00
SUMMER TIME BLUES	Sunset (S) SUS5123	3.00	4.50	6.00
VERY BEST OF EDDIE COCHRAN	United Artists (M) UA-LA428	2.00	3.00	4.00

COCHRAN, Jackie Lee (Waukeen)				
SWAMP FOX	Rollin Rock (M) LP005	4.00	6.00	8.00
COCHRAN, Wayne				
WAYNE COCHRAN	Chess (M) 1519	3.00	6.00	9.00
WAYNE COCHRAN	Chess (S) 1519	4.00	8.00	12.00

TITLE	LABEL & NO.	GOOD	VERY GOOD	NEAR MINT
COCHRAN, Wayne and His C.C. Riders				
ALIVE AND WELL	King (S) KS1116	3.00	6.00	9.00
HIGH AND RIDIN'	Bethlehem (M) 10002	5.00	10.00	15.00
COCKER, Joe				
I CAN STAND A LITTLE RAIN	A&M (S) SP 3633	2.50	3.75	5.00
JAMAICA SAY YOU WILL	A&M (S) SP 4529	2.00	3.00	4.00
JOE COCKER	A&M (S) SP 4368	2.50	3.75	5.00
JOE COCKER!	A&M (S) SP 4224	3.00	4.50	6.00
JOE COCKER!	A&M (Q) QU 54224	3.00	4.50	6.00
JOE COCKER'S GREATEST HITS	A&M (S) SP 4670	3.00	4.50	6.00
MAD DOGS & ENGLISHMEN	A&M (S) SP 6002	3.50	5.25	7.00
STINGRAY	A&M (S) SP 4574	2.00	3.00	4.00
WITH A LITTLE HELP FROM MY FRIENDS	A&M (S) SP 4182	3.00	4.50	6.00
WITH A LITTLE HELP FROM MY FRIENDS	A&M (Q) QU 54182	3.00	4.50	6.00
CODEN, Run				
AT THE RAVEN GALLERY	Hideout (M) 1003	6.00	12.00	18.00
CODY, Phillip				
LAUGHING SANDWHICH	Kirshner (S) KES113	2.50	3.75	5.00
COE, David Allen				
MYSTERIOUS RHINESTONE COWBOY	Columbia (S) KC-32942	2.00	3.00	4.00
MYSTERIOUS RHINESTONE COWBOY RIDES AGAIN	Columbia (S) KC-33085	2.00	3.00	4.00
COFFEY, Dennis				
ELECTRIC COFFEY	Sussex (S) 7021	2.50	3.75	5.00
INSTANT COFFEY	Sussex (S) 8031	2.50	3.75	5.00
COHEN, Leonard				
LEONARD COHEN, LIVE SONG	Columbia (S) KC-31724	2.50	3.75	5.00
NEW SKIN FOR THE OLD CEREMONY	Columbia (S) KC-33167	2.00	3.00	4.00
COHEN, Sidney				
L S D	Capitol (M) TA02574	2.00	3.00	4.00
L S D	Capitol (S) STA02574	2.50	3.75	5.00
COLD BLOOD				
COLD BLOOD	San Francisco (S) 200	4.00	6.00	8.00
FIRST TASTE OF SIN	Reprise (S) 2074	3.50	5.25	7.00
LYDIA	Warner Bros. (S) 2806	3.00	4.50	6.00
SISYPHUS	San Francisco (S) 205	4.00	6.00	8.00
THRILLER	Reprise (S) 2130	3.50	5.25	7.00
COLDER, Ben				
WACKY WORLD OF BEN COLDER	MGM (S) SE 4876	2.00	3.00	4.00
COLE, Cozy				
COZY COLE	King (M) 673	6.00	15.00	24.00
COZY COLE'S HITS	Love (M) 500	5.00	12.50	20.00
COZY CONCEPTION OF CARMEN	Charlie Parker (M) PLP-403	4.00	8.00	12.00
COZY'S CARAVAN AND EARL'S BACK ROOM	Felsted (M) FAJ7002	4.00	10.00	16.00
HOT & COZY	Continental (M) C16007	3.00	6.00	9.00
IT'S A COZY WORLD	Coral (M) CRL57457	4.00	10.00	16.00
IT'S A COZY WORLD	Coral (S) CRL757457	3.00	7.50	12.00
COLE, Don and Alleyne				
LIVE AT THE WHISKEY A-GO-GO	Tollie (M) T56001	4.00	6.00	8.00
LIVE AT THE WHISKEY A-GO-GO	Tollie (S) S56001	4.50	6.75	9.00
COLE, Ike				
TRIBUTE TO HIS BROTHER NAT	Dee Gee (M) D4001	5.00	10.00	15.00
TRIBUTE TO HIS BROTHER NAT	Dee Gee (S) DS4001	6.00	12.00	18.00
COLE, Ike, Quintet				
GET A LOAD O' COLE	Bally (M) 12020	2.00	3.00	4.00
COLE, Jerry and his Spacemen				
A GO GO GUITARS	Crown (S) CST539	3.00	6.00	9.00
HOT ROD DANCE PARTY	Capitol (M) T2061	3.00	6.00	9.00
HOT ROD DANCE PARTY	Capitol (S) ST2061	4.00	8.00	12.00
OUTER LIMITS	Capitol (M) T2044	3.00	6.00	9.00
OUTER LIMITS	Capitol (S) ST2044	4.00	8.00	12.00
SURF AGE	Capitol (M) T2112	3.00	6.00	9.00
SURF AGE	Capitol (S) ST2112	4.00	8.00	12.00
COLE, Natalie				
INSEPARABLE	Capitol (S) ST-11429	2.50	3.75	5.00
NATALIE	Capitol (S) ST 11517	2.50	3.75	5.00
THANKFUL	Capitol (S) SW 11708	2.00	3.00	4.00
UNPREDICTABLE	Capitol (S) SO 11600	2.00	3.00	4.00
COLE, Nat King				
AFTER MIDNIGHT	Capitol (EP) 7821	1.00	1.50	2.00
AFTER MIDNIGHT	Capitol (EP) 7822	1.00	1.50	2.00
AFTER MIDNIGHT	Capitol (EP) 7823	1.00	1.50	2.00
AFTER MIDNIGHT	Capitol (EP) 7824	1.00	1.50	2.00

(M) Mono (S) Stereo (EP) Extended Play (Q) Quad (RI) Re-issued

TITLE	LABEL & NO.	GOOD	VERY GOOD	NEAR MINT
NAT KING COLE STORY VOL 3	Capitol (M) W1928	2.50	3.75	5.00
NAT KING COLE STORY VOL 3	Capitol (S) SW1928	2.50	3.75	5.00
NAT KING COLE TOP POPS	Capitol (M) T1891	2.50	3.75	5.00
NAT KING COLE TOP POPS	Capitol (S) DT1891	2.50	3.75	5.00
NIGHT LIGHTS	Capitol (EP) 1801	1.50	2.25	3.00
NON DIMENTICAR	Capitol (EP) EAP1138	1.00	1.50	2.00
PENTHOUSE SERENADE	Capitol (M) T332	5.00	7.50	10.00
PENTHOUSE SERENADE	Capitol (EP) EAP 1332	1.50	2.25	3.00
PENTHOUSE SERENADE	Capitol (EP) EAP 2332	1.50	2.25	3.00
RAMBLIN ROSE	Capitol (M) T1793	2.50	3.75	5.00
RAMBLIN ROSE	Capitol (S) ST1793	2.50	3.75	5.00
SINGS THE BLUES	Capitol (M) W1713	2.50	3.75	5.00
SINGS THE BLUES	Capitol (S) SW1713	2.50	3.75	5.00
SONGS BY NAT KING COLE	Capitol (EP) EAP1500	1.50	2.25	3.00
STRIP FOR ACTION	Capitol (EP) EAP 1709	1.50	2.25	3.00
SWINGING SIDE OF NAT KING COLE	Capitol (M) W1724	2.50	3.75	5.00
SWINGING SIDE OF NAT KING COLE	Capitol (S) SW1724	2.50	3.75	5.00
TELL ME ALL ABOUT YOURSELF	Capitol (M) W1331	2.50	3.75	5.00
TELL ME ALL ABOUT YOURSELF	Capitol (S) SW1331	2.50	3.75	5.00
TENTH ANNIVERSARY ALBUM	Capitol (M) W514	4.00	6.00	8.00
TENTH ANNIVERSARY ALBUM	Capitol (EP) EAP 1514	1.00	1.50	2.00
TENTH ANNIVERSARY ALBUM	Capitol (EP) EAP 2514	1.00	1.50	2.00
TENTH ANNIVERSARY ALBUM	Capitol (EP) EAP 3514	1.00	1.50	2.00
TENTH ANNIVERSARY ALBUM	Capitol (EP) EAP 4514	1.00	1.50	2.00
THIS IS NAT KING COLE	Capitol (S) DT870	4.00	6.00	8.00
THOSE LAZY, HAZY, CRAZY DAYS OF SUMMER	Capitol (M) T1932	2.50	3.75	5.00
THOSE LAZY, HAZY, CRAZY DAYS OF SUMMER	Capitol (S) ST1932	2.50	3.75	5.00
TO WHOM IT MAY CONCERN	Capitol (M) W1190	3.00	4.00	6.00
TO WHOM IT MAY CONCERN	Capitol (S) SW1190	3.00	4.00	6.00
THE TOUCH OF YOUR LIPS	Capitol (M) W1574	2.50	3.75	5.00
THE TOUCH OF YOUR LIPS	Capitol (S) SW1574	2.50	3.75	5.00
TWO IN LOVE	Capitol (M) T 420	5.00	7.50	10.00
TWO IN LOVE	Capitol (S) DT420	2.50	3.75	5.00
TWO IN LOVE	Capitol (EP) EAP 4201	1.50	2.25	3.00
TWO IN LOVE	Capitol (EP) EAP4202	1.50	2.25	3.00
UNFORGETTABLE	Capitol (M) T357	5.00	7.50	10.00
UNFORGETTABLE	Capitol (S) DT357	2.50	3.75	5.00
VOCAL CLASSICS	Capitol (M) T591	5.00	7.50	10.00
WELCOME TO THE CLUB	Capitol (M) W1120	3.00	4.00	6.00
WELCOME TO THE CLUB	Capitol (S) SW1120	3.00	4.00	6.00
WELCOME TO THE CLUB	Capitol (EP) EAP11120	1.00	1.50	3.00
WHERE DID EVERYONE GO	Capitol (M) W1859	2.50	3.75	5.00
WHERE DID EVERYONE GO	Capitol (S) SW1859	2.50	3.75	5.00
WILD IS LOVE	Capitol (M) WAK1392	2.50	3.75	5.00
WILD IS LOVE	Capitol (S) SWAK1392	2.50	3.75	5.00

COLE, Nat King, Trio

KING COLE TRIO	Capitol (M) 8	10.00	15.00	20.00
KING COLE TRIO VOL 2	Capitol (M) 29	7.00	10.50	14.00
KING COLE TRIO VOL 3	Capitol (M) 59	7.00	10.50	14.00
KING COLE TRIO VOL 4	Capitol (M) 139	7.00	10.50	14.00

COLLECTORS

THE COLLECTORS	Warner Brothers (S) WS1746	3.50	5.25	7.00
GRASS AND WILD STRAWBERRIES	Warner Brothers (S) WS1774	3.50	5.25	7.00

COLLEGIANS

SING ALONG WITH THE COLLEGIANS	Winley (M) LP6004	7.00	17.50	28.00

COLLINS, Albert

THE COMPLETE ALBERT COLLINS	Imperial (S) LP12449	3.00	4.50	6.00
THE COOL SOUND OF ALBERT COLLINS	TCF Hall (M) TCF8002	4.00	8.00	12.00
LOVE CAN BE FOUND ANYWHERE	Imperial (S) LP12428	3.00	4.50	6.00
THERE'S GOTTA BE A CHANGE	Tumbleweed (S) TWS103	2.50	3.75	5.00
TRUCKIN' WITH ALBERT COLLINS	Blue Thumb (S) BTS8	2.50	3.75	5.00

COLLINS, Brian

LONELY TOO LONG	Dot (S) 26017	2.00	3.00	4.00
THAT'S THE WAY LOVE SHOULD BE	Dot (S) DOSD-2008	2.00	3.00	4.00

COLLINS, Dave and Ansell

DOUBLE BARREL	Big Tree (S) BTS2005	2.50	3.75	5.00

TITLE	LABEL & NO.	GOOD	VERY GOOD	NEAR MINT
A MIS AMIGOS	Capitol (M) W1220	2.50	3.75	5.00
A MIS AMIGOS	Capitol (S) ST1220	2.50	3.75	5.00
BALLADS OF THE DAY	Capitol (S) DT680	5.00	7.50	10.00
BY THE BEAUTIFUL SEA	Capitol (EP) EAP1535	1.50	2.25	3.00
CHRISTMAS SONG	Capitol (M) W1967	2.50	3.75	5.00
CHRISTMAS SONG	Capitol (S) SW1967	2.50	3.75	5.00
CHRISTMAS SONG, THE	Capitol (EP) EAP 19026	1.50	2.25	3.00
COLE ESPANOL	Capitol (S) DW1031	3.00	4.50	6.00
COLE SINGS	Capitol (EP) EAP 19120	1.00	1.50	2.00
COLE'S TOP POPS	Capitol (M) H9110	3.00	4.50	6.00
COLE'S TOP POPS	Capitol EP) EAP29110	1.00	1.50	2.00
DEAR LONELY HEARTS	Capitol (M) T1838	2.50	3.75	5.00
DEAR LONELY HEARTS	Capitol (S) ST1838	2.50	3.75	5.00
EVERY TIME I FEEL THE SPIRIT, WITH THE CHURCH OF DELIVERENCE CHOIR	Capitol (M) T1249	2.50	3.75	5.00
EVERY TIME I FEEL THE SPIRIT, WITH THE CHURCH OF DELIVERENCE CHOIR	Capitol (S) ST1249	2.50	3.75	5.00
EVERY TIME I FEEL THE SPIRIT, WITH THE CHURCH OF DELIVERENCE CHOIR	Capitol (EP) EAP11249	1.00	1.50	2.00
EVERY TIME I FEEL THE SPIRIT, WITH THE CHURCH OF DELIVERENCE CHOIR	Capitol (EP) EAP21249	1.00	1.50	2.00
EVERY TIME I FEEL THE SPIRIT, WITH THE CHURCH OF DELIVERENCE CHOIR	Capitol (EP) EAP31249	1.00	1.50	2.00
HAPPIEST CHRISTMAS TREE	Capitol (EP) EAP11346	1.00	1.50	2.00
HARVEST OF HITS	Capitol (M) L213	5.00	7.50	10.00
I DON'T WANT TO BE HURT ANYMORE	Capitol (M) T2118	2.00	3.00	4.00
I DON'T WANT TO BE HURT ANYMORE	Capitol (S) ST2118	2.00	3.00	4.00
IN THE BEGINNING	Decca (M) DL8260	4.50	6.75	9.00
IN THE BEGINNING	Decca (EP) ED405	2.00	3.00	4.00
JUST ONE OF THOSE THINGS	Capitol (M) W903	3.00	4.00	6.00
JUST ONE OF THOSE THINGS	Capitol (S) SW903	3.00	4.00	6.00
LET'S FACE THE MUSIC	Capitol (M) W2008	2.00	3.00	4.00
LET'S FACE THE MUSIC	Capitol (S) SW2008	2.00	3.00	4.00
LOOKING BACK	Capitol (EP) EAP960	1.50	2.25	3.00
L-O-V-E	Capitol (M) T2195	2.00	3.00	4.00
L-O-V-E	Capitol (S) ST2195	2.00	3.00	4.00
LOVE IS THE THING	Capitol (M) 824	3.00	4.00	6.00
LOVE IS THE THING	Capitol (S) SW824	3.00	4.00	6.00
LOVE IS THE THING	Capitol (EP) 8241	1.00	1.50	2.00
LOVE IS THE THING	Capitol (EP) 8242	1.00	1.50	2.00
LOVE IS THE THING	Capitol (EP) 8243	1.00	1.50	2.00
LOVE SONGS BY NAT KING COLE	Capitol (EP) EAP1696	1.00	1.50	2.00
MAGIC OF CHRISTMAS	Capitol (M) W1444	2.50	3.75	5.00
MAGIC OF CHRISTMAS	Capitol (S) SW1444	2.50	3.75	5.00
MIDNIGHT FLYER	Capitol (EP) EAP11317	1.00	1.50	2.00
MOODS IN SONG	Capitol (EP) EAP 1633	1.00	1.50	2.00
MORE COLE ESPANOL	Capitol (M) W1749	2.50	3.75	5.00
MORE COLE ESPANOL	Capitol (S) SW1749	2.50	3.75	5.00
MY FAIR LADY	Capitol (M) W2117	2.00	3.00	4.00
MY FAIR LADY	Capitol (S) SW2117	2.00	3.00	4.00
NAT KING COLE	Capitol (M) T2340	2.00	3.00	4.00
NAT KING COLE	Capitol (S) ST2340	2.00	3.00	4.00
NAT KING COLE	Capitol (EP) EAP19128	1.00	1.50	2.00
NAT KING COLE	Capitol (M) MA11579	2.50	3.75	5.00
NAT KING COLE, SINGS THE BLUES	Capitol (M) W1929	2.50	3.75	5.00
NAT KING COLE, SINGS THE BLUES	Capitol (S) SW1929	2.50	3.75	5.00
NAT KING COLE STORY VOL 1	Capitol (M) W1926	2.50	3.75	5.00
NAT KING COLE STORY VOL 1	Capitol (S) SW1926	2.50	3.75	5.00
NAT KING COLE STORY VOL 2	Capitol (M) W1927	2.50	3.75	5.00
NAT KING COLE STORY VOL 2	Capitol (S) SW1927	2.50	3.75	5.00

(M) Mono (S) Stereo (EP) Extended Play (Q) Quad (RI) Re-issued

COLLINS, Judy

TITLE	LABEL & NO.	GOOD	VERY GOOD	NEAR MINT
BREAD & ROSES	Elektra (S) 7E-1076	3.00	4.50	6.00
COLORS OF THE DAY/ THE BEST OF JUDY COLLINS	Elektra (S) EKS 75030	3.50	5.25	7.00
COLORS OF THE DAY/ THE BEST OF JUDY COLLINS	Elektra (Q) EQ 5030	3.00	4.50	6.00
IN MY LIFE	Elektra (M) EKL 320	4.00	6.00	8.00
IN MY LIFE	Elektra (S) EKS 7320	4.50	6.75	9.00
JUDITH	Elektra (S) 7E-1032	3.00	4.50	6.00
JUDY COLLINS #3	Elektra (M) EKL 243	4.00	6.00	8.00
JUDY COLLINS #3	Elektra (S) EKS 7243	4.50	6.75	9.00
JUDY COLLINS' FIFTH ALBUM	Elektra (M) EKL 300	4.00	6.00	8.00
JUDY COLLINS' FIFTH ALBUM	Elektra (S) EKS 7300	4.50	6.75	9.00
LIVING	Elektra (S) EKS 75014	3.50	5.25	7.00
RECOLLECTIONS	Elektra (S) EKS 74055	3.50	5.25	7.00
TRUE STORIES & OTHER DREAMS	Elektra (S) EKS 75053	3.50	5.25	7.00
WHALES & NIGHTINGALES	Elektra (S) EKS 75010	3.50	5.25	7.00
WHO KNOWS WHERE THE TIME GOES	Elektra (S) EKS 74033	3.50	5.25	7.00
WILDFLOWERS	Elektra (M) EKL 4012	3.50	5.25	7.00
WILDFLOWERS	Elektra (S) EKS 74012	4.00	6.00	8.00

COLLINS, Tommy

TITLE	LABEL & NO.	GOOD	VERY GOOD	NEAR MINT
DYNAMIC TOMMY COLLINS	Columbia (M) CL2510	2.00	3.00	4.00
DYNAMIC TOMMY COLLINS	Columbia (S) CS9310	2.00	3.00	4.00
LET'S LIVE A LITTLE	Tower (M) 5021	2.00	3.00	4.00
LET'S LIVE A LITTLE	Tower (S) 5021	2.00	3.00	4.00
LIGHT OF THE LORD	Capitol (M) T1125	2.50	3.75	5.00
LIGHT OF THE LORD	Capitol (EP) EAP11125	1.00	1.50	2.00
LIGHT OF THE LORD	Capitol (EP) EAP21125	1.00	1.50	2.00
LIGHT OF THE LORD	Capitol (EP) EAP31125	1.00	1.50	2.00
SONGS I LOVE TO SING	Capitol (M) T1436	2.50	3.75	5.00
SONGS I LOVE TO SING	Capitol (S) ST1436	2.50	3.75	5.00
THIS IS TOMMY COLLINS	Capitol (EP) EAP11196	1.00	1.50	2.00
THIS IS TOMMY COLLINS	Capitol (EP) EAP21196	1.00	1.50	2.00
THIS IS TOMMY COLLINS	Capitol (EP) EAP31196	1.00	1.50	2.00
TOMMY COLLINS	Capitol (EP) EAP1607	1.50	2.25	3.00
WORDS & MUSIC COUNTRY STYLE	Capitol (M) T776	4.00	6.00	8.00
WORDS & MUSIC COUNTRY STYLE	Capitol (EP) EAP1776	1.50	2.25	3.00
WORDS & MUSIC COUNTRY STYLE	Capitol (EP) EAP2776	1.50	2.50	3.00
WORDS & MUSIC COUNTRY STYLE	Capitol (EP) EAP T3776	1.50	2.25	3.00

COLOURS

TITLE	LABEL & NO.	GOOD	VERY GOOD	NEAR MINT
ATMOSPHERE	Dot (S) 25935	3.00	4.50	6.00
COLOURS	Dot (S) 25854	3.50	5.25	7.00

COLTER, Jessi

TITLE	LABEL & NO.	GOOD	VERY GOOD	NEAR MINT
I'M JESSI COLTER	Capitol (S) ST-11363	2.00	3.00	4.00

COLTRANE, Chi

TITLE	LABEL & NO.	GOOD	VERY GOOD	NEAR MINT
LET IT RIDE	Columbia (S) KC-32463	2.50	3.75	5.00

COMFORTABLE CHAIR

TITLE	LABEL & NO.	GOOD	VERY GOOD	NEAR MINT
THE COMFORTABLE CHAIR	Ode (S) Z12 44005	4.00	6.00	8.00

COMMANDE CODY & HIS LOST PLANET AIRMEN

TITLE	LABEL & NO.	GOOD	VERY GOOD	NEAR MINT
COUNTRY CASANOVA	Paramount (S) 6054	3.00	4.50	6.00
LIVE FROM DEEP IN THE HEARTS OF TEXAS	Paramount (S) 1017	3.00	4.50	6.00

COMMODORES

TITLE	LABEL & NO.	GOOD	VERY GOOD	NEAR MINT
CAUGHT IN THE ACT	Motown (S) 820	3.00	4.50	6.00
MACHINE GUN	Motown (S) 798	3.50	5.25	7.00
MOVIN' ON	Motown (S) 848	3.00	4.50	6.00

COMO, Perry

TITLE	LABEL & NO.	GOOD	VERY GOOD	NEAR MINT
COMO'S GOLDEN RECORDS	RCA (M) LOP1007	2.50	3.75	5.00
COMO'S GOLDEN RECORDS	RCA (EP) EPA 5012	1.00	1.50	2.00
COMO'S GOLDEN RECORDS	RCA (EP) EPA 5029	1.00	1.50	2.00
COMO'S GOLDEN RECORDS	RCA (EP) EPA 5030	1.00	1.50	2.00
I BELIEVE	RCA (M) LPM1172	2.00	3.00	4.00
P.C.	RCA (EP) EPA642	1.00	1.50	2.00
PERRY COMO	RCA (M) LPC160	4.00	6.00	8.00
PERRY COMO SINGS	RCA (EP) EPA903	1.00	1.50	2.00
PERRY COMO SINGS HITS FROM BROADWAY SHOWS	RCA (M) LPM1191	2.00	3.00	4.00
PERRY COMO SINGS HITS FROM BROADWAY SHOWS	RCA (EP) EPA728	1.00	1.50	2.00
PERRY COMO SINGS MERRY CHRISTMAS MUSIC	RCA (M) LPM51	2.50	3.75	5.00
PERRY COMO SINGS MERRY CHRISTMAS MUSIC	RCA (M) LPM1243	2.00	3.00	4.00
PERRY COMO SINGS MERRY CHRISTMAS MUSIC	RCA (EP) EPA920	1.00	1.50	2.00
RELAXING WITH PERRY COMO	RCA (M) LPM1176	2.00	3.00	4.00
RELAXING WITH PERRY COMO	RCA (EP) EPA738	1.00	1.50	2.00
SENTIMENTAL DATE	RCA (M) LPM3035	2.50	3.75	5.00
A SENTIMENTAL DATE WITH PERRY COMO	RCA (M) LPC187	4.00	6.00	8.00
SENTIMENTAL DATE WITH PERRY COMO	RCA (M) LPM1177	2.50	3.75	5.00
SENTIMENTAL DATE WITH PERRY COMO	RCA (EP) EPA739	1.00	1.50	2.00
SO SMOOTH	RCA (M) LPM1085	2.50	3.75	5.00
TILL THE END OF TIME	RCA (M) LPC-109	5.00	7.50	10.00
TV FAVORITES	RCA (M) LPM3013	2.50	3.75	5.00
WANTED	RCA (EP) EPA563	1.00	1.50	2.00
WE GET LETTERS	RCA (M) LPM1463	2.00	3.00	4.00

COMPETITORS

TITLE	LABEL & NO.	GOOD	VERY GOOD	NEAR MINT
HITS OF THE STREET & STRIP	Dot (M) DLP3542	3.00	6.00	9.00
HITS OF THE STREET & STRIP	Dot (S) DLP 25542	4.00	8.00	12.00

COMSTOCK, Bobby and The Counts

TITLE	LABEL & NO.	GOOD	VERY GOOD	NEAR MINT
OUT OF SIGHT	Ascot (M) ALM 13026	4.00	8.00	12.00
OUT OF SIGHT	Ascot (S) ALS16026	5.00	10.00	15.00

CONDELLO, Mike

TITLE	LABEL & NO.	GOOD	VERY GOOD	NEAR MINT
PHASE 1	Scepter (S) SPS 542	6.00	9.00	12.00

CONGRESS OF WONDERS

TITLE	LABEL & NO.	GOOD	VERY GOOD	NEAR MINT
REVOLTING	Fantasy (S) 7016	3.00	4.50	6.00

CONLEY, Arthur

TITLE	LABEL & NO.	GOOD	VERY GOOD	NEAR MINT
SHAKE, RATTLE, AND ROLL	Atco (M) 33-220	3.00	4.50	6.00
SOUL DIRECTION	Atco (M) 33-243	2.50	3.75	5.00

CONNELLY, Chris

TITLE	LABEL & NO.	GOOD	VERY GOOD	NEAR MINT
BOY FROM PEYTON PLACE	Philips (M) PHM 200-173	2.50	3.75	5.00
BOY FROM PEYTON PLACE	Philips (S) PHS 600-173	3.00	4.50	6.00

CONNOR, Chris

TITLE	LABEL & NO.	GOOD	VERY GOOD	NEAR MINT
CHRIS CONNOR SINGS BALLADS OF THE SAD CAFE	Atlantic (S) 1307	2.50	5.00	7.50
CHRIS IN PERSON	Atlantic (M) 8040	2.00	4.00	6.00
CHRIS IN PERSON	Atlantic (S) SD-8040	2.50	5.00	7.50

CONRAD, William

TITLE	LABEL & NO.	GOOD	VERY GOOD	NEAR MINT
SPIRITS & SPOOKS FOR HALLOWEEN	Caedmon (S)1344	2.00	3.00	4.00

CONTINENTAL FOUR

TITLE	LABEL & NO.	GOOD	VERY GOOD	NEAR MINT
DREAM WORLD	Jay Walking (M) 1020	3.00	6.00	9.00

CONTOURS

TITLE	LABEL & NO.	GOOD	VERY GOOD	NEAR MINT
DO YOU LOVE ME	Gordy (M) 901	6.00	12.00	18.00

CONTRASTS

TITLE	LABEL & NO.	GOOD	VERY GOOD	NEAR MINT
BLONDE ON BLONDE	Janus (S) JLS3003	3.00	4.50	6.00

COODER, Ry

TITLE	LABEL & NO.	GOOD	VERY GOOD	NEAR MINT
BOOMER'S STORY	Reprise (S) 2117	3.00	4.50	6.00
INTO THE PURPLE VALLEY	Reprise (S) 2052	3.00	4.50	6.00
PARADISE & LUNCH	Reprise (S) 2179	3.00	4.50	6.00

COOKE, L.C.

TITLE	LABEL & NO.	GOOD	VERY GOOD	NEAR MINT
L.C. COOKE	Blue Rock (M) 24001	3.00	4.50	6.00
L.C. COOKE	Blue Rock (S) 64001	4.00	6.00	8.00

COOKE, Sam

TITLE	LABEL & NO.	GOOD	VERY GOOD	NEAR MINT
AIN'T THAT GOOD NEWS	RCA (M) 2899	4.00	6.00	8.00
AIN'T THAT GOOD NEWS	RCA (S) LSP 2899	3.00	4.50	6.00
ANOTHER SATURDAY NIGHT	RCA (EP) 4375	2.00	4.00	6.00
AT THE COPA	RCA (S) LSP 2970	3.00	4.50	6.00
AT THE COPA	RCA (M) 2970	4.00	6.00	8.00
BEST OF SAM COOKE	RCA (M) 2625	4.00	6.00	8.00
BEST OF SAM COOKE	RCA (S) LSP 2625	3.00	4.50	6.00
BEST OF SAM COOKE, Vol. 2	RCA (M) 3373	4.00	6.00	8.00
BEST OF SAM COOKE, Vol. 2	RCA (S) LSP 3373	3.00	4.50	6.00
COOKE'S TOUR	RCA (M) 2221	4.00	8.00	12.00
COOKE'S TOUR	RCA (S) LPS 2221	3.00	4.50	6.00
ENCORE	Keen (M) 2003	5.00	10.00	15.00
ENCORE	Keen (S) B2006	2.00	5.00	8.00
ENCORE VOL. 2	Keen (EP) B2008	2.00	5.00	8.00
HIT KIT	Keen (M) 86101	5.00	12.50	20.00
HITS OF THE 50'S	RCA (M) LPM 2236	4.00	8.00	12.00
HITS OF THE 50's	RCA (S) LSP 2236	3.00	4.50	6.00
I THANK GOD	Keen (M) 86103	5.00	10.00	15.00
THE MAN WHO INVENTED SOUL	RCA (M) 3991	4.00	6.00	8.00
MAN WHO INVENTED SOUL	RCA (S) LSP-3991	3.00	4.50	6.00
MR. SOUL	RCA (M) 2673	4.00	6.00	8.00
MR. SOUL	RCA (S) LSP 2673	3.00	4.50	6.00
MY KIND OF BLUES	RCA (M) 2392	4.00	8.00	12.00
MY KIND OF BLUES	RCA (S) LSP 2392	3.00	4.50	6.00
NIGHT BEAT	RCA (M) 2709	4.00	6.00	8.00
NIGHT BEAT	RCA (S) LSP 2709	3.00	4.50	6.00
ONLY SIXTEEN	Famous (M) 505	4.00	6.00	8.00
RIGHT ON	Cherie (M) 1001	3.00	4.50	6.00
SAM COOKE	RCA (S) LSP-2293	3.00	4.50	6.00
SAM COOKE	Keen (M) 2001	5.00	10.00	15.00
SAM COOKE SINGS	RCA (M) LPC-126	5.00	7.50	10.00
SAM'S SONGS	Famous (M) 502	4.00	6.00	8.00
SHAKE	RCA (M) 3367	4.00	6.00	8.00
SHAKE	RCA (S) LSP 3367	3.00	4.50	6.00
SINGS THE BILLIE HOLIDAY STORY	Up Front (M) 160	2.00	3.00	4.00
SINGS THE BILLIE HOLIDAY STORY	Up Front (S) 160	2.50	3.75	5.00
SONGS BY SAM COOKE	Keen (EP) B2001	2.00	5.00	8.00
SOUL STIRRERS FEATURING SAM COOKE	SAR (M) 105	4.00	6.00	9.00
SO WONDERFUL	Famous (M) 508	4.00	6.00	8.00
SWING LOW	RCA (M) 2293	4.00	8.00	12.00
THIS IS SAM COOKE	RCA (M) 6027	4.00	6.00	8.00
TRIBUTE TO THE LADY	Keen (M) 2004	5.00	10.00	15.00

(M) Mono (S) Stereo (EP) Extended Play (Q) Quad (RI) Re-issued

TITLE	LABEL & NO.	GOOD	VERY GOOD	NEAR MINT
TRIBUTE TO THE LADY	Keen (S) 2004	7.00	14.00	21.00
TRIBUTE TO THE LADY, Vol. 1	Keen (EP) B2012	2.00	5.00	8.00
TRIBUTE TO THE LADY Vol. 2	Keen (EP) B2013	2.00	5.00	8.00
TRIBUTE TO THE LADY Vol. 3	Keen (EP) B2014	2.00	5.00	8.00
TRY A LITTLE LOVE	RCA (M) LPM-3435	4.00	6.00	8.00
TRY A LITTLE LOVE	RCA (S) LSP-3435	3.00	4.50	6.00
TWISTIN' THE NIGHT AWAY	RCA (M) LPM-2555	4.00	6.00	8.00
TWISTIN' THE NIGHT AWAY	RCA (S) LSP-2555	3.00	4.50	6.00
TWO SIDES OF SAM COOKE	Specialty (M) SP 2119	4.00	6.00	8.00
UNFORGETTABLE SAM COOKE	Camden (M) 2610	2.50	3.75	5.00
UNFORGETTABLE SAM COOKE	Camden (S) 2610	3.00	4.50	6.00
UNFORGETTABLE SAM COOKE	RCA (S) LSP-3517	3.00	4.50	6.00
WONDERFUL WORLD OF SAM COOKE	Keen (M) 86106	5.00	10.00	15.00
YOU SEND ME	Famous (M) 509	4.00	6.00	8.00
YOU SEND ME	Camden (S) ACL1-0445	2.50	3.75	5.00

COOKER
NOWHERE AT ALL	Scepter (S) 5116	2.50	3.75	5.00

COOL ONES
THE COOL ONES	(S)	10.00	20.00	30.00

COOL CALVIN & THE SURF KNOBS
SURFERS BEAT, THE	Charter (S) CLS103	3.50	7.00	10.50

COOLEY, Spade
DANCE-O-RAMA	Decca (M) DL5563	5.00	7.50	10.00
DANCE-O-RAMA	Decca (EP) ED2225-26	1.50	2.25	3.00
FIDOODLIN'	Raynote (M) RN-5007	5.00	10.00	15.00
ROY ROGERS SOUVENIR ALBUM	RCA (M) LPM3041	6.00	9.00	12.00
ROY ROGERS SOUVENIR ALBUM	RCA (EP) EPB3041	1.50	2.25	3.00
SAGEBRUSH SWING	Columbia (M) HL9007	5.00	7.50	10.00

COOLIDGE, Rita
ANYTIME ... ANYWHERE	A&M (S) SP 4616	2.00	3.00	4.00
FALL INTO SPRING	A&M (S) SP 3627	2.00	3.00	4.00
IT'S ONLY LOVE	A&M (S) SP 4531	2.00	3.00	4.00
LADY'S NOT FOR SALE	A&M (S) SP 4370	2.00	3.00	4.00
NICE FEELIN'	A&M (S) SP 4325	2.00	3.00	4.00
RITA COOLIDGE	A&M (S) SP 4291	2.00	3.00	4.00

COOLIDGE, Rita & Kris Kristofferson
BREAKAWAY	Monument (S) PZ-33278	2.50	3.75	5.00
FULL MOON	A&M (S) SP 4403	2.50	3.75	5.00

COOPER, Les and The Soul Rockers'
WIGGLE WOBBLE	Everlast (M) ELP202	6.00	15.00	24.00

COPAS, Cowboy
BROKEN HEARTED MELODIES	King (M) 720	3.00	4.50	6.00
COWBOY COPAS	Starday (M) 145	3.00	4.50	6.00
COWBOY COPAS, SINGS HIS FAVORITE SONGS VOL 1	King (EP) EP213/319-1	2.00	3.00	4.00
COWBOY COPAS SINGS HIS FAVORITE SONGS VOL 2	King (EP) EP213/319-2	2.00	3.00	4.00
FAVORITE SACRED SONGS	King (M) LP556	2.50	3.75	5.00
TRAGIC TALES OF LOVE & LIFE	King (M) 714	3.00	4.50	6.00

COPPERHEAD
COPPERHEAD	Columbia (S) KC 32250	4.00	6.00	8.00

COREY, Jill
SOMETIMES I'M HAPPY SOMETIMES BLUE	Columbia (M) CL1095	2.50	3.75	5.00
SOMETIMES I'M HAPPY SOMETIMES BLUE	Columbia (EP) B10951	1.00	1.50	2.00
SOMETIMES I'M HAPPY SOMETIMES BLUE	Columbia (EP) B10952	1.00	1.50	2.00

CORNELIUS BROTHERS & SISTER ROSE
BIG TIME LOVER	United Artists (S) UA-LA121-F	2.50	3.75	5.00
GOT TO TESTIFY	United Artists (S) UA-LA327-G	2.50	3.75	5.00

CORNELL, Don
DON CORNELL	Vocalion (M) VL-3657	2.00	3.00	4.00
DON CORNELL SINGS LOVE SONGS	Signature (M) SM-1001	2.00	4.00	6.00
DON CORNELL SINGS LOVE SONGS	Signature (S) SS-1001	3.00	6.00	9.00
DON'S GREAT HITS	Dot (M) DLP-3160	2.50	3.75	5.00
DON'S GREAT HITS	Dot (S) DLP-25160	3.00	4.50	6.00
FOR TEENAGERS ONLY!	Coral (M) CRL 57133	2.00	4.00	6.00

CORNELLS
BEACH BOUND	Garex (M) LPGA100	6.00	12.00	18.00

CORPORATE BODY
PROSPECTUS 69	MGM (S) SE 4624	4.50	6.75	9.00

CORTEZ, Dave "Baby"
DAVE "BABY" CORTEZ	Clock (M) C-331	4.00	8.00	12.00
DAVE "BABY" CORTEZ AND JERRY'S HOUSE ROCKERS	Crown (S) CST357	4.00	8.00	12.00
FABULOUS ORGAN	Metro (M) M550	3.00	6.00	9.00

TITLE	LABEL & NO.	GOOD	VERY GOOD	NEAR MINT
FABULOUS ORGAN	Metro (S) MS550	4.00	8.00	12.00
HAPPY ORGAN	RCA (M) LPM 2099	5.00	10.00	15.00
HAPPY ORGAN	RCA (EP) EPA4342	2.00	4.00	6.00
IN ORBIT WITH	Roulette (M) R25328	4.00	8.00	12.00
IN ORBIT WITH	Roulette (S) SR25328	5.00	10.00	15.00
MUSIC ROUND THE CLOCK	Clock (M) CX201	4.00	8.00	12.00
ORGAN SHINDIG	Roulette (M) R25298	4.00	8.00	12.00
ORGAN SHINDIG	Roulette (S) SP25298	5.00	10.00	15.00
RINKY DINK	Chess (M) LP1473	6.00	12.00	18.00

CORY, Troy
CLOSEST I EVER CAME, THE	Cinema Prize (M) 1686	2.00	3.00	4.00
TODAYS PUZZLE VOLUME 2	Cinema Prize (M) 1687	2.00	3.00	4.00

COSBY, Bill
AT LAST BILL COSBY REALLY SINGS	Partee (S) 2405	3.00	4.50	6.00
BILL	MCA (S) 2-8005	2.00	3.00	4.00
FAT ALBERT	MCA (S) 333	2.00	3.00	4.00
FAT ALBERT	UNI (S) 73143	2.50	3.75	5.00
FOR ADULTS ONLY	UNI (S) 73145	2.50	3.75	5.00
INSIDE THE MIND OF BILL COSBY	UNI (S) 73139	2.50	3.75	5.00
I STARTED OUT AS A CHILD	Warner Bros. (M) W-1567	2.50	3.75	5.00
MORE OF THE BEST OF BILL COSBY	Warner Bros (S) 1836	3.00	4.50	6.00
TO RUSSELL, MY BROTHER, WHOM I SLEPT WITH	Warner Bros. (S) 1734	3.00	4.50	6.00
200 M.P.H.	Warner Bros. (S) 1757	3.00	4.50	6.00
WONDERFULNESS	Warner Bros. (M) 1634	2.50	3.75	5.00
WONDERFULNESS	Warner Bros. (S) 1634	3.00	4.50	6.00

COSTA, Don
DON COSTA CONDUCTS HIS 15 HITS	ABC Paramount (M) ABC362	2.50	3.75	5.00

COSTANDINOS, Alec R. & The Syncophonic Orchestra
ROMEO & JULIET	Casablanca (S) NBLP 7086	2.00	3.00	4.00

COSTELLO, Elvis
LIVE AT THE EL MOCAMBO (Canadian)	CBS (S)	15.00	22.50	30.00
MY AIM IS TRUE	Columbia (S) JC 35037	2.00	3.00	4.00
THIS YEAR'S MODEL	Columbia (S) JC 35331	2.00	3.00	4.00

COTTON, James, Blues Band
COTTON IN YOUR EARS	Verve Forecast (S) FTS 3060	3.00	4.50	6.00
HIGH ENERGY	Buddah (S) 5650	3.00	4.50	6.00
THE JAMES COTTON BLUES BAND	Verve-Folkways (M) FT 3023	2.50	3.75	5.00
THE JAMES COTTON BLUES BAND	Verve-Folkways (S) FTS 3023	3.00	4.50	6.00
100 PERCENT COTTON	Buddah (S) 5620	3.00	4.50	6.00
PURE COTTON	Verve/Folkways (S) FTS3038	3.00	4.50	6.00

COTTON, LLOYD & CHRISTIAN
LLOYD & CHRISTIAN COTTON	20th Century (S) 487	2.00	3.00	4.00

COULSON, McGuiness, Flint
LO AND BEHOLD	Sire (S) SAS 7405	2.50	3.75	5.00

COUNT FIVE
PSYCHOTIC REACTION	Double Shot (M) DSM 1001	5.00	10.00	15.00
PSYCHOTIC REACTION	Double Shot (S) DSS 5001	6.00	12.00	18.00

COUNTRY JOE & THE FISH
C.J. FISH	Vanguard (S) 6555	3.50	5.25	7.00
COUNTRY JOE AND THE FISH	Rag Baby (M)	20.00	30.00	40.00
COUNTRY JOE & THE FISH	Vanguard (M) VRS 9244	3.00	4.50	6.00

(M) Mono (S) Stereo (EP) Extended Play (Q) Quad (RI) Re-issued

43

COUNTRY JOE & THE FISH (continued)

TITLE	LABEL & NO.	GOOD	VERY GOOD	NEAR MINT
GREATEST HITS	Vanguard (S) 6545	3.50	5.25	7.00
HERE WE ARE AGAIN	Vanguard (S) VSD 79299	3.00	4.50	6.00
I-FEEL-LIKE-I'M-FIXIN'-TO-DIE	Vanguard (M) VRS 9266	3.00	4.50	6.00
I-FEEL-LIKE-I'M-FIXIN'-TO-DIE	Vanguard (S) VSD 79266	3.50	5.25	7.00
LIFE & TIMES OF COUNTRY JOE & THE FISH	Vanguard (S) VSD 27/28	3.50	5.25	7.00
TOGETHER	Vanguard (S) VSD 79277	3.00	4.50	6.00

Also see McDONALD, COUNTRY JOE.

COUNTS
TITLE	LABEL & NO.	GOOD	VERY GOOD	NEAR MINT
LOVE SIGN	GRC (S) 2002	3.00	4.50	6.00

COUSIN BRUCIE
TITLE	LABEL & NO.	GOOD	VERY GOOD	NEAR MINT
COUSIN BRUCIE MEETS MOTHER GOOSIE	5 Star (M) 55555	3.00	7.50	12.00

COUSIN JOE
TITLE	LABEL & NO.	GOOD	VERY GOOD	NEAR MINT
COUSIN JOE OF NEW ORLEANS	Bluesway (M) 6078	2.00	3.00	4.00

COVAY, Don
TITLE	LABEL & NO.	GOOD	VERY GOOD	NEAR MINT
HOT BLOOD	Mercury (S) SRM-1-1020	2.50	3.75	5.00
MERCY	Atlantic (M) 8104	2.00	3.00	4.00
MERCY	Atlantic (S) 8104	3.00	4.50	6.00
SEE SAW	Atlantic (M) 8120	2.00	3.00	4.00
SEE SAW	Atlantic (S) 8120	3.00	4.50	6.00

COVEN
TITLE	LABEL & NO.	GOOD	VERY GOOD	NEAR MINT
BLOOD ON THE SNOW	Buddah (S) 5614	3.50	5.25	7.00

COVINGTON, Warren & The Commanders
TITLE	LABEL & NO.	GOOD	VERY GOOD	NEAR MINT
TEENAGE HOP	Decca (M) DL 8577	4.00	6.00	8.00

COWBOY
TITLE	LABEL & NO.	GOOD	VERY GOOD	NEAR MINT
WHY QUIT WHEN YOU'RE LOSING	Capricorn (S) 2CX-0121	2.50	3.75	5.00

COWBOY CHURCH SUNDAY SCHOOL
TITLE	LABEL & NO.	GOOD	VERY GOOD	NEAR MINT
COWBOY CHURCH SUNDAY SCHOOL SINGS	Decca (EP) ED2208	2.00	3.00	4.00

COWSILL, Bill
TITLE	LABEL & NO.	GOOD	VERY GOOD	NEAR MINT
NERVOUS BREAKTHROUGH	MGM (S) SE4706	2.50	3.75	5.00

COWSILLS
TITLE	LABEL & NO.	GOOD	VERY GOOD	NEAR MINT
BEST OF THE COWSILLS	MGM (S) SE4597	2.50	3.75	5.00
CAPTAIN SAD AND HIS SHIP OF FOOLS	MGM (S) SE4554	2.50	3.75	5.00
COWSILLS IN CONCERT	MGM (S) SE4619	2.50	3.75	5.00
COWSILLS PLUS THE LINCOLN PARK ZOO, THE	Wing (S) SRW16354	3.00	4.50	6.00
11 BY 11	MGM (S) SE 4639	2.50	3.75	5.00
ON MY SIDE	London (S) PS587	2.50	3.75	5.00
WE CAN FLY	MGM (S) SE 4534	3.00	4.50	6.00

COX, Danny
TITLE	LABEL & NO.	GOOD	VERY GOOD	NEAR MINT
BIRTH ANNOUNCEMENT	Together (M) 1011	5.00	7.50	10.00

COXHILL, Lol
TITLE	LABEL & NO.	GOOD	VERY GOOD	NEAR MINT
EAR OF THE BEHOLDER	Ampex (S) C10132	5.00	7.50	10.00

COX, Mick, Band
TITLE	LABEL & NO.	GOOD	VERY GOOD	NEAR MINT
THE MICK COX BAND	Capitol (S) ST11175	2.50	3.75	5.00

COYLE, Jim and Mal Sharpe
TITLE	LABEL & NO.	GOOD	VERY GOOD	NEAR MINT
INSANE (BUT HILARIOUS) MINDS OF COYLE & SHARPE	Warner Bros. (M) W1573	7.00	14.00	21.00

CRABBY APPLETON
TITLE	LABEL & NO.	GOOD	VERY GOOD	NEAR MINT
CRABBY APPLETON	Elektra (S) EKS 74067	4.50	6.75	9.00
ROTTEN TO THE CORE	Elektra (S) EKS74106	4.50	6.75	9.00

CRACK THE SKY
TITLE	LABEL & NO.	GOOD	VERY GOOD	NEAR MINT
ANIMAL NOTES	Lifesong (S) 6005	3.50	5.25	6.00
ANIMAL NOTES (RI)	Lifesong (S) PZ 34998	2.50	3.75	5.00
CRACK THE SKY	Lifesong (S) 6000	3.50	5.25	6.00
CRACK THE SKY (RI)	Lifesong (S) PZ 34994	2.50	3.75	5.00
SAFETY IN NUMBERS	Lifesong (S) JZ 35041	2.00	3.00	4.00

CRADDOCK, Billy "Crash"
TITLE	LABEL & NO.	GOOD	VERY GOOD	NEAR MINT
BILLY "CRASH" CRADDOCK	Harmony (S) KH-32186	2.00	3.00	4.00
BILLY "CRASH" CRADDOCK	Capitol (S) ST 11758	2.00	3.00	4.00
BILLY "CRASH" CRADDOCK'S GREATEST HITS, VOL. 1	ABC (S) 850	2.50	3.75	5.00
"CRASH"	Dot (S) DOSD 2063	2.50	3.75	5.00
KNOCK THREE TIMES	ABC (S) 725	3.00	4.50	6.00
MR. COUNTRY ROCK	ABC (S) 788	3.00	4.50	6.00
TWO SIDES OF CRASH	ABC (S) 777	3.00	4.50	6.00
YOU BETTER MOVE ON	ABC (S) 753	3.00	4.50	6.00

CRAMER, Floyd
TITLE	LABEL & NO.	GOOD	VERY GOOD	NEAR MINT
LAST DATE	RCA (M) LPM2350	2.00	3.00	4.00
LAST DATE	RCA (S) LSP2350	2.50	3.75	5.00
LAST DATE	RCA (EP) EPA 4377	1.00	1.50	2.00
ON THE REBOUND	RCA (M) LPM2359	2.00	3.00	4.00
ON THE REBOUND	RCA (S) LSP2359	2.50	3.75	5.00
ON THE REBOUND	RCA (EP) LPC134	1.00	1.50	2.00

CRANE, Bob
TITLE	LABEL & NO.	GOOD	VERY GOOD	NEAR MINT
FUNNY SIDE OF TV	Epic (M) 24224	4.00	8.00	12.00
FUNNY SIDE OF TV	Epic (S) 26224	5.00	10.00	15.00

CRAWFORD, Johnny
TITLE	LABEL & NO.	GOOD	VERY GOOD	NEAR MINT
CAPTIVATING JOHNNY CRAWFORD	Del Fi (M) DF1220	5.00	10.00	15.00
GREATEST HITS, VOL 2	Del Fi (M) DFLP1248	6.00	12.00	18.00
GREATEST HITS, VOL 2	Del Fi (S) 1248	5.00	10.00	15.00
HIS GREATEST HITS	Del Fi (M) DFLP 1229	5.00	10.00	15.00
HIS GREATEST HITS	Del Fi (S) DFS1229	4.00	8.00	12.00
JOHNNY CRAWFORD SINGS SONGS FROM 'THE RESTLESS ONES'	Supreme (M) M110	4.00	8.00	12.00
RUMORS	Del Fi (M) DFLP 1224	4.00	8.00	12.00
RUMORS	Del Fi (S) DFS1224	3.00	6.00	9.00
YOUNG MAN'S FANCY, A	Del Fi (M) DFLP1223	4.00	8.00	12.00
YOUNG MAN'S FANCY, A	Del Fi (S) DFS 1223	3.00	6.00	9.00

CRAYTON, Pee Wee
TITLE	LABEL & NO.	GOOD	VERY GOOD	NEAR MINT
PEE WEE CRAYTON	Crown (M) CLP5175	4.00	10.00	16.00
THINGS I USED TO DO	Vanguard (S) VSD6566	3.00	4.50	6.00

CRAZY ELEPHANT
TITLE	LABEL & NO.	GOOD	VERY GOOD	NEAR MINT
CRAZY ELEPHANT	Bell (S) 6034	4.00	6.00	8.00

CRAZY HORSE
TITLE	LABEL & NO.	GOOD	VERY GOOD	NEAR MINT
CRAZY HORSE	Reprise (S) 6438	3.00	4.50	6.00
CRAZY HORSE AT CROOKED LAKE	Epic (S) KE31710	2.50	3.75	5.00
LOOSE	Reprise (S) MS2059	3.00	4.50	6.00

CRAZY OTTO
TITLE	LABEL & NO.	GOOD	VERY GOOD	NEAR MINT
CRAZY OTTO	Decca (M) DL 8113	4.00	6.00	8.00
CRAZY OTTO GOES SENTIMENTAL	Vocalion VL-3663	3.00	4.50	6.00
GOLDEN AWARD SONGS	Decca (M) DL-8919	3.00	4.50	6.00
GOLDEN AWARD SONGS	Decca (S) DL1-78919	3.50	5.25	7.00

CREACH, "Papa" John
TITLE	LABEL & NO.	GOOD	VERY GOOD	NEAR MINT
FILTHY	Grunt (S) 1009	3.50	5.25	7.00
I'M THE FIDDLE MAN	Buddah (S) 5649	3.50	5.25	7.00
PAPA JOHN CREACH	Grunt (S) 1003	4.00	6.00	8.00
PLAYING MY FIDDLE FOR YOU	Grunt (S) BFL1-0418	3.00	4.50	6.00

Also see JEFFERSON STARSHIP

CREAM
TITLE	LABEL & NO.	GOOD	VERY GOOD	NEAR MINT
DISRAELI GEARS	Atco (S) 33-232	4.00	6.00	8.00
EARLY CREAM	Springboard (S) 4037	4.00	6.00	8.00
FRESH CREAM	Atco (S) 33-206	4.00	6.00	8.00
GOODBYE	Atco (S) 7001	3.50	5.25	7.00
HEAVY CREAM	Polydor (S) 24-3502	3.00	4.50	6.00
OFF THE TOP	Polydor (S) 5529	3.00	4.50	6.00
WHEELS OF FIRE	Atco (S) 2-700	4.50	6.75	9.00

Also see CLAPTON, Eric; DEREK & THE DOMINOES; BAKER'S, Ginger, Air Force

CREATIVE SOURCE
TITLE	LABEL & NO.	GOOD	VERY GOOD	NEAR MINT
CREATIVE SOURCE	Sussex (S) 8027	2.50	3.75	5.00
MIGRATION	Sussex (S) 8035	2.50	3.75	5.00
PASS THE FEELIN' ON	Polydor (S) 6052	2.00	3.00	4.00

CREATURES
TITLE	LABEL & NO.	GOOD	VERY GOOD	NEAR MINT
MONSTER RALLY	RCA (M) LPM1923	2.50	3.75	5.00
MONSTER RALLY	RCA (S) LSP1923	3.50	5.25	7.00

CREDIBILITY GAP
TITLE	LABEL & NO.	GOOD	VERY GOOD	NEAR MINT
A GREAT GIFT IDEA	Reprise (S) MS2154	2.50	3.75	5.00

CREEDENCE CLEARWATER REVIVAL
TITLE	LABEL & NO.	GOOD	VERY GOOD	NEAR MINT
BAYOU COUNTRY	Fantasy (S) 8387	3.00	4.50	6.00
CHRONICLE	Fantasy (S) CCR-2	3.00	4.50	6.00
COSMO'S FACTORY	Fantasy (S) 8402	3.00	4.50	6.00
CREEDENDE CLEARWATER REVIVAL	Fantasy (S) 8382	3.00	4.50	6.00
CREEDENCE GOLD	Fantasy (S) 9418	2.50	3.75	5.00
GREEN RIVER	Fantasy (S) 8393	3.00	4.50	6.00
LIVE IN EUROPE	Fantasy (S) CCR-1	3.00	4.50	6.00
MARDI GRAS	Fantasy (S) 9404	2.50	3.75	5.00
MORE CREEDENCE GOLD	Fantasy (S) 9430	2.50	3.75	5.00
PENDULUM	Fantasy (S) 8410	3.00	4.50	6.00
WILLY AND THE POORBOYS	Fantasy (S) 8397	3.00	4.50	6.00

Also see JOHN FOGERTY, TOM FOGERTY & DON HARRISON BAND.

CREME SODA
TITLE	LABEL & NO.	GOOD	VERY GOOD	NEAR MINT
TRICKY ZINGERS	Trinity (S) CST11 LA	3.50	5.25	7.00

CRESCENDOS
TITLE	LABEL & NO.	GOOD	VERY GOOD	NEAR MINT
OH JULIE	Guest Star (M) 1453	4.00	10.00	16.00

CRESTS
TITLE	LABEL & NO.	GOOD	VERY GOOD	NEAR MINT
BEST OF THE CRESTS	Coed (M) 904	10.00	25.00	40.00
BEST OF THE CRESTS	Coed (S) 904	20.00	50.00	80.00
CRESTS SING	Post (M) 3000	4.00	6.00	8.00
CRESTS SING ALL BIGGIES	Coed (M) 901	12.00	30.00	48.00

(M) Mono   (S) Stereo   (EP) Extended Play   (Q) Quad   (RI) Re-issued

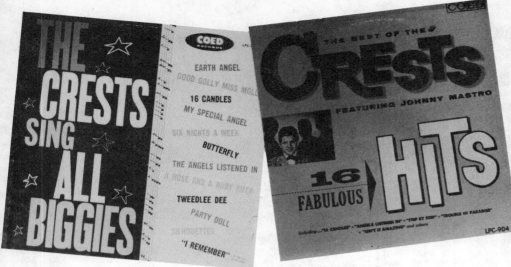 

TITLE	LABEL & NO.	GOOD	VERY GOOD	NEAR MINT
CREW CUTS				
CRAZY BOUT YOU BABY	Mercury (EP) E13261	2.00	4.00	6.00
CREW CUT CAPERS	Mercury (M) MG20143	6.00	12.00	18.00
CREW CUTS	Wing (M) MGW 12177	5.00	10.00	15.00
CREW CUTS GO LONG HAIR	Mercury (M) MG20067	5.00	10.00	15.00
CREW CUTS GO LONG HAIR	Mercury (EP) EP13325	2.00	4.00	6.00
CREW CUTS SING	RCA (M) LPM2037	2.50	3.75	5.00
CREW CUTS SING	RCA (S) LSP2037	2.50	3.75	5.00
CREW CUTS SING FOLK	Camay (M) 3002	2.00	3.00	4.00
CREW CUTS SING FOLK	Camay (S) CA3002	2.00	3.00	4.00
CREW CUTS SWING THE MASTERS	Mercury (EP) EP13327	2.00	4.00	6.00
CREW CUTS- TOPS IN POPS	Mercury (EP) EP13290	2.00	4.00	6.00
GREAT NEW SOUND OF THE CREW CUTS	Camay (M) 3002	2.50	3.75	5.00
HIGH SCHOOL FAVORITES	Wing (M) MGW-12180	5.00	10.00	15.00
LONG HAIR SWING WITH THE CREW CUTS	Mercury (EP) EP13326	2.00	3.00	6.00
MUSIC ALA CARTE	Mercury (M) MG20199	5.00	10.00	15.00
ON THE CAMPUS	Mercury (M) MG20140	5.00	10.00	15.00
ROCK AND ROLL BASH	Mercury (M) MG20144	6.00	12.00	18.00
SURPRISE PACKAGE	RCA (M) LPM1933	2.50	3.75	5.00
SURPRISE PACKAGE	RCA (S) LSP1933	2.50	3.75	5.00
3 CHEERS FOR THE CREW CUTS	Mercury (EP) EP13274	2.00	4.00	6.00
3 CHEERS FOR THE CREW CUTS	Mercury (EP) 13275	2.00	4.00	6.00
YOU MUST HAVE BEEN A BEAUTIFUL BABY	RCA (M) LPM2067	2.50	3.75	5.00
YOU MUST HAVE BEEN A BEAUTIFUL BABY	RCA (S) LSP2067	2.50	3.75	5.00
CREWE, Bob				
CRAZY IN THE HEART	Warwick (M) W 2034	4.00	10.00	16.00
KICKS	Warwick (M) W2009	4.00	10.00	16.00
KICKS	Warwick (S) WST2009	5.00	12.50	20.00
CREWE, Bob, Generation				
MUSIC TO WATCH GIRLS BY	DynoVoice (M) 9003	2.50	3.75	5.00
MUSIC TO WATCH GIRLS BY	DynoVoice (S) 9003	3.00	4.50	6.00
STREET TALK	Elektra (S) 7E-1083	2.50	3.75	5.00
CRICKETS				
CALIFORNIA SUN	Liberty (M) LRP3351	5.00	12.50	20.00
CALIFORNIA SUN	Liberty (S) LST7351	6.00	15.00	24.00
CHIRPING CRICKETS	Brunswick (M) BL54038	16.00	40.00	64.00
CHIRPING CRICKETS	Brunswick (EP) EB 71036	6.00	12.00	18.00
CRICKETS, THE	Coral (EP) EC81192	5.00	12.50	20.00
IN STYLE WITH THE CRICKETS	Coral (M) CRL57320	8.00	20.00	32.00
REMNANTS	Vertigo (S) VEL1020	6.00	9.00	12.00
ROCKIN' 50'S ROCK 'N' ROLL	Barnaby (S) Z 30268	5.00	7.50	10.00
SOMETHING OLD, SOMETHING NEW, SOMETHING BLUE, SOMETHIN' ELSE	Liberty (M) LRP3272	4.00	10.00	16.00
SOMETHING OLD, SOMETHING NEW, SOMETHING BLUE, SOMETHIN' ELSE	Liberty (S) LST7272	5.00	12.50	20.00
SOUND OF THE CRICKETS	Brunswick (EP) EB 71038	6.00	12.00	18.00
Also see HOLLY, Buddy				
CRITTERS				
CRITTERS	Project 3 (S) PR4002	3.50	5.25	7.00
TOUCH'N GO WITH THE CRITTERS	Project 3 (S) PR4001	3.50	5.25	7.00
YOUNGER GIRL	Kapp (M) 1485	3.50	5.25	7.00
YOUNGER GIRL	Kapp (S) 3485	4.00	6.00	8.00
CROCE, Ingrid and Jim				
CROCE	Capitol (S) ST315	10.00	15.00	20.00
CROCE, Jim				
FACES I'VE BEEN	Lifesong (S) 900	5.00	7.50	10.00
I GOT A NAME	ABC (S) 797	4.00	6.00	8.00
I GOT A NAME	Command (Q) 40008	3.00	4.50	6.00
I GOT A NAME (RI)	Lifesong (S) JZ 35009	2.50	3.75	5.00
LIFE & TIMES	ABC (S) 769	4.00	6.00	8.00
LIFE & TIMES	Command (Q) 40007	3.00	4.50	6.00
LIVE & TIMES (RI)	Lifesong (S) JZ 35008	2.50	3.75	5.00
PHOTOGRAPHS & MEMORIES	ABC (S) 835	4.00	6.00	8.00
PHOTOGRAPHS & MEMORIES	Command (S) 40020	3.00	4.50	6.00
PHOTOGRAPHS & MEMORIES (RI)	Lifesong (S) JZ 35010	2.50	3.75	5.00
YOU DON'T MESS AROUND WITH JIM	ABC (S) 756	4.00	6.00	8.00
YOU DON'T MESS AROUND WITH JIM	Command (Q) 40006	3.00	4.50	6.00
YOU DON'T MESS AROUND WITH JIM (RI)	Lifesong (S) JZ 34993	2.50	3.75	5.00
CROCHET, Cleveland and All The Sugar Bees				
CLEVELAND CROCHET AND ALL THE SUGAR BEES	Goldband (M) GRLP7749	5.00	7.50	10.00
CRONKITE, Walter				
BIG NEWS OF '59	Columbia (M) ML-5461	3.00	6.00	9.00
CROPPER, Steve				
WITH A LITTLE HELP FROM MY FRIENDS	Volt (S) VOS6006	3.50	5.25	7.00
CROSBY, Bing				
ACCENTUATE THE POSITIVE	Decca (M) DL4258	3.00	4.50	6.00
ANYTHING GOES	Decca (M) DL4264	3.00	4.50	6.00
AROUND THE WORLD WITH BING CROSBY	Decca (M) DL8687	2.50	3.74	5.00
BELLS OF ST. MARY'S	Decca (M) DL5052	3.00	4.50	6.00
BING CROSBY	Brunswick (M) BL58000-1	3.00	4.50	6.00
BING IN PARIS	Decca (M) DL8780	2.50	3.75	5.00
BINGLE DER	Columbia (M) CL2502	2.50	3.75	5.00
BING-MUSICAL AUTOBIOGRAPHY, 1927-1934	Decca (M) DL9054	2.50	3.75	5.00
BING SINGS HITS	Decca (M) DL5520	2.50	3.75	5.00
BING WITH DIXIELAND BANDS	Decca (M) DL5323	2.50	3.75	5.00
BLUE OF THE NIGHT	Decca (M) DL5105	2.50	3.75	5.00
BLUE SKIES	Decca (M) DL4259	3.00	4.50	6.00
BUT BEAUTIFUL	Decca (M) DL4260	3.00	4.50	6.00
CHRISTMAS GREETINGS	Decca (M) DL5020	3.00	4.50	6.00
A CHRISTMAS SING WITH BING	Decca (M) DL8419	2.50	3.75	5.00
A CHRISTMAS SING WITH BING	Decca (EP) ED850	1.00	1.50	2.00
CHRISTMAS TIME	Decca (EP) ED2547	1.00	1.50	2.00
COLLECTION OF EARLY RECORDINGS VOLUMES 1 & 2	Brunswick (EP) EB1011	1.50	2.25	3.00
COLLECTION OF EARLY RECORDINGS VOLUMES 1 & 2	Brunswick (EP) EB1010	1.50	2.25	3.00
COLLECTORS CLASSICS VOL 1	Decca (M) DL6008	2.50	3.75	5.00
COLLECTORS CLASSICS VOL 2	Decca (M) DL6009	2.50	3.75	5.00
COLLECTORS CLASSICS VOL 3	Decca (M) DL6010	2.50	3.75	5.00
COLLECTORS CLASSICS VOL 4	Decca (M) DL6011	2.50	3.75	5.00
COLLECTORS CLASSICS VOL 5	Decca (M) DL6012	2.50	3.75	5.00
COLLECTORS CLASSICS VOL 6	Decca (M) DL6013	2.50	3.75	5.00
COLLECTORS CLASSICS VOL 7	Decca (M) DL6014	2.50	3.75	5.00
COLLECTORS CLASSICS VOL 8	Decca (M) DL6015	2.50	3.75	5.00
COOL OF THE EVENING	Decca (M) DL4262	3.00	4.50	6.00
COUNTRY GIRL	Decca (M) DL5556	2.50	3.75	5.00
COUNTRY STYLE	Decca (M) DL5331	2.50	3.75	5.00
COWBOY SONGS VOL 1	Decca (M) DL5107	2.50	3.75	5.00
COWBOY SONGS VOL 2	Decca (M) DL5129	2.50	3.75	5.00
CROSBY CLASSICS VOL 1	Columbia (M) CL6027	3.00	4.50	6.00
CROSBY CLASSICS VOL 1	Columbia (EP) B280	1.00	1.50	2.00
CROSBY CLASSICS VOL 2	Columbia (M) CL6105	3.00	4.50	6.00
CROSBY CLASSICS VOL 2	Columbia (EP) B281	1.00	1.50	2.00
DON'T FENCE ME IN	Decca (M) DL5063	3.00	4.50	6.00
DOWN MEMORY LANE	Decca (M) DL5340	2.50	3.75	5.00
DOWN MEMORY LANE VOL. 2	Decca (M) DL 5343	2.50	3.75	5.00
DRIFTING AND DREAMING	Decca (M) DL5119	2.50	3.75	5.00
EAST SIDE OF HEAVEN	Decca (M) DL4253	3.00	4.50	6.00
EASY TO REMEMBER	Decca (M) DL4250	3.00	4.50	6.00
EL BINGO	Decca (M) DL5011	3.00	4.50	6.00
EMPEROR WALTZ	Decca (M) DL5272	2.50	3.75	5.00
FAVORITE HAWAIIAN SONGS	Decca (M) DL5299	2.50	3.75	5.00

(M) Mono (S) Stereo (EP) Extended Play (Q) Quad (RI) Re-issued

TITLE	LABEL & NO.	GOOD	VERY GOOD	NEAR MINT
FOSTER	Decca (M) DL5010	3.00	4.50	6.00
GERSHWIN	Decca (M) DL5081	3.00	4.50	6.00
GO WEST YOUNG MAN	Decca (M) DL5302	2.50	3.75	5.00
HAWIIAN FAVORITES VOL 1	Decca (M) DL5122	2.50	3.75	5.00
HITS FROM BROADWAY SHOWS	Decca (M) DL5298	2.50	3.75	5.00
HOLIDAY INN	Decca (M) DL4256	3.00	4.50	6.00
HOLIDAY INN SELECTIONS	Decca (M) DL5092	3.00	4.50	6.00
HOME ON THE RANGE	Decca (M) DL8210	2.50	3.75	5.00
HOME ON THE RANGE	Decca (EP) ED566	1.00	1.50	2.00
ICHABOD CRANE	Decca (M) DLP 6001	2.50	3.75	5.00
JERRY KERN SONGS	Decca (M) DLP5001	3.00	4.50	6.00
KING IN THE 1930'S	Brunswick (M) BL54005	3.00	4.50	6.00
LITTLE BOY LOST	Decca (M) DL5556	2.50	3.75	5.00
LULLABY TIME	Decca (M) DL8110	2.50	3.75	5.00
MERRY CHRISTMAS	Decca (M) DL5019	2.50	3.75	5.00
MERRY CHRISTMAS	Decca (EP) ED547	1.00	1.50	2.00
MR. MUSIC	Decca (M) DL5284	2.50	3.75	5.00
MY GOLDEN FAVORITES	Decca (M) DL4086	2.00	3.00	4.00
ONCE OVER LIGHTLY	Decca (EP) ED2550	1.00	1.50	2.00
ONLY FOREVER	Decca (M) DL4255	3.00	4.50	6.00
PENNIES FROM HEAVEN	Decca (M) DL4251	3.00	4.50	6.00
POCKET FULL OF DREAMS	Decca (M) DL4252	3.00	4.50	6.00
PORTER	Decca (M) DL5064	3.00	4.50	6.00
ROAD BEGINS	Decca (M) DL4254	3.00	4.50	6.00
ST. PATRICKS DAY	Decca (M) DL5037	3.00	4.50	6.00
ST VALENTINE'S DAY	Decca (M) DL5039	3.00	4.50	6.00
SMALL ONE	Decca (M) DL6000	2.50	3.75	5.00
SOME FINE OLD CHESTNUTS	Decca (M) DL5508	2.50	3.75	5.00
SOME FINE OLD CHESTNUTS	Decca (M) DL8374	2.50	3.75	5.00
SOME FINE OLD CHESTNUTS	Decca (EP) ED2107	1.00	1.50	2.00
SOME FINE OLD CHESTNUTS	Decca (EP) ED2108	1.00	1.50	2.00
SONG HITS OF PARIS	Decca (M) DL5499	2.50	3.75	5.00
SONGS I WISH I HAD SUNG	Decca (M) DL8352	2.50	3.75	5.00
SONGS I WISH I HAD SUNG	Decca (S) DL7-8352	2.50	3.75	5.00
SONGS I WISH I HAD SUNG	Decca (EP) ED2426	1.00	1.50	2.00
SONGS I WISH I HAD SUNG	Decca (EP) ED 2427	1.00	1.50	2.00
SONGS I WISH I HAD SUNG	Decca (EP) ED 2428	1.00	1.50	2.00
STARDUST	Decca (M) DL5126	2.50	3.75	5.00
SUNSHINE CAKE	Decca (M) DL4261	3.00	4.50	6.00
SWINGING ON A STAR	Decca (M) DL4257	3.00	4.50	6.00
THAT CHRISTMAS FEELING	Decca (M) DL8781	2.50	3.75	5.00
TWILIGHT ON THE TRAIL	Decca (M) DL8365	2.50	3.75	5.00
WAY BACK HOME	Decca (M) DL5310	2.50	3.75	5.00
WHEN IRISH EYES ARE SMILING	Decca (M) DL8262	2.50	3.75	5.00
WHEN IRISH EYES ARE SMILING	Decca (M) DL5403	2.50	3.75	5.00
WHITE CHRISTMAS	Decca (M) DL8083	2.50	3.75	5.00
YOURS IS MY HEART ALONE	Decca (M) DL5326	2.50	3.75	5.00
ZING A LITTLE ZONG	Decca (M) DL4263	3.00	4.50	6.00

CROSBY, Chris

MEET CHRIS CROSBY	MGM (M) E4226	3.50	5.25	7.00
MEET CHRIS CROSBY	MGM (S) SE4226	4.50	6.75	9.00

CROSBY, David & Graham Nash

LIVE	ABC (S) 1042	2.00	3.00	4.00
WHISTLING DOWN THE WIRE	ABC (S) 956	2.00	3.00	4.00
WIND ON THE WATER	ABC (S) 902	2.00	3.00	4.00

CROSBY, STILLS & NASH

CROSBY, STILLS & NASH	Atlantic (S) SD 8229	2.50	3.75	5.00
CSN	Atlantic (S) SD 19104	2.00	3.00	4.00

Crosby, Stills & Nash

CROSBY, STILLS, NASH & YOUNG

DEJA VU	Atlantic (S) SD 7200	3.00	4.50	6.00
GREATEST HITS	Atlantic (S) 7284	3.00	4.50	6.00
SO FAR	Atlantic (S) 18100	2.50	3.75	5.00

Also see BUFFALO SPRINGFIELD; NASH, Graham; STILLS, Stephen; YOUNG, Neil.

CROSSFIRES

TITLE	LABEL & NO.	GOOD	VERY GOOD	NEAR MINT
GUITARS IN MOTION	Edgemont (S)	3.00	4.50	6.00
LIMBO ROCK	Strand (M) SL1083	3.00	6.00	9.00
LIMBO ROCK	Strand (S) SLS1083	2.00	4.00	6.00

CROTHERS, Scatman

ROCK & ROLL WITH SCAT MAN	Tops (M) L1511	4.00	8.00	12.00
SCAT MAN CROTHERS AND JOE WILLIAMS	Grand Prix (M) K419	3.00	6.00	9.00

BEST OF CROW	Amaret (S) ST5012	3.00	4.50	6.00
CROW BY CROW	Amaret (S) ST5006	3.00	4.50	6.00
CROW MUSIC	Amaret (S) ST5002	3.00	4.50	6.00

CROWBAR

BAD MANORS	Paramount (S) PAS 6007	3.50	5.25	7.00
CROWBAR	Epic (S) KE32746	3.00	4.50	6.00
OFFICIAL MUSIC	Paramount (S) PAS 5030	3.50	5.25	7.00

CRUDUP, Arthur Big Boy

ARTHUR BIG BOY CRUDUP	Fire (M) 103	10.00	15.00	20.00
CRUDUP'S MOOD	Delmark (S) DS621	4.00	6.00	8.00
FATHER OF ROCK AND ROLL	RCA (M) 573	2.00	3.00	4.00
THE FATHER OF ROCK AND ROLL	RCA (S) LSP573	3.50	5.25	7.00
LOOK ON YONDERS WALL	Delmark (S) DS614	4.00	6.00	8.00
MEAN OLD FRISCO	Blue Horizon (M) 763855	4.00	6.00	8.00
MEAN OL' FRISCO	Fire (M) 103	8.00	20.00	32.00

CRUM, Simon (Ferlin Husky)

UNPREDICTABLE SIMON CRUM	Capitol (M) T-1880	3.00	6.00	9.00
UNPREDICTABLE SIMON CRUM	Capitol (S) ST1880	4.00	8.00	12.00

CRYAN SHAMES

A SCRATCH IN THE SKY	Columbia (M) CL2786	3.00	4.50	6.00
A SCRATCH IN THE SKY	Columbia (S) CS9586	4.00	6.00	8.00
SUGAR AND SPICE	Columbia (M) CL2589	4.00	6.00	8.00
SYNTHESIS	Columbia (S) CS9719	4.00	6.00	8.00

CRYSTAL MANSION

THE CRYSTAL MANSION	Rare Earth (S) R540L	2.50	3.75	5.00

CRYSTALS

CRYSTALS SING THE GREATEST HITS VOL. 1	Philles (M) PHLP 4003	8.00	20.00	32.00
HE'S A REBEL	Philles (M) PHLP 4001	9.00	22.50	36.00

TWIST UPTOWN	Philles (M) PHLP 4000	11.00	27.50	44.00

CUBY & THE BLIZZARDS

KING OF THE WORLD	Philips (S) 600-331	3.00	4.50	6.00
LIVE	Philips (S) 600-307	3.00	4.50	6.00

CULLEN, Bill

BILL CULLEN'S MINSTREL SHOW	ABC (M) ABC-264	2.50	3.75	5.00
BILL CULLEN'S MINSTREL SHOW	ABC (S) ABCS-264	3.00	4.50	6.00

(M) Mono (S) Stereo (EP) Extended Play (Q) Quad (RI) Re-issued

CULT
MAIL MUST GO THROUGH, The	Starburst (S) SLT-500	3.00	4.50	6.00

BURTON CUMMINGS	Portrait (S) PR 34261	2.00	3.00	4.00
BURTON CUMMINGS	Portrait (Q) PRQ 34261	2.00	3.00	4.00
MY OWN WAY TO ROCK	Portrait (S) PR 34698	2.00	3.00	4.00

Also see GUESS WHO.

CUNHA, Rick
CUNHA: SONGS	GRC (S) 5004	3.00	4.50	6.00
MOVING PICTURES	Columbia (S) PC-33697	2.50	3.75	5.00

CUPID'S INSPIRATION
CUPID'S INSPIRATION	Date (S) TES 4020	3.00	3.75	6.00

CURB, Mike, Congregation
IT'S A SMALL WORLD	Vista (S) 5006	2.00	3.00	4.00

CURLESS, Dick
DICK CURLESS	Capitol (S) ST 11119	1.50	2.25	3.00
LAST BLUES SONG	Capitol (S) ST 11211	1.50	2.25	3.00
SOUL OF DICK CURLESS	Tower (M) T 5013	2.00	4.00	6.00
TOMBSTONE EVERY MILE	Tower (M) T 5005	2.00	4.00	6.00
WILD SIDE OF TOWN	Tower (M) T 5137	2.00	4.00	6.00

CURTIS, Ken (Festus)
GUNSMOKE'S FESTUS	Capitol (M) T-2418	2.00	3.00	4.00
GUNSMOKE'S FESTUS	Capitol (S) ST-2418	2.00	3.00	4.00

CURTIS, Mac
GOOD ROCKIN TOMORROW	Rollin Rock (M) LP007	4.00	6.00	8.00
RUFFABILLY	Rollin Rock (M) LP 002	4.00	6.00	8.00
SUNSHINE MAN	Epic (S) BN 26419	4.50	6.75	9.00

CURTIS, Sonny
BEATLE HITS (Flamenco Guitar Style)	Imperial (M) 9276	3.00	6.00	9.00
BEATLE HITS (Flamenco Guitar Style)	Imperial (S) 12276	4.00	8.00	12.00
1ST OF SONNY CURTIS	Viva (S) V 36012	3.00	4.50	6.00
SONNY CURTIS STYLE, THE	Viva (S) V36021	3.00	4.50	6.00

CYMANDE
CYMANDE	Janus (S) 3044	3.00	4.50	6.00

CYMARRON
RINGS	Entrance (S) Z 30962	3.50	5.25	7.00

CYMBAL, Johnny
MR. BASS MAN	Kapp (M) KL 1324	4.00	8.00	12.00
MR. BASS MAN	Kapp (S) KS 3324	5.00	10.00	15.00

CYRKLE
NEON	Columbia (M) CL2632	4.00	6.00	8.00
NEON	Columbia (S) CS9432	5.00	7.50	10.00
RED RUBBER BALL	Columbia (M) CL2544	4.00	6.00	8.00
RED RUBBER BALL	Columbia (S) CS9344	5.00	7.50	10.00

D

DADA
DADA	Atco (S) SD33 352	5.00	7.50	10.00

DADDY COOL
DADDY COOL	Reprise (R) SS 6471	5.50	8.25	11.00
TEENAGE HEAVEN	Reprise (S) MS 2088	4.50	6.75	9.00

DAE, Tommy
TOMMY DAE	Hitt (M) 7001	6.00	9.00	12.00

DAHLSTROM, Patti
PATTI DAHLSTROM	UNI (S) 73127	5.00	7.50	10.00
WAY I AM	20th Century (S) 421	2.00	3.00	3.00
YOUR PLACE OR MINE	20th Century (S) 461	2.00	3.00	4.00

DAILEY, Don
SURF STOMPIN	Crown (S) CST 314	3.00	6.00	9.00

DAISEY CHAIN
STRAIGHT OR LAME	United International (M) LPM 13001	3.00	6.00	9.00
STRAIGHT OR LAME	United International (S) LPS 13001	4.00	8.00	12.00

DAKUS, Wes, with the Rebels
THE WES DAKUS ALBUM	Capitol (M) T 6120	6.00	15.00	24.00
WES DAKUS' REBELS	Kapp (S) KS 3536	3.50	5.25	7.00

DALE, Dick, & His Deltones
CHECKERED FLAG	Capitol (M) T 2002	5.00	10.00	15.00
CHECKERED FLAG	Capitol (S) ST 2002	6.00	12.00	18.00
GREATEST HITS	GNP/Crescendo (S) GNPS2095	3.00	4.50	6.00
KING OF THE SURF GUITAR	Capitol (M) T 1930	5.00	10.00	15.00
KING OF THE SURF GUITAR	Capitol (S) ST 1930	6.00	12.00	18.00
MR. ELIMINATOR	Capitol (M) T 2053	5.00	10.00	15.00
MR. ELIMINATOR	Capitol (S) ST 2053	6.00	12.00	18.00
ROCK OUT WITH DICK DALE AND HIS DELTONES LIVE AT CIRO'S	Capitol (M) T 2293	5.00	10.00	15.00
ROCK OUT WITH DICK DALE AND HIS DELTONES LIVE AT CIRO'S	Capitol (S) ST 2293	6.00	12.00	18.00
SUMMER SURF	Capitol (S) ST 2111	6.00	12.00	18.00
SURFER'S CHOICE	Deltone (M) LPM 1001	5.00	10.00	15.00

DALE, Dick and The Hollywood Surfers
SURF FAMILY	Dubtone (M) LP 1246	3.50	7.00	10.50

DALE, Dick, Bo Troy and his Hot Rods
WILD HOT ROD	Diplomat (M) D 2304	2.50	5.00	7.50

DALE, Dick, The Surfaris, The Fireballs
HOT ROD DRAG RACES	Almor (M) A 109	3.50	7.00	10.50
HOT ROD DRAG RACES	Almor (S) AS 109	3.00	6.00	9.00
WORLD OF SURFING	Almor (M) A 108	3.50	7.00	10.50
WORLD OF SURFING	Almor (S) AS 108	3.00	6.00	9.00

DALE, Dick, The Surfaris, The Surf Boys, The Surf Kings
SURFING	Guest Star (M) G 1433	3.50	7.00	10.50

DALE & GRACE
I'M LEAVING IT UP TO YOU	Montel-Mitchelle (M) LP 100	4.00	8.00	12.00

DALE, Jimmy, & The Ding-A-Lings
ROCK PRETTY BABY	Decca (M) DL 8429	6.00	15.00	24.00
ROCK PRETTY BABY	Decca (EP) ED 2480	2.00	5.00	8.00
ROCK PRETTY BABY	Decca (EP) ED2431	2.00	5.00	8.00
ROCK PRETTY BABY	Decca (EP) ED2432	2.00	5.00	8.00

DALLAS COUNTY
DALLAS COUNTY	Enterprise (S) ENS 1011	2.50	3.75	5.00

DALTON, Kathy
AMAZING	Disc Reet (S) 2168	2.00	3.00	4.00
BOOGIE BANDS & ONE NIGHT STANDS	Disc Reet (S) 2208	2.50	3.75	5.00

DALTREY, Roger
DALTREY	MCA (S) 328	3.00	4.50	6.00
RIDE A ROCK HORSE	MCA (S) 2147	3.00	4.50	6.00

Also see WHO.

DAMITA JO
DAMITA JO	Mercury (M) MGC 201	2.00	3.00	4.00
DAMITA JO AT THE DIPLOMAT	Mercury (M) MG 20703	2.00	3.00	4.00
DAMITA JO AT THE DIPLOMAT	Mercury (S) SR 60703	2.00	3.00	4.00
DAMITA JO WITH STEVE GIBSON & THE RED CAPS	ABC Paramount (M) ABC378	2.50	3.75	5.00
I'LL SAVE THE LAST DANCE FOR YOU	Mercury (M) MG20642	2.00	3.00	4.00
I'LL SAVE THE LAST DANCE FOR YOU	Mercury (S) SR 60642	2.00	3.00	4.00
I'LL SAVE THE LAST DANCE FOR YOU	Mercury (EP) 1-4047	1.00	1.50	2.00

(M) Mono   (S) Stereo   (EP) Extended Play   (Q) Quad   (RI) Re-issued

47

DAMNATION

THE DAMNATION OF	LABEL & NO.	GOOD	VERY GOOD	NEAR MINT
ADAM BLESSING	United Artist (S) UAS 6738	3.00	4.50	6.00
THE SECOND DAMNATION	United Artists (S) UAS 6773	3.00	4.50	6.00
WHICH IS THE JUSTICE, WHICH IS THE THEIF	United Artists (S) UAS 5533	3.00	4.50	6.00

DAMONE, Vic

ANGELA MIA	Columbia (S) CS-8046	2.00	3.00	4.00
CLOSER THAN A KISS	Columbia (S) CS-8019	2.00	3.00	4.00
YOURS FOR A SONG	Wing (M) MGW-12182	2.00	3.00	4.00

DANA, Bill

JOSE JIMENEZ AT THE HUNGRY I	Kapp (M) KL 1238	2.50	3.75	5.00
JOSE JIMENEZ IN HOLLYWOOD	Kapp (M) KL 1332	2.00	3.00	4.00
JOSE JIMENEZ IN HOLLYWOOD	Kapp (S) KS 3332	2.00	3.00	4.00
JOSE JIMENEZ IN LAS VEGAS	Kapp (M) KL 1402	2.00	3.00	4.00
JOSE JIMENEZ IN LAS VEGAS	KAPP (S) KS 3402	2.00	3.00	4.00
JOSE JIMENEZ IN ORBIT (Bill Dana on Earth)	Kapp (M) KL 1257	2.50	3.75	5.00
JOSE JIMENEZ OUR SECRET WEAPON	Kapp (M) KL 1320	2.00	3.00	4.00
JOSE JIMENEZ OUR SECRET WEAPON	Kapp (S) KS 3320	2.00	3.00	4.00
JOSE JIMENEZ TALKS TO TEENAGERS	Kapp (M) KL 1304	2.50	3.75	5.00
MORE JOSE JIMENEZ	Kapp (M) KL 1215	2.50	3.75	5.00
MY NAME---JOSE JIMENEZ	Signature (M) 1013	3.50	5.25	7.00

Also see Jose Jimenez

DANA, Vic

CRYSTAL CHANDELIER	Dolton (M) B 2041	2.00	3.00	4.00
CRYSTAL CHANDELIER	Dolton (S) BST 8041	2.00	3.00	4.00
GOLDEN GREATS	Dolton (M) BL 2048	2.50	3.75	5.00
GOLDEN GREATS	Dolton (S) BST 8048	2.50	3.75	5.00
LITTLE ALTAR BOY	Dolton (M) BL 2049	2.00	3.00	4.00
LITTLE ALTAR BOY	Dolton (S) BST 8049	2.00	3.00	4.00
RED ROSES FOR A BLUE LADY	Dolton (M) B 2034	2.50	3.75	5.00
RED ROSES FOR A BLUE LADY	Dolton (S) BST 8034	2.50	3.75	5.00
SHANGRI-LA	Dolton (M) BL 2028	2.00	3.00	4.00
SHANGRI-LA	Dolton (S) BST 8028	2.00	3.00	4.00
TOWN & COUNTRY	Dolton (M) BL 2046	2.00	3.00	4.00
TOWN & COUNTRY	Dolton (S) BST 8046	2.00	3.00	4.00
VIVA	Dolton (M) BL 2044	2.00	3.00	4.00
VIVA	Dolton (S) BST 8044	2.00	3.00	4.00
WARM & WILD	Dolton (M) BLP 2015	2.00	3.00	4.00
WARM & WILD	Dolton (S) BST 8015	2.00	3.00	4.00

DANIEL, Godfrey

TAKE A SAD SONG	Atlantic (S) SD 7219	4.50	6.75	9.00

DANIELS, Charlie, Band

CHARLIE DANIELS	Capitol (S) ST-11414	2.50	3.75	5.00
FIRE ON THE MOUNTAIN	Kama Sutra (S) 2603	3.00	4.50	6.50
FIRE ON THE MOUNTAIN (RI)	Epic (S) 34365	2.00	3.00	4.00
HIGH LONESOME	Epic (S) PE 34377	2.00	3.00	4.00
HONEY IN THE ROCK	Kama Sutra (S) 2071	3.00	4.50	6.00
NIGHT RIDER	Kama Sutra (S) 2607	3.00	4.50	6.00
NIGHTRIDER (RI)	Epic (S) 34402	2.00	3.00	4.00
MIDNIGHT WIND	Epic (S) PE 34970	2.00	3.00	4.00
SADDLE TRAMP	Epic (S) 34150	2.00	3.00	4.00
TE JOHN, GREASE & WOLFMAN	Epic (S) JE 34665	2.00	3.00	4.00
UNEASY RIDER	Epic (S) 34369	2.00	3.00	4.00
WAY DOWN YONDER	Kama Sutra (S) 2076	3.00	4.50	6.00
WHISKEY	Epic (S) 34664	2.00	3.00	4.00

DANKS

DANKS	Colossus (S) CS 1005	2.25	3.50	4.50

DANTE, Ron

BRINGS YOU UP	Kirshner (S) KES 106	4.50	6.75	9.00

Also see ARCHIES & CUFF LINKS

DANTE AND THE EVERGREENS

	LABEL & NO.	GOOD	VERY GOOD	NEAR MINT
DANTE AND THE EVERGREENS	Madison (M) LP 1002	10.00	25.00	40.00

DARIN, Bobby

BEST OF BOBBY DARIN	Capitol (M) T 2571	3.00	6.00	9.00
BEST OF BOBBY DARIN	Capitol (S) ST 2571	4.00	8.00	12.00
BOBBY DARIN	Atco (M) 33-102	8.00	20.00	32.00
BOBBY DARIN	Atco (EP) 4502	1.50	3.75	6.00
BOBBY DARIN	Atco (EP) 4505	1.50	3.75	6.00
BOBBY DARIN	Direction (S) 1936	3.00	6.00	9.00
BOBBY DARIN	Motown (S) 753	3.00	4.50	6.00
BOBBY DARIN SINGS DOCTOR DOLITTLE	Atlantic (M) 8154	4.00	8.00	12.00
BOBBY DARIN SINGS DOCTOR DOLITTLE	Atlantic (S) SD 8154	5.00	10.00	15.00
BOBBY DARIN SINGS RAY CHARLES	Atco (M) 33 140	4.00	8.00	12.00
BOBBY DARIN SINGS RAY CHARLES	Atco (S) SD 33 140	5.00	10.00	15.00
BOBBY DARIN STORY (White Cover)	Atco (M) 33 131	5.00	12.50	20.00
BOBBY DARIN STORY (White Cover)	Atco (S) SD 33131	6.00	15.00	24.00
BOBBY DARIN STORY (Black Cover)	Atco (S) SD33 131	2.50	3.75	5.00
BOBBY DARIN WINNERS	Atco (S) SD 33 167	5.00	12.50	15.00
COMMITMENT	Direction (S) 1937	3.00	6.00	9.00
DARIN AT THE COPA	Atco (M) 33 122	4.00	10.00	16.00
DARIN AT THE COPA	Atco (S) SD 33 122	5.00	12.50	20.00
DARIN AT THE COPA	Atco (EP) 4512	1.50	3.75	6.00
DARIN 1936 - 1973	Motown (S) 813	3.00	4.50	6.00
EARTHY	Capitol (M) T 1826	3.00	6.00	9.00
EARTHY	Capitol (S) ST 1826	4.00	8.00	12.00
18 YELLOW ROSES	Capitol (M) T 1942	3.00	6.00	9.00
18 YELLOW ROSES	Capitol (S) ST 1942	4.00	8.00	12.00
FOR TEENAGERS ONLY	Atco (S) SP1001	6.00	12.00	18.00
FOR TEENAGERS ONLY	Atco (EP) 4513	1.50	3.75	6.00
FROM HELLO DOLLY TO GOODBYE CHARLIE	Capitol (M) T 2194	3.00	6.00	9.00
FROM HELLO DOLLY TO GOODBYE CHARLIE	Capitol (S) ST 2194	4.00	8.00	12.00
GOLDEN FOLK HITS	Capitol (S) T2007	3.00	6.00	9.00
GOLDEN FOLK HITS	Capitol (S) ST 2007	4.00	8.00	12.00
IF I WERE A CARPENTER	Atlantic (M) 8135	4.00	8.00	12.00
IF I WERE A CARPENTER	Atlantic (S) SD 8135	5.00	10.00	15.00
IN A BROADWAY BAG	Atlantic (M) 8126	4.00	8.00	12.00
IN A BROADWAY BAG	(S) SD 8126	5.00	10.00	15.00
INSIDE OUT	Atlantic (M) 8142	4.00	8.00	12.00
INSIDE OUT	Atlantic (S) SD 8142	5.00	10.00	15.00
LOVE SWINGS	Atco (M) 33 134	4.00	8.00	12.00
LOVE SWINGS	Atco (S) SD 33 134	5.00	10.00	15.00
OH! LOOK AT ME NOW	Capitol (M) T 1791	3.00	6.00	9.00
OH! LOOK AT ME NOW	Capitol (S) ST 1791	4.00	8.00	12.00
SHADOW OF YOUR SMILE	Atlantic (M) 8121	4.00	8.00	12.00
SHADOW OF YOUR SMILE	Atlantic (S) 8121	5.00	10.00	15.00
THAT'S ALL	Atco (M) 33-104	6.00	15.00	24.00
THAT'S ALL	Atco (S) SD 33104	7.00	17.50	28.00
THAT'S ALL	Atco (EP) 4504	1.50	3.75	6.00
THINGS AND OTHER THINGS	Atco (M) 33 146	6.00	15.00	24.00
THINGS AND OTHER THINGS	Atco (S) SD 33 146	5.00	10.00	15.00
THIS IS DARIN	Atco (M) 33 115	6.00	15.00	24.00
THIS IS DARIN	Atco (S) SD 33 115	7.00	17.50	28.00
THIS IS DARIN	Atco (EP) 4508	1.50	3.75	6.00
25TH DAY OF DECEMBER WITH BOBBY DARIN	Atco (M) 33 125	4.00	10.00	16.00
25TH DAY OF DECEMBER WITH BOBBY DARIN	Atco (S) SD 33-125	5.00	12.50	20.00
TWIST WITH BOBBY DARIN	Atco (M) 33 138	4.00	10.00	16.00
TWIST WITH BOBBY DARIN	Atco (S) SD 33 138	5.00	12.50	20.00
TWO OF A KIND (With Johnny Mercer)	Atco (M) 33 126	4.00	10.00	16.00
TWO OF A KIND (With Johnny Mercer)	Atco (S) SD 33 126	5.00	12.50	20.00
VENICE BLUE	Capitol (M) T 2322	3.00	6.00	9.00
VENICE BLUE	Capitol (S) ST 2322	4.00	8.00	12.00
YOU'RE THE REASON I'M LIVING	Capitol (M) T 1866	3.00	6.00	9.00
YOU'RE THE REASON I'M LIVING	Capitol (S) ST 1866	4.00	8.00	12.00

(M) Mono (S) Stereo (EP) Extended Play (Q) Quad (RI) Re-issued

TITLE	LABEL & NO.	GOOD	VERY GOOD	NEAR MINT
DARREN, JAMES				
ALBUM NO. 1	Colpix (M) CP 406	4.00	8.00	12.00
GIDGET GOES HAWAIIAN (James Darren sings The Movies)	Colpix (M) CP 418	3.00	6.00	9.00
GIDGET GOES HAWAIIAN (James Darren sings The Movies)	Colpix (S) SCP 418	4.00	8.00	12.00
JAMES DARREN SINGS FOR ALL SIZES	Colpix (M) CP 424	3.00	6.00	9.00
LOVE AMONG THE YOUNG	Colpix (M) CP 428	3.00	6.00	9.00
LOVE SONGS FROM THE MOVIES	Kirshner (S) 116	2.50	3.75	5.00
MAMMY BLUE	Kirshner (S) 115	2.50	3.75	5.00
DARRELL, Johnny				
WATER GLASS OF WHISKEY	Capricorn (S) 0153	2.00	3.00	4.00
DARROW, Chris				
CHRIS DARROW	United Artists (S) UA-LA048	2.00	3.00	4.00
UNDER MY OWN DISGUISE	United Artists (S) UA-LA242	2.00	3.00	4.00
DARTELLS				
HOT PASTRAMI	Dot (M) DLP 3522	7.00	14.00	21.00
HOT PASTRAMI	Dot (S) DLP 25522	6.00	12.00	18.00
DARTS				
HOLLYWOOD DRAG	Del Fi (S) DFST 1244	4.00	8.00	12.00
DAUGHTERS OF ALBION				
DAUGHTERS OF ALBION	Fontana (S) SRF 67586	5.00	7.50	10.00
DAVE, DEE, DOZY, BEAKY, MICK, & TICH				
GREATEST HITS	Fontana (M) MGF 27567	4.00	6.00	8.00
GREATEST HITS	Fontana (S) SRF 67567	5.00	7.50	10.00
TIME TO TAKE OFF	Imperial (M) LP 12402	4.00	6.00	8.00
DAVEY & THE BADMEN				
WANTED	KRW (M) WA 63 054	15.00	37.50	60.00
DAVID, The				
ANOTHER DAY, ANOTHER LIFE TIME	VMC (S) VS 124	4.50	6.75	9.00
DAVID and JONATHAN				
MICHELLE	Capitol (M) T 2473	5.00	10.00	15.00
DAVIDSON, Brian				
EVERY WHICH WAY	Mercury (S) SR 61340	4.00	6.00	8.00
DAVIDSON, John				
TOUCH ME	20th Century (S) 429	2.00	3.00	4.00
WELL, HERE I AM	Mercury (S) SRM-1-658	2.00	3.00	4.00
DAVIE, Hutch				
MUCH HUTCH	Atco (M) 105	2.50	5.00	7.50
DAVIS, Danny & Nashville Brass				
CARIBBEAN CRUISE	RCA (S) APL1-0232	2.00	3.00	4.00
TURN ON SOME HAPPY	RCA (S) LSP-4803	2.50	3.75	5.00
DAVIS, Jesse Ed				
JESSE ED DAVIS	Atco (S) SD 33 346	3.00	4.50	6.00
KEEP ON COMMIN	Epic (S) KE 32133	2.50	3.75	5.00
ULULU	Atco (S) SD 33 382	3.00	4.50	6.00
DAVIS, Jimmie				
BEST OF JIMMIE DAVIS	MCA (S) 2-4085	2.00	3.00	4.00
NO ONE STANDS ALONE	Vocalion (M) VL-3676	2.00	3.00	4.00
SOMEONE TO CARE	Decca (M) DL-4037	2.00	3.00	4.00
SOMEONE TO CARE	Decca (S) DL-74037	2.00	3.00	4.00
SOUVENIRS OF YESTERDAY	Paula (S) 2226	2.00	3.00	4.00
SUNSHINE	Paula (S) 2230	2.00	3.00	4.00
SUPPERTIME	Decca (M) DL-8953	2.50	3.75	5.00
SUPPERTIME	Decca (S) DL-78953	2.50	3.75	5.00
YOU ARE MY SUNSHINE	Decca (EP) ED-2654	1.00	1.50	2.00
YOU ARE MY SUNSHINE	Decca (SEP) ED-72654	1.00	1.50	2.00
YOU ARE MY SUNSHINE	Decca (M) DL-8896	2.50	3.75	5.00
YOU ARE MY SUNSHINE	Decca (S) DL-78896	2.00	3.00	4.00
DAVIS, Mac				
ALL THE LOVE IN THE WORLD	Columbia (S) PC 32927	2.50	3.75	5.00
ALL THE LOVE IN THE WORLD	Columbia (Q) PCQ 32927	2.50	3.75	5.00
BABY DON'T GET HOOKED ON ME	Columbia (S) 31770	2.50	3.75	5.00
BABY DON'T GET HOOKED ON ME	Columbia (Q) 31770	2.50	3.75	5.00
BURNIN' THING	Columbia (S) PC 33551	2.50	3.75	5.00
BURNIN' THING	Columbia (Q) PCQ 33551	2.50	3.75	5.00
FOREVER LOVERS	Columbia (S) PC 34105	2.50	3.75	5.00
FOREVER LOVERS	Columbia (Q) PCQ 34105	2.50	3.75	5.00
I BELIEVE IN MUSIC	Columbia (S) 30926	2.50	3.75	5.00
MAC DAVIS	Columbia (S) KG 32206	2.50	3.75	5.00
STOP AND SMELL THE ROSES	Columbia (S) KC 32582	2.50	3.75	5.00
STOP AND SMELL THE ROSES	Columbia (Q) CQ 32582	2.50	3.75	5.00
THUNDER IN THE AFTERNOON	Columbia (S) PC 34313	2.50	3.75	5.00
THUNDER IN THE AFTERNOON	Columbia (Q) PCQ 34313	2.50	3.75	5.00

TITLE	LABEL & NO.	GOOD	VERY GOOD	NEAR MINT
DAVIS, Maxwell				
MAXWELL DAVIS AND HIS TENOR SAX (10")	Aladdin (M) 709	8.00	20.00	32.00
DAVIS, Paul				
PAUL DAVIS	Bang (S) 226	4.00	6.00	8.00
PAUL DAVIS (Orig. title)	Bang (S) 410	4.00	6.00	8.00
RIDE 'EM COWBOY	Bang (S) 401	3.00	4.50	6.00
SINGER OF SONGS, TELLER OF TALES	Bang (S) 410	2.50	3.75	5.00
SOUTHERN TRACKS AND FANTASIES	Bang (S) 405	3.00	4.50	6.00

Starring Sammy Davis Jr. — DECCA RECORDS — DL 8118

TITLE	LABEL & NO.	GOOD	VERY GOOD	NEAR MINT
DAVIS, Sammy Jr.				
ALL-STAR SPECTACULAR	Reprise (M) R-6033	2.00	3.00	4.00
ALL-STAR SPECTACULAR	Reprise (S) R9-6033	2.00	3.00	4.00
ALL THE WAY AND THEN SOME	Decca (M) DL8779	2.00	3.00	4.00
ALL THE WAY AND THEN SOME	Decca (EP) ED 2621	1.00	1.50	2.00
AS LONG AS SHE NEEDS ME	Reprise (M) R-6082	2.00	3.00	4.00
AS LONG AS SHE NEEDS ME	Reprise (S) R9-6082	2.00	3.00	4.00
AT THE COCONUT GROVE (2 LP's)	Reprise (M) R-6063/2	2.50	3.75	5.00
AT THE COCONUT GROVE (2 LP's)	Reprise (S) R9-6063/2	3.00	5.25	6.00
FEATURING SAMMY DAVIS JR	Capitol (EP) EAP 1 555	1.50	2.25	3.00
HERE'S LOOKIN' AT YOU	Decca (M) DL 8351	2.50	3.75	5.00
HERE'S LOOKIN AT YOU	Decca (EP) 2424	1.00	1.50	2.00
HERE'S LOOKIN AT YOU	Decca (EP) 2425	1.00	1.50	2.00
I GOTTA BE ME	Reprise (S) RS 6324	3.00	4.50	6.00
I GOTTA RIGHT TO SWING	Decca (M) DL8981	2.50	3.75	5.00
I GOTTA RIGHT TO SWING	Decca (S) DL7 8981	2.00	3.00	4.00
JUST FOR LOVERS	Decca (M) DL 8170	2.50	3.75	5.00
JUST FOR LOVERS	Decca (EP) 2237	1.00	1.50	2.00
JUST FOR LOVERS	Decca (EP) 2236	1.00	1.50	2.00
JUST FOR LOVERS	Decca (EP) 2285	1.00	1.50	2.00
MISTER WONDERFUL	Decca (M) DL 9032	2.50	3.75	5.00
MISTER WONDERFUL	(EP) ED 848	1.00	1.50	2.00
NOW	MGM (S) SE-4832	2.00	3.00	4.00
PORGY & BESS	Decca (M) DL 8854	2.50	3.75	5.00
PORGY & BESS	Decca (S) DL78854	2.00	3.00	4.00
PORGY & BESS	Decca (EP) ED 2647	1.00	1.50	2.00
PORGY & BESS	Decca (EP) ED7 2647	1.00	1.50	2.00
PORTRAIT OF SAMMY DAVIS JR	MGM (S) 4852	2.00	3.00	4.00
SALUTES THE STARS OF THE LONDON PALLADIUM	Reprise (M) R-6095	2.00	3.00	4.00
SALUTES THE STARS OF THE LONDON PALLADIUM	Reprise (S) R9-6095	2.00	3.00	4.00
SAMMY	MGM (S) 4914	2.00	3.00	4.00
SAMMY DAVIS JR., AT TOWN HALL	Decca (M) DL8841	2.50	3.75	5.00
SAMMY DAVIS JR., AT TOWN HALL	Decca (S) DL7 8841	2.00	3.00	4.00
SAMMY'S BACK ON BROADWAY	Reprise (M) R-6169	2.00	3.00	4.00
SAMMY'S BACK ON BROADWAY	Reprise (S) RS-6169	2.00	3.00	4.00
SHELTER OF YOUR ARMS	Reprise (M) R-6114	2.50	3.75	5.00
SHELTER OF YOUR ARMS	Reprise (S) RS-6114	3.00	4.50	6.00
STARRING SAMMY DAVIS JR.	Decca (M) DL 8118	2.50	3.75	5.00
STARRING SAMMY DAVIS JR.	Decca (EP) 2214	1.00	1.50	2.00
STARRING SAMMY DAVIS JR.	Decca (EP) 2215	1.00	1.50	2.00
STARRING SAMMY DAVIS JR	Decca (EP) 2216	1.00	1.50	2.00
SWING IS THE THING	Decca (EP) ED 2509	1.00	1.50	2.00
THAT'S ENTERTAINMENT	MGM (M) M3G 4965	2.00	3.00	4.00
A TREASURY OF GOLDEN HITS	Reprise (M) R-6096	2.00	3.00	4.00
A TREASURY OF GOLDEN HITS	Reprise (S) R9-6096	2.00	3.00	4.00
WHAT KIND OF FOOL AM I & OTHER SHOW-STOPPERS	Reprise (M) R-6051	3.50	5.25	7.00
WHAT KIND OF FOOL AM I & OTHER SHOW-STOPPERS	Reprise (S) R9-6051	4.00	6.00	8.00

(M) Mono (S) Stereo (EP) Extended Play (Q) Quad (RI) Re-issued

DAVIS, Skeeter

TITLE	LABEL & NO.	GOOD	VERY GOOD	NEAR MINT
BEST OF SKEETER DAVIS	RCA (S) APL1-0190	2.50	3.75	5.00
END OF THE WORLD	RCA (M) LPM 2699	3.00	4.50	6.00
END OF THE WORLD	RCA (S) LSP 2699	3.50	5.25	7.00
END OF THE WORLD	Camden (S) 2607	2.00	3.00	4.00
HILLBILLY SINGER	RCA (S) LSP-4818	2.00	3.00	4.00

DAVIS, Spencer, Group

TITLE	LABEL & NO.	GOOD	VERY GOOD	NEAR MINT
GIMME SOME LOVIN'	United Artists (M) UAL 3578	4.00	6.00	8.00
GIMME SOME LOVIN'	United Artists (S) UAS6578	5.00	7.50	10.00
GLUGGO	Vertigo (S) 1015	3.00	4.50	6.00
HEAVIES	United Artists(S) UAS 6691	5.00	7.50	10.00
I'M A MAN	United Artists (M) UAL 3589	4.00	6.00	8.00
I'M A MAN	United Artists (S) UAS 6589	5.00	7.50	10.00
SPENCER DAVIS GREATEST HITS	United Artists (M) UAL 3641	4.00	6.00	8.00
SPENCER DAVIS GREATEST HITS	United Artists (S) UAS 6641	5.00	7.50	10.00
VERY BEST OF THE SPENCER DAVIS GROUP	United Artists (S) UA-LA433	2.50	3.75	5.00
WITH THEIR NEW FACE ON	United Artists (M) UAL 3652	4.00	6.00	8.00
WITH THEIR NEW FACE ON	United Artists (S) UAS 6652	5.00	7.50	10.00

DAVIS, Tim

TITLE	LABEL & NO.	GOOD	VERY GOOD	NEAR MINT
PIPE DREAM	Metromedia (M) KMD 1054	3.00	4.50	6.00
TAKE ME AS I AM	Metromedia (S) BML 10175	3.00	4.50	6.00

DAWE, Tim

TITLE	LABEL & NO.	GOOD	VERY GOOD	NEAR MINT
PENROD	Straight (S) 1058	2.50	3.75	5.00

DAWKINS, Jimmy

TITLE	LABEL & NO.	GOOD	VERY GOOD	NEAR MINT
TRANSATLANTIC 770	Excello (M) 8024	2.00	4.00	6.00

DAY, Bobby

TITLE	LABEL & NO.	GOOD	VERY GOOD	NEAR MINT
ROCKIN' WITH ROBIN	Class (M) LP 5002	8.00	20.00	32.00

DAY, Doris

TITLE	LABEL & NO.	GOOD	VERY GOOD	NEAR MINT
APRIL IN PARIS	Columbia (EP) B 1581	1.00	1.50	2.00
BOYS AND GIRLS TOGETHER (With Danny Thomas)	Columbia (M) CL 2530	3.00	4.50	6.00
BY THE LIGHT OF THE SILVERY MOON	Columbia (M) CL 6248	2.50	3.75	5.00
BY THE LIGHT OF THE SILVERY MOON	Columbia (EP) B 334	1.00	1.50	2.00
CALAMITY JANE (With Howard Keel) (Soundtrack)	Columbia (M) CL 6273	2.50	3.75	5.00
CALAMITY JANE (With Howard Keel) (Soundtrack)	Columbia (EP) B 347	1.00	1.50	2.00
CALAMITY JANE (With Howard Keel) (Soundtrack)	Columbia (EP) B 1803	1.00	1.50	2.00
CALAMITY JANE (With Howard Keel) (Soundtrack)	Columbia (EP B 1804	1.00	1.50	2.00
CHRISTMAS ALBUM	Columbia (M) CL2226	2.00	3.00	4.00
CHRISTMAS ALBUM	Columbia (S) CS9026	2.00	3.00	4.00
CUTTIN' CAPERS	Columbia (M) CL 1232	2.00	3.00	4.00
CUTTIN' CAPERS	Columbia (S) CS 8078	2.00	3.00	4.00
CUTTIN' CAPERS	Columbia (EP) B-12321	1.00	1.50	2.00
CUTTIN' CAPERS	Columbia (EP) B-12322	1.00	1.50	2.00

(M) Mono (S) Stereo (EP) Extended Play (Q) Quad (RI) Re-issued

TITLE	LABEL & NO.	GOOD	VERY GOOD	NEAR MINT
CUTTIN' CAPERS	Columbia (EP) B-12323	1.00	1.50	2.00
DAY BY DAY	Columbia (M) CL942	2.50	3.75	5.00
DAY BY DAY	Columbia (EP) B9421	1.00	1.50	2.00
DAY BY DAY	Columbia (EP) 9422	1.00	1.50	2.00
DAY BY DAY	Columbia (EP) 9423	1.00	1.50	2.00
DAY BY NIGHT	Columbia (S) CS 8089	1.00	1.50	2.00
DAY DREAMS	Columbia (M) CL 624	3.00	4.50	6.00
DAY DREAMS	Columbia (EP) B 952	1.50	2.25	3.00
DAY IN HOLLYWOOD	Columbia (M) CL 749	3.00	4.50	6.00
DAY IN HOLLYWOOD	Columbia (EP) 7491	1.50	2.25	3.00
DAY IN HOLLYWOOD	Columbia (EP) 7492	1.50	2.25	3.00
DAY IN HOLLYWOOD	Columbia (EP) 7493	1.50	2.25	3.00
DAY IN HOLLYWOOD	Columbia (EP) B 1563	1.00	1.50	2.00
DORIS DAY	Columbia (EP) B2545	1.00	1.50	2.00
DORIS DAY	Columbia (EP) 2558	1.00	1.50	2.00
DORIS DAY	Columbia (EP) B 2615	1.00	1.50	2.00
DORIS DAY	Columbia (EP) B 2634	1.00	1.50	2.00
DORIS DAY'S GREATEST HITS	Columbia (M) CL 1210	2.50	3.75	5.00
FLOWER DRUM SONG (HITS)	Columbia (EP) B-2151	1.00	1.50	2.00
HITS FROM LIL ABNER	Columbia (EP) B2119	1.00	1.50	2.00
HOORAY FOR HOLLYWOOD, VOL 1	Columbia (S) CS-8066	2.00	3.00	4.00
HOORAY FOR HOLLYWOOD, VOL. 2	Columbia (S) CS-8067	2.00	3.00	4.00
HOT CANARIES (With Peggy Lee)	Columbia (M) CL2534	3.00	4.50	6.00
I'LL SEE YOU IN MY DREAMS	Columbia (M) CL 6198	2.50	3.75	5.00
I'LL SEE YOU IN MY DREAMS	Columbia (EP) B 289	1.00	1.50	2.00
LIGHTS, CAMERA, ACTION	Columbia (M) CL 2518	3.00	4.50	6.00
LOVE HIM	Columbia (M) CL 2131	2.00	3.00	4.00
LOVE HIM	Columbia (S) CS 8931	2.00	3.00	4.00
LOVE ME OR LEAVE ME (Soundtrack)	Columbia (M) CL 710	3.00	4.50	6.00
LOVE ME OR LEAVE ME (Soundtrack)	Columbia (EP B 540	1.50	2.25	3.00
LOVE ME OR LEAVE ME (Soundtrack)	Columbia (EP) B 2090	1.50	2.25	3.00
LULLABY OF BROADWAY	Columbia (M) CL 6168	3.00	4.50	6.00
LULLABY OF BROADWAY	Columbia (EP) B235	1.50	2.25	3.00
ON MOONLIGHT BAY	Columbia (M) CL 6186	3.00	4.50	6.00
ON MOONLIGHT BAY	Columbia (EP) B 267	1.50	2.25	3.00
PILLOW TALK	Columbia (EP) B-2156	1.00	1.50	2.00
SHOW TIME	Columbia (M) CL-1470	2.00	3.00	4.00
SHOW TIME	Columbia (S) CS-8261	2.00	3.00	4.00
SONGS FROM PETER PAN & CHRISTIAN ANDERSEN	Columbia (EP) B 1590	1.00	1.50	2.00
TEA FOR TWO	Columbia (M) CL 6149	3.00	4.50	6.00
TEA FOR TWO	Columbia (EP) B 215	1.50	2.25	3.00
WITH A SMILE & A SONG	Columbia (M) CL 2266	2.00	3.00	4.00
WITH A SMILE & A SONG	Columbia (S) CS9066	2.00	3.00	4.00
YOUNG AT HEART (With Frank Sinatra)	Columbia (M) CL 6339	2.50	3.75	5.00
YOUNG MAN WITH A HORN	Columbia (M) CL6106	3.00	4.50	6.00
YOUNG MAN WITH A HORN	Columbia (EP) B 198	1.50	2.25	3.00
YOU'RE MY THRILL	Columbia (M) CL 6071	3.00	4.50	6.00
YOU'RE MY THRILL	Columbia (EP) B 189	1.50	2.25	3.00

DAY BLINDNESS

TITLE	LABEL & NO.	GOOD	VERY GOOD	NEAR MINT
DAY BLINDNESS	Studio 10 (M) DBX 101	6.00	9.00	12.00

DEAD BOYS

TITLE	LABEL & NO.	GOOD	VERY GOOD	NEAR MINT
YOUNG, LOUD & SNOTTY	Sire (S) 6038	2.50	3.75	5.00

DEADLY ONES

TITLE	LABEL & NO.	GOOD	VERY GOOD	NEAR MINT
IT'S MONSTER SURFING TIME	Vee Jay (M) VJVLP 1090	3.00	6.00	9.00

DEAL, Bill and the Rhondels

TITLE	LABEL & NO.	GOOD	VERY GOOD	NEAR MINT
BEST OF BILL DEAL AND THE RHONDELS	Heritage (S) HTS 35006	4.00	6.00	8.00
VINTAGE ROCK	Heritage (S) HTS 35003	4.00	6.00	8.00

DEAN, Eddie

TITLE	LABEL & NO.	GOOD	VERY GOOD	NEAR MINT
HILLBILLY HEAVEN	Sage (M) C 16	2.50	3.75	5.00

DEAN, James

TITLE	LABEL & NO.	GOOD	VERY GOOD	NEAR MINT
JAMES DEAN	Warner Bros. (S) BS 2843	2.50	3.75	5.00

DEAN, Russell

TITLE	LABEL & NO.	GOOD	VERY GOOD	NEAR MINT
RUSSELL DEAN	Metromedia (S) K 1046	2.00	3.00	4.00

DEBRIS

TITLE	LABEL & NO.	GOOD	VERY GOOD	NEAR MINT
DEBRIS	Static Disposal (S) PIG 0000	3.50	5.25	7.00

DE BURGH, Chris

TITLE	LABEL & NO.	GOOD	VERY GOOD	NEAR MINT
AT THE END OF A PERFECT DAY	A&M (S) SP 4647	2.00	3.00	4.00
FAR BEYOND THESE CASTLE WALLS	A&M (S) SP 4516	2.00	3.00	4.00
SPANISH TRAIN & OTHER STORIES	A&M (S) SP 4568	2.00	3.00	4.00

DE CARO, Nick

TITLE	LABEL & NO.	GOOD	VERY GOOD	NEAR MINT
HAPPY HEART	A&M (S) SP 4176	2.00	3.00	4.00
ITALIAN GRAFFITI	Blue Thumb (S) 6011	2.00	3.00	4.00

DE CASTRO SISTERS

TITLE	LABEL & NO.	GOOD	VERY GOOD	NEAR MINT
DE CASTRO'S SING	Capitol (M) T 1402	2.50	3.75	5.00
DE CASTRO'S SING	Capitol (S) ST 1402	2.50	3.75	5.00
DE CASTRO SISTERS	Abbott (M) 5002	6.00	12.00	18.00

DECEMBERS CHILDREN

TITLE	LABEL & NO.	GOOD	VERY GOOD	NEAR MINT
DECEMBERS CHILDREN	Mainstream (S) S 6128	5.00	7.50	10.00

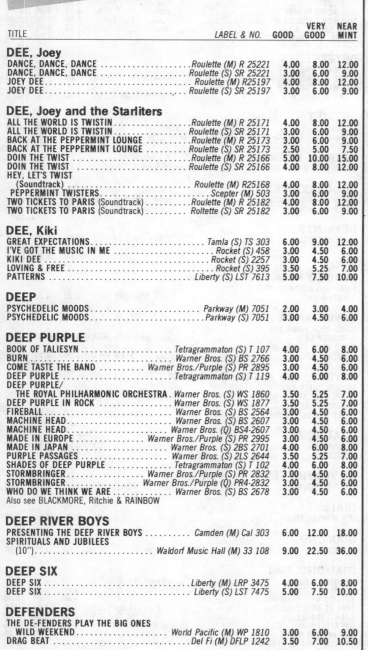

TITLE	LABEL & NO.	GOOD	VERY GOOD	NEAR MINT
DEE, Joey				
DANCE, DANCE, DANCE	Roulette (M) R 25221	4.00	8.00	12.00
DANCE, DANCE, DANCE	Roulette (S) SR 25221	3.00	6.00	9.00
JOEY DEE	Roulette (M) R25197	4.00	8.00	12.00
JOEY DEE	Roulette (S) SR 25197	3.00	6.00	9.00
DEE, Joey and the Starliters				
ALL THE WORLD IS TWISTIN	Roulette (M) R 25171	4.00	8.00	12.00
ALL THE WORLD IS TWISTIN	Roulette (S) SR 25171	3.00	6.00	9.00
BACK AT THE PEPPERMINT LOUNGE	Roulette (M) R 25173	3.00	6.00	9.00
BACK AT THE PEPPERMINT LOUNGE	Roulette (S) SR 25173	2.50	5.00	7.50
DOIN THE TWIST	Roulette (M) R 25166	5.00	10.00	15.00
DOIN THE TWIST	Roulette (S) SR 25166	4.00	8.00	12.00
HEY, LET'S TWIST (Soundtrack)	Roulette (M) R25168	4.00	8.00	12.00
PEPPERMINT TWISTERS	Scepter (M) 503	3.00	6.00	9.00
TWO TICKETS TO PARIS (Soundtrack)	Roulette (M) R 25182	4.00	8.00	12.00
TWO TICKETS TO PARIS (Soundtrack)	Roltette (S) SR 25182	3.00	6.00	9.00
DEE, Kiki				
GREAT EXPECTATIONS	Tamla (S) TS 303	6.00	9.00	12.00
I'VE GOT THE MUSIC IN ME	Rocket (S) 458	3.00	4.50	6.00
KIKI DEE	Rocket (S) 2257	3.00	4.50	6.00
LOVING & FREE	Rocket (S) 395	3.50	5.25	7.00
PATTERNS	Liberty (S) LST 7613	5.00	7.50	10.00
DEEP				
PSYCHEDELIC MOODS	Parkway (M) 7051	2.00	3.00	4.00
PSYCHEDELIC MOODS	Parkway (S) 7051	3.00	4.50	6.00
DEEP PURPLE				
BOOK OF TALIESYN	Tetragrammaton (S) T 107	4.00	6.00	8.00
BURN	Warner Bros. (S) BS 2766	3.00	4.50	6.00
COME TASTE THE BAND	Warner Bros./Purple (S) PR 2895	3.00	4.50	6.00
DEEP PURPLE	Tetragrammaton (S) T 119	4.00	6.00	8.00
DEEP PURPLE/ THE ROYAL PHILHARMONIC ORCHESTRA	Warner Bros. (S) WS 1860	3.50	5.25	7.00
DEEP PURPLE IN ROCK	Warner Bros. (S) WS 1877	3.50	5.25	7.00
FIREBALL	Warner Bros. (S) BS 2564	3.00	4.50	6.00
MACHINE HEAD	Warner Bros. (S) BS 2607	3.00	4.50	6.00
MACHINE HEAD	Warner Bros. (Q) BS4-2607	3.00	4.50	6.00
MADE IN EUROPE	Warner Bros./Purple (S) PR 2995	3.00	4.50	6.00
MADE IN JAPAN	Warner Bros. (S) 2BS 2701	3.00	6.00	9.00
PURPLE PASSAGES	Warner Bros. (S) 2LS 2644	3.50	5.25	7.00
SHADES OF DEEP PURPLE	Tetragrammaton (S) T 102	4.00	6.00	8.00
STORMBRINGER	Warner Bros./Purple (S) PR 2832	3.00	4.50	6.00
STORMBRINGER	Warner Bros./Purple (Q) PR4-2832	3.00	4.50	6.00
WHO DO WE THINK WE ARE	Warner Bros. (S) BS 2678	3.00	4.50	6.00
Also see BLACKMORE, Ritchie & RAINBOW				
DEEP RIVER BOYS				
PRESENTING THE DEEP RIVER BOYS	Camden (M) Cal 303	6.00	12.00	18.00
SPIRITUALS AND JUBILEES (10")	Waldorf Music Hall (M) 33 108	9.00	22.50	36.00
DEEP SIX				
DEEP SIX	Liberty (M) LRP 3475	4.00	6.00	8.00
DEEP SIX	Liberty (S) LST 7475	5.00	7.50	10.00
DEFENDERS				
THE DE-FENDERS PLAY THE BIG ONES WILD WEEKEND	World Pacific (M) WP 1810	3.00	6.00	9.00
DRAG BEAT	Del Fi (M) DFLP 1242	3.50	7.00	10.50
DE FRANCO FAMILY				
HEARTBEAT, IT'S A LOVEBEAT	20th Century (S) 422	3.00	4.50	6.00
SAVE THE LAST DANCE FOR ME	20th Century (S) 441	3.00	4.50	6.00

(M) Mono (S) Stereo (EP) Extended Play (Q) Quad (RI) Re-issued

TITLE	LABEL & NO.	GOOD	VERY GOOD	NEAR MINT
DEKKER, Desmond and the Aces				
ISRAELITES	UNI (S) 73059	3.00	4.50	6.00
DEL SATINS				
OUT TO LUNCH	B.T. Puppy (S) 1019	6.00	12.00	18.00
DEL VIKINGS				
COME GO WITH ME	Dot (M) DLP3695	5.00	12.50	20.00
COME GO WITH THE DEL VIKINGS	Luniverse (M) LP 1000	20.00	50.00	80.00
COME GO WITH US	Dot (EP) DEP 1058	2.00	5.00	8.00
DEL VIKINGS	Mercury (EP) MEP 35A	2.00	5.00	8.00
NEWIES & OLDIES	Fee Bee (M) 205	2.00	5.00	8.00
SWINGING, SINGING DEL VIKINGS RECORD SESSION	Mercury (M) MG 20353	9.00	22.50	36.00
THEY SING-THEY SWING	Mercury (EP) EP1 3362	2.00	5.00	8.00
THEY SING-THEY SWING	Mercury (M) MG 20314	9.00	22.50	36.00
DE JOHN SISTERS				
DE JOHN SISTERS	Epic (M) LN 1116	3.00	4.50	6.00
NO MORE	Epic (EP) EG7093	2.00	3.00	4.00
DEL VIKINGS and the Sonnets				
DEL VIKINGS AND THE SONNETS	Crown (M) CLP 5368	5.00	12.50	20.00
DELANEY AND BONNIE				
BEST OF DELANEY AND BONNIE	Atco (S) SD 7014	2.50	3.75	5.00
D AND B TOGETHER	Columbia (S) KC 31377	2.50	3.75	5.00
GENESIS	GNP-Crescendo (S) GNPS 2054	3.50	5.25	7.00
HOME	Star (S) STS 2026	4.00	6.00	8.00
MOTEL SHOT	Atco (S) SD 33 358	2.50	3.75	5.00
ON TOUR	Atco (S) 33 326	2.50	3.75	5.00
ORIGINAL DELANEY AND BONNIE	Elektra (S) EKS 74039	2.50	3.75	5.00
TO DELANEY FROM BONNIE	Atco (S) SD 33 341	2.50	3.75	5.00
Also see BRAMLETT, Bonnie				
DELEGATES				
DELEGATES	Mainstream (S) 100	5.00	7.50	10.00
DELICATO, Paul				
CARA MIA	Artists of America (S) 5002	2.50	3.75	5.00
ICE CREAM SODAS & LOLLIPOPS & A RED HOT SPINNING TOP	Artists of America (S) 5001	2.50	3.75	5.00
OFF ON AN ISLAND	AVI 6029	2.00	3.00	4.00
DELLS				
DELLS SING DIONNE WARWICK'S GREATEST HITS	Cadet (S) 50017	2.50	3.75	5.00
FREEDOM MEANS	Cadet (S) 50004	2.50	3.75	5.00
GREATEST HITS	Cadet (S) 824	3.00	4.50	6.00
IT'S NOT UNUSUAL	VeeJay (M) 1141	3.00	6.00	9.00
LIKE HIS	Cadet (S) 837	3.00	4.50	6.00
LOVE IS BLUE	Cadet (S) 829	3.00	4.50	6.00
MUSICAL MENU	Cadet (S) 822	3.00	4.50	6.00
OH WHAT A NITE	VeeJay (M) 1010	8.00	16.00	24.00
THERE IS	Cadet (S) 804	3.00	4.50	6.00
DELLS and Joe South				
COME TOGETHER	Apple (S) SW 3377	4.00	6.00	8.00
DELTA RHYTHM BOYS				
DELTA RHYTHM BOYS (10")	Mercury (M) 25153	9.00	22.50	36.00
DRY BONES (10")	RCA (M) LPM 3085	9.00	22.50	36.00
DEMENSIONS				
MY FOOLISH HEART	Coral (M) 57430	5.00	12.50	20.00

TITLE	LABEL & NO.	GOOD	VERY GOOD	NEAR MINT
DEMIAN				
DEMIAN	ABC (S) ABCS 718	7.00	10.50	14.00
DENNY, Martin				
AFRO-DESIA	Liberty (M) LRP 3111	2.50	3.75	5.00
AFRO-DESIA	Liberty (M) LST 7111	2.50	3.75	5.00
ENCHANTED SEA	Liberty (M) LRP 3141	2.00	3.00	4.00
ENCHANTED SEA	Liberty (S) LST 7141	2.00	3.00	4.00
EXOTICA	Liberty (M) LRP 3034	2.50	3.75	5.00
EXOTICA	Liberty (S) LST 7034	2.50	3.75	5.00
EXOTICA, VOL 2	Liberty (M) LRP 3077	2.00	3.00	4.00
EXOTICA, VOL 2	Liberty (S) LST 7006	2.00	3.00	4.00
EXOTICA, VOL 3	Liberty (M) LRP 3116	2.00	3.00	4.00
EXOTICA, VOL 3	Liberty (S) LST 7116	2.00	3.00	4.00
FORBIDDEN ISLAND	Liberty (M) LRP 3081	2.00	3.00	4.00
FORBIDDEN ISLAND	Liberty (S) LST 7001	2.00	3.00	4.00
HAWAII TATTOO	Liberty (M) LRP 3394	2.00	3.00	4.00
HAWAII TATTOO	Liberty (S) LSP 7394	2.00	3.00	4.00
MARTIN DENNY'S EXOTIC SOUNDS FROM THE SILVER SCREEN	Liberty (M) LRP 3158	2.00	3.00	4.00
MARTIN DENNY'S EXOTIC SOUNDS FROM THE SILVER SCREEN	Liberty (S) LST 7158	2.00	3.00	4.00
MARTIN DENNY'S EXOTIC SOUNDS VISIT BROADWAY	Liberty (M) LRP 3163	2.00	3.00	4.00
MARTIN DENNY'S EXOTIC SOUNDS VISIT BROADWAY	Liberty (S) LST 7163	2.00	3.00	4.00
QUIET VILLAGE	Liberty (M) LRP 3122	2.00	3.00	4.00
QUIET VILLIAGE	Liberty (S) LST 7122	2.00	3.00	4.00
A TASTE OF HONEY	Liberty (M) LRP 3237	2.50	3.75	5.00
A TASTE OF HONEY	Liberty (S) LSP 7237	2.50	3.75	5.00
VERY BEST OF MARTIN DENNY	United Artists (S) UA-LA234	2.00	3.00	4.00
VERY BEST OF MARTIN DENNY (RI)	United Artists (S) UA-LA383	2.00	3.00	4.00
DENNY, Sandy				
LIKE AN OLD FASHIONED WALTZ	Island (S) SW-9340	2.00	3.00	4.00
LIKE AN OLD FASHIONED WALTZ (RI)	Island (S) 9258	2.00	3.00	4.00
NORTH STAR GRASSMAN AND THE RAVENS	A&M (S) SP 4317	2.00	3.00	4.00
SANDY	A&M (S) SP 4371	2.00	3.00	4.00
DENVER, John				
AERIE	RCA (S) LSP 4607	3.00	4.50	6.00
BACK HOME AGAIN	RCA (S) CPL1-0548	2.50	3.75	5.00
BEGINNINGS (With Chad Mitchell Trio)	Mercury (S) SRM-1-704	2.50	3.75	5.00
AN EVENING WITH JOHN DENVER	RCA (S) CPL2-0764	2.50	3.75	5.00
FAREWELL ANDROMEDA	RCA (S) APL1-0101	2.50	3.75	5.00
I WANT TO LIVE	RCA (S) AFL1-2521	2.00	3.00	4.00
JOHN DENVER'S GREATEST HITS	RCA (S) CPL1-0374	2.50	3.75	5.00
JOHN DENVER'S GREATEST HITS, VOL. 2	RCA (S) CPL1-2195	2.00	3.00	4.00
JOHN DENVER SINGS	HJD (S) 66	12.00	24.00	36.00
POEMS, PRAYERS & PROMISES	RCA (S) LSP 4499	3.00	4.50	6.00
RHYMES & REASONS	RCA (S) LSP 4207	3.00	4.50	6.00
ROCKY MOUNTAIN CHRISTMAS	RCA (S) APL1-1201	2.50	3.75	5.00
ROCKY MOUNTAIN HIGH	RCA (S) LSP 4731	3.00	4.50	6.00
TAKE ME TO TOMORROW	RCA (S) LSP 4278	3.00	4.50	6.00
WINDSONG/ROCKY MOUNTAIN CHRISTMAS	RCA (S) APL2-1263	2.50	3.75	5.00
Also see MITCHELL, CHAD, TRIO				
DEPENDABLES				
KLATU, BERRADA NIKTU VOL. 1	United Artists (S) UAS6799	3.00	4.50	6.00
DEREK & THE DOMINOS				
DEREK & THE DOMINOS IN CONCERT	RSO (S) 2-8800	5.00	7.50	10.00
LAYLA	Atco (S) SD 2-704	5.00	7.50	10.00
LAYLA (RI)	Polydor (S) 2-3501	3.00	4.50	6.00
LAYLA (& OTHER ASSORTED LOVE SONGS)	RSO (S) RS 3801	3.00	4.50	6.00
Also see CLAPTON, ERIC & CREAM				
DERRINGER, RICK				
ALL-AMERICAN BOY	Blue Sky (S) KZ-32481	2.50	3.75	5.00
DERRINGER	Blue Sky (S) PZ 34181	2.50	3.75	5.00
LIVE	Blue Sky (S) PZ 34848	2.50	3.75	5.00
OUTSIDE STUFF (WITH THE MCCOYS)	Mercury (S) SRM-2-7506	3.50	5.25	7.00
SPRING FEVER	Blue Sky (S) PZ 33423	2.50	3.75	5.00
SWEET EVIL	Blue Sky (S) PZ 34470	2.50	3.75	5.00
Also see WINTER, EDGAR, GROUP & MCCOYS				
DESANTO, Sugar Pie				
SUGAR PIE	Checker (M) LP 2979	4.00	6.00	8.00
SUGAR PIE	Checker (EP) LP 2979	2.00	3.00	4.00
DESERT STRING BAND				
LAND OF MILK AND HONEY	Okehdoree (M)	3.00	4.50	6.00
DE SHANNON, Jackie				
ARE YOU READY FOR THIS	Imperial (M) LP 9328	3.00	6.00	9.00
ARE YOU READY FOR THIS	Imperial (S) LP 12328	4.00	8.00	12.00
BREAKIN IT UP ON THE BEATLES TOUR	Liberty (M) LRP 3390	5.00	10.00	15.00
BREAKIN IT UP ON THE BEATLES TOUR	Liberty (S) LST 7390	6.00	12.00	18.00
C'MON LET'S LIVE A LITTLE (Soundtrack)	Liberty (M) LP LRP 3430	5.00	10.00	15.00
C'MON LET'S LIVE A LITTLE (Soundtrack)	Liberty (S) LST 7430	6.00	12.00	18.00
FOR YOU	Imperial (M) LP 9352	3.00	6.00	9.00
FOR YOU	Imperial (S) LP 12352	4.00	8.00	12.00
IN THE WIND	Imperial (M) LP 9296	4.00	8.00	12.00
IN THE WIND	Imperial (S) LP 12296	5.00	10.00	15.00
JACKIE	Atlantic (S) SD 7231	2.50	3.75	5.00
JACKIE DE SHANNON	Liberty (M) LRP 3320	4.00	8.00	12.00
JACKIE DE SHANNON	Liberty (S) LST 7320	5.00	10.00	15.00
JACKIE DE SHANNON	Sunset (S) SUS-5322	2.50	3.75	5.00
LAUREL CANYON	Imperial (S) LP 12415	3.00	4.50	6.00
LONELY GIRL	Sunset (S) SUS 5225	2.50	3.75	5.00
ME ABOUT YOU	Imperial (S) LP 12386	3.00	4.50	6.00
NEW ARRANGEMENT	Columbia (S) PC 33500	2.50	3.75	5.00
NEW IMAGE	Imperial (M) LP 9344	3.00	6.00	9.00
NEW IMAGE	Imperail (S) LP 12344	4.00	8.00	12.00
PUT A LITTLE LOVE IN YOUR HEART	Imperial (S) LP 12442	3.00	4.50	6.00
SONGS	Capitol (S) ST 772	4.00	6.00	8.00
THIS IS JACKIE DE SHANNON	Imperial (M) LP9286	4.00	8.00	12.00
THIS IS JACKIE DE SHANNON	Imperial (S) LP 12286	5.00	10.00	15.00
TO BE FREE	Imperial (S) LP 12453	3.00	4.50	6.00
VERY BEST OF JACKIE DE SHANNON	United Artists (S) UA-LA434	2.50	3.75	5.00
WHAT THE WORLD NEEDS NOW IS LOVE	Imperial (S) LP 12404	3.00	4.50	6.00
YOU WON'T FORGET ME	Imperial (M) LP 9294	4.00	8.00	12.00
YOU WON'T FORGET ME	Imperial (S) LP 12294	5.00	10.00	15.00
YOUR BABY IS A LADY	Atlantic (S) SD 7303	2.50	3.75	5.00
YOU'RE THE ONLY DANCER	Amherst (S) AMH 1010	2.00	3.00	4.00
DETERGENTS				
THE MANY FACES OF THE DETERGENTS	Roulette (M) R 25308	5.00	7.50	10.00
THE MANY FACES OF THE DETERGENTS	Roulette (S) SR 25308	6.00	8.00	12.00
DETROIT				
DETROIT	Paramount (S) PAS 6010	4.00	6.00	8.00
Also see RYDER, MITCH & DETROIT WHEELS				
DETROIT EMERALDS				
I'M IN LOVE WITH YOU	Westbound (S) WB 2018	2.50	3.75	5.00
DEUCE COUPES				
HOT RODDER'S CHOICE	Del Fi (M) DFLP 1243	3.50	7.00	10.50
THE SHUT DOWNS	Crown (S) CST 393	3.00	6.00	9.00
DEVIANTS				
DISPOSABLE	Sire (S) SES 97005	10.00	15.00	20.00
PTOOEE	Sire (S) SES 97001	10.00	15.00	20.00
33	Sire (S) SES 97016	10.00	15.00	20.00
DEVILED HAM				
I HAD TOO MUCH TO DREAM LAST NIGHT	Super K (S) SKS 6003	6.00	9.00	12.00
DEVILS ANVIL				
HARD ROCK FROM THE MIDDLE EAST	Columbia (M) CL 2664	4.00	6.00	8.00
HARD ROCK FROM THE MIDDLE EAST	Columbia (S) CS 9464	5.00	7.50	10.00
DEVROE, Billy and the Devilaires				
DEVROE, BILLY AND THE DEVILAIRES VOL 1	Tampa (M) 31	5.00	12.50	20.00
DEVROE, BILLY AND THE DEVILAIRES VOL 2	Tampa (M) 39	5.00	12.50	20.00
DEXTER, Al				
AL DEXTER	Capitol (M) T 1701	3.00	4.50	6.00
AL DEXTER	Capitol (S) ST 1701	3.00	4.50	6.00
DE YOUNG, Cliff				
CLIFF DE YOUNG	MCA (S) 432	2.50	3.75	5.00
DIALS				
IT'S MONKEY TIME	Time (S) S 2100	3.00	6.00	9.00
DIAMOND				
DIAMOND	Paramount (S) 1021	2.50	3.75	5.00
DIAMOND, Neil				
BEAUTIFUL NOISE	Columbia (S) PC 33965	2.50	3.75	5.00
DO IT!	Bang (S) BLP 224	4.00	6.00	8.00
FEEL OF NEIL DIAMOND	Bang (M) BLP 214	4.00	6.00	8.00
FEEL OF NEIL DIAMOND	Bang (S) BLPS 214	5.00	7.50	10.00
GREATEST HITS	Bang (M) BLP 219	4.00	6.00	8.00
GREATEST HITS	Bang (S) BLPS219	5.00	7.50	10.00
HOT AUGUST NIGHT	MCA (S) 2-8000	3.00	4.50	6.00
I'M GLAD YOU'RE HERE WITH ME TONIGHT	Columbia (S) JC 34990	2.50	3.75	5.00
JONATHAN LIVINGSTON SEAGULL (Soundtrack)	Columbia (S) KS 32550	2.50	3.75	5.00
JUST FOR YOU	Bang (M) BLP 217	4.00	6.00	8.00
JUST FOR YOU	Bang (S) BLPS 217	5.00	7.50	10.00

(M) Mono (S) Stereo (EP) Extended Play (Q) Quad (RI) Re-issued

TITLE	LABEL & NO.	GOOD	VERY GOOD	NEAR MINT
LOVE AT THE GREEK	Columbia (S) KC2-34404	3.00	4.50	6.00
MOODS	UNI (S) 93136	3.00	4.50	6.00
MOODS (RI of UNI 93136)	MCA (S) 2005	2.50	3.75	5.00
NEIL DIAMOND	UNI (S) 73047	3.00	4.50	6.00
NEIL DIAMOND (Open End Radio Special with Neil Diamond)	UNI (M) 1913	4.00	6.00	8.00
NEIL DIAMOND GOLD	UNI (S) 73084	3.00	4.50	6.00
NEIL DIAMOND GOLD (RI of UNI 73084)	MCA (S) 2007	2.50	3.75	5.00
NEIL DIAMOND - HIS 12 GREATEST HITS	MCA (S) 2106	2.50	3.75	5.00
RAINBOW	MCA (S) 2103	2.50	3.75	5.00
SERENADE	Columbia (S) PC 32919	2.50	3.75	5.00
SERENADE	Columbia (Q) PCQ 32919	2.50	3.75	5.00
SHILO	Bang (S) BLPS 221	4.00	6.00	8.00
STONES	UNI (S) 93106	2.00	3.00	4.00
STONES (RI of UNI 93106)	MCA (S) 2008	2.50	3.75	5.00
TAP ROOT MANUSCRIPT	UNI (S) 73092	2.00	3.00	4.00
TAP ROOT MANUSCRIPT (RI of UNI 73092)	MCA (S) 2013	2.50	3.75	5.00
TOUCHING YOU TOUCHING ME	UNI (S) 73071	2.00	3.00	4.00

DIAMONDS

	LABEL & NO.	GOOD	VERY GOOD	NEAR MINT
DIAMONDS	Brunswick (EP) EB 71031	2.50	6.25	10.00
DIAMONDS	Mercury (M) MG 20309	7.00	17.50	28.00
DIAMONDS MEET PETE RUGOLO	Mercury (M) MG 20368	10.00	25.00	40.00
DIAMONDS MEET PETE RUGOLO	Mercury (S) SR-60076	12.50	31.25	50.00
OLD WEST	Mercury (S) 60159	5.00	12.50	20.00
POP HITS	Wing (M) MGW 12178	5.00	12.50	20.00
STROLL	Mercury (EP) EP 13390	3.00	6.00	9.00

DICK & DEE DEE

	LABEL & NO.	GOOD	VERY GOOD	NEAR MINT
SONGS WE'VE SUNG ON SHINDIG	Warner Brothers (M) W1623	3.00	6.00	9.00
SONGS WE'VE SUNG ON SHINDIG	Warner Brothers (S) WS1623	4.00	8.00	12.00
TELL ME	Liberty (M) LRP 3236	3.00	6.00	9.00
TELL ME	Liberty (S) LST 7236	4.00	8.00	12.00
THOU SHALT NOT STEAL	Warner Bros. (M) W 1586	3.00	6.00	9.00
THOU SHALT NOT STEAL	Warner Bros. (S) WS 1586	4.00	8.00	12.00
TURN AROUND	Warner Brothers (M) W 1538	3.00	6.00	9.00
TURN AROUND	Warner Brothers (S) WS 1538	4.00	8.00	12.00
YOUNG AND IN LOVE	Warner Brothers (M) W 1500	3.00	6.00	9.00
YOUNG AND IN LOVE	Warner Brothers (S) WS 1500	4.00	8.00	12.00

DICKENS, Little Jimmy

	LABEL & NO.	GOOD	VERY GOOD	NEAR MINT
BIG SONGS BY LITTLE JIMMY DICKENS	Columbia (M) CL 1545	3.00	6.00	9.00
BIG SONGS BY LITTLE JIMMY DICKENS	Columbia (S) CS 9242	2.00	3.00	4.00
LITTLE JIMMY DICKENS	Columbia (EP) H 1664	1.50	2.25	3.00
LITTLE JIMMY DICKENS	Columbia (EP) B 2813	4.00	8.00	12.00
LITTLE JIMMY DICKENS BEST	Harmony (M) HL7311	2.00	3.00	4.00
LITTLE JIMMY DICKENS GREATEST HITS	Columbia (M) CL 2551	2.50	3.75	5.00
LITTLE JIMMY DICKENS GREATEST HITS	Columbia (S) CS 9351	2.50	3.75	5.00
MAY THE BIRD OF PARADISE FLY UP YOUR NOSE	Columbia (M) CL 2442	2.00	3.00	4.00
MAY THE BIRD OF PARADISE FLY UP YOUR NOSE	Columbia (S) CS 9242	2.00	3.00	4.00
OUT BEHIND THE BARN	Columbia (M) CL 1887	3.00	6.00	9.00
OUT BEHIND THE BARN	Columbia (S) CS 8687	3.00	6.00	9.00
RAISIN THE DICKENS	Columbia (M) CL 1047	4.00	8.00	12.00
RAISIN THE DICKENS	Columbia (EP) B 10471	1.50	2.25	3.00

DICKEY DOO & THE DON'TS

	LABEL & NO.	GOOD	VERY GOOD	NEAR MINT
MADISON	United Artists (M) UAL 3094	6.00	12.00	18.00
MADISON	United Artists (S) UAS 6094	7.00	14.00	21.00

(M) Mono (S) Stereo (EP) Extended Play (Q) Quad (RI) Re-issued

TITLE	LABEL & NO.	GOOD	VERY GOOD	NEAR MINT
TEEN SCENE	United Artists (M) UAL 3097	6.00	12.00	18.00
TEEN SCENE	United Artists (S) UAS 6097	7.00	14.00	21.00

DICTATORS

	LABEL & NO.	GOOD	VERY GOOD	NEAR MINT
THE DICTATORS GO GIRL CRAZY	Epic (M) KE 33348	4.00	6.00	8.00

DIDDLEY, Bo

	LABEL & NO.	GOOD	VERY GOOD	NEAR MINT
ANOTHER DIMENSION	Chess (S) CH 50001	2.50	3.75	5.00
BIG BAD BO	Chess (S) CH50047	3.00	4.50	6.00
BLACK GLADIATOR	Checker (S) LPS 3013	3.00	4.50	6.00
BO DIDDLEY	Checker (M) 1431	10.00	15.00	20.00
BO DIDDLEY	Checker (M) LP 2984	4.00	10.00	16.00
BO DIDDLEY AND COMPANY	Checker (M) LP 2985	4.00	8.00	12.00
BO DIDDLEY IS A GUN SLINGER	Checker (M) LP 2977	5.00	12.50	20.00
BO DIDDLEY IS A LOVER	Checker (M) LP 2980	5.00	12.50	20.00
BO DIDDLEY'S A TWISTER	Checker (M) LP 2982	4.00	10.00	16.00
BO DIDDLEY'S BEACH PARTY	Checker (M) LP 2988	4.00	8.00	12.00
500% MORE MAN	Checker (M) LP 2996	4.00	10.00	16.00
GO BO DIDDLEY	Checker (M) 1436	10.00	15.00	20.00
GO BO DIDDLEY	Checker (M) LP 3006	4.00	6.00	8.00
GOT MY OWN BAG OF TRICKS	Chess (S) 2CH 60005	4.00	6.00	8.00
HAVE GUITAR WILL TRAVEL	Checker (M) LP 2974	5.00	12.50	20.00
HEY GOOD LOOKIN	Checker (M) LP2992	4.00	8.00	12.00
IN THE SPOTLIGHT	Checker (M) LP 2976	5.00	12.50	20.00
LONDON BO DIDDLEY SESSIONS	Chess (S) CH 50029	3.00	4.50	6.00
THE ORIGINATOR	Checker (M) LP 3001	4.00	6.00	8.00
16 ALL TIME GREATEST HITS	Checker (M) LP 2989	4.00	8.00	12.00
SURFIN' WITH	Checker (M) 2987	4.00	8.00	12.00
20TH ANNIVERSARY OF ROCK AND ROLL	RCA (M) APL1 1229	2.50	3.75	5.00
WHERE IT ALL BEGAN	Chess (S) CH50016	3.00	4.50	6.00

NOTE: Stereo reissues of these Checker LP's are worth 25-50% of the MONO versions.

DIDDLEY, Bo & Chuck Berry

	LABEL & NO.	GOOD	VERY GOOD	NEAR MINT
TWO GREAT GUITARS	Checker (M) 2991	5.00	10.00	15.00

DIETRICH, Marlene

	LABEL & NO.	GOOD	VERY GOOD	NEAR MINT
DIETRICH IN RIO	Columbia (M) WL-164	5.00	12.50	20.00
LILI MARLENE	Columbia (M) CL 1275	4.00	10.00	16.00

DILCHER, Cheryl

	LABEL & NO.	GOOD	VERY GOOD	NEAR MINT
MAGIC	A&M (S) 3640	2.00	3.00	4.00

DILLARD & CLARK

	LABEL & NO.	GOOD	VERY GOOD	NEAR MINT
THE FANTASTIC EXPEDITION OF DILLARD AND CLARK	A & M (S) SP 4158	3.50	5.25	7.00
THROUGH THE MORNING THROUGH THE NIGHT	A & M (S) SP 4203	3.50	5.25	7.00

DILLARD, Doug

	LABEL & NO.	GOOD	VERY GOOD	NEAR MINT
DUELIN' BANJO	20th Century (S) 409	2.00	3.00	4.00
YOU DON'T NEED A REASON TO SING	20th Century (S) 426	2.00	3.00	4.00

Also see DILLARD & CLARK

DILLARD, Douglas Flint

	LABEL & NO.	GOOD	VERY GOOD	NEAR MINT
BANJO ALBUM (Original)	Together (M) 1003	12.00	18.00	24.00
DUELIN' BANJO	20TH Century (M) 409	3.00	4.50	6.00
YOU DON'T NEED A REASON TO SING	20TH Century (M) T426	4.00	6.00	8.00

DILLARDS

	LABEL & NO.	GOOD	VERY GOOD	NEAR MINT
COPPERFIELDS	Elektra (S) EKS 74054	2.50	3.75	5.00
ROOTS AND BRANCHES	Anthem (S) 5901	3.50	5.25	7.00
TRIBUTE TO THE AMERICAN DUCK	Poppy (S) PP LA 175F	2.00	3.00	4.00
WHEATSTRAW SUITE	Elektra (S) EKS 74035	2.50	3.75	5.00

DILLER, Phyllis

	LABEL & NO.	GOOD	VERY GOOD	NEAR MINT
WET TOE IN A HOT SOCKET	Mirrosonic (S) SP-6002	4.00	6.00	8.00

DI MEOLA, Al

	LABEL & NO.	GOOD	VERY GOOD	NEAR MINT
CASINO	Columbia (S) JC 35277	2.00	3.00	4.00
ELEGANT GYPSY	Columbia (S) PC 34461	2.00	3.00	4.00
LAND OF THE MIDNIGHT SUN	Columbia (S) PC 34074	2.00	3.00	4.00

DINNING, Mark

	LABEL & NO.	GOOD	VERY GOOD	NEAR MINT
TEEN ANGEL	MGM (M) E 3828	4.00	8.00	12.00
TEEN ANGEL	MGM (S) SE 3828	5.00	10.00	15.00
WANDERIN'	MGM (M) E 3855	3.00	6.00	9.00
WANDERIN'	MGM (S) SE 3855	4.00	8.00	12.00

DINO, DESI & BILLY

	LABEL & NO.	GOOD	VERY GOOD	NEAR MINT
I'M A FOOL	Reprise (M) R 6176	3.00	4.50	6.00
I'M A FOOL	Reprise (S) RS 6176	4.00	6.00	8.00
MEMORIES ARE MADE OF THIS	Reprise (M) R 6198	3.00	4.50	6.00
MEMORIES ARE MADE OF THIS	Reprise (S) RS 6198	4.00	6.00	8.00
OUR TIMES COMING	Reprise (M) R 6194	3.00	4.50	6.00
OUR TIMES COMING	Reprise (S) RS 6194	4.00	6.00	8.00
SOUVENIR	Reprise (M) R 6224	3.00	4.50	6.00
SOUVENIR	Reprise (S) RS 6224	4.00	6.00	8.00

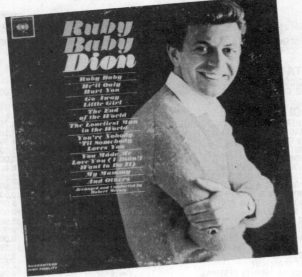

DION

Title	Label & No.	Good	Very Good	Near Mint
ALONE WITH DION	Laurie (M) LLP2004	5.00	10.00	15.00
BORN TO BE WITH YOU (Eng. Issue)	Phil Spector (S) 002	4.00	6.00	8.00
DION	Laurie (S) SLP2047	4.00	8.00	12.00
DION'S GREATEST HITS	Columbia (S) KC31942	3.00	4.50	6.00
DION SINGS HIS GREATEST HITS	Laurie (M) LLP2013	5.00	10.00	15.00
DION SINGS THE 15 MILLION SELLERS	Laurie (M) LLP 2019	4.00	8.00	12.00
DION SINGS TO SANDY	Laurie (M) LLP2017	4.00	8.00	12.00
DONNA THE PRIMA DONNA	Columbia (M) CL 2107	4.00	8.00	12.00
DONNA THE PRIMA DONNA	Columbia (S) CS8907	5.00	10.00	15.00
LOVE CAME TO ME	Laurie (M) LLP2015	5.00	10.00	15.00
LOVERS WHO WANDER	Laurie (M) LLP2012	5.00	10.00	15.00
MORE OF DION'S GREATEST HITS	Laurie (M) 2022	4.00	8.00	12.00
RETURN OF THE WANDERER	Lifesong (S) JZ 35356	2.50	3.75	5.00
RUBY BABY	Columbia (M) CL2010	4.00	8.00	12.00
RUBY BABY	Columbia (S) CS8810	5.00	10.00	15.00
RUNAROUND SUE	Laurie (M) LLP2009	5.00	10.00	15.00
SANCTUARY	Warner Bros. (S) WS 1945	3.00	4.50	6.00
SIT DOWN OLD FRIEND	Warner Bros. (S) WS 1826	3.00	4.50	6.00
STREETHEART	Warner Bros. (S) BS 2954	3.00	4.50	6.00
SUITE FOR LATE SUMMER	Warner Brothers (S) BS2642	3.00	4.50	6.00
WONDER WHERE I'M BOUND	Columbia (S) CS9773	4.00	8.00	12.00
YOU'RE NOT ALONE	Warner Bros. (S) WS1872	3.00	4.50	6.00

DION & THE BELMONTS

Title	Label & No.	Good	Very Good	Near Mint
BY SPECIAL REQUEST: DION AND THE BELMONTS TOGETHER ON RECORD	Laurie (M) LLP2016	4.00	8.00	12.00
DION AND THE BELMONTS LIVE AT MADISON SQUARE GARDEN 1972	Warner Brothers (S) BS2664	3.00	4.50	6.00
DION AND THE BELMONTS TOGETHER AGAIN	ABC (M) 599	3.00	6.00	9.00
DION AND THE BELMONTS TOGETHER AGAIN	ABC (S) ABCS599	4.00	8.00	12.00
PRESENTING DION AND THE BELMONTS	Laurie (M) LLP 2002	6.00	12.00	18.00
WHERE OR WHEN	Laurie (EP) LEP302	3.00	6.00	9.00
WISH UPON A STAR WITH DION AND THE BELMONTS	Laurie (M) LLP2006	5.00	10.00	15.00

Also see BELMONTS

DIRTY BLUES BAND

Title	Label & No.	Good	Very Good	Near Mint
DIRTY BLUES BAND	Blues Way (M) BL6010	3.50	5.25	7.00
DIRTY BLUES BAND	Blues Way (S) BLS6010	4.00	6.00	8.00
STONE DIRT	Blues Way (S) BLS6020	4.00	6.00	8.00

DISCO-TEX & HIS SEX-O-LETTES

Title	Label & No.	Good	Very Good	Near Mint
DISCO-TEX & HIS SEX-O-LETTES	Chelsea (S) CHL 505	3.00	4.50	6.00
MANHATTAN MILLIONAIRE	Chelsea (S) CHL 516	3.00	4.50	6.00

DISNEY, Walt

Title	Label & No.	Good	Very Good	Near Mint
SONGS FROM THE MICKEY MOUSE CLUB SERIES	Disneyland (M) DQ1229	5.00	10.00	15.00

DIXIE BELLES

Title	Label & No.	Good	Very Good	Near Mint
DOWN AT PAPA JOE'S	Sound Stage 7 (M) SSM5000	4.00	8.00	12.00
DOWN AT PAPA JOE'S	Sound Stage 7 (S) SM1500	5.00	10.00	15.00

DIXIE CUPS

Title	Label & No.	Good	Very Good	Near Mint
CHAPEL OF LOVE	Red Bird (M) RB 20-100	4.00	8.00	12.00
CHAPEL OF LOVE	Red Bird (S) RBS 20-100	5.00	10.00	15.00
IKO IKO	Red Bird (M) RB20-103	5.00	10.00	15.00
IKO IKO	Red Bird (S) RBS20-103	6.00	12.00	18.00
RIDING HIGH	ABC Paramount (M) ABC525	4.00	8.00	12.00
RIDING HIGH	ABC Paramount (S) ABCS525	5.00	10.00	15.00

DIXON, Errol

Title	Label & No.	Good	Very Good	Near Mint
BLUES IN THE POT	London (S) PS550	4.50	6.75	9.00

TITLE	LABEL & NO.	GOOD	VERY GOOD	NEAR MINT

DIXON, Willie and Memphis Slim

Title	Label & No.	Good	Very Good	Near Mint
WILLIE'S BLUES	Prestige (M) 1003	5.00	10.00	15.00

DOBKINS, Carl Jr.

Title	Label & No.	Good	Very Good	Near Mint
CARL DOBKINS JR.	Decca (M) DL8938	5.00	12.50	20.00
CARL DOBKINS JR.	Decca (S) DL7-8938	7.00	17.50	28.00
MY HEART IS AN OPEN BOOK	Decca (EP) ED 2664	3.00	6.00	9.00

DOCTOR FEELGOOD

Title	Label & No.	Good	Very Good	Near Mint
SOMETHING TO TAKE UP TIME	Number one (M)	8.00	10.00	16.00

DOCTOR FEELGOOD & THE INTERNS

Title	Label & No.	Good	Very Good	Near Mint
DOCTOR FEELGOOD	Okeh (M) OKM 12101	4.00	8.00	12.00
DOCTOR FEELGOOD	Okeh (S) OKS 14101	4.00	8.00	12.00

DR. HOOK

Title	Label & No.	Good	Very Good	Near Mint
BEST OF DR. HOOK	Columbia (S) C 34147	2.00	3.00	4.00
DR. HOOK & THE MEDICINE SHOW	Columbia (S) 30898	2.50	3.75	5.00
LITTLE BIT MORE	Capitol (S) ST 11522	2.00	3.00	4.00
WALK RIGHT IN	Capitol (S) SW 11632	2.00	3.00	4.00

DOCTOR JOHN

Title	Label & No.	Good	Very Good	Near Mint
ANYTIME, ANYPLACE	Barometer (S) BRM 67001	3.50	5.25	7.00
DESITIVELY BONNAROO	Atco (S) 7043	2.50	3.75	5.00
DOCTOR JOHN AND HIS NEW ORLEANS CONGREGATION	Ace (M) 2020	3.50	5.25	7.00
DR. JOHN'S GUMBO	Atco (S) 7006	2.50	3.75	5.00
HOLLYWOOD BE THY NAME	United Artists (S) UA-LA552	2.00	3.00	4.00
IN THE RIGHT PLACE	Atco (S) 7018	2.50	3.75	5.00
SUN, MOON & HERBS (LISTED AS "DR. JOHN THE NIGHT TRIPPER")	Atco (S) SD 33-362	3.00	4.50	6.00
TRIUMVIRATE (WITH JOHN HAMMOND & MIKE BLOOMFIELD)	Columbia (S) KC 32172	2.50	3.75	5.00
ZU ZU MAN	Trip (M) TLP 9518	3.50	5.25	7.00

DR. K'S BLUES BAND

Title	Label & No.	Good	Very Good	Near Mint
DR. K'S BLUES BAND	World Pacific (S) WPS-21903	4.00	6.00	8.00

DOCTOR ROSS

Title	Label & No.	Good	Very Good	Near Mint
DOCTOR ROSS	Testament (M) 2206	2.50	3.75	5.00
DOCTOR ROSS, THE HARMONICA BOSS	Fortune (S) FS 3011	6.00	12.00	18.00

DOCTOR WEST'S MEDICINE SHOW & JUNK BAND

Title	Label & No.	Good	Very Good	Near Mint
THE EGG PLANT THAT ATE CHICAGO	GoGo (M) 22 17001	5.00	7.50	10.00

Also see GRENBAUM, Norman

DODD, Dick

Title	Label & No.	Good	Very Good	Near Mint
FIRST EVOLUTION OF DICK DODD	Tower (M) T5142	5.00	10.00	15.00
FIRST EVOLUTION OF DICK DODD	Tower (S) ST 5142	6.00	12.00	18.00

DODD, Ken

Title	Label & No.	Good	Very Good	Near Mint
TEARS AND THE RIVER	Liberty (M) LRP 3442	2.00	3.00	4.00
TEARS AND THE RIVER	Liberty (S) LST 7442	3.00	4.50	6.00

DOLENZ, JONES, BOYCE & HART

Title	Label & No.	Good	Very Good	Near Mint
DOLENZ, JONES, BOYCE & HART	Capitol (S) ST 11513	3.00	4.50	6.00

DOMINO, Fats

Title	Label & No.	Good	Very Good	Near Mint
COOKING WITH FATS	United Artists (M) 122	3.00	4.50	6.00
FABULOUS MR. D	Imperial (M) LP9055	6.00	15.00	24.00
FATS	Reprise (M) 6439	8.00	20.00	32.00
FATS DOMINO	Everest (M) 280	6.00	12.00	18.00
FATS DOMINO	Sunset (M) 1103	3.00	6.00	9.00
FATS DOMINO	Sunset (S) 5103	2.00	4.00	6.00
FATS DOMINO	Grand Award (M) 267	5.00	10.00	15.00
FATS DOMINO SINGS	Imperial (M) LP 9103	6.00	12.50	20.00
FATS DOMINO '65	Mercury (S) SR 61039	6.00	12.00	18.00
FATS DOMINO SWINGS	Imperial (M) LP9062	6.00	15.00	24.00
FATS IS BACK	Reprise (M) 6304	5.00	10.00	15.00
FATS ON FIRE	ABC Paramount (M) ABC479	4.00	8.00	12.00
FATS ON FIRE	ABC Paramount (S) ABCS479	5.00	10.00	15.00
GETAWAY WITH FATS DOMINO	ABC Paramount (M) ABC510	4.00	8.00	12.00
GETAWAY WITH FATS DOMINO	ABC Paramount (S) ABCS 510	5.00	10.00	15.00
HERE COMES FATS	Imperial (EP) EP147	3.00	7.50	12.00
HERE COMES FATS DOMINO	ABC Paramount (M) ABC455	4.00	8.00	12.00
HERE COMES FATS DOMINO	ABC Paramount (S) ABCS455	5.00	10.00	15.00
HERE HE COMES AGAIN	Imperial (M) LP9248	5.00	16.00	15.00
HERE STANDS FATS DOMINO	Imperial (M) LP 9038	7.00	17.50	28.00
HERE STANDS FATS	Imperial (EP) EP148	3.00	7.50	12.00
JUST DOMINO	Imperial (M) LP9208	5.00	10.00	15.00
LEGENDARY MASTERS	United Artists (M) 9958	5.00	7.50	10.00
LET'S DANCE WITH DOMINO	Imperial (M) LP 9239	5.00	10.00	15.00
LET'S PLAY FATS DOMINO	Imperial (M) LP 9065	6.00	15.00	24.00
LET THE FOUR WINDS BLOW	Imperial (M) LP 9153	5.00	12.50	20.00
A LOT OF DOMINOS	Imperial (M) LP 9138	5.00	12.50	20.00
MILLION SELLERS	Imperial (M) LP9195	5.00	10.00	15.00
ROCK AND ROLLIN'	Imperial (M) LP 9009	8.00	20.00	32.00
ROCK AND ROLLIN' WITH FATS DOMINO	Imperial (M) LP9004	8.00	20.00	32.00
ROCKIN WITH FATS	Imperial (EP) EP152	3.00	7.50	12.00
SOUTHLAND USA	Mercury (M) MG21065	5.00	10.00	15.00

(M) Mono (S) Stereo (EP) Extended Play (Q) Quad (RI) Re-issued

TITLE	LABEL & NO.	GOOD	VERY GOOD	NEAR MINT
SOUTHLAND USA	Mercury (S) SR 61065	6.00	12.00	18.00
30 HITS-				
THE FATS DOMINO SOUND	United Artists (M) 104	4.00	6.00	8.00
THIS IS FATS	Imperial (M) LP9040	7.00	17.50	28.00
THIS IS FATS DOMINO	Imperial (M) LP 9028	7.00	17.50	28.00
TROUBLE IN MIND	Sunset (S) 5200	2.00	4.00	6.00
TWISTIN THE STOMP	Imperial (M) LP9170	5.00	10.00	15.00
WALKING TO NEW ORLEANS	Imperial (M) LP9227	5.00	10.00	15.00
WHAT A PARTY	Imperial (M) LP 9164	5.00	12.50	20.00
VERY BEST OF FATS DOMINO	United Artists (M) 233	1.50	2.25	3.00
VERY BEST OF FATS DOMINO (RI)	United Artists (M) 380	1.50	2.25	3.00

Note: Stereo reissues of Imperial LP's
are worth only 25-50% as much as MONO pressings.

DON & DEWEY

THEY'RE ROCKIN' TIL MIDNIGHT,				
ROLLIN' TIL DAWN	Specialty (S) SPS 2131	4.50	6.75	9.00

DON & THE GOODTIMES

GREATEST HITS	Burdette (M) 300	7.00	10.50	14.00
SO GOOD	Epic (M) LN24311	4.00	6.00	8.00
SO GOOD	Epic (S) BN 26311	5.00	7.50	10.00
WHERE THE ACTION IS	Wand (M) WDM679	5.00	7.50	10.00

DONALDSON, Bo & the Heywoods

BO DONALDSON & THE HEYWOODS	ABC (S) 824	2.50	3.75	5.00
SPECIAL SOMEONE	Family Productions (S) FPS 2711	3.00	4.50	6.00

DONEGAN, Lonnie

AN ENGLISHMAN SINGS AMERICAN				
FOLK SONGS	Mercury (M) MG 20229	4.00	10.00	16.00
LONNIE DONEGAN	Dot (M) DLP 3394	5.00	12.50	20.00
PUTTIN' ON THE STYLE	United Artists (S) UA-LA827	2.00	3.00	4.00
SING HALLELUJAH	ABC Paramount (M) ABC433	5.00	12.50	20.00
SING HALLELUJAH	ABC Paramount (S) ABCS433	4.00	10.00	16.00
SKIFFLE FOLK MUSIC	Atlantic (M) 8038	4.00	10.00	16.00
SKIFFLE FOLK MUSIC	Atlantic (S) SD-8038	5.00	12.50	20.00

DONLEY, Jimmy

MEMORIAL TO THE UNFORGETTABLE				
JIMMY DONLEY	Starfire (M) LP 2002	4.00	6.00	8.00

DONNER, Ral

TAKIN CARE OF BUSINESS	Gone (M) LP 5012	15.00	37.50	60.00

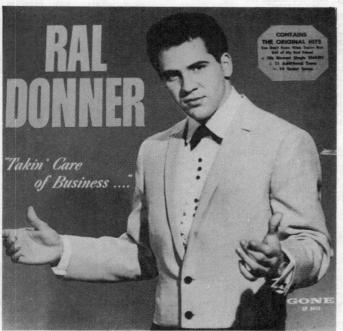

DONNER, Ral, Ray Smith & Bobby Dale

RAL DONNER, RAY SMITH AND				
BOBBY DALE	Crown (M) CLP 5335	4.00	10.00	16.00

DONOVAN

BARABAJAGAL	Epic (S) BN26481	2.50	3.75	5.00
BARABAJAGAL/HURDY GURDY MAN	Epic (S) BG 33731	3.00	4.50	6.00
BEST OF DONOVAN	Hickory (S) 149	4.00	6.00	8.00
CATCH THE WIND	Hickory (M) LPM123	4.50	6.75	9.00
DONOVAN	Arista (S) 4143	2.00	3.00	4.00
DONOVAN IN CONCERT	Epic (S) BN 26386	2.50	3.75	5.00
DONOVAN P. LEITCH	Janus (S) 3022	2.50	3.75	5.00

(M) Mono (S) Stereo (EP) Extended Play (Q) Quad (RI) Re-issued

TITLE	LABEL & NO.	GOOD	VERY GOOD	NEAR MINT
EARLY TREASURES	Bell (S) 1135	3.50	5.25	7.00
ESSENCE TO ESSENCE	Epic (S) KE 32800	2.50	3.75	5.00
FAIRYTALE	Hickory (M) 127	5.00	7.50	10.00
FAIRYTALE	Hickory (S) 127	4.00	6.00	8.00
A GIFT FROM A FLOWER TO				
A GARDEN	Epic (M) L2N6071	3.50	5.25	7.00
A GIFT FROM A FLOWER TO				
A GARDEN	Epic (S) B2N 171	4.00	6.00	8.00
HURDY GURDY MAN	Epic (S) BN 26420	2.50	3.75	5.00
LIKE IT IS, WAS &				
EVERMORE SHALL BE	Hickory (M) 143	5.00	7.50	10.00
LIKE IT IS, WAS &				
EVERMORE SHALL BE	Hickory (S) 143	4.00	6.00	8.00
MELLOW YELLOW	Epic (M) LN24239	2.50	3.75	5.00
MELLOW YELLOW	Epic (S) BN 26239	3.00	4.50	6.00
OPEN ROAD	Epic (S) E30125	2.50	3.75	5.00
REAL DONOVAN, THE	Hickory (M) LP135	4.50	6.75	9.00
7-TEASE	Epic (S) PE 33245	2.50	3.75	5.00
SLOW DOWN WORLD	Epic (S) PE 33945	2.50	3.75	5.00
SUNSHINE SUPERMAN	Epic (M) LN24217	3.50	3.75	5.00
SUNSHINE SUPERMAN	Epic (S) BN26217	3.00	4.50	6.00
SUNSHINE SUPERMAN/IN CONCERT	Epic (S) BG 33734	3.00	4.50	6.00

DOOBIE BROTHERS

BEST OF THE DOOBIE BROTHERS	Warner Bros. (S) BS 2978	2.50	3.75	5.00
BEST OF THE DOOBIES				
(RI of WB 2978)	Warner Bros. (S) BSK 3112	2.00	3.00	4.00
CAPTAIN & ME	Warner Bros. (S) BS 2694	3.00	4.50	6.00
CAPTAIN & ME	Warner Bros. (Q) BS4-2694	2.50	3.75	5.00
LIVIN' ON THE FAULT LINE	Warner Bros. (S) BSK 3045	2.50	3.75	5.00
STAMPEDE	Warner Bros. (S) BS 2835	2.50	3.75	5.00
STAMPEDE	Warner Bros. (Q) BS4-2835	2.50	3.75	5.00
TAKIN' IT TO THE STREETS	Warner Bros. (S) BS 2899	2.50	3.75	5.00
TOULOUSE STREET	Warner Bros. (S) BS 2634	3.00	4.50	6.00
TOULOUSE STREET	Warner Bros. (Q) BS4-2634	2.50	3.75	5.00
WHAT WERE ONCE VICES				
ARE NOW HABITS	Warner Bros. (S) WS 2750	3.00	4.50	6.00
WHAT WERE ONCE VICES				
ARE NOW HABITS	Warner Bros. (Q) WS4-2750	2.50	3.75	5.00

DOORS

ABSOLUTELY LIVE	Elektra (S) EKS 2-9002	4.00	6.00	8.00
BEST OF THE DOORS	Elektra (Q) EQ 5035	2.50	3.75	5.00
DOORS	Elektra (M) EKL 4007	3.00	4.50	6.00
DOORS	Elektra (S) EKS 74007	3.00	4.50	6.00
DOORS 13	Elektra (S) EKS 74079	3.00	4.50	6.00
FULL CIRCLE	Elektra (S) EKS 75038	3.00	4.50	6.00
L.A. WOMAN	Elektra (S) EKS 75011	3.00	4.50	6.00
MOONLIGHT DRIVE	Takal (S) 1954	5.00	7.50	10.00
MORRISON HOTEL	Elektra (S) EKS 75007	3.00	4.50	6.00
OTHER VOICES	Elektra (S) EKS 75017	3.00	4.50	6.00
SOFT PARADE	Elektra (S) EKS 75005	3.00	4.50	6.00
STRANGE DAYS	Elektra (M) EKL 4014	3.00	4.50	6.00
STRANGE DAYS	Elektra (S) EKS 74014	3.00	4.50	6.00
WAITING FOR THE SUN	Elektra (S) EKS 74024	3.00	4.50	6.00
WEIRD SCENES INSIDE THE GOLD MINE	Elektra (S) EKS 2-6001	4.00	6.00	8.00

DORSEY, Lee

RIDE YOUR PONY-GET OUT OF				
MY LIFE WOMAN	Amy (M) 8010	4.00	8.00	12.00
RIDE YOUR PONY-GET OUT OF				
MY LIFE WOMAN	Amy (S) S8010	5.00	10.00	15.00
WORKING IN THE COAL MINE	Amy (M) 8011	4.00	8.00	12.00
WORKING IN THE COAL MINE	Amy (S) 8011	5.00	10.00	15.00
YA YA	Fury (M) FULP1002	7.00	17.50	28.00
YA YA	Sphere Sound (S) SSR 7003	6.00	15.00	24.00

DOUCETTE

MAMA LET HIM PLAY	Mushroom (S) MRS 5009	2.00	3.00	4.00

DOUD, Earle

HONEST TO GOD, WE REALLY MEAN IT,				
VERY LAST NIXON ALBUM	Brunswick (S) 754201	3.00	4.50	6.00

TITLE	LABEL & NO.	GOOD	VERY GOOD	NEAR MINT

DOUD, Earle & Alen Robin

TITLE	LABEL & NO.	GOOD	VERY GOOD	NEAR MINT
LYNDON JOHNSON'S LONELY HEARTS CLUB BAND	Atco (M) 33-230	3.50	5.25	7.00
LYNDON JOHNSON'S LONELY HEARTS CLUB BAND	Atco (S) SD 33-230	4.00	6.00	8.00
WELCOME TO THE LBJ RANCH	Capitol (M) W 2423	3.50	5.25	7.00
WELCOME TO THE LBJ RANCH	Capitol (S) SW 2423	4.00	6.00	8.00

DOUGLAS, K. C.

TITLE	LABEL & NO.	GOOD	VERY GOOD	NEAR MINT
K.C. DOUGLAS	Bluesville (M) 1023	5.00	7.50	10.00
K.C. DOUGLAS	Bluesville (M) 1050	5.00	7.50	10.00

DOUGLAS, Mike

TITLE	LABEL & NO.	GOOD	VERY GOOD	NEAR MINT
DEAR MIKE, PLEASE SING	Epic (M) 24205	2.00	3.00	4.00
DEAR MIKE, PLEASE SING	Epic (S) 26205	2.00	3.00	4.00
MEN IN MY LITTLE GIRL'S LIFE	Epic (M) LM24186	2.00	3.00	4.00
MEN IN MY LITTLE GIRL'S LIFE	Epic (S) LN26186	2.00	3.00	4.00
YOU DON'T HAVE TO BE IRISH	Epic (M) LN24179	2.00	3.00	4.00
YOU DON'T HAVE TO BE IRISH	Epic (S) LN26179	2.00	3.00	4.00
YOUNG AT HEART	Harmony (M) 11263	2.00	3.00	4.00

DOUGLAS, Steve and the Rebel Rousers

TITLE	LABEL & NO.	GOOD	VERY GOOD	NEAR MINT
TWIST	Crown (M) CLP5254	3.00	6.00	9.00

DOUGLAS, Tony

TITLE	LABEL & NO.	GOOD	VERY GOOD	NEAR MINT
HIS 'N' HERS	Sims (M) 121	2.50	3.75	5.00
HIS 'N' HERS	Sims (S) S 121	2.50	3.75	5.00
MR. NICE GUY	Sims (M) 131	2.00	3.00	4.00
MR. NICE GUY	Sims (S) 131	2.00	3.00	4.00

DOVE, Ronnie

TITLE	LABEL & NO.	GOOD	VERY GOOD	NEAR MINT
BEST OF RONNIE DOVE	Diamond (M) 5005	2.50	3.75	5.00
BEST OF RONNIE DOVE	Diamond (S) 5005	2.50	3.75	5.00
Many Stereo Copies of This Lp were In True Stereo-But Labeled as Mono on Both Cover and Record				
BEST OF RONNIE DOVE, Vol 2	Diamond (M) D5008	2.50	3.75	5.00
BEST OF RONNIE DOVE, Vol 2	Diamond (S) SD5008	2.50	3.75	5.00
CRY	Diamond (M) D 5007	2.50	3.75	5.00
CRY	Diamond (S) SD 5007	2.50	3.75	5.00
GREATEST ALL TIME HITS	Certron (S) CST011	2.00	3.00	4.00
I'LL MAKE ALL YOUR DREAMS COME TRUE	Diamond (M) D5004	2.50	3.75	5.00
I'LL MAKE ALL YOUR DREAMS COME TRUE	Diamond (S) SD 5004	2.50	3.75	5.00
ONE KISS FOR OLD TIMES' SAKE	Diamond (M) D 5003	2.50	3.75	5.00
ONE KISS FOR OLD TIMES' SAKE	Diamond (S) SD 5003	2.50	3.75	5.00
RIGHT OR WRONG	Diamond (M) D 5002	2.50	3.75	5.00
RIGHT OR WRONG	Diamond (S) SD5002	2.50	3.75	5.00
RONNIE DOVE	MCA (S) 309	2.00	3.00	4.00
RONNIE DOVE SINGS THE HITS FOR YOU	Diamond (M) D5006	2.50	3.75	5.00
RONNIE DOVE SINGS THE HITS FOR YOU	Diamond (S) SD5006	2.50	3.75	5.00
SWINGIN' TEEN SOUNDS	Design (M) DLP186	2.00	3.00	4.00

DOVELLS

TITLE	LABEL & NO.	GOOD	VERY GOOD	NEAR MINT
ALL THE HITS OF THE TEEN GROUPS	Parkway (M) P 7010	4.00	8.00	12.00
BIGGEST HITS	Wyncote (M) 9114	3.00	6.00	9.00
BRISTOL STOMP	Parkway (M) P 7006	4.00	8.00	12.00
DISCOTHEQUE	Wyncote (S) SW 9052	3.00	6.00	9.00
FOR YOUR HULLY GULLY PARTY	Parkway (M) P 7021	4.00	8.00	12.00
YOU CAN'T SIT DOWN	Parkway (M) P 7025	4.00	8.00	12.00

Also see BARRY, Len

DOWELL, Joe

TITLE	LABEL & NO.	GOOD	VERY GOOD	NEAR MINT
JOE DOWELL SINGS THE GERMAN AMERICAN HITS	Smash (M) MGS 27011	2.50	3.75	5.00
JOE DOWELL SINGS THE GERMAN AMERICAN HITS	Smash (S) SRS 67011	2.50	3.75	5.00
WOODEN HEART	Smash (M) MGS 27000	2.50	3.75	5.00
WOODEN HEART	Smash (S) SRS 67000	3.00	4.50	6.00

DOWNS, Hugh

TITLE	LABEL & NO.	GOOD	VERY GOOD	NEAR MINT
EVENING WITH HUGH DOWNS	Epic (M) LN-3597	3.00	7.50	12.00
EVENING WITH HUGH DOWNS	Epic (S) BN-541	4.00	10.00	16.00

DRACULA

TITLE	LABEL & NO.	GOOD	VERY GOOD	NEAR MINT
DRACULA'S GREATEST HITS	RCA (M) LPM 2977	3.00	7.50	12.00

DRAGONFLY

TITLE	LABEL & NO.	GOOD	VERY GOOD	NEAR MINT
DRAGONFLY	Megophone (S) MS 1202	6.00	9.00	12.00

DRAMATICS

TITLE	LABEL & NO.	GOOD	VERY GOOD	NEAR MINT
DRAMA V	ABC (S) ABCD 916	2.00	3.00	4.00
A DRAMATIC EXPERIENCE	Volt (S) VOS 6019	3.00	4.50	6.00
JACKPOT	ABC (S) ABCD 867	2.00	3.00	4.00
WHATCHA SEE IS WHATCHA GET	Volt (S) VOS 6018	3.00	4.50	6.00

DRAPER, Rusty

TITLE	LABEL & NO.	GOOD	VERY GOOD	NEAR MINT
COUNTRY & WESTERN GOLDEN GREATS	Mercury (M) MG 20657	2.50	3.75	5.00
COUNTRY & WESTERN GOLDEN GREATS	Mercury (S) SR 60657	2.50	3.75	5.00
COUNTRY CLASSICS	Mercury/Wing (M) MGW 12274	2.00	3.00	4.00
COUNTRY CLASSICS	Mercury/Wing (S) SRW 16274	2.00	3.00	4.00
DRAPER SINGS FAVORITE HITS	Mercury (EP) 13192	1.00	1.50	2.00
ENCORES	Mercury (M) MG 20117	4.00	6.00	8.00
HITS THAT SOLD A MILLION	Mercury (M) MG20499	2.50	3.75	5.00
HITS THAT SOLD A MILLION	Mercury (S) SR60176	2.50	3.75	5.00
MUSIC FOR A RAINY NIGHT	Mercury (M) MG 20068	3.00	4.50	6.00
POP PARTY	Mercury	2.50	3.75	5.00
POP PARTY	Mercury (EP) 1 3199	1.00	1.50	2.00
RUSTY DRAPER'S GREATEST HITS	Harmony (S) H31051	2.00	3.00	4.00
RUSTY DRAPER SINGS	Mercury (M) MG 20118	2.50	3.75	5.00
RUSTY SINGS	Mercury (EP) 13079	1.00	1.50	2.00
SING-A-LONG WITH RUSTY	Mercury (M) MP 26	3.00	4.50	6.00
SWINGIN' COUNTRY/SOMETHING OLD, SOMETHING NEW	Monument (S) BZ33870	2.50	3.75	5.00
TOUR THE U.S.A. WITH RUSTY DRAPER	Golden Crest (S) 31030	3.00	4.50	6.00

DREAMLOVERS

TITLE	LABEL & NO.	GOOD	VERY GOOD	NEAR MINT
BIRD, THE	Columbia (M) CL 2020	5.00	12.50	20.00
BIRD, THE	Columbia (S) CS 8820	6.00	15.00	24.00

DREAMS

TITLE	LABEL & NO.	GOOD	VERY GOOD	NEAR MINT
DREAMS	Columbia (S) C 30225	1.50	3.00	5.00

DREAMS & ILLUSIONS

TITLE	LABEL & NO.	GOOD	VERY GOOD	NEAR MINT
DREAMS AND ILLUSIONS	Verve-Forecast (S) FTS-3040	3.00	4.50	6.00

DREAM WEAVERS

TITLE	LABEL & NO.	GOOD	VERY GOOD	NEAR MINT
DREAM WEAVERS	Decca (EP) ED 2376	2.50	6.25	10.00

DREW, Patti

TITLE	LABEL & NO.	GOOD	VERY GOOD	NEAR MINT
TELL HIM	Capitol (M) T 2804	4.00	8.00	12.00
TELL HIM	Capitol (S) ST2804	5.00	10.00	15.00
WILD IS LOVE	Capitol (S) ST 408	3.00	4.50	6.00

DRIFTERS

TITLE	LABEL & NO.	GOOD	VERY GOOD	NEAR MINT
CLYDE MCPHATTER AND THE DRIFTERS	Atlantic (M) 8003	9.00	22.s0	36.00
DRIFTERS FEATURING CLYDE MC PHATTER	Atlantic (EP) EP 534	3.00	7.50	12.00
DRIFTER'S GOLDEN HITS	Atlantic (M) 8153	5.00	10.00	15.00
DRIFTER'S GOLDEN HITS	Atlantic (S) SD 8153	6.00	12.00	18.00
DRIFTERS' GREATEST HITS	Atlantic (M) 8041	8.00	20.00	32.00
DRIFTERS-THEIR GREATEST RECORDINGS	Atco (S) SD 33 375	3.00	4.50	6.00
GOOD LIFE WITH THE DRIFTERS	Atlantic (M) 8103	5.00	10.00	15.00
GOOD LIFE WITH THE DRIFTERS	Atlantic (S) 8103	6.00	12.00	18.00
I'LL TAKE YOU WHERE THE MUSIC'S PLAYING	Atlantic (M) 8113	5.00	10.00	15.00
I'LL TAKE YOU WHERE THE MUSIC'S PLAYING	Atlantic (S) SD 8113	6.00	12.00	18.00
NOW	Bell (M) 219	4.00	6.00	8.00
OUR BIGGEST HITS	Atlantic (M) 8093	6.00	12.00	18.00
OUR BIGGEST HITS	Atlantic (S) SD 8093	7.00	14.00	21.00
ROCKIN' AND DRIFTIN'	Atlantic (M) 8022	8.00	20.00	32.00
SAVE THE LAST DANCE FOR ME	Atlantic (M) 8059	6.00	15.00	24.00
SAVE THE LAST DANCE FOR ME	Atlantic (S) SD 8059	7.00	17.50	28.00
UNDER THE BOARDWALK	Atlantic (M) 8099	6.00	12.00	18.00
UNDER THE BOARDWALK	Atlantic (S) SD 8099	7.00	14.00	21.00
UNDER THE BOARDWALK	Atlantic (EP) EP 592	3.00	7.50	12.00
UP ON THE ROOF	Atlantic (M) 8073	6.00	12.00	18.00
UP ON THE ROOF	Atlantic (S) SD 8073	7.00	14.00	21.00

Also see MC PHATTER, Clyde; & KING, Ben E.

DRIFTWOOD, Jimmy

TITLE	LABEL & NO.	GOOD	VERY GOOD	NEAR MINT
DRIFTWOOD AT SEA	RCA (M) LPM 2443	3.00	6.00	9.00
DRIFTWOOD AT SEA	RCA (S) LSP 2443	3.00	6.00	9.00
FOLK SONG FESTIVAL AT CARNEGIE HALL	United Artists (M) UAL-3050	2.50	3.75	5.00
FOLK SONG FESTIVAL AT CARNEGIE HALL	United Artists (S) UAS-6050	2.50	3.75	5.00
JIMMY DRIFTWOOD SINGS NEWLY DISCOVERED EARLY AMERICAN FOLK SONGS	RCA (M) LPM 1635	5.00	7.50	10.00
SOLDIER'S JOY	RCA (EP) EPA 4345	2.00	3.00	4.00
SONGS OF BILLY YANK AND JOHNNY REB	RCA (M) LPM 2316	3.00	6.00	9.00
SONGS OF BILLY YANK AND JOHNNY REB	RCA (S) LSP 2316	3.00	6.00	9.00
TALL TALES IN SONG	RCA (M) LPM 2228	3.00	6.00	9.00
TALL TALES IN SONG	RCA (S) LSP 2228	3.00	6.00	9.00
WESTWOOD MOVEMENT	RCA (M) LPM 2171	5.00	7.50	10.00
WESTWOOD MOVEMENT	RCA (S) LSP 2171	6.00	9.00	12.00

DRISCOLL, Julie and Brian Auger and the Trinity

TITLE	LABEL & NO.	GOOD	VERY GOOD	NEAR MINT
JOOLS AND BRIAN	Capitol (S) DT 136	2.50	3.75	5.00
OPEN	Atco (S) SD 33 258	3.50	5.25	7.00
STREETNOISE	Atco (S) SD 2-701	3.50	5.25	7.00

DRUIDS OF STONEHENGE

TITLE	LABEL & NO.	GOOD	VERY GOOD	NEAR MINT
CREATION	UNI (M) 3004	2.50	3.75	5.00
CREATION	UNI (S) 73004	3.50	5.25	7.00

DRUSKY, Roy

TITLE	LABEL & NO.	GOOD	VERY GOOD	NEAR MINT
DOIN' SOMETHING RIGHT	Mercury (S) SR 61377	2.00	3.00	4.00
PEACEFUL EASY FEELING	Capitol (S) ST-11339	2.00	3.00	4.00

(M) Mono (S) Stereo (EP) Extended Play (Q) Quad (RI) Re-issued

TITLE	LABEL & NO.	GOOD	VERY GOOD	NEAR MINT
DRY CITY SCAT BAND				
DRY CITY SCAT BAND	Elektra (S) 7292	5.00	10.00	15.00
DRY DOCK COUNTY				
DRY DOCK COUNTY	Mercury (S) SR 61286	3.00	4.50	6.00
DUALS				
STICK SHIFT	Sue (M) LP 2002	5.00	10.00	15.00
DUBS				
BEST OF THE DUBS	Candlelite (M) 1004	4.00	6.00	8.00
DUBS MEET THE SHELLS	Josie (M) JM 4001	9.00	22.50	36.00
YOU'VE GOT TO BE GOOD TO MAKE IT IN NEW YORK CITY	Candlelite (M) 1003	4.00	6.00	8.00
DUCEY, CHRIS				
DUCE OF HEARTS	Warner Bros. (S) BS-2841	2.00	3.00	4.00
DUCHIN, Eddy				
CHILD OF MINE	Capitol (S) ST-11146	2.00	3.00	4.00
GREAT EDDY DUCHIN	Harmony (M) HL-7209	2.00	3.00	4.00
DUCKS				
DUCKS	Just Sunshine (S) 6	2.50	3.75	5.00
DUCKS DELUXE				
DUCKS DELUXE	RCA (S) LPL1-5008	3.00	4.50	6.00
DUDEK, Les				
GHOST TOWN PARADE	Columbia (S) JC 35088	2.00	3.00	4.00
LES DUDEK	Columbia (S) PC 33702	2.00	3.00	4.00
SAY NO MORE	Columbia (S) PC 34397	2.00	3.00	4.00
DUDES				
WE'RE NO ANGELS	Columbia (S) PC 33577	2.50	3.75	5.00
DUDLEY, Dave				
KEEP ON TRUCKIN'	Mercury (S) SRM-1-669	2.00	3.00	4.00
SIX DAYS ON THE ROAD	Golden Ring (M) G 110	3.00	4.50	6.00
SPECIAL DELIVERY	United Artists (S) UA-LA366	2.00	3.00	4.00
DU DROPPERS				
DU DROPPERS	Groove (M) 0104	8.00	20.00	32.00
DUDZIAK, Urszula				
URSZULA	Arista (S) 4065	2.00	3.00	4.00
DUKE & THE DRIVERS				
CRUISING	ABC (S) 911	2.00	3.00	4.00
DUKE, Doris				
I'M A LOSER	Canyon (M) 7704	3.00	4.50	6.00
DUKE, Patty				
DON'T JUST STAND THERE	United Artists (M) UAL 3452	4.00	8.00	12.00
DON'T JUST STAND THERE	United Artists (S) UAS 6452	5.00	10.00	15.00
GUIDEPOSTS FOR CHRISTMAS	Guideposts (M) GP 101	4.00	8.00	12.00
PATTY	United Artists (S) UAS 6492	3.00	6.00	9.00
PATTY DUKE GREATEST HITS	United Artists (S) UAS 6535	4.00	8.00	12.00
PATTY DUKE SINGS SONGS FROM VALLEY OF THE DOLLS AND OTHER SELECTIONS	United Artists (M) UAL 3623	3.00	6.00	9.00
PATTY DUKE SINGS SONGS FROM VALLEY OF THE DOLLS AND OTHER SELECTIONS	United Artists (S) UAS 6623	4.00	8.00	12.00
TV'S TEEN STAR	Unart (M) M 20005	4.00	8.00	12.00
TV'S TEEN STAR	Unart (S) S 21005	5.00	10.00	15.00
DUNCAN, Johnny				
SWEET COUNTRY WOMAN	Columbia (S) KC-32440	2.00	3.00	4.00
YOU'RE GONNA NEED A MAN	Harmony (S) KH-32477	2.00	3.00	4.00
DUPREE, Champion Jack				
BLUES FOR EVERYBODY	King (M) 1084	4.00	10.00	16.00
BLUES FROM THE GUTTER	Atlantic (M) 8019	4.00	10.00	16.00
BLUES FROM THE GUTTER	Atlantic (S) SD 8019	5.00	12.50	20.00
CHAMPION OF THE BLUES	Atlantic (M) 8056	4.00	10.00	16.00
CHAMPION OF THE BLUES	Atlantic (S) SD 8056	5.00	12.50	20.00
CHAMPION JACK DUPREE	King (M) 735	5.00	7.50	10.00
CHAMPION JACK DUPREE	Folkways (M) 3825	2.50	4.00	5.00
CHAMPION JACK DUPREE	Everest (M) 217	2.50	4.00	5.00
CHAMPION JACK DUPREE SINGS THE BLUES	King (M) 735	4.00	10.00	16.00
DUPREE'S NATURAL AND SOULFUL BLUES	Atlantic (M) 8045	4.00	10.00	16.00
DUPREE'S NATURAL AND SOULFUL BLUES	Atlantic (S) SD 8045	5.00	12.50	20.00
DUPREE, Simon and the Big Sound				
WITHOUT RESERVATIONS	Tower (M) T 5097	4.00	8.00	12.00

(M) Mono   (S) Stereo   (EP) Extended Play   (Q) Quad   (RI) Re-issued

TITLE	LABEL & NO.	GOOD	VERY GOOD	NEAR MINT
DUPREES				
DUPREES SING	Post (M) 1000	3.00	4.50	6.00
HAVE YOU HEARD	Coed (M) LPC 906	8.00	20.00	32.00
YOU BELONG TO ME	Coed (M) LPC 905	8.00	20.00	32.00
DURANTE, Jimmy				
JIMMY DURANTE AT THE PIANO	Decca (M) DL-8884	2.00	4.00	6.00
JIMMY DURANTE AT THE PIANO	Decca (S) DL-78884	2.00	4.00	6.00
DURHAM, Judith				
GIFT OF SONG	A & M (S) SP 4240	4.50	6.75	9.00
DURY, Ian				
NEW BOOTS & PANTIES	Stiff (S) 0001	2.50	3.75	5.00
DUST				
DUST	Kama Sutra (S) KSBS 2041	5.00	7.50	10.00
HARD ATTACK	Kama Sutra (S) KSBS 2059	5.00	7.50	10.00
DUSTY CHAPS				
DOMINO JOE	Capitol (S) ST 11755	2.00	3.00	4.00
HONKY TONK MUSIC	Bandolier (S) 1021	5.00	7.50	10.00
DYLAN, Bob				
ANOTHER SIDE OF BOB DYLAN	Columbia (M) CL 2193	7.00	10.00	14.00
ANOTHER SIDE OF BOB DYLAN	Columbia (S) CS 8993	3.50	5.25	7.00
BASEMENT TAPES (WITH THE BAND)	Columbia (S) C2-33682	2.50	3.75	5.00
BEFORE THE FLOOD	Asylum (S) AB 201	4.00	6.00	8.00
BLONDE ON BLONDE	Columbia (M) C2L 41	6.00	9.00	12.00
BLONDE ON BLONDE	Columbia (S) CS 841	5.00	7.50	10.00
BLOOD ON THE TRACKS	Columbia (S) PC 33235	2.50	3.75	5.00
BOB DYLAN	Columbia (M) CL 1779	8.00	12.00	16.00
BOB DYLAN	Columbia (S) CS 8579	8.00	12.00	16.00
BOB DYLAN'S GREATEST HITS	Columbia (M) KCL 2663	7.00	10.50	14.00
BOB DYLAN'S GREATEST HITS	Columbia (S) KCS 9463	2.50	3.75	5.00
BOB DYLAN'S GREATEST HITS, VOL. 2	Columbia (S) 31120	2.50	3.75	5.00
BRINGING IT ALL BACK HOME	Columbia (M) CL 2328	7.00	10.50	14.00
BRINGING IT ALL BACK HOME	Columbia (S) CS 9128	3.50	5.25	7.00
BRINGING IT ALL BACK HOME (Compact 33)	Columbia (EP) 7-928	25.00	37.50	50.00
BROADSIDE BALLADS VOL 1	Broadside (M) BR 301	8.00	16.00	24.00
DESIRE	Columbia (S) PC 33893	2.50	3.75	5.00
DYLAN	Columbia (S) PC 32747	2.50	3.75	5.00
FREEWHEELIN (LP Containing 'Let Me Die in My Footsteps')	Columbia (M) CL 1936	40.00	100.00	160.00
FREEWHEELIN' BOB DYLAN	Columbia (M) CL 1986	8.00	12.00	16.00
FREEWHEELIN' BOB DYLAN	Columbia (S) CS 8786	4.00	6.00	8.00
HARD RAIN	Columbia (S) PC 34349	2.50	3.75	5.00
HIGHWAY 61 REVISITED	Columbia (M) 2389	7.00	10.00	14.00
HIGHWAY 61 REVISITED	Columbia (S) CS 9189	6.00	22.50	67.50
(This LP has an alternate version of ''From A Buick'' on it)				
JOHN WESLEY HARDING	Columbia (M) CL 2804	5.00	7.50	10.00
JOHN WESLEY HARDING	Columbia (S) CS 9604	3.00	4.50	6.00
NASHVILLE SKYLINE	Columbia (S) KCS 9825	3.00	4.50	6.00
NEW MORNING	Columbia (S) 30290	3.00	4.50	6.00
PLANET WAVES	Asylum (S) 7E-1003	4.00	6.00	8.00
SELF PORTRAIT	Columbia (S) C2X 30050	3.00	4.50	6.00
TIMES THEY ARE A CHANGIN'	Columbia (M) CL 2105	7.00	10.50	14.00
TIMES THEY ARE A CHANGIN'	Columbia (S) CS 8905	3.50	5.25	7.00
DYNAMICS (With Jimmy Hanna)				
DYNAMICS WITH JIMMY HANNA	Bolo (M) BLP 8001	6.00	12.00	18.00
DYNAMIC SUPERIORS				
DYNAMIC SUPERIORS	Motown (S) 822	2.50	3.75	5.00
DYNATONES				
FIFE PIPER	Hanna Barbera (M) HLP 8509	3.00	4.50	6.00
FIFE PIPER	Hanna Barbera (S) HST 9509	4.00	6.00	8.00

E

TITLE	LABEL & NO.	GOOD	VERY GOOD	NEAR MINT
EAGLE				
EAGLE	Janus (S) JLS 3011	6.00	9.00	12.00
EAGLES				
DESPERADO	Asylum (S) 5068	3.50	5.25	7.00
EAGLES	Asylum (S) 5054	3.50	5.25	7.00
HOTEL CALIFORNIA	Asylum (S) 7E-1084	2.50	3.75	5.00
ONE OF THESE NIGHTS	Asylum (S) 7E-1039	2.50	3.75	5.00
ON THE BORDER	Asylum (S) 7E-1004	2.50	3.75	5.00
THEIR GREATEST HITS 1971-1975	Asylum (S) 7E-1052	2.50	3.75	5.00
EAGLIN, Snooks				
NEW ORLEANS STREET SINGER	Folkways (M) FA 2476	6.00	12.00	18.00
SNOOLIS EAGLIN	Folkways (M) 2476	2.50	4.00	5.00
EARLS				
REMEMBER ME BABY	Old Town (M) LP 104	10.00	25.00	40.00
EARP, Wyatt (Hugh O'Brian)				
WYATT EARP SINGS	ABC (M) LP 203	2.50	3.75	5.00
EARTH & FIRE				
EARTH AND FIRE	Red Bullet (M) PRBLP 3000	5.00	7.50	10.00
EARTH ISLAND				
WE MUST SURVIVE	Philips (S) 600-340	4.00	6.00	8.00
EARTH OPERA				
EARTH OPERA	Elektra (S) EKS 74016	3.50	5.25	7.00
THE GREAT AMERICAN EAGLE TRAGEDY	Elektra (S) 74038	3.50	5.25	7.00
EARTH QUAKE				
EARTH QUAKE	A&M (S) SP 4308	2.50	3.75	5.00
8.5	Beserkley (S) 0047	4.00	6.00	8.00
8.5 (RI of BESERKLEY 0047)	Beserkley (S) PZ 34754	2.50	3.75	5.00
LEVELED	Beserkley (S) PZ 34801	3.00	4.50	6.00
ROCKIN' THE WORLD	Beserkley (S) 0045	4.00	6.00	8.00
ROCKIN' THE WORLD (RI of BESERKLEY 0045)	Beserkley (S) PZ 34752	2.50	3.75	5.00
WHY DON'T YOU TRY ME	A&M (S) SP 4337	5.00	7.50	10.00
EASTFIELD MEADOWS				
EASTFIELD MEADOWS	VMC (S) VS133	3.00	4.50	6.00
EAST OF EDEN				
EAST OF EDEN	Harvest (S) SW 806	2.50	3.75	5.00
SNAFU	Dream (S) DES 18043	2.50	3.75	5.00
EAST SIDE KIDS				
TIGER AND THE LAMB	UNI (S) 73032	4.00	6.00	8.00
EASTWOOD, Clint				
COWBOY FAVORITES	Cameo (M) C-1056	3.00	4.50	6.00
COWBOY FAVORITES	Cameo (S) SC 1056	3.00	4.50	6.00
EASYBEATS				
FALLING OFF THE EDGE OF THE WORLD	United Artists (S) UAS 6667	6.00	9.00	12.00
FRIDAY ON MY MIND	United Artists (M) UAL 3588	5.00	7.50	10.00
FRIDAY ON MY MIND	United Artists (S) UAS 6588	6.00	9.00	12.00
EASY RIDERS				
MARIANNE AND OTHER SONGS	Columbia (M) CL 990	5.00	7.50	10.00
MARIANNE AND OTHER SONGS	Columbia (EP) B 9901	1.50	2.25	3.00
MARIANNE AND OTHER SONGS	Columbia (EP) B 9902	1.50	2.25	3.00
WANDERIN FOLK SONGS	Columbia (M) CL 1272	2.50	3.75	5.00
WANDERIN FOLK SONGS	Columbia (S) CS 8102	2.50	3.75	5.00
ECKSTINE, Billy				
BILLY ECKSTINE	MGM (EP) X1078	1.50	2.25	3.00
BILLY ECKSTINE FAVORITES	MGM (M) E548	3.00	4.50	6.00
BILLY ECKSTINE FAVORITES	MGM (EP) X1103	1.50	2.25	3.00
BILLY ECKSTINE FAVORITES	MGM (EP) X 1104	1.50	2.25	3.00
BILLY ECKSTINE SINGS (10")	National (M) 2001	4.00	10.00	16.00
BLOWING THE BLUES AWAY	King (EP) EP258	2.00	3.00	4.00
DEDICATED TO YOU	MGM (EP) X1002	1.50	2.25	3.00
EARLY AUTUMN	MGM (EP) X 1152	1.50	2.25	3.00
A FOOL IN LOVE	MGM (EP) X1084	1.50	2.25	3.00
THE GREAT MR. B.	King (M) 265-12	5.00	7.50	10.00
I APOLOGIZE	MGM (EP) X1015	1.50	2.25	3.00
I LET A SONG GO OUT OF MY HEART	MGM (M) E257	3.00	6.00	9.00
I LET A SONG GO OUT OF MY HEART	MGM (EP) X1110	1.50	2.25	3.00
I LET A SONG GO OUT OF MY HEART	MGM (EP) X 1111	1.50	2.25	3.00
LOVE SONGS	MGM (EP) X1099	1.50	2.25	3.00
LOVE SONGS	MGM (EP) X 1100	1.50	2.25	3.00
MISTER 'B' WITH A BEAT	MGM (M) E3176	3.00	4.50	6.00
MY FOOLISH HEART	MGM (EP) X1011	1.50	2.25	3.00
RENDEZVOUS	MGM (M) E3209	3.00	4.50	6.00
SMOKE GETS IN YOUR EYES	MGM (EP) X1053	1.50	2.25	3.00
SONGS BY BILLY ECKSTINE	MGM (M) E523	3.00	6.00	9.00
SONGS BY BILLY ECKSTINE	MGM (M) X1041	1.50	2.25	3.00
STORMY MONDAY BLUES	RCA (M) 212XX	6.00	9.00	12.00
TENDERLY	MGM (M) E219	3.00	6.00	9.00
TENDERLY	MGM (M) X1052	1.50	2.25	3.00
THAT OLD FEELING	MGM (M) E3275	3.00	4.50	6.00
ECLECTION				
ECLECTION	Elektra (S) 74023	3.50	5.25	7.00
EDDY, Duane				
A-GO-GO	Colpix (M) CP 490	5.00	10.00	15.00
A-GO-GO	Colpix (S) CPS 490	6.00	12.00	18.00
BECAUSE THEY'RE YOUNG	Jamie (EP) JEP 304	1.50	3.75	6.00
BEST OF DUANE EDDY	RCA (M) LPM 3477	4.00	10.00	16.00
BEST OF DUANE EDDY	RCA (S) LSP 3477	5.00	12.50	20.00
BIGGEST TWANG OF THEM ALL	Reprise (M) R 6218	4.00	8.00	12.00
BIGGEST TWANG OF THEM ALL	Reprise (S) RS 6218	5.00	10.00	15.00
DANCE WITH THE GUITAR MAN	RCA (M) LPM 2648	4.00	10.00	16.00
DANCE WITH THE GUITAR MAN	RCA (S) LSP 2648	5.00	12.50	20.00
DETOUR	Jamie (EP) JEP 301	1.50	3.75	6.00
DUANE EDDY DOES BOB DYLAN	Colpix (S) CPS 494	6.00	12.00	18.00
DUANE EDDY DOES BOB DYLAN	Colpix (M) CP 494	5.00	10.00	15.00
DUANE EDDY, MOVIN' & GROOVIN'	Jamie (EP) JEP100	1.50	3.75	6.00
ESPECIALLY FOR YOU	Jamie (M) JLP 70 3006	5.00	12.50	20.00
ESPECIALLY FOR YOU	Jamie (S) JLP 3006	7.00	17.50	28.00
GIRLS, GIRLS, GIRLS	Jamie (M) JLP 70 3019	5.00	12.50	20.00
GIRLS, GIRLS, GIRLS	Jamie (S) JLP 3019	7.00	17.50	28.00
HAVE TWANGY GUITAR WILL TRAVEL	Jamie (M) JLP 70 3000	6.00	15.00	24.00
HAVE TWANGY GUITAR WILL TRAVEL	Jamie (S) JLP 3000	8.00	20.00	32.00
IN PERSON	Jamie (M) JLP 70 3025	4.00	10.00	16.00
IN PERSON	Jamie (S) JLP 3025	6.00	15.00	24.00
LONELY GUITAR	RCA (M) LPM 2798	4.00	10.00	16.00
LONELY GUITAR	RCA (S) LSP 2798	5.00	12.50	20.00
$1,000,000 WORTH OF TWANG	Jamie (M) JLP 70 3014	5.00	12.50	20.00
$1,000,000 WORTH OF TWANG	Jamie (S) JLP 3014	7.00	17.50	28.00
$1,000,000 WORTH OF TWANG (VOL. 2)	Jamie (M) JLP 70 3021	5.00	12.50	20.00
$1,000,000 WORTH OF TWANG (VOL. 2)	Jamie (S) JLP 3021	7.00	17.50	28.00
PURE GOLD	RCA (S) ANL1-2671	2.50	3.75	5.00
ROARING TWANGIES	Reprise (M) R 6240	4.00	8.00	12.00
ROARING TWANGIES	Reprise (S) RS 6240	5.00	10.00	15.00
SHAZAM	Jamie (EP) JEP 303	1.50	3.75	6.00
16 GREATEST HITS	Jamie (M) JLP 70 3026	4.00	10.00	16.00
16 GREATEST HITS	Jamie (S) JLP 3026	6.00	15.00	24.00
SONGS OF OUR HERITAGE (With Book Cover)	Jamie (M) JLP 70 3011	6.00	15.00	24.00
SONGS OF OUR HERITAGE (With Book Cover)	Jamie (S) JLP 3011	8.00	20.00	32.00
SONGS OF OUR HERITAGE	Jamie (M) JLP 70 3011	5.00	12.50	20.00
SONGS OF OUR HERITAGE	Jamie (S) JLP 3011	7.00	17.50	28.00
SURFIN	Jamie (M) JLP 3024	4.00	10.00	16.00
SURFIN	Jamie (S) JLP 3024	6.00	15.00	24.00
TWANG A COUNTRY SONG	RCA (M) LPM 2681	4.00	10.00	16.00
TWANG A COUNTRY SONG	RCA (S) LSP 2681	5.00	12.50	20.00
TWANGIN' THE GOLDEN HITS	RCA (M) LPM 2993	4.00	10.00	16.00
TWANGIN' THE GOLDEN HITS	RCA (S) LSP 2993	5.00	12.50	20.00
TWANGIN UP A STORM	RCA (M) LPM 2700	4.00	10.00	16.00
TWANGIN UP A STORM	RCA (S) LSP 2700	5.00	12.50	20.00
TWANGS THE THANG	Jamie (M) JLP 70 3009	5.00	12.50	20.00
TWANGS THE THANG	Jamie (S) JLP 3009	7.00	17.50	28.00
TWANGSVILLE	RCA (M) 3432	4.00	10.00	16.00
TWANGSVILLE	RCA (S) 3432	5.00	12.50	20.00
TWANGY GUITAR, SILKY STRINGS	RCA (M) LPM 2576	4.00	10.00	16.00
TWANGY GUITAR, SILKY STRINGS	RCA (S) LSP 2576	5.00	12.50	20.00
TWISTIN' AND TWANGIN'	RCA (M) LPM 2525	4.00	10.00	16.00
TWISTIN' AND TWANGIN'	RCA (S) LSP 2525	5.00	12.50	20.00
TWISTING WITH DUANE EDDY	Jamie (M) JLP 70-3022	4.00	10.00	16.00
TWISTING WITH DUANE EDDY	Jamie (S) JLP 70-3022	6.00	15.00	24.00
VINTAGE YEARS	Sire (S) Sash 3707-2	4.00	6.00	8.00
WATER SKIING	RCA (M) LPM 2918	4.00	10.00	16.00
WATER SKIING	RCA (S) LSP 2918	5.00	12.50	20.00
YEP!	Jamie (EP) JEP 302	1.50	3.75	6.00
EDELMAN, Randy				
FAREWELL FAIRBANKS	20th Century (S) T 494	2.00	3.00	4.00
IF LOVE IS REAL	Arista (S) 4139	2.00	3.00	4.00
LAUGHTER & TEARS	Lion (S) 1013	2.50	3.75	5.00
PRIMECUTS	20th Century (S) T 448	2.00	3.00	4.00
EDEN'S CHILDREN				
EDEN'S CHILDREN	ABC (S) ABCS624	5.00	7.50	10.00
SURE LOOKS REAL	ABC (S) ABCS652	5.00	7.50	10.00
EDGE				
EDGE	Nose Records (S) NRS 48003	4.00	6.00	8.00

(M) Mono (S) Stereo (EP) Extended Play (Q) Quad (RI) Re-issued

TITLE	LABEL & NO.	GOOD	VERY GOOD	NEAR MINT

EDGE, GRAEME, BAND
KICK OFF YOUR MUDDY BOOTS	Threshold (S) THS15	3.00	4.50	6.00
PARADISE BALLROOM (WITH ADRIAN GURVITZ)	London (S) PS 686	2.50	3.75	5.00

Also see MOODY BLUES

EDMUNDS, Dave
ROCKPILE	MAM (M) 3	15.00	22.50	30.00
SUBTLE AS A FLYING MALLET	RCA (M) LPL1 5003	3.00	4.50	6.00

EDWARD BEAR
BEARINGS	Capitol (S) SKAO 426	3.50	5.25	7.00
CLOSE YOUR EYES	Capitol (S) SMAS 11192	3.00	4.50	6.00
ECLIPSE	Capitol (S) ST 580	3.50	5.25	7.00
EDWARD BEAR	Capitol (S) ST 11157	3.00	4.50	6.00

EDWARDS HAND
EDWARDS HAND	GRT (S) 1005	3.00	4.50	6.00
STRANDED	RCA (S) LSP	3.00	4.50	6.00

EDWARDS, Jackie
PUT YOUR TEARS AWAY	Veep (S) VPS 16533	4.00	8.00	12.00

EDWARDS, Jonathan
HAVE A GOOD TIME FOR ME	Atco (S) 7036	2.50	3.75	5.00
HONKY-TONK STARDUST COWBOY	Atco (S) 7015	3.00	4.50	6.00
JONATHAN EDWARDS	Capricorn (S) 8021	3.00	4.50	6.00
LUCKY DAY	Atco (S) 36-104	2.50	3.75	5.00
ROCKIN' CHAIR	Reprise (S) MS 2238	2.00	3.00	4.00
SAILBOAT	Warner Bros. (S) BS 3020	2.00	3.00	4.00

EDWARDS, Jonathan & Darlene
AMERICAN POPULAR SONG	Westminster (S) WGAP 68014	3.00	4.50	6.00
SING ALONG WITH JONATHAN & DARLENE EDWARDS	RCA (M) LPM 2495	2.00	3.00	4.00
SING ALONG WITH JONATHAN & DARLENE EDWARDS	RCA (S) LSP 2495	3.00	4.50	6.00

EDWARDS, Tommy
FOR YOUNG LOVERS	MGM (M) E 3760	2.50	3.75	5.00
FOR YOUNG LOVERS	MGM (S) SE 3760	2.50	3.75	5.00
GREATEST HITS	MGM (M) E3884	2.50	3.75	5.00
GREATEST HITS	MGM (S) SE 3884	2.50	3.75	5.00
IT'S ALL IN THE GAME	MGM (M) E 3732	2.50	3.75	5.00
IT'S ALL IN THE GAME	MGM (S) SE 3732	3.00	4.50	6.00
IT'S ALL IN THE GAME (Contains the 1951 version of this song)	MGM (EP) X1003	3.00	4.50	6.00
STEP OUT SINGING	MGM (M) E 3822	2.50	3.75	5.00
STEP OUT SINGING	MGM (S) SE 3822	2.50	3.75	5.00
TOMMY EDWARDS	Lion (M) L-70120	2.50	3.75	5.00
TOMMY EDWARDS IN HAWAII	MGM (M) E 3838	2.50	3.75	5.00
TOMMY EDWARDS IN HAWAII	MGM (S) SE 3838	2.50	3.75	5.00
TOMMY EDWARDS SINGS	Regent (M) MG 6096	4.00	6.00	8.00
TOMMY EDWARDS SINGS GOLDEN COUNTRY HITS	MGM (M) E 3959	2.50	3.75	5.00
TOMMY EDWARDS SINGS GOLDEN COUNTRY HITS	MGM (S) SE 3959	3.00	4.50	6.00
YOU STARTED ME DREAMING	MGM (M) E 3805	2.50	3.75	5.00
YOU STARTED ME DREAMING	MGM (S) SE 3805	2.50	3.75	5.00

EDWARDS, Vincent
SOMETIMES I'M HAPPY, SOMETIMES I'M BLUE	Decca (M) DL 4336	3.00	7.50	12.00
SOMETIMES I'M HAPPY, SOMETIMES I'M BLUE	Decca (S) DL7 4336	4.00	10.00	16.00
VINCE EDWARDS (In Person at the Riviera)	Decca (M) DL 4399	3.00	7.50	12.00
VINCE EDWARDS (In Person at the Riviera)	Decca (S) DL7 4399	4.00	10.00	16.00
VINCENT EDWARDS SINGS	Decca (M) DL 4311	3.00	7.50	12.00
VINCENT EDWARDS SINGS	Decca (S) DL 74311	4.00	10.00	16.00
VINCENT EDWARDS SINGS	Decca (EP) ED 2731	1.50	3.75	6.00

EGAN, Walter
FUNDAMENTAL ROLL	Columbia (S) PC 34679	2.00	3.00	4.00
NOT SHY	Columbia (S) JC 35077	2.00	3.00	4.00

EIGHTH DAY
EIGHTH DAY, THE	Kapp (M)	3.00	4.50	6.00

EIRE APPARENT
SUNRISE	Buddah (S) BDS5031	6.00	9.00	12.00

ELBERT, Donnie
HAVE I SINNED	Deluxe (M) DLP 12003	6.00	15.00	24.00
SENSATIONAL DONNIE ELBERT SINGS	King (M) 629	10.00	25.00	40.00
WHERE DID OUR LOVE GO	All Platinum (M) 3007	3.00	4.50	6.00

ELDERS
LOOKING FOR THE ANSWER	Audio Fidelity (M)	7.00	10.50	14.00

ELDORADOS
CRAZY LITTLE MAMA	Vee Jay (M) VJLP 1001	15.00	37.50	60.00

(M) Mono (S) Stereo (EP) Extended Play (Q) Quad (RI) Re-issued

TITLE	LABEL & NO.	GOOD	VERY GOOD	NEAR MINT

ELECTRIC FLAG
BAND KEPT PLAYING	Atlantic (S) SD 18112	3.00	4.50	6.00
ELECTRIC FLAG	Columbia (S) CS 9714	4.00	6.00	8.00
A LONG TIME COMIN'	Columbia (S) CS 9597	4.00	6.00	8.00

ELECTRIC INDIAN
KEEM'O'SABE	United Artist (S) UAS 6728	3.00	4.50	6.00

ELECTRIC LIGHT ORCHESTRA
ELDORADO	United Artists (S) UA-LA339	2.50	3.75	5.00
ELECTRIC LIGHT ORCHESTRA	United Artists (S) UA-LA040	3.00	4.50	6.00
ELECTRIC LIGHT ORCHESTRA ("NO ANSWER" RE-TITLED)	United Artists (S) UAS 5573	2.50	3.75	5.00
ELECTRIC LIGHT ORCHESTRA II (UA 040 RE-TITLED.)	United Artists (S) UA-LA040	2.50	3.75	5.00
FACE THE MUSIC	United Artists (S) UA-LA546	2.50	3.75	5.00
JOYRIDE (SOUNDTRACK)	United Artists (S) UA-LA784	2.50	3.75	5.00
NEW WORLD RECORD	United Artists/Jet (S) UA-LA 679	2.50	3.75	5.00
NIGHT THE LIGHT WENT ON IN LONG BEACH	United Artists (S) UA-LA318	2.50	3.75	5.00
NO ANSWER	United Artists (S) UAS 5573	4.00	6.00	8.00
OLE ELO	United Artists/Jet (S) UA-LA 630	2.50	3.75	5.00
ON THE THIRD DAY	United Artists (S) UA-LA188	2.50	3.75	5.00
OUT OF THE BLUE	Jet (S) JT-LA823	5.00	7.50	10.00
OUT OF THE BLUE	Jet (S) JT-LA 823	10.00	15.00	20.00

(Promotional issue, pressed in blue vinyl)

ELECTRIC PRUNES
I HAD TO MUCH TO DREAM	Reprise (M) R 6248	5.00	7.50	10.00
I HAD TO MUCH TO DREAM	Reprise (S) RS 6248	6.00	9.00	12.00
JUST GOOD OLD ROCK N' ROLL	Reprise (S) RS 6342	5.00	7.50	10.00
MASS IN F MINOR	Reprise (S) RS 6275	6.00	9.00	12.00
RELEASE OF AN OATH	Reprise (S) RS 6316	5.00	7.50	10.00
UNDERGROUND	Reprise (S) RS 6262	6.00	9.00	12.00

TITLE	LABEL & NO.	GOOD	VERY GOOD	NEAR MINT

ELECTRIC TOILET
| ELECTRIC TOILET, THE | Nasco (M) | 4.00 | 6.00 | 8.00 |

ELECTRIC TOMMY
| ELECTRIC TOMMY: THE WORLDS FIRST ROCK OPERA | Viva (S) V 36025 | 3.00 | 4.50 | 6.00 |

ELEPHANT
| ELEPHANT | Capitol (S) SMAS-11154 | 2.00 | 3.00 | 4.00 |

ELEPHANT CANDY
| FUN AND GAMES | UNI (S) 73042 | 3.00 | 4.00 | 6.00 |

ELEPHANTS MEMORY
ANGELS FOREVER	RCA (S) APL1-0569	2.50	3.75	5.00
ELEPHANTS MEMORY	Buddah (S) BDS 5033	3.50	5.25	7.00
ELEPHANTS MEMORY	Apple (S) SMAS 3389	3.00	4.50	6.00
OUR ISLAND MUSIC	Muse (S) MR 5072	2.50	3.75	5.00
SONGS FROM MIDNIGHT COWBOY	Buddah (S) BDS 5038	4.00	6.00	8.00
TAKE IT TO THE STREETS	Metromedia (S) MD 1035	3.50	5.25	7.00
(Also see LENNON, John)				

ELF
ELF	Epic (S) KE-31789	2.00	3.00	4.00
L.A. 59	MGM (S) M3G-4974	2.50	3.75	5.00
TRYING TO BURN THE SUN	MGM (S) M3G-4994	2.50	3.75	5.00

ELGINS
| DARLING BABY | VIP (M) 400 | 5.00 | 7.50 | 10.00 |

ELIMINATORS
| LIVERPOOL, DRAGSTERS, CYCLES AND SURFING | Liberty (M) LRP 3365 | 4.00 | 8.00 | 12.00 |
| LIVERPOOL, DRAGSTERS, CYCLES AND SURFING | Liberty (S) LST 7365 | 5.00 | 10.00 | 15.00 |

ELIZABETH
| ELIZABETH | Vanguard (S) VSD 6501 | 3.00 | 4.50 | 6.00 |

ELLIE POP
| ELLIE POP | Mainstream (S) S 6115 | 3.50 | 5.25 | 7.00 |

ELLIMAN, Yvonne
FOOD OF LOVE	MCA (S) 356	2.50	3.75	5.00
LOVE ME	RSO (S) RS-1-3018	2.00	3.00	4.00
NIGHT FLIGHT	RSO (S) RS-1-3031	2.00	3.00	4.00

ELLIOT, Ron
| CANDLESTICKMAKER | Warner Brothers (M) L1833 | 5.00 | 7.50 | 10.00 |

ELLIOTT, Ramblin' Jack
RAMBLIN' COWBOY	Monitor (M) MF 379	4.00	8.00	12.00
RAMBLIN JACK ELLIOTT SINGS WOODIE GUTHRIE AND JIMMIE RODGERS	Monitor (M) MF 380	4.00	8.00	12.00
RAMBLIN' JACK ELLIOTT SINGS WOODY GUTHRIE AND JIMMIE RODGERS	Monitor (S) MS 380	5.00	10.00	15.00

ELLIOTT, Shawn
| SHAME & SCANDAL IN THE FAMILY | Roulette (M) R-25316 | 4.00 | 6.00 | 8.00 |
| SHAME & SCANDAL IN THE FAMILY | Roulette (S) SR-25316 | 4.50 | 6.75 | 9.00 |

ELLIS, Shirley
NAME GAME	Congress (M) CGL 3003	3.00	6.00	9.00
SUGAR, LET'S SHING A LING	Columbia (M) CL 2679	3.00	6.00	9.00
SUGAR, LET'S SHING A LING	Columbia (S) CS 9479	4.00	8.00	12.00

ELLISON, Lorraine
LORRAINE ELLISON	Warner Brothers (S) BS 2780	2.50	3.75	5.00
MISS LORRAINE ELLISON HEART AND SOUL	Warner Brothers (S) WS 1821	5.00	10.00	15.00
STAY WITH ME	Warner Brothers (S) WS 1821	5.00	10.00	15.00

ELOY
| INSIDE | Janus (S) 3062 | 2.00 | 3.00 | 4.00 |

EL ROACHO
| BEST OF EL ROACHO | Columbia (S) KC-32468 | 3.00 | 4.50 | 6.00 |
| BIGGEST HITS | Columbia (S) KC 32468 | 3.00 | 4.50 | 6.00 |

EMBERS
| BURN YOU A NEW ONE | EEE (M) No. 1069 | 4.00 | 8.00 | 12.00 |
| BURN YOU A NEW ONE | EEE (S) No. 1069 | 5.00 | 10.00 | 15.00 |

EMERSON, LAKE & PALMER
BRAIN SALAD SURGERY ("EMERSON, LAKE & PALMER ON TOUR" RE-TITLED)	Manticore (S) 66669	5.00	7.50	10.00
EMERSON, LAKE & PALMER	Cotillion (S) 9040	4.00	6.00	8.00
EMERSON, LAKE & PALMER ON TOUR	Manticore (S) 66669	6.00	9.00	12.00
LADIES & GENTLEMEN	Manticore (S) 3-200	5.00	7.50	10.00

TITLE	LABEL & NO.	GOOD	VERY GOOD	NEAR MINT
PICTURES AT AN EXIBITION	Cotillion (S) ELP 66666	6.00	9.00	12.00
TARKUS	Cotillion (S) 9900	4.00	6.00	8.00
TRILOGY	Cotillion (S) SD 9903	4.00	6.00	8.00

EMERSON'S OLD TIMEY CUSTARD-SUCKIN' BAND
| EMERSON'S OLD TIMEY CUSTARD SUCKIN BAND | ESP (M) ESP2006 | 4.00 | 6.00 | 8.00 |

EMOTIONS
SO I CAN LOVE YOU	Volt (S) VOS 6008	3.00	4.50	6.00
SONGS OF INNOCENCE AND EXPERIENCE	Volt (S) VOS 6021	3.00	4.50	6.00
UNTOUCHED	Volt (S) VOS 6015	3.00	4.50	6.00

EMPEROR HUDSON (Bob Hudson)
| ADVENTURES OF EMPEROR HUDSON | Hook (M) 100 | 9.00 | 13.50 | 18.00 |

ENCHANTMENTS
| ENCHANTMENTS PRESENTS ACCAPELLA, The | Rogue (M) 1000 | 3.00 | 4.50 | 6.00 |

END, THE
| INTROSPECTION | London (S) PS 560 | 5.00 | 7.50 | 10.00 |

ENDINGS, THE
| BRING BACK THOSE YEARS | Chris Mike (M) 8919 | 2.50 | 3.75 | 5.00 |

ENDLE ST. CLOUD
| THANK YOU ALL VERY MUCH | International Artists (M) IALP12 | 8.00 | 16.00 | 24.00 |

ENGEL, Scott
| I ONLY CAME TO DANCE WITH YOU | Tower (M) T-5026 | 5.00 | 10.00 | 15.00 |
| I ONLY CAME TO DANCE WITH YOU | Tower (S) ST 5026 | 4.00 | 8.00 | 12.00 |

ENGLAND DAN & JOHN FORD COLEY
DOWDY FERRY ROAD	Big Tree (S) BT 76000	2.00	3.00	4.00
FABLES	A&M (S) SP 4350	2.50	3.75	5.00
I HEAR THE MUSIC	A&M (S) SP 4613	2.00	3.00	4.00
NIGHTS ARE FOREVER	Big Tree (S) BT 89517	2.50	3.75	5.00
SOME THINGS DON'T COME EASY	Big Tree (S) BT 76006	2.00	3.00	4.00
Also see SOUTHWEST F.O.B.				

ENO
| HERE COME THE WARM JETS | Island (S) 9268 | 2.50 | 3.75 | 5.00 |
| TAKING TIGER MOUNTAIN BY STRATEGY | Island (S) 9309 | 2.50 | 3.75 | 5.00 |

ENTWISTLE, John
JOHN ENTWISTLE'S RIGOR MORTIS SETS IN (WITH RIGOR MORTIS)	MCA (S) 321	3.00	4.50	6.00
MAD DOG (LISTED AS "JOHN ENTWISTLE'S OX")	MCA (S) 2129	3.00	4.50	6.00
SMASH YOUR HEAD AGAINST THE WALL	Decca (S) DL 79183	4.00	6.00	8.00
WHISTLE RHYMES	Decca (S) DL 79190	4.00	6.00	8.00
Also see WHO				

EON
| EON | Scepter (S) 5122 | 2.50 | 3.75 | 5.00 |

EPPS, Preston
| BONGOLA | Top Rank (M) RM 349 | 6.00 | 15.00 | 24.00 |
| BONGO ROCK | Original Sound (EP) OSREP1001 | 2.00 | 4.00 | 6.00 |

(M) Mono (S) Stereo (EP) Extended Play (Q) Quad (RI) Re-issued

TITLE	LABEL & NO.	GOOD	VERY GOOD	NEAR MINT
SURFIN' BONGOS	Original Sound (M) 5009	3.00	6.00	9.00
(With Bongo Teens)				
SURFIN' BONGOS	Original Sound (S) 8872	4.00	8.00	12.00
(With Bongo Teens)				

EQUALS
TITLE	LABEL & NO.	GOOD	VERY GOOD	NEAR MINT
BABY COME BACK	RCA (S) LSP 4078	5.00	7.50	10.00
EQUALS SUPREME	President (M) PTL 1025	6.00	9.00	12.00
UNEQUALLED	Laurie (S) SLP2045	6.00	9.00	12.00

ERIK
TITLE	LABEL & NO.	GOOD	VERY GOOD	NEAR MINT
LOOK WHERE I AM	Vanguard (S) VDS 79267	4.00	6.00	8.00
SING ALONG ROCK 'N ROLL	Karate (M) 1401	3.00	6.00	9.00

ERVIN, Senator Sam
TITLE	LABEL & NO.	GOOD	VERY GOOD	NEAR MINT
SENATOR SAM AT HOME	Columbia (S) KC-32756	2.50	3.75	5.00

ESQUERITA
TITLE	LABEL & NO.	GOOD	VERY GOOD	NEAR MINT
ESQUIRITA	Capitol (M) T-1186	18.00	45.00	72.00

ESQUIRES
TITLE	LABEL & NO.	GOOD	VERY GOOD	NEAR MINT
GET ON UP AND GET AWAY	Bunky (S) 300	3.00	4.50	6.00

ESSEX
TITLE	LABEL & NO.	GOOD	VERY GOOD	NEAR MINT
EASIER SAID THAN DONE	Roulette (M) R25234	4.00	8.00	12.00
EASIER SAID THAN DONE	Roulette (S) SR 25234	5.00	10.00	15.00
A WALKIN' MIRACLE	Roulette (M) R25235	4.00	8.00	12.00
A WALKIN' MIRACLE	Roulette (S) SR 25235	5.00	10.00	15.00
YOUNG AND LIVELY FEATURING ANITA HUMES	Roulette (M) R 25246	3.00	6.00	9.00

ESSEX, David
TITLE	LABEL & NO.	GOOD	VERY GOOD	NEAR MINT
ALL THE FUN OF THE FAIR	Columbia (S) PC-33813	2.00	3.00	4.00
DAVID ESSEX	Columbia (S) PC-33289	2.00	3.00	4.00
ROCK ON	Columbia (S) KC-32560	2.50	3.75	5.00
ROCK ON	Columbia (Q) CQ-32560	2.50	3.75	5.00

ESSO TRINADAD STEEL BAND
TITLE	LABEL & NO.	GOOD	VERY GOOD	NEAR MINT
ESSO TRINADAD STEEL BAND	Warner Brothers (S) WS 1917	3.00	4.50	6.00

ESTES, Sleepy John
TITLE	LABEL & NO.	GOOD	VERY GOOD	NEAR MINT
SLEEPY JOHN ESTES	Selmark (M) 613	2.50	4.00	5.00

ETERNITYS CHILDREN
TITLE	LABEL & NO.	GOOD	VERY GOOD	NEAR MINT
ETERNITY'S CHILDREN	Tower (S) ST 5123	5.00	7.50	10.00

EUPHONIOUS WAIL
TITLE	LABEL & NO.	GOOD	VERY GOOD	NEAR MINT
EUPHONIOUS WAIL	Kapp (S) 3668	4.50	6.75	9.00

EUPHORIA
TITLE	LABEL & NO.	GOOD	VERY GOOD	NEAR MINT
EUPHORIA	Heritage (S) HTS-35,005	2.50	3.75	5.00

EVANS, Paul
TITLE	LABEL & NO.	GOOD	VERY GOOD	NEAR MINT
ANOTHER TOWN ANOTHER JAIL	Kapp (M) KL1475	3.00	7.50	12.00
ANOTHER TOWN ANOTHER JAIL	Kapp (S) KS3475	4.00	10.00	16.00
FABULOUS TEENS	Guaranteed (M) GUL1000	6.00	15.00	24.00
FABULOUS TEENS	Guaranteed (S) GUS1000	7.00	17.50	28.00
HEAR PAUL EVANS IN YOUR HOME TONIGHT	Carlton 129 (M)	5.00	12.50	20.00

(M) Mono (S) Stereo (EP) Extended Play (Q) Quad (RI) Re-issued

TITLE	LABEL & NO.	GOOD	VERY GOOD	NEAR MINT
HEAR PAUL EVANS IN YOUR HOME TONIGHT	Carlton (S) S129	6.00	15.00	24.00
PAUL EVANS, FOLK SONGS OF MANY LANDS	Carlton 130 (M)	4.00	10.00	16.00
PAUL EVANS, FOLK SONGS OF MANY LANDS	Carlton (S) S 130	5.00	12.50	20.00
21 YEARS IN A TENNESSEE JAIL	Kapp (M) KL 1346	3.00	7.50	12.00
21 YEARS IN A TENNESSEE JAIL	Kapp (S) KS 3346	4.00	10.00	16.00

EVE
TITLE	LABEL & NO.	GOOD	VERY GOOD	NEAR MINT
TAKE IT AND SMILE	LHI (M) 3100	4.00	6.00	8.00

EVEN DOZEN JUG BAND
TITLE	LABEL & NO.	GOOD	VERY GOOD	NEAR MINT
EVEN DOZEN JUG BAND	Elektra (M) EKL 246	8.00	12.00	16.00

EVERETT, Betty
TITLE	LABEL & NO.	GOOD	VERY GOOD	NEAR MINT
BLACK GIRL	Fantasy (M) 9447	2.00	3.00	4.00
HAPPY ENDINGS	Fantasy (M) F 9480	2.00	3.00	4.00
IT'S IN HIS KISS	VJ (M) VJ 1077	4.00	8.00	12.00
LOVE RHYMES	Fantasy (M) F 9447	2.00	3.00	4.00
VERY BEST OF BETTY EVERETT	VJ (M) VJLP1122	3.00	6.00	9.00
VERY BEST OF BETTY EVERETT	VJ (S) VJS 1122	4.00	8.00	12.00

EVER GREEN BLUES BAND
TITLE	LABEL & NO.	GOOD	VERY GOOD	NEAR MINT
7 DO ELEVEN	Mercury (S) SR 61157	4.00	6.00	8.00

EVERETT, Betty and Ketty Lester
TITLE	LABEL & NO.	GOOD	VERY GOOD	NEAR MINT
BETTY EVERETT AND KETTY LESTER	Grand Prix (M) K 125	3.00	6.00	9.00

EVERGREEN BLUE SHOES
TITLE	LABEL & NO.	GOOD	VERY GOOD	NEAR MINT
BALLAD OF EVERGREEN BLUE SHOES	Amos (M) 7002	6.50	9.75	13.00

EVERLY BROTHERS
TITLE	LABEL & NO.	GOOD	VERY GOOD	NEAR MINT
BEAT N' SOUL	Warner Bros. (M) W 1605	4.00	8.00	12.00
BEAT N' SOUL	Warner Brothers (S) WS 1605	5.00	10.00	15.00
CHAINED TO A MEMORY	Harmony (S) 11388	2.50	3.75	5.00
CHRISTMAS WITH THE EVERLY BROTHERS (WITH THE BOYS TOWN CHOIR)	Harmony (S) 11350	2.50	3.75	5.00
CHRISTMAS WITH THE EVERLY BROTHERS	Warner Bros. (M) W 1483	5.00	10.00	15.00
CHRISTMAS WITH THE EVERLY BROTHERS	Warner Brothers (S) WS 1483	6.00	12.00	18.00
A DATE WITH THE EVERLY BORTHERS	Warner Bros. (M) W 1395	5.00	10.00	15.00
A DATE WITH THE EVERLY BROTHERS	Warner Brothers (S) WS 1395	6.00	12.00	18.00
A DATE WITH THE EVERLY BROTHERS (Fold Out Cover)	Warner Bros. (M) W 1395	9.00	18.00	27.00
A DATE WITH THE EVERLY BROTHERS (Fold out Cover)	Warner Brothers (S) WS1395	9.00	18.00	27.00
DREAM WITH THE EVERLY BROTHERS	Cadence (EP) CEP 334	2.00	5.00	8.00
END OF AN ERA	Barnaby (M) 30260	4.00	6.00	8.00
ESPECIALLY FOR YOU	Warner Bros. (EP) EB 1381-1	2.00	4.00	6.00
ESPECIALLY FOR YOU PART 2	Warner Bros. (EP) EB 1381-2	2.00	4.00	6.00
EVERLY BROTHERS	Cadence (M) CLP 3003	9.00	22.50	36.00
EVERLY BROTHERS	Cadence (EP) CEP 104	2.00	5.00	8.00
EVERLY BROTHERS	Cadence (EP) CEP 105	2.00	5.00	8.00
EVERLY BROTHERS	Cadence (EP) CEP 107	2.00	5.00	8.00
EVERLY BROTHERS	Cadence (EP) CEP 111	2.00	5.00	8.00
EVERLY BROTHERS	Cadence (EP) CEP 118	2.00	5.00	8.00
EVERLY BROTHERS (FEATURING 'WAKE UP LITTLE SUSIE')	Harmony (S) 11304	2.50	3.75	5.00
EVERLY BROTHERS, THE	Warner Bros. (M) W 1418	5.00	10.00	15.00
EVERLY BROTHERS, THE	Warner Bros. (S) WS 1418	6.00	12.00	18.00
EVERLY BROTHERS BEST	Cadence (M) CLP 3025	9.00	22.50	36.00
EVERLY BROTHERS GREATEST HITS	Barnaby (S) 6006	3.00	4.50	6.00
EVERLY BROTHERS PLUS TWO OLDIES	Warner Bros. (EP) 5501	2.00	4.00	6.00
EVERLY BROTHERS SHOW	Warner Brothers (S) 1858	4.00	8.00	12.00
EVERLY BROTHERS SING	Warner Brothers (M) 1708	4.00	8.00	12.00
EVERLY BROTHERS SING	Warner Brothers (S) WS 1708	5.00	10.00	15.00
EVERLY BROTHERS SING GREAT COUNTRY HITS	Warner Brothers (M) 1513	4.00	8.00	12.00
EVERLY BROTHERS SING GREAT COUNTRY HITS	Warner Brothers (S) WS 1513	5.00	10.00	15.00
FABULOUS STYLE OF THE EVERLY BROTHERS	Cadence (M) CLP 3040	8.00	20.00	32.00
FABULOUS STYLE OF THE EVERLY BROTHERS	Cadence (S) CLP 25040	7.00	17.50	28.00
15 EVERLY HITS	Cadence (M) CLP 3062	8.00	20.00	32.00
15 EVERLY HITS	Cadence (S) CLP 25062	7.00	17.50	28.00
FOLK SONGS	Cadence (M) CLP 3059	8.00	20.00	32.00
FOLK SONGS	Cadence (S) 25059	7.00	17.50	28.00
GOLDEN HITS OF THE EVERLY BROTHERS	Warner Bros. (M) W 1471	5.00	10.00	15.00
GOLDEN HITS OF THE EVERLY BROTHERS	Warner Brothers (S) WS 1471	6.00	12.00	18.00
GONE, GONE, GONE	Warner Bros. (M) W 1585	4.00	8.00	12.00
GONE, GONE, GONE	Warner Brothers (S) WS 1585	5.00	10.00	15.00
HISTORY OF THE EVERLY BROTHERS	Barnaby (S) 2 BRS 15008	5.00	7.50	10.00
IN OUR IMAGE	Warner Brothers (M) 1620	4.00	8.00	12.00
IN OUR IMAGE	Warner Brothers (S) WS 1620	5.00	10.00	15.00
INSTANT PARTY	Warner Brothers (M) 1430	5.00	10.00	15.00
INSTANT PARTY	Warner Brothers (S) WS 1430	6.00	12.00	18.00

TITLE	LABEL & NO.	GOOD	VERY GOOD	NEAR MINT
IT'S EVERLY TIME	Warner Brothers (M) 1381	5.00	10.00	15.00
IT'S EVERLY TIME	Warner Brothers (S) 1381	6.00	12.00	18.00
PASS THE CHICKEN AND LISTEN	RCA (S) LSP 4781	3.00	4.50	6.00
ROCKIN WITH THE EVERLY BROTHERS	Cadence (EP) CEP 333	2.00	5.00	8.00
ROCK N' SOUL	Warner Brothers (M) 1578	4.00	8.00	12.00
ROCK N' SOUL	Warner Brothers (S) WS 1578	5.00	10.00	15.00
ROOTS	Warner Brothers(M) 1752	3.00	6.00	9.00
ROOTS	Warner Brothers (S) WS 1752	4.00	8.00	12.00
SONGS OUR DADDY TAUGHT US	Cadence (M) CLP 3016	9.00	22.50	36.00
SONGS OUR DADDY TAUGHT US, VOL. 1	Cadence (EP) CEP 108	2.00	5.00	8.00
SONGS OUR DADDY TAUGHT US, VOL. 2	Cadence (EP) CEP 109	2.00	5.00	8.00
SONGS OUR DADDY TAUGHT US, VOL. 3	Cadence (EP) CEP 110	2.00	5.00	8.00
STORIES WE COULD TELL	RCA (S) LSP 4620	3.00	4.50	6.00
TWO YANKS IN LONDON	Warner Bros. (M) W 1646	4.00	8.00	12.00
TWO YANKS IN LONDON	Warner Brothers (S) WS 1646	5.00	10.00	15.00
VERY BEST OF THE EVERLY BROTHERS	Warner Bros. (M) W 1554	4.00	8.00	12.00
VERY BEST OF THE EVERLY BROTHERS	Warner Brothers (S) WS 1554	5.00	10.00	15.00
VERY BEST OF THE EVERLY BROTHERS	Cadence (EP) CEP 121	2.00	5.00	8.00

EVERLY, Don

SUNSET TOWERS	Ode (S) 77023	2.50	3.75	5.00

EVERLY, Phil

MYSTIC LINE	Pye (S) 12121	2.50	3.75	5.00
PHIL'S DINER	Pye (S) 12104	2.50	3.75	5.00
STAR SPANGLED SPRINGER	RCA (S) APL1-0092	2.00	3.00	4.00

EVERPRESENT FULLNESS

EVERPRESENT FULLNESS	White Whale (S) WW 7132	6.00	9.00	12.00

EVERY MOTHER'S SON

BACK	MGM (S) SE 4504	2.50	3.75	5.00
EVERY MOTHER'S SON	MGM (M) 3471	2.00	3.00	4.00
EVERY MOTHER'S SON	MGM (S) SE 4471	2.50	3.75	5.00

EVERYTHING IS EVERYTHING

EVERYTHING IS EVERYTHING FEATURING CHRIS HILL	Vanguard (S) VSD 6512	6.00	9.00	12.00

EXCITERS

BLACK BEAUTY	Today (M) TLP 1001	3.00	4.50	6.00
CAVIAR AND CHITLINS	RCA (S) LSP 4211	4.00	6.00	8.00
EXCITERS	Roulette (M) R 25326	4.00	8.00	12.00
EXCITERS	Roulette (S) SR 25326	5.00	10.00	15.00
TELL HIM	United Artists (M) UAL 3264	4.00	8.00	12.00
TELL HIM	United Artists (S) UAS 6264	5.00	10.00	15.00

EXILE

EXILE	Wooden Nickel (S) BWL1-0120	2.50	3.75	5.00

EXUMA

LIFE	Kama Sutra (S) 2074	2.00	3.00	4.00

EYES OF BLUE

CROSSROADS OF TIME	Mercury (S) SR 61184	5.00	7.50	10.00
IN FIELDS OF ARDATH	Mercury (S) SR 61220	5.00	7.50	10.00

EZBA, Denny

HIS GREATEST HITS FROM 4000 YEARS AGO	Texas Record (M) 1001	3.00	4.50	6.00

F

FABARES, Shelly

SHELLY	Colpix (M) CP 426	4.00	8.00	12.00
THINGS WE DID LAST SUMMER	Colpix (S) SCP 431	5.00	10.00	15.00

FABIAN

FABIAN 'FACADE'

YOUNG AND WONDERFUL	Chancellor (M) CHL 69802	4.00	10.00	16.00
FABIAN'S 16 FABULOUS HITS	Chancellor (M) CHL 5024	5.00	12.50	20.00
FABULOUS FABIAN	Chancellor (M) CHL 5005	4.00	10.00	16.00
FABULOUS FABIAN	Chancellor (S) CHLX 5005	5.00	12.00	20.00
GOOD OLD SUMMERTIME	Chancellor (M) CHL 5012	4.00	10.00	16.00
GOOD OLD SUMMERTIME	Chancellor (S) CHLS 5012	5.00	12.50	20.00
HOLD THAT TIGER	Chancellor (M) CHL 5003	5.00	12.50	20.00
HOLD THAT TIGER	Chancellor (S) CHLS 5003	6.00	15.00	20.00
HOLD THAT TIGER	Chancellor (EP) A-5003	2.00	4.00	6.00
HOLD THAT TIGER	Chancellor (EP) B-5003	2.00	4.00	6.00
HOLD THAT TIGER	Chancellor (EP) C-5003	2.00	4.00	6.00
HOUND DOG MAN	Chancellor (EP) EP 301	2.00	4.00	6.00
ROCKIN' HOT	Chancellor (M) CHL 5019	6.00	15.00	24.00
16 GREATEST HITS	ABC (S) ABCX806	2.50	3.75	5.00
VERY BEST OF FABIAN	United Artists (S) UA-LA449	1.50	2.25	3.00

FABIAN AND FRANKIE AVALON

FABIAN AND AVALON THE HIT MAKERS	Chancellor (M) CHL 5009	6.00	15.00	24.00

FABRIC, Bent

ALLEY CAT	Atco (M) 33-148	4.00	6.00	8.00
ALLEY CAT	Atco (S) SD 33-148	4.50	6.75	9.00
HAPPY PUPPY	Atco (M) 33-155	3.00	4.50	6.00
HAPPY PUPPY	Atco (S) SD 33-155	3.50	5.25	7.00
ORGAN GRINDER'S SWING	Atco (M) 33-164	3.00	4.50	6.00
ORGAN GRINDER'S SWING	Atco (S) SD 33-164	3.50	4.50	7.00

FABULOUS FLIPPERS

SOMETHING TANGIBLE	Veritas (S) VS 2570	8.00	12.00	16.00

FACES

LONG PLAYER	Warner Bros. (S) WS 1892	3.50	5.25	7.00
A NOD IS AS GOOD AS A WINK TO A BLIND HORSE	Warner Bros. (S) BS 2574	3.00	4.50	6.00
OOH-LA-LA	Warner Bros. (S) BS 2665	3.00	4.50	6.00

FAINE JADE

INTROSPECTION: A FAINE JADE RECITAL	RSVP (S) ES 8002	6.00	12.00	18.00

FAIRCHILD, Barbara

FREE AND EASY	Columbia (S) PC 34868	2.00	3.00	4.00
KID STUFF	Columbia (S) KC-32711	2.00	3.00	4.00
LOVE IS A GENTLE THING	Columbia (S) C-32960	2.00	3.00	4.00
MISSISSIPPI	Columbia (S) PC 34307	2.00	3.00	4.00
STANDING IN YOUR LINE	Columbia (S) KC-33058	2.00	3.00	4.00

FAIRFIELD FOUR

FAIRFIELD FOUR	Old Town (M)	16.00	40.00	64.00

FAIRPORT CONVENTION

ANGEL DELIGHT	A&M (S) SP 4319	3.00	4.50	6.00
"BABBACOMBE" LEE	A&M (S) SP 4333	3.00	4.50	6.00
FAIRPORT CONVENTION	Cotillion (S) SD 9024	4.50	6.75	9.00
FAIRPORT CONVENTION	A&M (S) SP 4185	2.00	3.00	4.00
FAIRPORT CHRONICLES	A&M (S) SP 3530	2.00	3.00	4.00
FULL HOUSE	A&M (S) SP 4265	2.00	3.00	4.00
LIEGE & LIEF	A&M (S) SP 4257	2.00	3.00	4.00
MOVEABLE FEAST	Island (S) 9285	2.00	3.00	4.00
NINE	A&M (S) SP 4407	2.50	3.75	5.00
NINE (RI)	A&M (S) SP 3603	2.00	3.00	4.00
RISING FOR THE MOON	Island (S) 9313	2.00	3.00	4.00
ROSIE	A&M (S) SP 4386	2.50	3.75	5.00
UNHALFBRICKING	A&M (S) SP 4206	2.00	3.00	4.00

FAIRWEATHER LOW, Andy

BE-BOP 'N' HOLLA	A&M (S) SP 4602	2.00	3.00	4.00
LA BOOGA ROOGA	A&M (S) SP 4542	2.00	3.00	4.00
SPIDER JIVING	A&M (S) SP 3646	2.00	3.00	4.00

FAITH, Adam

ADAM FAITH	AMY (M) 8005	5.00	10.00	15.00
ENGLAND'S TOP SINGER	MGM (M) E3951	6.00	12.00	18.00
I SURVIVE	Warner Bros. (S) BS-2791	2.00	3.00	4.00

FAITH, Percy

ACADEMY AWARD WINNER "BORN FREE"	Columbia (M) CL 2650	2.00	3.00	4.00
ACADEMY AWARD WINNER "BORN FREE"	Columbia (S) CS 9450	2.00	3.00	4.00
ALL TIME GREATEST HITS	Columbia (S) KG 31588	2.00	3.00	4.00
ANGEL OF THE MORNING	Columbia (S) CS 9706	2.00	3.00	4.00
BLACK MAGIC WOMAN	Columbia (S) 30800	2.00	3.00	4.00
BLACK MAGIC WOMAN	Columbia (Q) CQ 30800	2.00	3.00	4.00
BOUQUET	Columbia (M) CL 1322	2.00	3.00	4.00
BOUQUET	Columbia (S) CS 8124	2.00	3.00	4.00
BOUQUET OF LOVE	Columbia (M) CL 1681	2.00	3.00	4.00
BOUQUET OF LOVE	Columbia (S) CS 8481	2.00	3.00	4.00
BROADWAY BOUQUET	Columbia (M) CL 2356	2.00	3.00	4.00
BROADWAY BOUQUET	Columbia (S) CS 9156	2.00	3.00	4.00
CAREFREE	Columbia (M) CL 1560	2.00	3.00	4.00
CAREFREE	Columbia (S) CS 8360	2.00	3.00	4.00
CHINATOWN	Columbia (S) KC 33244	2.00	3.00	4.00
CHINATOWN	Columbia (Q) CQ 33244	2.00	3.00	4.00
DAY BY DAY	Columbia (S) 31627	2.00	3.00	4.00
DAY BY DAY	Columbia (Q) CQ 31627	2.00	3.00	4.00
DISCO PARTY	Columbia (S) KC 33549	2.00	3.00	4.00
FOR THOSE IN LOVE	Columbia (M) CL 2810	2.00	3.00	4.00
FOR THOSE IN LOVE	Columbia (S) CS 9610	2.00	3.00	4.00
GREAT FOLK THEMES	Columbia (M) CL 2108	2.00	3.00	4.00
GREAT FOLK THEMES	Columbia (S) CS 8908	2.00	3.00	4.00
GREAT MOMENTS OF PERCY FAITH	Columbia (S) CG 33895	2.00	3.00	4.00
HELD OVER! TODAY'S GREAT MOVIE THEMES	Columbia (S) CS 1019	2.00	3.00	4.00
I THINK I LOVE YOU	Columbia (S) 30502	2.00	3.00	4.00
JEALOUSY	Columbia (M) CL 1501	2.00	3.00	4.00
JEALOUSY	Columbia (S) CS 8292	2.00	3.00	4.00
JESUS CHRIST, SUPERSTAR	Columbia (S) 31042	2.00	3.00	4.00
JOY	Columbia (S) 31301	2.00	3.00	4.00
KISMET	Columbia (M) 6275	2.00	5.00	8.00

(M) Mono   (S) Stereo   (EP) Extended Play   (Q) Quad   (RI) Re-issued

TITLE	LABEL & NO.	GOOD	VERY GOOD	NEAR MINT
LEAVING ON A JET PLANE	Columbia (S) CS 9983	2.00	3.00	4.00
LOVE THEME FROM "ROMEO & JULIET"	Columbia (S) CS 9906	2.00	3.00	4.00
MORE THEMES FOR YOUNG LOVERS	Columbia (M) CL 2167	2.00	3.00	4.00
MORE THEMES FOR YOUNG LOVERS	Columbia (S) CS 8967	2.00	3.00	4.00
MUCHO GUSTO!	Columbia (M) CL 1639	2.00	3.00	4.00
MUCHO GUSTO!	Columbia (S) CS 8439	2.00	3.00	4.00
MUSIC FROM HOLLYWOOD	Columbia (M) 6255	2.00	5.00	8.00
MUSIC FROM LERNER & LOEWE'S "CAMELOT"	Columbia (M) CL 1570	2.00	3.00	4.00
MUSIC FROM LERNER & LOEWE'S "CAMELOT"	Columbia (S) CS 8370	2.00	3.00	4.00
MUSIC FROM RODGERS & HAMMERSTEIN'S "THE SOUND OF MUSIC"	Columbia (M) CL 1418	2.00	3.00	4.00
MUSIC FROM RODGERS & HAMMERSTEIN'S "THE SOUND OF MUSIC"	Columbia (S) CS 8215	2.00	3.00	4.00
MUSIC OF BRAZIL!	Columbia (M) CL 1822	2.00	3.00	4.00
MUSIC OF BRAZIL!	Columbia (S) CS 8622	2.00	3.00	4.00
MUSIC OF CHRISTMAS	Columbia (M) CL 588	2.00	3.00	4.00
MY FAIR LADY	Columbia (M) CL 895	2.00	4.00	6.00
PERCY FAITH PLAYS THE BEATLES	Columbia (S) 30097	2.00	3.00	4.00
PERCY FAITH'S GREATEST HITS	Columbia (M) CL 1493	3.00	4.50	6.00
PORGY AND BESS	Columbia (S) CS 8105	2.00	4.00	6.00
SHANGRI-LA	Columbia (M) CL 2024	2.00	3.00	4.00
SHANGRI-LA	Columbia (S) CS 8824	2.00	3.00	4.00
SUMMER PLACE '76	Columbia (S) KC 33915	2.00	3.00	4.00
TARA'S THEME FROM "GONE WITH THE WIND" AND OTHER MOVIE THEMES	Columbia (M) CL 1627	2.00	3.00	4.00
TARA'S THEME FROM "GONE WITH THE WIND" AND OTHER MOVIE THEMES	Columbia (S) CS 8427	2.00	3.00	4.00
THEMES FOR YOUNG LOVERS	Columbia (M) CL 2023	2.00	3.00	4.00
THEMES FOR YOUNG LOVERS	Columbia (S) CS 8823	2.00	3.00	4.00
TIME FOR LOVE	Columbia (S) 30230	2.00	3.00	4.00
VIVA!/MUCHO GUSTO!	Columbia (S) CG 33606	2.00	3.00	4.00
THOSE WERE THE DAYS	Columbia (S) CS 9762	2.00	3.00	4.00
TODAY'S THEMES FOR YOUNG LOVERS	Columbia (M) CL 2704	2.00	3.00	4.00
TODAY'S THEMES FOR YOUNG LOVERS	Columbia (S) CS 9504	2.00	3.00	4.00
WINDMILLS OF YOUR MIND	Columbia (S) CS 9835	2.00	3.00	4.00

FAITHFULL, Marianne

TITLE	LABEL & NO.	GOOD	VERY GOOD	NEAR MINT
FAITHFULL FOREVER	London (M) LL 3482	4.50	6.75	9.00
FAITHFULL FOREVER	London (S) PS 482	5.00	7.50	10.00
GO AWAY FROM MY WORLD	London (M) LL 3452	4.50	6.75	9.00
GO AWAY FROM MY WORLD	London (S) PS 452	5.00	7.50	10.00
GREATEST HITS	London (S) PS 547	5.00	7.50	10.00
MARIANNE FAITHFULL	London (M) LL3423	4.50	6.75	9.00
MARIANNE FAITHFULL	London (S) PS 423	5.00	7.50	10.00

FALLEN ANGELS

TITLE	LABEL & NO.	GOOD	VERY GOOD	NEAR MINT
FALLEN ANGELS	Roulette (S) SR 25358	4.50	6.75	9.00
IT'S A LONG WAY DOWN	Roulette (S) SR 42011	5.00	7.50	10.00

FALLENROCK

TITLE	LABEL & NO.	GOOD	VERY GOOD	NEAR MINT
WATCH FOR FALLENROCK	Capricorn (S) 0143	2.50	3.75	5.00

FAME GANG, THE

TITLE	LABEL & NO.	GOOD	VERY GOOD	NEAR MINT
SOLID GOLD FROM MUSCLE SHOALS	Fame (S) SKAO-4200	2.50	3.75	5.00

FAME, Georgie

TITLE	LABEL & NO.	GOOD	VERY GOOD	NEAR MINT
BALLAD OF BONNIE AND CLYDE	Epic (S) 26368	3.00	4.50	6.00
GEORGIE FAME	Island (S) 9293	2.50	3.75	5.00
GET AWAY	Imperial (S) 9331	3.00	4.50	6.00
GET AWAY	Imperial (S) 12331	4.00	6.00	8.00
YEH, YEH	Imperial (M) 9282	3.00	4.50	6.00
YEH, YEH	Imperial (S) 12282	4.00	6.00	8.00

FAMILY

TITLE	LABEL & NO.	GOOD	VERY GOOD	NEAR MINT
ANYWAY	United Artists (S) UAS 5527	3.00	4.50	6.00
BANDSTAND	United Artists (S) 5644	3.00	4.50	6.00
FAMILY ENTERTAINMENT	Reprise (S) 6340	4.00	6.00	8.00
FAMILY OF APOSTOLIC	Vanguard-Apostolic (S) VSD793012	4.00	6.00	8.00
FEARLESS	United Artists (S) 5562	3.00	4.50	6.00
IT'S ONLY A MOVIE	United Artists (S) UA-LA 181	3.00	4.50	6.00
MUSIC IN A DOLLS HOUSE	Reprise (S) 6312	5.00	7.50	10.00
A SONG FOR ME	Reprise (S) 6384	4.00	6.00	8.00

FAMILY DOGG

TITLE	LABEL & NO.	GOOD	VERY GOOD	NEAR MINT
VIEW FROM ROWLAND'S HEAD	Buddah (S) BDS 5100	2.50	3.75	5.00

FAMILY TREE

TITLE	LABEL & NO.	GOOD	VERY GOOD	NEAR MINT
MISS BUTTERS	RCA (S) LSP 3955	6.00	9.00	12.00

FANCY

TITLE	LABEL & NO.	GOOD	VERY GOOD	NEAR MINT
FANCY MEETING YOU HERE	Poison Ring (M) PRR 2238	6.00	9.00	12.00
WILD THING	Big Tree (S) 89502	3.00	4.50	6.00

FANKHAUSER, Merrell and His Trusty H.M.S. Bounty

TITLE	LABEL & NO.	GOOD	VERY GOOD	NEAR MINT
MERRELL FANKHAUSER AND HIS TRUSTY H.M.S. BOUNTY	Shamley (S) SS 701	7.00	10.50	14.00

FANNY

TITLE	LABEL & NO.	GOOD	VERY GOOD	NEAR MINT
CHARITY BALL	Reprise (S) 6456	2.50	3.75	5.00
FANNY	Reprise (S) 6416	2.50	3.75	5.00
FANNY HILL	Reprise (S) MS 2058	2.50	3.75	5.00
MOTHERS PRIDE	Reprise (S) MS 2137	2.50	3.75	5.00
ROCK & ROLL SURVIVORS	Casablanca (S) NBLP 7007	2.50	3.75	5.00

FANNY ADAMS

TITLE	LABEL & NO.	GOOD	VERY GOOD	NEAR MINT
FANNY ADAMS	Kapp (S) KS 3644	5.00	7.50	10.00

FANTASTIC BAGGYS (Phil Sloan & Steve Barri)

TITLE	LABEL & NO.	GOOD	VERY GOOD	NEAR MINT
TELL 'EM I'M SURFIN'	Imperial (M) LP 9270	8.00	16.00	24.00
TELL 'EM I'M SURFIN'	Imperial (S) LP 12270	11.00	22.00	33.00

FANTASTIC D.J.S

TITLE	LABEL & NO.	GOOD	VERY GOOD	NEAR MINT
FANTASTIC D.J.'S	Stone (S)	9.00	13.00	18.00

FANTASTIC FOUR

TITLE	LABEL & NO.	GOOD	VERY GOOD	NEAR MINT
ALVIN STONE-THE BIRTH AND DEATH OF A GANGSTER	Westbound (S) W 201	2.00	3.00	4.00

FANTASTIC JOHNNY C.

TITLE	LABEL & NO.	GOOD	VERY GOOD	NEAR MINT
BOOGALOO DOWN BROADWAY	Phil L.A. of Soul (M) 4000	3.00	4.50	6.00
BOOGALOO DOWN BROADWAY	Phil L.A. of Soul (S) 4000	4.00	6.00	8.00

FANTASY

TITLE	LABEL & NO.	GOOD	VERY GOOD	NEAR MINT
FANTASY	Liberty (S) LST 7643	2.50	3.75	5.00

FAR CITY

TITLE	LABEL & NO.	GOOD	VERY GOOD	NEAR MINT
THE FAR CITY	Vanguard-Apostolic VSD 6510	3.00	4.50	6.00

FARDON, Don

TITLE	LABEL & NO.	GOOD	VERY GOOD	NEAR MINT
I'VE PAID MY DUES	Decca (S) DL 75225	4.00	6.00	8.00
THE LAMENT OF THE CHEROKEE INDIAN RESERVATION	GNP/Crescendo (S) GNPS 2044	3.50	5.25	7.00

FARGO, Donna

TITLE	LABEL & NO.	GOOD	VERY GOOD	NEAR MINT
ALL ABOUT A FEELING	Dot (S) 26019	3.00	4.50	6.00
HAPPIEST GIRL IN THE WHOLE U.S.A.	Dot (S) 26000	3.00	4.50	6.00
MISS DONNA FARGO	Dot (S) DOSD-2002	2.50	3.75	5.00
MY SECOND ALBUM	Dot (S) 26006	3.00	4.50	6.00
WHATEVER I SAY MEANS I LOVE YOU	Dot (S) DOSD-2029	2.50	3.75	5.00

FARINA, Richard and Mimi

TITLE	LABEL & NO.	GOOD	VERY GOOD	NEAR MINT
CELEBRATIONS FOR A GRAY DAY	Vanguard (M) VRS 9174	3.50	5.25	7.00
CELEBRATIONS FOR A GRAY DAY	Vanguard (S) VSD 79174	4.00	6.00	8.00
REFLECTIONS IN A CRYSTAL WIND	Vanguard (M) VSR-9204	3.50	5.25	7.00
REFLECTIONS IN A CRYSTAL WIND	Vanguard (S) VSR 79204	4.00	6.00	8.00

FARLOWE, Chris

TITLE	LABEL & NO.	GOOD	VERY GOOD	NEAR MINT
FABULOUS CHRIS FARLOWE AND THE THUNDERBIRDS	Columbia (M) CL 2593	4.00	8.00	12.00
FABULOUS CHRIS FARLOWE AND THE THUNDERBIRDS	Columbia (S) CS 9393	5.00	10.00	15.00
FROM HERE TO MAMA ROSA WITH THE HILL	Polydor (S) 24-4041	3.50	4.25	7.00
PAINT IT FARLOWE	Immediate (S) Z12 52010	5.00	7.50	10.00

FARMBAND

TITLE	LABEL & NO.	GOOD	VERY GOOD	NEAR MINT
FARM BAND	Mantra (M) 777	3.00	4.50	6.00

FARQUAHR

TITLE	LABEL & NO.	GOOD	VERY GOOD	NEAR MINT
FABULOUS FARQUAHR	Verve-Forecast (S) FTS 3053	3.50	5.25	7.00
FARQUAHR	Elektra (S) EKS 74083	3.00	4.50	6.00

FARR, Gary

TITLE	LABEL & NO.	GOOD	VERY GOOD	NEAR MINT
ADDRESSED TO THE CENSORS OF LOVE	Atco (S) SD 7034	2.50	3.75	5.00

FARRELL, Eileen

TITLE	LABEL & NO.	GOOD	VERY GOOD	NEAR MINT
I'VE GOT A RIGHT TO SING THE BLUES	Columbia (M) CL 1465	3.00	6.00	9.00

FARYAR, Cyrus

TITLE	LABEL & NO.	GOOD	VERY GOOD	NEAR MINT
ISLANDS	Elektra (S) EKS 75068	3.00	4.50	6.00

FAT CITY

TITLE	LABEL & NO.	GOOD	VERY GOOD	NEAR MINT
REINCARNATION	Probe (M) CPL1-4508	3.00	4.50	6.00

FAT FRED & THE KAPE MEN

TITLE	LABEL & NO.	GOOD	VERY GOOD	NEAR MINT
WHEELIN' AND DEALIN'	California (M) 101	7.50	11.25	15.00

FAT MATTRESS

TITLE	LABEL & NO.	GOOD	VERY GOOD	NEAR MINT
FAT MATTRESS	Atco (S) SD 33-309	3.00	4.50	6.00
FAT MATTRESS 2	Atco (S) SD 33-347	4.00	6.00	8.00

FAUN

TITLE	LABEL & NO.	GOOD	VERY GOOD	NEAR MINT
FAUN	Gregar (S) GG 7000	4.50	6.75	9.00

FEAR ITSELF

TITLE	LABEL & NO.	GOOD	VERY GOOD	NEAR MINT
FEAR ITSELF	Dot (S) DLP 25942	4.00	6.00	8.00

FEATHERS, Charlie

TITLE	LABEL & NO.	GOOD	VERY GOOD	NEAR MINT
GOOD ROCKIN TONIGHT	Barrelhouse (S) BH 03	5.00	7.50	10.00
ROCK N ROLL	Star (M)	6.00	9.00	12.00

(M) Mono (S) Stereo (EP) Extended Play (Q) Quad (RI) Re-issued

TITLE	LABEL & NO.	GOOD	VERY GOOD	NEAR MINT

FEDERAL DUCK
FEDERAL DUCK .... Musicor (S) MS 3162		4.00	6.00	8.00

FELICIANO, Jose
ALIVE ALIVE-O! .... RCA (S) LPS 6021		4.00	6.00	8.00
AND THE FEELING'S GOOD .... RCA (S) CPL1-0407		2.50	3.75	5.00
COMPARTMENTS .... RCA (S) APD1-0141		2.50	3.75	5.00
ENCORE! (JOSE FELICIANO'S FINEST PERFORMANCES) ...... RCA (S) LSPX 1005		4.00	6.00	8.00
FELICIANO! .... RCA (M) LPM 3957		3.50	5.25	7.00
FELICIANO! .... RCA (S) LPS 3957		3.00	4.50	6.00
FELICIANO 10 to 23 .... RCA (S) LPS 4185		3.00	4.50	6.00
FIREWORKS .... RCA (S) LPS 4370		3.00	4.50	6.00
FOR MY LOVE ... MOTHER MUSIC .... RCA (S) APL1-0266		2.50	3.75	5.00
SOULED .... RCA (S) LPS 4045		3.00	4.50	6.00
THAT THE SPIRIT NEEDS .... RCA (S) LSP 4573		3.00	4.50	6.00

FELIX HARP
FIRST OF FELIX HARP .... Western World (S) WWM 2000		3.00	4.50	6.00

FELIX, Julie
THIS WORLD GOES ROUND & ROUND ...... Fontana (S) SRF 67596		3.00	4.50	6.00

FELLER, Dick
NO WORD ON ME .... Asylum (S) CM-1		3.00	4.50	6.00
SOME DAYS ARE DIAMONDS .... Asylum (S) CM-4		3.00	4.50	6.00
SOME DAYS ARE DIAMONDS .... Asylum (S) 7E-1044		2.00	3.00	4.00

FELTS, Narvel
DRIFT AWAY .... Cinnamon (S) 5000		4.00	6.00	8.00
GREATEST HITS, VOL. 1 .... Dot (S) DOSD-2036		3.00	4.50	6.00
NARVEL FELTS .... Dot (S) DOSD-2025		3.00	4.50	6.00

FEMININE COMPLEX
LIVIN' LOVE .... Athena (S) 6001		6.00	9.00	12.00

FENDER, Freddy
ARE YOU READY FOR FREDDY ...... Dot (S) DOSD 2044		2.50	3.75	5.00
OUT OF REACH .... Starflite (M) LP 2001		3.00	4.50	6.00
SINCE I MET YOU BABY .... GRT (S) 8005		3.00	4.50	6.00

FENDERMEN
MULE SKINNER BLUES .... Soma (M) MG 1240		14.00	35.00	56.00

FERGUSON, Jay
THUNDER ISLAND .... Asylum (S) 7E-1115		2.00	3.00	4.00

Also see SPIRIT, JO JO GUNNE.

FERRIER, Al & His Boppin' Billies
BIRTH OF ROCKABILLY .... Goldstar		4.50	6.75	9.00
SOUND OF ROCKABILLY .... Showtime		4.00	6.00	8.00

FERRIS WHEEL
FERRIS WHEEL .... Uni (S) 73093		3.00	4.50	6.00

FERRY, Bryan
ANOTHER TIME, ANOTHER PLACE ..... Atlantic (S) SD 18113		2.50	3.75	5.00
THESE FOOLISH THINGS .... Atlantic (S) SD 7304		3.00	4.50	6.00

Also see ROXY MUSIC

FEVER TREE
ANOTHER TIME, ANOTHER PLACE ... Uni (S) 73040		4.50	5.75	9.00
CREATION .... Uni (S) 73067		4.50	5.75	9.00
FEVER TREE .... Uni (M) 3024		6.00	9.00	12.00
FEVER TREE .... Uni (S) 73024		6.00	9.00	12.00
FOR SALE .... Ampex (S) A10113		2.50	3.75	5.00

FIELD, Sally
SALLY FIELD, STAR OF "THE FLYING NUN" .... Colgems (M) COM-106		2.50	3.75	5.00
SALLY FIELD, STAR OF "THE FLYING NUN" ..... Colgems (S) COS-106		3.00	4.50	6.00

FIELDS
FIELDS .... Uni (M) 73050		2.50	3.75	5.00

FIELDS, Ernie
IN THE MOOD .... Rendezvous (M) M1309		5.00	10.00	15.00
IN THE MOOD .... Rendezvous (S) S 1309		6.00	12.00	18.00

FIELDS, Richard "Dimples"
SPOILED ROTTEN! .... DRFK (S) ?#1?		4.00	6.00	8.00

FIELDS, W.C.
BEST OF W.C. FIELDS .... Columbia (S) CG 34144		2.50	3.75	5.00
HIS GREAT MOVIES .... Decca (S) DL 79164		4.50	6.75	9.00
HIS ONLY RECORDING (WITH MAE WEST) .... American (S) 120		3.50	5.25	7.00
ORIGINAL VOICE TRACKS FROM W.C. FIELDS(2 Disc Set) ...... Variety (M) V101		5.00	12.50	20.00
W.C. FIELDS ON RADIO (WITH EDGAR BERGEN & CHARLIE MCCARTHY) .... Columbia (S) CS 9890		4.50	6.75	9.00

FIFTH ESTATE
DING DONG THE WITCH IS DEAD .... Jubilee (M) JGM 8005		3.00	4.50	6.00
DING DONG THE WITCH IS DEAD .... Jubilee (S) JGS 8005		4.00	6.00	8.00

FIFTY FOOT HOSE
CAULDRON .... Limelight (S) LS 86062		5.00	7.50	10.00

FINCHLEY BOYS
EVERLASTING TRIBUTE .... Golden Throat (S) 200-19		3.50	5.25	7.00

FINNIGAN & WOOD
CRAZED HIPSTERS .... Blue Thumb (S) BTS 35		3.00	4.50	6.00

FIREBALLS
FIREBALLS .... Top Rank (M) RM 324		8.00	20.00	32.00
HERE ARE THE FIREBALLS .... Warwick (M) W 2042		6.00	15.00	24.00
TORQUAY .... Dot (M) DLP 3512		5.00	10.00	15.00
TORQUAY .... Dot (S) DLP 25512		6.00	12.00	18.00
VAQUERO .... Top Rank (M) RM 343		7.00	17.50	28.00
VAQUERO .... Top Rank (S) RS-643		8.00	20.00	32.00

FIREBALLS Featuring Jimmy Gilmer
BOTTLE OF WINE .... Atco (S) SD 33-239		4.00	6.00	8.00
CAMPUSOLOGY .... Dot (M) DLP 3709		5.00	10.00	15.00
CAMPUSOLOGY .... Dot (S) DLP 25709		6.00	12.00	18.00
FIREWATER .... Dot (M) DLP 3856		4.00	8.00	12.00
FIREWATER .... Dot (S) DLP 25856		5.00	10.00	15.00
SENSATIONAL JIMMY GILMER AND THE FIRE BALLS ...... Crown (S) SCT 387		3.00	6.00	9.00
SUGAR SHACK .... Dot (M) DLP 3545		4.00	8.00	12.00
SUGAR SHACK .... Dot (S) DLP 25545		5.00	10.00	15.00

FIRE ESCAPE
PSYCHOTIC REACTION .... GNP-Crescendo (S) GNP 2034		7.00	10.50	14.00

FIREFLIES
YOU WERE MINE .... Taurus (S) 1002		16.00	40.00	64.00

FIRESIGN THEATRE
DEAR FRIENDS .... Columbia (S) PG 31099		2.50	3.75	5.00
DON'T CRUSH THAT DWARF, HAND ME THE PLIERS ...... Columbia (S) C 30102		2.50	3.75	5.00
FIRESIGN THEATRE SEZ .... Columbia (S) KC 33141		2.00	3.00	4.00
FIRESIGN THEATRE SEZ .... Columbia (Q) CQ 33141		2.50	3.75	5.00
FORWARD INTO THE PAST .... Columbia (S) PG 34391		2.00	3.00	4.00
GIANT RAT OF SUMATRA .... Columbia (S) KC 32730		2.00	3.00	4.00
HOW CAN YOU BE IN TWO PLACES AT ONCE WHEN YOU'RE NOT ANYWHERE AT ALL? ...... Columbia (S) CS 9884		3.50	5.25	7.00
IN THE NEXT WORLD YOU'RE ON YOUR OWN ...... Columbia (S) PC 33475		2.00	3.00	4.00
I THINK WE'RE ALL BOZOS ON THIS BUS ..... Columbia (S) C 30737		2.50	3.75	5.00
NOT INSANE OR ANYTHING YOU WANT TO ... Columbia (S) C 31585		2.50	3.75	5.00

FIRK, Backwards Sam
TRUE BLUES AND GOSPEL .... Adelphi (S) AD1001		3.50	5.25	7.00

FIRK, Backwards Sam and Delta X
FIRK, BACKWARDS SAM AND DELTA X .... Adelphi (S) AD 1006		2.50	5.25	7.00

(M) Mono   (S) Stereo   (EP) Extended Play   (Q) Quad   (RI) Re-issued

TITLE	LABEL & NO.	GOOD	VERY GOOD	NEAR MINT
FIRST CLASS				
FIRST CLASS	UK (S) UKS 53109	2.50	3.75	5.00
FISCHER & EPSTEIN				
TWO FACED	Greene Bottle (S) GBS 1006	6.00	9.00	12.00
FISHER, Al and Lou Marks				
IT'S A BEATLE (COO COO) WORLD	Swan (M) 514	5.00	10.00	15.00
FISHER, Chip				
CHIPPER AT THE SUGAR BOWL	RCA (M) LPM 1797	5.00	12.50	20.00
FISHER, Eddie				
BERLIN FAVORITES	RCA (M) LPM 3122	3.00	4.50	6.00
BERLIN FAVORITES	RCA (EP) EPA 448	1.50	2.25	3.00
BEST OF EDDIE FISHER	RCA (M) LPM 3375	3.50	5.25	7.00
BROADWAY CLASSICS	RCA (EP) EPA 561	1.50	2.25	3.00
BUNDLE OF JOY	RCA (M) LPM 1399	3.00	4.50	6.00
BUNDLE OF JOY	RCA (EP) EPA 4018	1.50	2.25	3.00
CHEEK TO CHEEK	RCA (EP) EPA 1426	1.50	2.25	3.00
DUNGAREE DOLL	RCA (EP) EPA 710	1.50	2.25	3.00
FISHER SINGS	RCA (M) LPM 3025	3.00	4.50	6.00
GIRL A GIRL	RCA (EP) EPA 572	1.50	2.25	3.00
I'M IN THE MOOD FOR LOVE	RCA (M) LPM 1180	3.00	4.40	6.00
I'M IN THE MOOD FOR LOVE	RCA (M) LPM 3058	3.00	4.50	6.00
I'M IN THE MOOD FOR LOVE	RCA (EP) EPA 742	1.50	2.25	3.00
MAY I SING TO YOU	RCA (M) LPM 1181	3.00	4.50	6.00
MAY I SING TO YOU	RCA (M) LPM 3185	3.00	4.50	6.00
THINKING OF YOU	RCA (M) LPM 1548	3.00	4.50	6.00
XMAS WITH FISHER	RCA (M) LPM 3065	3.00	4.50	6.00
FISHER, Toni				
BIG HURT	Signet (M) WP 509	5.00	12.50	20.00
FIVE AMERICANS				
I SEE THE LIGHT	Hanna Barbera (M) HLP 8503	4.00	6.00	8.00
NOW AND THEN	Abnak (S) ABST 2071	5.00	7.50	10.00
PROGRESSIONS	Abnak (S) ABSTM 2069	4.00	6.00	8.00
WESTERN UNION	Abnak (M) ABLP 1967	3.00	4.50	6.00
WESTERN UNION	Abnak (S) ABST 2067	4.00	6.00	8.00
FIVE EMPREES				
FIVE EMPREES	Freeport (M) FR 3001	8.00	16.00	24.00
FIVE EMPREES	Freeport (S) FRS 4001	9.00	18.00	27.00
LITTLE MISS SAD (2nd Press)	Freeport (M) FR 3001	5.00	7.50	10.00
LITTLE MISS SAD (2nd Press)	Freeport (S) FRS 4001	6.00	9.00	12.00
FIVE BY FIVE				
NEXT EXIT	Paula (S) LPS 2202	5.00	7.50	10.00

TITLE	LABEL & NO.	GOOD	VERY GOOD	NEAR MINT
FIVE KEYS	King (M) 688	20.00	50.00	80.00
FIVE KEYS ON STAGE	Capitol (M) T 828	18.00	45.00	72.00
FIVE KEYS ON STAGE	Capitol (EP) EPA 1 828	5.00	12.50	20.00
FIVE KEYS ON STAGE	Capitol (EP) EPA 2 828	5.00	12.50	20.00
FIVE KEYS ON STAGE	Capitol (EP) EAP 3 828	5.00	12.50	20.00
FIVE KEYS VOL 2	Aladdin (M) 808	25.00	62.50	100.00
JUST FOR A THRILL	Capitol (EP) EAP 572	5.00	12.50	20.00
ON THE TOWN	Aladdin (M) LP 806	25.00	62.50	100.00
ON THE TOWN	Score (M) LP 4003	20.00	50.00	80.00
RHYTHM & BLUES HITS PAST & PRESENT	King (M) 692	20.00	50.00	80.00
FIVE MAN ELECTRICAL BAND				
COMING OF AGE	Lionel (S) 1101	3.50	5.25	7.00
FIVE MAN ELECTRICAL BAND	Capitol (S) ST 165	2.50	3.75	5.00
GOOD-BYES & BUTTERFLIES	Lionel (S) 1100	3.50	5.25	7.00
SWEET PARADISE	Lion (S) LN 1009	3.00	4.50	6.00
5 ROYALES				
ALL TIME HITS	King (M) 955	9.00	22.50	36.00
DEDICATED TO YOU	King (M) 580	10.00	25.00	40.00
FIVE ROYALES	King (M) 678	9.00	22.50	36.00
ROCKIN' 5 ROYALES	Apollo (M) LP 488	15.00	37.50	60.00

FIVE KEYS				
BEST OF THE FIVE KEYS	Group Classics (M) 304	3.00	4.50	6.00
BEST OF THE FIVE KEYS VOL 3	Aladdin (M) 810	25.00	62.50	100.00
BEST OF THE FIVE KEYS VOL 5	Capitol (M) 1001	4.00	6.00	8.00
BEST OF THE FIVE KEYS VOL 6	Capitol (M) 1006	4.00	6.00	8.00
CONNOISSEUR COLLECTION OF THE FIVE KEYS	Harlem Hitparade (M) HHP 5004	4.00	6.00	8.00
FANTASTIC FIVE KEYS	Capitol (M) T1769	14.00	35.00	56.00

FIVE SATINS				
FIVE SATINS ENCORE	Ember (M) ELP 401	10.00	25.00	40.00
FIVE SATINS SING	Ember (M) ELP 100	12.00	30.00	48.00
FIVE SATINS SING	Mt. Vernon (M) 108	8.00	20.00	32.00
OUR ANNIVERSARY	Ember (EP) 102	3.00	7.50	12.00
TO THE AISLE	Ember (EP) 101	3.00	7.50	12.00

(M) Mono (S) Stereo (EP) Extended Play (Q) Quad (RI) Re-issued

TITLE	LABEL & NO.	GOOD	VERY GOOD	NEAR MINT
FLACK, Roberta				
BLUE LIGHTS IN THE BASEMENT	Atlantic (S) SD 19149	2.00	3.00	4.00
CHAPTER TWO	Atlantic (S) SD 1569	2.50	3.75	5.00
FIRST TAKE	Atlantic (S) SD 8230	2.50	3.75	5.00
KILLING ME SOFTLY	Atlantic (S) SD 7271	2.50	3.75	5.00
KILLING ME SOFTLY	Atlantic (Q) QD-7271	2.50	3.75	5.00
QUIET FIRE	Atlantic (S) SD 1594	2.50	3.75	5.00
FLACK, Roberta & Donny Hathaway				
ROBERTA FLACK & DONNY HATHAWAY	Atlantic (S) SD 7216	2.50	3.75	5.00
FLAGG, Fannie				
RALLY 'ROUND THE FLAGG	RCA (M) LPM 3856	2.50	3.75	5.00
RALLY 'ROUND THE FLAGG	RCA (S) LPS 3856	2.50	3.75	5.00
FLAIRS				
THE FLAIRS	Crown (M) CLP 5356	6.00	15.00	24.00
FLAME				
THE FLAME	Brother (S) BR 2500	4.50	6.75	9.00
FLAMING EMBER				
WESTBOUND #9	Hot Wax (S) HA 702	2.50	3.75	5.00
FLAMINGOS				
FLAMINGO FAVORITES	End (M) LP 307	6.00	15.00	24.00
FLAMINGOS	Checker (M) LP 1433	7.00	14.00	21.00
FLAMINGOS	End (EP) 205	2.50	6.25	10.00
FLAMINGO SERENADE	End (M) STLP 304	6.00	15.00	24.00
REQUESTFULLY YOURS	End (M) LP 308	6.00	15.00	24.00
SOUND OF THE FLAMINGOS	End (M) LP 316	6.00	15.00	24.00
THEIR HITS-THEN AND NOW	Phillips (M) 200206	4.00	6.00	8.00
THEIR HITS-THEN AND NOW	Philips (S) 600206	5.00	7.50	10.00
FLAMINGOS & THE MOONGLOWS				
THE FLAMINGOS MEET THE MOONGLOWS	Vee Jay (M) LP 1052	7.00	21.50	28.00
FLAMIN GROOVIES				
FLAMINGO (Blue Label)	Kama Sutra (S) KSBS2021	4.00	6.00	8.00
FLAMINGO (Pink Label Fold Open Cover)	Kama Sutra (S) KSBS 2021	6.00	9.00	12.00
SUPERSNAZZ	Epic (S) BN 26487	8.00	16.00	24.00
TEENAGE HEAD (Blue Label)	Kama Sutra (S) KSBS 2031	4.00	6.00	8.00
TEENAGE HEAD (Pink Label)	Kama Sutra (S) KSBS 2031	6.00	9.00	12.00
FLAMING YOUTH				
ARK 2	UNI (S) 73075	3.00	4.50	6.00
FLANDERS, Tommy				
MOONSTONE	Verve-Forecast (S) FTS 3075	2.50	3.75	5.00
FLARES				
ENCORE OF FOOTSTOMPIN HITS	Press (M) PR73001	4.00	8.00	12.00
ENCORE OF FOOTSTOMPIN HITS	Press (S) PRS83001	5.00	10.00	15.00
FLASH				
FLASH	Capitol (S) SMAS 11040	2.50	3.75	5.00
FLASH IN THE CAN	Capitol (S) SMAS-11115	2.50	3.75	5.00

(M) Mono (S) Stereo (EP) Extended Play (Q) Quad (RI) Re-issued

TITLE	LABEL & NO.	GOOD	VERY GOOD	NEAR MINT
FLASH CADILLAC & The Continental Kids				
FLASH CADILLAC AND THE CONTINENTAL KIDS	Epic (S) KE 31787	2.50	3.75	5.00
SONS OF THE BEACHES	Private Stock (S) 2003	3.00	4.50	6.00
THERE'S NO FACE LIKE CHROME	Epic (S) KE32488	2.50	3.75	5.00
FLATT, Lester				
BEFORE YOU GO	RCA (S) APL1-0470	2.00	3.00	4.00
BEST OF LESTER FLATT	RCA (S) APL1-0578	2.00	3.00	4.00
COUNTRY BOY	RCA (S) APL1-0131	2.00	3.00	4.00
FOGGY MOUNTAIN BREAKDOWN	RCA (S) LSP-4789	2.50	3.75	5.00
LESTER FLATT LIVE BLUEGRASS FESTIVAL	RCA (S) APL1-0588	2.00	3.00	4.00
OVER THE HILLS TO THE POORHOUSE (WITH MAC WISEMAN)	RCA (S) APL1-0309	2.00	3.00	4.00
FLATT, Lester & Earl Scruggs				
CHANGIN' TIMES	Columbia (M) CL 2796	3.00	4.50	6.00
CHANGIN' TIMES	Columbia (S) CS 9596	3.00	4.50	6.00
FLATT & SCRUGGS AT CARNEGIE HALL	Columbia (M) CL2045	3.00	4.00	6.00
FLATT & SCRUGGS AT CARNEGIE HALL	Columbia (S) CS 8845	3.00	4.00	6.00
FOGGY MOUNTAIN BANJO	Columbia (M) CL 1564	3.00	4.00	6.00
FOGGY MOUNTAIN BANJO	Columbia (S) CS 8364	3.00	4.00	6.00
FOGGY MOUNTAIN JAMBOREE	Columbia (M) CL 1019	4.00	6.00	8.00
FOGGY MOUNTAIN JAMBOREE	Columbia (EP) B10191	1.50	2.25	3.00
FOLK SONGS OF OUR LAND	Columbia (M) CL 1830	3.00	4.00	6.00
FOLK SONGS OF OUR LAND	Columbia (S) CS8630	3.00	4.00	6.00
GREATEST HITS	Columbia (M) CL 2570	3.00	4.00	6.00
GREATEST HITS	Columbia (S) CS 9370	3.00	4.00	6.00
HARD TRAVELIN'	Columbia (M) CL1951	3.00	4.00	6.00
HARD TRAVELIN'	Columbia (S) CS 8751	3.00	4.00	6.00
ORIGINAL THEME FROM BONNIE & CLYDE	Mercury (M) MG 21162	3.50	5.25	7.00
ORIGINAL THEME FROM BONNIE & CLYDE	Mercury (S) SR 61162	3.50	5.25	7.00
SONGS OF GLORY	Columbia (M) CL 1424	3.00	4.50	6.00
SONGS OF GLORY	Columbia (S) CS 8221	3.00	4.50	6.00
SONGS OF THE FAMOUS CARTER FAMILY	Columbia (M) CL1664	3.00	4.00	6.00
SONGS OF THE FAMOUS CARTER FAMILY	Columbia (S) CS8464	3.00	4.00	6.00
STORY OF BONNIE & CLYDE	Columbia (S) CS 9649	3.00	4.50	6.00
WORLD OF FLATT & SCRUGGS	Columbia (S) KG 31964	2.00	3.00	4.00
FLEETWOOD MAC				
BARE TREES	Reprise (S) MS 2080	3.00	4.50	6.00
BARE TREES (RI of Reprise 2080)	Reprise (S) MSK-2278	2.00	3.00	4.00
BLACK MAGIC WOMAN (RI of Epic 26402 & 26446)	Epic (S) KE 30632	3.50	5.25	7.00
ENGLISH ROSE	Epic (S) BN 26446	4.00	6.00	8.00
FLEETWOOD MAC	Reprise (S) MS 2225	2.50	3.75	5.00
FLEETWOOD MAC (RI of Reprise 2225)	Reprise (S) MSK-2281	2.00	3.00	4.00
FLEETWOOD MAC	Epic (S) BN 26402	4.00	6.00	8.00
FLEETWOOD MAC/ENGLISH ROSE (RI of Epic 30632)	Epic (S) BG 33740	2.50	3.75	5.00
FLEETWOOD MAC IN CHICAGO	Blue Horizon (S) 3801	3.50	5.25	7.00
FLEETWOOD MAC IN CHICAGO (RI of Blue Horizon 3801)	Sire (S) SASH-3715	3.00	4.50	6.00
FLEETWOOD MAC IN CHICAGO (RI of Sire 3715)	Sire (S) 2XS-6009	3.00	4.50	6.00
FUTURE GAMES	Reprise (S) 6465	3.50	5.25	7.00
HEROES ARE HARD TO FIND	Reprise (S) MS 2196	3.00	4.50	6.00
KILN HOUSE	Reprise (S) 6408	3.50	5.25	7.00
MYSTERY TO ME	Reprise (S) MS 2158	3.00	4.50	6.00
MYSTERY TO ME (RI of Reprise 2158)	Reprise (S) MSK-2279	2.00	3.00	4.00
ORIGINAL FLEETWOOD MAC	Sire (S) 6045	2.00	3.00	4.00
PENGUIN	Reprise (S) MS 2138	3.00	4.50	6.00
THEN PLAY ON	Reprise (S) 6368	3.50	5.25	7.00
VINTAGE YEARS	Sire (S) SASH-3706	3.00	4.50	6.00
VINTAGE YEARS (RI of Sire 3706)	Sire (S) 2XS-6006	3.00	4.50	6.00

Also see BOB WELCH, CHRISTINE McVIE, BUCKINGHAM NICKS.

FLEETWOODS

TITLE	LABEL & NO.	GOOD	VERY GOOD	NEAR MINT
BEFORE AND AFTER	Dolton (M) BLP 2030	3.00	6.00	9.00
BEFORE AND AFTER	Dolton (S) BST 8030	4.00	8.00	12.00
DEEP IN A DREAM	Dolton (M) BLP 2007	3.00	6.00	9.00
DEEP IN A DREAM	Dolton (S) BST 8007	4.00	8.00	12.00
ESPECIALLY FOR YOU	Jamie (S) JLP3006	7.00	17.50	28.00
FLEETWOODS	Dolton (M) BLP 2002	4.00	8.00	12.00
FLEETWOODS	Dolton (S) BST-8002	5.00	10.00	15.00
FLEETWOODS	Dolton (EP) BEP-502	2.00	4.00	6.00
FLEETWOODS GREATEST HITS	Dolton (M) BLP 2018	4.00	8.00	12.00
FLEETWOODS GREATEST HITS	Dolton (S) BST 8018	5.00	10.00	15.00
FLEETWOODS SING FOR LOVERS BY NIGHT	Dolton (M) BLP 2020	3.00	6.00	9.00
FLEETWOODS SING FOR LOVERS BY NIGHT	Dolton (S) BST 8020	4.00	8.00	12.00
FLEETWOODS SING THE BEST OF THE OLDIES	Dolton (M) BLP 2011	3.00	6.00	9.00
FLEETWOODS SING THE BEST OF THE OLDIES	Dolton (S) BST 8011	4.00	8.00	12.00
FOLK ROCK	Dolton (M) BLP 2039	3.00	6.00	9.00
FOLK ROCK	Dolton (S) BST 8039	4.00	8.00	12.00
GOODNIGHT MY LOVE	Dolton (M) BLP 2025	3.00	6.00	9.00
GOODNIGHT MY LOVE	Dolton (S) BST 8025	4.00	8.00	12.00
IN A MELLOW MOOD	Sunset (M) 1131	2.00	3.00	4.00
IN A MELLOW MOOD	Sunset (S) 5131	3.00	4.50	6.00
MR. BLUE	Dolton (M) BLP 2001	4.00	8.00	12.00
MR BLUE	Dolton (S) BS 8001	5.00	10.00	15.00
SOFTLY	Dolton (M) BLP 2005	3.00	6.00	9.00
SOFTLY	Dolton (S) BST 8005	4.00	8.00	12.00
VERY BEST OF THE FLEETWOODS	United Artists (S) UA-LA 334	2.00	3.00	4.00

FLEMONS, Wade

TITLE	LABEL & NO.	GOOD	VERY GOOD	NEAR MINT
WADE FLEMONS	Vee Jay (M) LP 1011	6.00	15.00	24.00

FLINT, Shelby

TITLE	LABEL & NO.	GOOD	VERY GOOD	NEAR MINT
CAST YOUR FATE TO THE WIND	Valiant (M) VLM 5003	2.50	5.00	7.50
CAST YOUR FATE TO THE WIND	Valiant (S) VLS 25003	3.50	7.00	10.50
SHELBY FLINT	Valiant (M) LP 401	4.50	9.00	13.50
SHELBY FLINT SINGS FOLK	Valiant (M) LP 403	3.00	6.00	9.00
SHELBY FLINT SINGS FOLK	Valiant (S) WS 403	4.00	8.00	12.00

FLIRTATIONS

TITLE	LABEL & NO.	GOOD	VERY GOOD	NEAR MINT
NOTHING BUT A HEARTACHE	Dream (S) DES 18028	4.50	6.75	9.00

FLO AND EDDIE

TITLE	LABEL & NO.	GOOD	VERY GOOD	NEAR MINT
FLO AND EDDIE	Warner Brothers (EP) PRO 564	4.00	6.00	8.00
FLO AND EDDIE	Reprise (S) MS 2141	2.50	3.75	5.00
ILLEGAL, IMMORAL & FATTENING	Columbia (S) PC-33554	2.00	3.00	4.00
MOVING TARGETS	Columbia (S) PC 34262	2.00	3.00	4.00
THE PHLORESCENT LEECH AND EDDIE	Reprise (S) MS 2099	2.50	3.75	5.00

Also see TURTLES

FLOCK

TITLE	LABEL & NO.	GOOD	VERY GOOD	NEAR MINT
DINOSAUR SWAMPS	Columbia (S) C 30007	2.50	3.75	5.00
FLOCK	Columbia (S) CS 9911	3.00	4.50	6.00
INSIDE OUT	Mercury (S) SRM-1-1035	2.50	3.75	5.00

FLOWERS, Phil

TITLE	LABEL & NO.	GOOD	VERY GOOD	NEAR MINT
I AM THE GREATEST	Guest Star (M) G 1456	4.00	10.00	16.00
PHIL FLOWERS SINGS A TRIBUTE	Guest Star (M) G1457	6.00	15.00	24.00

FLOYD, Eddie

TITLE	LABEL & NO.	GOOD	VERY GOOD	NEAR MINT
BABY LAY YOUR HEAD DOWN	Stax (S) STS3016	3.00	4.50	6.00
CALIFORNIA GIRL	Stax (S) STS2029	3.00	4.50	6.00
DOWN TO EARTH	Stax (S) STS2041	3.00	4.50	6.00
I NEVER FOUND A GIRL	Stax (S) STS2002	4.00	6.00	8.00

TITLE	LABEL & NO.	GOOD	VERY GOOD	NEAR MINT
KNOCK ON WOOD	Stax (S) S 714	3.50	5.25	7.00
RARE STAMPS	Stax (S) STS 2011	3.00	4.50	6.00
SOUL SISTER	Stax (S) STS 5512	3.00	4.50	6.00
THINK ABOUT IT	Atco (S) 7023	3.00	4.50	6.00
YOU'VE GOT TO HAVE EDDIE	Stax (S)2017	3.00	4.50	6.00

FLUFF

TITLE	LABEL & NO.	GOOD	VERY GOOD	NEAR MINT
FLUFF	Roulette (S) SR3011	3.00	4.50	6.00

FLYING BURRITO BROTHERS

TITLE	LABEL & NO.	GOOD	VERY GOOD	NEAR MINT
AIRBORNE	Columbia (S) PC 34222	2.00	3.00	4.00
BURRITO DELUXE	A&M (S) SP 4258	2.50	3.75	5.00
CLOSE UP THE HONKY TONKS	A&M (S) SP 3631	2.50	3.75	5.00
FLYING AGAIN	Columbia (S) PC 33817	2.00	3.00	4.00
FLYING BURRITO BROTHERS	A&M (S) SP 4295	2.50	3.75	5.00
GILDED PALACE OF SIN	A&M (S) SP 4175	2.50	3.75	5.00
LAST OF THE RED HOT BURRITOS	A&M (S) SP 4343	2.50	3.75	5.00
SLEEPLESS NIGHTS	A&M (S) SP 4578	2.00	3.00	4.00

FLYING CIRCUS

TITLE	LABEL & NO.	GOOD	VERY GOOD	NEAR MINT
FLYING CIRCUS	Capitol (S) ST 11147	2.50	3.75	5.00

FLYING SAUCERS

TITLE	LABEL & NO.	GOOD	VERY GOOD	NEAR MINT
WATERGATE	IX Chains (S) NCS 9000	2.50	3.75	5.00

FLYING MACHINE

TITLE	LABEL & NO.	GOOD	VERY GOOD	NEAR MINT
SMILE A LITTLE SMILE FOR ME	Janus (S) JLS 3007	4.00	6.00	8.00

FOCUS

TITLE	LABEL & NO.	GOOD	VERY GOOD	NEAR MINT
FOCUS/DUTCH MASTERS	Sire (S) 7505	3.50	5.25	7.00
FOCUS LIVE AT THE RAINBOW	Sire (S) 7408	3.50	5.25	7.00
FOCUS 3	Sire (S) 3901	4.00	6.00	8.00
HAMBURGER CONCERTO	Atco (S) 36-100	3.00	4.50	6.00
IN & OUT OF FOCUS	Sire (S) 7404	3.50	5.25	7.00
MOTHER FOCUS	Atco (S) 36-117	3.00	4.50	6.00
MOVING WAVES	Sire (S) 7401	3.50	5.25	7.00

FOGELBERG, Dan

TITLE	LABEL & NO.	GOOD	VERY GOOD	NEAR MINT
CAPTURED ANGEL	Epic (S) PE-33499	2.00	3.00	4.00
HOME FREE	Columbia (S) KC-31751	2.50	3.75	5.00
NETHER LANDS	Epic/Full Moon (S) PE-34185	2.00	3.00	4.00
SOUVENIRS	Epic (S) KE-33137	2.50	3.75	5.00

FOGERTY, John

TITLE	LABEL & NO.	GOOD	VERY GOOD	NEAR MINT
HOODOO	Asylum (S) 7E-1081	3.50	5.25	7.00
JOHN FOGERTY	Asylum (S) 7E-1046	3.00	4.50	6.00

Also see CREEDENCE CLEARWATER REVIVAL

FOGERTY, Tom

TITLE	LABEL & NO.	GOOD	VERY GOOD	NEAR MINT
EXCALIBUR	Fantasy (S) 9413	2.50	3.75	5.00
MYOPIA	Fantasy (S) 9469	2.50	3.75	5.00
TOM FOGERTY	Fantasy (S) 9407	3.00	4.50	6.00
ZEPHYR NATIONAL	Fantasy (S) 9448	2.50	3.75	5.00

Also see CREEDENCE CLEARWATER REVIVAL

FOGHAT

TITLE	LABEL & NO.	GOOD	VERY GOOD	NEAR MINT
ENERGIZED	Bearsville (S) 6950	3.00	4.50	6.00
FOGHAT	Bearsville (S) BR 2077	3.00	4.50	6.00
FOGHAT	Bearsville (S) BR 2136	3.00	4.50	6.00

Also see SAVOY BROWN

FOLKSWINGERS

TITLE	LABEL & NO.	GOOD	VERY GOOD	NEAR MINT
RAGA ROCK	World Pacific (M) WP1846	2.00	3.00	4.00
RAGA ROCK	World Pacific (S) WPS 21846	3.00	4.50	6.00

FONDA, Henry

TITLE	LABEL & NO.	GOOD	VERY GOOD	NEAR MINT
VOICES OF THE 20TH CENTURY	Coral (M) CRL-57308	3.00	6.00	9.00

FONTAINE, Frank

TITLE	LABEL & NO.	GOOD	VERY GOOD	NEAR MINT
FRANK FONTAINE SINGS LIKE CRAZY	ABC (M) ABC460	2.50	3.75	5.00
FRANK FONTAINE SINGS LIKE CRAZY	ABC (S) ABCS460	2.50	3.75	5.00
HOW SWEET IT IS	ABC (M) ABC 470	2.50	3.75	5.00
HOW SWEET IT IS	ABC (S) ABCS 470	2.50	3.75	5.00
MORE SONGS I SING ON THE JACKIE GLEASON SHOW	ABC (M) ABC490	2.50	3.75	5.00
MORE SONGS I SING ON THE JACKIE GLEASON SHOW	ABC (S) ABCS490	2.50	3.75	5.00
SONGS I SING ON THE JACKIE GLEASON SHOW	ABC (M) ABC442	3.00	4.50	6.00
SONGS I SING ON THE JACKIE GLEASON SHOW	ABC (S) ABCS442	3.00	4.50	6.00

FONTANA, Wayne

TITLE	LABEL & NO.	GOOD	VERY GOOD	NEAR MINT
WAYNE FONTANA	MGM (M) E4459	4.00	8.00	12.00

FONTANA, Wayne, & The Mindbenders

TITLE	LABEL & NO.	GOOD	VERY GOOD	NEAR MINT
GAME OF LOVE	Fontana (M) MGF 27542	4.00	6.00	8.00
GAME OF LOVE	Fontana (S) SRF 67542	5.00	7.50	10.00

FONTANE SISTERS

TITLE	LABEL & NO.	GOOD	VERY GOOD	NEAR MINT
FONTANE SISTERS	Dot (M) DLP3004	3.00	4.50	6.00

(M) Mono (S) Stereo (EP) Extended Play (Q) Quad (RI) Re-issued

TITLE	LABEL & NO.	GOOD	VERY GOOD	NEAR MINT
FONTANE SISTERS	Dot (EP) DEP1019	1.50	2.25	3.00
FONTANE SISTERS	Dot (EP) DEP 1020	1.50	2.25	3.00
FONTANES SING	Dot (M) DLP3042	3.00	4.50	6.00
TIP OF MY FINGERS	Dot (M) DLP3531	2.50	3.75	5.00
TIP OF MY FINGERS	Dot (S) DLP25531	2.50	3.75	5.00

FOOL

THE FOOL	Mercury (S) SR61178	3.50	5.25	7.00

FORD, Frankie

BEST OF FRANKIE FORD	Ace (EP) 105EP	2.00	5.00	8.00
FRANKIE FORD	Briarmeade (S) BR5002	3.00	4.50	6.00
ON A SEA CRUISE WITH FRANKIE FORD	ACE (M) LP1005	6.00	15.00	24.00

FORD, Neal & The Fanatics

NEAL FORD AND THE FANATICS	Hickory (S) LPS141	3.50	7.00	10.50

FORD, Tennessee Ernie

SIXTEEN TONS	Capitol (M) T1380	3.00	4.50	6.00

FORD THEATRE

FORD THEATRE PRESENTS TIME CHANGES	ABC (S) ABCS681	4.00	6.00	8.00

FOREIGNER

FOREIGNER	Atlantic (S) SD 19109	2.50	3.75	5.00

FOREST

FOREST	Harvest (S) SKAO-419	5.00	7.50	10.00

FOREVERMORE

WORDS ON BLACK PLASTIC	RCA (S) LSP4425	3.00	4.50	6.00
YOURS FOREVER MORE	RCA (S) LSP4272	3.00	4.50	6.00

FORMULA V

FORMULA V	Burlinguen (S)	6.00	12.00	18.00
VOLUME IV	Miami (S) 6076	6.00	12.00	18.00

FORT MUDGE MEMORIAL DUMP

FORT MUDGE MEMORIAL DUMP	Mercury (S) SR61256	2.50	3.75	5.00

FORTUNE, Johnny

SOUL SURFER	Park Ave. (S) 401	4.00	8.00	12.00

FORTUNES

FORTUNES	Press (M) PR73002	3.00	4.50	6.00
FORTUNES	Press (S) PRS83002	4.00	6.00	8.00
HERE COMES THAT RAINY DAY FEELING AGAIN	Capitol (S) ST809	3.00	4.00	6.00
IT'S THE REAL THING	Coca Cola (S)	5.25	8.00	16.00
STORM IN A TEACUP	Capitol (S) ST11041	2.50	3.75	5.00
THAT SAME OLD FEELING	World Pacific (S) WPS 21904	3.50	5.25	7.00

49TH PARALLEL

49TH PARALLEL	Maverick (S) MAS7001	3.50	5.25	7.00

FOSTER, Larry & Marty Brill

OTHER FAMILY	Laurie (M) LC 5000	4.00	6.00	8.00

FOTOMAKER

FOTOMAKER	Atlantic (S) SD 19165	2.00	3.00	4.00

FOUNDATIONS

BABY, NOW THAT I'VE FOUND YOU	UNI (S) 73016	3.00	4.50	6.00
BUILD ME UP BUTTERCUP	UNI (S) 73043	3.00	4.50	6.00
FOUNDATIONS	UNI (S) 73058	3.00	4.50	6.00

FOUR ACES

TITLE	LABEL & NO.	GOOD	VERY GOOD	NEAR MINT
AMOR	Decca (EP) ED2324	1.50	2.25	3.00
BEST OF THE FOUR ACES	MCA (S) 2-4033	2.50	3.75	5.00
BEYOND THE BLUE HORIZON	Decca (M) DL-8944	3.00	4.50	6.00
BEYOND THE BLUE HORIZON	Decca (S) DL-78944	3.00	4.50	6.00
BEYOND THE BLUE HORIZON	Decca (EP) ED-2675	1.00	1.50	2.00
BEYOND THE BLUE HORIZON	Decca (SEP) ED-72675	2.00	3.00	4.00
DREAM	Decca (EP) ED2170	1.50	2.25	3.00
FOUR ACES	Decca (M) DL5429	4.00	10.00	16.00
FOUR ACES	Decca (EP) ED2004	2.00	3.00	4.00
FOUR ACES	Decca (EP) ED573	1.50	2.25	3.00
FOUR ACES SING	Vocalion (M) VL3604	3.00	4.00	6.00
FOUR ACES SING	Decca (EP) ED-2665	1.00	1.50	2.00
FOUR ACES SING	Decca (SEP) ED-742665	2.00	3.00	4.00
GOLDEN HITS OF THE FOUR ACES	Decca (M) DL-4013	2.50	3.75	5.00
HEART AND SOUL	Decca (M) DL8228	4.00	8.00	12.00
HITS FROM BROADWAY	Decca (M) DL-8855	3.00	4.50	6.00
HITS FROM BROADWAY	Decca (S) DL-78855	3.00	4.50	6.00
HITS FROM BROADWAY	Decca (EP) ED-2658	1.00	1.50	2.00
HITS FROM BROADWAY	Decca (SEP) ED-72658	2.00	3.00	4.00
HITS FROM HOLLYWOOD	Decca (M) DL8693	3.00	4.00	6.00
KISMET	Decca (EP) ED2117	1.50	2.25	3.00
LONELY WINE	Decca (EP) ED2530	1.00	2.00	3.00
MOOD FOR LOVE	Decca (M) DL8122	4.00	8.00	12.00
MOOD FOR LOVE	Decca (EP) ED 2211	1.50	2.25	3.00
MOOD FOR LOVE	Decca (EP) ED 2212	1.50	2.25	3.00
MOOD FOR LOVE	Decca (EP) ED 2213	1.50	2.25	3.00
PEG O' MY HEART	Decca (EP) ED2531	1.50	2.25	3.00
SENTIMENTAL SOUVENIRS, MERRY CHRISTMAS WITH THE FOUR ACES	Decca (M) DL8191	4.00	8.00	12.00
SENTIMENTAL SOUVENIRS, MERRY CHRISTMAS WITH THE FOUR ACES	Decca (EP) ED2309	1.50	2.25	3.00
SENTIMENTAL SOUVENIRS, MERRY CHRISTMAS WITH THE FOUR ACES	Decca (EP) ED 2310	1.50	2.25	3.00
SENTIMENTAL SOUVENIRS, MERRY CHRISTMAS WITH THE FOUR ACES	Decca (EP) ED 2311	1.50	2.25	3.00
SHE SEES ALL THE HOLLYWOOD HITS	Decca (M) DL8312	4.00	8.00	12.00
SHE SEES ALL THE HOLLYWOOD HITS	Decca (EP) ED2390	1.50	2.25	3.00
SHUFFLIN ALONG	Decca (M) DL8567	3.00	4.50	6.00
SHUFFLIN ALONG	Decca (EP) ED2529	1.00	2.00	3.00
SWINGIN ACES	Decca (M) DL8766	3.00	4.50	6.00
SWINGIN ACES	Decca (S) DL78766	3.00	4.50	6.00
SWINGIN ACES	Decca (EP) ED2636	1.00	2.00	3.00
SWINGIN' ACES	Decca (SEP) ED-72636	2.00	3.00	4.00

FOUR CHESSMAN

ON A KNIGHT OUT	Rondo (EP) EPRR504	2.00	5.00	8.00

FOUR COINS

CURLY HEADED KID IN THE THIRD ROW	Epic (EP) EG7201	1.50	2.25	3.00
FOUR COINS	Epic (M) LN1104	3.00	6.00	9.00
FOUR COINS	Epic (EP) EG7121	1.50	2.25	3.00
FOUR COINS IN SHANGRI LA	Epic (M) LN3445	2.00	4.00	6.00
FOUR COINS IN SHANGRI LA	Epic (EP) EG7186	1.50	2.25	3.00
FOUR COINS SING	Epic (EP) EG7196	1.50	2.25	3.00
FOUR COINS SING	Epic (EP) EG 7197	1.50	2.25	3.00

FOUR FRESHMAN

BEST OF THE FOUR FRESHMEN	Capitol (M) T1640	2.50	3.75	5.00
BEST OF THE FOUR FRESHMEN	Capitol (S) ST1640	2.50	3.75	5.00
FIRST AFFAIR	Capitol (M) T-1378	2.50	3.75	5.00
FIRST AFFAIR	Capitol (S) ST-1378	2.50	3.75	5.00
FOUR FRESHMEN	Capitol (EP) EAP1433	1.50	2.25	3.00
FOUR FRESHMEN & FIVE GUITARS	Capitol (M) T-1255	2.50	3.75	5.00
FOUR FRESHMEN & FIVE GUITARS	Capitol (S) ST-1255	2.50	3.75	5.00
FOUR FRESHMEN & FIVE GUITARS	Capitol (EP) EAP-1-1255	1.50	2.25	3.00
FOUR FRESHMEN & FIVE GUITARS	Capitol (EP) EAP-2-1255	1.50	2.25	3.00
FOUR FRESHMEN & FIVE GUITARS	Capitol (EP) EAP-3-1255	1.50	2.25	3.00
FOUR FRESHMEN AND FIVE SAXES	Capitol (M) T-844	3.00	4.50	6.00
FOUR FRESHMEN AND FIVE TROMBONES	Capitol (M) T683	4.00	6.00	8.00
FOUR FRESHMAN AND FIVE TROMBONES	Capitol (EP) EAP1 683	1.50	2.25	3.00
FOUR FRESHMAN AND FIVE TROMBONES	Capitol (EP) EAP2 683	1.50	2.25	3.00
FOUR FRESHMAN AND FIVE TROMBONES	Capitol (EP) EAP3 683	1.50	2.25	3.00
FOUR FRESHMEN AND FIVE TRUMPETS	Capitol (M) T763	3.00	4.50	6.00
FOUR FRESHMEN AND FIVE TRUMPETS	Capitol (EP) EAP1763	1.50	2.25	3.00
FOUR FRESHMEN AND FIVE TRUMPETS	Capitol (EP) EAP2763	1.50	2.25	3.00
FOUR FRESHMEN AND FIVE TRUMPETS	Capitol (EP) EAP3763	1.50	2.25	3.00
FOUR FRESHMEN IN PERSON	Capitol (M) T-1008	3.00	4.50	6.00
FOUR FRESHMEN IN PERSON	Capitol (S) ST-1008	3.00	4.50	6.00
FRESHMEN FAVORITES	Capitol (M) T-743	3.00	4.50	6.00
FRESHMEN FAVORITES (RI)	Capitol (S) SM-743	2.00	3.00	4.00
FRESHMEN FAVORITES, VOL. 2	Capitol (M) T-1103	3.00	4.50	6.00
FRESHMAN FAVORITES, VOL. 2	Capitol (S) ST-1103	3.00	4.50	6.00
LOVE LOST	Capitol (M) T-1189	3.00	4.50	6.00
LOVE LOST	Capitol (S) ST-1189	3.00	4.50	6.00
VOICES & BRASS	Capitol (M) T-1295	2.50	3.75	5.00
VOICES & BRASS	Capitol (S) ST-1295	2.50	3.75	5.00
VOICES IN LOVE	Capitol (M) T-1074	3.00	4.50	6.00
VOICES IN LOVE	Capitol (S) ST-1074	3.00	4.50	6.00
VOICES IN MODERN	Capitol (M) T522	4.00	6.00	8.00
VOICES IN MODERN	Capitol (EP) 1522	1.50	2.25	3.00
VOICES IN MODERN	Capitol (EP) 2522	1.50	2.25	3.00

(M) Mono (S) Stereo (EP) Extended Play (Q) Quad (RI) Re-issued

FOUR JACKS AND A JILL

TITLE	LABEL & NO.	GOOD	VERY GOOD	NEAR MINT
FABLES	RCA (S) LSP4103	2.50	3.75	5.00
MASTER JACK	RCA (M) LPM4019	2.00	3.00	4.00
MASTER JACK	RCA (S) LSP4019	2.25	3.50	4.50

FOUR KNIGHTS

TITLE	LABEL & NO.	GOOD	VERY GOOD	NEAR MINT
FOUR KNIGHTS	Coral (M) 52221	4.00	10.00	16.00
FOUR KNIGHTS SING	Capitol (EP) EAP1414	2.50	7.50	10.00
I GET SO LONELY	Capitol (EP) EAP1506	2.50	7.50	10.00
MILLION DOLLAR BABY	Coral (M) CRL57309	3.00	7.50	12.00
MILLION DOLLAR BABY	Coral (S) CRL757309	4.00	10.00	16.00
SPOTLIGHT SONGS	Capitol (M) T 346	5.00	12.50	20.00

FOUR LADS

TITLE	LABEL & NO.	GOOD	VERY GOOD	NEAR MINT
BREEZIN' ALONG	Columbia (S) CS 8035	4.00	6.00	8.00
FLOWER DRUM SONG	Columbia (EP) B-2151	1.50	2.25	3.00
FOUR LADS	Columbia (EP) B2538	1.50	2.25	3.00
FOUR LADS	Columbia (EP) B2557	1.50	2.25	3.00
FOUR LADS	Columbia (EP) B-2617	1.50	2.25	3.00
FOUR LADS FEATURING FRANKIE LAINE	Columbia (M) LC861	5.00	7.50	10.00
FOUR LADS FEATURING FRANKIE LAINE	Columbia (EP) B8611	1.50	2.25	3.00
FOUR LADS FEATURING FRANKIE LAINE	Columbia (EP) B8612	1.50	2.25	3.00
FOUR LADS FEATURING FRANKIE LAINE	Columbia (EP) B8613	1.50	2.25	3.00
FOUR LADS GREATEST HITS	Columbia (M) CL 1235	4.00	6.00	8.00
FOUR LADS SING FOUR HITS	Columbia (EP) B2135	1.50	2.25	3.00
FOUR LADS SWING ALONG	Columbia (M) CL 1299	3.00	4.50	6.00
FOUR LADS SWING ALONG	Columbia (S) CS 8106	3.00	4.50	6.00
FOUR LADS SWING ALONG	Columbia (EP) B-12991	1.50	2.25	3.00
FOUR ON THE AISLE	Columbia (M) CL1111	4.00	6.00	8.00
FOUR ON THE AISLE	Columbia (S) CS 8047	4.00	6.00	8.00
HIGH SPIRITS!	Columbia (M) CL 1407	3.00	4.50	6.00
HIGH SPIRITS!	Columbia (S) CS 8203	3.00	4.50	6.00
LOVE AFFAIR	Columbia (M) CL 1502	3.00	4.50	6.00
LOVE AFFAIR	Columbia (S) CS 8293	3.00	4.50	6.00
NO NOT MUCH	Columbia (EP) B2110	1.50	2.25	3.00
ON THE SUNNY SIDE	Columbia (M) DL912	4.00	6.00	8.00
ON THE SUNNY SIDE	Columbia (EP) B9121	1.50	2.25	3.00
ON THE SUNNY SIDE	Columbia (EP) B9122	1.50	2.25	3.00
ON THE SUNNY SIDE	Columbia (EP) B9123	1.50	2.25	3.00
SPOTLIGHT SONGS (10")	Capitol (M) H 346	8.00	20.00	32.00
STAGE SHOW	Columbia (M) CL2577	3.00	4.50	6.00
STINGIEST MAN IN TOWN	Columbia (M) CL950	4.00	6.00	8.00
WHO NEEDS YOU	Columbia (EP) B2125	1.50	2.25	3.00

FOUR LOVERS

TITLE	LABEL & NO.	GOOD	VERY GOOD	NEAR MINT
FOUR LOVERS	RCA (EP) EPA 869	35.00	55.00	85.00
JOYRIDE	RCA (M) LPM1317	65.00	100.00	150.00
JOYRIDE	RCA (EP) EPA 871	35.00	55.00	85.00

FOUR PREPS

TITLE	LABEL & NO.	GOOD	VERY GOOD	NEAR MINT
BIG MAN	Capitol (EP) EAP11064	1.00	1.50	2.00
CAMPUS ENCORE	Capitol (M) T 1647	3.50	5.25	7.00
CAMPUS ENCORE	Capitol (S) ST 1647	3.50	5.25	7.00
DANCING AND DREAMING	Capitol (M) T 1216	4.00	6.00	8.00
DANCING AND DREAMING	Capitol (S) ST 1216	4.00	6.00	8.00
DOWN BY THE STATION	Capitol (M) T 1291	4.00	6.00	8.00
DREAMY EYES	Capitol (EP) EAP1862	1.00	1.50	2.00
FOUR PREPS	Capitol (M) T994	4.50	6.75	9.00
FOUR PREPS ON CAMPUS	Capitol (M) T1566	3.50	5.25	7.00
FOUR PREPS ON CAMPUS	Capitol (S) ST 1566	3.50	5.25	7.00
LAZY SUMMER NIGHT	Capitol (EP) EAP1139	1.00	1.50	2.00
THINGS WE DID LAST SUMMER	Capitol (EP) EAP11090	1.00	1.50	2.00
TWENTY SIX MILES	Capitol (EP) EAP1015	1.00	1.50	2.00

FOUR SEASONS

TITLE	LABEL & NO.	GOOD	VERY GOOD	NEAR MINT
AIN'T THAT A SHAME	Vee Jay (M) LP 1059	5.00	10.00	15.00
AIN'T THAT A SHAME	Vee Jay (S) SR 1059	10.00	15.00	20.00
ALL THE SONG HITS OF THE FOUR SEASONS	Philips (M) 200150	4.00	6.00	8.00

TITLE	LABEL & NO.	GOOD	VERY GOOD	NEAR MINT
ALL THE SONG HITS OF THE FOUR SEASONS	Philips (S) 600150	5.00	7.50	10.00
ALONE + 3	Vee Jay (EP) EP 902	2.00	4.00	6.00
BIG GIRLS DON'T CRY	Vee Jay (M) LP1056	5.00	10.00	15.00
BIG GIRLS DON'T CRY	Vee Jay (S) SR1056	10.00	15.00	20.00
BORN TO WANDER	Philips (M) PHM200129	4.00	6.00	8.00
BORN TO WANDER	Philips (S) 600129	8.00	10.00	12.00
BROTHERHOOD OF MAN	Pickwick (M) 3223	4.00	8.00	12.00
BROTHERHOOD OF MAN	Pickwick (S) 3223	2.00	4.00	6.00
BROTHERHOOD OF MAN	Sears (S) 609	10.00	12.50	15.00
CHAMELEON	Mowest (S) MW108L	3.00	6.00	9.00
CHRISTMAS ALBUM	Philips (M) PHM 200-223	8.00	10.00	12.00
CHRISTMAS ALBUM	Philips (S) PHS 600-223	4.00	8.00	10.00
DAWN (GO AWAY) & 11 OTHER GREAT HITS	Philips (M) PHM 200-124	4.00	6.00	8.00
DAWN (GO AWAY) & 11 OTHER GREAT HITS	Philips (S) PHS 600-124	6.00	8.00	10.00
EDIZONE D'ORO (Gold Edition)				
1ST COVER: Gold Foil; Red "4"	Philips (S) PHS 2-6501	10.00	15.00	20.00
2ND COVER: Gold Foil; White "4"	Philips (S) PHS 2-6501	15.00	20.00	25.00
3RD COVER: Gold Matte; White "4"	Philips (S) PHS 2-6501	15.00	20.00	25.00
FOLK-NANNY (Re-titled "Stay")	Vee Jay (M) LP 1082	10.00	15.00	20.00
FOLK-NANNY (Re-titled "Stay")	Vee Jay (S) SR 1082	12.50	15.00	20.00
FOUR SEASONS ENTERTAIN YOU				
1ST COVER: "Bye Bye Baby" on Orange Seal	Philips (M) PHM 200-164	4.00	6.00	8.00
Orange Seal	Philips (S) PHS 600-164	6.00	8.00	10.00
2ND COVER: "Bye Bye Baby" & "Toy Soldier" on Orange Seal	Philips (M) PHM 200-164	5.00	7.00	9.00
Orange Seal	Philips (S) PHS 600-164	7.00	9.00	11.00
3RD COVER: "Bye Bye Baby" — "Toy Soldier" on Blue Label	Philips (M) PHM 200-164	10.00	15.00	20.00
Blue Label	Philips (S) PHS 600-164	10.00	15.00	20.00
FOUR SEASONS GREETINGS	Vee Jay (M) LP 1055	10.00	15.00	20.00
FOUR SEASONS GREETINGS	Vee Jay (S) SR 1055	7.50	10.00	15.00
FOUR SEASONS STORY	Private Stock (S) PS 7000	3.50	5.25	7.00
GENUINE IMITATION LIFE GAZETTE				
1ST COVER: White; 2 Pages	Philips (S) PHS 600-290	1.50	3.00	5.00
2ND COVER: Yellow; 1 Page	Philips (S) PHS 600-290	10.00	15.00	20.00
GOLDEN HITS	Vee Jay (M) LP 1065	5.00	7.50	10.00
GOLDEN HITS	vee Jay (S) SR 1065	10.00	12.50	15.00
GOLD VAULT OF HITS				
1ST COVER: Red Logo; No Title Outline	Philips (M) PHM 200-196	10.00	12.50	15.00
No Title Outline	Philips (S) PHS 600-196	15.00	17.50	20.00
2ND COVER: Red Logo Black Outline	Philips (M) PHM 200-196	10.00	12.50	15.00
Black Outline	Philips (S) PHS 600-196	6.00	8.00	10.00
3RD COVER: Black Logo & Outline	Philips (M) PHM 200-196	6.00	8.00	10.00
Black Logo & Outline	Philips (S) PHS 600-196	4.00	6.00	8.00
1967 RI: Different Photo on Back	Philips (S) PHS 600-196	4.00	6.00	8.00
GREATEST HITS OF FRANKIE VALLI & THE FABULOUS FOUR SEASONS				
1ST COVER: "As Seen on TV" Label	Longines (S) 95833	15.00	20.00	25.00
2ND COVER: "As Seen on TV" & "4 Record Collection" Labels	Longines (S) 95833	10.00	15.00	20.00
3RD COVER: Both Phrases Removed	Longines (S) 95833	10.00	15.00	20.00
Box Set:	Longines (S) 95833	20.00	25.00	30.00
HALF AND HALF	Philips (S) PHS 600-341	3.00	6.00	8.00
HELICON	Warner/Curb (S) BS 3016	2.50	3.75	5.00
LOOKIN' BACK	Philips (M) PHM 200-222	4.00	8.00	10.00
LOOKIN' BACK	Philips (S) PHS 600-222	8.00	10.00	12.00
MORE GOLDEN HITS BY THE FOUR SEASONS	Vee Jay (M) LP 1088	10.00	12.50	15.00
MORE GOLDEN HITS BY THE FOUR SEASONS	Vee Jay (S) SR 1088	12.50	15.00	20.00
NEW GOLD HITS	Philips (M) PHM 200-243	4.00	8.00	10.00
NEW GOLD HITS	Philips (S) PHS 600-243	3.00	6.00	8.00
PEANUTS + 3 (Cardboard Cover)	Vee Jay EP 1-901	2.00	4.00	6.00
PEANUTS + 3 (Paper Title Sleeve)	Vee Jay EP 1-901	2.50	5.00	10.00
RAG DOLL				
1ST COVER	Philips (M) PHM 200-146	4.00	6.00	8.00
1ST COVER	Philips (S) PHS 600-146	6.00	8.00	10.00

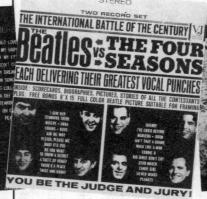

(M) Mono   (S) Stereo   (EP) Extended Play   (Q) Quad   (RI) Re-issued

TITLE	LABEL & NO.	GOOD	VERY GOOD	NEAR MINT
2ND COVER:				
Has "Save It For Me" on Yellow Seal	Philips (S) PHS 600-146	8.00	10.00	12.00
2ND COVER	Philips (M) PHM 22-146	6.00	8.00	10.00
RECORDED LIVE ON STAGE	Vee Jay (M) LP 1154	5.00	7.50	10.00
RECORDED LIVE ON STAGE	Vee Jay (S) SR 1154	5.00	7.50	10.00
2ND GOLD VAULT OF HITS	Philips (S) PHS 600-221	4.00	8.00	10.00
SHERRY & 11 OTHERS	Vee Jay (M) LP 1053	5.00	10.00	15.00
SHERRY & 11 OTHERS	Vee Jay (S) SR 1053	7.50	15.00	20.00
SING BIG HITS BY BURT BACHARACH, HAL DAVID, BOB DYLAN				
1ST COVER: Open, Medieval-Style Book	Philips (M) PHM 200-193	6.00	8.00	10.00
Style Book	Philips (S) PHS 600-193	10.00	12.50	15.00
2ND COVER: Plain Yellow Book	Philips (M) PHM 200-193	8.00	10.00	12.00
Plain Yellow Book	Philips (S) PHS 600-193	10.00	12.50	15.00
3RD COVER: '70 RI with Photos of Group on Front & Back	Philips (S) PHS 600-193	30.00	40.00	50.00
STAY & OTHER GREAT HITS ("Folk-Nanny" LP Re-titled)	Vee Jay (M) LP 1082	5.00	7.50	1.00
STAY & OTHER GREAT HITS ("Folk-Nanny" LP Re-titled)	Vee Jay (S) SR 1082	10.00	12.50	15.00
WE LOVE GIRLS	Vee Jay (M) LP 1121	10.00	12.50	15.00
WE LOVE GIRLS	Vee Jay (S) SR 1121	12.50	15.00	20.00
WHO LOVES YOU	Warner/Curb (S) BS 2900	2.50	3.75	5.00
WORKING MY WAY BACK TO YOU	Philips (M) PHM 200-201	3.00	6.00	8.00
WORKING MY WAY BACK TO YOU	Philips (S) PHS 600-201	4.00	8.00	10.00

FOUR SEASONS & Others

TITLE	LABEL & NO.	GOOD	VERY GOOD	NEAR MINT
AT THE HOP	Coronet (S) CXS244	2.00	3.00	4.00
FOUR SEASONS NEIL SEDAKA AND JOHNNY RIVERS	Pickwick (M) DLP185	2.50	3.75	5.00
FOUR SEASONS AND THE BARRONS	Guest Star (S) GS1481	2.00	3.00	4.00
FOUR SEASONS, TOMMY ROE JOHNNY RIVERS, AND TONY BANON	Diplomat (S) DS 2430	2.00	3.00	4.00

FOUR SEASONS & The Beatles

TITLE	LABEL & NO.	GOOD	VERY GOOD	NEAR MINT
BEATLES VERSUS THE FOUR SEASONS	Vee Jay (M) DX30	18.00	27.00	36.00
BEATLES VERSUS THE FOUR SEASONS	Vee Jay (S) DXS30	30.00	45.00	60.00

FOUR TOPS

TITLE	LABEL & NO.	GOOD	VERY GOOD	NEAR MINT
ANTHOLOGY	motown (S) 809	3.00	4.50	6.00
BEST OF THE FOUR TOPS	Motown (S) 764	2.00	3.00	4.00
FOUR TOPS	Motown (M) 622	5.00	7.50	10.00
FOUR TOPS NO. 2	Motown (S) 634	4.00	6.00	8.00
FOUR TOPS NO. 2	Motown (S) 634	5.00	7.50	10.00
GREATEST HITS VOL. 2	Motown (S) MS740	2.00	3.00	4.00
JAZZ IMPRESSIONS	Workshop (M) 217	15.00	37.50	60.00
KEEPER OF THE CASTLE	Dunhill (S) X50129	2.00	3.00	4.00
KEEPER OF THE CASTLE	Command (S) QD40011	2.00	3.00	4.00
LIVE	Motown (M) 654	3.00	4.50	6.00
LIVE AND IN CONCERT	Dunhill (S) D50188	2.00	3.00	4.00
MAIN STREET PEOPLE	Dunhill (S) X50144	2.00	3.00	4.00
MEETING OF THE MINDS	Dunhill (S) D50166	2.00	3.00	4.00
NATURE PLANNED IT	Motown (S) M748L	2.00	3.00	4.00
NIGHT LIGHTS HARMONY	ABC (S) D862	2.00	3.00	4.00
NOW	Motown (S) MS675	2.50	3.75	5.00
ON TOP	Motown (M) 647	4.00	6.00	8.00
ON TOP	Motown (S) 647	5.00	7.50	10.00
SOUL SPIN	Motown (S) MS695	2.50	3.75	5.00
STILL WATERS RUN DEEP	Motown (S) MS704	2.50	3.75	5.00
YESTERDAY DREAMS	Motown (S) 669	2.00	3.00	4.00

FOUR TOPS & The Supremes

TITLE	LABEL & NO.	GOOD	VERY GOOD	NEAR MINT
DYNAMITE	Motown (S) 745	2.50	3.75	5.00

FOUR TUNES

TITLE	LABEL & NO.	GOOD	VERY GOOD	NEAR MINT
FOUR TUNES	RCA (EP) EPA586	2.00	3.00	4.00
TWELVE TIMES FOUR	Jubilee (M) LP 1039	5.00	7.50	10.00

FOWLEY, Kim

TITLE	LABEL & NO.	GOOD	VERY GOOD	NEAR MINT
AUTOMATIC	Capitol (S) ST11248	2.50	3.75	5.00
BORN TO BE WILD	Imperial (S) LP 12413	4.00	6.00	8.00
GOOD CLEAN FUN	Imperial (S) LP12443	4.00	6.00	8.00
I'M BAD	Capitol (S) ST11075	2.50	3.75	5.00
INTERNATIONAL HEROES	Capitol (S) ST11159	2.50	3.75	5.00
LOVE IS ALIVE AND WELL	Tower (M) T5080	4.00	6.00	8.00
OUTRAGEOUS	Imperial (S) LP12423	4.00	6.00	8.00

FOWLKES, Doug and The Airdales

TITLE	LABEL & NO.	GOOD	VERY GOOD	NEAR MINT
AIRDALE WALK	Atco (S) 33145	4.00	6.00	8.00

FOXX, Inez

TITLE	LABEL & NO.	GOOD	VERY GOOD	NEAR MINT
AT MEMPHIS	Volt (S) VOS6022	2.50	3.75	5.00
MOCKINGBIRD	Symbol (M) SYM4400	6.00	12.00	18.00
MOCKINGBIRD	Sue (M) LP1027	5.00	10.00	15.00

FOXX, Inez and Charlie

TITLE	LABEL & NO.	GOOD	VERY GOOD	NEAR MINT
INEZ AND CHARLIE FOXX	Sue (M) LP 1037	5.00	10.00	15.00

FRAMPTON, Peter

TITLE	LABEL & NO.	GOOD	VERY GOOD	NEAR MINT
FRAMPTON	A&M (S) 4512	2.50	3.75	5.00
FRAMPTON COMES ALIVE	A&M (S) SP 3703	3.50	5.25	7.00
FRAMPTON'S CAMEL	A&M (S) SP 4389	2.50	3.75	5.00
I'M IN YOU	A&M (S) SP 4704	2.50	3.75	5.00
I'M IN YOU	A&M (S) 4704	20.00	30.00	40.00
(This is a special promotional disc A&M had made to give to the various companies that have helped them become successful. The record is made of clear vinyl, with a picture of Peter Frampton pressed in the plastic. The "picture record" came in a clear plastic bag which had a sticker on it saying, "From your friends at A&M.")				
SOMETHIN'S HAPPENING	A&M (S) SP 3619	2.50	3.75	5.00
WIND OF CHANGE	A&M (S) SP 4348	2.50	3.75	5.00

FRANCIS, Connie

TITLE	LABEL & NO.	GOOD	VERY GOOD	NEAR MINT
AWARD WINNING MOTION PICTURE HITS	MGM (M) E 4048	3.00	4.50	6.00
AWARD WINNING MOTION PICTURE HITS	MGM (S) SE-4048	3.00	4.50	6.00
BRYLCREAM PRESENTS SING ALONG WITH CONNIE FRANCIS	Mati-Mor (M) 8002	3.00	4.50	6.00
CHRISTMAS IN MY HEART	MGM (M) E3792	4.00	6.00	8.00
CHRISTMAS IN MY HEART	MGM (S) SE3792	4.00	6.00	8.00
CONNIE & CLYDE	MGM (S) SE-4573	2.50	3.75	5.00
CONNIE FRANCIS	MGM (EP) X 1599	1.50	2.25	3.00
CONNIE FRANCIS	MGM (EP) X1687	1.50	2.25	3.00
CONNIE FRANCIS	MGM (EP) X1703	1.50	2.25	3.00
CONNIE FRANCIS	Metro (M) M-519	2.00	3.00	4.00
CONNIE FRANCIS	Metro (S) MS-519	2.00	3.00	4.00
CONNIE FRANCIS AT THE COPA	MGM (M) E3913	2.50	3.25	5.00
CONNIE FRANCIS AT THE COPA	MGM (S) SE3913	2.50	3.25	5.00
CONNIE FRANCIS MORE ITALIAN FAVORITES	MGM (M) E3871	2.50	3.75	5.00
CONNIE FRANCIS MORE ITALIAN FAVORITES	MGM (S) SE3871	2.50	3.75	5.00
CONNIE FRANCIS SINGS	MGM (M) E-4049	3.00	4.50	6.00
CONNIE FRANCIS SINGS	MGM (S) SE-4049	3.00	4.50	6.00
CONNIE FRANCIS SINGS FOLK SONG FAVORITES	MGM (M) E3969	2.50	3.75	5.00
CONNIE FRANCIS SINGS FOLK SONG FAVORITES	MGM (S) SE3969	2.50	3.75	5.00
CONNIE FRANCIS SINGS FOR MAMA	MGM (M) E-4294	2.50	3.75	5.00
CONNIE FRANCIS SINGS FOR MAMA	MGM (S) SE-4294	2.50	3.75	5.00
CONNIE FRANCIS SINGS JEWISH FAVORITES	MGM (M) E 3869	3.00	4.50	6.00
CONNIE FRANCIS SINGS JEWISH FAVORITES	MGM (S) SE 3869	3.00	4.50	6.00
CONNIE FRANCIS SINGS "NEVER ON SUNDAY"	MGM (M) E 3965	3.00	4.50	6.00
CONNIE FRANCIS SINGS "NEVER ON SUNDAY"	MGM (S) SE 3965	3.00	4.50	6.00
CONNIE FRANCIS SINGS ROCK 'N ROLL MILLION SELLERS	MGM (M) E 3794	4.00	6.00	8.00
CONNIE FRANCIS SINGS ROCK 'N ROLL MILLION SELLERS	MGM (S) SE 3794	4.00	6.00	8.00
CONNIE FRANCIS SINGS SPANISH & LATIN AMERICAN FAVORITES	MGM (M) E 3853	3.00	4.50	6.00
CONNIE FRANCIS SINGS SPANISH & LATIN AMERICAN FAVORITES	MGM (S) SE 3853	3.00	4.50	6.00
CONNIE'S GREATEST HITS	MGM (M) E3793	4.00	6.00	8.00
CONNIE'S GREATEST HITS	MGM (EP) X1688	1.50	2.25	3.00
CONNIE'S GREATEST HITS	MGM (EP) X1689	1.50	2.25	3.00
CONNIE'S GREATEST HITS	MGM (EP) X1690	1.50	2.25	3.00
COUNTRY & WESTERN GOLDEN HITS	MGM (M) E3795	3.00	4.50	6.00
COUNTRY & WESTERN GOLDEN HITS	MGM (S) SE3795	3.00	4.50	6.00
COUNTRY & WESTERN GOLDEN HITS	MGM (EP) X 1694	1.50	2.25	3.00
COUNTRY & WESTERN GOLDEN HITS	MGM (EP) X 1695	1.50	2.25	3.00
COUNTRY & WESTERN GOLDEN HITS	MGM (EP) X 1696	1.50	2.25	3.00
COUNTRY MUSIC CONNIE STYLE	MGM (M) E-4079	3.00	4.50	6.00
COUNTRY MUSIC CONNIE STYLE	MGM (S) SE-4079	3.00	4.50	6.00
DO THE TWIST WITH CONNIE FRANCIS	MGM (M) E4022	2.50	3.75	5.00
DO THE TWIST WITH CONNIE FRANCIS	MGM (S) SE4022	2.50	3.75	5.00
EXCITING CONNIE FRANCIS	MGM (M) E3761	2.50	3.75	5.00
EXCITING CONNIE FRANCIS	MGM (S) SE3761	2.50	3.75	5.00
EXCITING CONNIE FRANCIS	MGM (EP) X1663	1.50	2.25	3.00
EXCITING CONNIE FRANCIS	MGM (EP) X1664	1.50	2.25	3.00
EXCITING CONNIE FRANCIS	MGM (EP) X1665	1.50	2.25	3.00
FOLLOW THE BOYS	MGM (M) E-4123	2.50	3.75	5.00
FOLLOW THE BOYS	MGM (S) SE-4123	3.00	4.50	6.00
GREATEST AMERICAN WALTZES	MGM (M) E-4145	3.00	4.50	6.00
GREATEST AMERICAN WALTZES	MGM (S) SE-4145	3.00	4.50	6.00
HAPPINESS	MGM (M) E-4472	2.50	3.75	5.00
HAPPINESS	MGM (S) SE-4472	2.50	3.75	5.00
HAWAII CONNIE	MGM (S) SE-4522	3.00	4.50	6.00
IF I DIDN'T CARE	MGM (EP) X1662	1.50	2.25	3.00
INCOMPARABLE CONNIE FRANCIS	Metro (M) M-603	2.00	3.00	4.00
INCOMPARABLE CONNIE FRANCIS	Metro (S) MS-603	2.00	3.00	4.00
IN THE SUMMER OF HIS YEARS	MGM (M) E-4210	2.50	3.75	5.00
IN THE SUMMER OF HIS YEARS	MGM (S) SE-4210	2.50	3.75	5.00
ITALIAN FAVORITES	MGM (M) E3791	2.50	3.75	5.00
ITALIAN FAVORITES	MGM (S) SE3791	2.50	3.75	5.00
LIVE AT THE SAHARA IN LAS VEGAS	MGM (M) E-4411	2.50	3.75	5.00
LIVE AT THE SAHARA IN LAS VEGAS	MGM (S) SE-4411	2.50	3.75	5.00
LOOKING FOR LOVE	MGM (M) E-4229	2.50	3.75	5.00
LOOKING FOR LOVE	MGM (S) SE-4229	2.50	3.75	5.00
LOVE ITALIAN STYLE	MGM (M) E-4448	2.50	3.75	5.00
LOVE ITALIAN STYLE	MGM (S) SE-4448	2.50	3.75	5.00
MALA FEMMENA (EVIL WOMAN)	MGM (M) E-4161	3.00	4.50	6.00
MALA FEMMENA (EVIL WOMAN)	MGM (S) SE-4161	3.00	4.50	6.00
MODERN ITALIAN HITS	MGM (M) E-4102	3.00	4.50	6.00
MODERN ITALIAN HITS	MGM (S) SE-4102	3.00	4.50	6.00
MORE GREATEST HITS	MGM (M) E3942	3.00	4.50	6.00
MORE GREATEST HITS	MGM (S) SE3942	3.00	4.50	6.00
MOVIE GREATS OF THE 60'S	MGM (M) E-4382	2.50	3.75	5.00
MOVIE GREATS OF THE 60'S	MGM (S) SE-4382	2.50	3.75	5.00
MY HAPPINESS	MGM (EP) X1655	1.50	2.25	3.00
MY HEART CRIES FOR YOU	MGM (M) E-4487	2.50	3.75	5.00
MY HEART CRIES FOR YOU	MGM (S) SE-4487	2.50	3.75	5.00

(M) Mono   (S) Stereo   (EP) Extended Play   (Q) Quad   (RI) Re-issued

Connie Francis Sings Folk Song Favorites

TITLE	LABEL & NO.	GOOD	VERY GOOD	NEAR MINT
MY THANKS TO YOU	MGM (M) E 3776	4.00	6.00	8.00
MY THANKS TO YOU	MGM (S) SE 3776	4.00	6.00	8.00
A NEW KIND OF CONNIE	MGM (M) E-4253	2.50	3.75	5.00
A NEW KIND OF CONNIE	MGM (S) SE-4253	2.50	3.75	5.00
ROCK 'N ROLL MILLION SELLERS	MGM (EP) X 1691	1.50	2.25	3.00
ROCK 'N ROLL MILLION SELLERS	MGM (EP) X1692	1.50	2.25	3.00
ROCK 'N ROLL MILLION SELLERS	MGM (EP) X1693	1.50	2.25	3.00
SINGS BACHARACH AND DAVID	MGM (S) SE-4585	2.50	3.75	5.00
SINGS GERMAN FAVORITES	MGM (M) E-4124	3.00	4.50	6.00
SINGS GERMAN FAVORITES	MGM (S) SE-4124	3.00	4.50	6.00
SINGS THE ALL TIME INTERNATIONAL HITS	MGM (M) E-4298	2.50	3.75	5.00
SINGS THE ALL TIME INTERNATIONAL HITS	MGM (S) SE-4298	2.50	3.75	5.00
SONGS TO A SWINGIN BAND	MGM (M) E3893	2.50	3.75	5.00
SONGS TO A SWINGIN BAND	MGM (S) SE3893	2.50	3.75	5.00
VERY BEST OF CONNIE FRANCIS	MGM (M) E-4167	3.00	4.50	6.00
VERY BEST OF CONNIE FRANCIS	MGM (S) SE-4167	3.00	4.50	6.00
WEDDING CAKE	MGM (S) SE-4637	2.50	3.75	5.00
WHO'S SORRY NOW	MGM (M) E3686	3.00	6.00	9.00
WHO'S SORRY NOW	MGM (EP) X1603	1.50	2.25	3.00
WHO'S SORRY NOW	MGM (EP) X1604	1.50	2.25	3.00
WHO'S SORRY NOW	MGM (EP) X1605	1.50	2.25	3.00

FRANKLIN, Aretha

TITLE	LABEL & NO.	GOOD	VERY GOOD	NEAR MINT
ARETHA	Columbia (M) CL1612	4.00	6.00	8.00
ARETHA	Columbia (S) CS8402	5.00	7.50	10.00
ARETHA FRANKLIN'S GREATEST HITS	Columbia (S) CS9601	3.00	4.50	6.00
ARETHA IN PARIS	Atlantic (S) 8207	2.50	3.75	5.00
ARETHA LIVE AT FILLMORE WEST	Atlantic (S) SD7205	2.50	3.75	5.00
ARETHA NOW	Atlantic (S) 8186	2.50	3.75	5.00
BEST OF ARETHA FRANKLIN	Atlantic (S) SD8305	2.50	3.75	5.00
ELECTRIFYING ARETHA FRANKLIN	Columbia (M) CL1761	3.00	4.50	6.00
ELECTRIFYING ARETHA FRANKLIN	Columbia (S) CS8561	4.00	6.00	8.00
FIRST TWELVE SIDES	Columbia (S) KC31953	2.50	3.75	5.00
GREATEST HITS VOLUME 2	Columbia (S) 9601	2.50	3.75	5.00
HEY, NOW, HEY	Atlantic (S) 7265	2.50	3.75	5.00
LADY SOUL	Atlantic (M) 8176	2.50	3.75	5.00
LADY SOUL	Atlantic (S) 8176	3.00	4.50	6.00
LAUGHING ON THE OUTSIDE	Columbia (M) CL2079	3.00	4.50	6.00
LAUGHING ON THE OUTSIDE	Columbia (S) CS8879	4.00	6.00	8.00
LET ME IN YOUR LIFE	Atlantic (S) 7292	2.50	3.75	5.00
QUEEN OF SOUL	Harmony (S) 11274	2.25	3.50	4.25
RUNNIN' OUT OF FOOLS				
TAKE IT LIKE YOU GIVE IT	Columbia (S) GP4	2.00	3.00	4.00
SOFT AND BEAUTIFUL	Columbia (S) 9776	2.50	3.75	5.00
SONGS OF FAITH	Checker (M) 10009	5.00	7.50	10.00
SOUL SISTER	Columbia (M) CL2521	3.00	4.50	6.00
SOUL SISTER	Columbia (S) CS9321	4.00	6.00	8.00
TENDER, MOVING SWINGING ARETHA FRANKLIN	Columbia (M) CL1876	3.00	4.50	6.00
TENDER, MOVING SWINGING ARETHA FRANKLIN	Columbia (S) CS8676	4.00	6.00	8.00
WITH EVERYTHING I FEEL IN ME	Atlantic (S) 18116	2.50	3.75	5.00
YEAH	Columbia (M) CL2351	3.00	4.50	6.00
YEAH	Columbia (S) CS9151	4.00	6.00	8.00
YOU	Atlantic (S) 18151	2.50	3.75	5.00
YOUNG, GIFTED & BLACK	Atlantic (S) 7213	2.50	3.75	5.00

FRANKLIN, Carolyn

TITLE	LABEL & NO.	GOOD	VERY GOOD	NEAR MINT
CHAIN REACTION	RCA (S) LSP4317	3.00	4.50	6.00

FRANKLIN, Erma

TITLE	LABEL & NO.	GOOD	VERY GOOD	NEAR MINT
HER NAME IS ERMA	Epic (M) LN3824	5.00	7.50	10.00
HER NAME IS ERMA	Epic (S) BN619	6.00	9.00	12.00

FRANTIC

TITLE	LABEL & NO.	GOOD	VERY GOOD	NEAR MINT
FRANTIC	Lizard (S) A20103	3.00	4.50	6.00

FRATERNITY OF MAN

TITLE	LABEL & NO.	GOOD	VERY GOOD	NEAR MINT
FRATERNITY OF MAN	ABC (S) ABCS647	3.50	5.25	7.00
GET IT ON	Dot (S) DLP25955	4.00	6.00	8.00

FREAK SCENE

TITLE	LABEL & NO.	GOOD	VERY GOOD	NEAR MINT
PSYCHEDELIC SOUL	Columbia (M) CL2556	2.00	3.00	4.00
PSYCHEDELIC SOUL	Columbia (S) CS9356	2.50	3.75	5.00

(M) Mono (S) Stereo (EP) Extended Play (Q) Quad (RI) Re-issued

FREBERG, Stan

TITLE	LABEL & NO.	GOOD	VERY GOOD	NEAR MINT
ANY REQUESTS	Capitol (EP) EAP1496	2.00	5.00	8.00
BEST OF STAN FREBERG	Capitol (M) T2020	6.00	15.00	24.00
BEST OF STAN FREBERG SHOWS	Capitol (M) WBO1035	6.00	15.00	24.00
A CHILD'S GARDEN OF FREBERG	Capitol (M) T777	6.00	15.00	24.00
FACE THE FUNNIES	Capitol (M) T1694	6.00	15.00	24.00
FREBERG UNDERGROUND SHOW #1	Capitol (M) T2551	5.00	12.50	20.00
FREBERG UNDERGROUND SHOW #1	Capitol (S) ST2551	6.00	15.00	24.00
FREBERG UNDERGROUND SHOW NO. 1 (RI)	Capitol (S) SM-2551	2.50	3.75	5.00
MADISON AVENUE WEREWOLF	Capitol (M) T 1816	6.00	15.00	24.00
MICKEY MOUSE'S BIRTHDAY PARTY	Capitol (M) J3264	5.00	12.50	20.00
OMAHA	Capitol (EP) EAP11101	2.00	5.00	8.00
REAL SAINT GEORGE	Capitol (EP) EAP1628	2.00	5.00	8.00
STAN FREBERG	Capitol (M) MA11589	6.00	15.00	24.00
STAN FREBERG PRESENTS THE UNITED STATES OF AMERICA, Vol. 2	Capitol (M) W 1573	4.00	10.00	16.00
STAN FREBERG PRESENTS THE UNITED STATES OF AMERICA, Vol. 2	Capitol (S) SW1573	5.00	12.50	20.00
STAN FREBERG WITH THE ORIGINAL CAST	Capitol (M) T1242	4.00	10.00	16.00
STAN FREBERG WITH THE ORIGINAL CAST	Capitol (S) SM1242	5.00	12.50	20.00

FRED, John & His Playboy Band

TITLE	LABEL & NO.	GOOD	VERY GOOD	NEAR MINT
AGNES ENGLISH (Original Title)	Paula (M) LP2197	5.00	7.50	10.00
AGNES ENGLISH (Original Title)	Paula (S) LPS 2197	6.00	9.00	12.00
JOHN FRED AND HIS PLAYBOYS	Paula (M) LP2191	6.00	9.00	12.00
JOHN FRED AND HIS PLAYBOYS	Paula (S) LPS2191	7.00	10.50	14.00
JUDY IN DISGUISE WITH GLASSES	Paula (M) LP2197	4.00	6.00	8.00
JUDY IN DISGUISE WITH GLASSES	Paula (S) LPS2197	5.00	7.50	10.00
LOVE IN MY SOUL	Uni (S) 73077	3.00	4.50	6.00
PERMANENTLY STATED	Paula (M) LPS2201	6.00	9.00	12.00
PERMANENTLY STATED	Paula (S) LPS 2201	6.00	9.00	12.00
34:40 OF JOHN FRED AND HIS PLAYBOYS	Paula (M) LP2193	5.00	7.50	10.00
34:40 OF JOHN FRED AND HIS PLAYBOYS	Paula (S) LPS2193	6.00	9.00	12.00

FREDDIE & The Dreamers

TITLE	LABEL & NO.	GOOD	VERY GOOD	NEAR MINT
DO THE FREDDIE	Mercury (M) MG21026	3.00	4.50	6.00
DO THE FREDDIE	Mercury (S) SR61026	4.00	6.00	8.00
FRANTIC FREDDIE	Mercury (M) MG21053	3.50	5.25	7.00
FRANTIC FREDDIE	Mercury (S) SR 61053	4.50	6.75	9.00
FREDDY AND THE DREAMERS	Mercury (M) MG21017	3.00	4.50	6.00
FREDDY AND THE DREAMERS	Mercury (S) SR 61017	4.00	6.00	8.00
FUN LOVIN FREDDIE	Mercury (M) MG21061	4.00	6.00	8.00
FUN LOVIN FREDDIE	Mercury (S) SR61061	5.00	7.50	10.00
I'M TELLING YOU NOW	Tower (M) T 5003	5.00	7.50	10.00
SEASIDE SWINGERS	Mercury (M) MG21031	3.50	5.25	7.00
SEASIDE SWINGERS	Mercury (S) SR61031	4.50	6.75	9.00

(M) Mono (S) Stereo (EP) Extended Play (Q) Quad (RI) Re-issued

TITLE	LABEL & NO.	GOOD	VERY GOOD	NEAR MINT
FUGS				
BELLE OF AVENUE A	Reprise (S) 6359	2.50	3.75	5.00
FUGS	Esp (S) 1028	3.00	4.50	6.00
FUGS FIRST ALBUM	Broadside (S) 304	5.00	7.50	10.00
FUGS FIRST ALBUM	Esp (S) 1018	3.50	5.00	7.00
(Reissue of Broadside 304)				
FUGS 4, ROUNDERS SCORE	Esp (S) 2018	3.00	4.50	6.00
IT CRAWLED INTO MY HAND, HONEST	Reprise (S) RS 6305	2.50	3.75	5.00
TENDERNESS JUNCTION	Reprise (S) 6280	2.50	3.75	5.00
VIRGIN FUGS: FOR ADULT MINDS ONLY	Esp (S) 1038	3.00	4.50	6.00

TITLE	LABEL & NO.	GOOD	VERY GOOD	NEAR MINT
FULLER, Bobby, Four				
CIVIL DEFENSE LP	Unknown	20.00	40.00	60.00
I FOUGHT THE LAW	Mustang (M) 901	5.00	7.50	10.00
I FOUGHT THE LAW	Mustang (S) MS 901	6.00	9.00	12.00
KRLA KING OF THE WHEELS	Mustang (M) 900	5.00	10.00	15.00
FULLER, Jerry				
TEENAGE LOVE	Lin (M) LP100	6.00	15.00	24.00
FULLER, Jesse				
BROTHER LOWDOWN	Fantasy (S) 24707	2.50	3.75	5.00
FULSOM, Lowell				
EVERYDAY I HAVE THE BLUES	Nashville (M) 2030	5.00	10.00	15.00
HUNG DOWN HEAD	Chess (M) 408	5.00	10.00	15.00
LOWELL FULSOM	Kent (M) 5016	2.50	4.00	5.00
LOWELL FULSOM	Kent (M) 5020	2.50	4.00	5.00
LOWELL FULSON	Arhoolie (M) R-2003	3.50	5.25	7.00
(Early recordings)				
NOW	Kent (S) KST531	3.50	5.25	7.00
TRAMP	Kent (S) KST520	4.00	6.00	8.00
FUMBLE				
FUMBLE	Sovereign (S) ST11125	3.00	4.50	6.00
POETRY IN MOTION	RCA (M) LPL15082	3.00	4.50	6.00
FUREY, Lewis				
HUMOURS OF LEWIS FUREY	A&M (S) SP 4594	2.00	3.00	4.00
LEWIS FUREY	A&M (S) SP 4522	2.00	3.00	4.00
FUSE				
FUSE	Epic (M) BN26502	3.00	4.50	6.00
FUZZ				
FUZZ	Calla (S) SD2001	3.00	4.50	6.00

G

TITLE	LABEL & NO.	GOOD	VERY GOOD	NEAR MINT
GABLES				
SNAKE DANCE	Unicrown	8.00	12.00	16.00
GAINSBOROUGH GALLERY				
LIFE IS A SONG	Evolution (S) 2012	2.50	3.75	5.00
GALE, Sunny				
IF I COULD BE WITH YOU	RCA (EP) EPA 600	1.00	1.50	2.00
SUNNY AND BLUE	RCA (M) LPM 1277	2.50	3.75	5.00
SUNNY GALE SINGS	King (EP) EP370	1.00	1.50	2.00
GALLAGHER AND LYLE				
BENNY GALLAGHER AND				
GRAHAM LYLE	Capitol (S) ST 11016	2.50	3.75	5.00
BREAKAWAY	A&M (S) SP 4566	2.00	3.00	4.00
GALLAGHER & LYLE (77 RI)	Capitol SM-11016	2.00	3.00	4.00
LAST COWBOY	A&M (S) SP 3665	2.00	3.00	4.00
LOVE ON THE AIRWAVES	A&M (S) SP 4620	2.00	3.00	4.00
SEEDS	A&M (S) SP 4425	2.50	3.75	5.00
SEEDS (RI)	A&M (S) SP 3605	2.00	3.00	4.00
SHOWDOWN	A&M (S) SP 4679	2.00	3.00	4.00
WILLIE & THE LAPDOG	A&M (S) SP 4384	2.00	3.00	4.00
GALLAGHER, Rory				
AGAINST THE GRAIN	Chrysalis (S) 1098	2.00	3.00	4.00
BLUEPRINT	Polydor (S) 24-5522	2.50	3.75	5.00
SINNER	Polydor (S) 6510	2.50	3.75	5.00
TATOO	Polydor (S) 24-5539	2.50	3.75	5.00
GAME				
GAME	Faithful Virtue (S) FVS 2003	2.50	3.75	5.00
LONG HOT SUMMER	Evolution (S) 3008	2.50	3.75	5.00
GANT, Cecil				
INCOMPARABLE CECIL GANT	Sound (M) 601	11.00	27.50	44.00

TITLE	LABEL & NO.	GOOD	VERY GOOD	NEAR MINT
GANTRY, Elmer and Velvet Opera				
ELMER GANTRY'S VELVET OPERA	Epic (S) BN 26415	5.00	7.50	10.00
GANTS				
GANTS AGAIN	Liberty (M) LRP 3473	4.00	6.00	8.00
GANTS AGAIN	Liberty (S) LST 7473	5.00	7.50	10.00
GANTS GALORE	Liberty (M) LRP 3455	4.00	6.00	8.00
GANTS GALORE	Liberty (S) LST 7455	5.00	7.50	10.00
ROAD RUNNER	Liberty (M) LRP 3432	5.00	7.50	10.00
ROAD RUNNER	Liberty (S) LST 7432	6.00	9.00	12.00

(M) Mono (S) Stereo (EP) Extended Play (Q) Quad (RI) Re-issued

TITLE	LABEL & NO.	GOOD	VERY GOOD	NEAR MINT

GARDNER, Don and Dee Dee Ford
THE DON GARDNER AND DEE DEE FORD

IN SWEDEN	Sue (M) LP 1044	4.00	8.00	12.00
NEED YOUR LOVIN	Fire (M)	6.00	12.00	18.00

GARFUNKEL, Art

ANGEL CLARE	Columbia KC-31474	2.00	3.00	4.00
ANGEL CLARE	Columbia (Q) CQ-31474	2.50	3.75	5.00
BREAKAWAY	Columbia PC 33700	2.00	3.00	4.00
BREAKAWAY	Columbia (Q) PCQ 33700	2.50	3.75	5.00
WATERMARK	Columbia (S) JC 34975	2.00	3.00	4.00

GARLAND, Judy

BEST OF JUDY GARLAND	MCA (S) 2-4003	3.00	4.50	6.00
BEST OF JUDY GARLAND	Decca (M) DXB 172	5.00	7.50	10.00
BEST OF JUDY GARLAND	Decca (SE) DXSB 7172	4.00	6.00	8.00
GARLAND AT THE GROVE	Capitol (M) T 1118	5.00	10.00	15.00
GARLAND AT THE GROVE	Capitol (S) ST 1118	6.00	12.00	18.00
GARLAND TOUCH	Capitol (M) W 1710	5.00	10.00	15.00
GARLAND TOUCH	Capitol (S) SW 1710	6.00	12.00	18.00
HITS OF JUDY GARLAND	Capitol (M) 1999	4.00	6.00	8.00
HITS OF JUDY GARLAND	Capitol (S) 1999	5.00	7.50	10.00
JUDY	Capitol (M) T 734	6.00	15.00	24.00
JUDY AT CARNEGIE HALL	Capitol (M) WBO 1569	5.00	10.00	15.00
JUDY AT CARNEGIE HALL	Capitol (S) SWBO 1569	6.00	12.00	18.00
JUDY GARLAND AT HOME AT THE PALACE	ABC (M) 620	3.50	5.25	7.00
JUDY GARLAND AT HOME AT THE PALACE	ABC (S) 620	4.00	6.00	8.00
JUDY GARLAND'S GREATEST HITS	Decca (S) DL 75150	3.00	4.50	6.00
JUDY IN LOVE	Capitol (M) T 1036	5.00	10.00	15.00
JUDY IN LOVE	Capitol (S) 1036	6.00	12.00	18.00
LETTER, THE (WITH JOHN IRELAND)	Capitol (M) TAO 1188	5.00	10.00	15.00
LETTER, THE (WITH JOHN IRELAND)	Capitol (S) STAO 1188	6.00	12.00	18.00
"LIVE" AT THE LONDON PALLADIUM (WITH LIZA MINNELLI)	Capitol (M) T 2295	7.50	11.25	15.00
"LIVE" AT THE LONDON PALLADIUM (WITH LIZA MINNELLI)	Capitol (S) ST 2295	8.00	12.00	16.00
MISS SHOW BUSINESS	Capitol (M) T 676	6.00	15.00	24.00

GARNETT, Gale

AN AUDIENCE WITH THE KING OF WANDS (With the Gentle Reign)	Columbia (S) CS 9625	6.00	9.00	12.00
GALE GARNETT, NEW ADVENTURES	RCA (M) LPM 3586	4.00	6.00	8.00
GALE GARNETT, NEW ADVENTURES	RCA (S) LSP 3586	5.00	7.50	10.00
LOVIN PLACE	RCA (M) LPM3305	4.00	6.00	8.00
LOVIN PLACE	RCA (S) LSP 3305	5.00	7.50	10.00
MANY FACES OF GALE GARNETT	RCA (M) LPM3325	4.00	6.00	8.00
MANY FACES OF GALE GARNETT	RCA (S) LSP2833	5.00	7.50	10.00
MY KIND OF FOLK SONGS	RCA (M) LPM2833	4.00	6.00	8.00
MY KIND OF FOLK SONGS	RCA (S) LSP2833	5.00	7.50	10.00
SINGS ABOUT FLYING & RAINBOWS & LOVE & OTHER GROOVY THINGS	RCA (S) LPM-3747	5.00	7.50	10.00
VARIETY IS THE SPICE OF GALE GARNETT	RCA (M) LPM3498	4.00	6.00	8.00
VARIETY IS THE SPICE OF GALE GARNETT	RCA (S) LSP3498	5.00	7.50	10.00

GARRISON, Glen

IF I LIVED HERE	Imperial (S) 12378	2.00	3.00	4.00

GARVIA, Rex and The Mighty Cravers

RAW FUNKY EARTH	Tower (S) ST 5130	2.00	3.00	4.00

GATES, David

DAVID GATES SONGBOOK	Elektra (S) 8E-6002	3.00	4.50	6.00
FIRST	Elektra (S) EKS 75066	3.00	4.50	6.00
FIRST	Elektra (Q) EQ-5066	2.50	3.75	5.00
NEVER LET HER GO	Elektra (S) 7E-1028	2.50	3.75	5.00
Also see BREAD

GATES, Hen and His Gaters

LET'S GO DANCING TO ROCK AND ROLL	Masterseal (M) M700	4.00	10.00	16.00

GAUCHOS

GAUCHOS FEATURING JIM DOVAL	ABC-Paramount (S) ABCS 506	3.50	5.25	7.00

GAYE, Marvin

ANTHOLOGY	Motown (S) 791	4.00	6.00	8.00
GREATEST HITS, VOL. 2	Tamla (S) 278	3.50	5.25	7.00
HELLO BROADWAY, THIS IS MARVIN	Tamla (S) 259	4.00	6.00	8.00
HOW SWEET IT IS TO BE LOVED BY YOU	Tamla (S) 258	4.00	6.00	8.00
I HEARD IT THROUGH THE GRAPEVINE	Tamla (S) 285	3.00	4.50	6.00
IN THE GROOVE (Original Title)	Tamla (S) 285	3.00	4.50	6.00
LET'S GET IT ON	Tamla (S) 329	2.50	3.75	5.00
MARVIN AND MARY TOGETHER (With Mary Wells)	Motown (S) 613	4.00	6.00	8.00
MARVIN GAYE AND KIM WESTON (With Kim Weston)	Tamla (S) 270	4.00	6.00	8.00
MARVIN GAYE LIVE	Tamla (S) 333	2.50	3.75	5.00
MARVIN GAYE ON STAGE	Tamla (S) 242	5.00	7.50	10.00
MARVIN GAYE'S GREATEST HITS	Tamla (S) 252	4.00	6.00	8.00
MOODS OF MARVIN GAYE	Tamla (S) 266	4.00	6.00	8.00

TITLE	LABEL & NO.	GOOD	VERY GOOD	NEAR MINT
SOULFUL MOODS OF MARVIN GAYE	Tamla (S) 221	6.00	8.00	12.00
THAT STUBBORN KINDA FELLOW	Tamla (S) 239	5.00	7.50	10.00
THAT'S THE WAY LOVE IS	Tamla (S) TS 299	3.00	4.50	6.00
WHEN I'M ALONE I CRY	Tamla (S) 251	5.00	7.50	10.00
YOU'RE ALL I NEED (With Tammi Terrell)	Tamla (S) 284	4.00	6.00	8.00

GAYLORDS

GAYLORDS	Mercury (EP) EP1-3235	1.50	2.25	3.00
GAYLORDS BY REQUEST (10")	Mercury (M) MG 25198	3.00	4.00	6.00
GAYLORDS BY REQUEST	Mercury (EP) 1-3263	1.50	2.25	3.00
GAYLORDS BY REQUEST	Mercury (EP) 1-3264	1.50	2.25	3.00
GAYLORDS SING AMERICAN HITS IN ITALIAN	Mercury (M) MG20620	2.50	3.75	5.00
GAYLORDS SING AMERICAN HITS IN ITALIAN	Mercury (S) SR60620	2.50	3.75	5.00
GAYLORDS SING WITHOUT A SONG	Mercury (EP) 1-3264	1.50	2.25	3.00
ITALIA	Mercury (M) MG 20186	4.00	6.00	8.00
LET'S HAVE A PIZZA PARTY	Mercury (M) MG 20356	3.00	4.00	6.00
LET'S HAVE A PIZZA PARTY	Mercury (S) SR60075	3.00	4.00	6.00
PAJAMA GAME	Mercury (EP) EP1-3235	1.50	2.25	3.00
PAJAMA GAME	Mercury (EP) 2-3255	1.50	2.25	3.00
SINGING SPELL	Mercury (EP) 1-3190	1.50	2.25	3.00
STRINGS OF MY HEART	Mercury (EP) EP1-3210	1.50	2.25	3.00
TOPS IN POPS	Mercury (EP) EP1-3288	1.00	2.00	3.00
TOPS IN POPS	Mercury (EP) 1-4004	1.00	2.00	3.00
TOPS IN POPS	Mercury (EP) 1-4010	1.00	2.00	3.00
TOPS IN POPS	Mercury (EP) 1-4012	1.00	2.00	3.00

GEDDES, David

RUN JOEY RUN	Big Tree (S) 89511	3.00	4.50	6.00

GEILS, J., Band

BLOODSHOT	Atlantic (S) 7260	3.00	4.50	6.00
BLOODSHOT	Atlantic (Q) QD-7260	2.50	3.75	5.00
FULL HOUSE	Atlantic (S) 7241	3.00	4.50	6.00
HOTLINE	Atlantic (S) 18147	2.50	3.75	5.00
J. GEILS BAND	Atlantic (S) SD 8275	3.00	4.50	6.00
MORNING AFTER	Atlantic (S) SD 8297	3.00	4.50	6.00
NIGHTMARES	Atlantic (S) 18107	2.50	3.75	5.00
NIGHTMARES	Atlantic (Q) QD-18107	2.50	3.75	5.00

(M) Mono   (S) Stereo   (EP) Extended Play   (Q) Quad   (RI) Re-issued

GENE AND EUNICE

HEAR AND NOW	TRX (S) TRXLPS 1001	3.00	4.50	6.00
ROCK AND ROLL SOCK HOP	Score (M) LP 4018	16.00	40.00	64.00

GENESIS

FROM GENSIS TO REVELATION	London (S) 643	3.00	4.50	6.00
IN THE BEGINNING	Mercury (S) SR 61175	3.00	4.50	6.00
TRESPASS	Impulse (S) AS9205	2.50	3.75	5.00

GENTLE GIANT

FREE HAND	Capitol (S) ST-11428	2.00	3.00	4.00
OCTOPUS	Columbia (S) KC-32022	2.50	3.75	5.00
POWER & THE GLORY	Capitol (S) ST-11337	2.00	3.00	4.00
THREE FRIENDS	Columbia (S) 31649	2.50	3.75	5.00

GENTLE SOUL

GENTLE SOUL	Epic (S) BN 26374	3.00	4.50	6.00

GENTRYS

GENTRYS	Sun (M) 117	2.50	3.75	5.00
GOLDEN ARCHIVE SERIES	MGM (S) GAS 127	2.00	3.00	4.00
KEEP ON DANCING	MGM (M) E 4336	2.50	3.75	5.00
KEEP ON DANCING	MGM (S) SE 4336	3.50	5.25	7.00
TIME	MGM (M) 4346	2.50	3.75	5.00
TIME	MGM (S) SE 4346	3.50	5.25	7.00

GEORGE AND TEDDY

EVERY NIGHT AT THE CONDOR	Mammoth (M) MA1011	3.00	4.50	6.00

GEORGE, Barbara

I KNOW (YOU DON'T LOVE ME ANYMORE)	AFO (M) 5001	6.00	12.00	18.00

GERDES, George

OBITUARY	United Artists (S) UAS 5549	2.50	3.75	5.00
SON OF OBITUARY	United Artists (S) UAS 5593	2.50	3.75	5.00

GERRY AND THE PACEMAKERS

DON'T LET THE SUN CATCH YOU CRYING	Laurie (M) LLP 2024	4.00	8.00	12.00
FERRY ACROSS THE MERSEY (Soundtrack)	United Artists (M) UAL 3387	3.00	4.50	6.00
FERRY ACROSS THE MERSEY (Soundtrack)	United Artists (M) T90812	4.00	6.00	8.00
GIRL ON A SWING	Laurie (M) LLP 2037	4.00	8.00	12.00
GIRL ON A SWING	Laurie (S) SLP 2037	5.00	10.00	15.00
GREATEST HITS	Laurie (M) LLP 2031	4.00	8.00	12.00
GREATEST HITS	Laurie (S) SLP 2031	5.00	10.00	15.00
I'LL BE THERE	Laurie (M) LLP 2030	4.00	8.00	12.00
SECOND ALBUM	Laurie (M) LLP 2027	4.00	8.00	12.00
I'LL BE THERE	Laurie (S) SP 2030	5.00	10.00	15.00
SECOND ALBUM	Laurie (S) SLP 2027	5.00	10.00	15.00

GHOULS

DRACULA'S DEUCE	Capitol (M) T 2215	3.00	6.00	9.00
DRACULA'S DEUCE	Capitol (S) ST 2215	4.00	8.00	12.00

GIANT CRAB

COOL IT HELIOS	Uni (S) 73057	3.00	4.50	6.00
A GIANT CRAB COMES FORTH	Uni (S) 73037	3.00	4.50	6.00

GIBB, Robin

ROBIN'S REIGN	Atco (S) SD 33 323	2.50	3.75	5.00
Also see BEE GEES				

GIBBS, Georgia

AFTER YOU'VE GONE	Mercury (EP) EP1-3266	1.00	1.50	2.00
BALLIN THE JACK	Coral (M) CRL 56037	3.00	4.00	6.00
BRIDGE OF SIGHS	Mercury (EP) EP1-3214	1.00	1.50	2.00

ENCORES	Mercury (EP) EP1-3082	1.00	1.50	2.00
FOR GENTLEMEN ONLY	Mercury (EP) EP1-3130	1.00	1.50	2.00
GEORGIA GIBBS SINGS	Halo (S) 50240	2.50	3.75	5.00
GEORGIA SINGS OLDIES (10")	?Mercury (M) MG 25175	1.00	1.50	2.00
GEORGIA SINGS OLDIES	Mercury (EP) EP1-3061	1.00	1.50	2.00
HER NIBBS, MISS GEORGIA GIBBS	Mercury (EP) EP1-3062	1.00	1.50	2.00
KISS OF FIRE	Mercury (EP) EP1-3242	1.00	1.50	2.00
MAN THAT GOT AWAY (10")	Mercury (M) MG 25199	2.50	3.75	5.00
MUSIC AND MEMORIES	Mercury (M) MG 20071	2.50	3.75	5.00
SO MADLY IN LOVE	Mercury (EP) EP1-3243	1.00	1.50	2.00
SOMEBODY BAD STOLE DE WEDDING BELL	Mercury (EP) EP3226	1.00	1.50	2.00
SONG FAVORITES OF GEORGIA GIBBS	Mercury (M) MG20114	2.50	3.75	5.00
SWINGIN WITH HER NIBS	Mercury (M) MG 20170	2.50	3.75	5.00
THUNDER AND LIGHTING	Mercury (EP) EP1-3241	1.00	1.50	2.00

GIBSON, Bob and Bob Camp

BOB GIBSON AND BOB CAMP AT THE GATE OF HORN	Elektra (S) EKS 7207	3.00	4.50	6.00

GIBSON, Don

BLUE & LONESOME	RCA (EP) EPA 5114	1.00	1.50	2.00
BLUE, BLUE DAY	RCA (EP) EPA4323	1.50	2.75	3.00
DON GIBSON	Columbia (M) B 2146	1.50	2.75	3.00
I WROTE A SONG	RCA (M) LPM 2707	2.50	3.75	5.00
I WROTE A SONG	RCA (S) LPS 2707	3.00	4.50	6.00
LOOK WHO'S BLUE	RCA (M) LPM-2184	2.50	3.75	5.00
LOOK WHO'S BLUE	RCA (S) LSP-2184	3.00	4.50	6.00
NO ONE STANDS ALONE	RCA (M) LPM 1918	2.50	3.75	5.00
NO ONE STANDS ALONE	RCA (S) LPS 1918	3.00	4.50	6.00
OH LONESOME ME	RCA (M) LPM 1743	5.00	10.00	15.00
THAT GIBSON BOY	RCA (M) LPM 2038	2.50	3.75	5.00
THAT GIBSON BOY	RCA (S) LSP 2038	3.00	4.00	6.00
THAT LONESOME VALLEY	RCA (EP) EPA4335	1.00	1.50	2.00

GIBSON, Harry The Hipster

ROCKIN RHYTHM	Sutton (M) SSU 313	4.00	8.00	12.00

GIBSON, Steve & The Red Caps

BLUEBERRY HILL (10")	Mercury (M) 25116	15.00	37.50	60.00
YOU'RE DRIVING ME CRAZY (10")	Mercury (M) 25115	15.00	37.50	60.00

GILDO, Rex

REX GILDO	Capitol (M) T 10338	2.50	3.75	5.00

GILLESPIE, Dana

FOOLISH SEASONS	London (S) S540	2.50	3.75	5.00

GILLESPIE, Darlene (Ex-Mouseketeer)

DARLENE GILLESPIE	Disneyland (M)	5.00	10.00	15.00

GILLEY, Mickey

CITY LIGHTS	Playboy (S) 403	2.50	3.75	5.00
DOWN THE LINE	Paula (M) LP 2195	4.00	8.00	12.00
FLYING HIGH	Playboy (S) KZ 35099	2.00	3.00	4.00
GILLEY'S GREATEST HITS	Playboy (S) PZ 34743	2.00	3.00	4.00
LONELY WINE	Astro (S)	5.00	10.00	15.00
MICKEY GILLEY AT HIS BEST	Paula (S) LPS 2224	3.50	5.25	7.00
MICKEY'S MOVIN' ON	Playboy (S) 405	2.50	3.75	5.00
OVERNIGHT SENSATION	Playboy (S) 408	2.50	3.75	5.00
ROOM FULL OF ROSES	Playboy (S) 128	3.00	4.50	6.00

GILMER, Jimmy

BUDDY'S BUDDY (BUDDY HOLLY SONGS BY JIMMY GILMER)	Dot (M) DLP 3577	5.00	10.00	15.00
BUDDY'S BUDDY (BUDDY HOLLY SONGS BY JIMMY GILMER)	Dot (S) DLP 25577	6.00	12.00	18.00
FOLKBEAT	Dot (M) DLP 3668	3.00	6.00	9.00
FOLKBEAT	Dot (S) DLP 25668	4.00	8.00	12.00
Also see FIREBALLS				

GLACIERS

FROM SEA TO SKI	Mercury (M) MG 20895	4.00	6.00	8.00

GLAD

FEELIN GLAD	ABC (S) ABCS 655	4.50	6.75	9.00

GLAHE, Will

GERMAN SING ALONG	London (M) TW 91237	3.00	4.50	6.00
GERMAN SING ALONG	London (S) SW 99009	3.00	4.50	6.00

GLASS HARP

GLASS HARP	Decca (S) DL 75261	3.00	4.50	6.00
IT MAKES ME GLAD	Decca (S) DL7 5358	2.50	3.75	5.00
SYNERGY	Decca (S) DL 75306	2.50	3.75	5.00

GLASS HOUSE

THANKS I NEEDED THAT	Invictus (S) T9810	2.00	3.00	4.00

GLAZER, Tom and The Do-Re-Mi-Childrens Chorus

ON TOP OF SPAGHETTI	Kapp (M) KL1331	2.50	3.75	5.00
ON TOP OF SPAGHETTI	Kapp (S) KS3331	2.50	3.75	5.00

(M) Mono (S) Stereo (EP) Extended Play (Q) Quad (RI) Re-issued

GLENN, Darrell

TITLE	LABEL & NO.	GOOD	VERY GOOD	NEAR MINT
CRYING IN THE CHAPEL	NRC (M) LPA 5	2.50	3.75	5.00
CRYING IN THE CHAPEL	NRC (S) SLPA 5	2.50	3.75	5.00

GLENN, Lloyd

CHICA-BOO (RED VINYL)	Aladdin (M) 808	5.00	12.50	20.00
LLOYD GLENN (10")	Swingtime (M) 1901	17.00	42.50	68.00

GLOVER, Henry

SOFT	King (EP) EP278	2.50	6.25	10.00

GOBEL, George

'LONESOME GEORGE' GOBEL	Decca (M) DL4163	3.00	4.00	6.00
'LONESOME GEORGE' GOBEL	Decca (S) DL7 4163	3.00	4.00	6.00

GODFREY, Arthur

ARTHUR GODFREY'S GREATEST HITS	Columbia (M) CL 1580	2.50	3.75	5.00
GODFREY SPOTLITE	Columbia (EP) B 615	1.50	2.25	3.00
OL' REDHEAD, THE	Columbia (M) CL 2529	4.00	6.00	8.00
OUR COUNTRY 'TIS OF THEE	RCA (S) DEL1-0010	2.00	3.00	4.00
TV SWEETHEARTS	Columbia (M) CL 576	4.00	6.00	8.00

GODZ

CONTACT HIGH WITH THE GODZ	ESP (S) 1037	3.00	4.50	6.00
GODZ	Millennium (S) MNLP 8003	2.00	3.00	4.00
GODZ 2	ESP (S) 1047	3.00	4.50	6.00
GODZUNHEIT	ESP (S) 2017	2.50	3.75	5.00
THIRD TESTAMENT	ESP (S) 1077	3.00	4.50	6.00

GOFFIN, Gerry

IT AIN'T EXACTLY ENTERTAINMENT	Adelphi (S) 4102	2.50	3.75	5.00

GOLD, Andrew

ALL THIS AND HEAVEN TOO	Asylum (S) 6E-116	2.00	3.00	4.00
ANDREW GOLD	Asylum (S) 7E-1047	2.00	3.00	4.00

GOLDBERG, Barry

BARRY GOLDBERG	Atco (S) 7040	2.50	3.75	5.00

GOLDBERG, Barry and The Blues Band

BLASTS FROM MY PAST	Buddah (S) BDS 5081	3.50	5.25	7.00
BLOWING MY MIND	Epic (S) BN 26199	3.00	4.50	6.00

GOLDBRIARS

GOLDBRIARS	Epic (M) LN 24087	5.00	7.50	10.00
GOLDBRIARS	Epic (S) BN26087	6.00	9.00	12.00
STRAIGHT AHEAD	Epic (M) LN 24114	5.00	7.50	10.00
STRAIGHT AHEAD	Epic (S) BN 26114	6.00	9.00	12.00

GOLDEN EARRING

GOLDEN EARRING	Dwarf (M) PDLP 2000	6.00	9.00	12.00
GOLDEN EARRING	Capitol (S) ST 11315	6.00	9.00	12.00
MIRACLE MIRROR	Capitol (S) ST 164	5.00	7.50	10.00
MOONTAN (ORIG. NUDE CVR.)	Track (S) 396	5.00	7.50	10.00
MOONTAN	Track (S) 396	2.50	3.75	5.00
SWITCH	MCA (S) 2139	2.50	3.75	5.00
WINTER HARVEST	Capitol (S) ST 2823	6.00	9.00	12.00

GOLDEN GATE QUARTET

GOLDEN GATE SPIRITUALS (10")	Columbia (M) 6102	9.00	22.50	36.00
SPIRITUALS SUNG BY THE GOLDEN GATE QUARTET (10")	Mercury (M) 25063	8.00	20.00	32.00

GOLDSBORO, Bobby

BLUE AUTUMN	United Artists (M) UAL 3552	3.00	4.50	6.00
BLUE AUTUMN	United Artists (S) UAS 6552	3.50	5.25	7.00
BOBBY GOLDSBORO'S GREATEST HITS	United Artists (S) UAS 5502	3.00	4.50	6.00
BOBBY GOLDSBORO'S 10TH ANNIVERSARY ALBUM	United Artists (S) UA-LA311	3.00	4.50	6.00
BRAND NEW KIND OF LOVE	United Artists (S) UA-LA019	2.50	3.75	5.00
BROOMSTICK COWBOY	United Artists (M) UAL 3471	3.50	5.25	7.00
BROOMSTICK COWBOY	United Artists (S) UAS 6471	4.00	6.00	8.00
COME BACK HOME	United Artists (S) UAS 5516	3.00	4.50	6.00
HONEY ("PLEDGE OF LOVE" re-titled)	United Artists (M) UAL 3642	3.00	4.50	6.00
HONEY ("PLEDGE OF LOVE" re-titled)	United Artists (S) UAS 6642	3.00	4.50	6.00
I CAN'T STOP LOVING YOU	United Artists (M) UAL 3381	3.00	4.50	6.00
I CAN'T STOP LOVING YOU	United Artists (S) UAS 6381	3.50	5.25	7.00
IT'S TOO LATE	United Artists (M) UAL 3486	3.50	5.25	7.00
IT'S TOO LATE	United Artists (S) UAS 6486	4.00	6.00	8.00
LITTLE THINGS	United Artists (M) UAL 3425	3.50	5.25	7.00
LITTLE THINGS	United Artists (S) UAS 6425	4.00	6.00	8.00
MUDDY MISSISSIPPI LINE	United Artists (S) UAS 6735	3.00	4.50	6.00
PLEDGE OF LOVE	United Artists (M) UAL 3642	5.00	7.50	10.00
PLEDGE OF LOVE	United Artists (S) UAS 6642	6.00	9.00	12.00
ROMANTIC, SOULFUL, WACKY	United Artists (M) UAL 3599	3.00	4.50	6.00
ROMANTIC, SOULFUL, WACKY	United Artists (S) UAS 6599	3.50	5.25	7.00
SOLID GOLDSBORO (BOBBY GOLDSBORO'S GREATEST HITS)	United Artists (M) UAL 3561	3.00	4.50	6.00
SOLID GOLDSBORO (BOBBY GOLDSBORO'S GREATEST HITS)	United Artists (S) UAS 6561	3.50	5.25	7.00
SUMMER (THE FIRST TIME)	United Artists (S) UA-LA124	2.50	3.75	5.00

(continued)

TODAY	United Artists (S) UAS 6704	3.00	4.50	6.00
WE GOTTA START LOVIN'	United Artists (S) UAS 6777	3.00	4.50	6.00
WORD PICTURES (AUTUMN OF MY LIFE)	United Artists (S) UAS 6657	3.00	4.50	6.00

GOLDTONES

GOLDTONES FEATURING RANDY SEOL	La Brea (M) L 8011	5.00	7.50	10.00

GOLIATH

GOLIATH	ABC (S) ABCS 702	3.00	4.50	6.00

GOOD AND PLENTY

WORLD OF GOOD AND PLENTY	Senate (M) 21001	3.00	4.50	6.00

GOODGUYS

SIDEWALK SURFING	GNP-Crescendo (M) GNP2001	4.00	8.00	12.00

GOODIES

CANDY COATED GOODIES	Hip (S) 7002	6.00	9.00	12.00

GOODMAN, Dickie

FLYING SAUCERS	Chains (M) 9000	3.00	4.50	6.00
MANY HEADS OF DICKIE GOODMAN	Rori (M) 3301	5.00	12.50	20.00
MY SON THE JOKE	Comet (M) C-69	3.00	4.50	6.00

GOODNESS AND MERCY

GOODNESS AND MERCY	MGM (S) SE 4730	2.00	3.00	4.00

GOOD RATS

GOOD RATS	Kapp (S) KS 3580	4.50	6.75	9.00

GOOD, THE BAD, AND THE UGLY

GOOD, THE BAD, AND THE UGLY	Mercury (S) SR 61253	2.00	3.00	4.00

GORDIAN KNOT

GORDIAN KNOT	Verve (S) V6 5062	3.50	5.25	7.00

GORE, Lesley

ALL ABOUT LOVE	Mercury (M) MG 21066	3.00	6.00	9.00
ALL ABOUT LOVE	Mercury (S) SR 61066	4.00	8.00	12.00
BOYS, BOYS, BOYS	Mercury (M) MG 20901	4.00	8.00	12.00
BOYS, BOYS, BOYS	Mercury (S) SR60901	5.00	10.00	15.00
CALIFORNIA NIGHTS	Mercury (M) MG 21120	3.00	6.00	9.00
CALIFORNIA NIGHTS	Mercury (S) SR 61120	4.00	8.00	12.00
GIRL TALK	Mercury (M) MG 20943	4.00	8.00	12.00
GIRL TALK	Mercury (S) SR 60943	5.00	10.00	15.00
GOLDEN HITS OF LESLEY GORE	Mercury (M) MG 21024	4.00	8.00	12.00
GOLDEN HITS OF LESLEY GORE	Mercury (S) SR 61024	5.00	10.00	15.00
GOLDEN HITS VOL 2	Mercury (S) SR 61185	4.00	8.00	12.00
I'LL CRY IF I WANT TO	Mercury (M) MG 20805	4.00	8.00	12.00
I'LL CRY IF I WANT TO	Mercury (S) SR 60805	5.00	10.00	15.00
LESLEY GORE SINGS OF MIXED UP HEARTS	Mercury (M) MG 20849	4.00	8.00	12.00
LESLEY GORE SINGS OF MIXED UP HEARTS	Mercury (S) SR 60849	5.00	10.00	15.00
LOVE, LOVE, LOVE	Wing (S) SRW 16382	3.00	6.00	9.00
MY TOWN, MY GUY AND ME	Mercury (M) MG 21042	4.00	8.00	12.00
MY TOWN, MY GUY AND ME	Mercury (S) SR 61042	4.00	8.00	12.00
SOMEPLACE ELSE NOW	Mowest (S) MW 117L	2.00	3.00	4.00
SOUND OF YOUNG LOVE, THE	Wing (S) PKW-2-119	3.00	6.00	9.00

GOULDMAN, Graham

GRAHAM GOULDMAN THING	RCA (S) LSP	5.50	8.25	11.00

GOZZO BAND

SOUNDS THAT ARE HAPPENING	Go Go (M) 22170003	3.00	4.50	6.00
SOUNDS THAT ARE HAPPENING	Go Go (S) 22170004	3.50	5.25	7.00

GRACIOUS

GRACIOUS	Capitol (S) ST 602	2.50	3.75	5.00

GRAMMER, Billy

TRAVELIN' ON	Monument (M) M 4000	4.00	6.00	8.00

GRAND FUNK RAILROAD

ALL THE GIRLS IN THE WORLD BEWARE	Capitol (S) SO 11356	2.50	3.75	5.00
CAUGHT IN THE ACT (LISTED AS GRAND FUNK)	Capitol (S) SABB 11445	3.00	4.50	6.00
CLOSER TO HOME	Capitol (S) SKAO 471	3.00	4.50	6.00
E PLURIBUS FUNK	Capitol (S) SW 853	3.00	4.50	6.00
GRAND FUNK	Capitol (S) SKAO 406	3.00	4.50	6.00
LIVE ALBUM	Capitol (S) SWBB 633	4.00	6.00	8.00
ON TIME	Capitol (S) ST 307	3.00	4.50	6.00
PHOENIX	Capitol (S) SMAS 11099	2.50	3.75	5.00
SHININ' ON	Capitol (S) SWAE 11278	2.50	3.75	5.00
SURVIVAL	Capitol (S) SW 764	3.00	4.50	6.00
WE'RE AN AMERICAN BAND	Capitol (S) SMAS 11207	2.50	3.75	5.00

Also see TERRY KNIGHT & THE PACK

(M) Mono (S) Stereo (EP) Extended Play (Q) Quad (RI) Re-issued

TITLE	LABEL & NO.	GOOD	VERY GOOD	NEAR MINT

GRANT, Earl
THE END	Decca (M) DL 8830	3.00	4.50	6.00
THE END	Decca (S) DL7 8830	3.50	5.25	7.00
THE END	Decca (EP) ED 2639	1.50	2.25	3.00
THE END	Decca (SEP) ED 7 2639	2.00	3.00	4.00

GRANT, Gogi
IF YOU WANT TO GET TO HEAVEN-SHOUT	Liberty (M) LRP-3144	2.50	3.75	5.00
IF YOU WANT TO GET TO HEAVEN-SHOUT	Liberty (S) LST-7144	2.50	3.75	5.00
KISS ME KATE	RCA (M) LPM 1984	2.50	3.75	5.00
KISS ME KATE	RCA (S) LSP 1984	2.50	3.75	5.00
SECRET LOVE	RCA (EP) EPA 902	1.50	2.25	3.00
SUDDENLY THERE'S GOGI GRANT	ERA (M) ED 20001	5.00	7.50	10.00
TORCH TIME	RCA (M) LPM 1940	2.50	3.75	5.00
TORCH TIME	RCA (S) LSP 1940	2.50	3.75	5.00
WAYWARD WIND	ERA (M) EL 106	4.00	6.00	8.00
WELCOME TO MY HEART	RCA (M) LPM 1717	2.50	3.75	5.00

GRAPEFRUIT
| AROUND GRAPEFRUIT | Dunhill (M) 50050 | 4.50 | 6.75 | 9.00 |
| DEEP WATER | RCA (S) LSP 4215 | 4.00 | 6.00 | 8.00 |

GRASS ROOTS
FEELINGS	Dunhill (S) DS 50027	3.00	4.50	6.00
GOLDEN GRASS (THEIR GREATEST HITS)	Dunhill (S) DS 50047	2.50	3.75	5.00
GRASS ROOTS	Haven (S) ST 9204	3.00	4.50	6.00
LEAVING IT ALL BEHIND	Dunhill (S) DS 50067	2.50	3.75	5.00
LET'S LIVE FOR TODAY	Dunhill (M) D 50020	3.00	4.50	6.00
LET'S LIVE FOR TODAY	Dunhill (S) DS 50020	3.00	4.50	6.00
A LOTTA MILEAGE	Dunhill (S) DSX 50137	2.50	3.75	5.00
LOVIN' THINGS	Dunhill (S) DS 50052	2.50	3.75	5.00
MORE GOLDEN GRASS	Dunhill (S) DS 50087	2.50	3.75	5.00
MOVE ALONG	Dunhill (S) DSX 50112	2.50	3.75	5.00
THEIR 16 GREATEST HITS	Dunhill (S) DSX 50107	2.50	3.75	5.00
THEIR 16 GREATEST HITS	Command (Q) QD 40013	2.50	3.75	5.00

GRATEFUL DEAD
AMERICAN BEAUTY	Warner Brothers (S) 1893	2.50	3.75	5.00
ANTHEM OF THE SUN	Warner Brothers (S) 1749	3.00	4.50	6.00
AOXOMOXOA	Warner Bros. (S) WS 1790	2.50	3.75	5.00
BEST OF SKELETONS FROM THE CLOSET	Warner Brothers (S) 2764	3.00	4.50	6.00
BLUES FOR ALLAH	Grateful Dead (S) GD-LA494G	2.00	3.00	4.00
EUROPE '72	Warner Brothers (S) 3WX2668	4.00	6.00	8.00
GRATEFUL DEAD	Warner Brothers (M) W 1689	3.00	4.50	6.00
GRATEFUL DEAD	Warner Brothers (S) 1689	3.00	4.50	6.00
GRATEFUL DEAD	Warner Brothers (S) 1935	3.00	4.50	6.00
GRATEFUL DEAD FROM THE MARS HOTEL	Grateful Dead (S) 102	2.50	3.75	5.00
HISTORIC DEAD	Sunflower (S) 5004	3.00	4.50	6.00
HISTORY OF THE GRATEFUL DEAD	Pride (S) 0016	3.00	4.50	6.00
HISTORY OF THE GRATEFUL DEAD VOL. 1	Warner Brothers (S) B2721	3.00	4.50	6.00
LIVE/DEAD	Warner Bros. (S) WS 1830	4.00	6.00	8.00
STEAL YOUR FACE	Grateful Dead GD-LA620	4.00	6.00	8.00
TERRAPIN STATION	Arista (S) AL 7001	2.00	3.00	4.00
VINTAGE DEAD	Sunflower (S) 5001	3.00	4.50	6.00
WAKE OF THE FLOOD	Grateful Dead (S) 01	2.50	3.75	5.00
WHAT A LONG, STRANGE TRIP IT'S BEEN	Warner Brothers (S) 2W 3091	3.00	4.50	6.00
WORKINGMAN'S DEAD	Warner Bros. (S) WS 1869	2.50	3.75	5.00

GRAY, Dobie
| DOBIE GRAY SINGS FOR IN CROWDERS | Charger (M) CHRM2002 | 3.00 | 6.00 | 9.00 |
| LOOK | Stripe (M) LPM2001 | 3.00 | 6.00 | 9.00 |
Also see POLLUTION

GREAT JONES
| ALL BOWED DOWN! | Tonsil (S) T-4002 | 2.50 | 3.75 | 5.00 |

GREAT SOCIETY With Grace Slick
| CONSPICUOUS ONLY IN ITS ABSENCE | Columbia (S) CS9624 | 2.50 | 3.75 | 5.00 |
| HOW IT WAS | Columbia (S) CS9702 | 2.50 | 3.75 | 5.00 |

TITLE	LABEL & NO.	GOOD	VERY GOOD	NEAR MINT

GREAT SPECKLED BIRD
| GREAT SPECKLED BIRD | Ampex (S) A 10103 | 2.50 | 3.75 | 5.00 |

GREEK FOUNTAIN RIVER FRONT BAND
| TAKES REQUESTS | Montel (S) LLP 110 | 3.00 | 4.50 | 6.00 |

GREEN, Guitar Slim
| STONE DOWN BLUES | United (M) 7764 | 2.00 | 3.00 | 4.00 |
Also see GUITAR SLIM

GREEN LYTE SUNDAY
| GREEN LYTE SUNDAY | RCA (S) LSP-4327 | 2.50 | 3.75 | 5.00 |

GREEN, Peter
| END OF THE GAME | Reprise (S) 6436 | 2.50 | 3.75 | 5.00 |

GREENBAUM, Norman
BACK HOME AGAIN	Reprise (S) RS 6422	2.50	3.75	5.00
PELALUMA	Reprise (S) MS 2084	2.50	3.75	5.00
SPIRIT IN THE SKY	Reprise (S) 6365	2.50	3.75	5.00
Also see DR. WEST'S MEDICINE SHOW & JUNK BAND

GREENFIELD
| BLUE SKY | RCA (S) APL1-0264 | 3.00 | 4.50 | 6.00 |

GREENWICH, Ellie
COMPOSES, PRODUCES AND SINGS	United Artists (M) UAL 3648	6.50	9.75	13.00
COMPOSES, PRODUCES AND SINGS	United Artists (S) UAS 6648	7.00	10.50	14.00
LET IT BE WRITTEN,LET IT BE SUNG	Verve (S) V6 5091	5.00	7.50	10.00

GREGG, Bobby and His Friends
| LET'S STOMP AND WILD WEEKEND | Epic (M) LN 24051 | 3.00 | 6.00 | 9.00 |

GRIER, Roosevelt
| SOUL CITY | Ric (M) M1008 | 2.50 | 3.75 | 5.00 |

GRIFFITH, Andy
ANDY & CLEOPATRA	Capitol (M) T2066	2.50	3.75	5.00
ANDY GRIFFITH SHOUTS THE BLUES & OLD TIME SONGS	Capitol (M) T1105	2.00	4.00	6.00
ANDY GRIFFITH SHOUTS THE BLUES & OLD TIME SONGS	Capitol (S) ST1105	2.00	4.00	6.00
ANDY GRIFFITH SHOW	Capitol (M) T1611	2.50	3.75	5.00
ANDY GRIFFITH SHOW	Capitol (S) ST1611	2.50	3.75	5.00
COMEDY CARAVAN	Capitol (M) T732	3.00	4.00	6.00
FACE IN THE CROWD	Capitol (EP) EPA1863	1.00	1.50	2.00
JUST FOR LAUGHS	Capitol (M) T 962	3.00	4.00	6.00
MAKE YOURSELF COMFORTABLE	Capitol (EP) EAP1630	1.00	1.50	2.00
ROMEO & JULIET	Capitol (EP) EAP1498	1.00	1.50	2.00

GRIMES, Tammy
| UNSINKABLE MOLLY BROWN | Capitol (M) WAO 1509 | 2.00 | 3.00 | 4.00 |
| UNSINKABLE MOLLY BROWN | Capitol (S) SWAO 1509 | 2.00 | 3.00 | 4.00 |

GRIN
ALL OUT	Spindizzy (S) KZ 31701	3.00	4.50	6.00
GONE CRAZY	A&M (S) SP 4415	2.00	3.00	4.00
GRIN	Spindizzy (S) Z30321	2.50	3.75	5.00
1 PLUS 1	Spindizzy (S) Z 31038	2.50	3.75	5.00

GRIND, Jody
| ONE STEP ON | United Artists (S) UAS 6774 | 3.50 | 5.25 | 7.00 |

GRISSOM, Jimmy
| WORLD OF TROUBLE | Argo (S) 729 | 4.00 | 8.00 | 12.00 |

GROOTNA
| GROOTNA | Columbia (S) C 31032 | 4.00 | 6.00 | 8.00 |

GROOV-U
| ON CAMPUS | Gateway (M) GLP 3010 | 7.00 | 10.50 | 14.00 |

GROSS, Henry
HENRY GROSS	A&M (S) SP 4416	2.00	3.00	4.00
ONE MORE TOMORROW	A&M (S) SP 4502	2.50	3.75	5.00
PLUG ME INTO SOMETHING ('77 Re-titled)	A&M (S) SP 4502	2.00	3.00	4.00
RELEASE	Lifesong (S) 6002	2.50	3.75	5.00
RELEASE ('77 RI)	Lifesong (S) PZ 34995	2.00	3.00	4.00
SHOW ME TO THE STAGE	Lifesong (S) -6010	2.50	3.75	5.00
SHOW ME TO THE STAGE ('77 RI)	Lifesong (S) PZ 35002	2.00	3.00	4.00

GROSVENOR, Luther
| UNDER OPEN SKIES | Island (S) ILPS 9168 | 2.50 | 3.75 | 5.00 |

(M) Mono (S) Stereo (EP) Extended Play (Q) Quad (RI) Re-issued

TITLE	LABEL & NO.	GOOD	VERY GOOD	NEAR MINT
GROUNDHOGS				
GROUNDHOGS BLUES OBITUARY	Imperial (S) 12452	3.50	5.25	7.00
GROUNDHOGS SCRATCHING				
THE SURFACE	World Pacific (S) 21892	3.50	5.25	7.00
GROUNDHOGS SPLIT	United Artists (S) 5513	2.50	3.75	5.00
GROUNDHOGS THANK CHRIST FOR				
THE BOMB	Liberty (S) LST 7644	3.00	4.50	6.00
GROUNDHOGS WITH JOHN LEE HOOKER				
& JOHN MAHALL, The	Cleve (S) CH-82871	9.00	13.50	18.00
HOGWASH	United Artists (S) UALA008F	2.50	3.75	5.00
SPLIT	United Artists (EP) SP 49	4.00	6.00	8.00
WHO WILL SAVE THE WORLD	United Artists (S) UAS 5570	2.50	3.75	5.00
GROUP				
GROUP, THE	Bell (S) 6038	5.00	7.50	10.00
GROUPIES				
THE GROUPIES	Earth (S) ELPS 1000	4.00	6.00	8.00
GROUP IMAGE				
A MOUTH IN THE CLOUDS	Community (S) A101	4.00	6.00	8.00
GROUP THERAPY				
PEOPLE GET READY FOR				
GROUP THERAPY	RCA (S) LSP 3976	3.00	4.50	6.00
37 MINUTES OF GROUP THERAPY	Philips (S) PHS 600303	3.00	4.50	6.00
GROWING CONCERN				
GROWING CONCERN	Mainstream (S) S6108	3.00	4.50	6.00
G.T.O.'S				
GIRLS TOGETHER OUTRAGEOUSLY				
PERMANENT DAMAGE	Straight (S) STS 1059	5.00	7.50	10.00
GUESS WHO				
AMERICAN WOMAN	RCA LSP 4266	3.50	5.25	7.00
ARTIFICIAL PARADISE	RCA (S) LSP 4830	3.00	4.50	6.00
BEST OF THE GUESS WHO	RCA LSPX 1004	4.00	6.00	8.00
BEST OF THE GUESS WHO, Vol. 2	RCA (S) APL1-0269	3.00	4.50	6.00
BEST OF THE GUESS WHO VOL 2	RCA (Q) APD1-0269	2.50	3.75	5.00
BORN IN CANADA	Wand (S) WDS 691	3.00	4.50	6.00
CANNED WHEAT PACKED BY THE GUESS WHO	RCA (S) LSP 4157	3.50	5.25	7.00
FLAVOURS	RCA CPL1-0636	3.00	4.50	6.00
GUESS WHO	Pickwick (S) SPC 3246	3.00	4.50	6.00
GUESS WHO LIVE AT THE PARAMOUNT	RCA LSP 4779	3.00	4.50	6.00
GUESS WHO NO. 10	RCA (S) APL1-0130	3.00	4.50	6.00
GUESS WHO NO. 10	RCA (Q) APD1-0130	2.50	3.75	5.00
GUESS WHO PLAY THE GUESS WHO	PIP (S) PIP6806	3.00	4.50	6.00
HISTORY OF THE GUESS WHO	Pride 0012	2.50	3.75	5.00
ROAD FOOD	RCA (S) APL1-0405	3.00	4.50	6.00
ROAD FOOD	RCA (Q) APD1-0405	2.50	3.75	5.00
ROCKIN'	RCA LSP 4602	3.00	4.50	6.00
SHAKIN' ALL OVER	Scepter (S) 533	3.00	4.50	6.00
SHARE THE LAND	RCA LSP 4359	3.50	5.25	7.00
SO LONG, BANNATYNE	RCA LSP 4574	3.00	4.50	6.00
WHEATFIELD SOUL	RCA (S) LSP 4141	3.50	5.25	7.00
Also see CUMMINGS, Burton				
GUITAR, Bonnie				
DARK MOON	Dot (M) DLP 3335	3.00	4.50	6.00
GUITAR SLIM				
THINGS THAT I USED TO DO	Specialty (S) SPS2120	4.50	6.75	9.00
Also see GREEN, Guitar Slim				
GULLIVER				
GULLIVER	Elektra (S) EKS 74070	2.50	3.75	5.00
GUN				
GUN	Epic (S) BN 26488	5.00	7.50	10.00
GUNSIGHT	Epic (S) BN 26551	6.00	9.00	12.00
GUNTER, Arthur				
BLACK AND BLUES	Excello (M) 8017	2.00	4.00	6.00
GUTHRIE, Arlo				
ALICE'S RESTAURANT	Reprise (M) R 6267	3.00	4.50	6.00
ALICE'S RESTAURANT	Reprise (S) RS 6267	3.50	5.25	7.00
ARLO	Reprise (S) RS 6299	3.00	4.50	6.00
ARLO GUTHRIE	Reprise (S) MS 2183	2.50	3.75	5.00
HOBO'S LULLABYE	Reprise (S) 2060	2.50	3.75	5.00
LAST OF THE BROOKLYN COWBOYS	Reprise (S) 2142	2.50	3.75	5.00
LAST OF THE BROOKLYN COWBOYS	Reprise (Q) MS4-2142	2.50	3.75	5.00
RUNNING DOWN THE ROAD	Reprise (S) RS 6346	3.00	4.50	6.00
WASHINGTON COUNTY	Reprise (S) RS 6411	3.00	4.50	6.00
GUY, Buddy				
LEFT MY BLUES IN SAN FRANCISCO	Chess (S) LPS 1527	3.00	4.50	6.00
A MAN AND THE BLUES	Vanguard (M) VRS 9272	3.00	4.50	6.00
A MAN AND THE BLUES	Vanguard (S) VSD 79272	4.00	6.00	8.00
GUY, Buddy and Others				
BUDDY & THE JUNIORS	Blue Thumb (S) 20	2.50	3.75	5.00

H

TITLE	LABEL & NO.	GOOD	VERY GOOD	NEAR MINT
HACKAMORE BRICK				
ONE KISS LEADS TO ANOTHER	Kama Sutra (S) KSBS 2025	3.50	5.25	7.00
HALEY, Bill & His Comets				
BILL HALEY AND HIS COMETS	Warner Brothers (M) W 1378	4.50	6.75	9.00
BILL HALEY AND HIS COMETS	Warner Brothers (S) WS 1378	4.50	6.75	9.00
BILL HALEY AND HIS COMETS	Decca (EP) ED 2670	2.00	3.00	4.00
BILL HALEY AND HIS COMETS	Decca (SEP) ED 7-2670	2.50	3.75	5.00
BILL HALEY, KING OF ROCK & ROLL	Alshire (S) 5313	2.50	3.75	5.00
BILL HALEY'S CHICKS	Decca (M) DL 8821	3.00	6.00	9.00
BILL HALEY'S CHICKS	Decca (S) DL 7 8821	4.00	8.00	12.00
BILL HALEY'S CHICKS	Decca (EP) ED 2638	2.00	3.00	4.00
BILLY HALEY'S CHICKS	Decca (SEP) ED 7-2638	2.50	3.75	5.00
DANCE PARTY	Essex (EP) EP 102	6.00	15.00	24.00
DIM, DIM THE LIGHTS	Decca (EP) ED 2209	2.50	3.75	5.00
GOLDEN HITS	Decca (S) DXSE 7211	4.00	6.00	8.00
HALEY'S JUKE BOX	Warner Brothers (M) W 1391	4.50	6.75	9.00
HALEY'S JUKE BOX	Warner Brothers (S) WS 1391	4.50	6.75	9.00
HE DIGS ROCK AND ROLL	Decca (S) DL 8315	4.00	8.00	12.00
HE DIGS ROCK AND ROLL	Decca (S) DL 7 8315	2.50	3.75	5.00
HE DIGS ROCK AND ROLL	Decca (EP) ED 2398	2.50	3.75	5.00
HE DIGS ROCK AND ROLL	Decca (EP) ED 2399	2.50	3.75	5.00
HE DIGS ROCK AND ROLL	Decca (EP) ED 2400	2.50	3.75	5.00
RAZZLE DAZZLE	Janus (S) JX2s-7003	2.50	3.75	5.00
ROCK AND ROLL	GNP/Crescendo (S) GNPS 2077	2.50	3.75	5.00
ROCK AND ROLL	Decca (EP) ED 2322	2.50	3.75	5.00
ROCK AND ROLL DANCE PARTY	Somerset (M) P 4600	5.00	12.50	20.00
ROCK AND ROLL PARTY	Decca (EP) ED 2533	2.50	3.75	5.00
ROCK AND ROLL STAGE SHOW	Decca (M) DL 8345	4.00	8.00	12.00
ROCK AND ROLL STAGE SHOW	Decca (S) DL 7 8345	2.50	3.75	5.00
ROCK AND ROLL STAGE SHOW	Decca (EP) ED 2416	2.50	3.75	5.00
ROCK AND ROLL STAGE SHOW	Decca (EP) ED 2417	2.50	3.75	5.00
ROCK AND ROLL STAGE SHOW	Decca (EP) ED 2418	2.50	3.75	5.00
ROCK AROUND THE CLOCK	Decca (M) DL 8225	4.00	8.00	12.00
ROCK AROUND THE CLOCK	Decca (S) DL 7 8225	2.50	3.75	5.00
ROCKIN' AND ROLLIN'	Decca (EP) ED 2534	2.00	3.00	4.00
ROCKIN' AROUND EUROPE	Decca (EP) ED 2576	2.00	3.00	4.00
ROCKIN' AROUND THE AMERICAS	Decca (EP) ED 2577	2.00	3.00	4.00
ROCKIN' AROUND THE WORLD	Decca (M) DL 8692	3.00	6.00	9.00
ROCKIN' AROUND THE WORLD	Decca (S) DL 7 8692	4.00	8.00	12.00
ROCKIN' AROUND THE WORLD	Decca (EP) ED 2564	2.00	3.00	4.00
ROCKIN' THE JOINT	Decca (M) DL 8775	3.00	6.00	9.00
ROCKIN' THE JOINT	Decca (S) DL 7 8775	4.00	8.00	12.00
ROCKIN' THE JOINT	Decca (EP) ED 2615	2.00	3.00	4.00
ROCKIN' THE JOINT	Decca (EP) ED 2616	2.00	3.00	4.00
ROCKIN' THE OLDIES	Decca (M) DL 8569	3.00	6.00	9.00
ROCKIN' THE OLDIES	Decca (S) DL 7 8569	2.50	3.75	5.00
ROCKIN' THE OLDIES	Decca (EP) ED 2532	2.00	3.00	4.00
ROCK THE JOINT	London (M) HAF 2037	5.00	10.00	15.00
ROCK WITH BILL HALEY & THE COMETS	Trans World 202	7.00	17.50	28.00
ROCK WITH BILL HALEY & THE COMETS	Essex (M) LP 202	25.00	62.50	100.00

ROCK WITH BILL HALEY & THE COMETS	Essex (EP) EP 117	6.00	15.00	24.00
ROCK WITH BILL HALEY & THE COMETS	Essex (EP) EP 118	6.00	15.00	24.00
SHAKE, RATTLE AND ROLL (10" LP)	Decca (M) DL 5560	15.00	37.50	60.00
SHAKE RATTLE AND ROLL	Decca (EP) ED 2168	2.50	3.75	5.00
STRICTLY INSTRUMENTAL	Decca (EP) ED 2671	2.00	3.00	4.00
STRICTLY INSTRUMENTAL	Decca (SEP) ED 72671	2.00	3.00	4.00
STRICTLY INSTRUMENTAL	Decca (M) DL 8964	3.00	6.00	9.00
STRICTLY INSTRUMENTAL	Decca (S) DL 7 8964	4.00	8.00	12.00
TOP TEEN HITS	Decca (EP) ED 2671	1.50	2.25	3.00
TOP TEEN HITS	Decca (SEP) ED7-2671	2.00	3.00	4.00
TRAVELIN' BAND	Janus (S) JLS 3035	2.50	3.75	5.00
TWISTIN' KNIGHTS AT THE ROUNDTABLE	Roulette (M) R 25174	4.00	6.00	8.00
TWISTIN' KNIGHTS AT THE ROUNDTABLE	Roulette (S) SR 25174	4.00	6.00	8.00

(M) Mono   (S) Stereo   (EP) Extended Play   (Q) Quad   (RI) Re-issued

HALFNELSON
HALFNELSON	Bearsville (S) BV 2048	5.00	7.50	10.00

HALL, Daryl & John Oates
ABANDONED LUNCHEONETTE	Atlantic (S) SD 7269	2.50	3.75	5.00
DARYL HALL & JOHN OATES	RCA (S) APL1-1144	2.00	3.00	4.00
PAST TIMES BEHIND	Chelsea (S) CHL 547	3.50	5.25	7.00
WAR BABIES	Atlantic (S) SD 18109	2.00	3.00	4.00
WHOLE OATS	Atlantic (S) SD 7242	2.50	3.75	5.00

HALL, Dora
DORA HALL SINGS TOP TEN TUNES	Calamo (M) 9201	2.00	4.00	6.00

HALL, Larry
SANDY, AND OTHER LARRY HALL HITS	Strand (M) SL 1005	8.00	16.00	24.00

"Sandy" and other LARRY HALL HITS

HIGH FIDELITY

HALLYDAY, Johnny
JOHNNY HALLYDAY SING AMERICA'S ROCKIN' HITS	Philips (M) 200-019	5.00	7.50	10.00
JOHNNY HALLYDAY SING AMERICA'S ROCKIN' HITS	Philips (S) 600-019	6.00	9.00	12.00

HALOS
THE HALOS	Warwick (M) W 2046	6.00	12.00	18.00

HAMBLEN, Stuart
SPELL OF THE YUKON	Columbia (M) CL-1588	2.50	3.75	5.00
SPELL OF THE YUKON	Columbia (S) CS-8388	2.50	3.75	5.00
STUART HAMBLEN	Columbia (EP) B-2827	1.50	2.25	3.00
THIS OLE HOUSE	RCA (EP) EPA-5115	1.50	2.25	3.00

HAMILTON, Bruce
SPARKLING STRINGS	Dot (M) DLP 3037	2.00	3.00	4.00

HAMILTON, George, IV
GEORGE HAMILTON IV BIG 15	ABC/Paramount (M) ABC-461	4.00	8.00	12.00
GEORGE HAMILTON IV BIG 15	ABC/Paramount (S) ABCS-461	5.00	10.00	15.00
MY GEORGE	ABC/Paramount (M) ABC 535	3.00	4.50	6.00
MY GEORGE	ABC/Paramount (S) ABCS 535	3.00	4.50	6.00
16 GREATEST HITS	ABC/Paramount (M) ABC-750	3.00	6.00	9.00

HAMILTON, JOE FRANK & REYNOLDS
FALLIN' IN LOVE	Playboy (S) 407	2.50	3.75	5.00
FALLIN' IN LOVE ('77 RI)	Playboy (S) PZ 34741	2.00	3.00	4.00
HALLWAY SYMPHONY	Dunhill (S) DSX 50113	3.00	4.50	6.00
HAMILTON, JOE FRANK & REYNOLDS	Dunhill (S) DSX 50103	3.00	4.50	6.00
LOVE & CONVERSATION	Playboy (S) 414	2.50	3.75	5.00
LOVE & CONVERSATION ('77 RI)	Playboy (S) PZ 34748	2.00	3.00	4.00

HAMILTON, Roy
EBB TIDE	Epic (EP) EG 7079	1.00	1.50	2.00
FAITH, HOPE AND HAMILTON	Epic (EP) EG 7080	1.50	2.25	3.00
HERE'S ROY HAMILTON	Epic (EP) EG 7065	1.50	2.25	3.00
ROY HAMILTON	Epic (M) LN 3176	3.00	4.50	6.00
ROY HAMILTON	Epic (EP) EG 7133	1.00	1.50	2.00
ROY HAMILTON	Epic (EP) EG 7158	1.00	1.50	2.00
ROY HAMILTON	Epic (EP) EG 7159	1.00	1.50	2.00
ROY HAMILTON GREATEST HITS	Epic (M) LN-24009	4.00	8.00	12.00
ROY HAMILTON GREATEST HITS	Epic (S) BN-26009	5.00	10.00	15.00

(M) Mono (S) Stereo (EP) Extended Play (Q) Quad (RI) Re-issued

VOICE OF ROY HAMILTON	Epic (M) LN 1103	3.00	4.50	6.00
YOU CAN HAVE HER	Epic (S) BN-595	7.00	14.00	21.00
YOU'LL NEVER WALK ALONE	Epic (M) LN 3294	3.00	4.50	6.00

HAMILTON, Russ
RAINBOWS	Kapp (M) KL 1076	8.00	16.00	24.00

HAMILTON FACE BAND
HAMILTON FACE BAND, THE	Philips (S) PHS 600-308	3.00	4.50	6.00

HAMILTON STREETCAR
HAMILTON STREETCAR	Dot (M) DLP 25939	3.00	4.50	6.00

HAMMER
HAMMER	San Francisco (S) SD 203	3.00	4.50	6.00

HAMMOND, John
CAN'T BEAT THE KID	Capricorn (S) 0153	2.00	3.00	4.00
COUNTRY BLUES	Vanguard (M) VRS 9198	2.50	3.75	5.00
COUNTRY BLUES	Vanguard (S) VSD 79198	3.00	4.50	6.00
I CAN TELL	Atlantic (S) SD 8152	3.00	4.50	6.00
JOHN HAMMOND	Vanguard (M) VRS 9132	2.50	3.75	5.00
JOHN HAMMOND	Vanguard (S) VSD 2148	3.00	4.50	6.00
SO MANY ROADS	Vanguard (M) VRS 9178	2.50	3.75	5.00
SO MANY ROADS	Vanguard (S) VSD 79178	3.00	4.50	6.00
SOONER OR LATER	Atlantic (S) SD 8206	3.00	4.50	6.00
SOUTHERN FRIED	Atlantic (S) SD 8251	2.50	3.75	5.00

HAMP, Monti
MONTI HAMP BLUES	Bluesville (M) 1027	5.00	7.50	10.00

HANGMEN
BITTER SWEET	Monument (M) MLP 8077	2.50	3.75	5.00

HA'PENNYS
LOVE IS NOT THE SAME	Fersch (M) FL 1110	8.00	16.00	24.00

HAPPENINGS
HAPPENINGS	B.T. Puppy (M) BTP 1001	2.50	3.75	5.00
HAPPENINGS, THE	BT Puppy (S) BTPS 1001	3.00	4.50	6.00
HAPPENINGS GOLDEN HITS!	BT Puppy (S) BTPS 1004	3.00	4.50	6.00
PIECE OF MIND	Jubilee (S) JGS 8028	2.50	3.75	5.00
PSYCHLE	B.T. Puppy (M) BTP 1003	2.50	3.75	5.00
PSYCHLE	B.T. Puppy (S) BTPS 1003	3.00	4.50	6.00

HAPSHASH AND THE COLOURED COAT
FEATURING THE HUMAN HOST AND
THE HEAVY METAL KIDS	Imperial (M) LP 12377	4.00	6.00	8.00
WESTERN FLIER	Imperial (M) LP 12430	4.00	6.00	8.00

HARDEN TRIO
SING ME BACK HOME	Columbia (S) CS-9633	2.00	3.00	4.00
TIPPY TOEING	Columbia (M) CL-2506	2.00	3.00	4.00
TIPPY TOEING	Columbia (S) CS-9306	2.00	3.00	4.00

HARDIN AND YORK
FOR THE WORLD	London (S) XPS 602	2.50	3.75	5.00
TOMORROW TODAY	Bell (M) 6043	3.00	4.50	6.00

HARDLY-WORTHIT PLAYERS
HARDLY-WORTHIT PLAYERS REPORT	Parkway (M) 7053	3.00	6.00	9.00
HARDLY-WORTHIT PLAYERS REPORT	Parkway (S) 7053	4.00	8.00	12.00

HARD STUFF
BOLEX DEMENTIA	Mercury (M) 663	3.00	4.50	6.00

HARDTIMES
BLEW MIND	World Pacific (M) WP 1867	4.00	6.00	8.00
BLEW MIND	World Pacific (S) WPS 21867	5.00	7.50	10.00

HARD WATER
HARD WATER	Capitol (S) ST 2954	2.50	3.75	5.00

HARDY BOYS
HERE COME THE HARDY BOYS	RCA (S) LSP 4217	4.00	6.00	8.00
WHEELS	RCA (S) LSP 4315	4.00	6.00	8.00

HARDY, Francoise
FRANCOISE	Four Corners (S) FCS 4231	5.00	10.00	15.00
FRANCOISE HARDY	Reprise (M) R 6290	4.00	8.00	12.00
FRANCOISE HARDY	Reprise (S) RS 6290	5.00	10.00	15.00
JE VUUS AIME	Four Corners (S) FCS 4238	5.00	10.00	15.00

HARMONAIRES MALE QUARTET, The
SPIRITUALS (10")	Varsity (M) 6915	8.00	20.00	32.00

HARMONICA FRANK (FRANK FLOYD)
GREAT ORIGINAL RECORDINGS OF
HARMONICA FRANK	Puritan (M) 3003	3.00	4.50	6.00

HARPE, Neil
Title	Label & No.	Good	Very Good	Near Mint
NEIL HARPE	Adelphi (M) AD 1013	2.50	3.75	5.00

HARPER, Roy
Title	Label & No.	Good	Very Good	Near Mint
FLAT, BAROQUE, AND BERSERK	Harvest (S) SKAO 418	3.50	5.25	7.00
FOLKJOKEOPUS	World Pacific (S) WPS 21888	4.00	6.00	8.00

HARPERS BIZARRE
Title	Label & No.	Good	Very Good	Near Mint
ANYTHING GOES	Warner Brothers (S) WS 1716	3.00	4.50	6.00
FEELIN' GROOVY	Warner Brothers (M) W 1693	2.50	3.75	5.00
FEELIN' GROOVY	Warner Brothers (S) WS 1693	3.00	4.50	6.00
HARPERS BIZARRE	Warner Brothers (S) WS 1784	3.00	4.50	6.00
SECRET LIFE OF HARPER'S BIZARRE	Warner Brothers (S) WS 1739	3.00	4.50	6.00

HARPO, Slim
Title	Label & No.	Good	Very Good	Near Mint
BABY SCRATCH MY BACK	Excello (M) 8005	5.00	7.50	10.00
BEST OF SLIM HARPO, THE	Excello (M) 8010	5.00	7.50	10.00
RAINING IN MY HEART	Excello (M) LP 8003	6.00	9.00	12.00
SLIM HARPO KNEW THE BLUES	Excello (M) EXC 8013	4.00	6.00	8.00
TIP ON IN	Excello (M) 8008	5.00	7.50	10.00
TRIGGER FINGER	Blue Horizon (M)	4.00	6.00	8.00

HARPTONES
Title	Label & No.	Good	Very Good	Near Mint
HARPTONES, THE	Harlem Hitparade (M) HHP 5006	3.00	4.50	6.00
HARPTONES FEATURING WILLIE WINFIELD	Relic (M) LP 5001	4.00	6.00	8.00
HARPTONES FEATURING WILLIE WINFIELD, THE VOL. 2	Relic (M) LP 5003	4.00	6.00	8.00

HARRIS, Betty
Title	Label & No.	Good	Very Good	Near Mint
BETTY HARRIS	Jubilee (M)	5.00	7.50	10.00

HARRIS, Emmy Lou
Title	Label & No.	Good	Very Good	Near Mint
GLIDING BIRD	Jubilee (M) 8031	9.00	13.50	18.00

HARRIS, Peppermint
Title	Label & No.	Good	Very Good	Near Mint
PEPPERMINT HARRIS	Time (M) 5	5.00	7.50	10.00
VOL. 5 BLUES/FOLK SERIES	Time (M) Vol.5	4.00	8.00	12.00

HARRIS, Richard
Title	Label & No.	Good	Very Good	Near Mint
I, IN THE MEMBERSHIP OF MY DAYS	Dunhill (S) DS 50159	2.50	3.75	5.00
JONATHAN LIVINGSTON SEAGULL	Dunhill (S) 50160	2.50	3.75	5.00
MY BOY	Dunhill (S) DSX 50116	2.50	3.75	5.00
PROPHET KAHLIL GIBRAN	Atlantic (S) SD 18120	2.50	3.75	5.00
PROPHET KAHLIL GIBRAN	Atlantic (Q) QS 18120	2.50	3.75	5.00
RICHARD HARRIS- HIS GREATEST PERFORMANCES	Dunhill (S) DSX 50139	2.50	3.75	5.00
SLIDES	Dunhill (S) DSX 50133	2.50	3.75	5.00
A TRAMP SHINING	Dunhill (S) DS 50032	3.00	4.50	6.00
YARD WENT ON FOREVER	Dunhill (S) DS 50042	3.00	4.50	6.00

HARRIS, Rolf
Title	Label & No.	Good	Very Good	Near Mint
COUNT OF KING CARACTACUS (AND OTHER FUN SONGS)	Epic (M) LN 24110	6.00	9.00	12.00
COUNT OF KING CARACTACUS (AND OTHER FUN SONGS)	Epic (S) BN 26110	7.00	10.50	14.00
TIE ME KANGAROO DOWN, SPORT	Epic (M) LN 24053	5.00	7.50	10.00
TIE ME KANGAROO DOWN, SPORT	Epic (S) BN 26053	6.00	9.00	12.00

HARRIS, Shaun
Title	Label & No.	Good	Very Good	Near Mint
SHAUN HARRIS	Capitol (S) ST 11168	2.50	3.75	5.00

HARRIS, Wynonie
Title	Label & No.	Good	Very Good	Near Mint
GOOD ROCKIN' BLUES	King (S) KS 1086	5.00	10.00	15.00
GOOD ROCKIN' TONIGHT	King (EP) EP 260	3.00	7.50	12.00
PARTY AFTER HOURS (10") (Red vinyl) (With Amos Milburn & Crown Prince Waterford.)	Aladdin (M) 703	33.00	82.50	132.00
PARTY AFTER HOURS (10") (Black vinyl) (With Amos Milburn and Crown Prince Waterford.)	Aladdin (M) 703	25.00	62.50	100.00

HARRISON, George
Title	Label & No.	Good	Very Good	Near Mint
ALL THINGS MUST PASS	Apple (S) STCH 639	6.00	9.00	12.00
BEST OF GEORGE HARRISON	Capitol (S) ST 11578	2.00	3.00	4.00
CONCERT FOR BANGLADESH, THE	Apple (S) STCX 3385	6.00	9.00	12.00
DARK HORSE	Apple (S) SMAS 3418	2.00	3.00	4.00
(Released with blue and white label or black and white label; YOGI on cover appears in either large yellow disc or small yellow disc. No difference in value.)				
ELECTRONIC SOUND	Zapple (S) ST 3358	2.50	3.75	5.00
EXTRA TEXTURE (Read All About It)	Apple (S) SW 3420	2.00	3.00	4.00
LIVING IN THE MATERIAL WORLD	Apple (S) SMAS 3410	2.00	3.00	4.00
PERSONAL MUSIC DIALOGUE WITH GEORGE HARRISON AT THRITY-THREE AND A THIRD, A	Dark Horse (S) PRO 649	12.50	18.75	25.00
THIRTY THREE & 1/3	Dark Horse (S) 3005	3.50	5.25	7.00
WONDERWALL MUSIC	Apple (S) ST 3350	3.50	5.25	7.00

HARRISON, Noel
Title	Label & No.	Good	Very Good	Near Mint
COLLAGE	Reprise (M) 6263	3.00	4.50	6.00
KING ARTHUR	Riverside (M) 1446	5.00	7.50	10.00

Title	Label & No.	Good	Very Good	Near Mint
NOEL HARRISON	London (M) LL 3459	3.00	4.50	6.00
NOEL HARRISON	London (S) PS 459	4.00	6.00	8.00
SANTA MONICA PIER	Reprise (S) 6295	3.00	4.50	6.00

HARRISON, Wilbert
Title	Label & No.	Good	Very Good	Near Mint
ANYTHING YOU WANT	Wet Soul (S) 1001	4.00	6.00	8.00
KANSAS CITY	Sphere (M) LP 7000	5.00	10.00	15.00
LET'S WORK TOGETHER	Sue (S) SSLP 8801	5.00	7.50	10.00
SHOOT YOU FULL OF LOVE	Juggernaut (S) ST 8803	3.50	5.25	7.00
WILBERT HARRISON	Buddah (S) BDS 5092	3.50	5.25	7.00

HARTFORD, John
Title	Label & No.	Good	Very Good	Near Mint
EARTHWORDS & MUSIC	RCA (M) LPM 3796	2.00	3.00	4.00
EARTHWORDS & MUSIC	RCA (S) LSP 3796	2.50	3.75	5.00
MORNING BUGLE	Warner Bros. (S) BS-2651	2.00	3.00	4.00

HARTLEY, Keef
Title	Label & No.	Good	Very Good	Near Mint
HALFBREED	Deram (S) DES 18024	3.00	4.50	6.00
LANCASHIRE HUSTLER	Deram (S) DES 13070	2.50	3.75	5.00
OVERDOG	Deram (S) DES 18057	3.00	4.50	6.00
TIME IS NEAR	Deram (S) DES 18047	3.00	4.50	6.00

HARUMI
Title	Label & No.	Good	Very Good	Near Mint
HARUMI	Verve/Forecast (S) FTS-3030-2X	6.00	9.00	12.00

HARVEY, Tina
Title	Label & No.	Good	Very Good	Near Mint
TINA HARVEY	UK (S) UKS 53103	3.00	4.50	6.00

HASSLES
Title	Label & No.	Good	Very Good	Near Mint
HASSLES, THE	United Artists (S) UAS 6631	3.00	4.50	6.00
HOUR OF THE WOLF	United Artists (S) UAS 6699	3.00	4.50	6.00

HAVENS, Richie
Title	Label & No.	Good	Very Good	Near Mint
ALARM CLOCK	Stormy Forest (S) 6005	2.50	3.75	5.00
ELECTRIC HAVENS	Douglas (M) 780	3.00	4.50	6.00
GREAT BLIND DEGREE, THE	Stormy Forest (S) 6010	2.50	3.75	5.00
MIXED BAG	MGM (M) 4698	3.00	4.50	6.00
MIXED BAG	Verve/Forecast (M) 3006	4.00	6.00	8.00
MIXED BAG 2	Stormy Forest (S) 6201	2.50	3.75	5.00
1983	Verve/Forecast (M) 3047	4.00	6.00	8.00
RICHARD P. HAVENS, PORTFOLIO	Stormy Forest (S) 6013	2.50	3.75	5.00
RICHIE HAVENS ON STAGE	Stormy Forest (S) 6012	2.50	3.75	5.00
RICHIE HAVENS' RECORD	Douglas (M) 779	3.00	4.50	6.00
SOMETHING ELSE AGAIN	Verve/Forecast (M) 3034	4.00	6.00	8.00
STONEHENGE	Stormy Forest (S) 6001	2.50	3.75	5.00

HAWKINS, Dale
Title	Label & No.	Good	Very Good	Near Mint
LET'S ALL TWIST (AT THE MIAMI BEACH PEPPERMINT LOUNGE)	Roulette (M) R-25175	4.00	10.00	16.00

Title	Label & No.	Good	Very Good	Near Mint
LET'S ALL TWIST (AT THE MIAMI BEACH PEPPERMINT LOUNGE)	Roulette (S) SR-25175	5.00	12.50	20.00
SUZIE-Q	Chess (M) 1429	19.00	47.50	76.00

HAWKINS, Hawkshaw
Title	Label & No.	Good	Very Good	Near Mint
HAWKINS, HAWKSHAW VOL 1	King (M) LP 587	3.00	4.50	6.00
HAWKINS, HAWKSHAW VOL 2	King (M) LP 592	3.00	4.50	6.00
HAWK OF W. VA. HILLS	King (EP) EP 231	1.50	2.25	3.00

HAWKINS, Jennell
Title	Label & No.	Good	Very Good	Near Mint
MANY MOODS OF JENNY, THE	Amazon (M) AM 1001	3.00	6.00	9.00
MANY MOODS OF JENNY, THE	Amazon (S) AS 1001	4.00	8.00	12.00
MOMENTS TO REMEMBER	Amazon (M) AM-1002	4.00	8.00	12.00
MOMENTS TO REMEMBER	Amazon (S) AS-1002	5.00	10.00	15.00

(M) Mono (S) Stereo (EP) Extended Play (Q) Quad (RI) Re-issued

HAWKINS, Ronnie

TITLE	LABEL & NO.	GOOD	VERY GOOD	NEAR MINT
BEST OF RONNIE HAWKINS	Roulette (M) R25255	5.00	10.00	15.00
FOLK BALLADS OF RONNIE HAWKINS, THE	Roulette (M) R 25120	5.00	12.50	20.00
FOLK BALLADS OF RONNIE HAWKINS, THE	Roulette (S) SR 25120	6.00	15.00	24.00
GIANT OF ROCK AND ROLL, THE	Monument (S) KZ 32940	2.00	3.00	4.00
HAWK, THE	Cotillion (S) SD 9039	2.50	3.75	5.00
MR. DYNAMO	Roulette (M) R 25102	7.00	17.50	28.00
MR. DYNAMO	Roulette (S) SR 25102	9.00	22.50	36.00
ROCK AND ROLL RESURRECTION	Monument (S) KZ 31330	2.00	3.00	4.00
RONNIE HAWKINS	Roulette (M) R 25078	7.00	17.50	28.00
RONNIE HAWKINS	Roulette (S) SR 25078	8.00	20.00	32.00
RONNIE HAWKINS	Cotillion (S) SD 9019	2.50	3.75	5.00
RONNIE HAWKINS SINGS THE SONGS OF HANK WILLIAMS	Roulette (M) R25137	5.00	12.50	20.00
RONNIE HAWKINS SINGS THE SONGS OF HANK WILLIAMS	Roulette (S) SR25137	6.00	15.00	24.00

Also see THE BAND

HAWKINS, Screamin' Jay

TITLE	LABEL & NO.	GOOD	VERY GOOD	NEAR MINT
AT HOME WITH SCREAMIN' JAY HAWKINS	Epic (M) LN 3448	8.00	20.00	32.00
I PUT A SPELL ON YOU	Epic (M) LN 3457	6.00	15.00	24.00
I PUT A SPELL ON YOU	Epic (S) BN 26457	4.00	6.00	8.00
SCREAMIN' JAY HAWKINS	Philips (S) PHS 600 336	4.00	8.00	12.00
WHAT THAT IS	Philips (S) PHS 600-319	4.00	8.00	12.00

HAYDEN, Willie

TITLE	LABEL & NO.	GOOD	VERY GOOD	NEAR MINT
BLAME IT ON THE BLUES	Dooto (M) 293	6.00	15.00	24.00

HAYES, Bill

TITLE	LABEL & NO.	GOOD	VERY GOOD	NEAR MINT
BILL HAYES SINGS BEST OF WALT DISNEY	ABC/Paramount (M) LP 194	4.00	6.00	8.00

HAYES, Isaac

TITLE	LABEL & NO.	GOOD	VERY GOOD	NEAR MINT
BLACK MOSES	Enterprise (S) ENS 5003	2.00	3.00	4.00
HOT BUTTERED SOUL	Enterprise (S) ENS 1001	3.00	4.50	6.00
IN THE BEGINNING	Atlantic (S) 1599	3.00	4.50	6.00
ISAAC HAYES	Enterprise 7510	2.50	3.75	5.00
ISAAC HAYES MOVEMENT, THE	Enterprise (S) ENS 1010	3.00	4.50	6.00
JOY	Enterprise (S) ENS 5007	3.00	4.50	6.00
JOY	Enterprise (Q) SQ-5007	2.50	3.75	5.00
LIVE AT THE SAHARA TAHOE	Enterprise (S) ENS 5005	2.00	3.00	4.00
SHAFT	Enterprise (S) ENS 2-5002	2.50	3.75	5.00
TO BE CONTINUED	Enterprise (S) ENS 1014	3.00	4.50	6.00

HAYWARD, Justin & John Lodge

TITLE	LABEL & NO.	GOOD	VERY GOOD	NEAR MINT
BLUE JAYS	Threshold (S) 14	3.50	5.25	7.00

Also see MOODY BLUES

HAZLEWOOD, Lee

TITLE	LABEL & NO.	GOOD	VERY GOOD	NEAR MINT
FRIDAY'S CHILD	Reprise (M) R-6163	2.50	3.75	5.00
FRIDAY'S CHILD	Reprise (S) RS-6163	3.00	4.50	6.00
LEE HAZLEWOODISM-ITS CAUSE AND CURE	MGM (S) SE 4403	3.00	4.50	6.00
N.S.V.I.P.'s, THE (NOT SO VERY IMPORTANT PEOPLE)	Reprise (M) R-6133	3.00	4.50	6.00
N.S.V.I.P.'s, THE (NOT SO VERY IMPORTANT PEOPLE)	Reprise (S) RS-6133	4.00	6.00	8.00
POET, FOOL OR BUM	Capitol (S) ST-11171	2.00	3.00	4.00
TROUBLE IS A LONESOME TOWN	Mercury (M) MG-20860	2.00	3.00	4.00
TROUBLE IS A LONESOME TOWN	Mercury (S) SR-60860	3.00	4.50	6.00
WORLD OF LEE HAZLEWOOD	MGM (M) 4362	2.50	3.75	5.00
WORLD OF LEE HAZLEWOOD	MGM (S) 4362	3.00	4.50	6.00

HAZLEWOOD, Lee/Nancy Sinatra

TITLE	LABEL & NO.	GOOD	VERY GOOD	NEAR MINT
NANCY & LEE	Reprise (S) 6273	2.50	3.75	5.00
NANCY & LEE AGAIN	RCA (S) LSP-4645	2.00	3.00	4.00

HAZZARD, Tony

TITLE	LABEL & NO.	GOOD	VERY GOOD	NEAR MINT
LOUDWATER HOUSE	Uni (S) 73126	2.00	3.00	4.00

HEAD

TITLE	LABEL & NO.	GOOD	VERY GOOD	NEAR MINT
HAVE YOU REACHED YET	Nova Sol (S) NSLP 1001	5.00	7.50	10.00

HEAD, Jim and His Del Rays

TITLE	LABEL & NO.	GOOD	VERY GOOD	NEAR MINT
HAYDEN PROFFITT PRESENTS JIM HEAD AND HIS DEL RAYS	HP (M) 22893	7.00	14.00	21.00

HEAD, Roy

TITLE	LABEL & NO.	GOOD	VERY GOOD	NEAR MINT
HEAD FIRST	Dot (S) DOSD 2051	2.00	3.00	4.00
ROY HEAD AND THE TRAITS	TNT (M) TLP 101	7.00	14.00	21.00
SOME PEOPLE	Dunhill (S) DS 50080	2.00	3.00	4.00
TREAT ME RIGHT	Scepter (M) 532	3.00	6.00	9.00
TREAT ME RIGHT	Scepter (S) SS 532	4.00	8.00	12.00

HEAD HANDS AND FEET

TITLE	LABEL & NO.	GOOD	VERY GOOD	NEAR MINT
HEAD HANDS AND FEET	Capitol (S) SVBB 680	2.50	3.75	5.00
OLD SOLDIERS NEVER DIE	Atco (S) SD 7025	2.50	3.75	5.00
TRACKS	Capitol (S) ST 11051	2.50	3.75	5.00

HEADS

TITLE	LABEL & NO.	GOOD	VERY GOOD	NEAR MINT
HEADS UP	Liberty (S) LST 7581	2.50	3.75	5.00

HEART

TITLE	LABEL & NO.	GOOD	VERY GOOD	NEAR MINT
HEART	Look (S) LLP 11000	4.50	6.75	9.00

(M) Mono (S) Stereo (EP) Extended Play (Q) Quad (RI) Re-issued

HEART

TITLE	LABEL & NO.	GOOD	VERY GOOD	NEAR MINT
DREAMBOAT ANNIE	Mushroom (S) MRS 5005	3.00	4.50	6.00
LITTLE QUEEN	Portrait (S) PR 34799	2.50	3.75	5.00
MAGAZINE (DUTCH IMPORT)	Arista (S) 1024	5.00	7.50	10.00
MAGAZINE	Mushroom (S) MRS 5008	2.50	3.75	5.00
MAGAZINE (Picture record)	Mushroom SP1	7.00	10.50	14.00

HEARTBEATS

TITLE	LABEL & NO.	GOOD	VERY GOOD	NEAR MINT
THOUSAND MILES AWAY	Roulette (M) R-25107	8.00	20.00	32.00
THOUSAND MILES AWAY	Roulette (S) SR-25107	9.00	22.50	36.00

Also see SHEP & THE LIMELIGHTS

HEARTS AND FLOWERS

TITLE	LABEL & NO.	GOOD	VERY GOOD	NEAR MINT
NOW IS THE TIME FOR HEARTS AND FLOWERS	Capitol (S) ST2762	4.00	6.00	8.00
OF HORSES-KIDS AND FORGOTTEN WOMEN	Capitol (S) ST 2868	5.00	7.50	10.00

HEAVY BALLOON

TITLE	LABEL & NO.	GOOD	VERY GOOD	NEAR MINT
16 TON	Elephant (S) EVS 104	2.50	3.75	5.00

HEBB, Bobby

TITLE	LABEL & NO.	GOOD	VERY GOOD	NEAR MINT
SUNNY	Philips (M) 200212	2.00	3.00	4.00
SUNNY	Philips (S) 600212	3.00	4.50	6.00

HELLO PEOPLE

TITLE	LABEL & NO.	GOOD	VERY GOOD	NEAR MINT
BRICKS	ABC (S) ABCD 882	2.00	3.00	4.00
FUSION	Philips (S) PHS 600-276	3.00	4.50	6.00
HAVE YOU SEEN THE LIGHT	Mediarts (S) 41-8	3.00	4.50	6.00
HELLO PEOPLE, THE	Philips (M) PHM 200-265	2.50	3.75	5.00
HELLO PEOPLE, THE	Philips (S) PHS 600-265	3.50	5.25	7.00

HELMS, Bobby

TITLE	LABEL & NO.	GOOD	VERY GOOD	NEAR MINT
BOBBY HELMS WITH ANITA KERR SINGERS	Decca (EP) ED 2629	1.50	2.25	3.00
SINGS TO MY SPECIAL ANGEL	Decca (M) DL 8638	4.50	6.75	9.00
SINGS TO MY SPECIAL ANGEL	Decca (EP) ED 2555	1.50	2.25	3.00
TONIGHT'S THE NIGHT	Decca (EP) ED 2586	1.50	2.25	3.00

HEMMINGS, David

TITLE	LABEL & NO.	GOOD	VERY GOOD	NEAR MINT
HAPPENS	MGM (M) 4490	2.50	3.75	5.00

HENDERSON, Joe

TITLE	LABEL & NO.	GOOD	VERY GOOD	NEAR MINT
SNAP YOUR FINGERS	Todd (M) MT 2701	3.00	6.00	9.00

HENDERSON, Tobias Wood

TITLE	LABEL & NO.	GOOD	VERY GOOD	NEAR MINT
BLUE STONE	Pulsar (S) AR-10605	3.50	4.25	7.00

HENDERSON, Willie and The Soul Explosions

TITLE	LABEL & NO.	GOOD	VERY GOOD	NEAR MINT
DANCE WITH THE MASTER	Brunswick (M) BL 754202	2.50	3.75	5.00
FUNKY CHICKEN	Brunswick (M) BL 754163	2.50	3.75	5.00

HENDRIX, Jimi

TITLE	LABEL & NO.	GOOD	VERY GOOD	NEAR MINT
AND A HAPPY NEW YEAR	Reprise (EP) PRO 595	30.00	35.00	45.00
ARE YOU EXPERIENCED	Reprise (M) 6261	3.00	4.50	6.00
ARE YOU EXPERIENCED	Reprise (S) 6261	3.50	5.25	7.00
AXIX: BOLD AS LOVE	Reprise (S) 6281	3.50	5.25	7.00
CRASH LANDING	Reprise (S) 2204	2.50	3.75	5.00
CRY OF LOVE, THE	Reprise (S) 2034	3.00	4.50	6.00
ELECTRIC LADYLAND	Reprise (S) 6307	3.50	5.25	7.00
ETERNAL JIMI HENDRIX, THE	Hallmark (S) SHM 732	3.00	4.50	6.00
FLASHING	Capitol (S) ST 2894	1.50	2.00	3.00
FRIENDS FROM THE BEGINNING	ALA (S) 1972	3.00	4.50	6.00
HENDRIX BAND OF GYPSYS (With Buddy Miles & Billy Cox)	Capitol (S) STAO 472	3.00	4.50	6.00
HENDRIX IN THE WEST	Reprise (S) 2049	2.50	3.75	5.00
IN CONCERT	Springboard (M) 4031	2.00	3.00	4.00
IN THE BEGINNING	Shout (M) 502	3.00	4.50	6.00
IN THE BEGINNING . . . THE ISLEY BROTHERS AND JIMI HENDRIX	T Neck (S) TNS 3007	5.00	8.00	12.00
JIMI HENDRIX AND CURTIS KNIGHT GET THAT FEELING	Capitol (S) ST 2856	3.00	4.50	6.00
JIMI HENDRIX TOGETHER WITH LONNIE YOUNGBLOOD	Maple (S) 6004	3.00	4.50	6.00
MIDNIGHT LIGHTNING	Reprise (S) 2229	2.50	3.75	5.00
SMASH HITS	Reprise (S) 2025	3.00	4.50	6.00
VERY BEST OF THE WORLD OF JIMI HENDRIX, THE	United Artists (S) UA-LA505	2.50	3.75	5.00
WAR HEROES	Reprise (S) 2103	2.50	3.75	5.00

HENRY, Clarence "Frogman"

TITLE	LABEL & NO.	GOOD	VERY GOOD	NEAR MINT
CLARENCE "FROGMAN" HENRY	Roulette (M) 42039	5.00	10.00	15.00
YOU ALWAYS HURT THE ONE YOU LOVE	Argo (M) LP 4009	6.00	15.00	24.00

HENSKE AND LESTER

TITLE	LABEL & NO.	GOOD	VERY GOOD	NEAR MINT
FAREWELL ALDEBARAN	Reprise (M) 6388	3.00	4.50	6.00

HENSUE, Judy

TITLE	LABEL & NO.	GOOD	VERY GOOD	NEAR MINT
LITTLE BIT OF SUNSHINE LITTLE BIT OF RAIN	Mercury (M) MG 21010	3.50	7.00	10.50
LITTLE BIT OF SUNSHINE LITTLE BIT OF RAIN	Mercury (S) SR 61010	4.00	8.00	12.00

HERD

TITLE	LABEL & NO.	GOOD	VERY GOOD	NEAR MINT
LOOKIN THRU YOU	Fontana (S) SRF 67579	5.00	7.50	10.00

TITLE	LABEL & NO.	GOOD	VERY GOOD	NEAR MINT
HERMAN'S HERMITS				
BEST OF HERMAN'S HERMITS, THE	MGM (M) E 4315	4.00	8.00	12.00
BEST OF HERMAN'S HERMITS, THE VOL. 2	MGM (M) E 4416	3.00	6.00	9.00
BEST OF HERMAN'S HERMITS, THE VOL. 2	MGM (S) SE 4416	4.00	8.00	12.00
BEST OF HERMAN'S HERMITS, THE VOL. 3	MGM (M) E 4505	3.00	6.00	9.00
BEST OF HERMAN'S HERMITS, THE VOL. 3	MGM (S) SE 4505	4.00	8.00	12.00
BLAZE	MGM (M) E 4478	3.50	7.00	10.50
BLAZE	MGM (S) SE 4478	4.50	9.00	13.50
BOTH SIDES OF HERMAN'S HERMITS	MGM (M) E 4386	3.00	6.00	9.00
BOTH SIDES OF HERMAN'S HERMITS	MGM (S) SE 4386	4.00	8.00	12.00
HERMAN'S HERMITS XX	ABKCO (S) 4227	2.50	3.75	5.00
INTRODUCING HERMAN'S HERMITS	MGM (M) E 4282	3.00	6.00	9.00
INTRODUCING HERMAN'S HERMITS	MGM (S) SE 4282	4.00	8.00	12.00
MRS. BROWN YOU'VE GOT A LOVELY DAUGHTER	MGM (M) E 4548	3.00	6.00	9.00
MRS. BROWN YOU'VE GOT A LOVELY DAUGHTER	MGM (S) SE 4548	4.00	8.00	12.00
ON TOUR	MGM (M) E 4295	3.00	6.00	9.00
ON TOUR	MGM (S) SE 4295	4.00	8.00	12.00
THERE'S A KIND OF HUSH ALL OVER THE WORLD	MGM (M) E 4438	3.00	6.00	9.00
THERE'S A KIND OF HUSH ALL OVER THE WORLD	MGM (S) SE 4438	4.00	8.00	12.00
HERON, Mike				
SMILING MEN WITH BAD REPUTATIONS	Elektra (S) EKS 74093	3.00	4.50	6.00
HESITATIONS				
BORN FREE (NEW)	Kapp (M) 1548	2.00	3.00	4.00
BORN FREE (NEW)	Kapp (S) 3548	3.00	4.50	6.00
SOLID GOLD	Kapp (M) 1574	2.00	3.00	4.00
SOLID GOLD	Kapp (S) 3574	3.00	4.50	6.00
WHERE WE'RE AT	Kapp (M) 1561	2.00	3.00	4.00
WHERE WE'RE AT	Kapp (S) 3561	3.00	4.50	6.00
HESTER, Carolyn				
CAROLYN HESTER	Columbia (M) 1796	7.00	14.00	21.00
(Features Bob Dylan on harmonica.)				
CAROLYN HESTER	Columbia (S) 3596	8.00	16.00	24.00
(Features Bob Dylan on harmonica.)				
CAROLYN HESTER AT TOWN HALL, ONE	Dot (M) DLP 3649	2.50	5.00	7.50
CAROLYN HESTER AT TOWN HALL, ONE	Dot (S) DLP 25649	3.00	6.00	9.00
THAT'S MY SONG	Dot (M) DLP 3604	2.50	5.00	7.50
THAT'S MY SONG	Dot (S) DLP 25604	3.00	6.00	9.00
HEYES, Mark				
WORDS AND MUSIC OF MARK HEYES, THE	Good Sounds (M) JAT-101	4.00	6.00	8.00
HIBBLER, Al				
AL HIBBLER REMEMBERS (BIG SONGS OF THE BIG BANDS)	Decca (M) DL-8862	3.00	4.50	6.00
AL HIBBLER REMEMBERS (BIG SONGS OF THE BIG BANDS)	Decca (S) DL-78862	4.00	6.00	8.00
AL HIBBLER SINGS DUKE ELLINGTON	Morgan (EP) N 24	3.00	4.50	6.00
AL HIBBLER SINGS DUKE ELLINGTON	Morgan (EP) 25	3.00	4.50	6.00
AL HIBBLER FAVORITES	Norgran (M) MG N4	6.00	9.00	12.00
AL HIBBLER FAVORITES	Norgran (EP) EP N 7	3.00	4.50	6.00
DUKE ELLINGTON PRESENTS AL HIBBLER	RCA (EP) EPAT 435	1.50	2.25	3.00
HERE'S HIBBLER	Decca (M) DL 8420	3.00	4.50	6.00
HERE'S HIBBLER	Decca (EP) ED 2445	1.50	2.25	3.00
HERE'S HIBBLER	Decca (EP) ED 2446	1.50	2.25	3.00
HERE'S HIBBLER	Decca (EP) ED 2447	1.50	2.25	3.00
STARRING AL HIBBLER	Decca (EP) ED 2410	1.50	2.25	3.00
STARRING AL HIBBLER	Decca (EP) ED 2411	1.50	2.25	3.00
STARRING AL HIBBLER	Decca (EP) ED 2412	1.50	2.25	3.00
UNCHAINED MELODIES	Decca (EP) ED 2283	1.50	2.25	3.00
VOICE OF HIBBLER AFTER THE LIGHTS GO DOWN, STARRING AL HIBBLER	Decca (M) DL 8328	3.00	4.50	6.00
HICKMAN, Dwayne				
SONGS BY DWAYNE HICKMAN	Capitol (M) 11441	6.00	12.00	18.00
HICKOK, Wild Bill				
ON THE SANTA FE TRAIL	Sunset (M) LP 500	3.00	4.50	6.00
ON THE SANTA FE TRAIL	Sunset (EP) SST 500	2.00	3.00	4.00
ON THE SANTA FE TRAIL	Sunset (EP) EP 2-500	2.00	3.00	4.00
HICKS, Joe				
MIGHTY	Enterprise (S) ENS 1028	3.00	4.50	6.00
HIGGINS, Chuck				
CHUCK HIGGINS	Combo (EP) EP-2	2.00	5.00	8.00
MOTOR HEAD CHUCK	Rollin Rock (S) LP 003	4.00	6.00	8.00
PACHUKO HOP	Combo (M) LP 300	10.00	25.00	40.00
RHYTHM ROCK AND ROLL	Dooto (EP) EP 208	2.00	5.00	8.00
HIGH TIDE				
SEA SHANTIES	Liberty (S) LST 7638	4.50	6.75	9.00
HIGHTOWER, Dean				
TWANGY WITH A BEAT	ABC/Paramount (M) ABC 312	5.00	10.00	15.00

(M) Mono (S) Stereo (EP) Extended Play (Q) Quad (RI) Re-issued

TITLE	LABEL & NO.	GOOD	VERY GOOD	NEAR MINT
HIGH TREASON				
HIGH TREASON	Abbott (S) ABS 1209	2.50	3.75	5.00
HIGHWAYMEN				
ENCORE	United Artists (M) UAL-3225	2.50	3.75	5.00
ENCORE	United Artists (S) UAS-6225	2.50	3.75	5.00
HIGHWAYMEN	United Artists (M) UAL-3125	3.00	4.50	6.00
HIGHWAYMEN	United Artists (S) UAS-6125	3.00	4.50	6.00
STANDING ROOM ONLY	United Artists (M) UAL-3168	2.50	3.75	5.00
STANDING ROOM ONLY	United Artists (S) UAS-6168	2.50	3.75	5.00
HI LITES				
FOR YOUR PRECIOUS LOVE	Dandee (M) DLP 206	4.00	8.00	12.00
HILL, Dan				
DAN HILL	20th Century (S) T-500	2.50	3.75	5.00
LONGER FUSE	20th Century (S) T-547	2.00	3.00	4.00
HILL, Jesse				
NATURALLY	Blue Thumb (S) BTS 31	2.00	3.00	4.00
HILL, Vince				
AT THE CLUB	Tower (M) T 5064	3.00	4.50	6.00
HILL, Z.Z.				
BEST THING THAT'S HAPPENED TO ME, THE	United Artists (S) UAS 5589	2.00	3.00	4.00
GREATEST HITS/DUES PAID IN FULL	Kent (S) KST 560	3.50	5.25	7.00
KEEP ON LOVIN' YOU	United Artists (S) UA-LA417	2.00	3.00	4.00
A WHOLE LOT OF SOUL	Kent (S) KST 528	3.50	5.25	7.00
HILLMEN				
HILLMEN, THE	Together (S) 1012	6.00	9.00	12.00
HILLOW HAMET				
HILLOW HAMET'S HAMMER	House of Fox (S) HOF LP 2	3.50	5.25	7.00
HILLTOPPERS				
HILL TOPPERS, THE	Dot (M) DLP 3073	3.00	4.50	6.00
HILLTOPPERS SING	Dot (M) 3003	4.00	6.00	8.00
HILLTOPPERS SING	Dot (EP) DEP 1006	2.00	3.00	4.00
HILLTOPPERS SING	Dot (EP) DEP 1007	2.00	3.00	4.00
HILLTOPPERS SING	Dot (EP) DEP 1008	2.00	3.00	4.00
HILLTOPPERS SING	Dot (EP) DEP 1009	2.00	3.00	4.00
HILLTOPPERS SING	Dot (EP) DEP 1011	2.00	3.00	4.00
HILLTOPPERS SING	Dot (EP) DEP 1012	2.00	3.00	4.00
TOWERING HILLTOPPERS	Dot (M) DLP 3029	3.00	4.50	6.00
HINES, Rupert & David McIver				
PICK UP A BONE	Capitol (S) SMAS 879	8.00	12.00	16.00
HINSON, Don & The Rigur Murticians				
MONSTER DANCE PARTY	Capitol (S) 2219	4.00	6.00	8.00
HINTON, Joe				
FUNNY (HOW TIME SLIPS AWAY)	Backbeat (M) B-60	4.00	8.00	12.00
HOBBITS				
DOWN TO MIDDLE EARTH	Decca (S) DL 74920	4.50	6.75	9.00
MEN AND DOORS	Decca (S) DL 75009	4.50	6.75	9.00
HOG HEAVEN				
HOG HEAVEN	Roulette (S) SR 42057	5.50	7.75	11.00
HOGAN, Silas				
TROUBLE	Excello (M) EX 8019	4.00	8.00	12.00

82

TITLE	LABEL & NO.	GOOD	VERY GOOD	NEAR MINT
HOGG, Smokey				
SMOKEY HOGG	Time (S) 6B	6.00	12.00	18.00
HOKUS POKUS				
HOKUS POKUS	Romar (S) RM 2002	3.00	4.50	6.00
HOLDEN, Ron				
I LOVE YOU SO	Donna (M) DLP 2111	5.00	12.50	20.00
HOLDER, Ram Jam				
BLACK LONDON BLUES	Philips (S) PHS 600-324	5.00	7.50	10.00
HOLIDAY, Jimmy				
TURNING POINT	Minit (M) LP 24005	3.00	4.50	6.00
HOLLAND, Eddie				
EDDIE HOLLAND	Motown (M) 604	4.00	8.00	12.00
HOLLIES				
ANOTHER NIGHT	Epic (S) PE-33387	3.00	4.50	6.00
BUS STOP	Imperial (M) LP 9330	4.00	8.00	12.00
BUS STOP	Imperial (S) LP 12330	5.00	10.00	15.00
DEAR ELOISE/KING MIDAS IN REVERSE	Epic (M) LN 24344	2.50	3.75	5.00
DEAR ELOISE/KING MIDAS IN REVERSE	Epic (S) BN 26344	3.50	5.25	7.00
DISTANT LIGHT	Epic (S) 30958	2.50	3.75	5.00
EVOLUTION	Epic (M) LN 24315	2.50	3.75	5.00
EVOLUTION	Epic (S) BN 26315	3.50	5.25	7.00
GREATEST HITS	Imperial (M) LP 9350	4.00	6.00	8.00
GREATEST HITS	Imperial (S) LP 12350	5.00	7.50	10.00
HE AIN'T HEAVY, HE'S MY BROTHER	Epic (S) BN 26538	3.50	5.25	7.00
HEAR! HERE!	Imperial (M) LP 9299	4.00	8.00	12.00
HEAR! HERE!	Imperial (S) LP 12299	5.00	10.00	15.00
HERE I GO AGAIN	Imperial (M) LP 9265	4.00	8.00	12.00
HERE I GO AGAIN	Imperial (S) LP 12265	5.00	10.00	15.00
HOLLIES, THE	Imperial (M) LP 9312	4.00	8.00	12.00
HOLLIES, THE	Imperial (S) LP 12312	5.00	10.00	15.00
MOVING FINGER	Epic (S) 30255	3.50	5.25	7.00
ROMANY	Epic (S) KE-31992	2.50	3.75	5.00
STOP! STOP! STOP!	Imperial (M) LP 9339	4.00	8.00	12.00
STOP! STOP! STOP!	Imperial (S) LP 12339	5.00	10.00	15.00
VERY BEST OF THE HOLLIES	United Artists (S) UA-LA329	2.00	3.00	4.00
WORDS AND MUSIC BY BOB DYLAN	Epic (S) BN 26447	3.50	5.25	7.00
HOLLOWAY, Brenda				
EVERY LITTLE BIT HURTS	Tamla (M) 257	4.00	8.00	12.00
HOLLY, Buddy				
BEST OF BUDDY HOLLY	Coral (M) CXB-8	5.00	10.00	15.00
BEST OF BUDDY HOLLY	Coral (SE) CXSB7-8	7.00	14.00	21.00
BROWN EYED HANDSOME MAN	Coral (EP) EC 81193	4.00	10.00	16.00
BUDDY HOLLY	Coral (M) CRL 57210	10.00	25.00	40.00

TITLE	LABEL & NO.	GOOD	VERY GOOD	NEAR MINT
BUDDY HOLLY	Coral (M) CRT-57279	6.00	15.00	24.00
(The back cover of the first pressing of this LP had no photoes. But was instead entirely text written in both black and red ink.)				
BUDDY HOLLY AND THE CRICKETS	Coral (M) CRL 57405	7.00	17.50	28.00
BUDDY HOLLY AND THE CRICKETS	Coral (S) CRL7 57405	6.00	15.00	24.00
BUDDY HOLLY STORY, THE	Coral (M) CRL 57279	10.00	15.00	20.00
BUDDY HOLLY STORY	Coral (M) CRL-57279	5.00	12.50	20.00
(The back cover of the second pressing was the same as the first, except the text on the back cover was only in black ink.)				
BUDDY HOLLY STORY, THE	Coral (S) CRL 7 57279	10.00	15.00	20.00
BUDDY HOLLY STORY	Coral (S) CRL7-57279	3.00	7.50	12.00
(The third pressing had a multi-color label, and pictures of other Buddy Holly albums on the back.)				
BUDDY HOLLY STORY,THE	Coral (EP) EC 81182	4.00	10.00	16.00
BUDDY HOLLY STORY, THE VOL. 2	Coral (M) CRL 57326	6.00	15.00	24.00
BUDDY HOLLY STORY, THE VOL. 2	Coral (S) CRL7 57326	10.00	15.00	20.00
GIANT	Coral (M) CRL 57504	4.00	6.00	8.00
GIANT	Coral (S) CRL 7 57504	5.00	7.50	10.00
GOOD ROCKIN'	Vocalion (M) 73923	7.00	14.00	21.00
GREAT BUDDY HOLLY, THE	Vocalion (M) VL 3811	3.00	4.50	6.00
GREATEST HITS	Coral (M) CRL 57492	7.00	14.00	21.00
GREATEST HITS	Coral (S) CRL 7 57492	5.00	10.00	15.00
HOLLY IN THE HILLS (WITH BOB MONTGOMERY)	Coral (M) CRL 57463	5.00	10.00	15.00
HOLLY IN THE HILLS (WITH BOB MONTGOMERY)	Coral (S) CRL7 57463	5.00	10.00	15.00
LISTEN TO ME	Coral (EP) EC 81169	5.00	12.50	20.00
PEGGY SUE GOT MARRIED	Coral (EP) EC 81191	4.00	10.00	16.00
REMINISCING	Coral (M) CRL 57426	8.00	16.00	24.00
REMINISCING	Coral (S) CRL7 57426	7.00	14.00	21.00
A ROCK AND ROLL COLLECTION	Decca (M) DXSE 7 207	8.00	12.00	16.00
SHOWCASE	Coral (M) CRL 57450	7.00	14.00	21.00
SHOWCASE	Coral (S) CRL7 57450	5.00	10.00	15.00
THAT'LL BE THE DAY	Decca (M) DL 8707	22.50	56.25	90.00
(Black label; pink label promo same price as black label.)				
THAT'LL BE THE DAY (Colored Label)	Decca (M) DL 8707	10.00	25.00	40.00
THAT'LL BE THE DAY	Decca (EP) ED 2575	40.00	80.00	120.00
All original first pressing Buddy Holly LP's are on the maroon Coral label. Also see CRICKETS				
HOLLYRIDGE STRINGS				
BEACH BOYS' SONG BOOK	Capitol (M) T-2156	2.50	3.75	5.00
BEACH BOYS' SONG BOOK	Capitol (S) ST-2156	2.50	3.75	5.00
BEATLES SONG BOOK	Capitol (M) T-2202	2.50	3.75	5.00
BEATLES SONG BOOK	Capitol (S) ST-2202	2.50	3.75	5.00
BEATLES SONG BOOK	Capitol (S) ST-2876	2.00	3.00	4.00
BEATLES SONG BOOK (VOL. 2)	Capitol (M) T-2116	2.50	3.75	5.00
BEATLES SONG BOOK (VOL. 2)	Capitol (S) ST-2116	2.50	3.75	5.00
FOUR SEASONS SONG BOOK	Capitol (M) T-2199	2.50	3.75	5.00
FOUR SEASONS SONG BOOK	Capitol (S) ST-2199	2.50	3.75	5.00
HOLLYRIDGE STRINGS PLAY (HITS OF SIMON & GARFUNKEL)	Capitol (S) ST-2998	2.00	3.00	4.00

(M) Mono   (S) Stereo   (EP) Extended Play   (Q) Quad   (RI) Re-issued

TITLE	LABEL & NO.	GOOD	VERY GOOD	NEAR MINT
HOLLYRIDGE STRINGS (PLAY HIT SONGS MADE FAMOUS BY ELVIS PRESLEY)	Capitol (M) T-2221	5.00	7.50	10.00
HOLLYRIDGE STRINGS (PLAY HIT SONGS MADE FAMOUS BY ELVIS PRESLEY)	Capitol (S) ST-2221	6.00	9.00	12.00
NAT KING COLE SONGBOOK	Capitol (M) T-2310	2.00	3.00	4.00
NAT KING COLE SONGBOOK	Capitol (S) ST-2310	2.00	3.00	4.00
NEW BEATLES SONG BOOK	Capitol (M) T-2429	2.50	3.75	5.00
NEW BEATLES SONG BOOK	Capitol (S) ST-2429	2.50	3.75	5.00
OLDIES BUT GOLDIES	Capitol (M) T-2564	2.50	3.75	5.00
OLDIES BUT GOLDIES	Capitol (S) ST-2564	2.50	3.75	5.00

HOLLYWOOD ARGYLES

TITLE	LABEL & NO.	GOOD	VERY GOOD	NEAR MINT
ALLEY OOP	Lute (M) L-9001	12.00	30.00	48.00

HOLMAN, Eddie

TITLE	LABEL & NO.	GOOD	VERY GOOD	NEAR MINT
I LOVE YOU	ABC (S) ABCS 701	3.00	4.50	6.00

HOLMBERG, Jim

TITLE	LABEL & NO.	GOOD	VERY GOOD	NEAR MINT
MIJ	ESP (S) 1098	4.00	6.00	8.00

HOLTS, Roosevelt

TITLE	LABEL & NO.	GOOD	VERY GOOD	NEAR MINT
PRESENTING THE COUNTRY BLUES	Blue Horizon (M) BH 7704	4.00	6.00	8.00

HOLY MACKEREL

TITLE	LABEL & NO.	GOOD	VERY GOOD	NEAR MINT
HOLY MACKEREL, THE	Reprise (S) 6311	2.50	3.75	5.00

HOLY MODAL ROUNDERS

TITLE	LABEL & NO.	GOOD	VERY GOOD	NEAR MINT
GOOD TASTE IS TIMELESS	Metromedia (S) MD 1039	3.50	5.25	7.00
HOLY MODAL ROUNDERS, THE	Prestige (M) 7451	5.00	7.50	10.00
HOLY MODAL ROUNDERS, THE	Prestige (M) 7410	5.00	7.50	10.00
INDIAN WAR WHOOP	ESP (M) 1068	4.00	6.00	8.00
STAMPFEL AND WEBER	Fantasy (S) 24711	2.50	3.75	5.00

HOMBRES

TITLE	LABEL & NO.	GOOD	VERY GOOD	NEAR MINT
LET IT OUT	Verve/Forecast (M) FT 3036	3.00	4.50	6.00
LET IT OUT	Verve/Forecast-(S) FTS 3036	4.00	6.00	8.00

HOME

TITLE	LABEL & NO.	GOOD	VERY GOOD	NEAR MINT
PAUSE FOR A HOARSE HORSE	Epic (S) E-31146	3.00	4.50	6.00

HOMEGAS

TITLE	LABEL & NO.	GOOD	VERY GOOD	NEAR MINT
HOMEGAS	Tacoma (S) 1026	2.50	3.75	5.00

HOMER & JETHRO

TITLE	LABEL & NO.	GOOD	VERY GOOD	NEAR MINT
ASSAULT TOP POPS	RCA (EP) EPA 499	2.00	3.00	4.00
BAREFOOT BALLADS	RCA (M) LPM 1412	3.00	4.50	6.00
BAREFOOT BALLADS	RCA (EP) EPA 1-1412	2.00	3.00	4.00
BAREFOOT BALLADS	RCA (EP) EPA 2-1412	2.00	3.00	4.00
CORNFUCIUS SAY	RCA (M) LPM-2928	2.00	3.00	4.00
CORNFUCIUS SAY	RCA (S) LSP-2928	2.00	3.00	4.00
CORNIER THAN CORN	King (M) 848	4.00	6.00	8.00
FRACTURED FOLK SONGS	RCA (M) LPM-2954	2.00	3.00	4.00
FRACTURED FOLK SONGS	RCA (S) LSP-2954	2.00	3.00	4.00
HERNANDO'S HIDEAWAY	RCA (EP) EPA 580	2.00	3.00	4.00
HOMER & JETHRO	Audio Lab (EP) 4	2.50	3.75	5.00
HOMER & JETHRO AT THE CONVENTION	RCA (M) LPM-2492	2.50	3.75	5.00
HOMER & JETHRO AT THE CONVENTION	RCA (S) LSP-2492	2.50	3.75	5.00
HOMER & JETHRO AT THE COUNTRY CLUB	RCA (M) LPM-2181	2.50	3.75	5.00
HOMER & JETHRO AT THE COUNTRY CLUB	RCA (S) LSP-2181	2.50	3.75	5.00
HOMER & JETHRO ENCORE	King (EP) EP 317	2.00	3.00	4.00
HOMER & JETHRO GO WEST	RCA (M) LPM-2674	2.50	3.75	5.00
HOMER & JETHRO GO WEST	RCA (S) LSP-2674	2.50	3.75	5.00
HOMER & JETHRO (THEIR VERSION OF THE STANDARDS)	King (M) 639	4.00	6.00	8.00
HUMOROUS SIDE OF COUNTRY MUSIC WITH HOMER & JETHRO	Camden (M) CAL-768	2.00	3.00	4.00
KID THE TOP POPS	RCA (EP) EPA 429	2.00	3.00	4.00
LET ME GO BLUBBER	RCA (EP) EPA 595	2.00	3.00	4.00
LIFE CAN BE MISERABLE	RCA (M) LPM-1880	3.00	4.50	6.00
LIFE CAN BE MISERABLE	RCA (S) LSP-1880	3.00	4.50	6.00
MURDER THE STANDARDS	King (EP) EP 226	2.00	3.00	4.00
OOH, THAT'S CORNY	RCA (M) LPM-2743	2.50	3.75	5.00
OOH, THAT'S CORNY	RCA (S) LSP 2743	2.50	3.75	5.00
PLAYING IT STRAIGHT	RCA (M) LPM-2459	2.50	3.75	5.00
PLAYING IT STRAIGHT	RCA (S) LSP-2459	2.50	3.75	5.00
SEASONED GREETINS	RCA (EP) EPA 1534	2.00	3.00	4.00
SONGS MY MOTHER NEVER SANG	RCA (M) LPM-2286	2.50	3.75	5.00
SONGS MY MOTHER NEVER SANG	RCA (S) LSP-2286	2.50	3.75	5.00
THIS IS MY WIFE	RCA (EP) EPA 716	2.00	3.00	4.00
WORST OF HOMER & JETHRO, THE	RCA (M) LPM 1560	3.00	4.50	6.00
WORST OF HOMER & JETHRO, THE	RCA (EP) EPA 1-1560	1.50	2.25	3.00
ZANY SONGS OF THE 30's	RCA (M) LPM-2455	2.50	3.75	5.00
ZANY SONGS OF THE 30's	RCA (S) LSP-2455	2.50	3.75	5.00

HOMESICK JAMES

TITLE	LABEL & NO.	GOOD	VERY GOOD	NEAR MINT
BLUES ON THE SOUTH SIDE	Prestige (M) PR 7388	5.00	10.00	15.00

HONDELLS

TITLE	LABEL & NO.	GOOD	VERY GOOD	NEAR MINT
GO LITTLE HONDA	Mercury (M) MG 20940	5.00	10.00	15.00
GO LITTLE HONDA	Mercury (S) SR 60940	6.00	12.00	18.00
HONDELLS, THE	Mercury (M) MG 20982	5.00	10.00	15.00
HONDELLS, THE	Mercury (S) SR 60982	6.00	12.00	18.00

HONEY & THE BEES

TITLE	LABEL & NO.	GOOD	VERY GOOD	NEAR MINT
HONEY AND THE BEES	Josie (S) JOS 4013	4.50	9.00	13.50

HONEYCOMBS

TITLE	LABEL & NO.	GOOD	VERY GOOD	NEAR MINT
HERE ARE THE HONEYCOMBS	Interphon (M) IN 88001	5.00	10.00	15.00
HERE ARE THE HONEYCOMBS	Interphon (M) 88001	9.00	13.50	18.00

HOODOO RHYTHM DEVILS

TITLE	LABEL & NO.	GOOD	VERY GOOD	NEAR MINT
BARBEQUE OF DEVILLE, THE	Blue Thumb (S) BTS 42	2.50	3.75	5.00
HOODOO RHYTHM DEVILS	Capitol (S) ST 842	3.00	4.50	6.00
JOE CRANE AND HIS HOODOO RHYTHM DEVILS	Funky Features (EP)	5.00	7.50	10.00
WHAT THE KIDS WANT	Blue Thumb (S) BTS 57	2.50	3.75	5.00

HOOK

TITLE	LABEL & NO.	GOOD	VERY GOOD	NEAR MINT
HOOK WILL GRAB YOU, THE	Uni (M) 73023	3.00	4.50	6.00
HOOKED	Uni (M) 73038	3.00	4.50	6.00

HOOKER, Earl

TITLE	LABEL & NO.	GOOD	VERY GOOD	NEAR MINT
DO YOU REMEMBER THE GREAT EARL HOOKER	Bluesway (M) 6072	2.50	4.00	5.00
GENIUS, THE	Cuca (M) 3400	3.00	4.50	6.00
HOOKER AND STEVE	Arhoolie (M) 1051	3.50	5.25	7.00
SWEET BLACK ANGEL	Blue Thumb (M) 12	2.00	3.00	4.00
TWO BUGS AND A ROACH	Arhoolie (M) 1044	2.00	3.00	4.00

HOOKER, John Lee

TITLE	LABEL & NO.	GOOD	VERY GOOD	NEAR MINT
BEST OF JOHN LEE HOOKER, THE	Vee Jay (M) LP1049	3.00	4.00	6.00
BEST OF JOHN LEE HOOKER, THE	Vee Jay (S) 1049	3.00	4.00	6.00
BIG BAND BLUES	Buddah (M) 7506	2.50	4.00	5.00
BIG SOUL OF JOHN LEE HOOKER, THE	Vee Jay (M) LP 1058	3.00	4.00	6.00
BIG SOUL OF JOHN LEE HOOKER, THE	Vee Jay (S) 1058	3.00	4.00	6.00
BLUES, THE	United (M) 7725	2.50	4.00	5.00
BORN IN MISSISSIPPI	ABC (M) 768	2.00	3.00	4.00
BURNIN'	Vee Jay (M) LP 1043	3.00	4.00	6.00
BURNIN'	Vee Jay (S) 1043	3.00	4.00	6.00
CONCERT AT NEWPORT	Vee Jay (M) LP 1078	3.00	4.00	6.00
CONCERT AT NEWPORT	Vee Jay (S) 1078	3.00	4.00	6.00
DETROIT SPECIAL	Atlantic (S) SD 7228	3.00	4.50	6.00
DON'T TURN ME FROM YOUR DOOR	Atco (M) 151	4.00	10.00	16.00
DRIFTIN' THROUGH THE BLUES	United (M) 7710	2.50	3.75	5.00
DRIFTIN' THROUGH THE BLUES	Custom (M) CM 2048	2.50	3.75	5.00
DRIFTIN' THROUGH THE BLUES	Custom (S) CS 2048	2.50	3.75	5.00
FOLK BLUES	United (M) 7729	2.50	3.75	5.00
FOLK BLUES	Crown (M) CLP 5295	2.50	3.75	5.00
FOLK LORE OF JOHN LEE HOOKER, THE	Vee Jay (M) LP 1033	3.00	4.50	6.00
GREAT BLUES SOUNDS OF JOHN LEE HOOKER, THE	United (M) UM 731	2.00	3.00	4.00
GREATEST HITS	United (M) 7746	2.50	3.75	5.00
GREATEST HITS OF JOHN LEE HOOKER	United (M) 7769	2.50	3.75	5.00
GREAT JOHN LEE HOOKER	Crown (M) CLP 5353	2.50	3.75	5.00
HOUSE OF THE BLUES	Chess (M) LP 1438	2.50	3.75	5.00
I FEEL GOOD	Jewel (M) 5005	2.00	3.00	4.00
IF YOU MISS IM	Bluesway (S) 6038	2.50	3.75	5.00
I'M JOHN LEE HOOKER	Vee Jay (M) LP 1007	3.00	4.50	6.00
IS HE THE WORLDS GREATEST BLUES SINGER	Exodus (M) 325	2.50	3.75	5.00
IT SERVE YOU RIGHT TO SUFFER	Impulse (EP) A 9103	1.50	2.25	3.00
JOHN LEE HOOKER	Galaxy (M) 201	2.50	3.75	5.00
JOHN LEE HOOKER	Galaxy (S) 8-201	2.50	3.75	5.00
JOHN LEE HOOKER	Battle (M) 6113	5.00	7.50	10.00
JOHN LEE HOOKER PLAYS AND SINGS THE BLUES	Chess (M) LP 1454	2.50	3.75	5.00
JOHN LEE HOOKER SINGS THE BLUES	King (M) 727	5.00	7.50	10.00
JOHN LEE HOOKER SINGS THE BLUES	Crown (M) CLP 5232	2.50	3.75	5.00
LIVE AT KABUKI WUKI	Bluesway (S) 6052	2.50	3.75	5.00
LIVE AT SOLEDAD PRISON	ABC (M) 761	2.00	3.00	4.00
MAD MANS BLUES	Chess (M) 2CH 60011	2.50	3.75	5.00
MOANIN' AND STOMPIN' BLUES	King (S) KS 1085	3.50	5.25	7.00
ON CAMPUS	Vee Jay (M) LP 1066	3.00	4.00	6.00
ON CAMPUS	Vee Jay (S) 1066	3.00	4.50	6.00
ORIGINAL FOLK BLUES	United (M) 7769	2.50	3.75	5.00
REAL BLUES	Tradition (M) 2089	2.50	3.75	5.00
SEVEN NIGHTS	Verve Folkways (M) 3003	2.00	3.00	4.00
SEVEN NIGHTS	Verve Folkways (S) 3003	2.00	3.00	4.00
SIMPLY THE TRUTH	Bluesway (S) 6023	2.50	3.75	5.00
THAT'S WHERE IT'S AT	Stax (M) 2013	2.50	3.75	5.00
TRAVELIN'	Vee Jay (M) LP 1023	3.00	4.00	6.00
URBAN BLUES	Bluesway (S) 6012	2.50	4.50	5.00
WITH JOHN MAYALL & THE GROUNDHOGS	Cleve (S) CH-82871	9.00	13.50	18.00
YOU RIGHT TO SUFFER	Impulse (S) 9103	2.50	3.75	5.00

HOPE, Lynn

TITLE	LABEL & NO.	GOOD	VERY GOOD	NEAR MINT
LYNN HOPE AND HIS TENOR SAX (10")	Aladdin (M) 707	10.00	25.00	40.00

HOPKIN, Mary

TITLE	LABEL & NO.	GOOD	VERY GOOD	NEAR MINT
EARTH SONG/OCEAN SONG	Apple (S) SMAS-3381	4.00	6.00	8.00
KIDNAPPED	Air (S) 1042	2.50	3.75	5.00
POSTCARD	Apple (S) SW 3351	4.00	6.00	8.00
THOSE WERE THE DAYS	Apple (S) SW 3395	4.00	6.00	8.00

(M) Mono (S) Stereo (EP) Extended Play (Q) Quad (RI) Re-issued

HOPKINS, Lightnin

TITLE	LABEL & NO.	GOOD	VERY GOOD	NEAR MINT
AUTOBIOGRAPHY IN BLUES	Tradition (M) TLP 1040	2.00	3.00	4.00
BEST OF LIGHTNIN HOPKINS	Tradition (M) 2056	2.50	3.75	5.00
BEST OF LIGHTNIN HOPKINS	Harlem Hit Parade (M) 5013	2.00	3.00	4.00
BLUES UNDERGROUND	"D" (M) 8000	5.00	12.50	20.00
CALIFORNIA MUDSLIDE	Vault (S) 129	3.00	6.00	9.00
COUNTRY BLUES	Tradition (M) TLP 1035	2.00	3.00	4.00
DOWN HOME BLUES	Prestige (M) 1986	2.50	3.75	5.00
EARLY RECORDINGS	Arhoolie (M) 2007	2.50	3.75	5.00
FREE FORM PATTERNS	International Artists (M) 1A LP 6	5.00	12.50	20.00
GOIN' AWAY	Prestige (M) 1073	2.50	3.75	5.00
HIS GREATEST HITS	Bluesville (M) 1084	4.00	6.00	8.00
LAST OF THE GREAT BLUES SINGERS	Time (S) T 70004	5.00	7.50	10.00
LEGEND IN HIS TIME	United (M) 7785	2.00	3.00	4.00
LIGHTNIN'	Prestige (M) 1019	2.50	3.75	5.00
LIGHTNIN' AND THE BLUES	Herald (M) 1012	5.00	12.50	20.00
LIGHTNIN' HOPKINS	Herald (M) 1012	10.00	15.00	20.00
LIGHTNIN HOPKINS	Everest (M) 241	2.50	3.75	5.00
LIGHTNIN' HOPKINS AND THE BLUES	Imperial (M) 9211	3.00	6.00	9.00
LIGHTNIN' HOPKINS AND THE BLUES	Imperial (S) 12211	3.00	6.00	9.00
LIGHTNIN' HOPKINS SINGS THE BLUES	Imperial (M) 9186	3.00	6.00	9.00
LIGHTNIN' HOPKINS SINGS THE BLUES	United (M) 7713	2.50	3.75	5.00
LIGHTNIN' HOPKINS STRUMS THE BLUES	Score (M) 4022	7.00	17.50	28.00
LIGHTNIN STRIKES	Tradition (M) 2103	2.50	3.75	5.00
LIGHTNIN' STRIKES	Vee Jay (M) 1044	4.00	6.00	8.00
LIGHTNIN' STRIKES	Verve Folkways (M) FV 9022	2.00	3.00	4.00
LIGHTNIN' STRIKES	Verve Folkways (S) FVS 9022	2.00	3.00	4.00
LOW DOWN AND DIRTY	Mainstream (M) 405	1.50	2.00	3.00
MOJO HAND	Fire (M) F 104	5.00	12.50	20.00
MY LIFE IN THE BLUES	Prestige (M) 7370	5.00	7.50	10.00
ON STAGE	Imperial (M) 9180	3.00	6.00	9.00
ORIGINAL FOLK BLUES	United (M) 7744	2.00	3.00	4.00
SOUL BLUES	Prestige (M) 7377	2.50	3.75	5.00
SOUL BLUES	Prestige (S) PRS 7377	2.50	3.75	5.00
WALKIN' THIS ROAD BY MYSELF	Prestige (M) 1057	2.50	3.75	5.00

HOPKINS, Lightnin'/Sonny Terry

TITLE	LABEL & NO.	GOOD	VERY GOOD	NEAR MINT
LAST NIGHT BLUES	Prestige (M) BV-SP101	2.50	3.75	5.00
LAST NIGHT BLUES	Prestige (M) BV-1029	2.50	3.75	5.00
SMOKES LIKE LIGHTNING	Prestige (M) BV-1070	2.50	3.75	5.00

HORN, Sam

TITLE	LABEL & NO.	GOOD	VERY GOOD	NEAR MINT
SAM HORN FATHER OF THE BLUES	Columbia (M) 9217	2.50	3.75	5.00

HORNETS

TITLE	LABEL & NO.	GOOD	VERY GOOD	NEAR MINT
BIG DRAG BOATS USA	Liberty (M) LRP 3364	3.00	6.00	9.00
BIG DRAG BOATS USA	Liberty (S) LST 7364	3.50	7.00	10.50
MOTORCYCLES USA	Liberty (M) LRP 3348	3.00	6.00	9.00
MOTORCYCLES USA	Liberty (S) LST 7348	3.50	7.00	10.50

HORSES

TITLE	LABEL & NO.	GOOD	VERY GOOD	NEAR MINT
HORSES	White Whale (S) WW 7121	4.00	6.00	8.00

HORTON, Big Walter & Carey Bell

TITLE	LABEL & NO.	GOOD	VERY GOOD	NEAR MINT
BIG WALTER HORTON WITH CAREY BELL	Alligator (M) 4702	3.00	4.50	6.00

HORTON, Johnny

TITLE	LABEL & NO.	GOOD	VERY GOOD	NEAR MINT
BUMMIN' AROUND	Starday (M) S-325	4.00	6.00	8.00
FANTASTIC JOHNNY HORTON	Mercury (M) MG-20478	4.00	8.00	12.00
HONKY TONK MAN	Columbia (M) CL-1721	5.00	10.00	15.00
HONKY TONK MAN	Columbia (S) CS-8779	6.00	12.00	18.00
HONKY TONK MAN	Columbia (EP) B 2130	5.00	10.00	15.00
I CAN'T FORGET YOU	Columbia (M) CL-2299	2.50	3.75	5.00
I CAN'T FORGET YOU	Columbia (S) CS-9099	2.50	3.75	5.00
JOHNNY HORTON	Dot (M) DLP-3221	3.00	4.50	6.00
JOHNNY HORTON	Dot (M) DLP-25221	3.00	4.50	6.00
JOHNNY HORTON GREATEST HITS	Columbia (M) CL-1596	3.00	6.00	9.00
JOHNNY HORTON GREATEST HITS	Columbia (S) CS-8396	4.00	8.00	12.00
JOHNNY HORTON'S GREATEST HITS (With photo inset)	Columbia (M) CL1596	5.00	10.00	15.00
JOHNNY HORTON MAKES HISTORY	Columbia (M) CL-1478	3.00	7.50	12.00
JOHNNY HORTON MAKES HISTORY	Columbia (S) CS-8269	3.00	7.50	12.00
JOHNNY HORTON MAKES HISTORY	Columbia (EP) B-14781	2.00	4.00	6.00
JOHNNY HORTON MAKES HISTORY	Columbia (EP) B-14782	2.00	4.00	6.00
JOHNNY HORTON MAKES HISTORY	Columbia (EP) B-14783	2.00	4.00	6.00
JOHNNY HORTON ON THE LOUISIANA HAYRIDE	Columbia (M) CL-2566	2.50	3.75	5.00
JOHNNY HORTON ON THE LOUISIANA HAYRIDE	Columbia (S) CS-9366	2.50	3.75	5.00
REQUESTFULLY YOURS	Mercury (EP) EP 1-3091	5.00	10.00	15.00
SPECTACULAR JOHNNY HORTON	Columbia (M) CL-1362	4.00	10.00	16.00
SPECTACULAR JOHNNY HORTON	Columbia (S) SC-8167	5.00	12.00	20.00
SPECTACULAR JOHNNY HORTON	Columbia (EP) B-13621	3.00	6.00	9.00
SPECTACULAR JOHNNY HORTON	Columbia (EP) B-13622	3.00	6.00	9.00
SPECTACULAR JOHNNY HORTON	Columbia (EP) B-13623	3.00	6.00	9.00
UNFORGETTABLE JOHNNY HORTON	Harmony (S) 11291	2.00	3.00	4.00

HORTON, Shakey

TITLE	LABEL & NO.	GOOD	VERY GOOD	NEAR MINT
SOUL OF BLUES HARMONICA, THE	Argo (M) 4037	4.00	8.00	12.00

HORWITZ, Bill

TITLE	LABEL & NO.	GOOD	VERY GOOD	NEAR MINT
LIES, LIES, LIES	ESP (M) 3020	3.00	4.50	6.00

HOT DOGS

TITLE	LABEL & NO.	GOOD	VERY GOOD	NEAR MINT
SAY WHAT YOU MEAN	Ardent (S) ADS 2805	3.50	5.25	7.00

HOT DOGGERS

TITLE	LABEL & NO.	GOOD	VERY GOOD	NEAR MINT
SURFIN' U.S.A.	Epic (M) LN-24054	8.00	16.00	24.00
SURFIN' U.S.A.	Epic (S) BN-26054	9.00	18.00	27.00

HOT LEGS

TITLE	LABEL & NO.	GOOD	VERY GOOD	NEAR MINT
HOTLEGS THINKS: SCHOOL STINKS	Capitol (S) ST 587	7.00	10.50	14.00

HOT POOP

TITLE	LABEL & NO.	GOOD	VERY GOOD	NEAR MINT
HOT POOP DOES THEIR STUFF	Hot Poop (S) HPS 3072	9.00	18.00	27.00

HOT RODDERS

TITLE	LABEL & NO.	GOOD	VERY GOOD	NEAR MINT
BIG HOT ROD	Crown (S) CST 378	3.00	6.00	9.00

HOT TUNA

TITLE	LABEL & NO.	GOOD	VERY GOOD	NEAR MINT
AMERICA'S CHOICE	Grunt (Q) BFD1-0820	3.00	4.50	6.00
AMERICA'S FAVORITE	Grunt (S) BFL1-0820	3.00	4.50	6.00
BURGERS	Grunt (S) 1004	4.00	6.00	8.00
DOUBLE DOSE	Grunt (S) CYL2-2545	3.00	4.50	6.00
ELECTRIC HOT TUNA	RCA (S) LSP 4550	3.50	5.25	7.00
HOT TUNA	RCA (S) LSP 4353	3.50	5.25	7.00
PHOSPHORESCENT RAT	Grunt (S) BFL1-0348	3.00	4.50	6.00
YELLOW FEVER	Grunt (S) BFL1-1238	3.00	4.50	6.00
YELLOW FEVER	Grunt (Q) BFD1-1238	3.00	4.50	6.00

HOUR GLASS

TITLE	LABEL & NO.	GOOD	VERY GOOD	NEAR MINT
HOUR GLASS, THE	United Artists (M) UA-LA 013-G2	6.00	9.00	12.00
HOUR GLASS	Liberty (M) LRP 3536	4.00	6.00	8.00
HOUR GLASS	Liberty (S) LST 7536	5.00	7.50	10.00
POWER OF LOVE	Liberty (M) LRP 3555	4.00	6.00	8.00
POWER OF LOVE	Liberty (S) LST 7555	5.00	7.50	10.00

HOUSTON, Bee

TITLE	LABEL & NO.	GOOD	VERY GOOD	NEAR MINT
BEE HOUSTON	Arhoolie (M) 1050	3.50	5.25	7.00

HOUSTON, David

TITLE	LABEL & NO.	GOOD	VERY GOOD	NEAR MINT
ALMOST PERSUADED	Epic (M) LN 24213	2.00	3.00	4.00
ALMOST PERSUADED	Epic (S) BN 26213	2.00	3.00	4.00
DAVID HOUSTON (NEW VOICE FROM NASHVILLE)	Epic (M) LN-24112	2.50	3.75	5.00
DAVID HOUSTON (NEW VOICE FROM NASHVILLE)	Epic (S) BN-26112	2.50	3.75	5.00
DAVID HOUSTON SINGS	Camden (M) 2126	2.00	3.00	4.00
DAVID HOUSTON SINGS	Camden (S) 2126	2.00	3.00	4.00
MAN NEEDS LOVE	Epic (M) KE-33350	2.00	3.00	4.00

HOUSTON, Joe

TITLE	LABEL & NO.	GOOD	VERY GOOD	NEAR MINT
BLOWS ALL NIGHT LONG	Modern (M) LMP 1206	5.00	12.50	20.00
BLOWS ALL NIGHT LONG	Modern (EP) M 200	2.00	5.00	8.00
ROCK AND ROLL WITH JOE HOUSTON AND HIS ROCKERS	Tops (M) L 1518	3.00	7.50	12.00
ROCKS AND ROLLS ALL NITE LONG	Crown (M) CLP 5006	3.00	7.50	12.00
SURF ROCKIN'	Crown (S) CST 313	3.50	8.75	14.00

HOUSTON, Thelma

TITLE	LABEL & NO.	GOOD	VERY GOOD	NEAR MINT
THELMA HOUSTON	Mowest (M) 102	3.00	4.50	6.00

HOUSTON FEARLESS

TITLE	LABEL & NO.	GOOD	VERY GOOD	NEAR MINT
HOUSTON FEARLESS	Imperial (M) LP 12421	2.50	3.75	5.00

HOWARD, Harlan

TITLE	LABEL & NO.	GOOD	VERY GOOD	NEAR MINT
HARLAN HOWARD SINGS HARLAN HOWARD	Capitol (M) T-1631	3.00	4.50	6.00
HARLAN HOWARD SINGS HARLAN HOWARD	Capitol (S) ST-1631	3.00	4.50	6.00

HOWARD, Paul/Ralph Willis

TITLE	LABEL & NO.	GOOD	VERY GOOD	NEAR MINT
FADED PICTURE BLUES	King (M) 1098	2.00	3.00	4.00

HOWLIN' WOLF

TITLE	LABEL & NO.	GOOD	VERY GOOD	NEAR MINT
BACK DOOR WOLF, THE	Chess (M) CH 50045	2.50	3.75	5.00
BIG CITY BLUES	Custom (M) CM 2055	6.00	9.00	12.00
BIG CITY BLUES	Custom (S) CS 2055	3.00	4.50	6.00
BIG CITY BLUES	United (M) 7717	2.00	3.00	4.00
EVIL	Chess (M) LP 1540	7.00	10.50	14.00
HOWLIN' WOLF	Chess (M) LP 1469	7.00	10.50	14.00
HOWLING WOLF SINGS THE BLUES	Crown (M) CLP 5240	4.00	6.00	8.00
LONDON HOWLIN' WOLF SESSIONS, THE	Chess (M) CH 60008	3.00	4.50	6.00
MOANIN' IN THE MOONLIGHT	Chess (M) LP 1434	8.00	12.00	16.00
MORE REAL FOLK BLUES	Chess (M) LP 1512	7.00	10.50	14.00
MORE REAL FOLK BLUES	Chess (S) LPS 1512	4.00	6.00	8.00
ORIGINAL FOLK BLUES	Kent (S) KST 526	3.00	4.50	6.00
ORIGINAL FOLK BLUES	United (M) 7747	2.50	3.75	5.00
REAL FOLK BLUES, THE	Chess (M) LP 1502	7.00	10.50	14.00

HOWLIN WOLF & CHUCK BERRY

TITLE	LABEL & NO.	GOOD	VERY GOOD	NEAR MINT
POP ORIGINS	Chess (M) 1544	4.00	6.00	8.00

H. P. LOVECRAFT

TITLE	LABEL & NO.	GOOD	VERY GOOD	NEAR MINT
H.P. LOVECRAFT	Philips (M) PHM 200-252	4.00	6.00	8.00
H.P. LOVECRAFT	Philips (S) PHS 600-252	4.50	6.75	9.00
LOVECRAFT	Philips (S) PHS 600-279	4.00	6.00	8.00
VALLEY OF THE MOON	Reprise (S) RS 6419	3.50	5.25	7.00
WE LOVE YOU (WHOEVER YOU ARE)	Mercury (S) SRM1-1031	4.00	6.00	8.00

(M) Mono   (S) Stereo   (EP) Extended Play   (Q) Quad   (RI) Re-issued

TITLE	LABEL & NO.	GOOD	VERY GOOD	NEAR MINT
HUDSON BROTHERS				
BA-FA	Rocket (S) PIG 2169	2.50	3.75	5.00
HOLLYWOOD SITUATION	Casablanca (S) NB 9008	3.00	4.50	6.00
HUDSON	Playboy (S) PB 102	5.00	7.50	10.00
TOTALLY OUT OF CONTROL	Rocket (S) 460	2.50	3.75	5.00
HUGHES, Freddie				
SEND MY BABY BACK	Scepter (S) WDS 664	3.00	4.50	6.00
HUGHES, Jimmy				
SOMETHING SPECIAL	Volt (S) VOS 6003	2.50	3.75	5.00
STEAL AWAY	Vee Jay (M) 1102	5.00	7.50	10.00
WHY NOT TONIGHT	Atco (M) 33-209	3.00	4.50	6.00
HUGHES, Lynne				
FREEWAY GYPSY	Fontana (S) SRF 67611	5.00	7.50	10.00
HULIN, T.K.				
HIT MEMORIES	Starlite (S) LP 2004	4.00	6.00	8.00
HULLABALLOOS				
ENGLAND'S NEWEST SINGING SENSATIONS	Roulette (M) R 25297	5.00	10.00	15.00
ENGLAND'S NEWEST SINGING SENSATIONS	Roulette (S) SR 25297	6.00	12.00	18.00
HULLABALLOOS ON HULLABALLOO, THE	Roulette (M) R 25310	6.00	12.00	18.00
HULLABALLOOS ON HULLABALLOO, THE	Roulette (S) SR 25310	7.00	14.00	21.00
HUMAN BEINZ				
EVOLUTIONS	Capitol (S) ST 2926	6.00	9.00	12.00
NOBODY BUT ME	Capitol (S) ST 2906	5.00	7.50	10.00
NOBODY BUT ME	Gateway (S) GLP 3012	7.00	14.00	21.00
(With the Mammals)				
HUMAN ZOO				
HUMAN ZOO, THE	Accent (S) ACS 5055	4.00	6.00	8.00
HUMBLE PIE				
AS SAFE AS YESTERDAY	Immediate (S) 101	4.00	6.00	8.00
EAT IT	A&M (S) SP 3701	2.50	3.75	5.00
HUMBLE PIE	A&M (S) SP 4270	2.50	3.75	5.00
LOST AND FOUND	A&M (S) SP 3513	2.00	3.00	4.00
ROCK ON	A&M (S) SP 4301	2.00	3.00	4.00
ROCKIN' THE FILLMORE	A&M (S) SP 3506	2.00	3.00	4.00
SMOKIN'	A&M (S) SP 4342	2.00	3.00	4.00
STREET RATS	A&M (S) SP 4514	2.00	3.00	4.00
THUNDERBOX	A&M (S) SP 4424	3.00	4.50	6.00
THUNDERBOX (RI)	A&M (S) SP 3611	2.00	3.00	4.00
HUMBLEBUMS				
HUMBLEBUMS	Liberty (S) LST 7636	3.50	5.25	7.00
OPEN UP THE DOOR	Liberty (S) LST 7656	3.50	5.25	7.00
HUMPERDINCK, Engelbert				
AFTER THE LOVIN'	Epic/MAM (S) PE 34381	2.00	3.00	4.00
ANOTHER TIME, ANOTHER PLACE	Parrot (S) XPAS 71048	2.50	3.75	5.00
CHRISTMAS TYME	Epic/MAM (S) PE 35031	2.00	3.00	4.00
ENGELBERT	Parrot (S) PAS 71026	2.50	3.75	5.00
ENGELBERT HUMPERDINCK	Parrot (S) PAS 71030	2.50	3.75	5.00
HIS GREATEST HITS	Parrot (S) XPAS 71067	2.00	3.00	4.00
IN TIME	Parrot (S) XPAS 71056	2.50	3.75	5.00
KING OF HEARTS	Parrot (S) XPAS 71061	2.00	3.00	4.00
LAST WALTZ	Parrot (M) PA 61015	2.50	3.75	5.00
LAST WALTZ	Parrot (S) PAS 71015	3.00	4.50	6.00
LIVE AND S.R.O. AT THE RIVIERA HOTEL, LAS VEGAS	Parrot (S) XPAS 71051	2.50	3.75	5.00
A MAN WITHOUT LOVE	Parrot (S) PAS 71022	2.50	3.75	5.00
MIRACLES	Epic/MAM (S) PE 34730	2.00	3.00	4.00
MY LOVE	Parrot (S) XPAS 71065	2.00	3.00	4.00
RELEASE ME	Parrot (M) PA 61012	2.50	3.75	5.00
RELEASE ME	Parrot (S) PAS 71012	3.00	4.50	6.00
SWEETHEART	Parrot (S) XPAS 71043	2.50	3.75	5.00
WE MADE IT HAPPEN	Parrot (S) XPAS 71038	2.50	3.75	5.00
HUNGER				
STRICKLY FROM HUNGER	Public (S) P 1006	4.00	6.00	8.00
HUNT, Pee Wee				
BEST OF PEE WEE HUNT	Capitol (M) T-1853	2.50	3.75	5.00
BEST OF PEE WEE HUNT	Capitol (S) ST-1853	2.50	3.75	5.00
PEE WEE AND FINGERS	Capitol (M) T 783	3.00	4.50	6.00
PEE WEE AND FINGERS	Capitol (EP) EAP 1-783	1.50	2.25	3.00
PEE WEE AND FINGERS	Capitol (EP) EAP 2-783	1.50	2.25	3.00
PEE WEE AND FINGERS	Capitol (EP) EAP 3-783	1.50	2.25	3.00
SWINGIN' AROUND	Capitol (M) T 492	3.50	5.25	7.00
HUNT, Tommy				
I JUST DON'T KNOW WHAT TO DO WITH MYSELF	Scepter (M) 506	2.50	3.75	5.00

(M) Mono (S) Stereo (EP) Extended Play (Q) Quad (RI) Re-issued

TITLE	LABEL & NO.	GOOD	VERY GOOD	NEAR MINT
HUNTER, Ivory Joe				
ARTISTRY OF, THE (WITH MEMPHIS SLIM)	Strand (M) 1123	2.50	3.75	5.00
FABULOUS	Goldisc (M) 403	3.00	4.00	6.00
GOLDEN HITS	Smash (M) MGS 27037	2.50	3.75	5.00
GOLDEN HITS	Smash (S) SRS 67037	2.50	3.75	5.00
I GET THAT LONESOME FEELING	MGM (M) E 3488	6.00	12.00	18.00
I GET THAT LONESOME FEELING	MGM (EP) 1376	4.00	6.00	8.00
I GET THAT LONESOME FEELING	MGM (EP) 1377	4.00	6.00	8.00
I GET THAT LONESOME FEELING	MGM (EP) 1378	4.00	6.00	8.00
I NEED YOU SO	Lion (M) L 70068	2.00	3.00	4.00
I'VE ALWAYS BEEN COUNTRY	Paramount (M) 6080	2.00	3.00	4.00
IVORY JOE HUNTER	King (EP) EP 265	2.00	3.00	4.00
IVORY JOE HUNTER	Sage (S) S 603	2.00	3.00	4.00
IVORY JOE HUNTER	Sound (M) 603	2.00	3.00	4.00
IVORY JOE HUNTER SINGS THE OLD AND THE NEW	Atlantic (M) 8015	5.00	7.50	10.00
MEAN WOMAN BLUES	Grand Prix (M) K 415	2.00	3.00	4.00
RETURN OF IVORY JOE HUNTER, THE	Epic (M) E 30348	2.00	3.00	4.00
ROCK AND ROLL	Atlantic (M) 8008	5.00	10.00	15.00
16 OF HIS GREATEST HITS	King (M) 605	4.00	6.00	8.00
THIS IS IVORY JOE HUNTER	Dot (M) DLP 3569	5.00	7.50	10.00
THIS IS IVORY JOE HUNTER	Dot (S) DLP 25569	5.00	7.50	10.00
HUNTER, Tab				
R.F.D. TAB HUNTER	Warner Brothers (M) W-1367	2.50	3.75	5.00
R.F.D. TAB HUNTER	Warner Brothers (S) WS-1367	2.50	3.75	5.00
TAB HUNTER	Warner Brothers (M) 1221	3.00	4.50	6.00
YOUNG LOVE	Dot (M) DLP-3370	4.00	6.00	8.00
YOUNG LOVE	Dot (S) DLP-25370	4.00	6.00	8.00
HURLEY, Michael & Pals				
ARMCHAIR BOOGIE	Warner Brothers (S) WS 1915	2.50	3.75	5.00
HURT, Mississippi John				
FOLKSONGS AND BLUES VOL. 1	Piedmont (M) PLP 13157	4.00	8.00	12.00
HUSKY, Ferlin				
BORN TO LOSE	Capitol (M) T-1204	3.00	4.50	6.00
BOULEVARD OF BROKEN DREAMS	Capitol (M) T 880	3.00	6.00	9.00
BOULEVARD OF BROKEN DREAMS	Capitol (EP) EAP 1-880	1.50	2.25	3.00
BOULEVARD OF BROKEN DREAMS	Capitol (EP) EAP 2-880	1.50	2.25	3.00
BOULEVARD OF BROKEN DREAMS	Capitol (EP) EAP 3-880	1.50	2.25	3.00
BY REQUEST	Capitol (M) T-2101	2.00	3.00	4.00
BY REQUEST	Capitol (S) ST-2101	2.00	3.00	4.00
CHAMPAGNE LADIES & BLUE RIBBON BABIES	ABC (S) 849	2.00	3.00	4.00
COUNTRY MUSIC HOLIDAY	Capitol (EP) EAP 921	1.50	2.25	3.00
EASY LIVIN'	King (M) 728	3.50	7.00	10.50
FERLIN' FAVORITES	Capitol (M) T-1280	3.00	4.50	6.00
FERLIN' FAVORITES	Capitol (EP) EAP 1-1280	1.50	2.25	3.00
FERLIN' FAVORITES	Capitol (EP) EAP 2-1280	1.50	2.25	3.00
FERLIN' FAVORITES	Capitol (EP) EAP 3-1280	1.50	2.25	3.00
FERLIN HUSKY	King (M) 647	4.00	8.00	12.00
FERLIN HUSKY	Capitol (EP) EAP 1-609	1.50	2.25	3.00
FOSTER & RICE SONG BOOK	ABC (S) 884	2.00	3.00	4.00
FRECKLES & POLLIWOG DAYS	ABC (S) 818	2.00	3.00	4.00
GONE	Capitol (M) T-1383	3.00	4.50	6.00
HEART & SOUL OF FERLIN HUSKY	Capitol (M) T-1885	2.50	3.75	5.00
HEART & SOUL OF FERLIN HUSKY	Capitol (S) ST-1885	2.50	3.75	5.00
HITS OF FERLIN HUSKY	Capitol (M) T-1991	2.50	3.75	5.00
HITS OF FERLIN HUSKY	Capitol (S) DT-1991	2.50	3.75	5.00
I COULD SING ALL NIGHT	Capitol (M) T-2548	2.00	3.00	4.00
I COULD SING ALL NIGHT	Capitol (S) ST-2548	2.00	3.00	4.00
MOUNTAIN OF EVERLASTING LIFE	ABC (S) 849	2.00	3.00	4.00
SOME OF MY FAVORITES	Capitol (M) T-1720	2.50	3.75	5.00
SOME OF MY FAVORITES	Capitol (S) ST-1720	2.50	3.75	5.00
SONGS OF THE HOME & HEART	Capitol (M) T 718	3.00	6.00	9.00
SONGS OF THE HOME & HEART	Capitol (EP) EAP 1-718	1.50	2.25	3.00
SONGS OF THE HOME & HEART	Capitol (EP) EAP 2-718	1.50	2.25	3.00
SONGS OF THE HOME & HEART	Capitol (EP) EAP 3-718	1.50	2.25	3.00
SONGS OF MUSIC CITY U.S.A.	Capitol (M) T-2439	2.00	3.00	4.00
SONGS OF MUSIC CITY U.S.A.	Capitol (S) ST-2439	2.00	3.00	4.00
TRUE TRUE LOVIN'	ABC (S) 776	2.00	3.00	4.00
WALKIN' AND HUMMIN'	Capitol (M) T 1546	2.50	3.75	5.00
WALKIN' AND HUMMIN'	Capitol (S) ST 1546	2.50	3.75	5.00
WINGS OF A DOVE	Capitol (EP) EAP-1-1516	1.50	2.25	3.00

TITLE	LABEL & NO.	GOOD	VERY GOOD	NEAR MINT
HUTTON, Danny				
PRE-DOG NIGHT	MGM (S) SE 4664	3.00	4.50	6.00
Also see THREE DOG NIGHT				
HYLAND, Brian				
BASHFUL BLONDE, THE	Kapp (M) KL 1202	3.00	6.00	9.00
BASHFUL BLONDE, THE	Kapp (S) KS 3202	3.00	6.00	9.00
BRIAN HYLAND	Uni (S) 73097	3.00	4.50	6.00
COUNTRY MEETS FOLK	ABC/Paramount (M) ABC 463	3.00	6.00	9.00
COUNTRY MEETS FOLK	ABC/Paramount (S) ABCS 463	4.00	8.00	12.00
HERE'S TO OUR LOVE	Philips (M) 200 136	3.00	6.00	9.00
HERE'S TO OUR LOVE	Philips (S) 600 136	4.00	8.00	12.00
IN A STATE OF BAYOU	Private Stock (S) PS 7003	2.00	3.00	4.00
JOKER WENT WILD, THE	Philips (M) 200 217	3.00	6.00	9.00
JOKER WENT WILD, THE	Philips (S) 600 217	4.00	8.00	12.00
LET ME BELONG TO YOU	ABC/Paramount (M) ABC 400	3.00	6.00	9.00
LET ME BELONG TO YOU	ABC/Paramount (S) ABCS 400	4.00	8.00	12.00
ROCKIN' FOLK	Philips (M) 200 158	3.00	6.00	9.00
ROCKIN' FOLK	Philips (S) 600 158	4.00	8.00	12.00
SEALED WITH A KISS	ABC/Paramount (M) ABC 431	3.00	6.00	9.00
SEALED WITH A KISS	ABC/Paramount (S) ABCS 431	4.00	8.00	12.00
STAY AND LOVE ME ALL SUMMER	Dot (S) DLP 25954	3.00	6.00	9.00
TRAGEDY	Dot (S) DLP 25926	3.00	6.00	9.00

I

TITLE	LABEL & NO.	GOOD	VERY GOOD	NEAR MINT
IAN, Janis				
AFTERTONES	Columbia (S) PC 33919	2.00	3.00	4.00
AFTERTONES	Columbia (Q) PCQ 33919	2.00	3.00	4.00
BETWEEN THE LINES	Columbia (S) PC-33394	2.00	3.00	4.00
BETWEEN THE LINES	Columbia (Q) PCQ-33394	2.00	3.00	4.00
FOR ALL THE SEASONS OF YOUR MIND	Verve/Forecast (M) FT 3024	2.50	3.75	5.00
FOR ALL THE SEASONS OF YOUR MIND	Verve/Forecast (S) FTS 3024	3.00	4.50	6.00
JANIS IAN	Verve/Forecast (M) FT 3017	4.00	6.00	8.00
JANIS IAN	Verve/Forecast (S) FTS 3017	4.50	6.75	9.00
JANIS IAN	Polydor (S) 6058	2.00	3.00	4.00
MIRACLE ROW	Columbia (S) PC 34440	2.00	3.00	4.00
PRESENT COMPANY	Capitol (S) SM-683	2.50	3.75	5.00
SECRET LIFE OF J. EDDY FINK	Verve/Forecast (S) 3048	3.00	4.50	6.00
STARS	Columbia (S) KC-32857	2.00	3.00	4.00
WHO REALLY CARES	Verve/Forecast (S) FT 3063	2.50	3.75	5.00
WHO REALLY CARES	Verve/Forecast (S) FTS 3063	3.00	4.50	6.00
IAN AND THE ZODIACS				
IAN AND THE ZODIACS	Philips (M) PHM 200-176	6.00	9.00	12.00
IAN AND THE ZODIACS	Philips (S) PHS 600 176	7.00	10.50	14.00
ICARUS				
MARVEL WORLD OF ICARUS	Grit (S) 2000	2.00	3.00	4.00
ICEBERG				
ICEBERG	United Artists (S) UA-LA 150	4.00	6.00	8.00
ID				
INNER SOUNDS OF THE ID, THE	RCA (S) LSP 3805	4.50	6.75	9.00
IDES OF MARCH				
COMMON BOND	Warner Bros. (S) WS 1896	3.00	4.50	6.00
MIDNIGHT OIL	RCA (M) APL1 0143	2.50	3.75	5.00
VEHICLE	Warner Bros. (S) WS 1863	3.00	4.50	6.00
WORLD WOVEN	RCA (S) LSP 4812	2.50	3.75	5.00
IDLE RACE				
BIRTHDAY PARTY	Liberty (S) LST 7603	7.00	10.50	14.00
IFIELD, Frank				
BEATLES AND FRANK IFIELD . . . (See "Beatles" for complete information on this album)				
I'M CONFESSIN' (THAT I LOVE YOU)	Capitol (M) T-10356	2.50	3.75	5.00
I'M CONFESSIN' (THAT I LOVE YOU)	Capitol (S) ST-10356	2.50	3.75	5.00
I REMEMBER YOU	Vee Jay (M) 1054	3.00	4.50	6.00
I REMEMBER YOU	Vee Jay (S) 1054	3.50	5.25	7.00
IGGY & THE STOOGES				
RAW POWER	Columbia (S) KC-32111	3.50	5.25	7.00
IKETTES				
GOLD AND NEW	United Artists (S) UA LA 190 F	2.50	3.75	5.00
SOUL HITS	Modern (S) MST 102	6.00	12.00	18.00
ILLINOIS SPEED PRESS				
DUET	Columbia (S) CS 9976	4.00	6.00	8.00
ILLINOIS SPEED PRESS	Columbia (S) CS 9792	4.50	6.75	9.00

(M) Mono (S) Stereo (EP) Extended Play (Q) Quad (RI) Re-issued

TITLE	LABEL & NO.	GOOD	VERY GOOD	NEAR MINT
ILLUSION				
IF IT'S SO	Steed (S) ST 37006	4.00	6.00	8.00
ILLUSION (Original Label)	Sinergia (S) SR 7654	9.00	13.50	18.00
ILLUSION, THE	Steed (S) ST 37003	4.00	6.00	8.00
TOGETHER AS A WAY OF LIFE	Steed (S) ST 37005	4.00	6.00	8.00
ILMO SMOKEHOUSE				
ILMO SMOKEHOUSE	Roulette (S) SR 3002	5.00	7.50	10.00
IMPACS				
IMPACT!	King (M) 886	3.00	7.50	12.00
IMPACTS				
WIPE OUT	Del Fi (M) DFLP 1234	4.00	8.00	12.00
WIPE OUT	Del Fi (S) DFST 1234	5.00	10.00	15.00
IMPALA SYNDROME				
IMPALA SYNDROME	Parallax (S) P 4002	6.00	9.00	12.00
IMPALAS				
SORRY (I RAN ALL THE WAY HOME)	Cub (M) 8003	9.00	22.50	36.00

TITLE	LABEL & NO.	GOOD	VERY GOOD	NEAR MINT
SORRY (I RAN ALL THE WAY HOME)	Cub (S) S-8003	10.00	25.00	40.00
SORRY (I RAN ALL THE WAY HOME)	Cub (EP) EP-CX 5000	2.50	6.25	10.00
IMPRESSIONS				
AMEN	Curtom (M)	2.00	3.00	4.00
BEST OF THE IMPRESSIONS	ABC (M) 654	3.00	4.50	6.00
FABULOUS IMPRESSION, THE	ABC (M) 607	3.00	6.00	9.00
FINALLY GOT MYSELF TOGETHER	Curtom (M) 8019	2.00	3.00	4.00
FIRST IMPRESSIONS	Curtom (M) 5003	2.00	3.00	4.00
FOR YOUR PRECIOUS LOVE	Vee Jay (M) 1075	5.00	12.50	20.00
FOR YOUR PRECIOUS LOVE	Vee Jay (S) 1075	6.00	15.00	24.00
IMPRESSIONS	ABC/Paramount (M) ABC-450	4.00	8.00	12.00
IMPRESSIONS	ABC/Paramount (S) ABCS-450	5.00	10.00	15.00
IMPRESSIONS GREATEST HITS	ABC/Paramount (M) ABC-515	3.00	6.00	9.00
IMPRESSIONS GREATEST HITS	ABC/Paramount (S) ABCS-515	4.00	8.00	12.00
KEEP ON PUSHING	ABC/Paramount (M) ABC-493	3.00	6.00	9.00
KEEP ON PUSHING	ABC/Paramount (S) ABCS-493	4.00	8.00	12.00
LOVING POWER	Curtom (M) 5009	2.00	3.00	4.00
NEVER ENDING	ABC/Paramount (M) ABC-468	3.00	6.00	9.00
NEVER ENDING	ABC/Paramount (S) ABCS-468	4.00	8.00	12.00
ONE BY ONE	ABC/Paramount (M) 523	3.00	6.00	9.00
PEOPLE GET READY	ABC/Paramount (M) ABC-505	3.00	6.00	9.00
PEOPLE GET READY	ABC/Paramount (S) ABCS-505	4.00	8.00	12.00
PREACHER MAN	Curtom (M) 8016	2.00	3.00	4.00
RIDIN HIGH	ABC/Paramount (M) 545	3.00	6.00	9.00
16 GREATEST HITS	ABC (M) 727	4.00	8.00	12.00
THIS IS MY COUNTRY	Curtom (M) 8001	2.00	3.00	4.00
THREE THE HARD WAY	Curtom (M) 8602	2.00	3.00	4.00
TIMES HAVE CHANGED	Curtom (M) 8012	2.00	3.00	4.00
WE'RE A WINNER	ABC (M) 635	3.00	4.50	6.00
YOUNG MOD'S FORGOTTEN STORY	Curtom (M) 8003	2.00	3.00	4.00
Also see BUTLER, Jerry & MAYFIELD, Curtis				
INCREDIBLES				
HEART AND SOUL	Audio Arts (S) AAS 7000	3.50	5.25	7.00
INDEPENDENTS				
FIRST TIME WE MET, THE	Wand (S) WDS 694	3.00	4.50	6.00
INDEPENDENTS	Wand (S) 696	3.00	4.50	6.00
INDIAN SUMMER				
INDIAN SUMMER	Neon (S) NE 3	2.50	3.75	5.00
INFLUENCE				
INFLUENCE	ABC (S) ABCS 630	3.00	4.50	6.00

TITLE	LABEL & NO.	GOOD	VERY GOOD	NEAR MINT
INGMANN, Jorgen				
APACHE	Atco (M) 130	3.00	6.00	9.00
MANY GUITARS OF JORGEN INGMANN	Atco (M) 139	2.50	5.00	7.50
SWINGING GUITAR	Mercury (M) MG 20200	2.50	5.00	7.50
INGRAM, Luther				
IF LOVING YOU IS WRONG—				
I DON'T WANT TO BE RIGHT	Ko Ko (S) KOS 2202	3.00	4.50	6.00
I'VE BEEN HERE ALL THE TIME	Ko Ko (S) 2201	3.00	4.50	6.00
IN GROUP				
SWINGING 12 STRING	IN (M) 1002	2.00	4.00	6.00
INK SPOTS				
GREAT SONGS OF OUR TIMES	King (EP) EP 376	3.00	6.00	9.00
INK SPOTS, Vol. 1 (10")	Decca (M) 5056	5.00	12.50	20.00
INK SPOTS, Vol. 2 (10")	Decca (M) 5071	5.00	12.50	20.00
SOMETHING OLD, SOMETHING NEW	King (M) LP 535	5.00	12.50	20.00
SONGS THAT WILL LIVE FOREVER	King (M) 642	5.00	12.50	20.00
SPIRITUALS AND JUBILEES (10")	Waldorf Music Hall (M) 33 144	4.00	10.00	16.00
SPIRITUALS AND JUBILEES (10")	Waldorf Music Hall (M) 33 152	4.00	10.00	16.00
INMAN, Jerry				
LENNON-McCARTNEY R.F.D. (BEATLES COUNTRY STYLE)	Columbia (S) CS-9593	3.00	4.00	6.00
INNOCENCE				
INNOCENCE, THE	Kama Sutra (M) KLP 8059	3.00	4.50	6.00
INNOCENCE, THE	Kama Sutra (S) KLPS 8059	4.00	6.00	8.00
INNOCENTS				
INNOCENTLY YOURS	Indigo (M) IND LP 503	6.00	12.00	18.00
IN-SECT				
INTRODUCING THE IN-SECT	Camden (M) CAL 909	6.00	9.00	12.00
INSECT TRUST				
HOBOKEN SATURDAY NIGHT	Atco (S) SD 33-313	4.50	6.75	9.00
INSECT TRUST, THE	Capitol (S) SKAO 109	4.50	6.75	9.00
INTERNATIONAL SUBMARINE BAND				
SAFE AT HOME	LHI (M) 12,001	12.00	24.00	36.00
SAFE AT HOME	LHI (S) S-12,001	13.00	26.00	39.00

TITLE	LABEL & NO.	GOOD	VERY GOOD	NEAR MINT
INTRUDERS				
SUPER HITS	Gamble (S) KZ 32131	2.50	3.75	5.00
INVICTAS				
A GO GO	Sahara (M) 101	9.00	18.00	27.00
IRON BUTTERFLY				
BALL	Atco (S) SD 33-280	3.00	4.50	6.00
BEST OF IRON BUTTERFLY/EVOLUTION	Atco (S) SD 33-369	3.50	5.25	7.00
HEAVY	Atco (M) 33-227	3.50	5.25	7.00
HEAVY	Atco (S) SD 33-227	3.00	4.50	6.00
IN-A-GADDA-DA-VIDA	Atco (S) SD 33-250	3.00	4.50	6.00
LIVE	Atco (S) SD 33-318	3.00	4.50	6.00
METAMORPHOSIS	Atco (S) SD 33-339	3.00	4.50	6.00
SCORCHING BEAUTY	MCA (S) 465	2.50	3.75	5.00
SUN & STEEL	MCA (S) 2164	2.50	3.75	5.00
ISLEY BROTHERS				
BEST OF ISLEY BROTHERS, THE	Buddah (S) BDS 5652-2	2.00	3.00	4.00
BROTHER, BROTHER, BROTHER	T-Neck (S) 3009	2.00	3.00	4.00
BROTHERS ISLEY, THE	T-Neck (S) 3002	2.00	3.00	4.00
DOIN' THEIR THING	Tamla (S) 287	3.00	6.00	9.00

(M) Mono (S) Stereo (EP) Extended Play (Q) Quad (RI) Re-issued

---

TITLE	LABEL & NO.	GOOD	VERY GOOD	NEAR MINT
FOREVER GOLD	T-Neck (S) PZ 34452	2.00	3.00	4.00
GET INTO SOMETHING	T-Neck 3006	3.00	4.50	6.00
GIVIN IT BACK	T-Neck (S) 3008	2.00	3.00	4.00
GO FOR YOUR GUNS	T-Neck (S) PZ 34432	2.00	3.00	4.00
GO FOR YOUR GUNS	T-Neck (Q) PZQ 34432	2.50	3.75	5.00
HARVEST FOR THE WORLD	T-Neck (S) PZ 33809	2.00	3.00	4.00
HARVEST FOR THE WORLD	T-Neck (Q) PZQ 33809	2.50	3.75	5.00
HEAT IS ON	T-Neck (S) PZ-33536	2.00	3.00	4.00
HEAT IS ON	T-Neck (Q) PZQ-33536	3.00	4.50	6.00
ISLEY BROTHERS AND MARVIN AND JOHNNY	Crown (S) CST 352	2.50	5.00	7.50
ISLEY'S GREATEST HITS	T-Neck (S) TNS 3011	2.00	3.00	4.00
ISLEYS LIVE	T-Neck (S) 3010	2.00	3.00	4.00
IT'S OUR THING	T-Neck (S) 3001	2.00	3.00	4.00
LIVE AT YANKEE STADIUM	T-Neck (S) 3004	2.00	3.00	4.00
LIVE IT UP	T-Neck (S) PZ-33070	2.00	3.00	4.00
LIVE IT UP	T-Neck (Q) ZQ-33070	2.00	3.00	4.00
SHOUT	RCA (M) LPM-2156	4.00	10.00	16.00
SHOUT	RCA (S) LSP-2156	6.00	12.00	18.00
SHOWDOWN	T-Neck (S) JZ 34930	2.00	3.00	4.00
SOUL ON THE ROCKS	Tamla (S) 275	3.00	6.00	9.00
STARRING THE ISLEY BROTHERS AND THE CHIFFONS	Spinorama (S) S 127	3.00	6.00	9.00
THIS OLD HEART OF MINE	Tamla (S) 269	3.00	6.00	9.00
3 + 3	T-Neck (S) KZ-32453	2.00	3.00	4.00
3 + 3	T-Neck (Q) ZQ-32453	3.00	4.50	6.00
TWIST AND SHOUT	Wand (M) 653	3.00	6.00	9.00
TWISTING AND SHOUTING	United Artists (S) UAS 6313	4.00	8.00	12.00
VERY BEST OF THE ISLEY BROTHERS	United Artists (S) UA-LA-500-E	1.50	2.25	3.00
IT'S A BEAUTIFUL DAY				
AT CARNEGIE HALL	Columbia (S) KC-31338	4.00	6.00	8.00
CHOICE QUALITY STUFF/ANYTIME	Columbia (S) C-30734	4.50	6.75	9.00
IT'S A BEAUTIFUL DAY	Columbia (S) CS 9768	5.00	7.50	10.00
IT'S A BEAUTIFUL DAY . . . TODAY	Columbia (S) KC-32181	4.00	6.00	8.00
MARRYING MAIDEN	Columbia (S) CS 1058	4.50	6.75	9.00
THOUSAND & ONE NIGHTS WITH	Columbia (S) KC-32660	3.00	4.50	6.00
IVES, Burl				
BALLADS	United Artists (M) UAL-3060	2.50	3.75	5.00
BALLADS	United Artists (S) UAS-6060	2.50	3.75	5.00
BEST OF BURL IVES, VOL. 2	MCA (S) 2-4089	2.50	3.75	5.00
BURL IVES SINGS IRVING BERLIN	United Artists (M) UAL-3117	2.50	3.75	5.00
BURL IVES SINGS IRVING BERLIN	United Artists (S) UAS-6117	2.50	3.75	5.00
CHEERS	Decca (M) DL-8886	2.50	3.75	5.00
CHEERS	Decca (S) DL-78886	3.00	4.50	6.00
CHEERS	Decca (EP) ED-2650	1.00	1.50	2.00
CHEERS	Decca (SEP) ED 2650	1.50	2.25	3.00
PAYING MY DUES AGAIN	MCA (S) 318	2.00	3.00	4.00
RETURN OF THE WAYFARING STRANGER	Columbia (M) CL-1459	2.00	4.00	6.00
WAYFARING STRANGER, THE	Columbia (M) CL 628	3.00	4.50	6.00
IVY LEAGUE				
TOSSING AND TURNING	Cameo (M) C-2000	5.00	10.00	15.00
TOSSING AND TURNING	Cameo (S) SC-2000	6.00	12.00	18.00

88

J

TITLE	LABEL & NO.	GOOD	VERY GOOD	NEAR MINT
J.K. AND CO.				
SUDDENLY ONE SUMMER	White Whale (S) WWS 7117	2.50	3.75	5.00
JACKS				
JACKS, THE	Crown (M) CST 372	6.00	15.00	24.00
JUMPIN' WITH THE JACKS	Crown (M) CLP 5021	8.00	20.00	32.00
JUMPIN' WITH THE JACKS	RPM (M) LRP 3006	10.00	25.00	40.00
JACKS, Terry				
SEASONS IN THE SUN	Bell (S) 1307	3.00	4.50	6.00
JACKSON, Bull Moose				
BULL MOOSE JACKSON	Audio Lab (M) 1524	12.00	30.00	48.00
BULL MOOSE JACKSON, Vol. 1 & 2	King (EP) EP 211	3.00	7.50	12.00
BULL MOOSE JACKSON VOL. 1 & 2	King (EP) EP 261	3.00	7.50	12.00
JACKSON, Chubby				
TWIST CALLING	Laurie (M) 2011	3.00	6.00	9.00
JACKSON, Chuck				
ANY DAY NOW	Wand (M) LP 654	3.00	6.00	9.00
CHUCK JACKSON AND YOUNG JESSIE	Crown (M) CLP 5354	5.00	12.50	20.00
DEDICATED TO THE KING	Wand (M) 680	5.00	10.00	15.00
(Elvis Tribute)				
DEDICATED TO THE KING	Wand (S) 5680	5.00	10.00	15.00
(Elvis Tribute)				
ENCORE	Wand (M) 665	2.50	5.00	7.50
GOIN BACK TO JACKSON	Motown (M) 687	3.00	4.50	6.00
GREATEST HITS	Wand (M) 683	2.50	3.75	5.00
I DON'T WANT TO CRY	Wand (M) LP 650	3.00	6.00	9.00
MR. EVERYTHING	Wand (M) 667	2.50	5.00	7.50
MR. EVERYTHING	Wand (S) S 667	3.00	6.00	9.00
STARRING CHUCK JACKSON AND				
HIS GREATEST HITS	Spinorama (M) 123	2.50	5.00	7.50
THROUGH ALL TIMES	ABC (S) X-798	2.00	3.00	4.00
TRIBUTE TO RHYTHM AND BLUES	Wand (M) 673	2.50	5.00	7.50
TRIBUTE TO RHYTHM AND BLUES	Wand (S) S 673	3.00	6.00	9.00
TRIBUTE TO RHYTHM & BLUES, VOL. 2	Wand (M) 676	2.50	5.00	7.50
VERY BEST OF CHUCK JACKSON	United Artists (S) UA-LA-499-E	1.50	2.25	3.00
JACKSON, Chuck & Maxine Brown				
SAYING SOMETHING	Wand (M) 669	2.50	5.00	7.50
JACKSON, Chuck & Tammi Terrell				
EARLY SHOW, THE	Wand (M) WDS 682	2.50	5.00	7.50
JACKSON, Deon				
LOVE MAKES THE WORLD GO 'ROUND	Atco (M) 33-188	3.00	6.00	9.00
LOVE MAKES THE WORLD GO 'ROUND	Atco (S) SD 33-188	4.00	8.00	12.00
JACKSON, J.J.				
J.J.	Calla (M) C 1101	3.00	4.50	6.00
JACKSON, John				
JOHN JACKSON	Arhoolie (M) 1025	2.50	3.75	5.00
JACKSON, Lil' SONNY				
LIL SON JACKSON	Arhoolie (M) 1004	2.50	3.75	5.00
ROCKIN' & ROLLIN'	Imperial (M) 9142	9.00	22.50	36.00

TITLE	LABEL & NO.	GOOD	VERY GOOD	NEAR MINT
JACKSON, Millie				
CAUGHT UP	Spring (S) SPR 6703	2.00	3.00	4.00
FREE AND IN LOVE	Spring (S) SP 1 6709	2.00	3.00	4.00
IT HURTS SO GOOD	Spring (S) SPR 5706	2.00	3.00	4.00
MILLIE	Spring (S) SPR 6701	2.00	3.00	4.00
MILLIE JACKSON	Spring (S) SPR 5703	2.00	3.00	4.00
JACKSON, Stonewall				
DYNAMIC STONEWALL JACKSON	Columbia (M) CL-1391	4.00	6.00	8.00
DYNAMIC STONEWALL JACKSON	Columbia (S) CS-8186	4.00	6.00	8.00
DYNAMIC STONEWALL JACKSON	Columbia (EP) B-13911	1.50	2.25	3.00
DYNAMIC STONEWALL JACKSON	Columbia (EP) B-13912	1.50	2.25	3.00
DYNAMIC STONEWALL JACKSON	Columbia (EP) B-13913	1.50	2.25	3.00
SADNESS IN A SONG	Columbia (M) CL-1770	3.00	4.50	6.00
SADNESS IN A SONG	Columbia (S) CS-8570	3.00	4.50	6.00
JACKSON, Walter				
IT'S ALL OVER	Okeh (M) OKM 12107	4.00	6.00	8.00
IT'S ALL OVER	Okeh (S) OKS 14107	5.00	7.50	10.00
SPEAK HER NAME	Okeh (M) OKM 12120	3.00	4.50	6.00
SPEAK HER NAME	Okeh (S) OKS 14120	4.00	6.00	8.00
WELCOME HOME	Okeh (M) OKM 12108	4.00	6.00	8.00
WELCOME HOME	Okeh (S) OKS 14108	5.00	7.50	10.00
JACKSON, Wanda				
LOVE ME FOREVER	Capitol (M) T1911	3.50	5.25	7.00
LOVE ME FOREVER	Capitol (S) ST 1911	4.00	6.00	8.00
LOVIN' COUNTRY STYLE	Decca (M) DL-4224	6.00	9.00	12.00
NOBODY'S DARLIN'	Vocalion (M) VL 73861	4.00	6.00	8.00
NOW I HAVE EVERYTHING	Myrrh (S) 6533	2.00	3.00	4.00
RIGHT OR WRONG	Capitol (M) T 1596	5.00	10.00	15.00
RIGHT OR WRONG	Capitol (S) ST 1596	6.00	12.00	18.00
ROCKIN' WITH WANDA!	Capitol (M) T 1384	9.00	22.50	36.00
THERE'S A PARTY GOIN' ON	Capitol (M) T 1511	8.00	16.00	24.00
THERE'S A PARTY GOIN' ON	Capitol (S) ST 1511	9.00	18.00	27.00
WANDA JACKSON	Capitol (M) T 1041	9.00	22.50	36.00
WONDERFUL WANDA	Capitol (M) T-1776	4.00	6.00	8.00
WONDERFUL WANDA	Capitol (S) ST-1776	4.00	6.00	8.00
JACKSON HEIGHTS				
JACKSON HEIGHTS	Verve (M) V6-5089	2.50	3.75	5.00
KING PROGRESS	Mercury (M) SR 61331	2.50	3.75	5.00
JACOBS, Dick & His Orchestra				
TEEN AGE BEAT	Sesac (EP) AD 25	1.50	3.00	4.50
JACOBS, Hank				
SO FAR AWAY	Sue (M) 1023	3.00	6.00	9.00
JACQUET, Illinois				
BATTLE OF THE SAXES (10")				
(With Lester Young)	Aladdin (M) 701	8.00	20.00	32.00
ILLINOIS JACQUET AND HIS TENOR SAX				
(10")	Aladdin (M) 708	8.00	20.00	32.00
JAMES, Elmore				
BLUES IN MY HEART,				
THE RHYTHM IN MY SOUL, THE	United (S) US 7716	4.00	8.00	12.00
BLUES MASTERS VOL. 1	Blue Horizon (M) BM 46021	4.00	6.00	8.00
ELMORE JAMES	Crown (M) 5168	5.00	7.50	10.00
I NEED YOU	Sphere Sound (M) 7008	5.00	10.00	15.00
LEGEND OF ELMORE JAMES	Kent (M) 9001	1.50	2.25	3.00
ORIGINAL FOLK BLUES	Kent (M) KLP 5022	5.00	10.00	15.00
ORIGINAL FOLK BLUES	United (M) 7743	2.50	3.75	5.00
RESURRECTION OF ELMORE JAMES	Kent (M) 9010	1.50	2.25	3.00
RESURRECTION OF ELMORE JAMES	United (M) 7787	2.50	3.75	5.00
SCREAMIN BLUES	Harlem Hit Parade (M) 5014	2.50	3.75	5.00
SKY IS CRYING, THE	Sphere Sound (M) 7002	5.00	10.00	15.00

(M) Mono (S) Stereo (EP) Extended Play (Q) Quad (RI) Re-issued

JAMES, Etta

TITLE	LABEL & NO.	GOOD	VERY GOOD	NEAR MINT
AT LAST (2nd Press)	Cadet (M) LP-4003	4.00	8.00	12.00
BEST OF ETTA JAMES, THE	Crown (M) CLP 5234	4.00	10.00	16.00
CALL MY NAME	Cadet (M) LP 4055	3.00	6.00	9.00
CALL MY NAME	Cadet (S) LPS 4055	4.00	8.00	12.00
COME A LITTLE BIT CLOSER	Chess (M) CH 60029	3.00	4.50	6.00
ETTA JAMES	Crown (M) CLP 5360	4.00	10.00	16.00
ETTA JAMES	Chess (M) CH 50042	4.00	6.00	8.00
ETTA JAMES	Westbound (M) W 203	2.50	3.75	5.00
ETTA JAMES	Argo (M) 4013	6.00	12.00	18.00
ETTA JAMES	Argo (S) 4013	7.00	14.00	21.00
ETTA JAMES (2nd Press)	Cadet (M) LP-4013	4.00	8.00	12.00
ETTA JAMES ROCKS THE HOUSE	Argo (M) 4032	5.00	10.00	15.00
ETTA JAMES ROCKS THE HOUSE	Argo (S) 4032	6.00	12.00	18.00
ETTA JAMES ROCKS THE HOUSE (2nd Press)	Cadet (M) LP-4032	3.50	7.00	10.50
ETTA JAMES SINGS	United (M) US 7712	4.00	8.00	12.00
ETTA JAMES SINGS FOR LOVERS	Argo (M) 4018	5.00	10.00	15.00
ETTA JAMES SINGS FOR LOVERS	Argo (S) 4018	6.00	12.00	18.00
ETTA JAMES SINGS FOR LOVERS (2nd Press)	Cadet (M) LP-4018	4.00	8.00	12.00
ETTA JAMES TOP TEN	Argo (M) LP 4025	4.00	8.00	12.00
ETTA JAMES TOP TEN	Argo (S) LPS 4025	5.00	10.00	15.00
ETTA JAMES TOP TEN (2nd Press)	Cadet (M) LP-4025	4.00	8.00	12.00
LOVE SHOUT	Prestige (M) PR 7272	4.00	8.00	12.00
LOVE SHOUT	Prestige (M) PRS 7272	5.00	10.00	15.00
PEACHES	Chess (M) 2CH 60004	4.00	6.00	8.00
QUEEN OF SOUL	Argo (M) 4040	4.00	8.00	12.00
QUEEN OF SOUL	Argo (S) 4040	5.00	10.00	15.00
QUEEN OF SOUL (2nd Press)	Cadet (M) LP-4040	3.50	7.00	10.50
SECOND TIME AROUND	Argo (M) 4011	5.00	10.00	15.00
SECOND TIME AROUND	Argo (S) 4011	6.00	12.00	18.00
SECOND TIME AROUND, THE (2nd Press)	Cadet (M) LP-4011	4.00	8.00	12.00
TELL MAMA	Cadet (M) 802	3.00	6.00	9.00
TELL MAMA	Cadet (S) 802	4.00	8.00	12.00
TWIST WITH ETTA JAMES	Crown (M) CL 5250	4.00	10.00	16.00

JAMES GANG

TITLE	LABEL & NO.	GOOD	VERY GOOD	NEAR MINT
JAMES GANG BAND	Atco (S) 7037	3.00	4.50	6.00
JAMES GANG LIVE IN CONCERT	ABC (S) 733	4.00	6.00	8.00
JAMES GANG RIDES AGAIN	ABC (S) 711	4.00	6.00	8.00
MIAMI	Atco (S) 36-102	4.00	6.00	8.00
PASSIN' THRU	ABC (S) 760	3.50	5.25	7.00
SIXTEEN GREATEST HITS	ABC (S) 801	3.00	4.50	6.00
STRAIGHT SHOOTER	ABC (S) 741	3.50	5.25	7.00
THIRDS	ABC (S) 721	4.00	6.00	8.00
YER ALBUM	Blues Way (S) 6034	5.00	7.50	10.00

Also see WALSH, Joe

JAMES, Homesick

TITLE	LABEL & NO.	GOOD	VERY GOOD	NEAR MINT
AIN'T SICK NO MORE	Bluesway (M) 6071	2.00	3.00	4.00
BLUES ON THE SOUTH SIDE	Prestige (M) 7388	5.00	7.50	10.00
COUNTRY BLUES, THE	Blues on Blues (S) BOB 10000	4.00	6.00	8.00

JAMES, Jesse

TITLE	LABEL & NO.	GOOD	VERY GOOD	NEAR MINT
JESSE JAMES	20th Century Fox (M) 3197	2.00	3.00	4.00
JESSE JAMES	20th Century Fox (S) S-3197	4.00	6.00	8.00

JAMES, Joni

TITLE	LABEL & NO.	GOOD	VERY GOOD	NEAR MINT
GIVE US THIS DAY	MGM (M) E 3528	2.50	3.75	5.00
GIVE US THIS DAY	MGM (EP) X 1389	1.00	1.50	2.00
GIVE US THIS DAY	MGM (EP) X 1390	1.00	1.50	2.00
GIVE US THIS DAY	MGM (EP) X 1391	1.00	1.50	2.00
HAVE YOURSELF A MERRY LITTLE CHRISTMAS	MGM (EP) 1172	1.00	1.50	2.00
I'M IN THE MOOD FOR LOVE	MGM (M) E-3837	2.50	3.75	5.00
I'M IN THE MOOD FOR LOVE	MGM (S) SE-3837	3.00	4.50	6.00
IN THE STILL OF THE NIGHT	MGM (M) E3328	3.00	6.00	9.00
IN THE STILL OF THE NIGHT	MGM (EP) X1211	1.00	1.50	2.00
IN THE STILL OF THE NIGHT	MGM (EP) X1212	1.00	1.50	2.00
IN THE STILL OF THE NIGHT	MGM (EP) X1213	1.00	1.50	2.00
JONI JAMES AT CARNEGIE HALL	MGM (M) E-3800	2.50	3.75	5.00
JONI JAMES AT CARNEGIE HALL	MGM (S) SE-3800	3.00	4.50	6.00
JONI JAMES' AWARD WINNING ALBUM (10")	MGM (M) E234	2.50	3.75	5.00
JONI JAMES' AWARD WINNING ALBUM	MGM (EP) X234	1.00	1.50	2.00
JONI JAMES' AWARD WINNING ALBUM	MGM (M) E3346	3.00	6.00	9.00
JONI JAMES' AWARD WINNING ALBUM	MGM (EP) X1219	1.00	1.50	2.00
JONI JAMES' AWARD WINNING ALBUM	MGM (EP) X1220	1.00	1.50	2.00
JONI JAMES' AWARD WINNING ALBUM	MGM (EP) X1221	1.00	1.50	2.00
JONI SINGS HOLLYWOOD	MGM (M) E-3840	2.50	3.75	5.00
JONI SINGS HOLLYWOOD	MGM (S) SE-3840	3.00	4.50	6.00
JONI SINGS IRISH FAVORITES	MGM (M) E-3749	2.50	3.75	5.00
JONI SINGS IRISH FAVORITES	MGM (S) SE-3749	3.00	4.50	6.00
JONI SWINGS SWEET	MGM (M) E-3772	2.50	3.75	5.00
JONI SWINGS SWEET	MGM (S) SE-3772	3.00	4.50	6.00
MERRY CHRISTMAS FROM JONI	MGM (M) E3468	2.50	3.75	5.00
MERRY CHRISTMAS FROM JONI	MGM (EP) X1399	1.00	1.50	2.00
MERRY CHRISTMAS FROM JONI	MGM (EP) X 1400	1.00	1.50	2.00
MERRY CHRISTMAS FROM JONI	MGM (EP) X 1401	1.00	1.50	2.00
100 STRINGS & JONI	MGM (M) E-3755	2.50	3.75	5.00
100 STRINGS & JONI	MGM (S) SE-3755	3.00	4.50	6.00
100 STRINGS & JONI	MGM (EP) X-1656	1.00	1.50	2.00
100 STRINGS & JONI	MGM (EP) X-1657	1.00	1.50	2.00
100 STRINGS & JONI	MGM (EP) X-1658	1.00	1.50	2.00
100 STRINGS & JONI ON BROADWAY	MGM (M) E-3839	2.50	3.75	5.00
100 STRINGS & JONI ON BROADWAY	MGM (S) SE-3839	3.00	4.50	6.00
SOMETHING FOR THE BOYS	MGM (M) E 4158	2.00	3.00	4.00
SONGS OF HANK WILLIAMS	MGM (M) E-3739	2.50	3.75	5.00
SONGS OF HANK WILLIAMS	MGM (S) SE-3739	3.00	4.50	6.00
SONGS OF HANK WILLIAMS	MGM (EP) X-1652	1.00	1.50	2.00
SONGS OF HANK WILLIAMS	MGM (EP) X-1653	1.00	1.50	2.00
SONGS OF HANK WILLIAMS	MGM (EP) X-1654	1.00	1.50	2.00

JAMES, Keef

TITLE	LABEL & NO.	GOOD	VERY GOOD	NEAR MINT
ONE TREE OF ANOTHER	Rare Earth (M) 539	2.50	3.75	5.00

JAMES, Leonard

TITLE	LABEL & NO.	GOOD	VERY GOOD	NEAR MINT
BOPPIN AND A-STROLLIN	Decca (M) DL8772	8.00	20.00	32.00

JAMES, Skip

TITLE	LABEL & NO.	GOOD	VERY GOOD	NEAR MINT
GREATEST OF THE DELTA BLUES SINGERS	Melodoon (M) MLP7321	5.00	7.50	10.00

JAMES, Sonny

TITLE	LABEL & NO.	GOOD	VERY GOOD	NEAR MINT
A MI ESPOSA CON AMOR	Columbia (S) KC 33056	2.00	3.00	4.00
ASTRODOME PRESENTS IN PERSON SONNY JAMES	Capitol (S) ST 320	2.50	3.75	5.00
BEHIND THE TEAR	Capitol (M) T 2415	2.50	3.75	5.00
BEHIND THE TEAR	Capitol (S) ST 2415	2.50	3.75	5.00
BEST OF SONNY JAMES	Capitol (M) 2615	3.00	4.50	6.00
BEST OF SONNY JAMES	Capitol (S) 2615	3.00	4.50	6.00
CHURCH IN THE WILDWOOD	Capitol (M) T 1113	3.00	4.50	6.00
CLOSE-UP	Capitol (S) SWBB 258	3.00	4.50	6.00
COUNTRY MALE ARTIST OF THE DECADE	Columbia (S) KC 33846	2.00	3.00	4.00
EMPTY ARMS	Capitol (S) 734	2.50	3.75	5.00
FIRST DATE, FIRST KISS, FIRST LOVE	Capitol (EP) EAP1861	1.50	2.25	3.00
GENTLEMAN FROM THE SOUTH	Capitol (S) ST 11144	2.00	3.00	4.00
GUITARS OF SONNY JAMES	Columbia (S) KC 33477	2.00	3.00	4.00
HONEY	Capitol (M) T988	2.50	3.75	5.00
HONEY	Capitol (S) ST 988	3.50	5.25	7.00
IF SHE HELPS ME GET OVER YOU	Columbia (S) KC 32291	2.00	3.00	4.00
I'LL KEEP HOLDING ON (JUST TO YOUR LOVE)	Capitol (M) T 2317	2.50	3.75	5.00
I'LL KEEP HOLDING ON (JUST TO YOUR LOVE)	Capitol (S) ST 2317	2.50	3.75	5.00
IN PRISON IN PERSON	Columbia (S) PC 34708	2.00	3.00	4.00
IS IT WRONG	Columbia (S) KC 32805	2.00	3.00	4.00
IT'S JUST A MATTER OF TIME	Capitol (S) 432	2.50	3.75	5.00
A LITTLE BIT SOUTH OF SASKATOON	Columbia (S) KC 33428	2.00	3.00	4.00
MY LOVE/DON'T KEEP ME HANGIN' ON	Capitol (S) 478	2.50	3.75	5.00
#1—THE BIGGEST HITS IN COUNTRY MUSIC HISTORY	Capitol (S) 629	2.50	3.75	5.00
ONLY THE LONELY	Capitol (S) 193	2.50	3.75	5.00
SENSATIONAL SONNY JAMES	Capitol (S) 804	2.50	3.75	5.00
SONNY	Capitol (M) T867	3.00	4.50	6.00
SONNY JAMES	Columbia (S) KC 32028	2.50	3.75	5.00
SOUTHERN GENTLEMEN	Capitol (M) T779	4.00	6.00	8.00
SOUTHERN GENTLEMEN	Capitol (EP) EAP 1 779	1.50	2.25	3.00
SOUTHERN GENTLEMEN	Capitol (EP) EAP 2 779	1.50	2.25	3.00
SOUTHERN GENTLEMEN	Capitol (EP) EAP 3 779	1.50	2.25	3.00
THIS IS SONNY JAMES	Capitol (M) T1178	3.00	4.50	6.00
200 YEARS OF COUNTRY MUSIC	Columbia (S) PC 34035	2.00	3.00	4.00
WHEN SOMETHING IS WRONG WITH MY BABY	Columbia (S) PC 34309	2.00	3.00	4.00
WHEN THE SNOW IS ON THE ROSES/ IF SHE HELPS ME GET OVER YOU	Columbia (S) CG 33627	2.00	3.00	4.00
WHEN THE SNOW IS ON THE ROSES	Columbia (S) 31646	2.50	3.75	5.00
YOUNG LOVE	Capitol (S) ST 11196	2.00	3.00	4.00
YOUNG LOVE	Capitol (EP) EAP1-827	1.50	2.25	3.00
YOU'RE FREE TO GO	Columbia (S) PC 34472	2.00	3.00	4.00
YOU'RE THE ONLY WORLD I KNOW	Capitol (M) T2209	2.50	3.75	5.00
YOU'RE THE ONLY WORLD I KNOW	Capitol (S) ST2209	2.50	3.75	5.00

JAMES, Tommy

TITLE	LABEL & NO.	GOOD	VERY GOOD	NEAR MINT
CHRISTIAN OF THE WORLD	Roulette (S) SR3001	4.00	6.00	8.00
IN TOUCH	Fantasy (S) 9509	2.00	3.00	4.00
MIDNIGHT RIDER	Fantasy (S) 9532	2.00	3.00	4.00
MY HEAD, MY BED AND MY RED GUITAR	Roulette (S) SR3007	4.00	6.00	8.00
TOMMY JAMES	Roulette (S) SR42051	3.50	5.25	7.00

JAMES, Tommy & The Shondells

TITLE	LABEL & NO.	GOOD	VERY GOOD	NEAR MINT
BEST OF TOMMY JAMES AND THE SHONDELLS	Roulette (S) SR 42040	3.00	4.50	6.00
CRIMSON AND CLOVER	Roulette (S) SR 42023	3.50	5.25	7.00
GETTIN TOGETHER	Roulette (M) R25357	3.50	5.25	7.00
GETTIN TOGETHER	Roulette (S) SR25357	4.50	6.75	9.00
HANKY PANKY	Roulette (M) R25336	3.50	5.25	7.00
HANKY PANKY	Roulette (S) S25336	4.50	6.75	9.00
I THINK WE'RE ALONE NOW (Picture Cover)	Roulette (M) R25353	3.50	5.25	7.00
I THINK WE'RE ALONE NOW (Black Cover with Footprints)	Roulette (S) SR25353	4.50	6.75	9.00
IT'S ONLY LOVE	Roulette (M) R25344	3.50	5.25	7.00
IT'S ONLY LOVE	Roulette (S) SR25344	4.50	6.75	9.00
SOMETHING SPECIAL-THE BEST OF TOMMY JAMES AND THE SHONDELLS	Roulette (M) R25355	3.00	4.50	6.00
SOMETHING SPECIAL-THE BEST OF TOMMY JAMES AND THE SHONDELLS	Roulette (S) SR25355	4.00	6.00	8.00
TRAVELIN'	Roulette (S) SR42044	3.50	5.25	7.00

JAMESON

TITLE	LABEL & NO.	GOOD	VERY GOOD	NEAR MINT
COLOR HIM IN	Verve (M) V5015	5.00	7.50	10.00
COLOR HIM IN	Verve (S) V65015	6.00	9.00	12.00

JAMESON, Bobby

TITLE	LABEL & NO.	GOOD	VERY GOOD	NEAR MINT
WORKING!	GRT (S) 10004	3.00	4.50	6.00

(M) Mono (S) Stereo (EP) Extended Play (Q) Quad (RI) Re-issued

TITLE	LABEL & NO.	GOOD	VERY GOOD	NEAR MINT
JAMME				
JAMME	Dunhill (S) DS50072	5.00	7.50	10.00
JAN & ARNIE				
JAN & ARNIE	Dot (EP) DEP 1097	18.00	36.00	54.00
JAN AND DEAN				
COKE COMMERCIAL LP	Coca Cola	20.00	40.00	60.00
COMMAND PERFORMANCE	Liberty (M) LRP3403	3.00	6.00	9.00
COMMAND PERFORMANCE	Liberty (S) LST 7403	4.00	8.00	12.00
DEAD MAN'S CURVE/ NEW GIRL IN SCHOOL	Liberty (M) LRP3361	3.00	6.00	9.00
DEAD MAN'S CURVE/ NEW GIRL IN SCHOOL	Liberty (S) LST7361	4.00	8.00	12.00
DRAG CITY	Liberty (M) LRP3339	3.00	6.00	9.00
DRAG CITY	Liberty (S) LST 7339	4.00	8.00	12.00
FILET OF SOUL	Liberty (M) LRP3441	3.00	6.00	9.00
FILET OF SOUL	Liberty (S) LST 7441	4.00	8.00	12.00
FOLK N' ROLL	Liberty (M) LRP3431	3.00	6.00	9.00
FOLK N' ROLL	Liberty (S) LST 7431	4.00	8.00	12.00
GOLDEN HITS VOL. 3	Liberty (M) LRP3460	4.00	8.00	12.00
GOLDEN HITS VOL. 3	Liberty (S) LST7460	5.00	10.00	15.00
GOTTA TAKE THAT ONE LAST RIDE	United Artists (S) UALA341H2	2.00	3.00	4.00
HEART & SOUL OF JAN & DEAN AND FRIENDS	Design (M) DLP 181	2.00	4.00	6.00
HEART & SOUL OF JAN & DEAN AND FRIENDS (LABEL SHOWS "STEREO SPECTRUM" AS NAME, CVR. LISTS "DESIGN")	Design (SE) SDLP-181	2.00	4.00	6.00
JAN & DEAN	Dore (M) LP101	4.00	12.00	20.00
JAN & DEAN (With photo insert)	Dore (M) LP 101	8.00	16.00	32.00
JAN AND DEAN	Sunset (M) SUM1156	3.00	6.00	9.00
JAN AND DEAN	Sunset (S) SUS 5156	3.00	6.00	9.00
JAN AND DEAN ANTHOLOGY ALBUM	United Artists (S) UAS9961	4.00	6.00	8.00
JAN AND DEAN MEET BATMAN	Liberty (M) LRP 3444	4.00	8.00	12.00
JAN AND DEAN MEET BATMAN	Liberty (S) LST7444	5.00	10.00	15.00
JAN & DEAN'S GOLDEN HITS	Liberty (M) LRP3248	3.00	6.00	9.00
JAN & DEAN'S GOLDEN HITS	Liberty (S) LST7248	4.00	8.00	12.00
JAN & DEAN'S GOLDEN HITS VOLUME 2	Liberty (M) LRP3417	2.00	4.00	6.00
JAN & DEAN'S GOLDEN HITS VOLUME 2	Liberty (S) LST 7417	3.00	6.00	9.00
JAN & DEAN'S POP SYMPHONY NUMBER 1	Liberty (M) LRP3414	6.00	12.00	18.00
JAN & DEAN'S POP SYMPHONY NUMBER 1	Liberty (S) LST7414	7.00	14.00	21.00
JAN & DEAN TAKE LINDA SURFING	Liberty (M) LRP3294	4.00	8.00	12.00
JAN & DEAN TAKE LINDA SURFING	Liberty (S) LST7294	4.00	8.00	12.00
JAN AND DEAN WITH THE SOUL SURFERS	L-J (M) 101	5.00	10.00	15.00
LITTLE OLD LADY FROM PASEDENA	Liberty (M) LRP3377	3.00	6.00	9.00
LITTLE OLD LADY FROM PASEDENA	Liberty (S) LST7377	4.00	8.00	12.00
POPSICLE	Liberty (M) LRP3458	3.00	6.00	9.00
POPSICLE	Liberty (S) LST7458	4.00	8.00	12.00
RIDE THE WILD SURF	Liberty (M) LRP3368	3.00	6.00	9.00
RIDE THE WILD SURF	Liberty (S) LST7368	4.00	8.00	12.00
SAVE FOR A RAINY DAY (DJ copy only)	Columbia (S) CS 9461	85.00	170.00	255.00
SAVE FOR A RAINY DAY	J and D (M) JD101	17.00	34.00	51.00
SURF CITY	Liberty (M) LRP3314	3.00	6.00	9.00
SURF CITY	Liberty (S) LST7314	4.00	8.00	12.00
VERY BEST OF JAN & DEAN VOL 1	United Artists UA-LA 443	2.50	3.75	5.00
JAN & KJELD				
BANJO BOY	Kapp (M) KL1190	3.00	6.00	9.00
JANERO, Triste				
MEET TRISTE JANERO	White Whale (M) WW7122	2.50	3.75	5.00
JANICE, Little				
TODAY'S YOUTH TOMORROW THE WORLD	Pzazz (S) SLP323	3.00	4.50	6.00

(M) Mono (S) Stereo (EP) Extended Play (Q) Quad (RI) Re-issued

TITLE	LABEL & NO.	GOOD	VERY GOOD	NEAR MINT
JANIS, Johnny				
FOR THE FIRST TIME	ABC (M) LP 140	5.00	7.50	10.00
START OF SOMETHING NEW	Columbia (M) CL1674	4.00	6.00	8.00
START OF SOMETHING NEW	Columbia (S) CS8474	4.50	6.75	9.00
JANUARY TIME				
FIRST TIME FROM MEMPHIS	Enterprise (S) ENS1004	2.50	3.75	5.00
JAY and The Americans				
BLOCKBUSTERS	United Artists (M) UAL3417	3.00	4.50	6.00
BLOCKBUSTERS	United Artists (S) UAS6417	4.00	6.00	8.00
CAPTURE THE MOMENT	United Artists (S) UAS6762	3.00	4.50	6.00
JAY & THE AMERICANS (AT THE CAFE WHA)	United Artists (M) UAL3300	5.00	7.50	10.00
JAY & THE AMERICANS (AT THE CAFE WHA)	United Artists (S) UAS6300	6.00	9.00	12.00
JAY AND THE AMERICANS GREATEST HITS	United Artists (M) UAL3453	3.00	4.50	6.00
JAY AND THE AMERICANS GREATEST HITS	United Artists (S) UAS6453	4.00	6.00	8.00
JAY & THE AMERICANS GREATEST HITS	United Artists (M) UAL 3555	4.00	6.00	8.00
JAY & THE AMERICANS GREATEST HITS	United Artists (S) UAS 6555	5.00	7.50	10.00
LIVIN ABOVE YOUR HEAD	United Artists (M) UAL3534	2.50	3.75	5.00
LIVIN ABOVE YOUR HEAD	United Artists (S) UAS6534	3.00	4.50	6.00
SANDS OF TIME	United Artists (S) 6671	3.50	5.25	7.00
SHE CRIED	United Artists (M) UAL3222	3.50	5.25	7.00
SHE CRIED	United Artists (S) UAS6222	4.50	7.00	9.00
SUNDAY & ME	United Artists (M) UAL3474	3.00	4.50	6.00
SUNDAY & ME	United Artists (S) UAS6474	4.00	6.00	8.00
TRY SOME OF THIS	United Artists (M) UAL3562	2.50	3.75	5.00
TRY SOME OF THIS	United Artists (S) UAS6562	3.00	4.50	6.00
VERY BEST OF JAY & THE AMERICANS	United Artists (S) UA-LA357	2.50	3.75	5.00
WAX MUSEUM	United Artists (S) UAS6719	3.00	4.50	6.00
WAX MUSEUM VOL. 2	United Artists (S) UAS6751	3.00	4.50	6.00
JAY & THE TECHNIQUES				
JAY & THE TECHNIQUES	Smash (S) SRS 67095	3.50	4.75	7.00
LOVE LOST AND FOUND	Smash (S) SRS67102	3.50	4.75	7.00
JAY, Bob, and The Hawks				
SKA VOL. 2	Warner Brothers (M) W1563	3.00	6.00	9.00
JAYE, Jerry				
MY GIRL JOSEPHINE	Hi (M) HL12038	5.00	10.00	15.00
MY GIRL JOSEPHINE	Hi (S) HLS 32038	6.00	9.00	12.00
JAYNETTES				
SALLY GO ROUND THE ROSES	Tuff (M) 13	5.00	10.00	15.00
JEFFERSON				
JEFFERSON	Janus (S) JLS3006	3.00	4.50	6.00
JEFFERSON AIRPLANE				
AFTER BATHING AT BAXTER'S	RCA (M) LOC 1511	3.50	5.25	7.00
AFTER BATHING AT BAXTER'S	RCA (S) LSO 1511	4.00	6.00	8.00
BARK	Grunt (S) FTR 1001	3.00	4.50	6.00
BLESS ITS POINTED LITTLE HEAD	RCA (S) LSP 4133	4.00	6.00	8.00
CROWN OF CREATION	RCA (S) LSP 4058	4.00	6.00	8.00
DRAGON FLY	Grunt (S) BFL1-0717	2.50	3.75	5.00
DRAGON FLY	Grunt (Q) BFD1-0717	2.50	3.75	5.00
EARLY FLIGHT	Grunt (S) CYL1-0437	2.50	3.75	5.00
EARTH	Grunt (S) BXL1-2515	2.50	3.75	5.00
FLIGHT LOG 1966-1976	Grunt CYL2-1255	3.00	4.50	6.00
JEFFERSON AIRPLANE TAKES OFF!	RCA (M) LPM 3584	3.50	5.25	7.00
JEFFERSON AIRPLANE TAKES OFF!	RCA (S) LSP 3584	4.00	6.00	8.00
LONG JOHN SILVER	Grunt (S) FTR 1007	3.00	4.50	6.00
RED OCTOPUS	Grunt (S) BFL1-0999	2.50	3.75	5.00
RED OCTOPUS	Grunt (Q) BFD1-0999	2.50	3.75	5.00
SPITFIRE	Grunt (S) BFL1-1557	2.50	3.75	5.00
SPITFIRE	Grunt (Q) BFD1-1557	2.50	3.75	5.00
SURREALISTIC PILLOW	RCA (M) LPM 3766	3.50	5.25	7.00
SURREALISTIC PILLOW	RCA (S) LSP 3766	4.00	6.00	8.00
THIRTY SECONDS OVER WINTERLAND	Grunt BFL1-0147	2.50	3.75	5.00
VOLUNTEERS	RCA (S) LSP 4238	3.00	4.50	6.00
VOLUNTEERS	RCA (Q) APD1-0320	2.50	3.75	5.00
WORST OF JEFFERSON AIRPLANE	RCA (S) LSP 4459	3.00	4.50	6.00

(Listed as "Jefferson Starship" beginning with Grunt 0147)

TITLE	LABEL & NO.	GOOD	VERY GOOD	NEAR MINT
JEFFERSON, Blind Lemon				
BLIND LEMON JEFFERSON	Biograph (M) 12000	5.00	10.00	15.00
FOLK BLUES	Riverside (M) RLP1014	6.00	12.00	18.00
FOLK BLUES CLASSICS	Riverside (M) RLP12-125	6.00	12.00	18.00
PENITENTIARY BLUES	Riverside (M) LP1053	6.00	12.00	18.00
JEFFREY, Joe				
MY PLEDGE OF LOVE	Wand (S) WDS 686	3.50	5.25	7.00
JELLY BEAN BANDITS				
JELLY BEAN BANDITS	Mainstream (M) 56103	4.00	6.00	8.00
JELLY BEAN BANDITS	Mainstream (S) S6103	5.00	7.50	10.00

TITLE	LABEL & NO.	GOOD	VERY GOOD	NEAR MINT

JELLYBREAD
| 1ST SLICE | Blue Horizon (S) BH4801 | 3.00 | 4.50 | 6.00 |

JENNIFER
I CAN REMEMBER EVERYTHING	Parrott (S) PAS71020	4.50	7.00	9.00
JENNIFER	Reprise (S) MS2065	4.00	6.00	8.00
SEE ME, FEEL ME, TOUCH ME, HEAL ME	Parrot (S) PAS71034	3.00	4.50	6.00

JENNINGS, Bill
| GUITAR MOODS | King (M) KEP342 | 1.50 | 3.75 | 6.00 |

JENNINGS, Waylon
AT JD'S	Sounds LTD.	8.00	20.00	32.00
DON'T THINK TWICE	A&M (S) S 4238	3.00	6.00	9.00
FOLK-COUNTRY	RCA (S) LSP 3523	3.00	6.00	9.00
HONKY TONK HEROES	RCA (S) APL1-0240	2.50	3.75	9.00
LEAVIN' TOWN	RCA (S) LSP 3620	3.00	6.00	9.00
NASHVILLE REBEL (Soundtrack)	RCA (S) LSP 3736	3.00	6.00	9.00
RAMBLIN' MAN	RCA (S) APL1-0734	2.50	3.75	5.00
SINGS 'OL HARLAN	RCA (S) LSP 3660	3.00	6.00	9.00
SOUVENIR OF ARIZONA (contains live studio interview with Waylon and one song 'RAVE ON')	LJR (M) 114	7.00	17.50	28.00
THIS TIME	RCA (S) APL1-0539	2.50	3.75	5.00
WAYLON JENNINGS	Vocalion (M) 73873	2.00	4.00	6.00

JENSEN, Kris
| TORTURE | Hickory (M) MH110 | 4.00 | 10.00 | 16.00 |

JETHRO TULL
AQUALUNG	Reprise (S) MS 2035	4.00	6.00	8.00
AQUALUNG (RI)	Chrysalis (S) 1044	3.00	4.50	6.00
AQUALUNG	Chrysalis (Q) CH4-1044	2.50	3.75	5.00
BENEFIT	Reprise (S) RS 6400	5.00	7.50	10.00
HEAVY HORSES	Chrysalis (S) CHR 1175	2.50	3.75	5.00
LIVING IN THE PAST	Chrysalis (S) 2106	4.00	6.00	8.00
MINSTREL IN THE GALLERY	Chrysalis (S) 1082	3.00	4.50	6.00
PASSION PLAY	Chrysalis (S) 1040	3.00	4.50	6.00
SONGS FROM THE WOOD	Chrysalis (S) 1132	2.50	3.75	5.00
STAND UP	Reprise (S) RS 6360	5.00	7.50	10.00
THICK AS A BRICK	Reprise (S) MS 2072	4.00	6.00	8.00
THIS WAS	Reprise (S) RS 6336	5.00	7.50	10.00
TOO OLD TO ROCK N' ROLL, TOO YOUNG TO DIE	Chrysalis (S) 1111	3.00	4.50	6.00
WAR CHILD	Chrysalis (S) 1067	3.00	4.50	6.00

JIM AND JEAN
JIM AND JEAN	Philips (M) PHM200-182	4.00	6.00	8.00
JIM AND JEAN	Philips (S) PHS600-182	5.00	7.50	10.00
PEOPLE WORLD	Verve-Forecast (S) FTS3015	3.50	4.75	7.00

JIMENEZ, Jose-see DANA, Bill

JIVE FIVE
JIVE 5	Relic (M) 5020	4.00	6.00	8.00
JIVE FIVE	United Artists (M) UAL 3455	4.00	8.00	12.00
JIVE FIVE	United Artists (S) UAS 6455	5.00	10.00	15.00

JO JO GUNNE
BITE DOWN HARD	Asylum (S) 5065	3.00	4.50	6.00
JUMPIN' THE GUNNE	Asylum (S) 5071	3.00	4.50	6.00
SO ... WHERE IS THE SHOW	Asylum (S) 7E-1022	2.50	3.75	5.00

Also see JAY FERGUSON, SPIRIT

JOBRIATH
| CREATURES OF THE STREET | Elektra (S) 7E1010 | 2.50 | 3.75 | 5.00 |
| JOBRIATH | Elektra (S) 75070 | 2.50 | 3.75 | 5.00 |

JOE & EDDIE
BEST OF JOE AND EDDIE	Crescendo (M) 2032	2.00	4.00	6.00
BEST OF JOE AND EDDIE	Crescendo (S) 2032	2.00	4.00	6.00
JOE & EDDIE	Crescendo (M) 99	2.00	4.00	6.00
JOE & EDDIE	Crescendo (S) 99	2.50	5.00	7.50
JOE & EDDIE COAST TO COAST	Crescendo (M) 96	2.00	4.00	6.00
JOE & EDDIE COAST TO COAST	Crescendo (S) 96	2.50	5.00	7.50
TEAR DOWN THE WALLS	Crescendo (M) 2005	2.00	4.00	6.00
TEAR DOWN THE WALLS	Crescendo (S) 2005	2.50	5.00	7.50
THERE'S A MEETIN HERE TONITE	Crescendo (M) 86	2.00	4.00	6.00
THERE'S A MEETIN HERE TONITE	Crescendo (S) 86	2.50	5.00	7.50

JOEL, Billy
PIANO MAN	Columbia (S) KC 32544	2.50	3.75	5.00
PIANO MAN	Columbia (Q) CQ 32544	2.50	3.75	5.00
STRANGER, THE	Columbia (S) JC 34987	2.00	3.00	4.00
STREETLIFE SERENADE	Columbia (S) PC 33146	2.00	3.00	4.00
STREETLIFE SERENADE	Columbia (Q) PCQ 33146	2.00	3.00	4.00
TURNSTILES	Columbia (S) PC 33848	2.00	3.00	4.00
TURNSTILES	Columbia (Q) PCQ 33848	2.00	3.00	4.00

JOHANSEN, David
| DAVID JOHANSEN | Blue Sky (S) JZ 34926 | 2.00 | 3.00 | 4.00 |

Also see NEW YORK DOLLS.

TITLE	LABEL & NO.	GOOD	VERY GOOD	NEAR MINT

JOHN, Elton
BLUE MOVES	MCA/Rocket (S) 2-11004	3.00	4.50	6.00
CAPTAIN FANTASTIC (& THE BROWN DIRT COWBOY)	MCA 2142	2.50	3.75	5.00
DON'T SHOOT ME, I'M ONLY THE PIANO PLAYER	MCA (S) 2100	2.50	3.75	5.00
11-17-70	Uni (S) 93105	5.00	7.50	10.00
11-17-70 (RI)	MCA (S) 2015	2.00	3.00	4.00
ELTON JOHN	Uni (S) 73090	6.00	9.00	12.00
ELTON JOHN (RI)	MCA 2012	2.00	3.00	4.00
ELTON JOHN'S GREATEST HITS, Vol. 2	MCA (S) 3027	2.00	3.00	4.00
EMPTY SKY	MCA (S) 2130	2.50	3.75	5.00
GOODBYE YELLOW BRICK ROAD	MCA 2-10003	3.00	4.50	6.00
GREATEST HITS	MCA 2128	2.50	3.75	5.00
HERE & THERE	MCA 2197	2.50	3.75	5.00
HONKEY CHATEAU	MCA (S) 2017	2.00	3.00	4.00
HONKEY CHATEAU	Uni (S) 93135	5.00	7.50	10.00
MADMAN ACROSS THE WATER	Uni (S) 93120	5.00	7.50	10.00
MADMAN ACROSS THE WATER (RI)	MCA (S) 2016	2.00	3.00	4.00
ROCK OF THE WESTIES	MCA 2163	2.50	3.75	5.00
TUMBLEWEED CONNECTION	Uni (S) 73096	5.00	7.50	10.00
TUMBLEWEED CONNECTION (RI)	MCA (S) 2014	2.00	3.00	4.00

JOHNNY & THE BLUE BEATS
| SMILE | Winsor (M) RL 1001 | 5.00 | 10.00 | 15.00 |

JOHNNY & THE HURRICANES
BEATNICK FLY	Twirl (M) 5002	7.00	14.00	21.00
BIG SOUND OF JOHNNY AND THE HURRICANES	Big Top (M) 12-1302	8.00	20.00	32.00
JOHNNY AND THE HURRICANES	Warwick (M) W2007	8.00	20.00	32.00
JOHNNY & THE HURRICANES	Warwick (EP) EX700	3.00	7.50	12.00
LIVE AT THE STAR CLUB Hamburg, Germany	Atila (M) ALP 1030	8.00	20.00	32.00
STORMSVILLE	Warwick (M) W2010	8.00	20.00	32.00
STORMSVILLE	Warwick (S) WST2010	10.00	25.00	40.00

JOHN'S CHILDREN
| ORGASM | White Whale (S) WW 7128 | 8.00 | 16.00 | 24.00 |

JOHNSON, Betty
BETTY JOHNSON	RCA (EP) EPA4059	1.00	1.50	2.00
BETTY JOHNSON	Atlantic (M) LP 8017	5.00	7.50	10.00
SONGS YOU HEARD WHEN YOU FELL IN LOVE	Atlantic (M) LP8027	3.00	4.50	6.00

JOHNSON, Bubber
| COME HOME | King (M) LP 569 | 5.00 | 10.00 | 15.00 |
| SWEET LOVE SONGS | King (M) 624 | 4.00 | 8.00 | 12.00 |

JOHNSON, Candy, Show
BIKINI BEACH	Canjo (M) LP1002	3.00	4.50	6.00
BIKINI BEACH	Canjo (S) CR1002	4.00	6.00	8.00
CANDY JOHNSON SHOW	Canjo (M) LP1001	3.00	4.50	6.00

JOHNSON, Col. Jubilation B.
| MOLDY GOLDIES | Columbia (M) 2532 | 5.00 | 7.50 | 10.00 |

(M) Mono (S) Stereo (EP) Extended Play (Q) Quad (RI) Re-issued

TITLE	LABEL & NO.	GOOD	VERY GOOD	NEAR MINT

JOHNSON, Lonnie
BLUES BY LONNIE JOHNSON	Prestige (M) BV1007	2.00	3.00	4.00
IDLE HOURS				
(With Victoria Spivey)	Prestige (M) BV1044	2.00	3.00	4.00
LONESOME ROAD	King (M) LP520	5.00	7.50	10.00
LONNIE JOHNSON, ANOTHER				
NIGHT TO CRY	Prestige (M) BV1062	2.00	3.00	4.00
LONNIE JOHNSON SINGS 24				
TWELVE BAR BLUES	King (M) 958	5.00	7.50	10.00
LOSING GAME	Prestige (M) BV1024	2.00	3.00	4.00
TOMORROW NIGHT	King (M) KS1083	4.00	6.00	8.00
TOMORROW NIGHT-PLEASING YOU	King (EP) EP267	2.50	3.75	5.00
WOMAN BLUES				
(With Victoria Spivey)	Prestige (M) BV1054	2.00	3.00	4.00

JOHNSON, Lou
WITH YOU IN MIND	Volt (S) VOS6016	2.50	3.75	5.00

JOHNSON, Luther & The Muddy Waters Blues Band
COME ON HOME	Douglas (S) SD 789	2.50	3.75	5.00

JOHNSON, Marv
I BELIEVE	United Artists (M) UAL 3187	5.00	10.00	15.00
MARVELOUS	United Artists (M) UAL 3081	6.00	12.00	18.00
MORE	United Artists (M) UAL 3118	5.00	10.00	15.00

JOHNSON, Pete
PETE JOHNSON & JOE TURNER	Savoy (M) MG14016	6.00	15.00	24.00
PETE'S BLUES	Savoy (M) MG14018	6.00	15.00	24.00

JOHNSON, Plas
PLAS JOHNSON	Tampa	6.00	12.00	18.00

JOHNSON, Robert
KING OF THE				
DELTA BLUES SINGERS	Columbia (M) CL1654	6.00	12.00	18.00

JOHNSON, Sly
BACK FOR A TASTE OF YOUR LOVE	Hi (S) XSHL 32081	2.50	3.75	5.00
DIAMOND IN THE ROUGH	Hi (S) SHL32085	2.50	3.75	5.00
IS IT BECAUSE I'M BLACK	Twinight (S) LPS1002	5.00	10.00	15.00
TOTAL EXPLOSION	Hi (S) SHL 32096	2.00	3.00	4.00

JOHNSTON, Bruce
GOING PUBLIC	Columbia (S) 34459	2.50	3.75	5.00
SURFIN ROUND THE WORLD	Columbia (M) CL2057	8.00	16.00	24.00
SURFIN ROUND THE WORLD	Columbia (S) CS8857	10.00	20.00	30.00

JOHNSTON, Bruce, Surfing Band
SURFERS PAJAMA PARTY	Del Fi (M) DELP1228	5.00	10.00	15.00
SURFERS PAJAMA PARTY	Del Fi (S) DFST 1228	6.00	12.00	18.00

JOLLIVER ARKANSAW
HOME	Bell (S) 6031	3.50	5.25	7.00

JOLSON, Al
AL JOLSON OVERSEAS	Decca (M) DL 9070	4.50	9.00	13.50
AL JOLSON WITH OSCAR LEVANT AT THE PIANO	Decca (M) DL 9095	4.00	6.00	8.00
BEST OF AL JOLSON	MCA (SE) 2-10002	3.00	4.50	6.00
BEST OF JOLSON	Decca (M) DXA 169	5.00	7.50	10.00
BEST OF JOLSON	Decca (SE) DXSA 7169	4.00	6.00	8.00
IMMORTAL AL JOLSON	Decca (M) DL 9063	4.50	9.00	13.50
JOLSON STORY-AMONG MY SOUVENIRS	Decca (M) DL 9050	4.50	9.00	13.50
JOLSON STORY-MEMORIES	Decca (M) DL 9037	5.00	10.00	15.00
JOLSON STORY-RAINBOW 'ROUND MY SHOULDER	Decca (M) DL 9036	5.00	10.00	15.00
JOLSON STORY-ROCK-A-BYE YOUR BABY	Decca (M) DL 9035	5.00	10.00	15.00
JOLSON STORY-YOU AIN'T HEARD NOTHIN' YET	Decca (M) DL 9037	5.00	10.00	15.00
JOLSON STORY-YOU MADE ME LOVE YOU	Decca (M) DL 9034	5.00	10.00	15.00
JOLSON STORY-YOU MADE ME LOVE YOU	Decca (SE) DL 79034	4.00	6.00	8.00
WORLD'S GREATEST ENTERTAINER	Decca (M) DL 9074	4.50	9.00	13.50

JON AND ROBIN
ELASTIC EVENT	Abnak (S) ABST M2070	4.00	6.00	8.00
SOUL OF A BOY & GIRL	Abnak (S) ABST M2068	4.00	6.00	8.00

JONES, Brian
BRIAN JONES PRESENTS THE				
PIPES OF PAN AT JOUJOUKA	Rolling Stones (S) 49100	5.00	7.50	10.00

JONES, Curtis
TROUBLE BLUES	Prestige-Bluesville (M) 1022	3.00	4.50	6.00

JONES, David
DAVID JONES	Colpix (M) CP493	5.00	7.50	10.00
DAVY JONES	Bell (M) 6067	7.00	10.50	14.00

JONES, Dean
INTRODUCING DEAN JONES	Valiant (M) W407	2.50	3.75	5.00
INTRODUCING DEAN JONES	Valiant (S) S407	3.00	4.50	6.00

JONES, Don
BIGFOOT (Northwest's				
Abominable Snowman)	Panorama (S) 204	5.00	7.50	10.00

JONES, George
FABULOUS COUNTRY MUSIC				
SOUND OF GEORGE JONES	Starday (M) S151	4.00	6.00	8.00
GEORGE JONES SONGS	Starday (M) SLP 101	5.00	10.00	15.00
HEARTBRAKE HOTEL (Features 2 Songs				
by George Jones - Issued without				
EP Jacket)	Dixie (EP) EP505	5.00	12.50	20.00
NOVELTY SIDE OF GEORGE JONES	Mercury (M) MG 20793	7.00	14.00	21.00

JONES, George & Gene Pitney
GEORGE JONES & GENE PITNEY	Musicor (M) MM2044	2.50	3.75	5.00
GEORGE JONES & GENE PITNEY	Musicor (S) MS3044	2.50	3.75	5.00
IT'S COUNTRY TIME AGAIN	Musicor (M) MM2065	2.50	3.75	5.00
IT'S COUNTRY TIME AGAIN	Musicor (S) MS3044	2.50	3.75	5.00

JONES, George & Tammy Wynette
GOLDEN RING	Epic (S) KE 34291	2.00	3.00	4.00
GREATEST HITS	Epic (S) KE 34716	2.00	3.00	4.00
WE GO TOGETHER	Epic (S) E 30802	2.00	3.00	4.00

JONES, Gloria
COME GO WITH ME	Uptown (M) T5700	4.00	6.00	8.00
SHARE MY LOVE	Motown (M) M790	2.50	3.75	5.00

JONES, Jack
CALL ME IRRESPONSIBLE	Kapp (M) KL 1328	3.00	4.50	6.00
CALL ME IRRESPONSIBLE	Kapp (S) KS 3328	3.00	4.50	6.00
DEAR HEART	Kapp (M) KL 1415	3.00	4.50	6.00
DEAR HEART	Kapp (S) KS 3415	3.00	4.50	6.00
IF YOU EVER LEAVE ME	RCA (S) LSP 3969	2.50	3.75	5.00
IMPOSSIBLE DREAM	Kapp (M) KL 1486	3.00	4.50	6.00
IMPOSSIBLE DREAM	Kapp (S) KS 3486	3.00	4.50	6.00
LADY	Kapp (M) KL 1511	3.00	4.50	6.00
LADY	Kapp (S) KS 3511	3.00	4.50	6.00
A TIME FOR US	RCA (S) LSP 4209	2.50	3.75	5.00
WHAT THE WORLD NEEDS NOW IS LOVE	Kapp (S) KS 3551	3.00	4.50	6.00
WHERE IS LOVE?	RCA (S) LSP 4048	2.50	3.75	5.00
WITHOUT HER	RCA (S) LSP 3911	2.50	3.75	5.00
WIVES AND LOVERS	Kapp (M) KL 1352	3.00	4.50	6.00
WIVES AND LOVERS	Kapp (S) KS 3352	3.00	4.50	6.00
WRITE ME A LOVE SONG, CHARLIE	RCA (S) APL1-0773	2.00	3.00	4.00

JONES, Jim & The Chaunteys
SOUL CLAP	Sunglow (M) SLP113	3.00	4.50	6.00

JONES, Jimmy
GOOD TIMIN'	MGM (M) E3847	7.00	17.50	28.00
GOOD TIMIN'	MGM (S) SE3847	9.00	22.50	36.00

JONES, Joe
YOU TALK TOO MUCH	Roulette (M) R25143	4.00	10.00	16.00
YOU TALK TOO MUCH	Roulette (S) SR25143	5.00	12.50	20.00

JONES, John Paul
JOHN PAUL JONES	Columbia (S) KC32047	3.00	4.50	6.00

JONES, Linda
HYPNOTIZED	Loma (S) 5907	4.00	6.00	8.00
YOUR PRECIOUS LOVE	Turbo (S) TU7007	3.00	4.50	6.00

JONES, Paul
PAUL JONES SINGS				
SONGS FROM THE FILM				
PRIVILEGE AND OTHERS	Capitol (S) ST2795	6.00	9.00	12.00

JONES, Ruby
RUBY JONES	Curtom (M) CRS8011	4.00	6.00	8.00

(M) Mono (S) Stereo (EP) Extended Play (Q) Quad (RI) Re-issued

TITLE	LABEL & NO.	GOOD	VERY GOOD	NEAR MINT
JONES, Spike				
BOTTOMS UP	RCA (M) LPM 3054	4.00	8.00	12.00
CHRISTMAS FUN WITH SPIKE JONES	RCA (EP) EYA18	2.00	4.00	6.00
CHRISTMAS SPECTACULAR	Verve (M) V 2021	5.00	12.50	20.00
CHRISTMAS SPECTACULAR	Verve (EP) EPV 5023	2.50	5.75	10.00
CHRISTMAS SPECTACULAR	Verve (EP) 5024	2.50	5.75	10.00
CHRISTMAS SPECTACULAR	Verve (EP) 5025	2.50	5.75	10.00
COUNTRY COUSINS	Verve (EP) EPA456	2.00	5.00	8.00
DINNER MUSIC FOR PEOPLE WHO AREN'T VERY HUNGRY	Verve (M) MGV4005	4.00	10.00	16.00
DINNER MUSIC FOR PEOPLE WHO AREN'T VERY HUNGRY	Verve (EP) EPV5056	2.50	5.75	10.00
DINNER MUSIC FOR PEOPLE WHO AREN'T VERY HUNGRY	Verve (EP) 5057	2.50	5.75	10.00
HANK WILLIAMS HITS	Liberty (M) LRP3401	2.50	3.75	5.00
HANK WILLIAMS HITS	Liberty (S) LST7401	2.50	3.75	5.00
JONES FAVORITES	RCA (EP) EPA288	2.00	4.00	6.00
KIDS THE CLASSICS	RCA (M) LPM3128	3.00	6.00	9.00
KIDS THE CLASSICS	RCA (EP) EPA415	2.00	4.00	6.00
MAN ON THE FLYING TRAPEZE	RCA (EP) EPA5080	2.00	3.00	4.00
MURDERS CARMEN	RCA LPM 3128	4.00	8.00	12.00
MURDERS CARMEN	RCA (EP) EPA440	2.00	4.00	6.00
MUSICAL DEPRECIATION (Box set)	RCA (M) 1893/5	8.00	16.00	24.00
MY MAN	Liberty (M) LRP3370	2.50	3.75	5.00
MY MAN	Liberty (S) LST7370	2.50	3.75	5.00
NUTCRACKER SUITE	RCA (EP) EPA143	2.00	4.00	6.00
60 YEARS OF MUSIC AMERICA HATES BEST	Liberty (M) LRP3154	3.00	4.50	6.00
60 YEARS OF MUSIC AMERICA HATES BEST	Liberty (S) LST7154	3.00	4.50	6.00
SOCK THE SMALLEST SNOWBALL	RCA (EP) EYA18	2.00	4.00	6.00
SPIKE JONES IN HI FI & STEREO	Warner Bros. (M) B1332	4.00	6.00	8.00
SPIKE JONES IN HI FI & STEREO	Warner Bros. (S) WS1332	4.00	6.00	8.00
SPIKE JONES IS MURDERING THE CLASSICS (Re-issue of 'Kids The Classics')	RCA (S) LSC3235	2.00	3.00	4.00
SPIKE JONES NEW BAND	Liberty (M) LRP3349	2.50	3.75	5.00
SPIKE JONES NEW BAND	Liberty (S) LST7349	2.50	3.75	5.00
SPIKE JONES PLAYS THE CHARLESTON	RCA (M) LPM 18	8.00	16.00	24.00
SPIKE JONES PLAYS THE CHARLESTON	RCA (EP) EPA277	2.00	4.00	6.00
SPIKE JONES PRESENTS OMNIBUST	Liberty (M) LRP3140	4.00	6.00	8.00
SPIKE JONES PRESENTS OMNIBUST	Liberty (S) LST7140	4.00	6.00	8.00
THANK YOU, MUSIC LOVERS	RCA (M) LPM2224	3.00	4.50	6.00
35 REASONS WHY CHRISTMAS CAN BE FUN	Verve (M) V8564	2.50	3.75	5.00
VERY BEST OF SPIKE JONES	United Artists (S) UA-LA439	2.00	3.00	4.00
WASHINGTON SQUARE	Liberty (M) LRP3338	2.50	3.75	5.00
WASHINGTON SQUARE	Liberty (S) LST7338	2.50	3.75	5.00
JONES, Tom				
ATOMIC JONES	Parrot (M) 61007	2.00	3.00	4.00
ATOMIC JONES	Parrot (S) 71007	2.50	3.75	5.00
BODY & SOUL OF TOM JONES	Parrot (S) 71060	2.50	3.75	5.00
CLASSIC TOM JONES	Epic/MAM (S) E 34383	2.00	3.00	4.00
CLOSE UP	Parrot (S) 71055	2.50	3.75	5.00
GREEN, GREEN, GRASS OF HOME	Parrot (M) 61009	2.00	3.00	4.00
GREEN, GREEN, GRASS OF HOME	Parrot (S) 71009	2.50	3.75	5.00
HELP YOURSELF	Parrot (S) 71025	2.50	3.75	5.00
IT'S NOT UNUSUAL	Parrot (M) 61004	2.00	3.00	4.00
IT'S NOT UNUSUAL	Parrot (S) 71004	2.50	3.75	5.00
I (WHO HAVE NOTHING)	Parrot (S) 71039	2.50	3.75	5.00
LIVE AT CAESARS' PALACE	Parrot (S) 71049	2.50	3.75	5.00
LIVE IN LAS VEGAS	Parrot (S) 71031	2.50	3.75	5.00
MEMORIES DON'T LEAVE LIKE PEOPLE DO	Parrot (S) PAS 71068	2.50	3.75	5.00
SAY YOU'LL STAY UNTIL TOMORROW	Epic/MAM (S) PE 34468	2.00	3.00	4.00
SHE'S A LADY	Parrot (S) 71046	2.50	3.75	5.00
THIS IS TOM JONES	Parrot (S) 71028	2.50	3.75	5.00
TOM	Parrot (S) 71037	2.50	3.75	5.00
TOM IS LOVE	Epic/MAM (S) E 34720	2.00	3.00	4.00
TOM JONES FEVER ZONE	Parrot (M) 61019	2.00	3.00	4.00
TOM JONES FEVER ZONE	Parrot (S) 71019	2.50	3.75	5.00
TOM JONES GREATEST HITS	London (S) LC 50002	2.00	3.00	4.00
TOM JONES' GREATEST HITS	Parrot (S) XPAS 71062	2.50	3.75	5.00
TOM JONES LIVE!	Parrot (M) 61014	2.00	3.00	4.00
TOM JONES LIVE!	Parrot (S) 71014	2.50	3.75	5.00
WHAT A NIGHT	Epic/MAM (S) JE 35023	2.00	3.00	4.00
WHAT'S NEW PUSSYCAT	Parrot (M) 61006	2.00	3.00	4.00
WHAT'S NEW PUSSYCAT	Parrot (S) 71006	2.50	3.75	5.00
JOPLIN, Janis				
I GOT DEM OL' KOZMIC BLUES AGAIN MAMA!	Columbia (S) CS 9913	4.00	6.00	8.00
JANIS JOPLIN'S GREATEST HITS	Columbia (S) KC 32168	2.50	3.75	5.00
JOPLIN IN CONCERT	Columbia (S) 33160	3.00	4.50	6.00
PEARL	Columbia (S) KC-30322	2.50	3.75	5.00
PEARL	Columbia (Q) CQ-30322	2.50	3.75	5.00
WICKED WOMAN	Memory 11-713	4.50	6.75	9.00
Also see Big Brother and the Holding Company				
JORDAN, Louis				
BEST OF LOUIS JORDAN	MCA (S) 24079	3.00	4.50	6.00
COME BLOW YOUR HORN	Score (M) 4007	14.00	35.00	56.00
LET THE GOOD TIMES ROLL	Decca (M) DL8551	9.00	22.50	36.00
LOUIS JORDAN VOLUME 1	Decca (EP) ED2029	2.50	6.25	10.00
LOUIS JORDAN VOLUME 2	Decca (EP) A645	2.50	6.25	10.00
LOUIS JORDAN'S GREATEST HITS	Decca (S) 5035	6.00	12.00	18.00
LOUIS JORDAN'S GREATEST HITS	Decca (S) 75035	7.00	14.00	21.00
MAN WERE WAILIN'	Mercury (M) MG 20331	3.00	7.50	12.00
SOMEBODY UP THERE DIGS ME	Mercury (M) MG20242	3.00	7.50	12.00

TITLE	LABEL & NO.	GOOD	VERY GOOD	NEAR MINT
JORDANAIRES				
BIG COUNTRY HITS	Columbia (M) CL2458	2.50	3.75	5.00
BIG COUNTRY HITS	Columbia (S) CS9258	2.50	3.75	5.00
SPOTLIGHT ON THE JORDANAIRES	Capitol (M) T1742	2.50	3.75	5.00
SPOTLIGHT ON THE JORDANAIRES	Capitol (S) ST1742	2.50	3.75	5.00
JOSEPHUS				
DEAD MAN	Hookah	7.00	10.50	14.00
JOSEPHUS	Mainstream	4.00	6.00	8.00
JOURNEY				
INFINITY	Columbia (S) JC 34912	2.00	3.00	4.00
JOURNEY	Columbia (S) PC-33388	2.00	3.00	4.00
LOOK INTO THE FUTURE	Columbia (S) PC 33904	2.00	3.00	4.00
NEXT	Columbia (S) PC 34311	2.00	3.00	4.00
JOY				
THUNDERFOOT	Puala (S) LPS2217	2.50	3.75	5.00
JOYFUL NOISE				
JOYFUL NOISE	RCA (S) LSP3963	3.00	4.50	6.00
JOY OF COOKING				
CLOSER TO THE GROUND	Capitol (S) SMAS828	4.00	6.00	8.00
JOY OF COOKING	Capitol (S) ST661	4.00	6.00	8.00
JOY OF COOKING	Capitol (S) ST11050	5.00	7.50	10.00
JOYRIDE				
FRIEND SOUND	RCA (S) LSP4114	6.00	9.00	12.00
JUDAS JUMP				
SCORTCH	Pride (S) 0003	4.50	6.75	9.00
JUICY LUCY				
GET A WHIFF OF THIS	Atco (S) SD33367	2.50	3.75	5.00
JUICY LUCY	Atco (S) SD33325	2.50	3.75	5.00
LIE BACK & ENJOY IT	Atco (S) SD33345	2.50	3.75	5.00
JULIAN, Don (Featuring The Meadowlarks)				
GREATEST OLDIES	Amazon (M) 1009	9.00	18.00	27.00
JULY				
JULY	Epic (S) BN26416	3.50	5.25	7.00
JR. CADILLAC				
JR. CADILLAC IS BACK	Great Northwest (M) GNWRC 1000001	4.50	6.75	9.00
JR. CADILLAC IS BACK VOLUME 2	Great Northwest (M) GNWRC 1000002	4.50	6.75	9.00
JUNIOR'S EYES				
JUNIOR'S EYES	A & M (S) SP4189	3.00	4.50	6.00
JUSTIS, Bill				
SOLID & RAUNCHY	Phillips International (M) 1950	5.00	10.00	15.00
JUST US				
I CAN'T GROW PEACHES ON A CHERRY TREE	Kapp (M) KL1502	2.50	3.75	5.00
I CAN'T GROW PEACHES ON A CHERRY TREE	Kapp (S) 3502	3.00	4.50	6.00

(M) Mono   (S) Stereo   (EP) Extended Play   (Q) Quad   (RI) Re-issued

K

TITLE	LABEL & NO.	GOOD	VERY GOOD	NEAR MINT
KAHN, Sajid				
SAJID	Colgems (S) COS-114	2.50	3.75	5.00
KAK				
KAK	Epic (S) BN26429	7.00	10.50	14.00
KAKKONEN, Peter				
BLACK KANGAROO	Grunt (S) FTR1006	3.00	4.50	6.00
KALEIDOSCOPE				
A BEACON FROM MARS	Epic (M) LN24333	6.00	9.00	12.00
A BEACON FROM MARS	Epic (S) BN26333	7.00	10.50	14.00
BERNICE	Epic (S) BN26508	5.00	7.50	10.00
KALEIDOSCOPE	Epic (S) BN26467	5.00	7.50	10.00
SIDE TRIPS	Epic (M) LN24304	5.00	7.50	10.00
SIDE TRIPS	Epic (S) BN26304	6.00	9.00	12.00
KALIN TWINS				
KALIN TWINS	Decca (M) DL8812	5.00	10.00	15.00
KALIN TWINS	Decca (S) DL78812	6.00	12.00	18.00
KALIN TWINS	Vocalion (S) VL73771	4.00	6.00	8.00
KALEN, Kitty				
HONKY TONK ANGEL	Columbia (M) CL1652	2.50	3.75	5.00
HONKY TONK ANGEL	Columbia (S) CS8452	2.50	3.75	5.00
IF I GIVE MY HEART TO YOU	Columbia (M) CL1409	3.00	4.50	6.00
IF I GIVE MY HEART TO YOU	Columbia (S) CS8204	3.00	4.50	6.00
IT'S A LONESOME OLD TOWN	Decca (M) DL8397	3.00	4.50	6.00
IT'S A LONESOME OLD TOWN	Decca (EP) ED 2467	1.00	1.50	2.00
IT'S A LONESOME OLD TOWN	Decca (EP) ED2468	1.00	1.50	2.00
IT'S A LONESOME OLD TOWN	Decca (EP) ED 2469	1.00	1.50	2.00
KITTY KALEN SINGS	Decca (EP) ED2164	1.00	1.50	2.00
KITTY KALEN SINGS	Mercury/Wing (M) MGW 12241	2.50	3.75	5.00
KITTY KALEN SINGS	Mercury/Wing (S) SRW16241	2.50	3.75	5.00
KITTY KALEN'S MY COLORING BOOK	RCA (M) LPM2640	2.50	3.75	5.00
KITTY KALEN'S MY COLORING BOOK	RCA (S) LSP2640	2.50	3.75	5.00
PRETTY KITTY KALEN SINGS (10")	Mercury (M) MG25206	2.50	3.75	5.00
PRETTY KITTY KALEN SINGS	Mercury (EP) EP13293	2.50	3.75	5.00
PRETTY KITTY KALEN SINGS	Mercury (EP) EP13294	2.50	3.75	5.00
KANNIBAL KOMIX				
KANNIBAL KOMIX	Colossus (S) CS1004	6.00	9.00	12.00
KANSAS				
KANSAS	Kirshner (S) KZ-32817	2.50	3.75	5.00
LEFTOVERTURE	Kirshner (S) JZ 34224	2.00	3.00	4.00
MASQUE	Kirshner (S) PZ-33806	2.00	3.00	4.00
POINT OF KNOW RETURN	Kirshner (S) JZ 34929	2.00	3.00	4.00
SONG FOR AMERICA	Kirshner (S) PZ 33385	2.00	3.00	4.00
KARAS, Anton				
ANTON KARAS AND HIS ZITHER	London (M) LB397	2.50	3.75	5.00
THIRD MAN THEME	London (M) LL560	2.50	3.75	5.00
ZITHER SOLOS	London (EP) BEP6035	1.00	1.50	2.00
KARTHAGO				
SECOND STEP	BASF (S) BB21780	3.50	5.25	7.00
K.C. & THE SUNSHINE BAND				
DO IT GOOD	TK (S) 500	3.00	4.50	6.00
KC & THE SUNSHINE BAND	T.K. (S) 603	2.50	3.75	5.00
PART 3	T.K. (S) 605	2.50	3.75	5.00
QUEEN OF CLUBS	TK (S) 600	2.50	3.75	5.00
SOUND OF SUNSHINE (SHOWN AS SUNSHINE BAND)	TK (S) 604	2.50	3.75	5.00
K-DOE, Ernie				
MOTHER-IN-LAW	Minit (M) LP0002	5.00	10.00	15.00
KEENE, Bob				
MASQUE D'AFRIQUE	Del Fi (M) DF1203	2.00	4.00	6.00
TWIST TO RADIO KRLA	Del Fi (M) DF1222	3.00	6.00	9.00
UNFORGETTABLE (Love Songs of The Sixties)	Del Fe (M) DF1202	2.00	4.00	6.00
KEITH				
ADVENTURES OF KEITH	RCA (S) LSP4143	5.00	7.50	10.00
98.6 AIN'T GONNA LIE	Mercury (M) MG21102	3.00	4.50	6.00
98.6 AIN'T GONNA LIE	Mercury (S) SR 61102	4.00	6.00	8.00
OUT OF CRANK	Mercury (M) MG21129	3.00	4.50	6.00
OUT OF CRANK	Mercury (S) SR61129	4.00	6.00	8.00

TITLE	LABEL & NO.	GOOD	VERY GOOD	NEAR MINT
KELLER, Jerry				
HERE COMES JERRY KELLER	Kapp (M) KL1178	5.00	12.50	20.00
HERE COMES JERRY KELLER	Kapp (S) KS3178	6.00	15.00	24.00
KELLY, Gene				
AMERICAN IN PARIS (Soundtrack)	MGM (M) E 3232	3.00	4.50	6.00
BROADWAY BALLET	MGM (EP) 1026	1.00	1.50	3.00
INVITATION TO THE DANCE	MGM (M) E 3207	3.00	4.50	6.00
IT'S ALWAYS FAIR WEATHER	MGM (M) E 3241	3.00	4.50	6.00
PIRATE	MGM (M) E 3234	3.00	4.50	6.00
SINGIN IN THE RAIN	MGM (M) E 3236	4.00	6.00	8.00
SONG AND DANCE MAN	MGM (M) E30	5.00	7.50	10.00
SONG AND DANCE MAN	MGM (EP) X1079	1.00	1.50	3.00
SUMMER STOCK (With Judy Garland)	MGM (M) E3234	4.00	6.00	8.00
KENDRICKS, Eddie				
ALL BY MYSELF	Tamla 309	3.00	4.50	6.00
BOOGIE DOWN	Tamla 330	2.50	3.75	5.00
EDDIE KENDRICKS AT HIS BEST	Tamla (S) T7-354	2.00	3.00	4.00
FOR YOU	Tamla (S) T6-335	2.00	3.00	4.00
GOIN' UP IN SMOKE	Tamla (S) T6-346	2.00	3.00	4.00
HE'S A FRIEND	Tamla (S) T6-343	2.00	3.00	4.00
HIT MAN	Tamla (S) T6-338	2.00	3.00	4.00
PEOPLE ... HOLD ON	Tamla 315	3.00	4.50	6.00
SLICK	Tamla (S) 356	2.00	3.00	4.00
VINTAGE '78	Arista (S) AB 4170	2.00	3.00	4.00
Also see TEMPTATIONS				
KENNEDY, Jerry				
JERRY KENNEDY DANCING GUITAR ROCKS ELVIS' HITS	Smash (M) MGS27004	3.00	4.00	6.00
JERRY KENNEDY DANCING GUITAR ROCKS ELVIS' HITS	Smash (S) SRS67004	4.00	6.00	8.00

TITLE	LABEL & NO.	GOOD	VERY GOOD	NEAR MINT
KENNEDY, John Fitzgerald				
MEMORIAL ALBUM, A	Premier (M) 2099	3.00	6.00	9.00
(Highlights of President Kennedy's speeches in a tribute produced and broadcast by Radio Station WMCA, New York on Friday, November 22, 1963.)				
KENNEDY, John F. and Richard M. Nixon				
GREAT DEBATES - 1960	Columbia (M) D2L372	5.00	7.50	10.00
KENNY and The KASUALS				
IMPACT	Mark (M) LP5000	40.00	100.00	160.00
KENSINGTON MARKET				
AARDVARK	Warner Brothers (S) WS1780	3.50	4.75	7.00
KEROUAC, Jack				
READINGS BY JACK KEROUAC ON THE BEAT GENERATION	Verve (M) MGV15005	9.00	22.50	36.00
KESEY, Ken				
THE ACID TEST	Sound City Prod. (M) EX27690	12.00	30.00	48.00
KICKSTANDS				
BLACK BOOTS AND BIKES	Capitol (M) T2078	3.00	6.00	9.00
BLACK BOOTS AND BIKES	Capitol (S) ST 2078	4.00	8.00	12.00
KIDS				
THE KIDS	RCA (EP) EPA4188	8.00	16.00	24.00
(Contains "Elvis and Me" an Elvis novelty)				
TEENAGERS DANCE THE HOP-A-DO	RCA (EP) EPA4061	2.00	4.00	6.00
KILLING FLOOR				
KILLING FLOOR	Sire (S) SES 97019	3.00	4.50	6.00

(M) Mono (S) Stereo (EP) Extended Play (Q) Quad (RI) Re-issued

KIM, Andy

TITLE	LABEL & NO.	GOOD	VERY GOOD	NEAR MINT
ANDY KIM	Capitol (S) ST11318	3.00	4.50	6.00
ANDY KIM	Uni (S) 73137	3.00	4.50	6.00
ANDY KIM'S GREATEST HITS	Steed (S) 37008	2.50	3.75	5.00
ANDY KIM'S GREATEST HITS (RI)	Dunhill (S) DSDP50193	2.50	3.75	5.00
BABY I LOVE YOU	Steed (S) ST37004	3.00	4.50	6.00
HOW'D WE EVER GET THIS WAY	Steed (S) ST37001	3.00	4.50	6.00
RAINBOW RIDE	Steed (S) ST 37002	3.00	4.50	6.00

KING, Albert

TITLE	LABEL & NO.	GOOD	VERY GOOD	NEAR MINT
I'LL PLAY THE BLUES FOR YOU	Stax (S) STS3009	2.50	3.75	5.00
I WANNA GET FUNKY	Stax (S) 5505	2.00	3.00	4.00
KING DOES THE KING'S THING	Stax (S) STS2015	2.50	3.75	5.00
LIVE WIRE/BLUES POWER	Stax (S) STS 2003	2.50	3.75	5.00
LOVE JOY	Stax (S) STS2040	2.50	3.75	5.00
MONTREUX FESTIVAL	Stax (S) 5520	2.00	3.00	4.00
YEARS GONE BY	Stax (S) STS2010	2.50	3.75	5.00

KING, Albert and Others

TITLE	LABEL & NO.	GOOD	VERY GOOD	NEAR MINT
JAMMED TOGETHER	Stax (S) STS 2020	2.50	3.75	5.00

KING, B.B.

TITLE	LABEL & NO.	GOOD	VERY GOOD	NEAR MINT
ALIVE & WELL	Bluesway (M) 6031	2.50	4.00	5.00
B.B.KING	Crown (S) CST359	2.50	3.75	5.00
B.B. KING IN LONDON	ABC (M) 730	2.00	3.00	4.00
B.B. KING 9 x 9-50	United (M) 7788	2.50	4.00	5.00
B. B. KING WAILS	Crown (S) C5115	2.00	3.00	4.00
B. B. KING WAILS	Crown (S) CST147	2.00	3.00	4.00
BETTER THAN EVER	United (M) 7771	2.50	4.00	5.00
BLUE, THE	United (M) 7732	2.50	4.00	5.00
BLUE FOR ME	United (M) 7708	2.50	4.00	5.00
BLUES FOR ME	Custom (M) CM2046	2.50	3.75	5.00
BLUES IN MY HEART	Crown (S) CST309	2.50	3.75	5.00
BLUES ON TOP OF BLUES	Bluesway (M) 6011	1.50	2.00	3.00
BOSS OF THE BLUES	Kent (M) KLP5029	2.00	3.00	4.00
BOSS OF THE BLUES	United (M) 7750	2.50	4.00	5.00
CONFESSIN THE BLUES	ABC (M) 528	5.00	7.50	10.00
EASY LISTENING BLUES	Crown (M) 5286	2.50	3.75	5.00
EASY LISTENING BLUES	United (M) 7705	2.50	4.00	5.00
ELECTIVE, THE	Bluesway (M) 6022	2.50	4.00	5.00
GREAT B.B.KING	Crown (M) CLP143	2.50	3.75	5.00
GREAT B. B. KING	Crown (M) 5143	2.50	3.75	5.00
GREATEST HITS VOL. 1	United (M) 7766	2.50	4.00	5.00
GREAT, THE	United (M) 7728	2.50	4.00	5.00
GUESS WHO	ABC (M) 759	2.50	4.00	5.00
HEART FULL OF BLUES	United (M) 7703	2.50	4.00	5.00
I LOVE YOU SO	Custom (M) CM2049	2.00	3.00	4.00
I LOVE YOU SO	United (M) 7711	2.50	4.00	5.00
INCREDIBLE SOUL	United (M) 7756	2.50	4.00	5.00
JUNGLE	Kent (S) KST521	2.00	3.00	4.00
JUNGLE, THE	United (M) 7742	2.50	4.00	5.00
KING OF THE BLUES	United (S) US7730	2.00	3.00	4.00
KING OF THE BLUES	Crown (M) 5167	2.50	3.75	5.00
LET ME LOVE YOU	Kent (M) K5013	2.00	3.00	4.00
LET ME LOVE YOU	Kent (S) KST513	2.00	3.00	4.00
LET ME LOVE YOU	United (M) 7734	2.50	4.00	5.00
LIVE	Kent (S) KST515	2.00	3.00	4.00
LIVE	United (M) 7771	2.50	4.00	5.00
LIVE AT REGAL	ABC (M) 509	5.00	7.50	10.00
LIVE, B.B.KING ON STAGE	Kent (M) K5015	2.00	3.00	4.00
MR. BLUES	ABC (M) 456	5.00	7.50	10.00
MY KIND OF BLUES	Crown (M) 5188	2.50	3.75	5.00
MY KIND OF BLUES	United (M) 7724	2.50	4.00	5.00
ON STAGE	United (M) 7736	2.50	4.00	5.00
ORIGINAL SWEET 16	United (M) 7773	2.50	4.00	5.00
ROCK ME BABY	Kent (M) KLP5012	2.00	3.00	4.00
ROCK ME BABY	Kent (S) KST512	2.00	3.00	4.00
ROCK ME BABY	United (M) 7733	2.50	4.00	5.00
SINGIN THE BLUES	Crown (M) 5020	2.50	3.75	5.00
SINGIN THE BLUES	United (S) US7726	2.00	3.00	4.00
SOUL OF B.B. KING	Kent (M) KLP 5016	2.00	3.00	4.00
SOUL OF B.B. KING	Kent (S) KST 516	2.00	3.00	4.00
SOUL OF B.B.KING	Custom (M) CM2052	2.00	3.00	4.00
SOUL OF B.B.KING	Custom (S) CS1052	2.00	3.00	4.00
SOUL OF	United (M) 7714	2.50	4.00	5.00
TURN ON	United (M) 7763	2.50	4.00	5.00
TWIST WITH B.B.KING	Crown (M) CLP5248	2.50	3.75	5.00

KING, B.B. and the Southern Calif. Community Choir

TITLE	LABEL & NO.	GOOD	VERY GOOD	NEAR MINT
B.B.KING LIVE	Kent (M) 365	2.00	3.00	4.00
DOING MY THING LORD	Kent (S) 563	2.00	3.00	4.00

KING, Ben E.

TITLE	LABEL & NO.	GOOD	VERY GOOD	NEAR MINT
AUDIO BIOGRAPHY INTERVIEW BY RICHARD ROBINSON	King (M) MA3008	5.00	7.50	10.00
BEGINNING OF IT ALL	Mandala (M) 3007	3.00	4.50	6.00
BEN E. KING SINGS FOR SOULFUL LOVERS	Atco (M) 137	5.00	10.00	15.00
BEN E. KING SINGS FOR SOULFUL LOVERS	Atco (S) 137	6.00	12.00	18.00
DON'T PLAY THAT SONG	Atco (M) 142	5.00	10.00	15.00
DON'T PLAY THAT SONG	Atco (S) 142	6.00	12.00	18.00
GREATEST HITS	Atco (M) 165	4.00	8.00	12.00
GREATEST HITS	Atco (S) 165	5.00	10.00	15.00
I HAVE A LOVE	Atlantic (S) SD18169	2.00	3.00	4.00
ROUGH EDGES	Maxwell (M) ML88001	3.50	5.25	7.00
SEVEN LETTERS	Atco (M) 174	4.00	8.00	12.00

(M) Mono (S) Stereo (EP) Extended Play (Q) Quad (RI) Re-issued

TITLE	LABEL & NO.	GOOD	VERY GOOD	NEAR MINT
SEVEN LETTERS	Atco (S) 174	5.00	10.00	15.00
SPANISH HARLEM	Atco (M) 133	5.00	10.00	15.00
SPANISH HARLEM	Atco (S) 133	6.00	12.00	18.00
SUPERNATURAL	Atlantic (S) SD18132	2.00	3.00	4.00

KING, Carole

TITLE	LABEL & NO.	GOOD	VERY GOOD	NEAR MINT
FANTASY	Ode (S) SP 77018	2.50	3.75	5.00
FANTASY	Ode (Q) SQ 88018	2.50	3.75	5.00
FANTASY ('77 RI)	Epic/Ode (S) PE 34962	2.00	3.00	4.00
HER GREATEST HITS	Epic/Ode (S) JE 34967	2.00	3.00	4.00
MUSIC	Ode (S) SP 77013	2.50	3.75	5.00
MUSIC	Ode (Q) SQ 88013	2.50	3.75	5.00
MUSIC ('77 RI)	Epic/Ode (S) PE 34949	2.00	3.00	4.00
REALLY ROSIE	Ode (S) SP 77027	2.50	3.75	5.00
REALLY ROSIE ('77 RI)	Epic/Ode (S) PE 34955	2.00	3.00	4.00
RHYMES AND REASONS	Ode (S) SP 77016	2.50	3.75	5.00
RHYMES AND REASONS	Ode (Q) SQ 88016	2.50	3.75	5.00
THYMES AND REASONS ('77 RI)	Epic/Ode (S) PE 34950	2.00	3.00	4.00
SIMPLE THINGS	Avatar (S) SMAS 11667	2.00	3.00	4.00
TAPESTRY	Ode (S) SP 77009	2.50	3.75	5.00
TAPESTRY	Ode (Q) SQ 88009	2.50	3.75	5.00
TAPESTRY ('77 RI)	Epic/Ode (S) PE 34956	2.00	3.00	4.00
THOROUGHBRED	Ode (S) SP 77034	2.50	3.75	5.00
THOROUGHBRED	Epic/Ode (S) PE 34963	2.00	3.00	4.00
WRAP AROUND JOY	Ode (S) SP 77024	2.50	3.75	5.00
WRAP AROUND JOY	Epic/Ode (S) PE 34953	2.00	3.00	4.00
WRITER	Ode (S) SP77006	4.00	6.00	8.00
WRITER	Epic/Ode (S) PE 34944	2.00	3.00	4.00

KING, Claude

TITLE	LABEL & NO.	GOOD	VERY GOOD	NEAR MINT
MEET CLAUDE KING	Columbia (M) CL1810	2.50	3.75	5.00
MEET CLAUDE KING	Columbia (S) CS8610	2.50	3.75	5.00
TIGER WOMAN	Columbia (M) CL2415	2.00	3.00	4.00
TIGER WOMAN	Columbia (S) CS9215	2.00	3.00	4.00

KING CRIMSON

TITLE	LABEL & NO.	GOOD	VERY GOOD	NEAR MINT
GROON	World Record Club (M) WRMB 448	6.00	9.00	12.00
IN THE COURT OF THE CRIMSON KING	Atlantic (S) SD 8245	3.00	4.50	6.00
IN THE WAKE OF POSEIDON	Atlantic (S) SD 8266	3.00	4.50	6.00
ISLANDS	Atlantic (S) SD 7212	3.00	4.50	6.00
LARKS TONGUE IN ASPIC	Atlantic (S) 7263	3.00	4.50	6.00
LIZARD	Atlantic (S) SD 8278	4.00	6.00	8.00
RED	Atlantic (S) 18110	2.50	3.75	5.00
STARLESS & BLACK BIBLE	Atlantic (S) 7298	3.00	4.50	6.00

KING PINS

TITLE	LABEL & NO.	GOOD	VERY GOOD	NEAR MINT
IT WON'T BE THIS WAY ALWAYS	King (M) 865	3.00	7.50	12.00

KING FLOYD

TITLE	LABEL & NO.	GOOD	VERY GOOD	NEAR MINT
WELL DONE	Chimneyville (S) 201	3.00	4.50	6.00

KING, Freddie

TITLE	LABEL & NO.	GOOD	VERY GOOD	NEAR MINT
BEST OF FREDDIE KING	Shelter (S) 2140	2.50	3.75	5.00
BURGLAR	RSO (S) 4803	3.50	3.75	5.00
FREDDY KING GIVES YOU A BONANZA OF INSTRUMENTALS	King (M) 928	4.00	8.00	12.00
FREDDY KING GOES SURFIN'	King (M) 856	6.00	15.00	24.00
FREDDY KING SINGS	King (M) 762	10.00	25.00	40.00
GETTING READY	Shelter (M) SHE8905	2.50	3.75	5.00
LARGER THAN LIFE	RSO (S) 4811	2.00	3.00	4.00
WOMAN ACROSS THE RIVER	Shelter (S) SW8919	2.50	3.75	5.00

KING HARVEST

TITLE	LABEL & NO.	GOOD	VERY GOOD	NEAR MINT
DANCING IN THE MOONLIGHT	Perception (S) 36	4.00	6.00	8.00

KING, Jonathon

TITLE	LABEL & NO.	GOOD	VERY GOOD	NEAR MINT
BUBBLE ROCK IS HERE TO STAY	UK (S) UKS53101	3.00	4.50	6.00
OR THEN AGAIN	Parrot (M) PA61013	4.00	6.00	8.00
OR THEN AGAIN	Parrot (S) PAS71013	5.00	7.50	10.00
PANDORA'S BOX	UK (S) UKS53104	3.00	4.50	6.00

KING, Martin Luther

TITLE	LABEL & NO.	GOOD	VERY GOOD	NEAR MINT
GREAT MARCH TO FREEDOM	Gordy (M) 906	6.00	12.00	18.00

TITLE	LABEL & NO.	GOOD	VERY GOOD	NEAR MINT
KING, Pee Wee				
COUNTRY CLASSICS	RCA (EP) EPB 3028	1.00	1.50	2.00
COUNTRY CLASSICS VOL. 2	RCA (M) LPM3109	3.00	4.50	6.00
SQUARE DANCES WITH CALLS	RCA (EP) EPA 256	1.00	1.50	2.00
SWING WEST	RCA (M) LPM1237	3.00	4.50	6.00
SWING WEST	RCA (EP) EPA797	1.00	1.50	2.00
SWING WEST	RCA (M) LPM3280	3.00	4.50	6.00
TOP COUNTRY HITS	RCA (EP) EPA 461	1.00	1.50	2.00
WESTERN HITS	RCA (M) LPM3071	3.00	4.50	6.00
KING CURTIS				
BEST OF KING CURTIS	Atco (S) SD 33-266	3.50	5.25	7.00
EVERYBODY'S TALKIN'	Atco (S) SD 33-385	2.50	3.75	5.00
GET READY	Atco (S) SD 33-338	2.50	3.75	5.00
GREAT MEMPHIS HITS	Atco (M) 33-211	3.00	4.50	6.00
GREAT MEMPHIS HITS	Atco (S) SD 33-211	3.50	5.25	7.00
HAVE TENOR SAX, WILL BLOW	Atco (M) 33-113	4.00	8.00	12.00
HAVE TENOR SAX, WILL BLOW	Atco (S) SD 33-113	5.00	10.00	15.00
INSTANT GROOVE	Atco (S) SD 33-293	3.00	4.50	6.00
KING SIZE SOUL	Atco (S) SD 33-231	3.00	4.50	6.00
KING SIZE SOUL	Atco (S) SD 33-231	3.50	5.25	7.00
LIVE AT FILLMORE WEST	Atco (S) SD 33-359	2.50	3.75	5.00
SOUL SERENADE	Capitol (M) T 2095	5.00	10.00	15.00
SOUL TWIST	Enjoy (S) 2001	3.00	4.50	6.00
SWEET SOUL	Atco (S) SD 33-247	3.00	4.50	6.00
KING'S HENCHMEN				
NEW ORLEANS ROCK 'N ROLL	Coral (M) CRL 57216	4.00	10.00	16.00
KINGSMEN				
IN PERSON	Wand (M) 657	3.00	6.00	9.00
ON CAMPUS	Wand (M) 670	3.00	6.00	9.00
16 GREATEST HITS	Wand (M) 674	3.00	6.00	9.00
UP AND AWAY	Wand (M) 675	3.00	6.00	9.00
VOL. 2	Wand (M) 659	3.00	6.00	9.00
VOL. 3	Wand (M) 662	3.00	6.00	9.00
KINGSTON TRIO				
BACK IN TOWN	Capitol (M) T2081	2.50	3.75	5.00
BACK IN TOWN	Capitol (S) ST2081	2.50	3.75	5.00
BEST OF THE KINGSTON TRIO	Capitol (M) T1705	2.50	3.75	5.00
BEST OF THE KINGSTON TRIO	Capitol (S) ST1705	2.50	3.75	5.00
BEST OF THE KINGSTON TRIO, Vol. 2	Capitol (M) T 2280	2.50	3.75	5.00
BEST OF THE KINGSTON TRIO, Vol. 2	Capitol (S) ST 2280	2.50	3.75	5.00
BEST OF THE KINGSTON TRIO, Vol. 3	Capitol (M) T2614	2.00	3.00	4.00
BEST OF THE KINGSTON TRIO, Vol. 3	Capitol (S) ST2614	2.00	3.00	4.00
CHILDREN IN THE MORNING	Decca (M) 4758	2.00	3.00	4.00
CHILDREN IN THE MORNING	Decca (S) 74758	2.00	3.00	4.00
CLOSE UP	Capitol (M) T1642	2.50	3.75	5.00
CLOSE UP	Capitol (S) ST1642	2.50	3.75	5.00
CLOSE UP	Capitol (EP) EAP11642	1.00	1.50	2.00
CLOSE UP	Capitol (EP) EAP21642	1.00	1.50	2.00
CLOSE UP	Capitol (EP) EAP31642	1.00	1.50	2.00
COLLEGE CONCERT	Capitol (M) T1658	2.50	3.75	5.00
COLLEGE CONCERT	Capitol (S) ST1658	2.50	3.75	5.00
FOLK ERA	Capitol (M) CL2180	2.50	3.75	5.00
FOLK ERA	Capitol (S) STCL2180	2.50	3.75	5.00
FROM THE HUNGRY I	Capitol (M) T1107	3.00	4.50	6.00
GOIN' PLACES	Capitol (M) T1564	2.50	3.75	5.00
GOIN' PLACES	Capitol (S) ST1564	2.50	3.75	5.00
HERE WE GO AGAIN!	Capitol (M) T1258	3.00	4.50	6.00
HERE WE GO AGAIN!	Capitol (S) ST1258	3.00	4.50	6.00
HERE WE GO AGAIN	Capitol (EP) EAP 11258	1.50	2.25	3.00
HERE WE GO AGAIN	Capitol (EP) EAP 21258	1.50	2.25	3.00
HERE WE GO AGAIN	Capitol (EP) EAP 31258	1.50	2.25	3.00
KINGSTON TRIO	Capitol (M) T996	4.00	6.00	8.00
KINGSTON TRIO	Capitol (EP) EAP1996	1.50	2.25	3.00
KINGSTON TRIO	Capitol (M) MA11577	2.50	3.75	5.00
KINGSTON TRIO	Decca (M) DL 4613	2.00	3.00	4.00
KINGSTON TRIO	Decca (S) DL 74613	2.00	3.00	4.00
KINGSTON TRIO ENCORES	Capitol (S) DT 1612	3.00	4.50	6.00
KINGSTON TRIO AT LARGE	Capitol (M) T1199	3.00	4.50	6.00
KINGSTON TRIO AT LARGE	Capitol (S) ST1199	3.00	4.50	6.00
KINGSTON TRIO AT LARGE	Capitol (EP) EAP11199	1.50	2.25	3.00
KINGSTON TRIO AT LARGE	Capitol (EP) EAP21199	1.50	2.25	3.00
KINGSTON TRIO AT LARGE	Capitol (EP) EAP31199	1.50	2.25	3.00
KINGSTON TRIO NO. 16	Capitol (M) T1871	2.50	3.75	5.00
KINGSTON TRIO NO. 16	Capitol (S) ST1871	2.50	3.75	5.00
LAST MONTH OF THE YEAR	Capitol (M) T1446	2.50	3.75	5.00
LAST MONTH OF THE YEAR	Capitol (S) ST1446	2.50	3.75	5.00
LAST MONTH OF THE YEAR	Capitol (EP) EAP11146	1.00	1.50	2.00
LAST MONTH OF THE YEAR	Capitol (EP) EAP21146	1.00	1.50	2.00
LAST MONTH OF THE YEAR	Capitol (EP) EAP31146	1.00	1.50	2.00
MAKE WAY	Capitol (S) ST1474	2.50	3.75	5.00
MAKE WAY	Capitol (EP) EAP11474	1.00	1.50	2.00
MAKE WAY	Capitol (EP) EAP21474	1.00	1.50	2.00
MAKE WAY	Capitol (EP) EAP31474	1.00	1.50	2.00
M.T.A.	Capitol (EP) EAP 1119	1.50	2.25	3.00
NEW FRONTIER	Capitol (M) T1809	2.50	3.75	5.00
NEW FRONTIER	Capitol (S) ST1809	2.50	3.75	5.00
ONCE UPON A TIME	Tetragrammation (S) 5101	3.00	4.50	6.00
RASBERRIES, STRAWBERRIES	Capitol (EP) EAP11182	1.50	2.25	3.00
7-UP (DJ Copy only)	Capitol Custom (EP) NKB 2670	2.00	3.00	4.00
SING A SONG WITH THE KINGSTON TRIO	Capitol (M) KAO2005	2.50	3.75	5.00
SING A SONG WITH THE KINGSTON TRIO	Capitol (S) SKAO2005	2.50	3.75	5.00
SOLD OUT	Capitol (M) T1352	2.50	3.75	5.00
SOLD OUT	Capitol (S) ST1352	2.50	3.75	5.00
SOLD OUT	Capitol (EP) EAP11352	1.00	1.50	2.00
SOLD OUT	Capitol (EP) EAP21352	1.00	1.50	2.00
SOLD OUT	Capitol (EP) EAP31352	1.00	1.50	2.00
SOMETHIN ELSE	Decca (M) DL4694	2.00	3.00	4.00
SOMETHIN ELSE	Decca (S) DL74694	2.00	3.00	4.00
SOMETHING SPECIAL	Capitol (M) T1747	2.50	3.75	5.00
SOMETHING SPECIAL	Capitol (S) ST1747	2.50	3.75	5.00
STAY AWHILE	Decca (M) DL4656	2.00	3.00	4.00
STAY AWHILE	Decca (S) DL7-4656	2.00	3.00	4.00
STEREO CONCERT	Capitol (S) ST 1183	3.00	4.50	6.00
STRING ALONG	Capitol (M) T1407	2.50	3.75	5.00
STRING ALONG	Capitol (S) ST 1407	2.50	3.75	5.00
STRING ALONG	Capitol (EP) EAP11407	1.00	1.50	2.00
STRING ALONG	Capitol (EP) EAP21407	1.00	1.50	2.00
STRING ALONG	Capitol (EP) EAP31407	1.00	1.50	2.00
SUNNY SIDE!	Capitol (M) T1935	2.50	3.75	5.00
SUNNY SIDE!	Capitol (S) ST1935	2.50	3.75	5.00
TIJUANA JAIL	Capitol (EP) SEP11120	2.00	3.00	4.00
TIME TO THINK	Capitol (M) T2011	2.50	3.75	5.00
TIME TO THINK	Capitol (S) ST2011	2.50	3.75	5.00
TOM DOOLEY	Capitol (EP) EAP1136	1.50	2.25	3.00
A WORRIED MAN	Capitol (EP) EAP11322	1.50	2.25	3.00
KINKS				
ARTHUR	Reprise (S) RS6366	4.00	6.00	8.00
EVERYBODY'S IN SHOW-BIZ	RCA (S) 6065	3.50	5.25	7.00
FACE TO FACE	Reprise (M) R6228	4.00	8.00	12.00
FACE TO FACE	Reprise (S) RS6228	4.50	9.00	13.50
GREAT LOST KINKS ALBUM	Reprise (S) MS 2127	4.00	6.00	8.00
KINDA KINKS	Reprise (M) R6173	4.00	8.00	12.00
KINDA KINKS	Reprise (S) RS6173	4.50	9.00	13.50
KINK KONTROVERSY	Reprise (M) R6197	4.00	8.00	12.00
KINK KONTROVERSY	Reprise (S) RS6197	4.50	9.00	13.50
KINK KRONIKLES	Reprise (S) 2XS 6454	5.00	10.00	15.00
KINKS GREATEST HITS	Reprise (M) R6217	4.00	8.00	12.00
KINKS GREATEST HITS	Reprise (S) RS6217	4.50	9.00	13.50
KINKS KINKDOM	Reprise (M) R6184	4.00	8.00	12.00
KINKS KINKDOM	Reprise (S) RS6184	4.50	9.00	13.50
KINKS SIZE	Reprise (M) R6158	4.00	8.00	12.00
KINKS SIZE	Reprise (S) RS6158	4.50	9.00	13.50
LIVE KINKS	Reprise (M) R6260	4.00	8.00	12.00
LIVE KINKS	Reprise (S) RS6260	4.50	9.00	13.50
LOLA VERSUS THE POWERMAN AND THE MONEY GO ROUND	Reprise (S) RS6423	3.50	5.25	7.00
MUSWELL HILLBILLIES	RCA (S) LSP 4644	3.50	5.25	7.00
PRESERVATION ACT 1	RCA (S) LPL1-5002	3.50	5.25	7.00
PRESERVATION ACT 2	RCA (S) CPL2-5040	4.50	6.75	9.00
SCHOOLBOYS IN DISGRACE	RCA (S) LPL1-5102	3.50	5.25	7.00
SLEEPWALKER	Arista (S) 4106	3.00	4.50	6.00

(M) Mono (S) Stereo (EP) Extended Play (Q) Quad (RI) Re-issued

...from the "Hungry i"

THE KINKS GREATEST HITS!

THE KINK KONTROVERSY

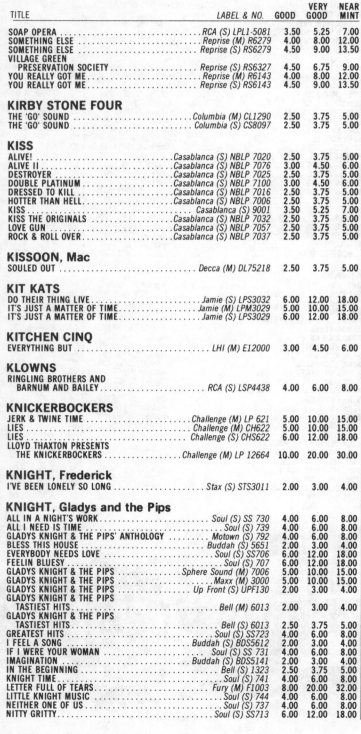

TITLE	LABEL & NO.	GOOD	VERY GOOD	NEAR MINT
SOAP OPERA	RCA (S) LPL1-5081	3.50	5.25	7.00
SOMETHING ELSE	Reprise (M) R6279	4.00	8.00	12.00
SOMETHING ELSE	Reprise (S) RS6279	4.50	9.00	13.50
VILLAGE GREEN PRESERVATION SOCIETY	Reprise (S) RS6327	4.50	6.75	9.00
YOU REALLY GOT ME	Reprise (M) R6143	4.00	8.00	12.00
YOU REALLY GOT ME	Reprise (S) RS6143	4.50	9.00	13.50

KIRBY STONE FOUR
TITLE	LABEL & NO.	GOOD	VERY GOOD	NEAR MINT
THE 'GO' SOUND	Columbia (M) CL1290	2.50	3.75	5.00
THE 'GO' SOUND	Columbia (S) CS8097	2.50	3.75	5.00

KISS
TITLE	LABEL & NO.	GOOD	VERY GOOD	NEAR MINT
ALIVE!	Casablanca (S) NBLP 7020	2.50	3.75	5.00
ALIVE II	Casablanca (S) NBLP 7076	3.00	4.50	6.00
DESTROYER	Casablanca (S) NBLP 7025	2.50	3.75	5.00
DOUBLE PLATINUM	Casablanca (S) NBLP 7100	3.00	4.50	6.00
DRESSED TO KILL	Casablanca (S) NBLP 7016	2.50	3.75	5.00
HOTTER THAN HELL	Casablanca (S) NBLP 7006	2.50	3.75	5.00
KISS	Casablanca (S) 9001	3.50	5.25	7.00
KISS THE ORIGINALS	Casablanca (S) NBLP 7032	2.50	3.75	5.00
LOVE GUN	Casablanca (S) NBLP 7057	2.50	3.75	5.00
ROCK & ROLL OVER	Casablanca (S) NBLP 7037	2.50	3.75	5.00

KISSOON, Mac
TITLE	LABEL & NO.	GOOD	VERY GOOD	NEAR MINT
SOULED OUT	Decca (M) DL75218	2.50	3.75	5.00

KIT KATS
TITLE	LABEL & NO.	GOOD	VERY GOOD	NEAR MINT
DO THEIR THING LIVE	Jamie (S) LPS3032	6.00	12.00	18.00
IT'S JUST A MATTER OF TIME	Jamie (M) LPM3029	5.00	10.00	15.00
IT'S JUST A MATTER OF TIME	Jamie (S) LPS3029	6.00	12.00	18.00

KITCHEN CINQ
TITLE	LABEL & NO.	GOOD	VERY GOOD	NEAR MINT
EVERYTHING BUT	LHI (M) E12000	3.00	4.50	6.00

KLOWNS
TITLE	LABEL & NO.	GOOD	VERY GOOD	NEAR MINT
RINGLING BROTHERS AND BARNUM AND BAILEY	RCA (S) LSP4438	4.00	6.00	8.00

KNICKERBOCKERS
TITLE	LABEL & NO.	GOOD	VERY GOOD	NEAR MINT
JERK & TWINE TIME	Challenge (M) LP 621	5.00	10.00	15.00
LIES	Challenge (M) CH622	5.00	10.00	15.00
LIES	Challenge (S) CHS622	6.00	12.00	18.00
LLOYD THAXTON PRESENTS THE KNICKERBOCKERS	Challenge (M) LP 12664	10.00	20.00	30.00

KNIGHT, Frederick
TITLE	LABEL & NO.	GOOD	VERY GOOD	NEAR MINT
I'VE BEEN LONELY SO LONG	Stax (S) STS3011	2.00	3.00	4.00

KNIGHT, Gladys and the Pips
TITLE	LABEL & NO.	GOOD	VERY GOOD	NEAR MINT
ALL IN A NIGHT'S WORK	Soul (S) SS 730	4.00	6.00	8.00
ALL I NEED IS TIME	Soul (S) 739	4.00	6.00	8.00
GLADYS KNIGHT & THE PIPS' ANTHOLOGY	Motown (S) 792	4.00	6.00	8.00
BLESS THIS HOUSE	Buddah (S) 5651	2.00	3.00	4.00
EVERYBODY NEEDS LOVE	Soul (S) SS706	6.00	12.00	18.00
FEELIN BLUESY	Soul (S) 707	6.00	12.00	18.00
GLADYS KNIGHT & THE PIPS	Sphere Sound (M) 7006	5.00	10.00	15.00
GLADYS KNIGHT & THE PIPS	Maxx (M) 3000	5.00	10.00	15.00
GLADYS KNIGHT & THE PIPS	Up Front (S) UPF130	2.00	3.00	4.00
GLADYS KNIGHT & THE PIPS TASTIEST HITS	Bell (M) 6013	2.00	3.00	4.00
GLADYS KNIGHT & THE PIPS TASTIEST HITS	Bell (S) 6013	2.50	3.75	5.00
GREATEST HITS	Soul (S) SS723	4.00	6.00	8.00
I FEEL A SONG	Buddah (S) BDS5612	2.00	3.00	4.00
IF I WERE YOUR WOMAN	Soul (S) SS 731	4.00	6.00	8.00
IMAGINATION	Buddah (S) BDS5141	2.00	3.00	4.00
IN THE BEGINNING	Bell (S) 1323	2.50	3.75	5.00
KNIGHT TIME	Soul (S) 741	4.00	6.00	8.00
LETTER FULL OF TEARS	Fury (M) F1003	8.00	20.00	32.00
LITTLE KNIGHT MUSIC	Soul (S) 744	4.00	6.00	8.00
NEITHER ONE OF US	Soul (S) 737	4.00	6.00	8.00
NITTY GRITTY	Soul (S) SS713	6.00	12.00	18.00

TITLE	LABEL & NO.	GOOD	VERY GOOD	NEAR MINT
SECOND ANNIVERSARY	Buddah (S) 5639	2.00	3.00	4.00
SILK & SOUL	Soul (S) SS 711	6.00	12.00	18.00
STANDING OVATION	Soul (S) 736	4.00	6.00	8.00
VERY BEST OF THE WORLD OF GLADYS KNIGHT & THE PIPS	United Artists (S) UA-LA503	1.50	2.00	3.00

KNIGHT, Jean
TITLE	LABEL & NO.	GOOD	VERY GOOD	NEAR MINT
MR. BIG STUFF	Stax (S) STS2045	3.00	4.50	6.00

KNIGHTS
TITLE	LABEL & NO.	GOOD	VERY GOOD	NEAR MINT
ACROSS THE BOARD	Ace (M) MG200854	8.00	20.00	32.00
HOT ROD HIGH	Capitol (M) T 2189	6.00	12.00	18.00
HOT ROD HIGH	Capitol (S) ST 2189	7.00	14.00	21.00
1967	Ace (M) MG201303	8.00	20.00	32.00

KNIGHT, Sonny
TITLE	LABEL & NO.	GOOD	VERY GOOD	NEAR MINT
IF YOU WANT THIS LOVE	Aura (M) AR3001	2.50	5.00	7.50
IF YOU WANT THIS LOVE	Aura (S) AS3001	3.00	6.00	9.00

KNIGHT, Terry and The Pack
TITLE	LABEL & NO.	GOOD	VERY GOOD	NEAR MINT
BEST OF MARK FARNER, TERRY KNIGHT AND DONNIE BREWER	Lucky Eleven (M) LE8001	4.00	6.00	8.00
1966-67	ABKCO (M) AB4217	3.50	5.25	7.00
REFLECTIONS	Cameo (M) C2007	5.00	10.00	15.00
TERRY KNIGHT & PACK	Lucky Eleven (M) LE8000	5.00	10.00	15.00

Also see GRAND FUNK RAILROAD

KNOCKOUTS
TITLE	LABEL & NO.	GOOD	VERY GOOD	NEAR MINT
GO APE WITH THE KNOCKOUTS	Tribute (M) LP1202	7.00	17.50	28.00

KNOWBODY ELSE
TITLE	LABEL & NO.	GOOD	VERY GOOD	NEAR MINT
KNOWBODY ELSE	Hip (S) HIS7003	3.00	4.50	6.00

KNOX, Buddy
TITLE	LABEL & NO.	GOOD	VERY GOOD	NEAR MINT
BUDDY KNOX	Roulette (M) R 25003	8.00	20.00	32.00
GOLDEN HITS	Liberty (M) LRP3251	4.00	8.00	12.00
GOLDEN HITS	Liberty (S) LST7251	5.00	10.00	15.00
GYPSY MAN	United Artists (S) UAS6689	4.00	8.00	12.00

KNOX, Buddy and Jimmy Bowen
TITLE	LABEL & NO.	GOOD	VERY GOOD	NEAR MINT
BUDDY KNOX & JIMMY BOWEN	Roulette (M) R 25048	9.00	22.50	36.00

KOALA
TITLE	LABEL & NO.	GOOD	VERY GOOD	NEAR MINT
KOALA	Capitol (S) SKOA176	4.00	6.00	8.00

KODAKS AND THE STARLITES
TITLE	LABEL & NO.	GOOD	VERY GOOD	NEAR MINT
KODAKS VERSUS THE STARLITES	Sphere Sound (M) LP7005	6.00	15.00	24.00

KOERNER, Ray and Glover
TITLE	LABEL & NO.	GOOD	VERY GOOD	NEAR MINT
BLUE RAGS AND HOLLERS	Elektra (M) 240	2.50	3.75	5.00
GOOD OLD KOERNER, RAY & GLOVER	Mil City (M) MCR172	5.00	7.50	10.00
LOTS MORE BLUES RAGS AND HOLLERS	Elektra (M) 267	2.50	3.75	5.00
RETURN OF KOERNER, RAY & GLOVER	Elektra (S) 7305	2.50	3.75	5.00

KOERNER, Spider John
TITLE	LABEL & NO.	GOOD	VERY GOOD	NEAR MINT
MUSIC IS JUST A BUNCH OF NOTES	Sweet Jane (S) SJL5872	5.00	7.50	10.00

KOKOMO
TITLE	LABEL & NO.	GOOD	VERY GOOD	NEAR MINT
ASIA MINOR	Felsted (M) 7513	4.00	10.00	16.00
ASIA MINOR	Felsted (S) 7513	5.00	12.50	20.00

KOLE, Jerry and The Strokers
TITLE	LABEL & NO.	GOOD	VERY GOOD	NEAR MINT
HOT ROD ALLEY	Crown (M) CLP5385	4.00	8.00	12.00

KONGOS, John
TITLE	LABEL & NO.	GOOD	VERY GOOD	NEAR MINT
KONGOS	Elektra (S) EKS75019	3.00	4.50	6.00
REFLECTIONS ON A GOLDFISH	Janus (S) JLS3032	4.50	6.75	9.00

(M) Mono (S) Stereo (EP) Extended Play (Q) Quad (RI) Re-issued

TITLE	LABEL & NO.	GOOD	VERY GOOD	NEAR MINT
KOOPER, Al and Shuggie Otis				
EASY DOES IT	Columbia (S) 30031	2.50	3.75	5.00
I STAND ALONE	Columbia (S) CS 9718	3.00	4.50	6.00
KOOPER SESSION (With Shuggie Otis)	Columbia (S) CS 9951	3.00	4.50	6.00
NAKED SONGS	Columbia (S) KC 31723	2.50	3.75	5.00
NEW YORK CITY (YOU'RE A WOMAN)	Columbia (S) 30506	2.50	3.75	5.00
POSSIBLE PROJECTION OF THE FUTURE/				
CHILDHOOD'S END	Columbia (S) 31189	2.50	3.75	5.00
YOU NEVER KNOW WHO YOUR FRIENDS ARE	Columbia (S) CS 9855	3.00	4.50	6.00
Also see BLUES PROJECT				
KORNER, Alexis				
BOOTLEG HIM	Warner Brothers (M) 2XS1966	2.50	3.75	5.00
KORNER, Alexis and Snape				
ACCIDENTLY BORNE				
IN NEW ORLEANS	Warner Brothers (S) BS2647	2.50	3.75	5.00
KORNFIELD, Artie				
TIME TO REMEMBER	Dunhill (S) DS50092	2.50	3.75	5.00
KRAFTWERK				
AUTOBAHN	Vertigo (S) 2003	4.00	6.00	8.00
MAN-MACHINE	Capitol (S) SW 11728	2.00	3.00	4.00
RADIO-ACTIVITY	Capitol (S) ST-11457	2.50	3.75	5.00
TRANS-EUROPE EXPRESS	Capitol (S) SW 11603	2.00	3.00	4.00
KRAMER, Billy J. and The Dakotas				
I'LL KEEP YOU SATISFIED	Imperial (M) LP9273	4.50	9.00	13.50
I'LL KEEP YOU SATISFIED	Imperial (S) LP12273	5.00	10.00	15.00
LITTLE CHILDREN	Imperial (M) LP9267	4.50	9.00	13.50
TRAINS & BOATS & PLANES	Imperial (M) LP 9291	4.50	9.00	13.50
TRAINS & BOATS & PLANES	Imperial (S) LP12291	5.00	10.00	15.00
KRAZY KATS				
MOVIN' OUT	Damon (M) 12478	6.00	15.00	24.00
KRISTOFFERSON, Kris				
BORDER LORD	Monument (S) 31302	2.50	3.75	5.00
EASTER ISLAND	Columbia/Monument (S) JZ 35310	2.00	3.00	4.00
JESUS WAS A CAPRICORN	Monument (S) KZ 31909	2.50	3.75	5.00
JESUS WAS A CAPRICORN	Monument (Q) ZQ 31909	2.50	3.75	5.00
ME AND BOBBY MCGEE	Monument (S) 30817	2.50	3.75	5.00
SILVER TONGUED DEVIL AND I	Monument (S) 30679	2.50	3.75	5.00
SONGS OF KRISTOFFERSON	Columbia/Monument (S) PZ 34687	2.50	3.75	5.00
SPOOKY LADY'S SIDESHOW	Monument (S) KZ 32914	2.50	3.75	5.00
SPOOKY LADY'S SIDESHOW	Monument (Q) PZQ 32914	2.50	3.75	5.00
SURREAL THING	Monument (S) PZ 34254	2.50	3.75	5.00
WHO'S TO BLESS & WHO'S TO BLAME	Monument (S) PZ 33379	2.50	3.75	5.00
Also see COOLIDGE, Rita & Kris Kristofferson				
KUBAN, Bob				
LOOK OUT FOR THE CHEATER	Musicland (M) 3500	2.50	5.00	7.50
LOOK OUT FOR THE CHEATER	Musicland (S) 3500	3.00	6.00	9.00
KUPFERBERG, Tuli				
NO DEPOSIT NO RETURN	ESP (S) 1035	3.00	4.50	6.00
KUSTOM KINGS				
KUSTOM CITY USA	Smash (M) MGS27051	3.00	6.00	9.00
KUSTOM CITY USA	Smash (S) SRS 67051	4.00	8.00	12.00
KWESKIN, Jim and The Jugband				
GARDEN OF JOY	Reprise (M) R 6266	4.00	6.00	8.00
GARDEN OF JOY	Reprise (S) RS 6266	5.00	7.50	10.00
JIM KWESKIN'S AMERICA	Reprise (M) 6464	5.00	7.50	10.00
JUG BAND MUSIC	Vanguard (S) VSD79163	2.50	3.75	5.00
SEE REVERSE SIDE				
FOR TITLE	Vanguard (S) VSD79234	2.50	3.75	5.00

L

TITLE	LABEL & NO.	GOOD	VERY GOOD	NEAR MINT
LA BEEF, Sleepy				
BULL'S NIGHT OUT	Sun (M)	5.00	7.50	10.00
LABELLE				
MERRY CHRISTMAS FROM LABELLE	Mistletoe (M) MLP 1204	4.00	6.00	8.00
LABELLE, Patti, and The Bluebelles				
APOLLO PRESENTS THE BLUEBELLES	Newtown (M) 631	7.50	15.00	22.50
AT THE APOLLO	Up Front (S) UPF129	2.50	3.75	5.00
OVER THE RAINBOW	Atlantic (M) 8119	4.00	8.00	12.00
OVER THE RAINBOW	Atlantic (S) SD8119	5.00	10.00	15.00
SLEIGH BELLS, JINGLE BELLS				
& BLUE BELLS	Newtown (M) 632	8.00	16.00	24.00

TITLE	LABEL & NO.	GOOD	VERY GOOD	NEAR MINT
LACE WING				
LACEWING	Mainstream (M) 6132	3.00	4.50	6.00
LAINE, Denny				
AHH LAINE!	Wizard/Reprise (S) MS 2190	4.00	6.00	8.00
HOLLY DAYS	Capitol ST-11588	3.00	4.50	6.00
Also see MCCARTNEY, Paul & Wings				
LAINE, Frankie				
BRING YOUR SMILE ALONG	Columbia (EP) B2086	1.00	1.50	2.00
CALL OF THE WILD	Columbia (M) CL1829	2.50	3.75	5.00
CALL OF THE WILD	Columbia (S) CS8629	2.50	3.75	5.00
CHRISTMAS FAVORITES	Mercury (EP) EP13028	1.00	1.50	2.00
COMMAND PERFORMANCE	Columbia (M) CL623	3.00	4.50	6.00
COMMAND PERFORMANCE	Columbia (M) CL625	3.00	4.50	6.00
COMMAND PERFORMANCE	Columbia (EP) B475	1.00	1.50	2.00
COMMAND PERFORMANCE	Columbia (EP) B4751	1.00	1.50	2.00
COMMAND PERFORMANCE	Mercury (EP) 13010	1.00	1.50	2.00
COMMAND PERFORMANCE	Mercury (EP) 13016	1.00	1.50	2.00
COMMAND PERFORMANCE	Mercury (EP) 13047	1.00	1.50	2.00
COMMAND PERFORMANCE	Mercury (EP) 13053	1.00	1.50	2.00
COMMAND PERFORMANCE	Mercury (EP) 13166	1.00	1.50	2.00
CONCERT DATE				
WITH FRANKIE LAINE	Mercury (M) MG20085	3.00	4.50	6.00
DEUCES WILD	Columbia (M) CL1696	2.50	3.75	5.00
DEUCES WILD	Columbia (S) CS8496	2.50	3.75	5.00
FOREIGN AFFAIR	Columbia (M) CL1116	2.50	3.75	5.00
FOREIGN AFFAIR	Columbia (EP) B11161	1.00	1.50	2.00
FOREIGN AFFARI	Columbia (EP) B11162	1.00	1.50	2.00
FRANKIE LAINE	Columbia (EP) B2503	1.00	1.50	2.00
FRANKIE LAINE	Mercury (M) MG25007	3.00	4.50	6.00
FRANKIE LAINE (10")	Mercury (M) MG25024	3.00	4.50	6.00
FRANKIE LAINE (10")	Mercury (M) MG25025	3.00	4.50	6.00
FRANKIE LAINE (10")	Mercury (M) MG25026	3.00	4.50	6.00
FRANKIE LAINE (10")	Mercury (M) MG25027	3.00	4.50	6.00
FRANKIE LAINE & FOUR LADS	Columbia (M) CL861	3.00	4.50	6.00
FRANKIE LAINE & FOUR LADS	Columbia (EP) B8611	1.00	1.50	2.00
FRANKIE LAINE & FOUR LADS	Columbia (EP) 8612	1.00	1.50	2.00
FRANKIE LAINE & FOUR LADS	Columbia (EP) 8613	1.00	1.50	2.00
FRANKIE LAINE, BALLADEER	Columbia (M) CL1393	2.50	3.75	5.00
FRANKIE LAINE, BALLADEER	Columbia (S) CS8188	2.50	3.75	5.00
FRANKIE LAINE GREATEST HITS	Columbia (M) CL1231	3.00	4.50	6.00
FRANKIE LAINE GREATEST HITS	Columbia (S) CS8636	2.00	3.00	4.00
FRANKIE LAINES GOLDEN HITS	Mercury (M) MG20587	2.50	3.75	5.00
FRANKIE LAINES GOLDEN HITS	Mercury (S) SR60587	2.50	3.75	5.00
FRANKIE LAINE				
SINGS FOR US	Mercury (M) MG20083	3.00	4.50	6.00
GEORGIA ON MY MIND	Mercury (EP) 13071	1.00	1.50	2.00
GET HAPPY	Mercury (EP) 13165	1.00	1.50	2.00
HELL BENT FOR LEATHER	Columbia (M) CL1615	3.00	4.50	6.00
HELL BENT FOR LEATHER	Columbia (S) CS8415	3.00	4.50	6.00
I BELIEVE	Capitol (M) T2277	2.00	3.00	4.00
I BELIEVE	Capitol (S) ST2277	2.00	3.00	4.00
JAZZ SPECTACULAR	Columbia (M) CL808	3.00	4.50	6.00
LAINE FAVORITES (10")	Mercury (M) MG25007	3.00	4.50	6.00

(M) Mono (S) Stereo (EP) Extended Play (Q) Quad (RI) Re-issued

99

TITLE	LABEL & NO.	GOOD	VERY GOOD	NEAR MINT
LAINE FAVORITES	Mercury (EP) EP13021	1.00	1.50	2.00
LAINE FAVORITES	Columbia (EP) B1685	1.00	1.50	2.00
LAINE SPOTLITE	Columbia (EP) B1582	1.00	1.50	2.00
LOVE IS A GOLDEN RING AND OTHER HITS	Columbia (EP) B2132	1.00	1.50	2.00
LOVER'S LANE	Columbia (M) CL2504	3.00	4.50	6.00
MISTER RHYTHM (10")	Columbia (M) CL6273	3.00	4.50	6.00
MISTER RHYTHM	Columbia (EP) B367	1.00	1.50	2.00
MR. RHYTHM SINGS (10")	Mercury0 (M) MG25097	3.00	4.50	6.00
MOONLIGHT GAMBLER	Columbia (EP) B2121	1.00	1.50	2.00
MUSIC MAESTRO, PLEASE (10")	Mercury (M) MG25124	3.00	4.50	6.00
MUSIC MAESTRO, PLEASE	Mercury (EP) 13001	1.00	1.50	2.00
NEW ORLEANS (With Jo Stafford) (10")	Columbia (M) CL6263	3.00	4.50	6.00
NEW ORLEANS (With Jo Stafford)	Columbia (EP) B342	1.00	1.50	2.00
ONE FOR MY BABY	Columbia (M) CL6200	3.00	4.50	6.00
ONE FOR MY BABY	Columbia (EP) B287	1.00	1.50	2.00
ONE FOR MY BABY	Columbia (M) CL2548	3.00	4.50	6.00
POPULAR FAVORITES	Columbia (EP) B1897	1.00	1.50	2.00
RAINBOW 'ROUND MY SHOULDER	Columbia (M)C302	3.00	4.50	6.00
RAINBOW 'ROUND MY SHOULDER	Columbia (EP) B1512	1.00	1.50	2.00
REUNION IN RHYTHM	Columbia (M) CL1277	2.50	3.75	5.00
REUNION IN RHYTHM	Columbia (S) CS8087	2.50	3.75	5.00
REUNION IN RHYTHM	Columbia (EP) B12771	1.00	1.50	2.00
ROCKIN'	Columbia (M) CL975	3.00	4.50	6.00
ROCKIN'	Columbia (EP) B2132	1.00	1.50	2.00
ROVING GAMBLER	Harmony (M) HS11129	2.50	3.75	5.00
SINGING THE BLUES	Mercury/Wing (M) MGW12158	2.50	3.75	5.00
SINGING THE BLUES	Mercury/Wing (S) SRW16158	2.50	3.75	5.00
SONGS BY LAINE	Mercury (M) MG20069	3.00	4.50	6.00
SONGS BY LAINE (10")	Mercury (M) MG25098	3.00	4.50	6.00
SPOTLITE	Columbia (EP) EPB1582	1.00	1.50	2.00
SUNNY SIDE OF THE STREET	Mercury (EP) EP13057	1.00	1.50	2.00
THAT'S MY DESIRE	Columbia (EP) B9752	1.00	1.50	2.00
THAT'S MY DESIRE	Mercury (M) MG20080	3.00	4.50	6.00
TORCHIN	Columbia (M) CL1176	2.50	3.75	5.00
TORCHIN	Columbia (S) CS8024	2.50	3.75	5.00
TORCHIN	Columbia (EP) B11761	1.00	1.50	2.00
WANDERLUST	Columbia (M) CL1962	2.50	3.75	5.00
WANDERLUST	Columbia (S) CS 8762	2.50	3.75	5.00
WITH ALL MY HEART	Mercury (M) MG20105	3.00	4.50	6.00
WITH ALL MY HEART	Mercury (EP) EP13175	1.00	1.50	2.00
YOU ARE MY LOVE	Columbia (M) CL1317	2.50	3.75	5.00
YOU ARE MY LOVE	Columbia (S) CS8119	2.50	3.75	5.00

LAMB
TITLE	LABEL & NO.	GOOD	VERY GOOD	NEAR MINT
BRING OUT THE SUN	Warner Brothers (M) WS1952	4.00	6.00	8.00

LAMBERT & NUTTYCOMBE
TITLE	LABEL & NO.	GOOD	VERY GOOD	NEAR MINT
AS YOU WILL	20TH Century (M) T415	2.50	3.75	5.00
AT HOME	A&M (S) SP 4250	3.00	4.50	6.00

LANCE, Major
TITLE	LABEL & NO.	GOOD	VERY GOOD	NEAR MINT
BEST OF MAJOR LANCE	Okeh (M) OKM12106	3.00	4.50	6.00
BEST OF MAJOR LANCE	Okeh (S) OKS14106	4.00	6.00	8.00
MAJOR'S GREATEST HITS	Okeh (M) OKM 12110	3.50	5.25	7.50
MAJRO'S GREATEST HITS	Okeh (S) OKS 14110	4.50	6.75	9.00
MONKEY TIME	Okeh (M) OKM12105	3.00	4.50	6.00
MONKEY TIME	Okeh (S) OKS14105	4.00	6.00	8.00
UM, UM, UM, UM, UM, UM	Okeh (M) OKM12106	3.00	4.50	6.00
UM, UM, UM, UM, UM, UM	Okeh (S) OKS 14106	4.00	6.00	8.00

LANCELOT LINK & THE EVOLUTION REVOLUTION
TITLE	LABEL & NO.	GOOD	VERY GOOD	NEAR MINT
LANCELOT LINK AND THE EVOLUTION REVOLUTION	ABC (S) ABCS715	3.50	5.25	7.00

LANCERS
TITLE	LABEL & NO.	GOOD	VERY GOOD	NEAR MINT
RHYTHM & BLUES	Coral (EP) EC81117	.3.00	7.50	12.00

LANIN, Lester
TITLE	LABEL & NO.	GOOD	VERY GOOD	NEAR MINT
40 BEATLES' HITS	Philips (M) 200211	2.00	3.00	4.00
40 BEATLES' HITS	Philips (S) 600-211	2.00	3.00	4.00

LANZA, Mario
TITLE	LABEL & NO.	GOOD	VERY GOOD	NEAR MINT
BECAUSE YOU'RE MINE	RCA (M) LM 7018	2.50	3.75	5.00
BECAUSE YOU'RE MINE	RCA (EP) ERA 51	1.00	1.50	2.00
BEST OF MARIO LANZA	RCA (M) LM2748	2.50	3.75	5.00
BEST OF MARIO LANZA	RCA (S) LSC2748	2.50	3.75	5.00
CAVALCADE OF SHOW TUNES	RCA (M) LM2090	2.50	3.75	5.00
CAVALCADE OF SHOW TUNES	RCA (EP) ERA12090	1.00	1.50	2.00
CAVALCADE OF SHOW TUNES	RCA (EP) 22090	1.00	1.50	2.00
CAVALCADE OF SHOW TUNES	RCA (EP) 32090	1.00	1.50	2.00
FOUR FAVORITE CHRISTMAS CAROLS	RCA (EP) ERA115	1.00	1.50	2.00
HILLS OF ROME	RCA (M) LM2211	2.50	3.75	5.00
KISS & OTHER LOVE SONGS	RCA (M) LM1860	1.00	1.50	2.00
KISS & OTHER LOVE SONGS	RCA (EP) ERA 1860	2.50	3.75	5.00
LANZA IN SERENADE	RCA (M) LM996	2.50	3.75	5.00
LANZA IN SERENADE	RCA (EP) ERB 70	1.00	1.50	2.00
LANZA ON BROADWAY	RCA (M) LM2070	2.50	3.75	5.00
LANZA ON BROADWAY	RCA (EP) ERA292	1.00	1.50	2.00
LANZA ON BROADWAY	RCA (EP) ERA293	1.00	1.50	2.00
LANZA ON BROADWAY	RCA (EP) ERA294	1.00	1.50	2.00
LANZA SINGS CHRISTMAS CAROLS	RCA (M) LM2029	2.50	3.75	5.00
LANZA SINGS CHRISTMAS CAROLS	RCA (EP) ERA288	1.00	1.50	2.00
LANZA SINGS CHRISTMAS CAROLS	RCA (M) 289	1.00	1.50	2.00
LANZA SINGS CHRISTMAS CAROLS	RCA (M) LM2333	2.00	3.00	4.00
LANZA SINGS CHRISTMAS CAROLS	RCA (S) LSC2333	2.00	3.00	4.00
LOVE IN A HOME	RCA (EP) ERA290	1.00	1.50	2.00
MAGIC MARIO	RCA (M) LM 1943	2.50	3.75	5.00
MAGIC MARIO	RCA (EP) ERB 67	1.00	1.50	2.00
MAGIC MARIO	RCA (EP) ERA 262	1.00	1.50	2.00
MARIO LANZA FILM HITS	RCA (EP) EPA5129	1.00	1.50	2.00
MOVIE HITS	RCA (EP) ERA130	1.00	1.50	2.00
STUDENT PRINCE	RCA (M) LM1837	2.50	3.75	5.00
STUDENT PRINCE	RCA (EP) ERB1837	1.00	1.50	2.00
THAT MIDNITE KISS	RCA (M) LM86	3.00	4.50	6.00
THERE'S GONNA BE A PARTY TONIGHT	RCA (EP) EPA 4242	1.00	1.50	2.00
TOAST OF NEW ORLEANS	RCA (M) LM75	3.00	4.50	6.00
TOAST OF NEW ORLEANS & THAT MIDNIGHT KISS	RCA (M) LM2422	2.00	3.00	4.00
TOUCH OF YOUR HANDS	RCA (M) LM 1927	2.50	3.75	5.00
TOUCH OF YOUR HANDS	RCA (EP) ERB65	1.00	1.50	2.00

LARKS
TITLE	LABEL & NO.	GOOD	VERY GOOD	NEAR MINT
JERK	Money (M) LP1102	4.00	6.00	8.00
SOUL KALEIDOSCOPE	Money (M) LP 1107	3.00	4.50	6.00
SOUL KALEIDOSCOPE	Money (S) MS1107	3.00	4.50	6.00
SUPERSLICK	Money (M) MY1110	2.50	3.75	5.00

LA ROSA, Julius
TITLE	LABEL & NO.	GOOD	VERY GOOD	NEAR MINT
CHRISTMAS	Cadence (EP) EP1234	1.00	1.50	2.00
JULIUS BEST	RCA (M) CLP1007	3.50	5.25	7.00
JULIUS LA ROSA	Cadence (M) CLP 107	3.00	4.50	6.00
JULIUS LA ROSA	RCA (M) LPM1299	2.00	3.00	4.00
JULIUS LA ROSA	RCA (EP) EPA841	1.00	1.50	2.00
LOVE SONGS A LA ROSA	Roulette (M) R-25054	3.00	4.50	6.00
LOVE SONGS A LA ROSA	Roulette (S) SR-25054	4.00	6.00	8.00
ON THE SUNNY SIDE	Roulette (M) R-25083	3.00	4.50	6.00
ON THE SUNNY SIDE	Roulette (S) SR-25083	4.00	6.00	8.00
OUR MONDAY DATE	RCA (EP) EPA4097	1.00	1.50	2.00

LA SALLE, Denise
TITLE	LABEL & NO.	GOOD	VERY GOOD	NEAR MINT
HERE I AM AGAIN	Westbound (M) W 209	3.00	4.50	6.00
ON THE LOOSE	Westbound (M) 2016	2.50	3.75	5.00

LAS MOSQUITAS
TITLE	LABEL & NO.	GOOD	VERY GOOD	NEAR MINT
LAS MOSQUITAS	Mardi Gras (M) LP5029	4.00	6.00	8.00

LAST WORDS
TITLE	LABEL & NO.	GOOD	VERY GOOD	NEAR MINT
LAST WORDS	Atco (M) 33235	4.00	6.00	8.00

LAUREN, Rod
TITLE	LABEL & NO.	GOOD	VERY GOOD	NEAR MINT
I'M ROD LAUREN	RCA (M) LPM2176	4.50	9.00	13.50
I'M ROD LAUREN	RCA (S) LSP2176	6.00	12.00	18.00

LAWRENCE, Eddie
TITLE	LABEL & NO.	GOOD	VERY GOOD	NEAR MINT
EDDIE LAWRENCE, THE OLD PHILOSOPHER	Epic (S) BN26159	5.00	7.50	10.00
EDDIE LAWRENCE, THE OLD PHILOSOPHER	Epic (M) LN24159	4.00	6.00	8.00
EDDIE "THE OLD PHILOSOPHER" LAWRENCE	Coral (M) 57155	5.00	10.00	15.00
GARDEN OF EDDIE LAWRENCE	Signature (M) SM1003	7.50	18.75	30.00
KINGDOM OF EDDIE LAWRENCE	Coral (M) 57203	5.00	10.00	15.00
OLD PHILOSOPHER, THE	Coral (M) LP57103	5.00	10.00	15.00
7 CHARACTERS IN SEARCH OF EDDIE LAWRENCE	Coral (M) 57411	5.00	10.00	15.00
7 CHARACTERS IN SEARCH OF EDDIE LAWRENCE	Coral (S) 757411	6.00	12.00	18.00
SIDE SPLITTING PERSONALITY OF EDDIE LAWRENCE	Coral (S) 757371	6.00	12.00	18.00
SIDE SPLITTING PERSONALITY OF EDDIE LAWRENCE	Coral (M) CRL57371	5.00	10.00	15.00

LAWRENCE, Steve
TITLE	LABEL & NO.	GOOD	VERY GOOD	NEAR MINT
ABOUT THAT GIRL	Coral (M) CRL57050	3.00	4.50	6.00
ALL ABOUT LOVE	Coral (M) CRL57268	2.00	3.00	4.00
ALL ABOUT LOVE	Coral (S) CRL757268	2.00	3.00	4.00
BEST OF STEVE LAWRENCE	ABC (M) ABC392	2.50	3.75	5.00
BEST OF STEVE LAWRENCE	ABC (S) ABCS392	3.50	5.25	7.00
BIG 15	ABC (M) ABC469	3.50	5.25	7.00
BIG 15	ABC (S) ABCS469	4.50	6.75	9.00
PORTRAIT OF MY LOVE	United Artists (M) UAL 3150	2.50	3.75	5.00
PORTRAIT OF MY LOVE	United Artists (S) UAS 6150	3.50	5.25	7.00
PORTRAIT OF STEVE	MGM (S) SE 4824	2.00	3.00	4.00
SONGS EVERYBODY KNOWS	Coral (M) CRL57434	2.00	3.00	4.00
SONGS EVERYBODY KNOWS	Coral (S) CRL757434	2.00	3.00	4.00
STEVE LAWRENCE	King (M) 593	3.00	6.00	9.00
STEVE LAWRENCE SOUND	United Artists (M) UAL-3098	2.50	3.75	5.00
STEVE LAWRENCE SOUND	United Artists (S) UAS-6098	3.50	5.25	7.00
STEVE LAWRENCE WINNERS!	Columbia (M) CL 1953	2.00	3.00	4.00
STEVE LAWRENCE WINNERS!	Columbia (S) CS 8753	2.50	3.75	5.00
SWING SOFTLY WITH ME	ABC (M) ABC290	2.00	3.00	4.00
SWING SOFTLY WITH ME	ABC (S) ABCS290	2.00	3.00	4.00

(M) Mono   (S) Stereo   (EP) Extended Play   (Q) Quad   (RI) Re-issued

LAWRENCE, Steve and Eydie Gorme

TITLE	LABEL & NO.	GOOD	VERY GOOD	NEAR MINT
FEELIN'	MGM (S) SE 4881	2.00	3.00	4.00
STEVE & EYDIE (Individually & Together)	ABC (S) X764	2.00	3.00	4.00
WE GOT US	ABC (M) ABC300	2.00	3.00	4.00
WE GOT US	ABC (S) ABCS300	2.00	3.00	4.00

LAWRENCE, Vicki

| NIGHT THE LIGHTS WENT OUT IN GEORGIA | Bell (S) 1120 | 3.00 | 4.50 | 6.00 |

LAY, Sam

| SAM LAY IN BLUESLAND | Blue Thumb (S) BTS14 | 3.50 | 5.25 | 7.00 |

LAZY LESTER

| TRUE BLUES | Excello (M) LP8006 | 5.00 | 10.00 | 15.00 |

LEADBELLY

FROM LAST SESSIONS	Verve/Folkways (M) 3019	2.50	3.75	5.00
HUDDIE LEDBETTER MEMORIAL ALBUM (10")	Folkways (M) 2013	7.50	10.75	15.00
HUDDIE LEDBETTER MEMORIAL ALBUM, Vol. 2 (10")	Folkways (M) 2014	7.50	10.75	15.00
LEADBELLY	Columbia (M) C 30035	2.50	3.75	5.00
LEADBELLY LAST SESSIONS Volumes 1 & 2	Folkways (M) FP24142	4.00	6.00	8.00
LEADBELLY LEGACY VOL 1	Folkways (M) FP4	4.00	6.00	8.00
LEADBELLY LEGACY VOL 2	Folkways (M) FP14	3.50	5.25	7.00
LEADBELLY LEGACY VOL 3	Folkways (M) FP24	3.50	5.25	7.00
LEADBELLY LEGACY, Vol. 4	Folkways (M) FP34	3.50	5.25	7.00
PLAY PARTY SONGS	Stinson (M) LP39	5.00	7.50	10.00

LEANDER, Mike

| FOLK HITS | London (M) LL3453 | 3.00 | 4.50 | 6.00 |
| FOLK HITS | London (S) PS453 | 4.00 | 6.00 | 8.00 |

LEARY, Timothy

| TURN ON, TUNE IN, DROP OUT | ESP (M) 1027 | 5.00 | 10.00 | 15.00 |

LEATHERCOATED MINDS

| TRIP DOWN THE SUNSET STRIP | Viva (M) V36003 | 4.00 | 6.00 | 8.00 |

LEAVES

ALL THE GOOD THAT'S HAPPENING	Capitol (M) T2638	3.50	5.25	7.00
ALL THE GOOD THAT'S HAPPENING	Capitol (S) ST2368	4.00	6.00	8.00
HEY JOE	Mire (M) 3005	4.00	6.00	8.00
HEY JOE	Mire (S) 3005	5.00	7.50	10.00

LED ZEPPELIN

LED ZEPPELIN	Atlantic (S) SD 8216	3.50	5.25	7.00
LED ZEPPELIN II	Atlantic (S) SD 8236	3.50	5.25	7.00
LED ZEPPELIN III	Atlantic (S) SD 7201	3.00	4.50	6.00
LED ZEPPELIN IV	Atlantic (S) SD 7208	3.00	4.50	6.00
PHYSICAL GRAFFITI	Swan Song (S) 2-200	4.00	6.00	8.00

LEE, Ada

| ADA LEE COMES ON | Atco (M) 33132 | 3.00 | 6.00 | 9.00 |

LEE, Alvin

ALVIN LEE	Columbia (S) PC-33796	2.50	3.75	5.00
IN FLIGHT	Columbia (S) PG-33187	2.00	3.00	4.00
ON THE ROAD TO FREEDOM (WITH MYLON LE FEVRE)	Columbia (S) KC-32729	2.50	3.75	5.00
ROCKET FUEL	RSO (S) RS-1-3033	2.00	3.00	4.00

Also see TEN YEARS AFTER

LEE, Arthur

| VINDICATOR | A&M (M) SP4356 | 4.00 | 6.00 | 8.00 |

LEE, Brenda

ALL ALONE AM I	Decca (M) DL4370	3.00	6.00	9.00
ALL ALONE AM I	Decca (S) DL74370	4.00	8.00	12.00
BRENDA	MCA (M) 305	2.50	3.75	5.00
BRENDA	MCA (S) 305	2.50	3.75	5.00
BRENDA LEE	Decca (M) DL4039	5.00	10.00	15.00
BRENDA LEE	Decca (S) DL74039	6.00	12.00	18.00
BRENDA LEE	Decca (EP) ED2682	2.00	5.00	8.00
BRENDA LEE	Decca (EP) ED2661	2.00	5.00	8.00
BRENDA LEE	Decca (EP) ED2678	2.00	5.00	8.00
BRENDA LEE	Decca (EP) ED2683	2.00	5.00	8.00
BRENDA LEE	Decca (EP) ED2702	2.00	5.00	8.00
BRENDA LEE	Decca (EP) ED2704	2.00	5.00	8.00
BRENDA LEE	Decca (EP) ED2712	2.00	5.00	8.00
BRENDA LEE	Decca (EP) ED2716	2.00	5.00	8.00
BRENDA LEE	Decca (EP) ED2730	2.00	5.00	8.00
BRENDA LEE	Decca (EP) ED2738	2.00	5.00	8.00
BRENDA LEE	Decca (EP) ED2745	2.00	5.00	8.00
BRENDA LEE	Decca (EP) ED2764	2.00	5.00	8.00
BRENDA LEE	Decca (EP) 2775	2.00	5.00	8.00
BRENDA LEE, ALL THE WAY	Decca (M) DL4176	5.00	10.00	15.00
BRENDA LEE, ALL THE WAY	Decca (S) DL74176	6.00	12.00	18.00
BRENDA LEE NOW	MCA (S) 433	2.50	3.75	5.00

TITLE	LABEL & NO.	GOOD	VERY GOOD	NEAR MINT
BRENDA LEE STORY	MCA (M) 24012	4.00	6.00	8.00
BRENDA, THAT'S ALL	Decca (M) DL4326	3.00	6.00	9.00
BRENDA, THAT'S ALL	Decca (S) DL74326	4.00	8.00	12.00
BYE BYE BLUES	Decca (M) DL4755	3.00	6.00	9.00
BYE BYE BLUES	Decca (S) DL74755	4.00	8.00	12.00
BY REQUEST	Decca (M) DL4509	3.00	4.50	6.00
BY REQUEST	Decca (S) DL74509	4.00	6.00	8.00
COMING ON STRONG	Decca (M) 4825	3.00	6.00	9.00
COMING ON STRONG	Decca (S) 74825	4.00	8.00	12.00
EMOTIONS	Decca (M) DL4104	5.00	10.00	15.00
EMOTIONS	Decca (S) DL74104	6.00	12.00	18.00
EVERYBODY LOVES ME BUT YOU	Decca (EP) ED2725	2.00	5.00	8.00
GRANDMA, WHAT GREAT SONGS YOU SANG	Decca (M) DL8873	3.00	4.50	6.00
GRANDMA, WHAT GREAT SONGS YOU SANG	Decca (S) DL78873	4.00	6.00	8.00
JOHNNY ONE TIME	Decca (S) DL 75111	3.00	4.50	6.00
LET ME SING	Decca (M) DL4439	3.00	6.00	9.00
LET ME SING	Decca (S) DL74439	4.00	8.00	12.00
MEMPHIS PORTRAIT	Decca (S) DL75232	3.00	4.50	6.00
MERRY CHRISTMAS FROM BRENDA LEE	Decca (M) DL4583	3.00	4.50	6.00
MERRY CHRISTMAS FROM BRENDA LEE	Decca (S) DL74583	4.00	6.00	8.00
NEW SUNRISE	MCA (S) 373	2.50	3.75	5.00
NOW	MCA (M) 433	2.50	3.75	5.00
REFLECTIONS IN BLUE	Decca (M) DL 4941	3.00	4.50	6.00
SINCERELY-BRENDA LEE	MCA (S) 477	2.50	3.75	5.00
SINCERELY, BRENDA LEE	Decca (M) DL4216	4.00	8.00	12.00
SINCERELY, BRENDA LEE	Decca (S) DL74216	5.00	10.00	15.00
10 GOLDEN YEARS	Decca (M) 4757	3.00	6.00	9.00
10 GOLDEN YEARS	Decca (S) 74757	4.00	8.00	12.00
THIS IS BRENDA	Decca (M) DL4082	5.00	10.00	15.00
THIS IS BRENDA	Decca (S) DL74082	6.00	12.00	18.00
TOO MANY RIVERS	Decca (M) DL 4684	3.00	4.50	6.00
TOO MANY RIVERS	Decca (S) DL 74684	4.00	6.00	8.00
TOP TEEN HITS	Decca (M) DL4626	3.00	6.00	9.00
TOP TEEN HITS	Decca (S) DL74626	4.00	8.00	12.00
VERSATILE BRENDA LEE	Decca (M) DL4661	3.00	4.50	6.00
VERSATILE BRENDA LEE	Decca (S) DL74661	4.00	6.00	8.00

LEE, BRENDA and Pete Fountain

| FOR THE FIRST TIME | Decca (M) 4955 | 3.00 | 4.50 | 6.00 |
| FOR THE FIRST TIME | Decca (S) 74955 | 4.00 | 6.00 | 8.00 |

LEE, Byron and The Dragonaires

BYRON LEE & THE DRAGONAIRES	JAD (M) JS1004	3.00	6.00	9.00
DANCE THE SKA	BMN (M) BLP004	3.00	6.00	9.00
SOUNDS OF JAMAICA	Towers Hall (M) LP006	3.50	7.00	10.50

LEE, Dickey

BABY, BYE BYE	RCA (S) LSP-4791	3.00	4.50	6.00
CRYING OVER YOU	RCA (S) LSP-4857	3.00	4.50	6.00
DICKEY LEE SINGS LAURA AND THE GIRL FROM PEYTON PLACE	TCF Hall (M) 8001	4.00	8.00	12.00
DICKEY LEE SINGS LAURA AND THE GIRL FROM PEYTON PLACE	TCF Hall (S) 8001	5.00	10.00	15.00
SPARKLIN' BROWN EYES	RCA (S) APL1-0311	2.50	3.75	5.00
TALE OF PATCHES	Smash (M) MGS27020	2.50	5.00	7.50
TALE OF PATCHES	Smash (SR(STS 67020	3.00	6.00	9.00

LEE, Jackie

| THE DUCK | Mirwood (M) MW7000 | 4.00 | 6.00 | 8.00 |
| THE DUCK | Mirwood (S) SW7000 | 4.50 | 6.75 | 9.00 |

LEE, Laura

BEST OF LAURA LEE	Hot Wax (M) HA715	3.00	4.50	6.00
I CAN'T MAKE IT ALONE	Invictus (M) KZ33133	2.50	3.75	5.00
LAURA LEE	Hot Wax (M) HA714	3.00	4.50	6.00

LEE, Leapy

| LITTLE ARROWS | Decca (M) DL5076 | 2.50 | 3.75 | 5.00 |
| LITTLE ARROWS | Decca (S) DL75076 | 2.50 | 3.75 | 5.00 |

(M) Mono (S) Stereo (EP) Extended Play (Q) Quad (RI) Re-issued

101

TITLE	LABEL & NO.	GOOD	VERY GOOD	NEAR MINT
LEE, Michele				
L. DAVID SLOANE				
& OTHER HITS OF TODAY	Columbia (S) CS9682	2.00	3.00	4.00
SEESAW	Buddah (S) 95006	2.50	3.75	5.00
TASTE OF THE FANTASTIC	Columbia (M) CL2486	2.00	3.00	4.00
TASTE OF THE FANTASTIC	Columbia (S) CS9286	2.00	3.00	4.00
LEE, Peggy				
ALL AGLOW AGAIN	Capitol (M) T-1366	2.50	3.75	5.00
ALRIGHT, OKAY, YOU WIN	Capitol (EP) EAP-1-1213	1.50	2.25	3.00
BEAUTY & THE BEAT (WITH GEORGE SHEARING)	Capitol T-1219	2.50	3.75	5.00
BEAUTY & THE BEAT (WITH GEORGE SHEARING)	Capitol (S) ST-1219	3.00	4.50	6.00
BEST OF PEGGY LEE	Decca (M) DXB-164	3.00	4.50	6.00
FEVER	Capitol (SEP) SEP-1-1232	2.00	3.00	4.00
I LIKE MEN	Capitol (M) T-1131	2.00	4.00	6.00
I LIKE MEN	Capitol (EP) EPA-1-1131	1.50	2.25	3.00
I'M A WOMAN	Capitol (S) SM-1857	2.50	3.75	5.00
JUMP FOR JOY	Capitol (S) ST-979	2.50	5.00	7.50
LATIN ALA LEE	Capitol (M) T-1290	2.00	4.00	6.00
LATIN ALA LEE	Capitol (S) ST-1290	2.50	5.00	7.50
LET'S LOVE	Atlantic (S) 18108	2.00	3.00	4.00
MAN I LOVE, THE	Capitol (M) T 864	3.00	6.00	9.00
(Orchestra conducted by Frank Sinatra.)				
PRETTY EYES	Capitol (M) T-1401	2.50	3.75	5.00
PRETTY EYES	Capitol (S) ST-1401	3.00	4.50	6.00
THINGS ARE SWINGIN'	Capitol (S) ST-1049	2.00	4.00	6.00
LEE, Pinky				
PINKY LEE, SURPRISE PARTY	Decca (M) DL8421	3.00	4.50	6.00
LEFT BANKE				
TOO	Smash (S) SRS67113	5.00	7.50	10.00
WALK AWAY RENEE	Smash (M) MGS27088	4.50	6.75	9.00
WALK AWAY RENEE	Smash (S) SRS67088	5.00	7.50	10.00
LEFT END				
SPOILED ROTTEN	Polydor (M) PD6022	5.00	7.50	10.00
LEGEND				
LEGEND	Bell (M) 6027	5.00	7.50	10.00
LEGEND	Megaphone (M) S101	3.00	6.00	9.00
LEGENDS				
DYNAMIC SOUNDS OF THE LEGENDS	Columbia (M) CL1707	6.00	15.00	24.00
DYNAMIC SOUNDS OF THE LEGENDS	Columbia (S) CS8507	7.00	17.50	28.00
LEGENDS LET LOOSE	Capitol (M) T1925	7.00	17.50	28.00
LEGENDS LET LOOSE	Capitol (S) ST1925	8.00	20.00	32.00
LEGENDS LET LOOSE	Ermine (M) 101	7.50	18.75	30.00
RUN TO THE MOVIES	Capitol Custom	8.00	20.00	32.00
LEIBER, Jerry				
SCOOBY DOO	Kapp (M) KL1127	4.00	10.00	16.00
LEIBER & STOLLER BIG BAND				
YAKETY YAK	Atlantic (M) 8047	3.00	7.50	12.00
LEIGH, Andrew				
MAGICIAN	Sire (S) SES97025	3.50	5.25	7.00
LEMON PIPERS				
GREEN TAMBOURINE	Buddah (S) BDS5009	3.00	4.50	6.00
JUNGLE MARMALADE	Buddah (S) BDS5016	3.00	4.50	6.00
LENIOR, J.B.				
NATURAL MAN	Chess (M) 410	4.00	6.00	8.00
LENNON, John				
IMAGINE	Apple (S) SW 3379	2.00	3.00	4.00
JOHN LENNON SINGS THE ROCK & ROLL HITS				
(ROOTS)	Adam VIII Ltd. (S) A8018	15.00	22.00	30.00
(Artists listed as "Plastic Ono Band")				
MIND GAMES	Apple (S) SW-3414	2.00	3.00	4.00
PLASTIC ONO BAND	Apple (S) SW-3372	5.00	7.50	10.00
ROCK N' ROLL	Apple (S) SK-3419	2.00	3.00	4.00
SHAVED FISH	Apple (S) SW-3421	2.00	3.00	4.00
WALLS & BRIDGES	Apple (S) SW 3416	2.00	3.00	4.00
Also see ELEPHANT'S MEMORY				
Also see ONO, Yoko				
LENNON, John and Yoko Ono				
LIVE PEACE IN TORONTO (WITH CALENDAR)	Apple (S) SW 3362	7.50	10.75	15.00
(Artist listed as: "Plastic Ono Band")				
SOME TIME IN NEW YORK CITY	Apple (S) SUBB 3392	4.00	6.00	8.00
UNFINISHED MUSIC NO. 1				
TWO VIRGINS (With Brown sleeve)	Apple (S) T 5001	15.00	22.50	30.00
UNFINISHED MUSIC NO. 2				
LIFE WITH THE LIONS	Zapple (S) ST3357	6.00	9.00	12.00
WEDDING ALBUM	Apple (S) SMAX 3361	10.00	25.00	40.00
LESTER, Ketty				
LOVE LETTERS	Era (M) EL108	3.00	4.50	6.00
LOVE LETTERS	Era (S) ES108	4.00	6.00	8.00

(M) Mono (S) Stereo (EP) Extended Play (Q) Quad (RI) Re-issued

TITLE	LABEL & NO.	GOOD	VERY GOOD	NEAR MINT
SOUL OF ME	RCA (M) LPM2945	2.00	3.00	4.00
SOUL OF ME	RCA (S) LSP2945	2.00	3.00	4.00
WHEN A WOMAN LOVES A MAN	Tower (M) T5029	2.00	3.00	4.00
WHERE IS LOVE	RCA (M) LPM3326	2.00	3.00	4.00
WHERE IS LOVE	RCA (S) LSP3326	2.00	3.00	4.00
LETTERMEN				
"ALIVE" AGAIN-NATURALLY	Capitol (S) SW-11183	2.00	3.00	4.00
ALL TIME GREATEST HITS	Capitol (S) SW-11249	2.00	3.00	4.00
CLOSE-UP	Capitol (S) 251	3.00	4.50	6.00
GOIN' OUT OF MY HEAD	Capitol (S) ST 2865	3.00	4.50	6.00
LETTERMEN!!! ... AND "LIVE!"	Capitol (M) T2758	2.50	3.75	5.00
LETTERMEN!!! ... AND "LIVE!"	Capitol (S) ST 2758	3.00	4.50	6.00
MAKE A TIME FOR LOVIN'	Capitol (S) SW-11424	2.00	3.00	4.00
NOW & FOREVER	Capitol (S) SW-11319	2.00	3.00	4.00
SPIN AWAY	Capitol (S) SW-11124	2.00	3.00	4.00
THERE IS NO GREATER LOVE	Capitol (S) SW-11364	2.00	3.00	4.00
TIME IS RIGHT	Capitol (S) SW-11470	2.00	3.00	4.00
LEVINE, Mark				
PILGRIMS PROGRESS	Hogfat (M) HLP1	4.00	6.00	8.00
LEWIS, Barbara				
BABY, I'M YOURS	Atlantic (M) 8110	4.00	6.00	8.00
BABY, I'M YOURS	Atlantic (S) SD8110	4.50	6.75	9.00
BABY I'M YOURS	Atlantic (EP) EP8110	2.00	4.00	6.00
BEST OF BARBARA LEWIS	Atlantic (S) SD8286	3.50	5.25	7.00
HELLO STRANGER	Atlantic (M) 8086	5.00	7.50	10.00
HELLO STRANGER	Atlantic (S) SD8086	5.50	8.50	11.00
IT'S MAGIC	Atlantic (M) 8118	4.00	6.00	8.00
IT'S MAGIC	Atlantic (S) SD8118	4.50	6.75	9.00
MANY GROOVES OF BARBARA LEWIS	Enterprise (S) ENS1006	3.00	4.50	6.00
SNAP YOUR FINGERS	Atlantic (M) 8090	5.00	7.50	16.00
SNAP YOUR FINGERS	Atlantic (S) SD8090	5.50	8.50	11.00
WORKIN' ON A GROOVY THING	Atlantic (S) SD8173	4.50	6.75	9.00
LEWIS, Bobby				
(Rhythm & Blues artist)				
TOSSIN' AND TURNIN'	Beltone (M) 4000	7.00	14.00	21.00
LEWIS, Bobby				
(Country/Western artist)				
FROM HEAVEN TO HEARTACHE	United Artists (S) 6673	2.50	3.75	5.00
LITTLE MAN WITH				
A BIG HEART	United Artists (M) 3499	3.00	4.50	6.00
LITTLE MAN WITH				
A BIG HEART	United Artists (S) 6499	2.50	3.75	5.00
ORDINARY MIRACLE	United Artists (S) 6629	2.50	3.75	5.00
LEWIS, Dave				
LITTLE GREEN THING	A & M (S) SP105	2.50	3.75	5.00
LEWIS, Furry				
BLUES MASTERS VOL. 5	Blue Horizon (M) BM4605	4.00	6.00	8.00
LIVE AT THE GASLIGHT	Ampex (M) A10140	2.50	3.75	5.00
SHAKE 'EM DOWN	Fantasy (M) 24709	3.00	4.50	6.00
LEWIS, Gary				
DOIN THE FLAKE	Liberty (EP) 277	1.50	2.25	3.00
LEWIS, Gary and The Playboys				
CLOSE COVER BEFORE PLAYING	Liberty (S) LST7606	3.00	4.50	6.00
EVERYBODY LOVES A CLOWN	Liberty (M) LRP3428	4.00	6.00	8.00
EVERYBODY LOVES A CLOWN	Liberty (S) LST7428	5.00	7.50	10.00
GOLDEN GREATS	Liberty (M) LRP3468	3.00	4.50	6.00
GOLDEN GREATS	Liberty (S) LST7468	4.00	6.00	8.00
HITS AGAIN	Liberty (M) LRP3452	4.00	6.00	8.00
HITS AGAIN	Liberty (S) LST7452	5.00	7.50	10.00
I'M ON THE ROAD NOW	Liberty (S) LST7633	3.00	4.50	6.00
LISTEN	Liberty (M) LRP3524	3.00	4.50	6.00
LISTEN	Liberty (S) LST7524	4.00	6.00	8.00
MORE GOLDEN GREATS	Liberty (S) LST 7589	3.00	4.50	6.00
NEW DIRECTIONS	Liberty (M) LRP3519	3.00	4.50	6.00

TITLE	LABEL & NO.	GOOD	VERY GOOD	NEAR MINT
NEW DIRECTIONS	Liberty (S) LST7519	4.00	6.00	8.00
NOW	Liberty (S) LST7568	4.00	6.00	8.00
RHYTHM OF THE RAIN	Liberty (S) LST7623	3.00	4.50	6.00
A SESSION WITH GARY LEWIS AND THE PLAYBOYS	Liberty (M) LRP3419	4.00	6.00	8.00
A SESSION WITH GARY LEWIS AND THE PLAYBOYS	Liberty (S) LST7419	5.00	7.50	10.00
SHE'S JUST MY STYLE	Liberty (M) LRP3435	4.00	6.00	8.00
SHE'S JUST MY STYLE	Liberty (S) LST7435	5.00	7.50	10.00
THIS DIAMOND RING	Liberty (M) LRP3408	4.00	6.00	8.00
THIS DIAMOND RING	Liberty (S) LST7408	5.00	7.50	10.00
VERY BEST OF GARY LEWIS AND THE PLAYBOYS	United Artists (S) UALA430	2.50	3.75	5.00

LEWIS, Jerry

TITLE	LABEL & NO.	GOOD	VERY GOOD	NEAR MINT
BIG SONGS FOR LITTLE PEOPLE	Decca (M) DL-8936	3.00	4.50	6.00
BIG SONGS FOR LITTLE PEOPLE	Decca (S) DL-78936	3.50	5.25	7.00
JERRY LEWIS JUST SINGS	Decca (M) DL8410	3.00	4.50	6.00
JERRY LEWIS JUST SINGS	Decca (EP) ED2455	1.00	1.50	2.00
JERRY LEWIS JUST SINGS	Decca (EP) ED2456	1.00	1.50	2.00
JERRY LEWIS JUST SINGS	Decca (EP) ED2457	1.00	1.50	2.00
JERRY LEWIS SINGS FROM THE HEART	Decca (EP) ED2566	1.00	1.50	2.00

LEWIS, Jerry Lee

TITLE	LABEL & NO.	GOOD	VERY GOOD	NEAR MINT
ANOTHER PLACE ANOTHER TIME	Smash (S) SRS67104	2.50	3.75	5.00
BEST OF JERRY LEE LEWIS	Smash (S) SRS67131	2.50	3.75	5.00
BY REQUEST	Smash (M) MGS27086	2.50	3.75	5.00
BY REQUEST	Smash (S) SRS67086	2.50	3.75	5.00
COUNTRY HITS, Vol. 1	Smash (S) SRS 67118	2.50	3.75	5.00
COUNTRY SONGS FOR CITY FOLKS	Smash (M) MGS27010	2.50	3.75	5.00
COUNTRY SONGS FOR CITY FOLKS	Smash (S) SRS67071	2.50	3.75	5.00
GOLDEN CREAM OF THE COUNTRY	Sun (M) 108	3.00	4.50	6.00
GOLDEN HITS OF JERRY LEE LEWIS	Smash (M) MGS27040	2.50	3.75	5.00
GOLDEN HITS OF JERRY LEE LEWIS	Smash (S) SRS67040	2.50	3.75	5.00
GREATEST LIVE SHOW ON EARTH	Smash (M) MGS27056	3.00	4.50	6.00
GREATEST LIVE SHOW ON EARTH	Smash (S) SRS67056	3.50	5.25	7.00
I-40 COUNTRY	Mercury (S) SRM-1-710	2.00	3.00	4.00
JERRY LEE LEWIS	Sun (M) LP1230	12.00	24.00	36.00
JERRY LEE LEWIS	Everest (S) 298	2.50	3.75	5.00
JERRY LEE LEWIS, DON'T BE CRUEL	Sun (EP) EP108	2.50	6.25	10.00
JERRY LEE LEWIS HIGH SCHOOL CONFIDENTIAL	Sun (EP) 110	2.50	6.25	10.00
JERRY LEE LEWIS SINGS HANK WILLIAMS WITH JOHNNY CASH (5 Songs by each)	Sun (M) 125	3.00	4.50	6.00
JERRY LEE LEWIS, UBANGI STOMP	Sun (EP) 109	2.50	6.25	10.00
JERRY LEE'S WHOLE LOT OF SHAKING	Sun (EP) 107	2.50	6.25	10.00
JERRY LEE'S GREATEST	Sun (M) LP1265	12.00	24.00	36.00
MEMPHIS BEAT	Smash (M) MGS 27079	2.50	3.75	5.00
MEMPHIS BEAT	Smash (S) SRS67079	2.50	3.75	5.00
MEMPHIS ROCK & ROLL	Sun (M) 116	3.00	4.50	6.00
MONSTERS	Sun (M) 124	4.00	6.00	8.00
ORIGINAL GOLDEN HITS VOL. 2	Sun (M) 103	3.00	4.50	6.00
ORIGINAL GOLDEN HITS VOL. 3	Sun (M) 128	3.00	4.50	6.00
ORIGINAL GREATEST HITS VOL. 1	Sun (M) 102	3.00	4.50	6.00
RETURN OF ROCK	Smash (M) MGS27063	3.00	4.50	6.00
RETURN OF ROCK	Smash (S) SRS67063	3.50	5.25	7.00
ROCKIN' RHYTHM & BLUES	Sun (M) 107	3.00	4.50	6.00
ROCKIN' WITH JERRY LEE LEWIS	Design (M) DLP165	4.00	8.00	12.00
SESSION, THE	Mercury (S) SRM-2-803	3.00	4.50	6.00
SHE EVEN WOKE ME UP TO SAY GOODBYE	Smash (S) SRS 67128	2.50	3.75	5.00
SHE STILL COMES AROUND	Smash (S) SRS67112	2.50	3.75	5.00
SOLID GOLD ROCK 'N ROLL, Vol. 2	Mercury (S) SR 61372	2.50	3.75	5.00
SOMETIMES A MEMORY AIN'T ENOUGH	Mercury (S) SRM-1-677	2.00	3.00	4.00
SOUL MY WAY	Smash (M) MGS27097	2.50	3.75	5.00
SOUL MY WAY	Smash (S) SRS67097	2.50	3.75	5.00
SUNDAY DOWN SOUTH, WITH JOHNNY CASH (5 Songs by each)	Sun (M) 119	3.00	4.50	6.00
TASTE OF THE COUNTRY	Sun (M) 114	3.00	4.50	6.00
TOGETHER WITH LINDA GAIL LEWIS	Smash (S) SRS 67126	2.50	3.75	5.00
WHO'S GONNA PLAY THIS OLD PIANO	Mercury (S) SR 61366	2.50	3.75	5.00

(NOTE: Sun 100 series are late 60's)

LEWIS, Linda

TITLE	LABEL & NO.	GOOD	VERY GOOD	NEAR MINT
HEART STRINGS	Reprise (M) MS 2192	3.00	4.50	6.00

LEWIS, Meade Lux

TITLE	LABEL & NO.	GOOD	VERY GOOD	NEAR MINT
BARREL HOUSE PIANO	Tops (M) L1533	4.00	10.00	16.00
BLUES PIANO ARTISTRY OF MEADE LUX LEWIS	Riverside (M) 9402	5.00	12.50	20.00

LEWIS, Smiley

TITLE	LABEL & NO.	GOOD	VERY GOOD	NEAR MINT
I HEAR YOU KNOCKING	Imperial (M) 9141	12.00	30.00	48.00

LIFEGUARDS

TITLE	LABEL & NO.	GOOD	VERY GOOD	NEAR MINT
C'MON AND SWIM	Wyncote (M) W 9043	2.50	5.00	7.50

LIGHTFOOT, Gordon

TITLE	LABEL & NO.	GOOD	VERY GOOD	NEAR MINT
CLASSIC LIGHTFOOT (BEST OF LIGHTFOOT, VOL. 2)	United Artists (S) UAS 5510	3.50	5.25	7.00
COLD ON THE SHOULDER	Reprise (S) 2206	3.00	4.50	6.00
COLD ON THE SHOULDER	Reprise (Q) MS4-2206	2.50	3.75	5.00
DON QUIXOTE	Reprise (S) MS 2056	3.00	4.50	6.00
GORD'S GOLD	Reprise (S) 2RS-2237	3.50	5.25	7.00
OLD DAN'S RECORDS	Reprise (S) 2116	3.00	4.50	6.00
SIT DOWN YOUNG STRANGER	Reprise (S) RS 6392	3.00	4.50	6.00
SUMMER SIDE OF LIFE	Reprise (S) MS 2037	3.00	4.50	6.00
SUNDAY CONCERT	United Artists (S) UAS 6714	3.50	5.25	7.00
SUNDOWN	Reprise (S) MS 2177	3.00	4.50	6.00
SUNDOWN	Reprise (Q) MS4-2177	2.50	3.75	5.00
VERY BEST OF GORDON LIGHTFOOT, VOL. 2	United Artists (S) UA-LA445	2.00	3.00	4.00

LIGHTHOUSE

TITLE	LABEL & NO.	GOOD	VERY GOOD	NEAR MINT
CAN YOU FEEL IT	Polydor (S) 5056	2.50	3.75	5.00
GOOD DAY	Polydor (S) 6028	2.50	3.75	5.00
LIGHTHOUSE LIVE!	Evolution (S) 3014	3.50	5.25	7.00
ONE FINE LIGHT	RCA (S) VPS 6047	3.00	4.50	6.00
ONE FINE MORNING	Evolution (S) 3007	3.00	4.50	6.00
PEACING IT ALL TOGETHER	RCA (S) LSP 4325	3.50	5.25	7.00
SUNNY DAYS	Evolution (S) 3016	3.50	5.25	7.00
THOUGHTS OF MOVIN' ON	Evolution (S) 3010	3.50	5.25	7.00

LIGHTNING

TITLE	LABEL & NO.	GOOD	VERY GOOD	NEAR MINT
LIGHTNING	P.I.P. (M) PIP 6807	5.00	7.50	10.00

LIGHTNIN' SLIM

TITLE	LABEL & NO.	GOOD	VERY GOOD	NEAR MINT
BELL RINGER	Excello (M) 8004	5.00	10.00	15.00
HIGH AND LOW DOWN	Excello (M) 8018	4.00	8.00	12.00
LIGHTNIN SLIMS BELL RINGER	Excello (M) 8000	5.00	7.50	10.00
ROOSTER BLUES	Excello (M) LP8000	5.00	10.00	15.00

LINCOLN STREET EXIT

TITLE	LABEL & NO.	GOOD	VERY GOOD	NEAR MINT
DRIVE IT	Mainstream (S) S 6126	4.50	6.75	9.00

LIND, Bob

TITLE	LABEL & NO.	GOOD	VERY GOOD	NEAR MINT
DON'T BE CONCERNED	World Pacific (M) WP1841	3.50	5.25	7.00
DON'T BE CONCERNED	World Pacific (S) WPS 21841	3.50	5.25	7.00
ELUSIVE BOB LIND	Verve-Folkways (M) FT 3005	3.00	4.00	6.00
ELUSIVE BOB LIND	Verve-Folkways (S) FTS 3005	3.00	4.00	6.00
PHOTOGRAPHS OF FEELING	World Pacific (M) WP 1851	3.50	5.25	7.00
PHOTOGRAPHS OF FEELING	World Pacific (S) WPS21851	3.50	5.25	7.00
SINCE THERE WERE CIRCLES	Capitol (S) ST 780	2.00	3.00	4.00

LINDEN, Kathy

TITLE	LABEL & NO.	GOOD	VERY GOOD	NEAR MINT
THAT CERTAIN BOY	Felsted (M) FL 7501	4.00	10.00	16.00

LINDSAY, Mark

TITLE	LABEL & NO.	GOOD	VERY GOOD	NEAR MINT
ARIZONA	Columbia (S) CS 9986	3.50	5.25	7.00
SILVER BIRD	Columbia (S) C 30111	3.00	4.50	6.00
YOU'VE GOT A FRIEND	Columbia (S) C 30735	3.00	4.50	6.00

Also see PAUL REVERE & THE RAIDERS

LINHART, Buzzy

TITLE	LABEL & NO.	GOOD	VERY GOOD	NEAR MINT
BUZZY	Philips (S) PHS 600291	4.00	6.00	8.00
BUZZY LINHART	Kama Sutra (S) KSBS 2042	3.50	5.25	7.00
PUSSY CATS CAN GO FAR	Atco (S) 7044	2.50	3.75	5.00
TIME TO LIVE IS NOW	Kama Sutra (S) KSBS 2037	3.50	5.25	7.00

LINKLETTER, Art

TITLE	LABEL & NO.	GOOD	VERY GOOD	NEAR MINT
HOWLS, BONERS AND SCHOCKERS	Columbia (M) CL 703	4.00	6.00	8.00
HOWLS, BONERS AND SCHOCKERS	Columbia (EP) B 530	1.50	2.25	3.00
KIDS SAY THE DARNDEST THINGS	Harmony (M) HL 7152	2.00	3.00	4.00
WE LOVE YOU, CALL COLLECT With His Daughter, Diane	Word (M) WEP 1101	2.50	3.75	5.00

LINN COUNTY

TITLE	LABEL & NO.	GOOD	VERY GOOD	NEAR MINT
TILL THE BREAK OF DAWN	Philips (M) PHS 600326	3.00	4.50	6.00

LIPSCOMB, Mance

TITLE	LABEL & NO.	GOOD	VERY GOOD	NEAR MINT
MANCE LIPSCOMB VOL. 1	Arhoolie (M) 1001	2.50	4.00	5.00
MANCE LIPSCOMB VOL. 2	Arhoolie (M) 1023	2.50	4.00	5.00
MANCE LIPSCOMB VOL. 3	Arhoolie (M) 1026	2.50	4.00	5.00

LIPTON, Peggy

TITLE	LABEL & NO.	GOOD	VERY GOOD	NEAR MINT
PEGGY LIPTON	Ode (S) Z12-44006	4.50	6.75	9.00

LIQUID SMOKE

TITLE	LABEL & NO.	GOOD	VERY GOOD	NEAR MINT
LIQUID SMOKE	Avco-Embassy (S) AVE-33005	3.50	5.25	7.00

LISTENING

TITLE	LABEL & NO.	GOOD	VERY GOOD	NEAR MINT
LISTENING	Vanguard (M) 6504	4.00	6.00	8.00

LITTER

TITLE	LABEL & NO.	GOOD	VERY GOOD	NEAR MINT
DISTORTIONS	Warick (M) WM 671A	12.00	24.00	36.00
EMERGE	Probe (M) CPLP 4504	5.00	7.50	10.00
$100 FINE	Hexagon (M) HX 681	10.00	20.00	30.00

LITTLE ANTHONY & THE IMPERIALS

TITLE	LABEL & NO.	GOOD	VERY GOOD	NEAR MINT
BEST OF LITTLE ANTHONY AND THE IMPERIALS	DCP (M) DC 3809	3.00	4.50	6.00
BEST OF LITTLE ANTHONY AND THE IMPERIALS	DCP (S) DS 6809	3.50	5.25	7.00
BEST OF LITTLE ANTHONY AND THE IMPERIALS Vol. 2	Veep (M) VP 13519	2.50	3.75	5.00

(M) Mono (S) Stereo (EP) Extended Play (Q) Quad (RI) Re-issued

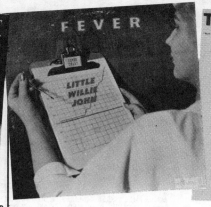
FEVER
THE LIVERPOOL BEATS!

TITLE	LABEL & NO.	GOOD	VERY GOOD	NEAR MINT
BEST OF LETTLE ANTHONY				
AND THE IMPERIALS Vol. 2 .... Veep (S) VPS 16519		3.00	4.50	6.00
GOIN OUT OF MY HEAD .... DCP (M) DC 3808		3.00	4.50	6.00
GOIN OUT OF MY HEAD .... DCP (S) DS 6808		3.50	5.25	7.00
GREATEST HITS OF				
LITTLE ANTHONY AND THE IMPERIALS .... Roulette (M) R25294		3.00	6.00	9.00
GREATEST HITS OF				
LITTLE ANTHONY AND THE IMPERIALS .... Roulette (S) SR25294		4.00	8.00	12.00
I'M ON THE OUTSIDE (Looking In) .... DCP (M) DC 3801		3.00	4.50	6.00
I'M ON THE OUTSIDE (Looking In) .... DCP (S) DCS 6801		3.50	5.25	7.00
LITTLE ANTHONY AND THE IMPERIALS				
SING THEIR BIG HITS .... Forum Circle (M) FC 9107		3.00	6.00	9.00
LITTLE ANTHONY AND THE IMPERIALS				
SING THEIR BIG HITS .... Forum Circle (S) FCS 9107		2.00	4.00	6.00
MOVIE GRABBERS .... Veep (M) VP 13516		2.00	3.00	4.00
MOVIE GRABBERS .... Veep (S) VPS 16516		2.50	3.75	5.00
ON A NEW STREET .... Avco (S) 11012		3.00	4.50	6.00
OUT OF SIGHT, OUT OF MIND .... United Artists (S) UAS 6720		2.50	3.75	5.00
PAYIN' OUR DUES .... Veep (M) VP 13513		2.50	3.75	5.00
PAYIN' OUR DUES .... Veep (S) VPS 16513		3.00	4.50	6.00
REFLECTIONS .... Veep (M) VP 13514		2.50	3.75	5.00
REFLECTIONS .... Veep (S) VPS 16514		3.00	4.50	6.00
VERY BEST OF LITTLE				
ANTHONY AND THE IMPERIALS .... United Artists (M) UALA 255		2.00	3.00	4.00
VERY BEST OF LITTLE ANTHONY				
AND THE IMPERIALS (RI) .... United Artists (S) UA-LA 382E		1.50	2.25	3.00
WE ARE LITTLE ANTHONY				
AND THE IMPERIALS .... End (M) LP303		6.00	12.00	18.00
WE ARE LITTLE ANTHONY				
AND THE IMPERIALS .... End (S) LP 303		3.00	4.50	6.00

LITTLE BLUE BOYS
IN THE WOODLAND OF WEIR .... Fontana (M) SRF 67578		4.00	6.00	8.00

LITTLE CEASAR & THE ROMANS
MEMORIES OF THOSE				
OLDIES BUT GOODIES Vol. 1 .... Del Fi (M) DFLP 1218		6.00	12.00	18.00

LITTLE EVA
L-L-L-L-LOCO-MOTION .... Dimension (M) DLP 6000		5.00	10.00	15.00
L-L-L-L-LOCO-MOTION .... Dimension (S) DLPS 6000		6.00	12.00	18.00

LITTLE FEAT
DIXIE CHICKEN .... Warner Bros. (S) BS-2686		2.50	3.75	5.00
FEATS DON'T FAIL ME NOW .... Warner Bros. (S) BS 2784		2.50	3.75	5.00
LAST RECORD ALBUM .... Warner Bros. (S) BS 2884		2.50	3.75	5.00
LITTLE FEAT .... Warner Bros. (S) WS 1890		3.50	5.25	7.00
SAILIN' SHOES .... Warner Bros. (S) BS 2600		2.50	3.75	5.00
TIME LOVES A HERO .... Warner Bros. (S) BS 3015		2.00	3.00	4.00
WAITING FOR COLUMBUS .... Warner Bros. (S) 2BS 3140		3.00	4.50	6.00

LITTLE JOE & THE THRILLERS
LITTLE JOE & THE THRILLERS .... Epic (EP) EG 7198		2.50	5.00	7.50

LITTLE JOHN
LITTLE JOHN .... Epic (M) E 30414		3.00	4.50	6.00

LITTLE MILTON
BLUES N' SOUL .... Stax (S) 5514		2.50	3.75	5.00
GREATEST HITS .... Chess (M) 50013		4.00	6.00	8.00
SINGS BIG BLUES .... Checker (M) 3002		4.00	8.00	12.00
WAITING FOR LITTLE MILTON .... Stax (S) STS 3012		2.50	3.75	5.00
WE'RE GONNA MAKE IT .... Checker (M) 2995		4.00	8.00	12.00

LITTLE RICHARD
BEST OF LITTLE RICHARD, THE				
(the same as Vee Jay 1124 minus 2 songs) .... Up Front (M) 123		2.00	3.00	4.00
BEST OF LITTLE RICHARD, THE				
(the same as Vee Jay 1124 minus 2 songs) .... Scepter (M) 18020		2.00	3.00	4.00
CLAP YOUR HANDS .... Spin O Rama (M) 119		2.00	3.00	4.00
CLAP YOUR HANDS .... Spin O Rama (S) S 119		2.00	3.00	4.00
COMING HOME .... Coral (M) CRL 757446		3.00	4.50	6.00
EVERY HOUR WITH LITTLE RICHARD .... RCamden (S) CAS 2430		3.00	4.50	6.00
EXPLOSIVE LITTLE RICHARD .... Okeh (M) OKS 14117		4.00	6.00	8.00
FABULOUS LITTLE RICHARD, THE .... Specialty (M) SP 2104		4.00	6.00	8.00
HERE'S LITTLE RICHARD .... Specialty (M) SP 2100		4.00	6.00	8.00
HERE'S LITTLE RICHARD Vol 1 .... Specialty (EP) SEP 400		2.00	3.00	4.00
HERE'S LITTLE RICHARD Vol 2 .... Specialty (EP) SEP 401		2.00	3.00	4.00
HERE'S LITTLE RICHARD Vol 3 .... Specialty (EP) SEP 402		2.00	3.00	4.00
INCREDIBLE LITTLE RICHARD SINGS HIS				
GREATEST HITS-RECORDED LIVE .... Modern (M) 100		2.00	3.00	4.00
INCREDIBLE LITTLE RICHARD SINGS HIS				
GREATEST HITS-RECORDED LIVE .... Modern (S) 1000		2.00	3.00	4.00
INCREDIBLE LITTLE RICHARD SINGS HIS				
GREATEST HITS-RECORDED LIVE .... United Records (M) 7775		2.00	3.00	4.00
KING OF ROCK AND ROLL .... Reprise (S) RS 6462		2.50	3.75	5.00
KING OF THE GOSPEL SINGERS .... Mercury (M) 20656		2.00	3.00	4.00
KING OF THE GOSPEL SINGERS .... Mercury/Wing (M) 12288		2.00	3.00	4.00
KING OF THE GOSPEL SINGERS .... Pickwick (S) SPC 3258		2.00	3.00	4.00
LITTLE RICHARD .... Buddah (S) BDS 7501		2.00	3.00	4.00
LITTLE RICHARD .... Kama Sutra (S) NSBS 2023		2.00	3.00	4.00
LITTLE RICHARD .... Camden (M) CAL 420		3.00	4.50	6.00
LITTLE RICHARD .... Camden (EP) CAE 4111		1.50	2.25	3.00
LITTLE RICHARD .... Specialty (EP) SEP 405		1.50	2.75	3.00
LITTLE RICHARD IS BACK .... Vee Jay (M) 1107		2.50	3.75	5.00
LITTLE RICHARD ROCKS .... Camden (EP) CAE 446		1.50	2.25	3.00
LITTLE RICHARD'S BIGGEST HITS .... Specialty (M) SP 2111		4.00	6.00	8.00
LITTLE RICHARD'S GREATEST HITS .... Vee Jay (M) 1124		2.00	3.00	4.00
LITTLE RICHARD'S GREATEST HITS				
RECORDED LIVE .... Okeh (M) OKM 12121		3.00	4.50	6.00
LITTLE RICHARD'S GREATEST HITS				
RECORDED LIVE .... Okeh (S) OKS 14121		3.00	4.50	6.00
LITTLE RICHARD'S GROOVIEST				
17 ORIGINAL HITS .... Specialty (M) SP 2113		3.00	4.50	6.00
LITTLE RICHARD'S GROOVIEST				
17 ORIGINAL HITS .... Specialty (S) SPS 2113		2.50	3.75	5.00
LITTLE RICHARD SINGS .... Summit (M) LSE 4029		2.00	3.00	4.00
LITTLE RICHARD SINGS FREEDOM SONGS .... Crown (M) CLP 5362		2.00	3.00	4.00
LITTLE RICHARD SINGS GOSPEL .... 20th Century (M) FXG 5010		2.50	3.75	5.00
LITTLE RICHARD SINGS SPIRITUALS .... Custom (M) 2061		2.00	3.00	4.00
LITTLE RICHARD SINGS SPIRITUALS .... United Records (M) UM 723		2.00	3.00	4.00
LITTLE RICHARD SINGS SPIRITUALS .... United Records (S) US 7723		2.00	3.00	4.00
LITTLE RICHARD Vol 1 .... Specialty (EP) SEP 403		1.50	2.25	3.00
LITTLE RICHARD VOL. 2 .... Specialty (M) SP 2103		4.00	6.00	8.00
LITTLE RICHARD Vol 2 .... Specialty (EP) SEP 404		1.50	2.25	3.00
LITTLE RICHARD WITH SISTER ROSETTA .... Guest Star (M) 1429		2.00	3.00	4.00
PRAY ALONG WITH LITTLE RICHARD VOL. 1 .... Goldisc (M) 4001		2.00	3.00	4.00
PRAY ALONG WITH LITTLE RICHARD VOL. 2 .... Goldisc (M) 4002		2.00	3.00	4.00
RIGHT NOW .... United (M) US 7791		2.00	3.00	4.00
RILL THING, THE .... Reprise (S) RS 6406		2.50	3.75	5.00
SECOND COMING, THE .... Reprise (S) MS 2107		2.50	3.75	5.00
WELL ALRIGHT .... Specialty (S) SPS 2136		3.00	4.50	6.00
WILD AND FRANTIC				
LITTLE RICHARD .... Modern (M) MST 103		2.00	3.00	4.00
WILD AND FRANTIC				
LITTLE RICHARD .... Modern (S) 1003		2.00	3.00	4.00
WILD AND FRANTIC				
LITTLE RICHARD .... United Records (M) US 7777		2.00	3.00	4.00

LITTLE ROYAL
JEALOUS .... Trius (S) KS 1145		2.50	3.75	5.00

LITTLE SONNY
BLACK AND BLUE .... Enterprise (S) ENS 1018		2.50	3.75	5.00
HARD GOIN' UP .... Enterprise (S) ENS 1036		2.50	3.75	5.00
NEW KING OF THE BLUES HARMONICA .... Enterprise (S) ENS 1005		2.50	3.75	5.00

LITTLE WALTER
BEST .... Checker (M) 3004		5.00	10.00	15.00
BEST OF LITTLE WALTER .... Chess (M) LP 1428		4.00	8.00	12.00
BOSS BLUES HARMONICA .... Chess (M) 2CH 60014		4.00	6.00	8.00
HATE TO SEE YOU GO .... Chess (M) LP 1535		4.00	6.00	8.00

LITTLE WILLIE JOHN
ACTION .... King (M) 691		4.00	8.00	12.00
COME ON AND JOIN .... King (M) 802		3.00	6.00	9.00
FEVER (BROWN COVER) .... King (M) 564		7.00	17.50	28.00
FEVER (BLUE COVER) .... King (M) 564		6.00	12.00	18.00
FREE AT LAST .... King (S) RS 1081		4.50	6.75	9.00
LITTLE WILLIE JOHN SINGS ALL ORIGINALS .... King (M) 949		4.00	6.00	8.00
MISTER LITTLE WILLIE JOHN .... King (M) 603		5.00	10.00	15.00
SURE THINGS .... King (M) 739		5.00	10.00	15.00
SWEET, THE HOT, THE TEEN AGE BEAT, THE .... King (M) 767		4.00	8.00	12.00
TALK TO ME .... King (M) 596		5.00	10.00	15.00
TALK TO ME .... King (EP) EP423		2.00	5.00	8.00
THESE ARE MY FAVORITE SONGS .... King (M) 895		4.00	6.00	8.00

(M) Mono (S) Stereo (EP) Extended Play (Q) Quad (RI) Re-issued

TITLE	LABEL & NO.	GOOD	VERY GOOD	NEAR MINT
LIVELY ONES				
GREAT SURF HITS	Del Fi (M) DFLP 1238	4.00	8.00	12.00
SURF DRUMS	Del Fi (M) DFLP 1231	4.00	6.00	8.00
SURF DRUMS	Del Fi (S) DFST 1231	4.50	6.75	9.00
SURFIN SOUTH OF THE BORDER	Del Fi (M) DFLP 1240	4.00	6.00	8.00
SURFIN SOUTH OF THE BORDER	Del Fi (S) DFST 1240	4.50	6.75	9.00
SURF-RIDER	Del Fi (M) DFLP 1226	4.00	6.00	8.00
SURF-RIDER	Del Fi (S) DFST 1226	4.50	6.75	9.00
THIS IS SURF CITY	Del Fi (M) DFLP 1237	4.00	6.00	8.00
THIS IS SURF CITY	Del Fi (S) DFST 1237	4.50	6.75	9.00
LIVERPOOL BEATS				
NEW MERSEYSIDE SOUND	Rondo (M) 2026	4.00	8.00	12.00
LIVERPOOL FIVE				
ARRIVE	RCA (S) LSP 3583	5.00	7.50	10.00
OUT OF SIGHT	RCA (M) LPM 3682	4.00	8.00	12.00
OUT OF SIGHT	RCA (S) LSP 3682	4.50	9.00	13.50
LIVERPOOL KIDS				
BEATLE MASH	Palace 777	3.50	7.00	10.50
LIVERPOOLS				
BEATLE MANIA IN THE USA	Wyncote (M) 9001	3.00	6.00	9.00
HIT SOUNDS FROM ENGLAND, THE	Wyncote (M) 9061	3.00	6.00	9.00
LIVERPOOL SCENE				
AMAZING ADVENTURES OF THE LIVERPOOL SCENE	RCA (S) LSP 4189	3.50	5.25	7.00
BREAD ON THE NIGHT	RCA (S) LSP 4267	3.50	5.25	7.00
INCREDIBLE NEW LIVERPOOL SCENE	Epic (S) BN 26336	4.00	6.00	8.00
LIVERPOOL STRINGS				
HERMAN'S HERMITS GREATEST HITS	Metro (S) MS 560	2.50	3.75	5.00
LLOYD, Sam				
SAM LLOYD	Charton (M) CHA 2001	3.00	4.50	6.00
LOADING ZONE				
LOADING ZONE, THE	RCA (S) LSP 3959	4.00	6.00	8.00
ONE FOR ALL	Umbrella (M) US 101	6.00	9.00	12.00
LOBO				
BEST OF LOBO	Big Tree (S) 89513	3.00	4.50	6.00
INTRODUCING LOBO	Big Tree (S) 2003	4.00	6.00	8.00
JUST A SINGER	Big Tree (S) 89501	3.00	4.50	6.00
OF A SIMPLE MAN	Big Tree (S) 2013	3.50	5.25	7.00
LOCKLIN, Hank				
BEST OF HANK LOCKLIN	King (M) 672	2.50	3.75	5.00
ENCORES OF HANK LOCKLIN	King (M) 738	2.50	3.75	5.00
FOREIGN LOVE	RCA (M) LPM 1673	2.00	3.00	4.00
FOREIGN LOVE	RCA (EP) EPA 4221	1.50	2.25	3.00
HANK LOCKLIN	RCA (EP) EPA-5096	1.00	1.50	2.00
HAPPY JOURNEY	RCA (M) LPM-2464	2.00	3.00	4.00
HAPPY JOURNEY	RCA (S) LSP-2464	2.00	3.00	4.00
MAYOR OF MCLELLAN	RCA (S) LSP 4800	2.00	3.00	4.00
PLEASE HELP ME, I'M FALLING	RCA (M) LPM-2291	2.00	3.00	4.00
PLEASE HELP ME, I'M FALLING	RCA (S) LSP-2291	2.00	3.00	4.00
PLEASE HELP ME, I'M FALLING	RCA (EP) EPA-4366	1.50	2.25	3.00
WAYS OF LIFE	RCA (M) LPM-2680	2.00	3.00	4.00
WAYS OF LIFE	RCA (S) LSP-2680	2.00	3.00	4.00
LOCKWOOD, Robert Jr.				
CONTRASTS	Trix (M) TRIX 3307	3.00	4.50	6.00
LOCOMOTIVE				
LOCOMOTIVE	MGM (S) SE 4653	2.50	3.75	5.00
LOFGREN, Nils				
AUTHORIZED BOOTLEG	A & M (S) SP 8362	15.00	22.00	30.00
CRY TOUGH	A&M (S) SP 4573	2.00	3.00	4.00

TITLE	LABEL & NO.	GOOD	VERY GOOD	NEAR MINT
I CAME TO DANCE	A&M (S) SP 4628	2.00	3.00	4.00
NIGHT AFTER NIGHT	A&M (S) SP 3707	2.50	3.75	5.00
NILS LOFGREN	A&M (S) SP 4509	2.00	3.00	4.00
Also see GRIN				
LOGGINS & MESSINA				
BEST OF FRIENDS	Columbia (S) PC 34388	2.50	3.75	5.00
FINALE	Columbia (S) JG-34167	3.00	4.50	6.00
FULL SAIL	Columbia (S) KC-32540	2.50	3.75	5.00
FULL SAIL	Columbia (Q) CQ-32540	2.50	3.75	5.00
KENNY LOGGINS (WITH JIM MESSINA SITTIN' IN)	Columbia (S) C 31044	4.00	6.00	8.00
LOGGINS WITH MESSINA (LISTED AS KENNY LOGGINS & JIM MESSINA)	Columbia (S) KC 31748	4.00	6.00	8.00
LOGGINS AND MESSINA ("LOGGINS WITH MESSINA" re-titled)	Columbia (S) KC 31748	2.50	3.75	5.00
LOGGINS AND MESSINA	Columbia (Q) CQ 31748	2.50	3.75	5.00
MOTHER LODE	Columbia (S) PC 33175	2.50	3.75	5.00
NATIVE SONS	Columbia (Q) PCQ 33578	2.50	3.75	5.00
NATIVE SONS	Columbia (S) PC 33578	2.50	3.75	5.00
ON STAGE	Columbia PG-32848	2.50	3.75	5.00
SITTIN' IN (KENNY LOGGINS" re-titled)	Columbia (S) C 31044	2.50	3.75	5.00
LOGGINS, Dave				
APPRENTICE (IN A MUSICAL WORKSHOP)	Epic (S) KE-32833	2.00	3.00	4.00
LOLITA				
LOLITA-SONGS YOU WILL NEVER FORGET	Kapp (M) KL-1229	2.00	3.00	4.00
LOLITA-SONGS YOU WILL NEVER FORGET	Kapp (S) KS-3229	2.00	3.00	4.00
SAILOR	Kapp (M) KL-1219	3.00	4.50	6.00
SAILOR	Kapp (S) KS-3219	3.00	4.50	6.00
LOLLIPOP SHOPPE				
LOLLIPOP SHOPPE JUST COLOUR, THE	Uni (M) 73019	6.00	9.00	12.00
LOMAX, Jackie				
HOME IS IN MY HEAD	Warner Brothers (S) WS 1914	3.00	4.50	6.00
IS THIS WHAT YOU WANT	Apple (S) ST 3354	6.00	9.00	12.00
THREE	Warner Brothers (S) BS 2591	3.00	4.50	6.00
LONDON, Julie				
ABOUT THE BLUES	Liberty (M) LRP 3043	2.00	4.00	6.00
ABOUT THE BLUES	Liberty (S) LST 7012	2.50	3.75	5.00
AROUND MIDNIGHT	Liberty (M) LRP 3164	2.50	3.75	5.00
AROUND MIDNIGHT	Liberty (S) LST 7164	2.50	3.75	5.00
CALENDAR GIRL	Liberty (M) SL9002	4.00	6.00	8.00
CRY ME A RIVER	Liberty (EP) LSX 1001	1.00	1.50	2.00
END OF THE WORLD	Liberty (M) LRP 3300	2.50	3.75	5.00
END OF THE WORLD	Liberty (S) LST 7300	2.50	3.75	5.00
JULIE	Liberty (M) LRP 3096	2.00	4.00	6.00
JULIE	Liberty (S) LST 7004	2.50	3.75	5.00
JULIE AT HOME	Liberty (M) LRP 3152	2.50	3.75	5.00
JULIE AT HOME	Liberty (S) LST 7152	2.50	3.75	5.00
JULIE HIS HER NAME	Liberty (M) LRP 3006	2.00	4.00	6.00
JULIE HIS HER NAME	Liberty (S) LST 7027	2.50	3.75	5.00
JULIE IS HER NAME, Vol. 2	liberty (M) LRP-3100	2.00	4.00	6.00
JULIE IS HER NAME, Vol. 2	liberty (S) LST-7100	2.00	4.00	6.00
JULIE'S GOLDEN GREATS	Liberty (M) LRP-3291	2.00	3.00	4.00
JULIE'S GOLDEN GREATS	Liberty (S) LST-7291	2.00	3.00	4.00
LONDON BY NIGHT	Liberty (M) LRP 3105	2.50	5.00	7.50
LONELY GIRL	Liberty (M) LRP 3012	2.50	5.00	7.50
MAKE LOVE TO ME	Liberty (M) LRP 3060	2.50	5.00	7.50
SEND FOR ME	Liberty (M) LRP 3171	2.50	3.75	5.00
SEND FOR ME	Liberty (S) LST 7171	2.50	3.75	5.00
SWING ME AN OLD SONG	Liberty (M) LRP 3119	2.00	4.00	6.00
SWING ME AN OLD SONG	Liberty (S) LST 7119	2.00	4.00	6.00
VERY BEST OF JULIE LONDON	United Artists (S) UA-LA437	2.00	3.00	4.00
WHATEVER JULIE WANTS	Liberty (M) LRP 3192	2.50	3.75	5.00
WHATEVER JULIE WANTS	Liberty (S) LST 7192	2.50	3.75	5.00
WONDERFUL WORLD OF JULIE LONDON	Liberty (M) LRP 3324	2.50	3.75	5.00
WONDERFUL WORLD OF JULIE LONDON	Liberty (S) LST 7324	2.50	3.75	5.00
YOUR NUMBER PLEASE	Liberty (M) LRP 3130	2.50	3.75	5.00
YOUR NUMBER PLEASE	Liberty (S) LST 7130	2.50	3.75	5.00
LONDON, Laurie				
LAURIE LONDON	Capitol (M) T 10169	2.50	6.25	10.00

(M) Mono (S) Stereo (EP) Extended Play (Q) Quad (RI) Re-issued

TITLE	LABEL & NO.	GOOD	VERY GOOD	NEAR MINT
LAURIE LONDON	Capitol (EP) EAP 1-10182	1.50	2.25	3.00
LAURIE LONDON SINGS	Capitol (EP) EAP 1-10191	1.50	2.25	3.00
ADVENTURES OF THE LONE RANGER	Decca (M) DL 8578	4.00	6.00	8.00

LONESOME SUNDOWN
LONESOME SUNDOWN	Excello (M) 8012	5.00	7.50	10.00

LONG, Shorty
PRIME OF SHORTY LONG, THE	Soul (M) SS 719	4.00	8.00	12.00

LONGET, Claudine
COLOURS	A & M (S) 4163	2.50	3.75	5.00
LET'S SPEND THE NIGHT TOGETHER	Barnaby (S) 15001	2.00	3.00	4.00
LOVE IS BLUE	A & M (S) 4142	2.00	3.00	4.00

LOOKING GLASS
SUBWAY SERENADE	Epic (S) KE-32167	3.00	4.50	6.00

LOPEZ, Trini
MORE OF TRINI LOPEZ	King (M) 877	2.00	3.00	4.00
MORE TRINI LOPEZ AT PJ'S	Reprise (M) R-6103	2.50	3.75	5.00
MORE TRINI LOPEZ AT PJ'S	Reprise (S) R9-6103	2.50	3.75	5.00
TEENAGE IDOL	King (EP) 483	2.00	3.00	4.00
TEENAGE LOVE SONGS	King (M) 863	2.00	3.00	4.00
TRINI	Reprise (M) R-6196	2.00	3.00	4.00
TRINI	Reprise (S) RS-6196	2.00	3.00	4.00
TRINI LOPEZ AT PJ'S	Reprise (M) R-6093	2.50	3.75	5.00
TRINI LOPEZ AT PJ'S	Reprise (S) R9-6093	2.50	3.75	5.00
TRINI LOPEZ GREATEST HITS	Reprise (M) 6226	2.50	3.75	5.00
TRINI LOPEZ GREATEST HITS	Reprise (S) 6226	2.50	3.75	5.00

LORD SITAR
LORD SITAR	Capitol (M) ST 3916	10.00	20.00	30.00

LORD SUTCH
HANDS OF JACK THE RIPPER	Cotillion (S) SD 9049	4.00	6.00	8.00
LORD SUTCH AND HIS HEAVY FRIENDS	Cotillion (S) SD 9015	4.00	6.00	8.00

LOREN, Donna
BEACH BLANKET BINGO	Capitol (M) ST 2323	3.00	6.00	9.00

LOS BRAVOS
BLACK IS BLACK	Press (M) PR73003	5.00	7.50	10.00
BLACK IS BLACK	Press (S) PRS 83003	6.00	9.00	12.00
BRING A LITTLE LOVIN	Parrot (M) PAS 71021	5.00	7.50	10.00

LOS INDIOS TABAJARAS
ALWAYS IN MY HEART	RCA (M) LPM-2912	2.00	3.00	4.00
ALWAYS IN MY HEART	RCA (S) LSP 2912	3.00	4.50	6.00
MARIA ELENA	RCA (M) LPM-2822	2.00	3.00	4.00
MARIA ELENA	RCA (S) LSP-2822	3.00	4.50	6.00
MELLOW GUITAR MOODS	RCA (M) LPM 2959	2.00	3.00	4.00
MELLOW GUITAR MOODS	RCA (S) LSP 2959	3.00	4.50	6.00

LOST AND FOUND
FOREVER LASTING PLASTIC WORDS	International Artists (M) IA LP 3	5.00	10.00	15.00

LOST NATION
PARADISE LOST	Rare Earth (M) RS 518	4.00	6.00	8.00

LOTHAR & THE HAND PEOPLE
PRESENTING LOTHAR AND THE HAND PEOPLE	Capitol (M) ST 2997	6.00	9.00	12.00
SPACE HYMN	Capitol (M) ST 247	6.00	9.00	12.00

LOUDERMILK, John D.
COUNTRY LOVE SONGS (PLAIN & SIMPLY SUNG)	RCA (S) LSP-4040	2.00	3.00	4.00
LANGUAGE OF LOVE	RCA (M) LPM-2434	5.00	7.50	10.00
LANGUAGE OF LOVE	RCA (S) LSP-2434	5.50	8.25	11.00
LOUDERMILK, JOHN D	RCA (M) LPM-3497	2.50	3.75	5.00
LOUDERMILK, JOHN D	RCA (S) LSP-3497	2.50	3.75	5.00
TWELVE SIDES OF LOUDERMILK	RCA (M) LPM-2539	3.00	4.50	6.00
TWELVE SIDES OF LOUDERMILK	RCA (S) LSP-2539	3.50	5.25	7.00

LOUIE & THE LOVERS
RISE	Epic (M) E 30026	4.00	6.00	8.00

LOUISIANA RED
LOUISIANA RED SINGS THE BLUES	Atco (M) 389	2.00	3.00	4.00
LOUISIANA RED SINGS THE BLUES	Atco (M) SD 33-389	4.00	8.00	12.00
LOW DOWN BACK PORCH BLUES, THE	Roulette (M) R 25200	5.00	10.00	15.00

LOUIS, Joe Hill
ONE MAN BAND	Muskadine (M) No, 101	5.00	7.50	10.00

LOVE
DA CAPO	Elektra (M) EKL 4005	3.50	5.25	7.00
DA CAPO	Elektra (S) EKS 74005	4.00	6.00	8.00

(M) Mono (S) Stereo (EP) Extended Play (Q) Quad (RI) Re-issued

TITLE	LABEL & NO.	GOOD	VERY GOOD	NEAR MINT
FALSE START	Blue Thumb (S) BTS 8822	4.00	6.00	8.00
FOREVER CHANGES	Elektra (M) EKL 4013	3.50	5.25	7.00
FOREVER CHANGES	Elektra (S) EKS 74013	4.00	6.00	8.00
FOUR SAIL	Elektra (S) EKS 74049	4.00	6.00	8.00
LOVE	Elektra (M) EKL 4001	3.50	5.25	7.00
LOVE	Elektra (S) EKS 74001	4.00	6.00	8.00
OUT THERE	Blue Thumb BTS 9000	4.50	6.75	9.00
REEL TO REAL	RSO (S) 4804	4.00	6.00	8.00
REVISITED	Elektra (S) EKS 74058	4.00	6.00	8.00

LOVE EXCHANGE
LOVE EXCHANGE	Tower (M) T 5115	3.00	4.50	6.00

LOVE, Hot Shot
HOT SHOT BOOGIE	Bo Weevil (EP) 1	2.00	4.00	6.00

LOVELITES
LOVELITES, THE	Uni (M) 73081	4.00	6.00	8.00

LOVE, Preston
OMAHA BAR B-Q	Kent (S) KST540	3.00	4.50	6.00

LOVE SCULPTURE
BLUES HELPING	Rare Earth (M) RS 505	6.00	9.00	12.00
FORMS AND FEELINGS	Parrot (S) PAS 71035	5.00	7.50	10.00

LOVE UNLIMITED
HE'S ALL I'VE GOT	Unlimited Gold (S) U 101	2.50	3.75	5.00
IN HEAT	20th Century (S) 443	2.50	3.75	5.00
LOVE UNLIMITED	UNI (S) 73131	3.00	4.50	6.00
UNDER THE INFLUENCE OF LOVE UNLIMITED	20th Century (S) T 414	2.00	3.00	4.00

LOVE UNLIMITED ORCHESTRA
MY SWEET SUMMER SUITE	20th Century (S) T 517	2.50	3.75	5.00
RHAPSODY IN WHITE	20th Century (S) T 433	2.50	3.75	5.00
WHITE GOLD	20th Century (S) T 458	2.50	3.75	5.00

LOVIN' SPOONFUL
BEST OF THE LOVIN' SPOONFUL	Kama Sutra (S) 2608-2	3.00	4.50	6.00
BEST OF THE LOVIN' SPOONFUL	Kama Sutra (S) KLPS 8056	4.00	6.00	8.00
BEST OF THE LOVIN' SPOONFUL VOL. 2	Kama Sutra (S) KLPS 8064	3.00	4.50	6.00
DAYDREAM	Kama Sutra (M) KLP 8051	3.50	5.25	7.00
DAYDREAM	Kama Sutra (S) KLPS 8051	4.00	6.00	8.00
DO YOU BELIEVE IN MAGIC	Kama Sutra (M) KLP 8050	3.50	5.25	7.00
DO YOU BELIEVE IN MAGIC	Kama Sutra (S) KLPS 8050	4.00	6.00	8.00
EVERYTHING PLAYING	Kama Sutra (S) KLPS 8061	3.50	5.25	7.00
HUMS OF THE LOVIN' SPOONFUL	Kama Sutra (M) KLP 8054	3.50	5.25	7.00
HUMS OF THE LOVIN' SPOONFUL	Kama Sutra (S) KLPS 8054	4.00	6.00	8.00
REVELATION REVOLUTION '69 (Featuring Joe Butler)	Kama Sutra (S) KLPS 8073	3.00	4.50	6.00

LOWE, Jim
DOOR OF FAME	Mercury (M) MG 20246	2.00	4.00	6.00
RAINBOW	Dot (EP) DEP 1061	1.00	1.50	2.00
SONGS THEY SING BEHIND THE GREEN DOOR	Dot (M) DLP 3051	5.00	10.00	15.00
SONGS THEY SANG BEHIND THE GREEN DOOR	Dot (M) DLP-3681	3.00	4.50	6.00
SONGS THEY SANG BEHIND THE GREEN DOOR	Dot (S) DLP-25681	3.00	4.50	6.00
WICKED WOMEN	Dot (M) DLP 3114	3.50	5.25	7.00

LOWERY, Fred
WALKING ALONG KICKING THE LEAVES	Decca (M) DL 8476	5.00	7.50	10.00

(Fred Lowery, blind since the age of two, is considered by many to be the world's finest whistler of popular songs.)

L.T.D.
GITTIN' DOWN	A & M (S) SP 3660	2.00	3.00	4.00
LOVE, TOGETHERNESS AND DEVOTION	A & M (S) SP 3602	2.00	3.00	4.00

LUCEY, Chris
SONG OF PROTEST AND ANTI PROTEST	Surrey (S) SS 1027	5.00	7.50	10.00

LUCIFER'S FRIEND
I'M JUST A ROCK & ROLL SINGER	Billingsgate (M) 1008	2.50	3.75	5.00
LUCIFER'S FRIEND	Billingsgate (M) 1002	2.50	3.75	5.00

LUKE, Robin

TITLE	LABEL & NO.	GOOD	VERY GOOD	NEAR MINT
SUSIE DARLIN	Dot (EP) DEP-1092	3.00	6.00	9.00

LULU

TITLE	LABEL & NO.	GOOD	VERY GOOD	NEAR MINT
FROM LULU WITH LOVE	Parrot (M) PA 61016	5.00	7.50	10.00
FROM LULU WITH LOVE	Parrot (S) PAS 71016	4.50	6.75	9.00
IT'S LULU	Epic (S) BN 26536	3.00	4.50	6.00
LULU	Chelsea (S) BCL1-0144	6.00	9.00	12.00
LULU	Pickwick (S) SPC 3237	4.50	6.75	9.00
MELODY FAIR	Atco (S) SD 33-330	3.00	4.50	6.00
NEW ROUTES	Atco (S) SD 33-310	3.00	4.50	6.00
TO LOVE SOMEBODY	Harmony (M) H 30249	2.50	3.75	5.00

LUMAN, Bob

TITLE	LABEL & NO.	GOOD	VERY GOOD	NEAR MINT
BOB LUMAN'S GREATEST HITS	Epic (S) KE-32759	2.00	3.00	4.00
LET'S THINK ABOUT LIVING	Warner Brothers (M) W-1396	3.00	4.50	6.00
LET'S THINK ABOUT LIVING	Warner Brothers (S) WS-1396	3.50	5.25	7.00
LET'S THINK ABOUT LIVING	Warner Brothers (EP) E-1396	1.50	2.25	3.00
LONELY WOMEN MAKE GOOD LOVERS	Epic (S) KE-31746	2.00	3.00	4.00
NEITHER ONE OF US	Epic (S) KE-32192	2.00	3.00	4.00
RED CADILLAC & BLACK MUSTACHE	Epic (S) KE-33177	2.00	3.00	4.00
STILL LOVING YOU	Hickory (S) 4508	2.00	3.00	4.00
WHEN YOU SAY LOVE/ LONELY WOMEN MAKE GOOD LOVERS	Epic (S) BG-33755	2.00	3.00	4.00

LUNDBERG, Victor

TITLE	LABEL & NO.	GOOD	VERY GOOD	NEAR MINT
OPEN LETTER (TO MY TEENAGE SON)	Liberty (S) LST 7547	3.00	4.50	6.00

LYMON, Frankie

TITLE	LABEL & NO.	GOOD	VERY GOOD	NEAR MINT
FRANKIE LYMON AT THE LONDON PALLADIUM	Roulette (M) R 25013	5.00	10.00	15.00
FRANKIE LYMON AT THE LONDON PALLADIUM	Roulette (EP) EPR 1 304	3.00	6.00	9.00
JERRY BLAVAT PRESENTS FRANKIE LYMON'S GREATEST HITS	Roulette (M) R 25250	5.00	10.00	15.00
ROCK AND ROLL	Roulette (M) R 25036	6.00	12.00	18.00

LYNN, Barbara

TITLE	LABEL & NO.	GOOD	VERY GOOD	NEAR MINT
HERE IS BARBARA LYNN	Atlantic (S) SD 8171	3.50	5.25	7.00
YOU'LL LOSE A GOOD THING	Jamie (M) JLP 70-3023	4.50	6.75	9.00

LYNN, Donna

TITLE	LABEL & NO.	GOOD	VERY GOOD	NEAR MINT
JAVA JONES	Capitol (M) T-2085	3.00	6.00	9.00
JAVA JONES	Capitol (S) ST-2085	4.00	8.00	12.00

LYNN, Loretta

TITLE	LABEL & NO.	GOOD	VERY GOOD	NEAR MINT
BACK TO THE COUNTRY	MCA (S) 471	2.00	3.00	4.00
BEFORE I'M OVER YOU	Decca (M) DL-4541	3.50	5.25	7.00
BEFORE I'M OVER YOU	Decca (S) DL7-4541	3.50	5.25	7.00
BEFORE I'M OVER YOU	Decca (EP) ED-2784	1.00	1.50	2.00
BLUE KENTUCKY GIRL	Decca (M) DL-4665	2.50	3.75	5.00
BLUE KENTUCKY GIRL	Decca (S) DL7-4665	2.50	3.75	5.00
COAL MINER'S DAUGHTER	Decca (S) DL 75253	2.50	3.75	5.00
COUNTRY CHRISTMAS	Decca (M) DL 4817	2.50	3.75	5.00
COUNTRY CHRISTMAS	Decca (S) DL7-4817	2.50	3.75	5.00
DON'T COME HOME A DRINKIN'	Decca (M) DL 4842	2.50	3.75	5.00
DON'T COME HOME A DRINKIN'	Decca (S) DL 74842	2.50	3.75	5.00
ENTERTAINER OF THE YEAR-LORETTA	MCA (S) 300	2.00	3.00	4.00
FEELINS'	MCA (S) 2143	2.00	3.00	4.00
HERE I AM AGAIN	Decca (S) DL 75381	2.50	3.75	5.00
HOME	MCA (S) 2146	2.00	3.00	4.00
I LIKE 'EM COUNTRY	Decca (M) DL 4744	2.50	3.75	5.00
I LIKE 'EM COUNTRY	Decca (S) DL7-4744	2.50	3.75	5.00
I WANNA BE FREE	Decca (S) DL 75282	2.50	3.75	5.00
LORETTA LYNN'S GREATEST HITS, VOL. 2	MCA (S) 420	2.00	3.00	4.00
LORETTA LYNN SINGS	Decca (M) DL-4457	3.50	5.25	7.00
LORETTA LYNN SINGS	Decca (S) DL7-4457	3.50	5.25	7.00
LOVE IS THE FOUNDATION	MCA (S) 355	2.00	3.00	4.00
ONE'S ON THE WAY	Decca (S) DL 75334	2.50	3.75	5.00
SONGS FROM MY HEART	Decca (M) DL-4620	2.50	3.75	5.00
SONGS FROM MY HEART	Decca (S) DL7-4620	2.50	3.75	5.00
SONGS FROM MY HEART	Decca (EP) ED-2800	1.00	1.50	2.00
WINGS UPON YOUR HORNS	Decca (S) DL 75163	2.50	3.75	5.00
WOMAN OF THE WORLD/TO MAKE A MAN	Decca (S) DL 75113	2.50	3.75	5.00
YOU AIN'T WOMAN ENOUGH	Decca (M) DL 4783	2.50	3.75	5.00
YOU AIN'T WOMAN ENOUGH	Decca (S) DL7-4783	2.50	3.75	5.00
YOUR SQUAW IS ON THE WARPATH	Decca (S) DL 75084	2.50	3.75	5.00

Also see TWITTY, CONWAY & LORETTA LYNN

LYNN, Tami

TITLE	LABEL & NO.	GOOD	VERY GOOD	NEAR MINT
LOVE IS HERE AND NOW YOU'RE GONE	Cotillion (S) SD 9052	3.00	4.50	6.00

LYNN, Vera

TITLE	LABEL & NO.	GOOD	VERY GOOD	NEAR MINT
VERA LYNN GOLDEN HITS	London (M) LL-3294	3.00	4.50	6.00
VERA LYNN SINGS SONGS OF THE 20's	London (M) PS-156	2.00	4.00	6.00

LYNYRD SKYNYRD

TITLE	LABEL & NO.	GOOD	VERY GOOD	NEAR MINT
GIMME BACK MY BULLETS	MCA (S) 2170	2.50	3.75	5.00
NUTHIN' FANCY	MCA (S) 2137	2.50	3.75	5.00
PRONOUNCED LEH-NERD SKIN-NERD	MCA/Sounds of the South (S) 363	3.50	5.25	7.00
SECOND HELPING	MCA/Sounds of the South (S) 413	3.50	5.25	7.00
STREET SURVIVORS	MCA (S) 3029	2.50	3.75	5.00

(M) Mono (S) Stereo (EP) Extended Play (Q) Quad (RI) Re-issued

M

TITLE	LABEL & NO.	GOOD	VERY GOOD	NEAR MINT

MABON, Willie

TITLE	LABEL & NO.	GOOD	VERY GOOD	NEAR MINT
WILLIE MABON	Chess (M) LP 1439	6.00	12.00	18.00

MacGREGOR, Byron

TITLE	LABEL & NO.	GOOD	VERY GOOD	NEAR MINT
AMERICANS, THE	Westbound (S) 1000	4.00	6.00	8.00

MACKAY, Bruce

TITLE	LABEL & NO.	GOOD	VERY GOOD	NEAR MINT
BRUCE MACKAY	ORO (M) 1	4.50	6.75	9.00

MACKAY, Rabbit and The Somis Rhythm Band

TITLE	LABEL & NO.	GOOD	VERY GOOD	NEAR MINT
BUG CLOTH	Uni (M) 73026	3.50	5.25	7.00
PASSING THROUGH	Uni (M) 73064	3.50	5.25	7.00

MACK, Lonnie

TITLE	LABEL & NO.	GOOD	VERY GOOD	NEAR MINT
HILLS OF INDIANA, THE	Elektra (S) EKS 74012	3.00	4.50	6.00
WHATEVER'S RIGHT	Elektra (S) EKS 74050	3.00	4.50	6.00
WHAT OF THAT MEMPHIS MAN, THE	Fraternity (M) SF 1014	3.00	6.00	9.00
WHAT OF THAT MEMPHIS MAN, THE (Reissue)	Fraternity (S) SF 1014	2.50	3.75	5.00

MACK, Lonnie/Rusty York

TITLE	LABEL & NO.	GOOD	VERY GOOD	NEAR MINT
DUELING BANJOS	QCA (S) 304	2.50	3.75	5.00

MAD DOG

TITLE	LABEL & NO.	GOOD	VERY GOOD	NEAR MINT
MAD DOG	Fish Head (S) 7701	3.00	4.50	6.00

MAD LADS

TITLE	LABEL & NO.	GOOD	VERY GOOD	NEAR MINT
A NEW BEGINNING	Volt (S) VOS 6020	3.50	5.25	7.00
MAD MAD MAD MAD MAD LADS, THE	Volt (S) VOS 6005	3.50	5.25	7.00
MEMPHIS GOLD	Stax (M) 710	3.00	4.50	6.00
MEMPHIS GOLD	Stax (S) 710	3.50	5.25	7.00

MAD RIVER

TITLE	LABEL & NO.	GOOD	VERY GOOD	NEAR MINT
MAD RIVER	Wee (EP) AEP-10021	4.00	8.00	12.00

MAESTRO, Johnny

TITLE	LABEL & NO.	GOOD	VERY GOOD	NEAR MINT
JOHNNY MAESTRO STORY, THE	Buddah (S) BDS 5091	2.50	3.75	5.00

Also see "CRESTS"

MAGIC LANTERNS

TITLE	LABEL & NO.	GOOD	VERY GOOD	NEAR MINT
HAYMARKET SQUARE	Chaparral (M) CRM-201	8.00	12.00	16.00
SHAME SHAME	Atlantic (M) SD 8217	3.00	4.50	6.00

MAGIC SAM

TITLE	LABEL & NO.	GOOD	VERY GOOD	NEAR MINT
BLUES MASTERS VOL. 3	Blue Horizon (M) BM 4603	4.50	6.75	9.00

MAGMA

TITLE	LABEL & NO.	GOOD	VERY GOOD	NEAR MINT
MAGMA	Polydor	15.00	22.50	30.00

MAGNIFICENT MEN

TITLE	LABEL & NO.	GOOD	VERY GOOD	NEAR MINT
"LIVE!"	Capitol (S) ST 2775	2.50	3.75	5.00
WORLD OF SOUL	Capitol (S) ST-2846	2.50	3.75	5.00

MAHARIS, George

TITLE	LABEL & NO.	GOOD	VERY GOOD	NEAR MINT
GEORGE MAHARIS SINGS	Epic (M) LN-24001	2.50	3.75	5.00
GEORGE MAHARIS SINGS	Epic (S) BN-26001	2.50	3.75	5.00

MAHOGANY RUSH

TITLE	LABEL & NO.	GOOD	VERY GOOD	NEAR MINT
CHILD OF THE NOVELTY	20th Century (S) T 451	2.50	3.75	5.00
MAXOOM	20th Century (S) T 463	2.50	3.75	5.00
STRANGE UNIVERSE	20th Century (S) T 482	2.50	3.75	5.00

MAILER MACKENZIE BAND

TITLE	LABEL & NO.	GOOD	VERY GOOD	NEAR MINT
MAILER MACKENZIE BAND	Ampex (M) A-10114	4.00	6.00	8.00

MAJIC SHIP

TITLE	LABEL & NO.	GOOD	VERY GOOD	NEAR MINT
MAJIC SHIP	Bel Ami (M) BA 711	8.00	16.00	24.00

MAJORS

TITLE	LABEL & NO.	GOOD	VERY GOOD	NEAR MINT
MEET THE MAJORS	Imperial (M) 9222	3.00	6.00	9.00
MEET THE MAJORS	Imperial (S) 12222	4.00	8.00	12.00

MALCOLM X

TITLE	LABEL & NO.	GOOD	VERY GOOD	NEAR MINT
MALCOLM X TALKS TO YOUNG PEOPLE	Douglas (S) 795	4.00	6.00	8.00

MAMA'S AND THE PAPA'S

TITLE	LABEL & NO.	GOOD	VERY GOOD	NEAR MINT
A GATHERING OF FLOWERS	Dunhill (S) DSY 50073	4.00	6.00	8.00
CASS, JOHN, MICHELLE, DENNIE	Dunhill (M) D 50010	2.50	3.75	5.00

TITLE	LABEL & NO.	GOOD	VERY GOOD	NEAR MINT
CASS, JOHN, MICHELLE, DENNIE	Dunhill (S) DS 50010	3.00	4.50	6.00
DELIVER	Dunhill (M) D 50014	2.50	3.75	5.00
DELIVER	Dunhill (S) DS 50014	3.00	4.50	6.00
FAREWELL TO THE FIRST GOLDEN ERA	Dunhill (S) DS 50025	3.00	4.50	6.00
GOLDEN ERA VOL. 2	Dunhill (S) DS 50038	3.00	4.50	6.00
IF YOU CAN BELIEVE YOUR EYES AND EARS	Dunhill (M) D 50006	2.50	3.75	5.00
IF YOU CAN BELIEVE YOUR EYES AND EARS	Dunhill (S) DS 50006	3.00	4.50	6.00
PAPA'S AND THE MAMA'S, THE	Dunhill (S) DS 50031	3.00	4.50	6.00
PEOPLE LIKE US	Dunhill (S) DSX 50106	2.50	3.75	5.00
16 OF THEIR GREATEST HITS	Dunhill (S) 50064	2.25	3.75	5.00
20 GOLDEN HITS	Dunhill (S) DSX 50145	2.50	3.75	5.00

MAN

MAN	Columbia (S) CS 9803	3.00	4.50	6.00
RHINOS, WINOS & LUNATICS	United Artists (S) UA-LA247	2.50	3.75	5.00
SLOW MOTION	United Artists (S) UA-LA345	2.50	3.75	5.00

MANCHESTER, Melissa

HOME TO MYSELF	Bell (S) 1123	3.00	4.50	6.00
MELISSA	Arista (S) 4031	2.50	3.75	5.00

MANCHESTERS

BEATLERAMA VOL. 2	Diplomat (M) 2310	4.00	8.00	12.00

MANCINI, Henry

BLUES & THE BEAT	RCA (M) LPM-2147	2.00	4.00	6.00
BLUES & THE BEAT	RCA (S) LSP-2147	2.50	5.00	7.50
COUNTRY GENTLEMAN	RCA (S) APL1-0270	2.00	3.00	4.00
COUNTRY GENTLEMAN	RCA (Q) APD1-0270	2.00	3.00	4.00
DEAR HEART	RCA (M) LPM 2990	2.50	3.75	5.00
DEAR HEART	RCA (S) LPS 2990	3.00	4.50	6.00
HANGIN' OUT WITH HENRY MANCINI	RCA (S) CPL1-0672	2.00	3.00	4.00
MANCINI TOUCH	RCA (EP) EPA-4351	2.00	3.00	4.00
MANCINI TOUCH	RCA (M) LPM-2101	2.00	4.00	6.00
MANCINI TOUCH	RCA (S) LSP-2101	2.50	5.00	7.50
MANCINI SALUTES SOUSA	RCA (Q) APD1-0013	2.00	3.00	4.00
MARCH STEP IN STEREO & HI FI	Warner Bros. (M) W-1312	3.00	6.00	9.00
MARCH STEP IN STEREO & HI FI	Warner Bros. (S) WS-1312	4.00	8.00	12.00
MORE MUSIC FROM "PETER GUNN"	RCA (M) LPM 2040	2.50	5.00	7.50
MORE MUSIC FROM "PETER GUNN"	RCA (S) LPS 2040	3.00	6.00	9.00
MORE MUSIC FROM "PETER GUNN"	RCA (EP) EPA 4339	2.00	3.00	4.00
MORE MUSIC FROM "PETER GUNN"	RCA (SEP) ESP 4339	2.50	3.75	5.00
MUSIC FROM MR. LUCKY	RCA (M) LPM-2198	2.50	5.00	7.50
MUSIC FROM MR. LUCKY	RCA (S) LSP-2198	3.00	6.00	9.00
MUSIC FROM MR. LUCKY	RCA (EP) EPA-4363	2.00	3.00	4.00
MUSIC FROM "PETER GUNN"	RCA (M) LPM 1956	2.50	5.00	7.50
MUSIC FROM "PETER GUNN"	RCA (S) LPS 1956	3.00	6.00	9.00
SYMPHONIC SOUL	RCA (S) APL1-1025	2.50	3.75	5.00
SYMPHONIC SOUL	RCA (Q) APD1-1025	2.50	3.75	5.00
UNIQUELY MANCINI	RCA (M) LPM 2692	2.50	3.75	5.00
UNIQUELY MANCINI	RCA (S) LPS 2692	3.00	4.50	6.00
VERSATILE HENRY MANCINI	Liberty (M) LRP 3121	3.00	4.50	6.00
VERSATILE HENRY MANCINI	Liberty (S) LST 7121	3.50	5.25	7.00

MANDO & THE CHILI PEPPERS

ON THE ROAD WITH ROCK & ROLL	Golden Crest (M) 3023	6.00	12.00	18.00

MANDRAKE MEMORIAL

MANDRAKE MEMORIAL	Poppy (M) PYS 40,002	5.00	7.50	10.00
MEDIUM	Poppy (M) PYS 40,003	5.00	7.50	10.00
PUZZLE	Poppy (M) PYS 40,006	4.00	6.00	8.00

MANFRED MANN

FIVE FACES OF MANFRED MANN, THE	Ascot (M) ALM 13018	4.00	6.00	8.00
FIVE FACES OF MANFRED MANN, THE	Ascot (S) ALS 16018	4.50	6.75	9.00
MANFRED MANN ALBUM, THE	Ascot (M) ALM 13015	4.00	6.00	8.00
MANFRED MANN ALBUM, THE	Ascot (S) ALS 16015	4.50	6.75	9.00
MANFRED MANN'S CHAPTER 3	Polydor (M) 24-4013	4.00	6.00	8.00
MANFRED MANN'S GREATEST HITS	United Artists (M) UAL 3551	4.00	6.00	8.00
MANFRED MANN'S GREATEST HITS	United Artists (S) UAS 6551	4.50	6.75	9.00
MANN MADE	Ascot (M) ALM 13024	4.00	6.00	8.00

TITLE	LABEL & NO.	GOOD	VERY GOOD	NEAR MINT
MANN MADE	Ascot (S) ALS 16024	4.50	6.75	9.00
MIGHTY QUINN, THE	Mercury (M) SR 61168	4.00	6.00	8.00
MY LITTLE RED BOOK OF WINNERS	Ascot (M) ALM 13021	4.00	6.00	8.00
MY LITTLE RED BOOK OF WINNERS	Ascot (S) ALS 16021	4.50	6.75	9.00
PRETTY FLAMINGO	United Artists (M) UAL 3549	4.00	6.00	8.00
PRETTY FLAMINGO	United Artists (S) UAS 6549	4.50	6.75	9.00

MANHATTANS

DEDICATED TO YOU	Carnival (M) CMLP 201	4.00	8.00	12.00
DEDICATED TO YOU	Carnival (S) CLPS 201	4.50	9.00	13.50
FOR YOU AND YOURS	Carnival (M) CMLP 202	4.00	8.00	12.00
FOR YOU AND YOURS	Carnival (S) CLPS 202	4.50	9.00	13.50
MILLION TO ONE	Deluxe (S) 12004	5.00	10.00	15.00
THAT'S HOW MUCH I LOVE YOU	Columbia (S) KC-33064	2.50	3.75	5.00
THERE'S NO ME WITHOUT YOU	Columbia (S) KC-32444	2.50	3.75	5.00
WITH THESE HANDS	Deluxe (M) 12000	5.00	10.00	15.00

MANHATTAN TRANSFER

JUKIN' (WITH GENE PISTILLI)	Capitol (S) ST-11405	2.50	3.75	5.00

MANILOW, Barry

BARRY MANILOW	Bell (S) 1129	4.50	6.75	9.00
BARRY MANILOW I	Arista (S) AL 4007	2.50	3.75	5.00
BARRY MANILOW 2	Bell (S) 1314	4.00	6.00	8.00
BARRY MANILOW 2	Arista (S) AL 4016	2.50	3.75	5.00
BARRY MANILOW 2	Arista (Q) AQ 4016	2.50	3.75	5.00
EVEN NOW	Arista (S) AB 4164	2.00	3.00	4.00
LIVE	Arista (S) AL 8500	3.50	5.25	7.00
THIS ONE'S FOR YOU	Arista (S) AB 4090	2.50	3.75	5.00
TRYIN' TO GET THE FEELIN'	Arista (S) AL 4060	2.50	3.75	5.00
TRYIN' TO GET THE FEELIN'	Arista (Q) AQ 4060	2.50	3.75	5.00

MANN, Barry

LAY IT ALL OUT	New Design (S) Z30876	4.00	6.00	8.00
SURVIVOR	RCA (S) APL1 0860	2.50	3.75	5.00
WHO PUT THE BOMP (IN THE BOMP)	ABC/Paramount (M) ABC 399	6.00	12.00	18.00
WHO PUT THE BOMP (IN THE BOMP)	ABC/Paramount (S) ABCS 399	7.00	14.00	21.00

MANN, Carl

LIKE, MANN	Phillips (M) PLP 1960	7.50	18.75	30.00

MANNING, Terry

HOME SWEET HOME	Enterprise (S) ENS 1008	3.50	5.25	7.00

MANN, Johnny Singers

BALLADS OF THE KING (ELVIS PRESLEY)	Liberty (M) LRP-3198	3.00	4.50	6.00
BALLADS OF THE KING (ELVIS PRESLEY)	Liberty (S) LST-7198	4.00	6.00	8.00
BEATLE BALLADS	Liberty (M) LRP-3391	2.50	3.75	5.00
BEATLE BALLADS	Liberty (S) LST-7391	2.50	3.75	5.00
SONGS OF SINATRA	Liberty (M) LRP-3217	2.00	3.00	4.00
SONGS OF SINATRA	Liberty (S) LST-7217	2.00	3.00	4.00

MANN, Steve

STRAIGHT LIFE	Custom Fidelity (S) CFS 1675	4.00	6.00	8.00

MANSON, Charles

LIE	Awareness (M) B 22145	7.00	10.50	14.00

MANTLE, Mickey

MICKEY MANTLE FAVORITE HITS	RCA (M) LPM 1704	2.50	3.75	5.00

MARATHONS

PEANUT BUTTER	Arvee (M) A 428	5.00	10.00	15.00

MARBLES

MARBLES, THE	Cotillion (S) SD 9029	3.50	5.25	7.00

MARCELS

BLUE MOON	Colpix (M) CP-416	9.00	14.00	18.00

MARCHAN, Bobby

THERE'S SOMETHING ON YOUR MIND	Sphere Sound (M) SSR 7004	5.00	10.00	15.00

MARCH, Little Peggy

I WILL FOLLOW HIM	RCA (M) LPM 2732	2.50	5.00	7.50
I WILL FOLLOW HIM	RCA (S) LSP 2732	3.00	6.00	9.00
I WISH I WERE A PRINCESS	RCA (EP) EPA-4376	2.00	3.00	4.00
LITTLE PEGGY MARCH	RCA (M) LPM-129	2.00	4.00	6.00
NO FOOLIN	RCA (M) LPM 3883	2.00	4.00	6.00
NO FOOLIN	RCA (S) LSP 3883	2.50	5.00	7.50

MARESCA, Ernie

SHOUT SHOUT (KNOCK YOURSELF OUT)	Seville (M) SV-77001	4.00	8.00	12.00
SHOUT SHOUT (KNOCK YOURSELF OUT)	Seville (S) 87001	5.00	10.00	15.00

MARIANO & THE UNBELIEVABLES

MARIANO AND THE UNBELIEVABLES	Capitol (M) 2831	3.00	4.50	6.00

(M) Mono   (S) Stereo   (EP) Extended Play   (Q) Quad   (RI) Re-issued

TITLE	LABEL & NO.	GOOD	VERY GOOD	NEAR MINT
MARKETTS				
AM FM/ETC.	Mercury (S) SRM-1-679	2.00	3.00	4.00
OUT OF LIMITS	Warner Brothers (M) W 1537	4.00	6.00	8.00
SUN POWER	World Pacific (M) WP 1870	3.50	5.25	7.00
SUN POWER	World Pacific (S) WPS 21870	4.00	6.00	8.00
SURFERS STOMP	Liberty (M) LRP 3226	4.00	8.00	12.00
TAKE TO WHEELS	Warner Brothers (M) W 1509	4.00	6.00	8.00
MAR-KEYS				
BACK TO BACK	Stax (S) S 720	2.50	3.75	5.00
DAMIFIKNEW	Stax (S) STS 2025	2.50	3.75	5.00
DO THE POP-EYE WITH THE MAR-KEYS	Atlantic (M) 8062	3.50	5.25	7.00
GREAT MEMPHIS SOUND	Stax (M) 707	2.50	3.75	5.00
LAST NIGHT	Atlantic (M) 8055	3.50	5.25	7.00
MEMPHIS EXPERIENCE	Stax (S) STS 2036	2.50	3.75	5.00
MARK IV				
MARK IV	Mercury (S) SRM 1 651	2.50	3.75	5.00
MARKLEY				
MARKLEY	Forward	7.00	10.50	14.00
MARKS, Guy				
LOVING YOU HAS MADE ME BANANAS	ABC (S) 648	2.00	3.00	4.00
MARLEY, Bob & The Wailers				
BURNIN'	Island (S) 9256	2.50	3.75	5.00
(Shown as Wailers only)				
CATCH A FIRE	Island (S) SW-9329	3.00	4.50	6.00
(Shown as Wailers only)				
KAYA	Island (S) ILPS 9517	2.00	3.00	4.00
NATTY DREAD	Island (S) 9281	2.50	3.75	5.00
MARMALADE				
BEST OF MARMALADE	Epic (S) BN 26553	4.00	6.00	8.00
REFLECTIONS OF MY LIFE	London (S) PS 575	4.50	6.75	9.00
MARSHALL TUCKER BAND				
MARSHALL TUCKER BAND	Capricorn (S) 0112	2.50	3.75	5.00
NEW LIFE	Capricorn (S) 0124	2.50	3.75	5.00
SEARCHIN' FOR A RAINBOW	Capricorn (S) 0161	2.00	3.00	4.00
TOGETHER FOREVER	Capricorn (S) 0205	2.00	3.00	4.00
WHERE WE ALL BELONG	Capricorn (S) 2C-0145	3.00	4.50	6.00
MARS, Kenneth				
HENRY THE FIRST	Dunhill (S) D-50191	2.00	3.00	4.00
MARTHA & THE VANDELLAS				
BLACK MAGIC	Gordy (S) GS 958	2.00	3.00	4.00
COME AND GET THESE MEMORIES	Gordy (M) 902	5.00	10.00	15.00
DANCE PARTY	Gordy (M) 915	3.50	5.25	7.00
HEAT WAVE	Gordy (M) 907	4.00	6.00	8.00
LIVE!	Gordy (M) 925	3.00	4.50	6.00
MARTHA AND THE VANDELLAS	Gordy (M) 917	3.50	5.25	7.00
NATURAL RESOURCES	Gordy (S) GS 952	2.00	3.00	4.00
RIDIN HIGH	Gordy (S) 926	3.00	4.50	6.00
SUGAR 'N SPICE	Gordy (S) 944	3.00	4.00	6.00
WATCHOUT	Gordy (M) 920	2.50	3.75	5.00
MARTIN, Bobbi				
DON'T FORGET I STILL LOVE YOU	Coral (M) CRL-57472	2.50	3.75	5.00
DON'T FORGET I STILL LOVE YOU	Coral (S) CRL7-57442	2.50	3.75	5.00
DON'T FORGET I STILL LOVE YOU	Coral (EP) EC-81194	1.50	2.25	3.00
MARTINDALE, Wink				
BIBLE STORY	Dot (M) DLP-3293	2.00	3.00	4.00
BIBLE STORY	Dot (S) DLP-25293	2.00	3.00	4.00
BIG BAD JOHN	Dot (M) DLP-3403	2.00	3.00	4.00
BIG BAD JOHN	Dot (S) DLP-25403	2.00	3.00	4.00
DECK OF CARDS	Dot (M) DLP-3245	2.50	3.75	5.00
DECK OF CARDS	Dot (S) DLP-25245	2.50	3.75	5.00
GIDDY UP GO	Dot (M) DLP 3571	2.50	3.75	5.00
GIDDY UP GO	Dot (S) DLP 25571	2.50	3.75	5.00
MARTIN, Dean				
ARTISTS AND MODELS	Capitol (EP) EAP 1-702	1.00	1.50	2.00
BELLS ARE RINGING	Capitol (M) W-1435	2.00	3.00	4.00
BELLS ARE RINGING	Capitol (S) SW-1435	2.00	3.00	4.00
DEAN MARTIN	Capitol (EP) EAP 1-9123	1.00	1.50	2.00
DEAN MARTIN SINGS	Capitol (M) T 401	4.00	6.00	8.00
DEAN MARTIN SINGS	Capitol (EP) EAP 1-401	1.50	2.25	3.00
DEAN MARTIN SINGS	Capitol (EP) EAP 2-401	1.50	2.25	3.00
DINO	Capitol (M) T-1659	2.00	3.00	4.00
DINO	Capitol (S) ST-1659	2.00	3.00	4.00
HOLLYWOOD OR BUST	Capitol (EP) EAP 1-806	1.00	1.50	2.00
LIVING IT UP	Capitol (EP) EAP 1-533	1.50	2.25	3.00
MEMORIES ARE MADE OF THIS	Capitol (EP) EAP 1-701	1.50	2.25	3.00
PRETTY BABY	Capitol (M) T 849	2.50	3.75	5.00
PRETTY BABY	Capitol (EP) EAP 1-849	1.00	1.50	2.00
PRETTY BABY	Capitol (EP) EAP 2-849	1.00	1.50	2.00
PRETTY BABY	Capitol (EP) EAP 3-849	1.00	1.50	2.00
RETURN TO ME	Capitol (EP) EAP 939	1.00	1.50	2.00

TITLE	LABEL & NO.	GOOD	VERY GOOD	NEAR MINT
SUNNY ITALY	Capitol (EP) EAP 1-481	1.50	2.25	3.00
SWINGIN DOWN YONDER	Capitol (M) T 576	3.00	4.50	6.00
TEN THOUSAND BEDROOMS	Capitol (EP) EAP 1-840	1.00	1.50	2.00
THIS IS MARTIN	Capitol (M) T 1047	2.50	3.75	5.00
THIS TIME I'M SWINGIN'	Capitol (M) T-1442	2.00	3.00	4.00
THIS TIME I'M SWINGIN'	Capitol (S) ST-1442	2.00	3.00	4.00
TO ME	Reprise (S) 2174	2.00	3.00	4.00
VOLARE	Capitol (EP) EAP 1027	1.00	1.50	2.00
WINTER ROMANCE	Capitol (M) T-1285	2.00	3.00	4.00
WINTER ROMANCE	Capitol (S) ST-1285	2.00	3.00	4.00
WINTER ROMANCE	Capitol (EP) EAP 1-1285	1.00	1.50	2.00
WINTER ROMANCE	Capitol (EP) EAP 2-1285	1.00	1.50	2.00
WINTER ROMANCE	Capitol (EP) EAP 3-1285	1.00	1.50	2.00
MARTIN, Dean & Jerry Lewis				
PARDNERS	Capitol (EP) AEP 1-752	2.00	3.00	4.00
MARTIN, Dean & Frank Sinatra				
DEAN MARTIN SINGS-SINATRA CONDUCTS	Capitol (M) T-2297	2.50	3.75	5.00
DEAN MARTIN SINGS-SINATRA CONDUCTS	Capitol (S) ST-2297	2.50	3.75	5.00
MARTIN, George				
BEATLE GIRLS	United Artists (M) UAL 3539	5.00	7.50	10.00
BEATLE GIRLS	United Artists (S) UAS 6539	6.00	9.00	12.00
GEORGE MARTIN	United Artists (M) UAL-3420	2.50	3.75	5.00
GEORGE MARTIN	United Artists (S) UAS-6420	2.50	3.75	5.00
HARD DAY'S NIGHT	United Artists (M) UAL-3383	3.00	4.50	6.00
HARD DAY'S NIGHT	United Artists (S) UAS-6383	4.00	6.00	8.00
OFF THE BEATLE TRACK	United Artists (M) UAL-3377	3.00	4.50	6.00
OFF THE BEATLE TRACK	United Artists (S) UAS-6377	4.00	6.00	8.00
MARTIN, Janis				
JUST SQUEEZE ME	RCA (EP) EPA 4093	5.00	10.00	15.00
MARTINO, Al				
COUNTRY STYLE	Capitol (S) ST-11184	2.00	3.00	4.00
DOOR OF THE SUN	Capitol (S) ST-11366	2.00	3.00	4.00
EXCITING VOICE OF AL MARTINO	Capitol (M) T 1774	2.50	5.00	7.50
EXCITING VOICE OF AL MARTINO	Capitol (S) ST 1774	3.00	6.00	9.00
I LOVE YOU BECAUSE	Capitol (M) T 1914	2.00	4.00	6.00
I LOVE YOU BECAUSE	Capitol (S) ST 1914	2.50	5.00	7.50
I WON'T LAST A DAY WITHOUT YOU	Capitol (S) ST-11302	2.00	3.00	4.00
PAINTED TAINTED ROSE	Capitol (M) T 1975	2.00	4.00	6.00
PAINTED TAINTED ROSE	Capitol (S) ST 1975	2.50	5.00	7.50
SING ALONG WITH AL MARTINO	20th Century Fox (M) FOX-3032	2.50	6.25	10.00
SING ALONG WITH AL MARTINO	20th Century Fox (S) SFX-3032	3.00	7.50	12.00
MARTIN, Trade				
LET ME TOUCH YOU	Buddah (M) BDS 5126	2.00	3.00	4.00
MARVELETTES				
ANTHOLOGY	Motown (M) M7 827	4.00	6.00	8.00
GREATEST HITS	Tamla (M) TM 253	3.00	4.50	6.00
MARVELETTES IN FULL BLOOM	Tamla (S) TS 288	2.50	3.75	5.00
MARVELETTES, THE	Tamla (M) TM 274	3.00	4.50	6.00
MARVELETTES SING, THE	Tamla (M) TM 229	3.50	7.00	10.50
MARVELOUS	Tamla (M) TM 237	3.50	5.25	7.00
ON STAGE	Tamla (M) TM 243	3.50	5.25	7.00
PLAYBOY	Tamla (M) TM 231	3.50	7.00	10.50
RETURN OF THE MARVELETTES	Tamla (S) TS 305	2.50	3.75	5.00
SOPHISTICATED SOUL	Tamla (S) TS 286	2.50	3.75	5.00
MARVIN AND FARRAR				
HANK MARVIN AND JOHN FARRAR	EMI (S) ST 11403	4.00	6.00	8.00
MARVIN, WELCH, AND FARRAR				
MARVIN, WELCH, AND FARRAR	Capitol (S) ST 760	4.00	6.00	8.00
SECOND OPINION	Sire (S) S AS 7403	3.50	5.25	7.00
MARVIN AND JOHNNY				
MARVIN AND JOHNNY	Crown (M) CLP 5381	5.00	12.50	20.00
MARX, Groucho				
EVENING WITH GROUCHO	A & M (S) 3515	2.50	3.75	5.00
HOORAY FOR CAPTAIN SPAULDING	Decca (M) DL 5405	5.00	7.50	10.00
MARX, Harpo				
HARPO BY HARPO	RCA (M) LPM 27	5.00	7.50	10.00
HARPO BY HARPO	RCA (EP) EPA 329	2.00	3.00	4.00
HARPO IN HI FI	Mercury (M) MG 20232	4.00	6.00	8.00
MASHMAKHAN				
FAMILY, THE	Epic (M) E 30813	3.00	4.50	6.00
MASHMAKHAN	Epic (M) E 30235	3.00	4.50	6.00
MASKED MARAUDERS				
MASKED MARAUDERS	Deity/Reprise (M) 6378	5.00	7.50	10.00
MASON, Barbara				
GIVE ME YOUR LOVE	Buddah (S) BDS 5117	2.00	3.00	4.00
IF YOU KNEW HIM LIKE I DO	GNC (M) 2001	3.00	4.50	6.00

(M) Mono (S) Stereo (EP) Extended Play (Q) Quad (RI) Re-issued

LADY LOVE	Buddah (S) BDS 5140	2.00	3.00	4.00
LOVES THE THING	Buddah (S) BDS 5628	2.00	3.00	4.00
OH HOW IT HURTS	Arctic (S) A LPS 1004	3.50	5.25	7.00
TRANSITION	Buddah (S) BDS 5610	2.00	3.00	4.00
YES, I'M READY	Arctic (M) A LPM 1000	3.00	4.50	6.00
YES, I'M READY	Arctic (S) A LPS 1000	3.50	5.25	7.00

MASON, Dave

TITLE	LABEL & NO.	GOOD	VERY GOOD	NEAR MINT
ALONE TOGETHER (Multi colored pressing)	Blue Thumb (S) 8819	6.00	9.00	12.00
BEST OF DAVE MASON	Blue Thumb (S) 6013	3.00	4.50	6.00
DAVE MASON	Columbia (S) PC 33096	2.50	3.75	5.00
DAVE MASON	Columbia (Q) PCQ-33096	2.50	3.75	5.00
DAVE MASON AT HIS VERY BEST	ABC (S) TD-880	2.50	3.75	5.00
DAVE MASON IS ALIVE	Blue Thumb (S) 54	3.50	5.25	7.00

MASON PROFFIT

TITLE	LABEL & NO.	GOOD	VERY GOOD	NEAR MINT
BAREBACK RIDER	Warner Bros. (S) BS-2704	2.50	3.75	5.00
COME & GONE	Warner Bros. (S) 2LS-2746	2.50	3.75	5.00
LAST NIGHT I HAD THE STRANGEST DREAM	Ampex (M) A 10138	3.00	4.50	6.00
MASON PROFFIT	Happy Tiger (M) HT 1009	4.00	6.00	8.00
ROCKFISH CROSSING	Warner Brothers (M) BS2657	2.50	3.75	5.00

MATHIS, Johnny

TITLE	LABEL & NO.	GOOD	VERY GOOD	NEAR MINT
BALLADS & RHYTHMS OF BROADWAY	Columbia (M) C2L-17	3.00	4.50	6.00
BALLADS & RHYTHMS OF BROADWAY	Columbia (S) C2S-803	3.50	5.25	7.00
FAITHFULLY	Columbia (M) CL-1422	2.50	3.75	5.00
FAITHFULLY	Columbia (S) CS-8219	3.00	4.50	6.00
FEELINGS	Columbia (S) PC-33887	2.00	3.00	4.00
FLOWER DRUM SONG (HITS)	Columbia (EP) B-2151	1.00	1.50	2.00
HEAVENLY	Columbia (M) CL-1351	2.50	3.75	5.00
HEAVENLY	Columbia (S) CS-8152	3.00	4.50	6.00
HEAVENLY	Columbia (EP) B-13511	1.00	1.50	2.00
HEAVENLY	Columbia (EP) B-13512	1.00	1.50	2.00
HEAVENLY	Columbia (EP) B-13513	1.00	1.50	2.00
HEAVENLY/FAITHFULLY	Columbia (S) CG-33621	2.00	3.00	4.00
I'M COMING HOME	Columbia (Q) CQ-32435	2.00	3.00	4.00
JOHNNY MATHIS	Columbia (EP) B-2640	1.00	1.50	2.00
JOHNNY'S GREATEST HITS	Columbia (S) CL 1133	2.00	3.00	4.00
JOHNNY'S MOOD	Columbia (M) CL-1526	2.50	3.75	5.00
JOHNNY'S MOOD	Columbia (S) CS-8326	3.00	4.50	6.00
JOHNNY'S MOOD	Columbia (EP) B-15261	1.00	1.50	2.00
JOHNNY'S MOOD	Columbia (EP) B-15262	1.00	1.50	2.00
JOHNNY'S MOOD	Columbia (EP) B-1563	1.00	1.50	2.00
KILLING ME SOFTLY WITH HER SONG	Columbia (S) KC-32258	2.00	3.00	4.00
ME & MRS. JONES	Columbia (S) KC-32114	2.00	3.00	4.00
ME & MRS. JONES	Columbia (Q) CQ-32114	2.00	3.00	4.00
MORE JOHNNY'S GREATEST HITS	Columbia (M) CL-1344	2.50	3.75	5.00
MORE JOHNNY'S GREATEST HITS	Columbia (S) CS-8150	3.00	4.50	6.00
OPEN FIRE, TWO GUITARS	Columbia (M) CL-1270	2.50	3.75	5.00
OPEN FIRE, TWO GUITARS	Columbia (S) CS-8056	3.00	4.50	6.00
OPEN FIRE, TWO GUITARS	Columbia (EP) B-12701	1.00	1.50	2.00
OPEN FIRE, TWO GUITARS	Columbia (EP) B-12702	1.00	1.50	2.00
OPEN FIRE, TWO GUITARS	Columbia (EP) B-12703	1.00	1.50	2.00
SONG SUNG BLUE	Columbia (S) KC-31626	2.00	3.00	4.00
SONG SUNG BLUE	Columbia (Q) CQ-31626	2.00	3.00	4.00
SWING SOFTLY	Columbia (M) CL 1165	2.50	3.75	5.00
WARM	Columbia (M) CL 1078	3.00	6.00	9.00
WHAT'LL I DO	Columbia (S) C-32963	2.00	3.00	4.00
WHEN WILL I SEE YOU AGAIN	Columbia (S) PC-33420	2.00	3.00	4.00
WHEN WILL I SEE YOU AGAIN	Columbia (Q) PCQ-33420	2.00	3.00	4.00
WONDERFUL! WONDERFUL!	Columbia (M) CL 1028	3.00	6.00	9.00

MATRIX

TITLE	LABEL & NO.	GOOD	VERY GOOD	NEAR MINT
MATRIX	Rare Earth (S) R 542L	3.00	4.50	6.00

MAUDS

TITLE	LABEL & NO.	GOOD	VERY GOOD	NEAR MINT
HOLD ON	Mercury (M) MG 21135	4.50	6.75	9.00
HOLD ON	Mercury (S) SR 61135	5.00	7.50	10.00

MAXWELL, Diane

TITLE	LABEL & NO.	GOOD	VERY GOOD	NEAR MINT
ALMOST SEVENTEEN	Challenge (M) CHL-607	4.00	8.00	12.00
ALMOST SEVENTEEN	Challenge (S) CHS-2501	5.00	10.00	15.00

MAYALL, John

TITLE	LABEL & NO.	GOOD	VERY GOOD	NEAR MINT
BEST OF JOHN MAYALL	Polydor (S) 2-3006	3.00	4.50	6.00

DOWN THE LINE	London (S) BP-618/9	3.00	4.50	6.00
LATEST EDITION	Polydor (S) 6030	2.50	3.75	5.00
MOVING ON	Polydor (S) 24-5036	2.50	3.75	5.00
10 YEARS ARE GONE	Polydor (S) 2-3005	3.00	4.50	6.00
WITH JOHN LEE HOOKER & THE GROUNDHOGS	Cleve (S) CH-82871	9.00	13.50	18.00

MAYER, Nathaniel

TITLE	LABEL & NO.	GOOD	VERY GOOD	NEAR MINT
GOING BACK TO THE VILLAGE OF LOVE	Fortune (M) 8014	5.00	10.00	15.00

MAYFIELD, Curtis

TITLE	LABEL & NO.	GOOD	VERY GOOD	NEAR MINT
CURTIS IN CHICAGO	Curtom (S) CRS 8018	2.00	3.00	4.00
GIVE, GET, TAKE, AND HAVE	Curtom (S) CL 5007	2.00	3.00	4.00
GOT TO FIND A WAY	Curtom (S) CRS 8604	2.00	3.00	4.00
HIS EARLY YEARS WITH THE IMPRESSIONS	ABC (S) X-780	3.00	4.50	6.00
RAPPING (special Promotional Radio Show)	Curtom (S) CRS SP	3.00	4.50	6.00
THERE'S NO PLACE LIKE AMERICA TODAY	Curtom (S) CU 5001	2.00	3.00	4.00

MAYFIELD, Percy

TITLE	LABEL & NO.	GOOD	VERY GOOD	NEAR MINT
BEST OF PERCY MAYFIELD, THE	Specialty (S) SPS 2126	4.50	6.75	9.00

MAYPOLE

TITLE	LABEL & NO.	GOOD	VERY GOOD	NEAR MINT
MAYPOLE	Colossus (S) CS 1007	4.50	6.75	9.00

MAZE

TITLE	LABEL & NO.	GOOD	VERY GOOD	NEAR MINT
ARMAGEDDON	MTA (S) MTS 5012	3.00	4.50	6.00

McCALLUM, David

TITLE	LABEL & NO.	GOOD	VERY GOOD	NEAR MINT
MCCALLUM	Capitol (M) T 2748	3.00	4.50	6.00
MCCALLUM	Capitol (S) ST 2748	3.50	5.25	7.00
MUSIC: A BIT MORE OF ME	Capitol (M) T 2498	3.00	4.50	6.00
MUSIC: A BIT MORE OF ME	Capitol (S) ST 2498	3.50	5.25	7.00

McCANN, Peter

TITLE	LABEL & NO.	GOOD	VERY GOOD	NEAR MINT
PETER MCCANN	20th Century (S) T 544	2.50	3.75	5.00

MCCARTNEY, Paul & Wings

TITLE	LABEL & NO.	GOOD	VERY GOOD	NEAR MINT
AT THE SPEED OF SOUND ("Speed of Sound" label)	Capitol (S) SW 11525	2.00	3.00	4.00
BAND ON THE RUN	Apple (S) SO-3415	2.00	3.00	4.00
LIVE AND LET DIE (Soundtrack; title song only)	United Artists (S) UAS 100G	2.00	3.00	4.00
LONDON TOWN	Capitol (S) SW 11777	2.00	3.00	4.00
McCARTNEY	Apple (S) STAO 3363	2.50	3.75	5.00
OPEN END INTERVIEW	Capitol	20.00	30.00	40.00
RAM	Apple (S) SMAS 3375	2.00	3.00	4.00
RED ROSE SPEEDWAY	Apple (S) SMAL-3409	2.00	3.00	4.00
VENUS AND MARS	Capitol (S) SMAS 11419	2.00	3.00	4.00
WILDLIFE (With Wings)	Apple (S) SW 3386	2.00	3.00	4.00
WINGS OVER AMERICA (3 Records)	Capitol (S) SWCO 11593	5.00	7.50	10.00

McCORMICK, Gayle

TITLE	LABEL & NO.	GOOD	VERY GOOD	NEAR MINT
FLESH & BLOOD	Decca (S) 75364	3.00	4.50	6.00
GAYLE MCCORMICK	Dunhill (S) DS 50109	3.00	4.50	6.00
ONE MORE HOUR	Fantasy (M) F-9467	2.50	3.75	5.00

McCOY, George and Ethel

TITLE	LABEL & NO.	GOOD	VERY GOOD	NEAR MINT
EARLY IN THE MORNING	Adelphi (M) AD 1004	3.00	4.50	6.00

McCOY, Roy

TITLE	LABEL & NO.	GOOD	VERY GOOD	NEAR MINT
LIVE	Funky (M) FR 2001	2.00	3.00	4.00

McCOYS

TITLE	LABEL & NO.	GOOD	VERY GOOD	NEAR MINT
HANG ON SLOOPY	Bang (M) BLP 212	4.00	8.00	12.00
HUMAN BALL	Mercury (S) SR 61207	4.00	6.00	8.00
INFINITE MCCOYS	Mercury (S) SR 61163	4.00	6.00	8.00
YOU MAKE ME FEEL SO GOOD	Bang (M) BLP 213	4.00	8.00	12.00

McCRACKLIN, Jimmy

TITLE	LABEL & NO.	GOOD	VERY GOOD	NEAR MINT
EVERY NIGHT, EVERY DAY	Imperial (M) LP 9285	3.50	7.00	10.50
EVERY NIGHT, EVERY DAY	Imperial (S) LP 12285	4.00	8.00	12.00
I JUST GOTTA KNOW	Imperial (M) 9219	4.00	8.00	12.00
JIMMY MCCRACKLIN SONGS	Chess (M) LP 1464	4.00	8.00	12.00
LET'S GET TOGETHER	Minit (M) LP 24011	4.00	6.00	8.00
NEW SOUL OF JIMMY MCCRACKLIN	Imperial (M) 9316	3.50	7.00	10.50
NEW SOUL OF JIMMY MCCRACKLIN	Imperial (S) 12316	4.00	8.00	12.00
THINK	Imperial (M) 9297	3.50	7.00	10.50
THINK	Imperial (S) 12297	4.00	8.00	12.00
TWIST WITH JIMMY MCCRACKLIN	Crown (M) CLP 5244	3.00	6.00	9.00

McCRAE, George

TITLE	LABEL & NO.	GOOD	VERY GOOD	NEAR MINT
DIAMOND TOUCH	TK (S) 606	2.00	3.00	4.00
GEORGE MC CRAE	TK (S) 602	2.50	3.75	5.00
ROCK YOUR BABY	TK (S) 501	2.00	3.00	4.00
ROCK YOUR BABY	TK (S) 501	2.50	3.75	5.00

McCRAE, George & Gwen

TITLE	LABEL & NO.	GOOD	VERY GOOD	NEAR MINT
TOGETHER	Cat (S) 2606	2.00	3.00	4.00

(M) Mono (S) Stereo (EP) Extended Play (Q) Quad (RI) Re-issued

TITLE	LABEL & NO.	GOOD	VERY GOOD	NEAR MINT
McCRAE, Gwen				
GWEN MCCRAE	Cat (S) 1603	2.00	3.00	4.00
ROCKIN' CHAIR	Cat (S) 2605	2.00	3.00	4.00
ROCKIN' CHAIR	Cat (S) 2605	2.50	3.75	5.00
SOMETHING SO RIGHT	Cat (S) 2608	2.50	3.75	5.00
McCULLOCH, Danny				
WINGS OF A MAN	Capitol (S) ST 174	3.50	5.25	7.00
McCURN, George				
COUNTRY BOY GOES TO TOWN	A & M (M) 102	2.50	3.75	5.00
COUNTRY BOY GOES TO TOWN	A & M (S) S 102	2.50	3.75	5.00
McDANIELS, Gene				
FACTS OF LIFE	Sunset (M) 1122	2.50	3.75	5.00
FACTS OF LIFE	Sunset (S) 5122	2.50	3.75	5.00
GENE MCDANIELS SINGS MOVIE MEMORIES	Liberty (M) LRP-3204	2.00	4.00	6.00
GENE MCDANIELS SINGS MOVIE MEMORIES	Liberty (S) LST-7204	2.50	5.00	7.50
HIT AFTER HIT	Liberty (M) LRP-3258	2.00	4.00	6.00
HIT AFTER HIT	Liberty (S) LST-7258	2.50	5.00	7.50
IN TIMES LIKE THESE	Liberty (M) LRP-3146	3.00	6.00	9.00
IN TIMES LIKE THESE	Liberty (S) LST-7146	3.50	7.00	10.50
100 LBS OF CLAY	Liberty (M) LRP 3191	3.00	6.00	9.00
100 LBS OF CLAY	Liberty (S) LST 7191	3.50	7.00	10.50
SOMETIMES I'M HAPPY (SOMETIMES I'M BLUE)	Liberty (M) LRP-3175	3.00	6.00	9.00
SOMETIMES I'M HAPPY (SOMETIMES I'M BLUE)	Liberty (S) LST-7175	3.50	7.00	10.50
SPANISH LACE	Liberty (M) LRP 3275	2.00	4.00	6.00
SPANISH LACE	Liberty (S) LST 7275	2.50	5.00	7.50
TOWER OF STRENGTH	Liberty (EP) LSX 1014	2.00	4.00	6.00
VERY BEST OF GENE MCDANIELS	United Artists (M) UALA 447	1.50	2.25	3.00
WONDERFUL WORLD OF GENE MCDANIELS	Liberty (M) LRP-3311	2.00	4.00	6.00
WONDERFUL WORLD OF GENE MCDANIELS	Liberty (S) LST-7311	2.50	5.00	7.50
McDONALD AND GILES				
MC DONALD AND GILES	Cotillion (S) SD 9042	3.00	4.50	6.00

Paul McCartney

Mike McGear

TITLE	LABEL & NO.	GOOD	VERY GOOD	NEAR MINT
McDONALD, Country Joe				
COUNTRY JOE	Vanguard (S) VSD 79348	3.00	4.50	6.00
ESSENTIAL (2 LP's)	Vanguard (S) VSD 85/86	3.00	4.50	6.00
GOODBYE BLUES	Fantasy (S) F 9525	2.00	3.00	4.00
INCREDIBLE! LIVE!	Vanguard (S) VSD 79316	3.50	5.25	7.00
LOVE IS A FIRE	Fantasy (S) F 9511	2.00	3.00	4.00
PARIS SESSIONS	Vanguard (S) VSD 79328	3.00	4.50	6.00
ROCK AND ROLL MUSIC FROM THE PLANET EARTH	Fantasy (S) F 9544	2.00	3.00	4.00
WAR, WAR, WAR	Vanguard (S) VSD 79315	3.50	5.25	7.00
Also see COUNTRY JOE & THE FISH				
McDOWELL, Fred				
MISS DELTA BLUES	Arhoolie (M) 1021	2.50	3.75	5.00
MISS DELTA BLUES VOL. 2	Arhoolie (M) 1027	2.50	3.75	5.00
MISSISSIPPI FRED MCDOWELL	Everest (M) 253	2.50	4.00	5.00
MC5				
BACK IN THE USA	Atlantic (S) SD 8247	4.00	6.00	8.00
HIGH TIME	Atlantic (S) SD 8285	4.00	6.00	8.00
KICK OUT THE JAMS (Liner notes by John Sinclair)	Elektra (S) EKS 74042	6.00	9.00	12.00
KICK OUT THE JAMS	Elektra (S) EKS 74042	5.00	7.50	10.00
McGEAR, Mike				
MC GEAR (Mike McGear is Paul McCartney's brother)	Warner Bros. (S) BS-2825	3.50	5.25	7.00
McGHEE, Brownie & Sonny Terry				
BROWNIE MCGHEE & SONNY TERRY	Everest (M) 242	2.50	4.00	5.00
I COULDN'T BELIEVE MY EYES	Bluesway (M) 6059	2.50	4.00	5.00
LONG WAY TO HOME	Bluesway (M) 6028	2.50	4.00	5.00
McGOVERN, Maureen				
ACADEMY AWARD PERFORMANCE	20th Century (S) 474	2.50	3.75	5.00

TITLE	LABEL & NO.	GOOD	VERY GOOD	NEAR MINT
MORNING AFTER	20th Century (S) 419	3.00	4.50	6.00
NICE TO BE AROUND	20th Century (S) 439	2.50	3.75	5.00
McGRATH, Suni				
CALL OF THE MOURNING DOVE, THE	Adelphi (M) AD 1014	2.50	3.75	5.00
CORNFLOWER SUITE	Adelphi (M) AD 1002	2.50	3.75	5.00
McGUINESS FLINT				
HAPPY BIRTHDAY RUTHY BABY	Capitol (S) ST 794	3.50	5.25	7.00
LO & BEHOLD	Sire (S) 7405	3.50	5.25	7.00
MC GUINESS FLINT	Capitol (S) SMAS 625	4.00	6.00	8.00
McGUINN, Roger				
PEACE ON YOU	Columbia (S) KC-32956	2.50	3.75	5.00
ROGER MCGUINN	Columbia (S) KC-31946	2.50	3.75	5.00
ROGER MCGUINN & BAND	Columbia (S) PC-33541	2.00	3.00	4.00
Also see BYRDS				
McGUIRE, Barry				
BARRY & BARRY HERE & NOW (With Barry Kane)	Horizon (M) WP-1608	3.00	6.00	9.00
BARRY & BARRY HERE & NOW (With Barry Kane)	Horizon (S) ST-1608	3.50	7.00	10.50
BARRY MCGUIRE ALBUM	Horizon (M) WP 1636	2.50	5.00	7.50
BARRY MCGUIRE ALBUM	Mira (S) LPS 3000	2.00	4.00	6.00
EVE OF DESTRUCTION	Dunhill (M) D 50003	2.50	5.00	7.50
LIGHTEN UP	Myrrh (S) MSA 6531	1.50	2.25	3.00
MC GUIRE AND THE DOCTOR	Ode (S) SP 77004	3.00	4.50	6.00
THIS PRECIOUS TIME	Dunhill (M) D 50005	2.50	5.00	7.50
THIS PRECIOUS TIME	Dunhill (S) DS 50005	3.00	6.00	9.00
WORLD'S LAST PRIVATE CITIZEN, THE	Dunhill (S) DS 50033	3.00	4.50	6.00
McGUIRE SISTERS				
BEST OF THE MCGUIRE SISTERS	Coral (M) CXB-6	3.50	5.25	7.00
BEST OF THE MCGUIRE SISTERS	Coral (S) CXBS7-6	3.50	5.25	7.00
BY REQUEST	Coral (M) CRL 56123	2.50	3.75	5.00
BY REQUEST	Coral (EP) EC 81098	1.00	1.50	2.00
CHILDREN'S HOLIDAY	Coral (M) CRL 57097	2.50	3.75	5.00
CHILDREN'S HOLIDAY	Coral (EP) EC 82031	1.00	1.50	2.00
DO YOU REMEMBER WHEN	Coral (M) CRL 57026	2.50	3.75	5.00
DO YOU REMEMBER WHEN	Coral (EP) EC 82022	1.00	1.50	2.00
GREETINGS FROM THE MCGUIRE SISTERS	Coral (M) CRL 57225	2.50	3.75	5.00
HE (WITH JOHNNY DESMOND)	Coral (M) CRL 57033	3.00	4.50	6.00
HE (WITH JOHNNY DESMOND)	Coral (EP) EC 81507	1.00	1.50	2.00
I'LL THINK OF YOU	Coral (EP) EC-81184	1.00	1.50	2.00
I'LL THINK OF YOU	Coral (SEP) EC-781184	2.00	3.00	4.00
MCGUIRE SISTERS	Coral (EP) EC 81074	1.00	1.50	2.00
MCGUIRE SISTERS SHOWCASE	Coral (M) CRL-57443	2.00	3.00	4.00
MCGUIRE SISTERS SHOWCASE	Coral (S) CRL7-57443	2.00	3.00	4.00
MUSICAL MAGIC	Coral (M) CRL 57180	3.00	4.50	6.00
SINCERELY	Coral (M) CRL 57052	3.00	4.50	6.00
SUGARTIME	Coral (M) CRL 57217	3.00	4.50	6.00
S' WONDERFUL	Coral (M) CRL 57026	3.00	4.50	6.00
S' WONDERFUL	Coral (EP) EC 81127	1.00	1.50	2.00
TEENAGE PARTY	Coral (M) CRL 57134	3.00	4.50	6.00
TV FAVORITES	Coral (EP) EC 81090	1.00	1.50	2.00
WHILE THE LIGHTS ARE LOW	Coral (M) CRL 57145	2.50	3.75	5.00
WHILE THE LIGHTS ARE LOW	Coral (EP) EC 81165	1.00	1.50	2.00
McKAY, Scotty				
TONIGHT IN PERSON	Ace (M) LP 1017	5.50	11.00	16.50
McKENZIE, Scott				
STAINED GLASS MORNING	Ode (M) SP 77007	4.00	6.00	8.00
VOICE OF SCOTT MCKENZIE	Ode (M) Z 12 44001	4.00	6.00	8.00
VOICE OF SCOTT MCKENZIE	Ode (S) Z12 44002	5.00	7.50	10.00
McKUEN, Rod				
ALONE	Warner Bros. (S) BS-2817	2.50	3.75	5.00
ALONE AFTER DARK	Decca (M) DL-8946	2.50	5.00	7.50
ALONE AFTER DARK	Decca (S) DL7-8946	3.00	6.00	9.00
ANYWHERE I WANDER	Decca (M) DL-8882	2.50	5.00	7.50
ANYWHERE I WANDER	Decca (S) DL-78882	3.00	6.00	9.00
BACK TO CARNEGIE HALL	Warner Bros. (S) 2WS-2731	3.00	4.50	6.00
BEATSVILLE	HIFI (M) R-419	3.00	6.00	9.00
BEATSVILLE	HIFI (S) SR-419	4.00	8.00	12.00
BEST OF ROD MCKUEN	RCA (M) LPM 4127	3.00	4.50	6.00
BEST OF ROD MCKUEN	RCA (S) LPS 4127	3.00	4.50	6.00
GOODTIME MUSIC	Warner Bros. (S) ES-2861	2.50	3.75	5.00
GREATEST HITS OF ROD MCKUEN, VOL. 4	Warner Bros. (S) BS-2688	2.50	3.75	5.00
IN SEARCH OF EROS	Epic (M) LN 3814	2.50	3.75	5.00
IN SEARCH OF EROS	Epic (S) BN 613	3.00	4.50	6.00
LISTEN TO THE WARM	RCA (M) LPM 3863	3.00	4.50	6.00
LISTEN TO THE WARM	RCA (S) LPS 3863	3.00	4.50	6.00
SEASONS IN THE SUN	Warner Bros. (S) B-2785	2.50	3.75	5.00
WINTER	Warner Bros. (S) BS-2622	2.50	3.75	5.00
McKUEN, Rod & The San Sebastian Strings				
BOUQUET	Warner Bros. (S) BS-2768	2.00	3.00	4.00
SLEEP WARM	Warner Bros. (S) BS-2889	2.00	3.00	4.00
SPRING-SUMMER-WINTER-AUTUMN	Warner Bros. (S) 4WS-2754	4.00	6.00	8.00
SUMMER	Warner Bros. (Q) BS4-2707	2.00	3.00	4.00
WITH LOVE	Warner Bros. (S) 2837	2.00	3.00	4.00

(M) Mono   (S) Stereo   (EP) Extended Play   (Q) Quad   (RI) Re-issued

TITLE	LABEL & NO.	GOOD	VERY GOOD	NEAR MINT

McLEAN, Don
AMERICAN PIE	United Artists (S) UAS 5535	4.00	6.00	8.00
DON MCLEAN	United Artists (S) UAS 5651	3.50	5.25	7.00
HOMELESS BROTHERS	United Artists (S) UA-LA315	2.50	3.75	5.00
PLAYING FAVORITES	United Artists (S) UA-LA161	2.50	3.75	5.00
SOLO	United Artists (S) UA-LA652	2.00	3.00	4.00
TAPESTRY	United Artists (S) UAS 5522	4.00	6.00	8.00

McLUHAN, Marshall
MEDIUE IS THE MASSAGE, THE	Columbia (M) CL 2701	4.00	6.00	8.00
MEDIUM IS THE MESSAGE, THE	Columbia (S) CS 9501	5.00	7.50	10.00

McNAMARA, Robin
LAY A LITTLE LOVIN' ON ME	Steed (S) STS 37007	2.50	3.75	5.00

McNEELY, Big Jay
BIG JAY IN 3 D	King (M) LP 530	5.00	12.50	20.00
BIG JAY McNEELY (10")	Federal (M) 295 96	13.00	30.50	52.00
BIG JAY McNEELY	King (M) LP 295-96	5.00	12.50	20.00
BIG JAY McNEELY	Warner Brothers (M) W-1523	3.00	6.00	9.00
BIG JAY McNEELY	Warner Brothers (S) WS-1523	4.00	8.00	12.00
BIG JAY McNEELY SELECTIONS	Savoy (M) MG 15045	6.00	15.00	24.00
JUST CRAZY VOL. 1	King (EP) EP 245	2.00	4.00	6.00
JUST CRAZY VOL. 2	King (EP) EP 301	2.00	4.00	6.00
JUST CRAZY VOL. 3	King (EP) EP 332	2.00	4.00	6.00
JUST CRAZY VOL. 4	King (EP) EP 373	2.00	4.00	6.00

McPHATTER, Clyde
BEST OF CLYDE MCPHATTER, THE	Atlantic (M) 8077	6.00	15.00	24.00
CLYDE	Atlantic (M) 8031	7.00	17.50	28.00
CLYDE MCPHATTER	Atlantic (EP) 618	2.50	6.25	10.00
CLYDE MCPHATTER AND THE DRIFTERS	Atlantic (M) 8003	9.00	22.00	36.00
GOLDEN BLUES HITS	Mercury (M) MG 20665	5.00	10.00	15.00
GOLDEN BLUES HITS	Mercury (S) SR 60655	6.00	12.00	18.00
GREATEST HITS	Mercury (M) MG 20783	5.00	10.00	15.00
GREATEST HITS	Mercury (S) SR 60783	6.00	12.00	18.00
GREATEST HITS	MGM (M) E-3866	4.00	8.00	12.00
GREATEST HITS	MGM (S) SE-3866	5.00	10.00	15.00
LET'S START OVER AGAIN	MGM (M) E-4133	6.00	12.00	18.00
LIVE AT THE APOLLO	Mercury (M) MG20915	5.00	10.00	15.00
LIVE AT THE APOLLO	Mercury (S) SR 60915	6.00	12.00	18.00
LOVE BALLADS	Atlantic (M) 8024	7.00	17.50	28.00
LOVER PLEASE	Mercury (M) MG 20711	5.00	10.00	15.00
LOVER PLEASE	Mercury (S) SR 60711	6.00	12.00	18.00
MAY I SING FOR YOU	Mercury/Wing (M) MGW 12224	4.00	8.00	12.00
MAY I SING FOR YOU	Mercury/Wing (S) SRW 16224	5.00	10.00	15.00
RHYTHM AND SOUL	Mercury (M) MG 20750	5.00	10.00	15.00
RHYTHM AND SOUL	Mercury (S) SR 60750	6.00	12.00	18.00
ROCK WITH CLYDE MCPHATTER	Atlantic (EP) EPS 605	2.50	6.25	10.00
SONGS OF THE BIG CITY	Mercury (M) MG 20902	5.00	10.00	15.00
SONGS OF THE BIG CITY	Mercury (S) SR 60902	6.00	12.00	18.00
TA TA	Mercury (M) MG 20597	5.00	10.00	15.00
TA TA	Mercury (S) SR 60252	6.00	12.00	18.00
WELCOME HOME	Decca (S) DL 75231	4.00	6.00	8.00

Also see DRIFTERS

McTELL, Blind Willie
ATLANTA TWELVE STRING	Atlantic (S) SD 7224	4.00	6.00	8.00
LAST SESSION	Bluesville (M) 1040	5.00	10.00	15.00

MEADER, Vaughn
FIRST FAMILY	Cadence (M) C-3060	3.00	4.00	6.00
FIRST FAMILY	Cadence (S) 25060	3.50	5.25	7.00
FIRST FAMILY VOL. 2	Cadence (M) C-3065	3.00	4.00	6.00
FIRST FAMILY VOL. 2	Cadence (S) 25065	3.50	5.25	7.00
SECOND COMING	Kama Sutra (S) KSBS 2038	2.50	3.75	5.00

MEADLOWLARKS
MEADLOWLARKS	Dooto (EP) EP 203	3.00	6.00	9.00

MECKI MARK MEN
MECKI MARK MEN	Limelight (S) LS 86054	3.50	5.25	7.00

MEDALLIONS
MEDALLIONS	Dooto (EP) EP 202	3.00	6.00	9.00
MEDALLIONS	Dooto (EP) EP 857	4.00	6.00	8.00
MEDALLIONS	Dooto (EP) EP 420	4.00	6.00	8.00

MEDIUM
MEDIUM	Gamma (S) GS 503	2.50	3.75	5.00

MEDLEY, Bill
BILL MEDLEY 100%	MGM (S) SE 4583	3.50	5.25	7.00
SMILE	A&M (S) 3517	3.00	4.50	6.00
SOFT AND SOULFUL	MGM (S) SE 4603	3.50	5.25	7.00

Also see RIGHTEOUS BROTHERS

MEL AND TIM
GOOD GUYS ONLY WIN IN THE MOVIES	Bamboo (S) BMS 8001	3.00	4.50	6.00
MEL & TIM	Stax (S) 5501	2.00	3.00	4.00
STARTING ALL OVER AGAIN	Stax (S) STS 3007	2.50	3.75	5.00

(M) Mono (S) Stereo (EP) Extended Play (Q) Quad (RI) Re-issued

TITLE	LABEL & NO.	GOOD	VERY GOOD	NEAR MINT

MELANIE
AS I SEE IT NOW	Neighborhood (S) 3000	2.50	3.75	5.00
FROM THE BEGINNING	ABC (S) ND-879	2.00	3.00	4.00
GATHER ME	Neighborhood (S) 4700	3.00	4.50	6.00
MADRUGADA	Neighborhood (S) 48001	3.00	4.50	6.00
MELANIE AT CARNEGIE HALL	Neighborhood (S) 49001	3.00	4.50	6.00
PLEASE LOVE ME	Buddah (S) 5132	2.50	3.75	5.00
STONEGROUND WORDS	Neighborhood (S) 47005	3.00	4.50	6.00
SUNSETS (& OTHER BEGINNINGS)	Neighborhood (S) 3001	2.50	3.75	5.00

MELLOKINGS
TONIGHT TONIGHT	Herald (M) H-1013	8.00	20.00	32.00

MELTON, Barry
BRIGHT SUN IS SHINING	Vanguard (S) VSD 6551	4.00	6.00	8.00

MEMPHIS SLIM
BAD LUCK & TROUBLES	Barnaby (M) 31291	2.50	4.00	5.00
BLUE MEMPHIS	Warner Brothers (S) WS 1899	3.50	5.25	7.00
BORN WITH THE BLUES	Jewell (M) 5004	2.00	3.00	4.00
BROKEN SOUL BLUES	United Artists (S) 6137	4.00	6.00	8.00
JUST BLUES	Prestige (M) BV 1018	5.00	10.00	15.00
LONESOME BLUES	Spinorama (M) M 149	3.00	6.00	9.00
MEMPHIS SLIM	Chess (M) LP 1455	4.00	8.00	12.00
MEMPHIS SLIM	Everest (M) 215	2.50	4.00	5.00
MEMPHIS SLIM	King (M) 885	5.00	10.00	15.00
MEMPHIS SLIM AT THE GATE OF HORN	Vee Jay (M) 1012	5.00	10.00	15.00
MEMPHIS SLIM, USA	Candid (M) 8024	4.00	8.00	12.00
MEMPHIS SLIM, USA	Candid (S) 9024	5.00	10.00	15.00
MEMPHIS SLIM VOL. 2	Everest (M) 286	2.50	4.00	5.00
MESSIN' AROUND WITH THE BLUES	King (S) KS 1082	3.00	4.50	6.00
NO STRAIN	Prestige (M) BV 1031	5.00	10.00	15.00
RAINING THE BLUES	Fantasy (M) 24705	3.00	4.50	6.00
RIGHT NOW	Trip (M) 8025	2.00	3.00	4.00
SELF PORTRAIT	Scepter (M) SM 535	4.00	6.00	8.00
SOUTH SIDE REUNION	Warner Brothers (S) BS 2646	3.50	5.25	7.00
WEST SIDE REUNION	Warner Brothers (M) 2646	2.50	4.00	5.00
WORLD FOREMOSTBLUES SINGER	Strand (M) 1046	5.00	10.00	15.00
WORLD'S FOREMOST BLUES SINGER, THE	Strand (S) SLS 1046	4.00	8.00	12.00

MEMPHIS SLIM & Willie Dixon
MEMPHIS SLIM & WILLIE DIXON IN PARIS	Battle (M) BM-6122	3.00	6.00	9.00
MEMPHIS SLIM & WILLIE DIXON IN PARIS	Battle (S) BS9-6122	4.00	8.00	12.00

MENDES, Sergio & Brasil '77
LOVE MUSIC	Bell (S) 1119	2.00	3.00	4.00
SERGIO MENDES & BRASIL '77 (LIVE AT THE GREEK CARNIVAL)	A&M (S) 4378	2.00	3.00	4.00
VINTAGE '74	Bell (S) 1305	2.00	3.00	4.00

MERCURY, Eric
FUNKY SOUND NURTURED IN THE FERTILE SOIL OF MEMPHIS THAT SMELL OF ROCK	Enterprise (S) ENS 1021	2.00	3.00	4.00
LOVE IS TAKING OVER	Enterprise (S) ENS 1033	2.00	3.00	4.00

MERCY
LOVE (CAN MAKE YOU HAPPY)	Sundi (S) SRLP 803	3.50	5.25	7.00

MERCY DEE
MERCY DEE	Arhoolie (M) 1007	2.50	3.75	5.00

MERRY GO ROUND
YOU'RE A VERY LOVELY WOMAN	A & M (S) SP 4132	5.00	7.50	10.00

MERRYWEATHER AND CAREY
VACUUM CLEANER	RCA (S) LSP 4485	3.00	4.50	6.00

MERRYWEATHER, Neil, John Richardson and Boers
NEIL MERRYWEATHER, JOHN RICHARDSON AND BOERS	Kent (S) KST 546	3.00	4.50	6.00

MERSEYBEATS
Title	Label & No.	Good	Very Good	Near Mint
ENGLAND'S BEST SELLERS	ARC International (M) 834	5.00	10.00	15.00

MERSEYBOYS
Title	Label & No.	Good	Very Good	Near Mint
15 GREATEST SONGS OF THE BEATLES	Vee Jay (M) 1101	4.00	8.00	12.00
15 GREATEST SONGS OF THE BEATLES	Vee Jay (S) 1101	4.00	8.00	12.00

MESMERIZING EYE
Title	Label & No.	Good	Very Good	Near Mint
PSYCHEDELIA/A MUSICAL LIGHT SHOW	Smash (M) MGS 27090	3.00	4.50	6.00

MESSINA, Jim and His Jesters
Title	Label & No.	Good	Very Good	Near Mint
DRAGSTERS, THE	Audio Fidelity (S) DFS 7037	5.00	10.00	15.00
JIM MESSINA AND THE JESTERS	Thimble (M) TLP-3	3.00	4.50	6.00

METERS
Title	Label & No.	Good	Very Good	Near Mint
LOOK-KA PY PY	Josie (S) JOS 4011	4.00	6.00	8.00
METERS, THE	Josie (S) JOS 4010	4.00	6.00	8.00

METRONOMES
Title	Label & No.	Good	Very Good	Near Mint
METRONOMES	Wynne (EP) EP 101	2.00	4.00	6.00

METROS
Title	Label & No.	Good	Very Good	Near Mint
EMOTION IN MOTION	RCA (M) LPM 3776	2.50	3.75	5.00
EMOTION IN MOTION	RCA (S) LSP 3776	2.50	3.75	5.00

METROTONES
Title	Label & No.	Good	Very Good	Near Mint
TOPS IN ROCK AND ROLL (10")	Columbia (M) 6341	3.00	7.50	12.00
TOPS IN ROCK AND ROLL	Columbia (EP) B 2026	1.50	2.25	3.00
TOPS IN ROCK AND ROLL	Columbia (EP) B 2027	1.50	2.25	3.00

MEYERS, Augie
Title	Label & No.	Good	Very Good	Near Mint
LIVE AT THE LONGNECK	Texas Re-cord (M) LP 1002	2.50	3.75	5.00
LIVE AT THE LONGNECK	Texas Re-Cord Co. (S) LP-1002	2.50	3.75	5.00

MG'S
Title	Label & No.	Good	Very Good	Near Mint
MG'S	Stax (S) 3024	2.50	3.75	5.00

MICHAELS, Lee
Title	Label & No.	Good	Very Good	Near Mint
BARREL	A&M (S) SP 4249	3.00	4.50	6.00
LEE MICHAELS	A&M (S) SP 4199	2.00	3.00	4.00
LEE MICHAELS "5TH"	A&M (S) SP 4302	3.00	4.50	6.00
LEE MICHAELS "LIVE"	A&M (S) 3518	3.00	4.50	6.00
NICE DAY FOR SOMETHING	Columbia (S) KC-32275	2.50	3.75	5.00
NICE DAY FOR SOMETHING	Columbia (Q) CQ-32275	2.50	3.75	5.00
SPACE & FIRST TAKES	A&M (S) SP 4336	3.00	4.50	6.00
TAILFACE	Columbia (S) KC-32846	2.00	3.00	4.00
MICHELE				
SATURN RINGS	ABC (M) 684	5.00	7.50	10.00

MICKEY & SYLVIA
Title	Label & No.	Good	Very Good	Near Mint
LOVE IS STRANGE	Camden (M) CAL-863	4.00	8.00	12.00
LOVE IS STRANGE	Camden (S) CAS-863	3.00	6.00	9.00
LOVE IS STRANGE	Groove (EP) EGA 18	3.00	6.00	9.00
MICKEY & SYLVIA	Vik (EP) EXA 262	3.00	4.50	6.00
MICKEY & SYLVIA DO IT AGAIN	RCA (M) APM1-0327	4.00	6.00	8.00
NEW SOUNDS	Vik (M) LX 1102	6.00	12.00	18.00

MIDDLE OF THE ROAD
Title	Label & No.	Good	Very Good	Near Mint
ACCELERATION	RCA (S) LSP 4674	2.00	3.00	4.00

MIDDLETON, Rex, Hi Fi's
Title	Label & No.	Good	Very Good	Near Mint
REX MIDDLETON'S HI FI'S	Verve (M) MG V 2035	4.00	8.00	12.00

MIDLER, Bette
Title	Label & No.	Good	Very Good	Near Mint
BETTE MIDLER	Atlantic (S) SD 7270	3.00	4.50	6.00
DIVINE MISS M	Atlantic (S) SD7238	3.00	4.50	6.00
DIVINE MISS M	Atlantic (Q) QD-7238	3.00	4.50	6.00
SINGS FOR THE NEW DEPRESSION	Atlantic (S) SD 18155	2.50	3.75	5.00

MIDNIGHTERS
Title	Label & No.	Good	Very Good	Near Mint
MIDNIGHTERS (YEL/GREY COLOR SCHEME)	Federal (M) 541	15.00	37.50	60.00
MIDNIGHTERS (PINK/BROWN COLOR SCHEME)	Federal (M) 541	15.00	37.50	60.00
MIDNIGHTERS SING THEIR GREATEST HITS	Federal (EP) FEP 333	2.00	5.00	8.00
MIDNIGHTERS SING THEIR HITS	King (M) LP 295-90	5.00	12.50	20.00
MIDNIGHTERS: THEIR GREATEST HITS, THE (10")	Federal (M) 295 90	40.00	100.00	160.00
MIDNIGHTERS VOLUME II	Federal (M) 581	15.00	37.50	60.00

Also see BALLARD, HANK & THE MIDNIGHTERS

MIGHTY BABY
Title	Label & No.	Good	Very Good	Near Mint
MIGHTY BABY	Head (S) LPS 025	4.00	6.00	8.00

MIGHTY DIAMONDS
Title	Label & No.	Good	Very Good	Near Mint
RIGHT TIME	Virgin (M) PZ 34235	3.50	5.25	7.00

MIGHTY MARVELOWS
Title	Label & No.	Good	Very Good	Near Mint
MIGHTY MARVELOWS	ABC (S) ABCS-643	4.00	6.00	8.00

MILBURN, Amos
Title	Label & No.	Good	Very Good	Near Mint
BLUES BOSS	Motown (M) 608	4.00	8.00	12.00
LET'S HAVE A PARTY	Score (M) LP 4012	10.00	25.00	40.00
MILLION SELLERS	Imperial (M) A-9176	5.00	10.00	15.00
ROCKIN' THE BOOGIE	Aladdin (M) AL 704	12.00	30.00	48.00
ROCKIN' THE BOOGIE	Aladdin (M) 810	9.00	22.50	36.00
ROCKIN' THE BOOGIE (10") (Red vinyl)	Aladdin (M) 704	40.00	100.00	160.00
ROCKIN' THE BOOGIE (10") (Black vinyl)	Aladdin (M) 704	30.00	75.00	120.00

Also see HARRIS, Wynonie

MILES, Garry
Title	Label & No.	Good	Very Good	Near Mint
LOOK FOR A STAR	Liberty (EP) LSX-1005	3.00	6.00	9.00

MILES, Long Gone
Title	Label & No.	Good	Very Good	Near Mint
COUNTRY BORN	World Pacific (M) 1820	5.00	7.50	10.00

MILLBURNAIRES
Title	Label & No.	Good	Very Good	Near Mint
MILLBURNAIRES '70	MB (M) 670	3.00	4.50	6.00

MILLENNIUM
Title	Label & No.	Good	Very Good	Near Mint
MILLENNIUM BEGIN	Columbia (S) CS 9663	5.00	7.50	10.00

MILLER, Art Jerry
Title	Label & No.	Good	Very Good	Near Mint
RATED X, SUGGESTED FOR MATURE SOULS	Enterprise (S) ENS 1007	2.00	3.00	4.00

MILLER, Big
Title	Label & No.	Good	Very Good	Near Mint
DID YOU EVER HEAR THE BLUES	United Artists (S) UAS 6047	4.50	6.75	9.00

MILLER, Chuck
Title	Label & No.	Good	Very Good	Near Mint
AFTER HOURS	Mercury (M) MG 20195	4.50	11.25	18.00

MILLER, Jamene
Title	Label & No.	Good	Very Good	Near Mint
JAMENE	United Artists (S) 5538	3.00	6.00	9.00

MILLER, Jody
Title	Label & No.	Good	Very Good	Near Mint
BEST OF JODY MILLER	Capitol (S) ST-11169	2.00	3.00	4.00
COUNTRY GIRL	Epic (S) KE-33349	2.00	3.00	4.00
GOOD NEWS	Epic (S) KE-32386	2.00	3.00	4.00
HOME OF THE BRAVE	Capitol (M) T-2412	2.50	3.75	5.00
HOME OF THE BRAVE	Capitol (S) ST-2412	2.50	3.75	5.00
HOUSE OF THE RISING SUN	Epic (S) KE-32569	2.00	3.00	4.00
JODY MILLER	Capitol (M) T-2446	2.50	3.75	5.00
JODY MILLER	Capitol (S) ST-2446	2.50	3.75	5.00
NASHVILLE SOUND OF JODY MILLER	Capitol (M) T-2996	2.00	3.00	4.00
NASHVILLE SOUND OF JODY MILLER	Capitol (S) ST-2996	2.00	3.00	4.00
QUEEN OF THE HOUSE	Capitol (M) T-2349	2.50	3.75	5.00
QUEEN OF THE HOUSE	Capitol (S) ST-2349	2.50	3.75	5.00
WEDNESDAY'S CHILD IS FULL OF WOE	Capitol (M) T-1913	2.50	3.75	5.00
WEDNESDAY'S CHILD IS FULL OF WOE	Capitol (S) ST-1913	2.50	3.75	5.00

MILLER, Ned
Title	Label & No.	Good	Very Good	Near Mint
FROM A JACK TO A KING	Fabor (M) F 1001	3.00	7.50	12.00

MILLER, Steve, Band
Title	Label & No.	Good	Very Good	Near Mint
ANTHOLOGY	Capitol (S) SVBB-11114	2.50	3.75	5.00
BOOK OF DREAMS	Capitol SO-11630	2.50	3.75	5.00
BRAVE NEW WORLD	Capitol (S) 184	3.00	4.50	6.00
CHILDREN OF THE FUTURE	Capitol SKAO-2920	4.00	6.00	8.00
CHILDREN OF THE FUTURE/ LIVING IN THE USA	Capitol STBB-717	3.00	4.50	6.00
FLY LIKE AN EAGLE	Capitol ST-11497	2.50	3.75	5.00
JOKER, THE	Capitol SMAS 11235	2.50	3.75	5.00
NUMBER 5	Capitol (S) 436	3.00	4.50	6.00
RECALL THE BEGINNING (A JOURNEY FROM EDEN)	Capitol SMAS-11022	2.50	3.75	5.00
ROCK LOVE	Capitol SW-748	3.00	4.50	6.00
SAILOR	Capitol ST-2984	3.50	5.25	7.00
YOUR SAVING GRACE	Capitol (S) 331	3.00	4.50	6.00

MILLINDER, Lucky
Title	Label & No.	Good	Very Good	Near Mint
LUCKY MILLINDER	King (EP) 268	2.00	5.00	8.00
LUCKY MILLINDER	King (EP) EP 336	2.00	5.00	8.00

MILLS BROTHERS
Title	Label & No.	Good	Very Good	Near Mint
FAMOUS BARBER SHOP BALLADS, Vol. 1 (10")	Decca (M) 5050	3.00	7.50	12.00
FAMOUS BARBER SHOP BALLADS, Vol. 2 (10")	Decca (M) 5051	3.00	7.50	12.00
LOUIS ARMSTRONG AND THE MILLS BROTHERS (10")	Decca (M) 5509	4.00	10.00	16.00
MEET THE MILLS BROTHERS (10")	Decca (M) 5506	3.00	7.50	12.00
MILLS BROTHERS SOUVENIR ALBUM (10")	Decca (M) 5102	3.00	7.50	12.00
WONDERFUL WORDS (10")	Decca (M) 5337	3.00	7.50	12.00

MILLS, Hayley
Title	Label & No.	Good	Very Good	Near Mint
LET'S GET TOGETHER	Buena Vista (M) BV 3311	3.00	6.00	9.00

(M) Mono (S) Stereo (EP) Extended Play (Q) Quad (RI) Re-issued

TITLE	LABEL & NO.	GOOD	VERY GOOD	NEAR MINT
MILLS, Stephanie				
FOR THE FIRST TIME	Motown (S) M6 859 S1	2.50	3.75	5.00
MOVIN' IN THE RIGHT DIRECTION	ABC (S) ABCD 869	5.00	7.50	10.00
MILTON, Roy				
ROCK 'N' ROLL VS R&B	Dooto (M) 223	8.00	20.00	32.00
MIMMS, Garnet & Enchanters				
AS LONG AS I HAVE YOU	United Artists (M) UAL 3396	2.00	4.00	6.00
AS LONG AS I HAVE YOU	United Artists (S) UAS 6396	2.50	5.00	7.50
CRY BABY (& 11 OTHER HITS)	United Artists (M) UAL-3305	2.50	5.00	7.50
CRY BABY (& 11 OTHER HITS)	United Artists (S) UAS-6305	3.50	7.00	10.50
GARNET MIMMS AND MAURICE MONK	Grand Prix (S) K 424	2.50	5.00	7.50
I'LL TAKE GOOD CARE OF YOU	United Artists (M) UAL 3498	2.00	4.00	6.00
I'LL TAKE GOOD CARE OF YOU	United Artists (S) UAS 6498	2.50	5.00	7.50
SENSATIONAL NEW STAR	Guest Star (S) G 1907	2.50	5.00	7.50
MINDBENDERS				
A GROOVY KIND OF LOVE	Fontana (M) MGF 27554	4.50	6.75	9.00
A GROOVY KIND OF LOVE	Fontana (S) SRF 67554	5.00	7.50	10.00
MINDEXPANDERS				
WHAT'S HAPPENING	Dot (M) DLP 3773	3.50	5.25	7.00
WHAT'S HAPPENING	Dot (S) DLP 25773	4.50	6.75	9.00
MINEO, Sal				
SAL	Epic (M) LN 3405	4.00	8.00	12.00
SAL	Epic (EP) EG 7194	1.50	2.25	3.00
SAL	Epic (EP) EG 7195	1.50	2.25	3.00
SAL MINEO	Epic (EP) EG 7187	1.50	2.25	3.00
SOUVENIRS OF SUMMERTIME	Epic (EP) EG 7204	1.50	2.25	3.00
MINNELLI, Liza				
"LIVE" AT THE LONDON PALLADIUM (WITH JUDY GARLAND)	Capitol (M) T 2295	7.50	11.25	15.00
"LIVE" AT THE LONDON PALLADIUM (WITH JUDY GARLAND)	Capitol (S) ST 2295	8.00	12.00	16.00
LIZA! LIZA!	Capitol (M) 2174	3.50	5.25	7.00
LIZA! LIZA!	Capitol (S) 2174	4.00	6.00	8.00
LIZA MINNELLI	A&M (S) SP 4141	2.00	3.00	4.00
LIZA WITH A "Z"	Columbia (S) 31762	2.00	3.00	4.00
NEW FEELIN'	A&M (S) SP 4272	2.00	3.00	4.00
MIRACLES				
AWAY WE A-GO-GO	Tamla (M) 271	3.00	4.50	6.00
AWAY WE A-GO-GO	Tamla (S) 271	4.00	6.00	8.00
CHRISTMAS WITH THE MIRACLES	Tamla (M) 236	4.00	8.00	12.00
COOKIN' WITH THE MIRACLES	Tamla (S) 223	5.00	10.00	15.00
DOIN' MICKEY'S MONKEY	Tamla (M) 245	3.00	4.50	6.00
DOIN' MICKEY'S MONKEY	Tamla (S) 245	4.00	6.00	8.00
FABULOUS MIRACLES, THE	Tamla (M) 238	4.00	6.00	8.00
FLYING HIGH TOGETHER	Tamla (M) 318	3.00	4.50	6.00
FOUR IN BLUE	Tamla (M) 297	3.00	4.50	6.00
FROM THE BEGINNING	Bell (M) 1063	2.50	3.75	5.00
GOING TO A-GO-GO	Tamla (M) 267	3.00	4.50	6.00
GOING TO A-GO-GO	Tamla (S) 267	4.00	6.00	8.00
GREATEST HITS VOL 2	Tamla (M) 280	3.50	5.25	
HI, WE'RE THE MIRACLES	Tamla (M) 220	6.00	12.00	18.00
I'LL TRY SOMETHING NEW	Tamla (M) 230	4.00	8.00	12.00
LIVE	Tamla (M) 289	3.00	4.50	6.00
MAKE IT HAPPEN	Tamla (M) 276	3.00	4.50	6.00
MIRACLES GREATEST HITS, Vol. 2	Tamla (M) 280	3.00	4.50	6.00
MIRACLES GREATEST HITS- FROM THE BEGINNING	Tamla (M) 254	3.00	4.50	6.00
MIRACLES GREATEST HITS- FROM THE BEGINNING	Tamla (S) 254	4.00	6.00	8.00
MIRACLES ON STAGE	Tamla (M) 241	4.00	6.00	8.00
ONE DOZEN ROSES	Tamla (S) 312	3.00	4.50	6.00
A POCKET FULL OF MIRACLES	Tamla (S) 306	3.00	4.50	6.00
SEASON FOR MIRACLES, THE	Tamla (S) TS 307	3.50	5.25	7.00
SHOP AROUND	Tamla (M) 224	5.00	10.00	15.00
SMOKEY ROBINSON & THE MIRACLES' ANTHOLOGY	Motown (S) 793	3.50	5.25	7.00
SPECIAL OCCASION	Tamla (M) 290	3.50	5.25	7.00
TEARS OF A CLOWN ("Make It Happen" re-titled)	Tamla (M) 276	3.00	4.50	6.00
TIME OUT FOR SMOKEY ROBINSON AND THE MIRACLES	Tamla (S) 295	3.00	4.50	6.00
WHAT LOVE HAS JOINED TOGETHER	Tamla (M) 301	3.00	4.50	6.00
(Shown as "Smokey Robinson & The Miracles" beginning with Tamla 276)				
MIRETTES				
IN THE MIDNIGHT HOUR	Revue (M) RS 7205	2.50	3.75	5.00
WHIRLPOOL	Uni (M) 73062	2.50	3.75	5.00
MR. GASSER and The Weirdos				
HOT ROD HOOTENANNY	Capitol (M) T 2010	3.00	6.00	9.00
HOT ROD HOOTENANNY	Capitol (S) ST 2010	3.50	7.00	10.50
RODS N' RATFINKS	Capitol (M) T 2057	3.00	6.00	9.00
RODS N' RATFINKS	Capitol (S) ST 2057	3.50	7.00	10.50
SURFIN	Capitol (M) T 2114	3.00	6.00	9.00
SURFIN	Capitol (S) ST 2114	3.50	7.00	10.50
MITCHELL, Chad Trio				
BEST OF CHAD MITCHELL TRIO	Kapp (M) K-1334	2.50	3.75	5.00

(M) Mono (S) Stereo (EP) Extended Play (Q) Quad (RI) Re-issued

TITLE	LABEL & NO.	GOOD	VERY GOOD	NEAR MINT
BEST OF CHAD MITCHELL TRIO	Kapp (S) KS-3324	2.50	3.75	5.00
BLOWIN' IN THE WIND	Kapp (M) KL-1313	2.50	3.75	5.00
BLOWIN' IN THE WIND	Kapp (S) KS-3313	2.50	3.75	5.00
CHAD MITCHELL TRIO ARRIVES	Colpix (M) CP 411	4.00	6.00	8.00
CHAD MITCHELL TRIO ARRIVES	Colpix (S) SCP 411	4.00	6.00	8.00
CHAD MITCHELL TRIO IN ACTION	Kapp (M) KL1313	2.00	3.00	4.00
CHAD MITCHELL TRIO IN ACTION	Kapp (S) KS3313	2.00	3.00	4.00
CHAD MITCHELL TRIO AT THE BITTER END	Kapp (M) KL-1281	2.50	3.75	5.00
CHAD MITCHELL TRIO AT THE BITTER END	Kapp (S) KS-3281	2.50	3.75	5.00
MIGHTY DAY ON CAMPUS, A	Kapp (M) KL-1262	2.50	3.75	5.00
MIGHTY DAY ON CAMPUS, A	Kapp (S) KS-3262	2.50	3.75	5.00
REFLECTING	Mercury (M) MG 20891	2.50	3.75	5.00
REFLECTING	Mercury (S) SR 60891	2.50	3.75	5.00
SINGIN' OUR MIND	Mercury (M) MG 20838	2.50	3.75	5.00
SINGIN' OUR MIND	Mercury (S) SR 60838	2.50	3.75	5.00
SLIGHTLY IRRELEVENT (MITCHELL TRIO)	Mercury (M) MG 20944	2.50	3.75	5.00
SLIGHTLY IRRELEVENT (MITCHELL TRIO)	Mercury (S) SR 60944	2.50	3.75	5.00
THAT'S THE WAY IT'S GONNA BE (FEATURING JOHN DENVER)	Mercury (M) MG 21049	5.00	7.50	10.00
THAT'S THE WAY IT'S GONNA BE (FEATURING JOHN DENVER)	Mercury (S) SR 61049	5.00	7.50	10.00
TYPICAL AMERICAN BOYS (MITCHELL TRIO)	Mercury (M) MG 20992	2.50	3.75	5.00
TYPICAL AMERICAN BOYS (MITCHELL TRIO)	Mercury (S) SR 60992	2.50	3.75	5.00
MITCHELL, Chad				
HOOTENANNY NO. 3	Kapp (M) KL-1344	2.00	3.00	4.00
HOOTENANNY NO. 3	Kapp (S) KS-3344	2.00	3.00	4.00
MITCHELL, Guy				
A GUY IN LOVE	Columbia (M) CL 1155	2.50	3.75	5.00
A GUY IN LOVE	Columbia (S) CS 8011	2.50	3.75	5.00
A GUY IN LOVE	Columbia (EP) B 11551	1.00	1.50	2.00
GUY MITCHELL	Columbia (EP) B 2502	1.00	1.50	2.00
GUY MITCHELL	Columbia (EP) B-2618	1.00	1.50	2.00
GUY'S GREATEST HITS	Columbia (M) CL 1226	4.00	6.00	8.00
KNEE DEEP IN THE BLUES	Columbia (EP) B 2126	1.50	2.25	3.00
MITCHELL SPOTLITE	Columbia (EP) B 1585	1.00	1.50	2.00
PAJAMA GAME	Columbia (EP) B 1863	1.00	1.50	2.00
RED GARTERS (10")	Columbia (M) CL 6282	2.50	3.75	5.00
RED GARTERS	Columbia (EP) B 377	1.00	1.50	2.00
ROCK-A-BILLY	Columbia (EP) B 2133	1.50	2.25	3.00
SINGING THE BLUES	Columbia (EP) B 2117	1.50	2.25	3.00
SONGS OF OPEN SPACES (10")	Columbia (M) CL 6231	2.50	3.75	5.00
SONGS OF OPEN SPACES	Columbia (EP) B 322	1.00	1.50	2.00
SUNSHINE GUITAR	Columbia (M) CL-1552	2.00	3.00	4.00
SUNSHINE GUITAR	Columbia (S) CS-8352	2.00	3.00	4.00
MITCHELL, Joni				
BLUE	Reprise (S) 2038	3.00	4.50	6.00
CLOUDS	Reprise (S) RS 6341	3.50	5.25	7.00
COURT & SPARK	Asylum 7E-1001	2.50	3.75	5.00
DON JUAN'S RECKLESS DAUGHTER	Asylum BB-701	4.00	6.00	8.00
FOR THE ROSES	Asylum 5057	3.00	4.50	6.00
HEJIRA	Asylum 7E-1087	2.00	3.00	4.00
HISSING OF SUMMER LAWNS	Asylum (S) 7E-1051	2.00	3.00	4.00
JONI MITCHELL	Reprise (S) RS 6293	4.00	6.00	8.00
LADIES OF THE CANYON	Reprise (S) RS 6376	3.50	5.25	7.00
MILES OF AISLES	Asylum (S) 202	2.50	3.75	5.00
MOB				
MOB, THE	Colossus (S) CS 1006	3.00	4.50	6.00
MOB, THE	Private Stock (S) 2005	3.00	4.50	6.00
MOBY GRAPE				
GRAPE JAM	Columbia (S) MGS 1	2.50	3.75	5.00
MOBY GRAPE	Columbia (S) CS 9498	3.50	5.25	7.00
MOBY GRAPE (With finger on cover & poster inside)	Columbia (S) CS 9498	6.00	9.00	12.00
MOBY GRAPE '69	Columbia (S) CS 9696	3.50	5.25	7.00
TRULY FINE CITIZEN	Columbia (S) CS 9912	3.00	4.50	6.00
20 GRANITE CREEK	Reprise (M) 6460	3.00	4.50	6.00
WOW	Columbia (S) CS 9613	3.00	4.50	6.00
MODERN FOLK QUARTET				
CHANGES	Warner Bros. (S) 1546	5.00	7.50	10.00
MFQ	Warner Bros. (M) 1511	5.00	7.50	10.00

MODUGNO, Domenico
Title	Label & No.	Good	Very Good	Near Mint
NEL BLU DIPINTI DI BLU	Decca (M) DL 8808	3.00	4.00	6.00
NEL BLU DIPINTI DI BLU	Decca (EP) ED 2633	1.00	1.50	2.00

MOGAN DAVID
SAVAGE YOUNG WINOS	Kosher (M) 1	5.00	7.50	10.00

MOLOCH
MOLOCH	Enterprise (S) ENS 1002	2.00	3.00	4.00

MOMENTS
LIVE	Stang (S) ST 1006	3.00	4.50	6.00
LIVE AT THE MISS BLACK AMERICA PAGEANT	Stang (S) 1015	2.50	3.75	5.00

MOMS APPLE PIE
MOMS APPLE PIE	Brown Bag (S) BB 14200	2.00	3.00	4.00
MOMS APPLE PIE (With original Vagina Cover)	Brown Bag (S) BB 14200	4.00	8.00	12.00
MUSIC	Brown Bag (S) BB-LA 073-F	2.00	3.00	4.00

MONAHAN, Stephen
STEPHEN MONAHAN	Kapp (M) KL 1528	3.00	4.50	6.00
STEPHEN MONAHAN	Kapp (S) KS 3528	4.00	6.00	8.00

MONDAY BLUES
PHIL SPECTOR SONG BOOK	Vault (M) 133	4.00	6.00	8.00

MONEY, Zoot
ALL HAPPENING ZOOT MONEY'S BIG ROLL BAND AT KLOOKS KLEEK	Epic (M) LN 24241	4.00	8.00	12.00

MONITORS
GREETINGS WE'RE THE MONITORS	Soul (M) 714	3.50	7.00	10.50

MONKEES
BARREL FULL OF MONKEES	Colgems (M) 1001	7.00	10.50	14.00
BIRDS, THE BEES, AND THE MONKEES, THE	Colgems (M) COM109	4.00	6.00	8.00
BIRDS, THE BEES, AND THE MONKEES, THE	Colgems (S) COS109	5.00	7.50	10.00
CHANGES	Colgems (S) 119	7.00	10.50	14.00
GREATEST HITS	RCA (S) PRS-329	8.00	12.00	16.00
GREATEST HITS	Colgems (S) 115	5.00	7.50	10.00
HEAD	Colgems (S) COSO 5008	6.00	9.00	12.00
HEADQUARTERS	Colgems (M) COM 103	4.00	6.00	8.00
HEADQUARTERS	Colgems (S) COS 103	5.00	7.50	10.00
INSTANT REPLAY	Colgems (S) COS 113	5.00	7.50	10.00
MONKEE BUSINESS	Wyncote (M) W 9199	3.50	5.25	7.00
MONKEES, THE	Colgems (M) COM 101	5.00	7.50	10.00
MONKEES, THE	Colgems (S) COS 101	6.00	9.00	12.00
MONKEES, THE	Colgems (EP) CGLP 101	3.00	4.50	6.00
MONKEES (SPEC. PRODUCTS 2-LP RELEASE)	RCA (S) DPL2-0188	4.00	6.00	8.00
MONKEES GREATEST HITS	Arista (S) AL 4089	2.50	3.75	5.00
MONKEES PRESENT, THE	Colgems (S) COS 117	6.00	9.00	12.00
MORE OF THE MONKEES	Colgems (M) COM 102	5.00	7.50	10.00
MORE OF THE MONKEES	Colgems (S) COS 102	6.00	9.00	12.00
MORE OF THE MONKEES	Colgems (EP) CGLP 102	3.00	4.50	6.00
PISCES, AQUARIUS, CAPRICORN, AND JONES, LTD	Colgems (M) COM 104	4.00	6.00	8.00
PISCES, AQUARIUS, CAPRICORN, AND JONES, LTD	Colgems (S) COS 104	5.00	7.50	10.00
REFOCUS	Bell (S) 6081	4.00	6.00	8.00

MONN, Jeff
REALITY	Vanguard (S) VSD-79291	3.50	5.25	7.00

MONROE, Vaughn
SURFER'S STOMP	Dot (M) DLP 3419	2.00	4.00	6.00
SURFER'S STOMP	Dot (S) DLP 25419	2.50	5.00	7.50

MONRO, Matt
MATT MONRO BEST	Liberty (M) LRP 3459	2.00	3.00	4.00
MATT MONRO BEST	Liberty (S) LST 7459	2.00	3.00	4.00
MY KIND OF GIRL	Warwick (M) W-2045	2.50	3.75	5.00
MY KIND OF GIRL	Warwick (S) WST-2045	2.50	3.75	5.00
WALK AWAY	Liberty (M) LRP-3402	2.00	3.00	4.00
WALK AWAY	Liberty (S) LST-7402	2.00	3.00	4.00

MONTAGE
MONTAGE	Laurie (S) SLP 2049	5.00	7.50	10.00

MONTE, Lou
BEST OF LOU MONTE	RCA (M) LPM-3672	3.00	4.50	6.00
BEST OF LOU MONTE	RCA (S) LSP-3672	4.00	6.00	8.00
ITALIAN HOUSEPARTY	RCA (M) LPM-1976	2.50	3.75	5.00
ITALIAN HOUSEPARTY	RCA (S) LSP-1976	2.50	3.75	5.00
PEPINO THE ITALIAN MOUSE	Reprise (M) R-6058	2.50	3.75	5.00
PEPINO THE ITALIAN MOUSE	Reprise (S) R9-6058	2.50	3.75	5.00
SONGS FOR PIZZA LOVERS	RCA (M) LPM 1877	3.00	4.50	6.00

MONTEZ, Chris
LET'S DANCE & SOME KINDA' FUN	Monogram (M) M-100	5.00	10.00	15.00
MORE I SEE YOU	A & M (M) 115	2.00	3.00	4.00
MORE I SEE YOU	A & M (S) 4115	2.50	3.75	5.00
TIME AFTER TIME	A & M (M) 120	2.00	3.00	4.00
TIME AFTER TIME	A & M (S) 4120	2.50	3.75	5.00

MONTGOMERY, Little Brother
NO SPECIAL RIDER	Adelphi (M) AD 1003	3.50	5.25	7.00

MONTROSE
MONTROSE	Warner Bros. (S) BS 2740	2.50	3.75	5.00
PAPER MONEY	Warner Bros. (S) BS-2823	2.50	3.75	5.00
(WARNER BROS. PRESENTS) MONTROSE	Warner Bros. (S) BS-2892	2.50	3.75	5.00

MONTY PYTHON
ALBUM OF THE SOUNDTRACK OF THE TRAILER OF THE FILM OF "MONTY PYTHON & THE HOLY GRAIL"	Arista (S) 4050	3.00	4.50	6.00
MONTY PYTHON, MATCHING TIE & HANDKERCHIEF	Arista (S) 4039	3.00	4.50	6.00
MONTY PYTHON'S FLYING CIRCUS	Pye (S) 12116	3.50	5.25	7.00
MONTY PYTHON'S PREVIOUS RECORD	Charisma (S) 1063	4.00	6.00	8.00

MOODY BLUES
DAYS OF FUTURE PASSED	Deram (M) DE 16012	3.00	4.50	6.00
DAYS OF FUTURE PASSED	Deram (S) DES 18012	3.50	5.25	7.00
EVERY GOOD BOY DESERVES FAVOUR	Threshold (S) THS 5	3.50	5.25	7.00
GO NOW—MOODY BLUES #1	London (M) LL 3428	5.00	10.00	15.00
GO NOW—MOODY BLUES #1	London (S) PS 428	6.00	12.00	18.00
IN SEARCH OF THE LOST CHORD	Deram (S) DES 18017	3.50	5.25	7.00
IN THE BEGINNING	Deram (S) DES 18051	3.50	5.25	7.00
MOODY BLUES CAUGHT LIVE PLUS 5	London (S) 2 PS-690	2.50	3.75	5.00
NOW FROM THE MOODY BLUES RAY THOMAS DISCUSSES THE RECORDING OF HIS FIRST SOLO ALBUM FROM MIGHTY OAKS	Threshold (M) THSX 102	3.00	4.50	6.00
ON THE THRESHOLD OF A DREAM	Deram (S) DES 18025	3.50	5.25	7.00
A QUESTION OF BALANCE	Threshold (S) THS 3	3.50	5.25	7.00
SEVENTH SOJOURN	Threshold (S) THS 7	3.50	5.25	7.00
SPECIAL MOODY BLUES INTERVIEW KIT	Threshold (M) THS 100	5.00	7.50	10.00
THIS IS THE MOODY BLUES (2 LP's)	Threshold (S) 2 THS 12/13	4.00	6.00	8.00
TO OUR CHILDREN'S CHILDREN'S CHILDREN	Threshold (S) THS 1	3.50	5.25	7.00

MOON
MOON	Imperial (S) LP12444	3.00	4.50	6.00
MOON WITHOUT EARTH	Imperial (S) LP 12381	4.00	6.00	8.00

MOON, Chris (Group)
CHRIS MOON GROUP, THE	Kinetic (S) Z 30228	4.00	6.00	8.00

MOONDOG
MOONDOG II	Columbia (S) KC-30897	4.00	6.00	8.00

MOONGLOWS
BEST OF BOBBY LESTER & MOONGLOWS	Chess (M) 1471	5.00	10.00	15.00
LOOK	Chess (M) LP 1430	6.00	12.00	18.00
MOONGLOWS MEET THE FLAMINGOS	Vee Jay (M) 1052	6.00	12.00	18.00
RETURN OF THE MOONGLOWS	RCA (S) LSP 4722	2.50	3.75	5.00

MOON, Keith
TWO SIDES OF THE MOON	MCA (S) 2136	2.50	3.75	5.00

Also see WHO

MOONLIGHTERS
AN EVENING WITH THE MOONLIGHTERS	Century (M) 29132	5.00	10.00	15.00

MOONRAKERS
MOONRAKERS	Shamley (S) SS 704	4.00	6.00	8.00

MOON, Roger
NOBODY KNOWS MY NAME	Capitol (S) ST 11370	5.00	7.50	10.00

(Peter Frampton played guitar on this LP)

(M) Mono (S) Stereo (EP) Extended Play (Q) Quad (RI) Re-issued

MOORE, Alex
ALEX MOORE .... Arhoolie (M) 1008 — 2.50 — 3.75 — 5.00

MOORE, Bob
MEXICO .... Monument (M) M-8008 — 2.50 — 3.75 — 5.00
MEXICO .... Monument (S) SM-18008 — 3.00 — 4.50 — 6.00

MOORE, Bobby and The Rhythm Aces
SEARCHING FOR MY LOVE .... Checker (M) LP 3000 — 3.00 — 6.00 — 9.00
SEARCHING FOR MY LOVE .... Checker (S) LPS 3000 — 3.50 — 7.00 — 10.50

MOORE, Gatemouth
I'M A FOOL TO CARE .... King (M) 684 — 6.00 — 15.00 — 24.00

MOORE, Merrill
MERRILL MOORE .... Capitol (EP) EAP 1-608 — 2.50 — 3.75 — 5.00

MOORE, Scotty
GUITAR THAT CHANGED THE WORLD
(PLAYS ELVIS HITS) .... Epic (M) LN-24103 — 6.00 — 15.00 — 24.00
GUITAR THAT CHANGED THE WORLD
(PLAYS ELVIS HITS) .... Epic (S) BN-26103 — 7.00 — 17.50 — 28.00

MORGAN, Dave
MORGAN .... Ampex (M) A-10118 — 4.50 — 6.75 — 9.00

MORGAN, George
DON'T CRY, FOR YOU I LOVE ..... Columbia (EP) B 2136 — 1.00 — 1.50 — 2.00
GEORGE MORGAN .... Columbia (M) CL 1044 — 2.50 — 3.75 — 5.00
GEORGE MORGAN .... Columbia (EP) B 10441 — 1.00 — 1.50 — 2.00
GEORGE MORGAN .... Columbia (EP) B 10442 — 1.00 — 1.50 — 2.00
GEORGE MORGAN .... Columbia (EP) B 10443 — 1.00 — 1.50 — 2.00
RED ROSES FOR A BLUE LADY ... Columbia (M) CL-2333 — 2.00 — 3.00 — 4.00
RED ROSES FOR A BLUE LADY ... Columbia (S) CS-9133 — 2.00 — 3.00 — 4.00
TENDER LOVIN' CARE .... Columbia (M) CL-2111 — 2.00 — 3.00 — 4.00
TENDER LOVIN' CARE .... Columbia (S) CS-8911 — 2.00 — 3.00 — 4.00
VOCAL SELECTIONS WITH STRING BAND ...... Columbia (EP) H 708 — 1.00 — 1.50 — 2.00

MORGAN, Jane
BALLADS OF LADY JANE .... Kapp (M) KL-1191 — 2.50 — 3.75 — 5.00
BALLADS OF LADY JANE .... Kapp (S) KS-3191 — 2.50 — 3.75 — 5.00
BROADWAY IN STEREO .... Kapp (S) KS-3001 — 3.50 — 4.50 — 6.00
DAY THE RAIN CAME .... Kapp (M) KL 1105 — 2.50 — 3.75 — 5.00
FASCINATION .... Kapp (M) KL 1068 — 2.50 — 3.75 — 5.00
FASCINATION .... Kapp (SEP) SE-415 — 2.00 — 3.00 — 4.00
JANE IN SPAIN .... Kapp (M) KL-1129 — 2.50 — 3.75 — 5.00
JANE MORGAN .... Kapp (M) KL 1023 — 2.50 — 3.75 — 5.00
JANE MORGAN .... Kapp (M) KL 1098 — 2.50 — 3.75 — 5.00
JANE MORGAN'S GREATEST HITS ... Kapp (M) KL-1329 — 2.50 — 3.75 — 5.00
JANE MORGAN'S GREATEST HITS ... Kapp (S) KS-3329 — 2.50 — 3.75 — 5.00
TWO DIFFERENT WORLDS .... Kapp (EP) KE 723 — 1.00 — 1.50 — 2.00

MORGEN
MORGEN .... Command/Probe (M) CPLP 4507 — 3.50 — 5.25 — 7.00

MORGON, Tim
THEY CALL THE WIND MARIA .... Fink (S) 1005 — 2.00 — 3.00 — 4.00

MORNING
MORNING .... Vault (M) 138 — 3.00 — 4.50 — 6.00

MORNING GLORY
TWO SUNS WORTH .... Fontana (S) SRF 67573 — 5.00 — 7.50 — 10.00

MORRILL, Kent
DREAM MAKER, THE .... Cream (M) CR 5001 — 3.00 — 4.50 — 6.00

MORRISON, Van
BACKTRACKIN' (WITH THEM) .... London (S) PS 639 — 2.50 — 3.75 — 5.00
BEST OF VAN MORRISON .... Bang (S) BLPS 222 — 5.00 — 7.50 — 10.00
BLOWIN' YOUR MIND! .... Bang (M) BLP 218 — 4.00 — 6.00 — 8.00
BLOWIN' YOUR MIND! .... Bang (S) BLPS 218 — 5.00 — 7.50 — 10.00
HARD NOSE THE HIGHWAY .... Warner Bros. BS-2712 — 3.00 — 4.50 — 6.00
IT'S TOO LATE TO STOP NOW ...... Warner Bros. 2ES-2760 — 3.00 — 4.50 — 6.00
MOONDANCE .... Warner Bros. (S) 1835 — 3.00 — 4.50 — 6.00
SAINT DOMINIC'S PREVIEW .... Warner Bros. (S) BS 2633 — 3.00 — 4.50 — 6.00
TUPELO HONEY .... Warner Bros. (S) 1950 — 3.00 — 4.50 — 6.00
VAN MORRISON, HIS BAND & STREET CHOIR ... Warner Bros. 1884 — 3.00 — 4.50 — 6.00
Also see THEM

MORROW, Buddy
BIG BAND BEATLEMANIA .... Epic (M) LN24095 — 2.50 — 5.00 — 7.50
BIG BAND BEATLEMANIA .... Epic (S) BN26095 — 3.00 — 6.00 — 9.00
DOUBLE IMPACT .... RCA (M) LPM-2180 — 3.00 — 4.50 — 6.00
DOUBLE IMPACT .... RCA (S) LSP-2180 — 4.00 — 6.00 — 8.00
IMPACT .... RCA (M) LPM-2042 — 3.00 — 4.50 — 6.00
IMPACT .... RCA (S) LSP-2042 — 4.00 — 6.00 — 8.00
NIGHT TRAIN .... RCA (M) LPM 1427 — 5.00 — 7.50 — 10.00

MORSE, Ella Mae
BARRELHOUSE BOOGIE AND THE BLUES
(10") .... Capitol (M) H 513 — 5.00 — 12.50 — 20.00
BARRELHOUSE, BOOGIE AND THE BLUES ...... Capitol (M) T513 — 3.00 — 7.50 — 12.00
BARRELHOUSE, BOOGIE AND THE BLUES ..... Capitol (EP) EAP-1-513 — 2.00 — 5.00 — 8.00
ELLA MAE MORSE SWINGS .... Capitol (EP) EAP-1-9126 — 2.00 — 5.00 — 8.00
HITS OF ELLA MAE MORSE
& FREDDIE SLACK .... Capitol (M) T-1802 — 5.00 — 10.00 — 15.00
MORSE CODE .... Capitol (M) T898 — 4.00 — 10.00 — 16.00
MORSE CODE .... Capitol (EP) EAP-1898 — 2.00 — 5.00 — 8.00

MORTIMER
MORTIMER .... Philips (S) PHS 600-267 — 3.00 — 4.50 — 6.00

MOSLEY, Bob
BOB MOSLEY .... Reprise (M) 2068 — 2.50 — 3.75 — 5.00

MOSS, Gene
DRACULA'S GREATEST HITS .... RCA (M) LPM-2977 — 3.00 — 4.50 — 6.00
DRACULA'S GREATEST HITS .... RCA (S) LSP-2977 — 3.00 — 4.50 — 6.00

MOTHERS OF INVENTION
ABSOLUTELY FREE .... Verve (M) V-5013 — 5.00 — 7.50 — 10.00
ABSOLUTELY FREE .... Verve (S) V6-5013 — 6.00 — 9.00 — 12.00
BURNT WEENY SANDWICH .... Bizarre (S) RS 6370 — 5.00 — 7.50 — 10.00
CRUISIN' WITH RUBEN & THE JETS ... Verve (S) V6-5055 — 6.00 — 9.00 — 12.00
FREAK OUT .... Verve (M) V-5005-2 — 6.00 — 9.00 — 12.00
FREAK OUT .... Verve (S) V6-5005-2 — 7.00 — 10.50 — 14.00
GRAND WAZOO .... Bizarre (S) MS 2093 — 4.00 — 6.00 — 8.00
JUST ANOTHER BAND FROM L.A. ... Bizarre (S) MS 2075 — 4.00 — 6.00 — 8.00
LIVE, FILLMORE EAST-JUNE 1971 ... Bizarre (S) MS2042 — 4.00 — 6.00 — 8.00
MOTHERMANIA-BEST OF THE MOTHERS ... Verve (S) V6-5068 — 6.00 — 9.00 — 12.00
MOTHERS .... Verve (S) V6-5074 — 6.00 — 9.00 — 12.00
MOTHERS OF INVENTION .... MGM (S) GAS 112 — 3.00 — 4.50 — 6.00
OVER-NITE SENSATION .... Disc Reet (S) MS 2149 — 4.00 — 6.00 — 8.00
OVER-NITE SENSATION .... Disc Reet (Q) MS4-2149 — 4.00 — 6.00 — 8.00
UNCLE MEAT .... Bizarre (S) MS 2024 — 4.00 — 6.00 — 8.00
WEASELS RIPPED MY FLESH .... Bizarre (S) MS 2028 — 4.00 — 6.00 — 8.00
WE'RE ONLY IN IT FOR THE MONEY ...... Verve (M) V-5045 — 5.00 — 7.50 — 10.00
WE'RE ONLY IN IT FOR THE MONEY ...... Verve (S) V6-5045 — 6.00 — 9.00 — 12.00
WORST OF THE MOTHERS .... MGM (S) SE 4754 — 3.50 — 5.25 — 7.00
Also see ZAPPA, Frank

MOTIONS
ELECTRIC BABY .... Philips (M) 600-317 — 4.00 — 6.00 — 8.00

MOTT THE HOOPLE
ALL THE YOUNG DUDES .... Columbia KC 31750 — 2.50 — 3.75 — 5.00
BRAIN CAPERS .... Atlantic (S) SD 8304 — 3.50 — 5.25 — 7.00
DRIVE ON (LISTED AS MOTT) .... Columbia (S) PC 33705 — 2.00 — 3.00 — 4.00
HOOPLE, THE .... Columbia (S) PC 32871 — 2.50 — 3.75 — 5.00
HOOPLE, THE .... Columbia (Q) PCQ 32871 — 2.50 — 3.75 — 5.00
MAD SHADOWS .... Atlantic (S) SD 8272 — 3.50 — 5.25 — 7.00
MOTT .... Columbia KC 32425 — 2.50 — 3.75 — 5.00
MOTT THE HOOPLE .... Atlantic (S) SP 8258 — 3.50 — 5.25 — 7.00
MOTT THE HOOPLE LIVE .... Columbia PC 33282 — 2.50 — 3.75 — 5.00
ROCK & ROLL QUEEN .... Atlantic (S) SD 7297 — 3.00 — 4.50 — 6.00
WILDLIFE .... Atlantic (S) SD 8284 — 3.50 — 5.25 — 7.00

MOUNT RUSHMORE
HIGH ON MOUNT RUSHMORE .... Dot (M) DLP 25898 — 3.00 — 4.50 — 6.00
MOUNT RUSHMORE '69 .... Dot (M) DLP 25934 — 3.00 — 4.50 — 6.00

MOUNTAIN
AVALANCHE .... Columbia (S) KC-33088 — 2.50 — 3.75 — 5.00
AVALANCHE .... Columbia (Q) CQ-33088 — 2.50 — 3.75 — 5.00
BEST OF MOUNTAIN .... Columbia (S) KC-32079 — 2.50 — 3.75 — 5.00
BEST OF MOUNTAIN .... Columbia (Q) CQ-32079 — 2.50 — 3.75 — 5.00
FLOWERS OF EVIL .... Windfall (S) 5501 — 3.00 — 4.50 — 6.00
MOUNTAIN .... Windfall (S) 4500 — 3.50 — 5.25 — 7.00
MOUNTAIN CLIMBING! .... Windfall (S) 4501 — 3.50 — 5.25 — 7.00
NANTUCKET SLEIGHRIDE .... Windfall (S) 5500 — 3.00 — 4.50 — 6.00
ROAD GOES EVER ON .... Windfall (S) 5502 — 3.00 — 4.50 — 6.00
TWIN PEAKS .... Columbia (S) PG-32818 — 2.50 — 3.75 — 5.00

MOUNTAIN BUS
SUNDANCE .... Good (M) G 101 — 3.00 — 4.50 — 6.00

MOVE
BEST OF THE MOVE ("FIRST MOVE" re-titled) ...... A&M (S) SP 3625 — 2.00 — 3.00 — 4.00
FIRST MOVE .... A&M (S) SP 3625 — 3.00 — 4.50 — 6.00
LOOKING ON .... Capitol (S) ST 658 — 5.00 — 7.50 — 10.00
MESSAGE FROM THE COUNTRY ..... Capitol (S) ST 811 — 6.00 — 9.00 — 12.00
SHAZAM .... A & M (S) SP 4259 — 2.50 — 3.75 — 5.00
SPLIT ENDS .... United Artists (S) UAS 5666 — 4.00 — 6.00 — 8.00

MOVING SIDEWALKS
FLASH .... Tantara (S) TS 6919 — 6.00 — 12.00 — 18.00

MU
MU .... RTV (M) RTV 300 — 7.50 — 11.00 — 15.00

(M) Mono (S) Stereo (EP) Extended Play (Q) Quad (RI) Re-issued

TITLE	LABEL & NO.	GOOD	VERY GOOD	NEAR MINT
MUD				
MUD	Uni (M) 73110	2.50	3.75	5.00
MUD ON MUDD	Uni (M) 73089	2.50	3.75	5.00
MUDDY WATERS & HOWLIN' WOLF				
LONDON REVISITED	Chess (M) 60026	2.00	3.00	4.00
MUGWUMPS (MAMAS & PAPAS)				
MUGWUMPS, THE	Warner Brothers (M) W 1697	3.00	4.50	6.00
MULLICAN, Moon				
GOOD TIMES GONNA ROLL AGAIN	Hilltop (M) 6033	3.50	5.25	7.00
MANY MOODS OF MOON MULLICAN	King (M) 681	5.00	7.50	10.00
MOON MULLICAN	Starday (SEP) SEP-154	2.00	3.00	4.00
MOON MULLICAN	King (EP) EP 214	2.00	4.00	6.00
MOON MULLICAN	King (EP) EP 227	2.00	4.00	6.00
MOON MULLICAN	King (EP) LEP314	2.00	3.00	4.00
MOON MULLICAN	King (EP) EP314	2.00	4.00	8.00
MOON MULLICAN SINGS AND PLAYS FAVORITE TUNES	King (M) 628	5.00	12.50	20.00
MOON MULLICAN SINGS HIS ALL TIME GREATEST HITS	King (M) LP 555	5.00	12.50	20.00
MOON OVER MULLICAN	Coral (M) CRL 57235	40.00	60.00	80.00
MUNGO JERRY				
MEMOIRS OF A STOCKBROKER	Janus (M) JLS 3027	4.00	6.00	8.00
MUNGO JERRY	Janus (M) JXS 7000	3.00	4.50	6.00
MUNSTERS				
MUNSTERS	Decca (M) DL-4588	2.50	3.75	5.00
MUNSTERS	Decca (S) DL7-4588	2.50	3.75	5.00
MURPHY, Elliot				
AQUASHOW	Polydor (M) PD 5061	4.00	6.00	8.00
MURPHY, Rose				
ROSE MURPHY AND QUARTETTE (10")	Royale (M) 1835	6.00	15.00	24.00
(With the Selah Jubilee Quartette)				
MURRAY, Mickey				
PEOPLE ARE TOGETHER	Federal (S) FS 13000	4.00	6.00	8.00
SHOUT BAMALAMA	SSS International (M) 102	3.50	5.25	7.00
MUSIC				
MUSIC	Eleuthera (S) ELS 3601	2.50	3.75	5.00
MUSIC EXPLOSION				
LITTLE BIT O' SOUL	Laurie (S) SLLP 2040	5.00	7.50	10.00
MUSIC MACHINE				
TURN ON THE MUSIC MACHINE	Original Sound (M) LPM 5015	4.00	6.00	8.00
TURN ON THE MUSIC MACHINE	Original Sound (S) LPS 8875	5.00	7.50	10.00
MUSSELWHITE, Charley				
LEAVE THE BLUES TO US	Capitol (S) ST 11450	2.00	3.00	4.00
LOUISIANA FOG	Cherry Red (M) CR 5102	2.00	3.00	4.00
STAND BACK	Vanguard (S) VSD 79232	2.50	3.75	5.00
MUSTANGS				
DARTELL STOMP	Providence (M) PLP 001	5.00	10.00	15.00
MYERS, Dave and The Surftones				
HANGIN' TWENTY	Del Fi (M) DFLP 1239	3.00	6.00	9.00
HANGIN' TWENTY	Del Fi (S) DFST 1239	4.00	8.00	12.00
MYERS, Dave, Effect				
GREATEST RACING THEMES	Carole (S) CARS 8002	4.00	8.00	12.00
MYSTIC ASTROLOGIC CRYSTAL BAND				
CLIP OUT, PUT ON BOOK	Carole (S) CARS 8003	2.50	3.75	5.00
MYSTIC ASTROLOGIC CRYSTAL BAND	Carole (M) CAR 8001	2.50	3.75	5.00
MYSTIC NUMBER NATIONAL BANK				
MYSTIC NUMBER NATIONAL BANK	Probe (M) CPLP 4501	2.50	3.75	5.00
MYSTIC NUMBER NATIONAL BANK	Probe (S) CPLPS 4501	2.50	4.25	5.00

N

TITLE	LABEL & NO.	GOOD	VERY GOOD	NEAR MINT
NAGLE, Ron				
BAD RICE	Warner Brothers (M) 1902	3.50	5.25	7.00

(M) Mono (S) Stereo (EP) Extended Play (Q) Quad (RI) Re-issued

TITLE	LABEL & NO.	GOOD	VERY GOOD	NEAR MINT
NANTOS, Nick & The Fireballers				
GUITARS ON FIRE	Summit (M) 4114	3.00	4.50	6.00
NANTUCKET				
NANTUCKET	Epic (S) JE 35253	2.00	3.00	4.00
NAPOLEON XIV				
THEY'RE COMING TO TAKE ME AWAY, HA, HAAA	Warner Brothers (M) W 1661	4.00	6.00	8.00
NASH, Graham				
WILD TALES	Atlantic (S) SD 7288	3.50	5.25	7.00
NASH, Johnny				
CELEBRATE LIFE	Epic (S) KE 32828	2.00	3.00	4.00
COMPOSER'S CHOICE	Argo (M) 4038	3.00	6.00	9.00
COMPOSER'S CHOICE	Argo (S) 4038	4.00	8.00	12.00
HOLD ME TIGHT	Jad (S) JS 1207	3.00	4.50	6.00
I CAN SEE CLEARLY NOW	Epic (S) KE 31607	2.00	3.00	4.00
I GOT RHYTHM	ABC/Paramount (M) ABC 299	3.00	4.50	6.00
I GOT RHYTHM	ABC-Paramount (S) ABCS-299	4.00	6.00	8.00
JOHNNY NASH	ABC/Paramount (M) ABC 244	3.00	4.50	6.00
JOHNNY NASH	ABC-Paramount (S) ABCS-244	4.00	6.00	8.00
LET'S GET LOST	ABC/Paramount (M) ABC 334	3.50	5.25	7.00
LET'S GET LOST	ABC/Paramount (S) ABCS 334	4.00	6.00	8.00
MY MERRY-GO-ROUND	Epic (S) KE-32158	2.00	3.00	4.00
QUIET HOUR	ABC (M) ABC-276	2.50	5.00	7.50
QUIET HOUR	ABC (S) ABCS-276	3.00	6.00	9.00
SOUL FOLK	Jad (S) JS 1006	3.00	4.50	6.00
STARRING JOHNNY NASH STUDIO TIME	ABC (M) ABC-383	2.00	4.00	6.00
STARRING JOHNNY NASH STUDIO TIME	ABC (S) ABCS-383	2.50	5.00	7.50
TEARDROPS IN THE RAIN	Cadet (S) 50034	3.00	4.50	6.00
NASHVILLE				
NASHVILLE	Epic (S) KE-32916	2.00	3.00	4.00
NASHVILLE TEENS				
TOBACCO ROAD	London (M) LL 3407	5.00	7.50	10.00
TOBACCO ROAD	London (S) PS 407	6.00	9.00	12.00
NATIONAL LAMPOON				
COLD TURKEY	Epic (S) PE-33410	3.00	4.50	6.00
LEMMINGS	Blue Thumb (S) 6006	5.00	7.50	10.00
MISSING WHITE HOUSE TAPES	Blue Thumb (S) 6008	5.00	7.50	10.00
RADIO DINNER	Banana (S) 38	4.00	6.00	8.00
NATURAL FOUR				
NATURAL FOUR	Curtom (S) 8600	3.00	4.50	6.00
NAVASOTA				
ROOTIN	ABC (S) ABCX 757	2.50	3.75	5.00
NAZARETH				
CLOSE ENOUGH FOR ROCK 'N' ROLL	A&M (S) SP 4562	2.00	3.00	4.00
EXERCISES	Warner Bros. (S) BS 2639	3.50	5.25	7.00
EXPECT NO MERCY	A&M (S) SP 4666	2.00	3.00	4.00
HAIR OF THE DOG	A&M (S) SP 4511	2.00	3.00	4.00
HOT TRACKS	A&M (S) SP 4643	2.00	3.00	4.00
LOUD 'N' PROUD	A&M (S) SP 3609	2.50	3.75	5.00
NAZARETH	Warner Bros. (S) BS 2615	3.50	5.25	7.00
PLAY 'N' THE GAME	A&M (S) SP 4610	2.00	3.00	4.00
RAMPANT	A&M (S) SP 3641	2.50	3.75	5.00
RAZAMANAZ	A&M (S) SP 4396	2.50	3.75	5.00
NAZZ (Featuring Todd Rundgren)				
NAZZ	SGC (S) SD 5001	7.50	11.00	15.00
NAZZ NAZZ	SGC (S) SD 5002	7.50	11.00	15.00
NAZZ 3	SGC (S) SD 5004	6.00	9.00	12.00
NEELY, Sam				
SAM NEELY	A&M (S) SP 3626	2.00	3.00	4.00

TITLE	LABEL & NO.	GOOD	VERY GOOD	NEAR MINT

NEELEY, Ted
TITLE	LABEL & NO.	GOOD	VERY GOOD	NEAR MINT
1974 A.D.	RCA (S) APL1-0317	2.25	3.38	4.50

NEIGHBORHOOD CHILDREN
TITLE	LABEL & NO.	GOOD	VERY GOOD	NEAR MINT
NEIGHBORHOOD CHILDREN	Acta (M) 38005	5.00	7.50	10.00

NEIHARDT, John G.
TITLE	LABEL & NO.	GOOD	VERY GOOD	NEAR MINT
FLAMING RAINBOW	United Artists (M) UA LA 157 J3	4.00	6.00	8.00

NEKTAR
TITLE	LABEL & NO.	GOOD	VERY GOOD	NEAR MINT
DOWN TO EARTH	Passport (S) 98005	3.50	5.25	7.00

NELSON, Ricky
TITLE	LABEL & NO.	GOOD	VERY GOOD	NEAR MINT
ALBUM SEVEN BY RICK	Imperial (M) LP 9167	4.00	8.00	12.00
ALBUM SEVEN BY RICK	Imperial (S) LP 12167	3.00	6.00	9.00
ANOTHER SIDE OF RICK	Decca (M) DL 4944	3.00	4.50	6.00
ANOTHER SIDE OF RICK	Decca (S) DL 74944	4.00	6.00	8.00
BEST ALWAYS	Decca (M) DL 4660	2.50	3.75	5.00
BEST ALWAYS	Decca (S) DL 74660	3.50	5.25	7.00
BEST ALWAYS	Decca (EP) DL 74660	1.50	3.00	4.50
BEST SELLERS	Imperial (M) LP 9218	4.00	8.00	12.00
BEST SELLERS	Imperial (S) LP 12218	3.00	6.00	9.00
BE TRUE TO ME	Imperial (EP) IMP 159	1.50	3.75	6.00
BRIGHT LIGHTS AND COUNTRY MUSIC	Decca (M) DL 4779	3.00	4.50	6.00
BRIGHT LIGHTS AND COUNTRY MUSIC	Decca (S) DL 74779	4.00	6.00	8.00
COUNTRY FEVER	Decca (M) DL 4837	3.00	4.50	6.00
COUNTRY FEVER	Decca (S) DL 74827	4.00	6.00	8.00
DON'T LEAVE ME	Imperial (EP) IMP 164	1.50	3.75	6.00
DOWN THE LINE	Imperial (EP) IMP 157	1.50	3.75	6.00
FOR YOUR SWEET LOVE	Decca (M) DL 4419	2.50	5.00	7.50
FOR YOUR SWEET LOVE	Decca (S) DL 74419	3.50	7.00	10.50
FOR YOUR SWEET LOVE	Decca (EP) DL 74419	1.50	3.00	4.50
GARDEN PARTY	Decca (S) DL 75391	3.00	4.50	6.00
HONEYCOMB	Imperial (EP) IMP 153	1.50	3.75	6.00
IF YOU CAN'T ROCK ME	Imperial (EP) IMP 154	1.50	3.75	6.00
IN CONCERT	Decca (S) DL 75162	3.50	5.25	7.00
IN CONCERT (RI)	MCA (S) 3	2.50	3.75	5.00
I NEED YOU	Sunset (S) SUS 5205	2.00	3.00	4.00
IT'S UP TO YOU	Imperial (M) LP 9223	4.00	8.00	12.00
IT'S UP TO YOU	Imperial (S) LP 12223	3.00	6.00	9.00
LEGENDARY MASTERS SERIES	United Artists (S) UAS 9960	5.00	7.50	10.00
A LONG VACATION	Imperial (M) LP 9244	4.00	8.00	12.00
A LONG VACATION	Imperial (S) LP 12244	3.00	6.00	9.00
LOVE AND KISSES	Decca (M) DL 4678	3.00	4.50	6.00
LOVE AND KISSES	Decca (S) DL 74678	4.00	6.00	8.00
MILLION SELLERS	Imperial (M) LP 9232	3.00	6.00	9.00
MILLION SELLERS	Imperial (S) LP 12232	3.00	6.00	9.00
MORE SONGS BY RICKY	Imperial (M) LP 9059	4.00	10.00	16.00
MORE SONGS BY RICKY	Imperial (S) LP 12059	3.00	6.00	9.00
MORE SONGS BY RICKY	Imperial (M) LP 9122	4.00	10.00	16.00
MORE SONGS BY RICKY	Imperial (S) LP 12122	3.00	6.00	9.00
OLD ENOUGH TO LOVE	Imperial (EP) EP 161	1.50	3.75	6.00
ONE MINUTE TO ONE	Imperial (EP) IMP 163	1.50	3.75	6.00
ON THE FLIP SIDE (cst album)	Decca (M) DL 4836	3.00	4.50	6.00
ON THE FLIP SIDE (cst album)	Decca (S) DL 74836	4.00	6.00	8.00
PERSPECTIVE	Decca (M) DL 5014	3.00	4.50	6.00
PERSPECTIVE	Decca (S) 75014	4.00	6.00	8.00
RESTLESS KID	Imperial (EP) EP 160	1.50	3.75	6.00
RICK IS 21	Imperial (M) LP 9152	4.00	10.00	16.00
RICK IS 21	Imperial (S) LP 12152	3.00	6.00	9.00
RICK NELSON	Sunset (M) SUM 1118	2.50	3.75	5.00
RICK NELSON	Sunset (S) SUS 5118	2.00	3.00	4.00
RICK NELSON COUNTRY	MCA (S) 2 4004	2.00	3.00	4.00
RICK NELSON SINGS FOR YOU	Decca (M) DL 4479	2.50	5.00	7.50
RICK NELSON SINGS FOR YOU	Decca (S) DL 74479	3.50	7.00	10.50
RICK SINGS NELSON	Decca (S) DL 75236	3.50	5.25	7.00
RICKY	Imperial (M) LP 9048	5.00	12.50	20.00
RICKY	Imperial (S) LP 12048	3.00	6.00	9.00
RICKY	Verve (EP) EPV 5048	6.00	15.00	24.00
RICKY NELSON	Imperial (M) LP 9050	4.00	10.00	16.00
RICKY NELSON	Imperial (S) LP 12050	3.00	6.00	9.00
RICKY NELSON SINGS FOR YOU	Imperial (M) LP 9251	4.00	8.00	12.00

TITLE	LABEL & NO.	GOOD	VERY GOOD	NEAR MINT
RICKY NELSON SINGS FOR YOU	Imperial (S) LP 12251	3.00	6.00	9.00
RICKY NELSON STORY (3 LP's)	ARI 1003	4.00	8.00	12.00
RICKY SINGS AGAIN	Imperial (M) LP 9061	4.00	10.00	16.00
RICKY SINGS AGAIN	Imperial (S) LP 12061	3.00	6.00	9.00
RICKY SINGS SPIRITUALS	Imperial (EP) EP 165	1.50	3.75	6.00
RUDY THE FIFTH	Decca (S) DL 75297	3.00	4.50	6.00
SOMEDAY	Imperial (EP) EP 156	1.50	3.75	6.00
SONGS BY RICKY	Imperial (M) LP 9082	4.00	10.00	16.00
SONGS BY RICKY	Imperial (S) LP 12082	3.00	6.00	9.00
SPOTLIGHT ON RICK	Decca (M) DL 4608	2.50	5.00	7.50
SPOTLIGHT ON RICK	Decca (S) DL 74608	3.50	7.00	10.50
TEEN TIME	Verve (M) MG V 2083	6.00	15.00	24.00
TRUE LOVE	Imperial (EP) IMP 155	1.50	3.75	6.00
UNCHAINED MELODY	Imperial (EP) EP 158	1.50	3.75	6.00
VERY BEST RICK NELSON, THE	United Artists (M) UA LA 330	2.00	3.00	4.00
VERY THOUGHT OF YOU, THE	Decca (M) DL 4559	2.50	5.00	7.50
VERY THOUGHT OF YOU, THE	Decca (S) DL 74559	3.50	7.00	10.50
WINDFALL	MCA (S) 383	2.00	3.00	4.00
YOU'LL NEVER KNOW WHAT YOU'RE MISSIN	Imperial (EP) EP 162	1.50	3.75	6.00

NELSON, Sandy
TITLE	LABEL & NO.	GOOD	VERY GOOD	NEAR MINT
AND THEN THERE WERE DRUMS	Sunset (M) SUM 1224	2.50	3.75	5.00
AND THEN THERE WERE DRUMS	Sunset (S) SUS 5224	2.00	3.00	4.00
BEAT THAT #!!@* DRUM	Imperial (M) LP 9329	3.00	4.50	6.00
BEAT THAT #!!@* DRUM	Imperial (S) LP 12329	3.00	4.50	6.00
BEST OF THE BEATS, THE	Imperial (M) LP 9224	4.00	8.00	12.00
BEST OF THE BEATS, THE	Imperial (S) LP 12224	3.00	6.00	9.00
BE TRUE TO YOUR SCHOOL	Imperial (M) LP 9258	4.00	6.00	8.00
BE TRUE TO YOUR SCHOOL	Imperial (S) LP 12258	3.00	4.50	6.00
BOOGALOO BEAT	Imperial (M) LP 9367	3.00	4.50	6.00
BOOGALOO BEAT	Imperial (S) LP 12367	3.00	4.50	6.00
BOSS BEAT	Imperial (M) LP 9298	3.00	4.50	6.00
BOSS BEAT	Imperial (S) LP 12298	3.00	4.50	6.00
COMPELLING PERCUSSION— AND THEN THERE WERE DRUMS	Imperial (M) LP 9204	4.00	8.00	12.00
COMPELLING PERCUSSION— AND THEN THERE WERE DRUMS	Imperial (S) LP 12204	4.00	8.00	12.00
DRUM DISCOTHEQUE	Imperial (M) LP 9283	3.00	4.50	6.00
DRUM DISCOTHEQUE	Imperial (S) LP 12283	3.00	4.50	6.00
DRUMMIN UP A STORM	Imperial (M) LP 9189	4.00	8.00	12.00
DRUMMIN UP A STORM	Imperial (S) LP 12189	3.00	6.00	9.00
DRUMS ARE MY BEAT	Imperial (M) LP 9168	4.00	8.00	12.00
DRUMS ARE MY BEAT	Imperial (S) LP 12168	3.00	6.00	9.00
GROOVY	Imperial (M) LP 9451	3.00	4.50	6.00
GROOVY	Imperial (S) LP 12451	3.00	4.50	6.00
HE'S A DRUMMER BOY	Imperial (M) LP 9136	4.00	8.00	12.00
HE'S A DRUMMER BOY	Imperial (S) LP 12136	3.00	6.00	9.00
LET THERE BE DRUMS	Imperial (M) LP 9159	4.00	8.00	12.00
LET THERE BE DRUMS	Imperial (S) LP 12159	3.00	6.00	9.00
ON THE WILD SIDE	Imperial (M) LP 9203	4.00	8.00	12.00
ON THE WILD SIDE	Imperial (S) LP 12203	3.00	6.00	9.00
ROCK AND ROLL REVIVAL	Imperial (M) LP 9400	3.00	4.50	6.00
ROCK AND ROLL REVIVAL	Imperial (S) LP 12400	3.00	4.50	6.00
SANDY NELSON PLAYS	Imperial (M) LP 9249	4.00	6.00	8.00
SANDY NELSON PLAYS	Imperial (S) LP 12249	3.00	4.50	6.00
SANDY NELSON PLAYS TEEN BEAT	Imperial (M) LP 9044	4.00	8.00	12.00
SANDY NELSON PLAYS TEEN BEAT	Imperial (S) LP 12044	3.00	6.00	9.00
SUPERDRUMS	Imperial (M) LP 9314	3.00	4.50	6.00
SUPERDRUMS	Imperial (S) LP 12314	3.00	4.50	6.00
TEEN AGE HOUSE PARTY	Imperial (M) LP 9215	4.00	8.00	12.00
TEEN AGE HOUSE PARTY	Imperial (S) LP 12215	3.00	6.00	9.00
TEEN BEAT '65	Imperial (M) LP 9278	4.00	6.00	8.00
TEEN BEAT '65	Imperial (S) LP 12278	3.00	4.50	6.00
VERY BEST OF SANDY NELSON, THE	United Artists (S) UA LA 440	2.00	3.00	4.00
WALKIN' BEAT	Sunset (M) SUM 1114	2.50	3.75	5.00
WALKIN' BEAT	Sunset (S) SUS 5114	2.00	3.00	4.00

NELSON, Tracy
TITLE	LABEL & NO.	GOOD	VERY GOOD	NEAR MINT
POOR MAN'S PARADISE	Columbia (S) KC-31759	2.50	3.75	5.00
SWEET SOUL MUSIC	MCA (S) 494	2.00	3.00	4.00
TRACY NELSON	Atlantic (S) 7310	3.00	4.50	6.00

NELSON, Willie
TITLE	LABEL & NO.	GOOD	VERY GOOD	NEAR MINT
AND THEN I WROTE	Liberty (M) LRP-3239	3.00	6.00	9.00
AND THEN I WROTE	Liberty (S) LST-7239	3.00	6.00	9.00
COUNTRY FAVORITES	RCA (M) LPM-3528	2.00	3.00	4.00
COUNTRY FAVORITES	RCA (S) LSP-3528	2.00	3.00	4.00
COUNTRY MUSIC CONCERT	RCA (M) LPM-3659	2.00	3.00	4.00
COUNTRY MUSIC CONCERT	RCA (S) LSP-3659	2.00	3.00	4.00
HERE'S WILLIE NELSON	Liberty (M) LRP-3308	3.00	6.00	9.00
HERE'S WILLIE NELSON	Liberty (S) LST-7308	3.00	6.00	9.00
PHASES & STAGES	Atlantic (S) 7291	4.00	6.00	8.00
SHOTGUN WILLIE	Atlantic (S) 7262	3.00	4.50	6.00
TEXAS IN MY SOUL	RCA (M) LPM-3937	2.00	3.00	4.00
TEXAS IN MY SOUL	RCA (S) LSP-3937	2.00	3.00	4.00

NERO, Peter
TITLE	LABEL & NO.	GOOD	VERY GOOD	NEAR MINT
DISCO DANCE (& LOVE THEMES OF THE 70's)	Arista (S) 4034	2.00	3.00	4.00
PETER NERO'S GREATEST HITS	Columbia (S) KC-33136	2.50	3.75	5.00
SAY, HAS ANYBODY SEEN MY SWEET GYPSY ROSE	Columbia (S) KC-32698	2.00	3.00	4.00
SUMMER OF '42/FIRST TIME EVER	Columbia (S) CG-33624	2.50	3.75	5.00

NESMITH, Michael
TITLE	LABEL & NO.	GOOD	VERY GOOD	NEAR MINT
PRISON, THE (RI)	Pacific Arts (S) 101	2.00	3.00	4.00

(M) Mono (S) Stereo (EP) Extended Play (Q) Quad (RI) Re-issued

NESMITH, Michael & The First National Band

TITLE	LABEL & NO.	GOOD	VERY GOOD	NEAR MINT
AND THE HITS KEEP ON COMING	RCA (S) LSP 4695	3.00	4.50	6.00
LOOSE SALUTE	RCA (S) LSP 4415	3.00	4.50	6.00
MAGNETIC SOUTH	RCA (S) LSP 4371	3.00	4.50	6.00
NEVADA FIGHTER	RCA (S) LSP 4497	3.00	4.50	6.00

NESMITH, Michael & The Second National Band

TITLE	LABEL & NO.	GOOD	VERY GOOD	NEAR MINT
TANTAMOUNT TO TREASON	RCA (S) LSP 4563	3.00	4.50	6.00

NEVILLE, Aaron

TITLE	LABEL & NO.	GOOD	VERY GOOD	NEAR MINT
LIKE IT 'TIS	Minit (M) LP 40007	4.00	8.00	12.00
LIKE IT 'TIS	Minit (S) LP 24007	3.00	6.00	9.00
TELL IT LIKE IT IS	Parlo (M) LP 1	4.50	9.00	13.50

NEWBEATS

TITLE	LABEL & NO.	GOOD	VERY GOOD	NEAR MINT
BIG BEAT SOUNDS	Hickory (M) LPM 122	4.00	8.00	12.00
BREAD AND BUTTER	Hickory (M) LPM 120	4.00	8.00	12.00
RUN BABY RUN	Hickory (M) LPM 128	4.00	8.00	12.00

NEW BIRTH

TITLE	LABEL & NO.	GOOD	VERY GOOD	NEAR MINT
BEST OF NEW BIRTH	RCA (S) APL1-1021	3.00	4.50	6.00
BIRTH DAY	RCA (S) LSP-4797	3.00	4.50	6.00
BLIND BABY	Buddah (S) 5636	4.00	6.00	8.00
COMIN' FROM ALL ENDS	RCA (S) APL1-0494	2.50	3.75	5.00
IT'S BEEN A LONG TIME	RCA (Q) APD1-0285	2.50	3.75	5.00

NEWBURY, Mickey

TITLE	LABEL & NO.	GOOD	VERY GOOD	NEAR MINT
'FRISCO MABEL JOY	Elektra (S) 74107	3.00	4.50	6.00
'FRISCO MABEL JOY	Elektra (Q) EQ-4107	3.50	5.25	7.00
HEAVEN HELP THE CHILD	Elektra (S) 75055	3.00	4.50	6.00
I CAME TO HEAR THE MUSIC	Elektra (S) 7E-1007	2.50	3.75	5.00
LOVERS	Elektra (S) 7E-1030	2.50	3.75	5.00

NEW CHRISTY MINSTRELS

TITLE	LABEL & NO.	GOOD	VERY GOOD	NEAR MINT
ACADEMY AWARD WINNER-CHIM CHIM CHER-EE (& OTHER HAPPY SONGS)	Columbia (M) CL 2369	2.00	3.00	4.00
ACADEMY AWARD WINNER-CHIM CHIM CHER-EE (& OTHER HAPPY SONGS)	Columbia (S) CS 9169	2.50	3.75	5.00
CHRISTMAS WITH THE CHRISTIES	Columbia (M) CL-2556	2.00	3.00	4.00
CHRISTMAS WITH THE CHRISTIES	Columbia (S) CS-9356	2.50	3.75	5.00
COWBOY & INDIANS	Columbia (M) CL-2303	2.00	3.00	4.00
COWBOY & INDIANS	Columbia (S) CS-9103	2.50	3.75	5.00
GREATEST HITS	Columbia (M) CL 2479	2.00	3.00	4.00
GREATEST HITS	Columbia (S) CS 9279	2.50	3.75	5.00
LAND OF GIANTS	Columbia (M) CL-2187	2.00	3.00	4.00
LAND OF GIANTS	Columbia (S) CS-8987	2.50	3.75	5.00
MERRY CHRISTMAS	Columbia (M) CL-2096	2.00	3.00	4.00
MERRY CHRISTMAS	Columbia (S) CS-8896	2.50	3.75	5.00
NEW KICK	Columbia (M) CL-2542	2.00	3.00	4.00
NEW KICK	Columbia (S) CS-9342	2.50	3.75	5.00
PRESENTING NEW CHRISTY MINSTRELS	Columbia (M) CL-1872	2.00	3.00	4.00
PRESENTING NEW CHRISTY MINSTRELS	Columbia (S) CS-8672	3.00	4.50	6.00
RAMBLIN (FEAT, GREEN, GREEN)	Columbia (M) CL-2055	2.00	3.00	4.00
RAMBLIN (FEAT, GREEN, GREEN)	Columbia (S) CS-8855	2.50	3.75	5.00
TALL TALES (LEGENDS & NONSENSE)	Columbia (M) CL 2017	2.00	3.00	4.00
TALL TALES (LEGENDS & NONSENSE)	Columbia (S) CS 8817	2.50	3.75	5.00
TODAY	Columbia (M) CL-2159	2.00	3.00	4.00
TODAY	Columbia (S) CS-8959	2.50	3.75	5.00

Also see MC GUIRE, Barry; First Edition

NEW COLONY SIX

TITLE	LABEL & NO.	GOOD	VERY GOOD	NEAR MINT
ATTACKING A STRAW MAN	Mercury (M) SR 61228	3.00	4.50	6.00
BREAKTHROUGH	Sentar (M) 101	5.00	7.50	10.00
COLONIZATION	Sentar (M) ST 3001	3.00	4.50	6.00
COLONIZATION	Sentar (S) SST 3801	4.00	6.00	8.00
REVELATIONS	Mercury (M) SR 61165	3.00	4.50	6.00

NEW DIMENSIONS

TITLE	LABEL & NO.	GOOD	VERY GOOD	NEAR MINT
DEUCES AND EIGHTS	Sutton (M) 331	3.00	6.00	9.00
SOUL SURF	Sutton (M) 336	3.00	6.00	9.00
SURF 'N' BONGOS	Sutton (M) 332	3.00	6.00	9.00

NEWHART, Bob

TITLE	LABEL & NO.	GOOD	VERY GOOD	NEAR MINT
BEHIND THE BUTTON-DOWN MIND OF BOB NEWHART	Warner Bros. (M) W 1417	3.00	6.00	9.00
BEHIND THE BUTTON-DOWN MIND OF BOB NEWHART	Warner Bros. (S) WS 1417	3.50	7.00	10.50
BOB NEWHART: DELUXE EDITION	Warner Bros. (M) 2N 1399	5.00	10.00	15.00
BOB NEWHART: DELUXE EDITION	Warner Bros. (S) 2NS 1399	4.50	6.75	9.00
BOB NEWHART FACES BOB NEWHART	Warner Bros. (M) W 1517	3.00	4.50	6.00
BOB NEWHART FACES BOB NEWHART	Warner Bros. (S) WS 1517	3.50	5.25	7.00
BUTTON-DOWN MIND OF BOB NEWHART	Warner Bros. (M) W 1379	3.00	6.00	9.00
BUTTON-DOWN MIND OF BOB NEWHART	Warner Bros. (S) WS 1379	3.50	7.00	10.50
BUTTON-DOWN MIND ON TV	Warner Bros. (M) W 1467	3.00	6.00	9.00
BUTTON-DOWN MIND ON TV	Warner Bros. (S) WS 1467	3.50	7.00	10.50
BUTTON-DOWN MIND STRIKES BACK	Warner Bros. (M) W 1393	3.00	6.00	9.00
BUTTON-DOWN MIND STRIKES BACK	Warner Bros. (S) WS 1393	3.50	7.00	10.50
THIS IS IT!	Warner Bros. (S) WS 1717	3.00	4.50	6.00
WINDMILLS ARE WEAKENING	Warner Bros. (M) W 1588	3.00	4.50	6.00

NEW HOPE

TITLE	LABEL & NO.	GOOD	VERY GOOD	NEAR MINT
TO UNDERSTAND IS TO LOVE	Jamie (S) LPS 3034	4.50	9.00	13.50

(M) Mono (S) Stereo (EP) Extended Play (Q) Quad (RI) Re-issued

NEWLEY, Anthony

TITLE	LABEL & NO.	GOOD	VERY GOOD	NEAR MINT
AIN'T IT FUNNY	Verve (S) V-5096	2.50	3.75	5.00

NEWMAN, Randy

TITLE	LABEL & NO.	GOOD	VERY GOOD	NEAR MINT
GOOD OLD BOYS	Reprise (S) MS 2193	3.00	4.50	6.00
GOOD OLD BOYS	Reprise (Q) MS4-2193	2.50	3.75	5.00
LITTLE CRIMINALS	Warner Bros. BS K-3079	2.00	3.00	4.00
LIVE	Reprise (S) 6459	4.00	6.00	8.00
RANDY NEWMAN	Reprise (S) 6286	5.00	7.50	10.00
SAIL AWAY	Reprise (S) 2064	3.00	4.50	6.00
12 SONGS	Reprise (S) 6373	4.00	6.00	8.00

NEW MIX

TITLE	LABEL & NO.	GOOD	VERY GOOD	NEAR MINT
NEW MIX, THE	United Artists (S) UAS 6678	2.50	3.75	5.00

NEW RENAISSANCE SOCIETY

TITLE	LABEL & NO.	GOOD	VERY GOOD	NEAR MINT
BAROQUE N' STONES (PERFORMED BY THE NEW RENAISSANCE SOCIETY)	Hanna Barbera (M) HLP 8504	4.00	6.00	8.00

NEW RIDERS OF THE PURPLE SAGE

TITLE	LABEL & NO.	GOOD	VERY GOOD	NEAR MINT
ADVENTURES OF PANAMA RED	Columbia (S) KC-32450	2.50	3.75	5.00
ADVENTURES OF PANAMA RED	Columbia (Q) CQ-32450	3.00	4.50	6.00
BRUJO	Columbia (S) 33145	2.50	3.75	5.00
GORDON'S WAR	Buddah (S) 5137	3.00	4.50	6.00
GYPSY COWBOY	Columbia (S) KC-31930	2.50	3.75	5.00
NEW RIDERS OF THE PURPLE SAGE	Columbia (S) 30888	3.00	4.50	6.00
POWERGLIDE	Columbia (S) 31284	2.50	3.75	5.00

NEW SEEKERS

TITLE	LABEL & NO.	GOOD	VERY GOOD	NEAR MINT
BEAUTIFUL PEOPLE	Elektra (S) 74088	3.00	4.50	6.00
BEST OF THE NEW SEEKERS	Elektra (S) 75051	3.50	5.25	7.00
CIRCLES	Elektra (S) 75034	3.00	4.50	6.00
COME SOFTLY TO ME	Verve (S) V-5090	4.00	6.00	8.00
HISTORY OF THE NEW SEEKERS	Verve (S) V-5095	4.00	6.00	8.00
WE'D LIKE TO TEACH THE WORLD TO SING	Elektra (S) 74115	3.00	4.50	6.00

Also see SEEKERS

NEWTON-JOHN, Olivia

TITLE	LABEL & NO.	GOOD	VERY GOOD	NEAR MINT
COME ON OVER	MCA 2186	2.50	3.75	5.00
DON'T STOP BELIEVIN'	MCA 2223	2.50	3.75	5.00
GREATEST HITS	MCA 3028	2.00	3.00	4.00
HAVE YOU NEVER BEEN MELLOW	MCA 2133	2.50	4.25	5.00
IF NOT FOR YOU	Uni (S) 73117	5.00	7.50	10.00
IF YOU LOVE ME, LET ME KNOW	MCA (S) 411	3.00	4.50	6.00
LET ME BE THERE	MCA (S) 389	3.00	4.50	6.00
MAKING A GOOD THING BETTER	MCA 2280	2.50	3.75	5.00

NEWTON, JUICE & SILVER SPUR

TITLE	LABEL & NO.	GOOD	VERY GOOD	NEAR MINT
JUICE NEWTON & SILVER SPUR	RCA (S) APL1-1004	3.00	4.50	6.00

NEWTON, Wayne

TITLE	LABEL & NO.	GOOD	VERY GOOD	NEAR MINT
BEST OF WAYNE NEWTON LIVE	Chelsea (S) CHL 504	2.50	3.75	5.00
BEST OF WAYNE NEWTON	Capitol (M) 2797	2.50	3.75	5.00
BEST OF WAYNE NEWTON	Capitol (S) 2797	3.00	4.50	6.00
CAN'T YOU HEAR THE SONG?	Chelsea (S) CHE 1003	2.50	3.75	5.00
CHRISTMAS EVERYWHERE	Chelsea (S) CHL 800	2.50	3.75	5.00
DADDY DON'T YOU WALK SO FAST	Chelsea (S) CHE 1001	3.00	4.50	6.00
DADDY DON'T YOU WALK SO FAST (RI)	Chelsea (S) CHL 513	2.50	3.75	5.00
DANKE SCHOEN	Capitol (M) T 1973	3.50	5.25	7.00
DANKE SCHOEN	Capitol (S) ST 1973	4.00	6.00	8.00
IT'S ONLY THE GOOD TIMES	Capitol (M) 2635	2.00	3.00	4.00
IT'S ONLY THE GOOD TIMES	Capitol (S) 2635	2.50	3.75	5.00
MIDNIGHT IDOL	Chelsea (S) CHL 507	2.50	3.75	5.00
NOW!	Capitol (M) 2445	2.50	3.75	5.00
NOW!	Capitol (S) 2445	2.50	3.75	5.00
ONE MORE TIME	MGM (S) SE 4549	2.50	3.75	5.00
RED ROSES FOR A BLUE LADY	Capitol (M) 2335	2.00	3.00	4.00
RED ROSES FOR A BLUE LADY	Capitol (S) 2335	2.50	3.75	5.00
SUMMER WIND	Capitol (M) T 2389	2.00	3.00	4.00
SUMMER WIND	Capitol (S) ST2389	2.50	3.75	5.00
TOMORROW	Chelsea (S) CHL 512	2.50	3.75	5.00
WALKING ON NEW GRASS	MGM (S) SE 4523	2.50	3.75	5.00
WHILE WE'RE STILL YOUNG	Chelsea (S) CHE 1006	2.50	3.75	5.00

NEW TWEEDY BROTHERS

TITLE	LABEL & NO.	GOOD	VERY GOOD	NEAR MINT
NEW TWEEDY BROTHERS, THE	Ridon (S) SLP 234	6.00	12.00	18.00

NEW VAUDEVILLE BAND

TITLE	LABEL & NO.	GOOD	VERY GOOD	NEAR MINT
WINCHESTER CATHEDRAL	Fontana (M) 27560	2.00	3.00	4.00
WINCHESTER CATHEDRAL	Fontana (S) 67560	2.50	3.75	5.00

NEW WAVE

TITLE	LABEL & NO.	GOOD	VERY GOOD	NEAR MINT
NEW WAVE, THE	Canterbury (M) CLPM 1501	2.50	3.75	5.00
NEW WAVE, THE	Canterbury (S) CLPS 1501	3.50	5.25	7.00

NEW YORK CITY

TITLE	LABEL & NO.	GOOD	VERY GOOD	NEAR MINT
I'M DOIN' FINE NOW	Chelsea (S) BCL1-0198	3.50	5.25	7.00

NEW YORK DOLLS

TITLE	LABEL & NO.	GOOD	VERY GOOD	NEAR MINT
NEW YORK DOLLS	Mercury (S) SRM 1 675	4.00	6.00	8.00
TOO MUCH, TOO SOON	Mercury (S) SRM 1 1001	4.00	6.00	8.00

Also see JOHANSEN, David

TITLE	LABEL & NO.	GOOD	VERY GOOD	NEAR MINT
NEW YORK ROCK 'N' ROLL ENSEMBLE				
FAITHFUL FREINDS	Atco (S) SD 33-294	3.00	4.50	6.00
NEW YORK ROCK AND ROLL ENSEMBLE	Atco (S) SD 33-240	3.00	4.50	6.00
NICE				
ARS LONGA VITA BREVIS	Immediate (S) Z12 52020	5.00	7.50	10.00
ELEGY	Mercury (S) SR 61324	4.00	6.00	8.00
EVERYTHING AS NICE AS MOTHER MAKES	Immediate (S) 102	5.00	7.50	10.00
FIVE BRIDGES SUITE	Mercury (S) SR 61295	4.00	6.00	8.00
KEITH EMERSON WITH THE NICE	Mercury (S) SRM 2 6500	3.00	4.50	6.00
NICE	Immediate (S) Z12 52022	5.00	7.50	10.00
NICE-IMMEDIATE STORY	Sire (S) SASH-3710-2	4.00	6.00	8.00
THOUGHTS OF EMERLIST DAVJACK	Immediate (S) Z12 52004	5.00	7.50	10.00
NICHOLS, Mike & Elaine May				
AN EVENING WITH MIKE NICHOLS AND ELAINE MAY	Mercury (M) 2200	2.50	3.75	5.00
IMPROVISATIONS TO MUSIC	Mercury (M) 20376	2.50	3.75	5.00
MIKE NICHOLS AND ELAINE MAY EXAMINE DOCTORS	Mercury (M) 20680	2.50	3.75	5.00
RETROSPECT	Mercury (M) SRM 2 628	2.50	3.75	5.00
NICO				
CHELSEA GIRL	Verve (M) V6-5032	6.00	9.00	12.00
DESERT SHORE	Reprise (S) 6424	5.00	7.50	10.00
END, THE	Island (S) 9311	4.00	6.00	8.00
MARBLE INDEX, THE	Elektra (S) EKS 74029	5.00	7.50	10.00
NIGHTCAPS				
WINE, WINE, WINE	Vandan (M) VRLP 8124	7.50	18.75	30.00
NIGHTCRAWLERS				
LITTLE BLACK EGG, THE	Kapp (M) KL 1520	4.00	8.00	12.00
NIGHTHAWKS				
ROCK & ROLL	Aladdin (S) 101	3.50	5.25	7.00
NIGHT OWLS				
TWISTING THE OLDIES	Valmor (M) 79	3.00	6.00	9.00
NILSSON				
AERIAL PANDEMONIUM BALLET	RCA (S) LSP 4543	4.00	6.00	8.00
EARLY TYMES	Musicor 2505	2.50	3.75	5.00
HARRY	RCA (S) LSP 4197	4.00	6.00	8.00
KNNILLSSONN	RCA AFL1-2276	2.00	3.00	4.00
LITTLE TOUCH OF SCHMILSSON IN THE NIGHT	RCA APL1-0097	3.00	4.50	6.00
NILSSON SCHMILSSON	RCA (Q) APD1-0319	2.50	3.75	5.00
NILSSON SINGS NEWMAN	RCA LSP 4289	3.00	4.50	6.00
NILSSON SINGS NEWMAN (RI)	RCA (S) APL1-0203	2.00	3.00	4.00
POINT, THE	RCA LSPX-1003	3.50	5.25	7.00
PUSSY CATS	RCA (S) CPL1-0570	2.50	3.75	5.00
PUSSY CATS	RCA (Q) APD1-0570	2.50	3.75	5.00
SANDMAN	RCA APL1-1031	2.50	3.75	5.00
SANDMAN	RCA (Q) APD1-1031	2.50	3.75	5.00
SCATALOGUE (ORIGINAL)		10.00	20.00	30.00
SON OF DRACULA (WITH RINGO STARR)	Rapple (S) ABLI-0220	4.00	6.00	8.00
SON OF SCHMILSSON	RCA (S) LSP 4717	3.50	5.25	7.00
NIMOY, Leonard				
MR. SPOCK'S MUSIC FROM OUTER SPACE	Dot (M) DLP 3794	2.50	3.75	5.00
MR. SPOCK'S MUSIC FROM OUTER SPACE	Dot (S) DLP 25794	2.50	3.75	5.00
OUTER SPACE/INNER MIND	Paramount (S) 2-1030	2.00	3.00	4.00
TWO SIDES OF LEONARD NIMOY	Dot (S) 25835	2.00	3.00	4.00
WAY I FEEL	Dot (S) 25883	2.00	3.00	4.00
WAY I FEEL, THE	Dot (M) 883	2.50	3.75	5.00

TITLE	LABEL & NO.	GOOD	VERY GOOD	NEAR MINT
1910 FRUITGUM COMPANY				
GOODY, GOODY, GUM DROPS	Buddah (S) BDS 5027	3.00	4.50	6.00
HARD RIDE	Buddah (S) BDS 5043	3.00	4.50	6.00
INDIAN GIVER	Buddah (S) BDS 5036	3.00	4.50	6.00
JUICIEST FRUITGUM	Buddah (S) BDS 5057	3.00	4.50	6.00

(M) Mono (S) Stereo (EP) Extended Play (Q) Quad (RI) Re-issued

TITLE	LABEL & NO.	GOOD	VERY GOOD	NEAR MINT
1, 2, 3 RED LIGHT	Buddah (S) BDS 5022	4.00	6.00	8.00
SIMON SAYS	Buddah (S) BDS 5010	4.00	6.00	8.00
NINTH CREATION, THE				
BUBBLE GUM	Rite Track (M) RKA 01M	3.00	4.50	6.00
NIRVANA				
ALL OF US	Bell (S) 6024	6.00	9.00	12.00
NIRVANA	Metromedia (S) 1018	6.00	9.00	12.00
STORY OF SIMON SIMOPATH, THE	Bell (S) 6015-S	5.00	7.50	10.00
NISKER, Scoop				
IF YOU DON'T LIKE THE NEWS.. GO OUT AND MAKE SOME OF YOUR OWN		4.00	6.00	8.00
NITECAPS				
FRUG	Forum Circle (M) 7G 110	2.00	4.00	6.00
FRUG	Forum Circle (S) 7GS 2110	3.00	6.00	9.00
NITTY GRITTY DIRT BAND				
ALIVE	Liberty (S) LST 7611	4.00	6.00	8.00
ALL THE GOOD TIMES	United Artists 5553	3.50	5.25	7.00
ALL THE GOOD TIMES	United Artists (EP) EP 69	2.50	3.75	5.00
BANJOMAN	Sire 7527	2.50	3.75	5.00
CHICKEN CHRONICLES	United Artists UA-LA830	2.00	3.00	4.00
DIRT, SILVER & GOLD	United Artists UA-LA670	2.50	3.75	5.00
DREAM	United Artists UA-LA469	2.50	3.75	5.00
NITTY GRITTY DIRT BAND, THE	Liberty (M) LRP 3501	3.00	4.50	6.00
NITTY GRITTY DIRT BAND, THE	Liberty (S) LST 7501	4.00	6.00	8.00
RICOCHET	Liberty (M) LRP 3516	3.00	4.50	6.00
RICOCHET	Liberty (S) LST 7516	4.00	6.00	8.00
UNCLE CHARLIE AND HIS DOG TEDDY	Liberty (S) LST 7642	2.50	3.75	5.00
WILL THE CIRCLE BE UNBROKEN	United Artists (S) 9801	2.50	3.75	5.00
NITZSCHE, Jack				
CHOPIN '66	Reprise (M) 6200	4.50	9.00	13.50
HITS OF THE BEATLES	Reprise (M) 6115	5.00	10.00	15.00
LONELY SURFER, THE	Reprise (M) R 6101	4.00	8.00	12.00
LONELY SURFER, THE	Reprise (S) R9 6101	5.00	10.00	15.00
ST. GILES CRIPPLEGATE	Reprise (M) MS 2092	4.00	6.00	8.00
NIX, Don				
HOBOES, HEROES, & STREET CORNER CLOWNS	Enterprise (S) 1032	3.00	4.50	6.00
LIVING BY THE DAYS	Elektra (S) 74101	3.00	4.50	6.00
NIXON, Richard M.				
RESIGNATION OF A PRESIDENT	Capitol (S) SJ-11350	2.00	3.00	4.00
NIXON, Richard M. & John F. Kennedy				
GREAT DEBATES-1960	Columbia (M) D2L-372	2.50	3.75	5.00
NOBLE, Cliff				
PONY THE HORSE	Moon Shot (M) MS 601	3.00	4.50	6.00
NOBLES, Cliff & Co.				
HORSE, THE	Phil L.A. Of Soul (S) 4001	3.00	4.50	6.00
NO GO				
NO GO	Island (S) SMAS-9333	3.00	4.50	6.00
NOGUEZ, Jacky				
CHOW CHOW BAMBINA	Jamie (M) J-3007	2.50	3.75	5.00
CHOW CHOW BAMBINA	Jamie (S) JS-3007	3.00	4.00	6.00
DANCE ALONG WITH JACKY NOGUEZ	Jamie (M) J-3013	2.50	3.75	5.00
DANCE ALONG WITH JACKY NOGUEZ	Jamie (S) JS-3013	2.50	3.75	5.00
NOLAND, Terry				
TERRY NOLAND	Brunswick (M) BL 54041	19.00	47.50	76.00
NOLAN, Kenny				
KENNY NOLAN	20th Century (S) T 532	2.50	3.75	5.00
NOONAN, Steve				
STEVE NOONAN	Elektra (S) EKS 74017	3.00	4.50	6.00
NORDINE, Ken				
CLASSIC COLLECTION- BEST OF WORDS JAZZ	Dot (S) DLP 25880	5.00	7.50	10.00
CONCERT IN THE SKY	Decca (M) DL 8550	3.00	6.00	9.00
HOW ARE THINGS IN YOUR TOWN	Blue Thumb (S) 33	3.00	4.50	6.00
LOVE WORDS	Dot (M) DLP 3115	5.00	10.00	15.00
LOVE WORDS	Dot (S) DLP-25115	5.50	11.00	16.50
MY BABY	Dot (M) DLP-3142	4.50	9.00	13.50
NEXT	Dot (M) DLP-3196	4.00	8.00	12.00
NEXT	Dot (S) DLP-25196	4.50	9.00	13.50
SON OF WORD JAZZ	Dot (M) DLP 3096	6.00	15.00	24.00
SON OF WORD JAZZ	Dot (S) DLP 25096	7.00	17.50	28.00
TWINK	Philips (M) 200258	4.00	6.00	8.00
TWINK	Philips (S) 600258	5.00	7.50	10.00

TITLE	LABEL & NO.	GOOD	VERY GOOD	NEAR MINT
WORD JAZZ	Dot (M) DLP 3075	8.00	20.00	32.00
WORD JAZZ (VOL. 2)	Dot (M) DLP-3301	4.00	8.00	12.00
WORD JAZZ (VOL. 2)	Dot (S) DLP-25301	5.00	10.00	15.00

NORTHERN LITES
GABRIELLE	United Artists International (M) 14507	4.00	6.00	8.00

NOTES FROM THE UNDERGROUND
NOTES FROM THE UNDERGROUND	Vanguard (S) VSD 6502	4.00	6.00	8.00

NOVA LOCAL
NOVA 1	Decca (S) DL 79477	4.50	6.75	9.00

NOVELLS
MOTHERS RECORDS AND THE SNARF COMPANY PRESENT A HAPPENING WITH THE NOVELLS	Mothers (S) MRS 73	2.50	3.75	5.00

NRBQ
BOPPIN THE BLUES	Columbia (S) CS 9981	4.00	6.00	8.00
NRBQ	Columbia (S) CS 9858	5.00	7.50	10.00
SCRAPS	Kama Sutra (S) KSBS 2045	3.00	4.50	6.00
WORKSHOP	Kama Sutra (S) KSBS 2065	3.00	4.50	6.00

Also see PERKINS, Carl

NUCLEUS
NUCLEUS	Mainstream (S) S/6120	3.00	4.50	6.00

NUGENT, Ted
CAT SCRATCH FEVER	Epic (S) JE 34700	2.50	3.75	5.00
DOUBLE LIVE GONZO	Epic (S) KE2 35069	3.00	4.50	6.00
FREE FOR ALL	Epic (S) PE 34121	2.50	3.75	5.00
FREE FOR ALL	Epic (Q) PEQ 34121	2.50	3.75	5.00
TED NUGENT	Epic (S) PE 33692	2.50	3.75	5.00

Also see AMBOY DUKES

NUTMEGS
NUTMEGS, THE	Herald (EP) EP-452	4.00	6.00	8.00
NUTMEGS FEATURING LEROY GRIFFIN	Relic (M) 5002	4.00	6.00	8.00

NUTTY SQUIRRELS
BIRD WATCHING	Columbia (M) CL-1589	4.00	6.00	8.00
BIRD WATCHING	Columbia (S) CS-8389	5.00	7.50	10.00
HARD DAY'S NIGHT	MGM (M) E-4272	3.00	4.50	6.00
HARD DAY'S NIGHT	MGM (S) SE-4272	4.00	6.00	8.00
NUTTY SQUIRRELS	Hanover (EP) DP-301	2.00	4.00	6.00

NUTZ
HARD NUTZ	A&M (S) SP 4623	2.00	3.00	4.00
NUTZ	A&M (S) SP 3648	2.00	3.00	4.00

NYRO, Laura
MORE THAN A NEW DISCOVERY	Verve Folkways (M) FT 3020	4.00	6.00	8.00
MORE THAN A NEW DISCOVERY	Verve/Folkways (S) FTS 3020	5.00	7.50	10.00

O

O'BRIEN, Hugh
WYATT EARP SINGS	ABC (M) 203	2.50	3.75	5.00

(M) Mono (S) Stereo (EP) Extended Play (Q) Quad (RI) Re-issued

OCEAN
TITLE	LABEL & NO.	GOOD	VERY GOOD	NEAR MINT
GIVE TOMORROW'S CHILDREN ONE MORE CHANCE	Kama Sutra (S) 2064	2.50	3.75	5.00
PUT YOUR HAND IN THE HAND	Kama Sutra (S) 2033	3.00	5.25	6.00

OCHS, Phil
ALL THE NEWS THAT'S FIT TO SING	Elektra (S) EKS 7269	2.50	3.75	5.00
GREATEST HITS	A & M (S) SP 4253	3.00	6.00	9.00
I AIN'T MARCHING ANYMORE	Elektra (M) EKL-287	3.00	4.50	6.00
I AIN'T MARCHING ANYMORE	Elektra (S) EKS7-287	4.00	6.00	8.00
PHIL OCHS IN CONCERT	Elecktra (M) EKL 310	2.50	3.75	5.00
PHIL OCHS IN CONCERT	Elektra (S) EKS 7-310	3.50	5.25	7.00
PLEASURES OF THE HARBOR	A & M (S) SP 4133	2.50	3.75	5.00
REHEARSALS FOR RETIREMENT	A & M (S) SP 4181	2.50	3.75	5.00
TAPE FROM CALIFORNIA	A & M (S) SP 4148	2.50	3.75	5.00

OCTOBER COUNTRY
OCTOBER COUNTRY	Epic (S) BN 26381	3.00	4.50	6.00

O'DELL, Kenny
KENNY O'DELL	Capricorn (S) 0140	4.00	6.00	8.00

ODETTA
BALLAD FOR AMERICANS	Vanguard (M) VRS-9066	3.00	4.50	6.00
BALLAD FOR AMERICANS	Vanguard (S) VSD-2057	3.50	5.25	7.00
MY EYES HAVE SEEN	Vanguard (M) VRS-9059	3.00	4.50	6.00
MY EYES HAVE SEEN	Vanguard (S) VSD-2046	3.50	5.25	7.00
ODETTA SINGS FOLK SONGS	RCA (M) LPM 2643	2.50	3.75	5.00
ODETTA SINGS FOLK SONGS	RCA (S) LSP 2643	3.00	4.50	6.00

ODOM, Andrew
FATHER DOWN THE ROAD	Bluesway (M) 6055	2.50	4.00	5.00

O'HARA, Maureen
LOVE LETTERS FROM MAUREEN O'HARA	RCA LPM-1953	3.00	6.00	9.00
LOVE LETTERS FROM MAUREEN O'HARA	RCA (S) LSP-1953	4.00	8.00	12.00

O'HARA'S PLAYBOYS
GET READY	Fontana (S) SRF 6 7581	3.50	5.25	7.00

OHIO EXPRESS
BEG, BORROW, AND STEAL	Cameo (S) CS,20,000	4.00	6.00	8.00
CHEWY CHEWY	Buddah (S) BDS 5026	3.00	4.50	6.00
MERCY	Buddah (S) BDS 5037	3.00	4.50	6.00
OHIO EXPRESS	Buddah (S) BDS 5018	3.00	4.50	6.00
SALT WATER TAFFY	Buddah (S) BDS 5021	3.00	4.50	6.00
VERY BEST OF THE OHIO EXPRESS	Buddah (S) BDS 5058	3.00	4.50	6.00

OHIO PLAYERS
CLIMAX	Westbound 1003	3.50	5.25	7.00
ECSTASY	Westbound (S) 2021	5.00	7.50	10.00
ECSTASY (RI)	20th Century/Westbound 222	3.00	4.50	6.00
FIRE	Mercury (S) SRM-1-1013	3.00	4.50	6.00
HONEY	Mercury SRM-1-1038	2.00	3.00	4.00
OBSERVATIONS IN TIME	Capitol (S) ST 192	4.50	6.75	9.00
OHIO PLAYERS (RI OF CAPITOL 192)	Capitol (S) ST 11291	2.50	3.75	5.00
OHIO PLAYERS GREATEST HITS	Westbound (S) 1005	3.50	5.25	7.00
PAIN	Westbound (S) 2045	5.00	7.50	10.00
PAIN (RI)	20th Century/Westbound (S) 219	3.00	4.50	6.00
PLEASURE	Westbound (S) 2017	5.00	7.50	10.00
PLEASURE (RI)	20th Century/Westbound (S) 220	3.00	4.50	6.00
RATTLESNAKE	20th Century/Westbound 211	3.00	4.50	6.00
SKIN TIGHT	Mercury SRM-1-705	3.00	4.50	6.00
VERY BEST OF THE WORLD OF OHIO PLAYERS	United Artists UA-LA502	2.00	3.00	4.00

O'JAYS
BACK STABBERS	Phila. Intl (S) KZ 31712	3.00	4.50	6.00
COMIN' THROUGH	Imperial (M) LP 9290	3.00	4.50	6.00
COMIN' THROUGH	Imperial (S) LP 12290	4.00	6.00	8.00
EVERYTHING YOU ALWAYS WANTED TO HEAR BY THE O'JAYS BUT WERE AFRAID TO ASK FOR	Phila. Int'l (M) ASZ 140	3.00	4.50	6.00
FAMILY REUNION	Phila. Int'l. (S) PZ 33807	2.00	3.00	4.00
FAMILY REUNION	Phila. Int'l. (Q) PZQ 33807	3.00	4.50	6.00
FULL OF SOUL	Sunset (S) SUS-5222	3.00	4.50	6.00
GREATEST HITS, THE	United Artists (S) UAS 5655	3.00	4.50	6.00
LIVE IN LONDON	Phila. Int'l. (S) KZ 32953	2.00	3.00	4.00
LIVE IN LONDON	Phila. Int'l. (Q) ZQ 32953	3.00	4.50	6.00
O'JAYS	Bell (S) 6082	3.00	4.50	6.00
O'JAYS IN PHILADELPHIA	Neptune (S) NLPS 202	4.00	6.00	8.00
O'JAYS MEET THE MOMENTS	Stang (S) 1024	3.50	5.25	7.00
SHIP AHOY	Phila. Int'l. (S) KZ 32408	2.50	3.75	5.00
SHIP AHOY	Phila. Int'l. (Q) ZQ 32408	3.00	4.50	6.00
SOUL SOUNDS	Minit (M) LP 40008	4.00	6.00	8.00
SURVIVAL	Phila. Int'l. (S) KZ 33150	2.00	3.00	4.00

O'KEEFE, Danny
BREEZY STORIES	Atlantic (S) SD 7264	3.50	5.25	7.00
O'KEEFE	Signpost (S) SP8404	4.50	6.75	9.00

OLATUNJI
AFRO PERCUSSION	Columbia (S) CS 8434	3.00	4.50	6.00

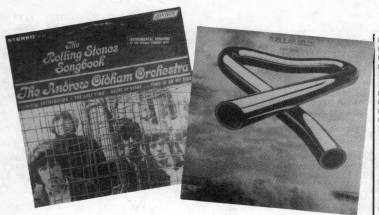

TITLE	LABEL & NO.	GOOD	VERY GOOD	NEAR MINT
CRYING	Monument (M) 4007	6.00	12.00	18.00
CRYING	Monument (S) 14007	8.00	16.00	24.00
CRY SOFTLY LONELY ONE	MGM (M) E 4514	3.00	4.50	6.00
CRY SOFTLY LONELY ONE	MGM (S) SE 4514	4.00	6.00	8.00
EARLY ORBISON	Monument (M) 8023	3.50	5.25	7.00
EARLY ORBISON	Monument (S) 18023	4.50	6.75	9.00
GREATEST HITS	Monument (M) 4009	5.00	10.00	15.00
GREATEST HITS	Monument (S) 14009	6.00	12.00	18.00
GREATEST HITS (RI of 4009 LP)	Monument (M) MLP 8000	4.00	8.00	12.00
GREATEST HITS (RI of 14009 LP)	Monument (S) SLP 18000	5.00	10.00	15.00
HANK WILLIAMS THE ROY ORBISON WAY	MGM (S) SE 4683	3.50	5.25	7.00
I'M STILL IN LOVE WITH YOU	Mercury (S) SRM 1 1045	3.00	4.50	6.00
IN DREAMS	Monument (M) 8003	5.00	10.00	15.00
IN DREAMS	Monument (S) 18003	6.00	12.00	18.00
LONELY AND BLUE	Monument (M) 4002	7.50	18.75	30.00
LONELY AND BLUE	Monument (S) 14002	8.00	20.00	32.00
MILESTONES	MGM (S) SE 4934	3.00	4.50	6.00
MORE OF ROY ORBISON'S GREATEST HITS	Monument (M) 8024	3.50	5.25	7.00
MORE OF ROY ORBISON'S GREATEST HITS	Monument (S) 18024	4.50	6.75	9.00
ORBISONGS	Monument (M) 8035	3.50	5.25	7.00
ORBISONGS	Monument (S) 18035	4.50	6.75	9.00
ORBISON WAY, THE	MGM (M) E 4322	3.00	4.50	6.00
ORBISON WAY, THE	MGM (S) SE 4322	4.00	6.00	8.00
ORBITING WITH ROY ORBISON	Spectrum (M) DLP 164	4.00	8.00	12.00
ORIGINAL SOUND, THE	Sun (M) 113	4.00	6.00	8.00
REGENERATION	Monument (M) MG7600	2.50	3.75	5.00
ROY ORBISON AT THE ROCK HOUSE	Sun (M) LP 1260	8.00	20.00	32.00
ROY ORBISON SINGS	MGM (S) SE 4835	3.50	5.25	7.00
ROY ORBISON SINGS DON GIBSON	MGM (M) E 4424	3.00	4.50	6.00
ROY ORBISON SINGS DON GIBSON	MGM (S) SE 4424	4.00	6.00	8.00
THERE IS ONLY ONE ROY ORBISON	MGM (M) E 4308	3.00	4.50	6.00
THERE IS ONLY ONE ROY ORBISON	MGM (S) SE 4308	4.00	6.00	8.00
VERY BEST OF ROY ORBISON	Monument (M) 8045	3.50	5.25	7.00
VERY BEST OF ROY ORBISON	Monument (S) 18045	4.50	6.75	9.00

ORCHIDS

TITLE	LABEL & NO.	GOOD	VERY GOOD	NEAR MINT
TWISTIN' AT THE ROUNDTABLE WITH THE ORCHIDS	Roulette (M) R-25169	2.50	3.75	5.00
TWISTIN' AT THE ROUNDTABLE WITH THE ORCHIDS	Roulette (S) SR-25169	3.50	5.25	7.00

ORIGINALS

TITLE	LABEL & NO.	GOOD	VERY GOOD	NEAR MINT
CALIFORNIA SUNSET	Motown (S) M6-826	3.00	4.50	6.00
DEFINITIONS	Soul (S) SS 734	3.50	5.25	7.00
GAME CALLED LOVE	Soul (S) 740	3.50	5.25	7.00
PORTRAIT OF THE ORIGINALS	Soul (S) SS 724	3.50	5.25	7.00

ORIOLES

TITLE	LABEL & NO.	GOOD	VERY GOOD	NEAR MINT
GREATEST ALL TIME HITS	Big A Records (M) SBA 2001	6.00	12.00	18.00
MODERN SOUNDS OF THE ORIOLES	Parker (M) PLP 816	4.00	8.00	12.00
MODERN SOUNDS OF THE ORIOLES	Parker (S) SP-816	5.00	10.00	15.00
SONNY TIL AND THE ORIOLES OLD GOLD/NEW GOLD	RCA (S) LSP 4538	3.00	4.50	6.00

ORION

TITLE	LABEL & NO.	GOOD	VERY GOOD	NEAR MINT
SOMETIMES WORDS JUST GET IN THE WAY	London (S) SP-44230	2.50	3.75	5.00

ORION, P.J. & The Magnates

TITLE	LABEL & NO.	GOOD	VERY GOOD	NEAR MINT
P.J. ORION AND THE MAGNATES	Magnate (M) XTV 122459	6.00	12.00	18.00

ORLANDO, Tony

TITLE	LABEL & NO.	GOOD	VERY GOOD	NEAR MINT
BEFORE DAWN	Epic (S) BG-33785	2.00	3.00	4.00
BLESS YOU (& 11 OTHER GREAT HITS)	Epic (M) LN-3808	9.00	18.00	27.00
BLESS YOU (& 11 OTHER GREAT HITS)	Epic (S) BN-611	12.00	24.00	36.00
PRIME TIME	Bell (S) 1317	2.00	3.00	4.00

ORLANDO, Tony & Dawn

TITLE	LABEL & NO.	GOOD	VERY GOOD	NEAR MINT
CANDIDA	Bell (S) 6052	3.00	4.50	6.00
DAWN FEATURING TONY ORLANDO	Bell (S) 6069	3.50	5.25	7.00
DAWN'S NEW RAGTIME FOLLIES	Bell (S) 1130	3.00	4.50	6.00
GREATEST HITS	Arista 4045	2.00	3.00	4.00
HE DON'T LOVE YOU LIKE I LOVE YOU	Elektra 7E-1034	2.50	3.75	5.00
PRIME TIME	Bell 1317	3.00	4.50	6.00
SKYBIRD	Arista 4059	4.00	6.00	8.00
TUNEWEAVING	Bell (S) 1112	3.00	4.50	6.00
YOU'RE ALL I NEED TO GET BY	Elektra 7E-1049	2.50	3.75	5.00

ORLEANS

TITLE	LABEL & NO.	GOOD	VERY GOOD	NEAR MINT
LET THERE BE MUSIC	ABC (S) ABCD 814	5.00	7.50	10.00
LET THERE BE MUSIC	Asylum (S) 7E-1029	3.50	4.75	7.00

ORLONS

TITLE	LABEL & NO.	GOOD	VERY GOOD	NEAR MINT
ALL THE HITS	Cameo (M) C 1033	2.50	3.75	5.00
BIGGEST HITS	Cameo (M) C 1061	2.50	3.75	5.00
DOWN MEMORY LANE	Cameo (M) C 1073	2.50	3.75	5.00
GOLDEN HITS	Cameo (M) C 1067	2.50	3.75	5.00
NOT ME	Cameo (M) C 1054	2.50	3.75	5.00
SOUTH STREET	Cameo (M) C 1041	2.50	3.75	5.00

ORPHAN EGG

TITLE	LABEL & NO.	GOOD	VERY GOOD	NEAR MINT
ORPHAN EGG	Carole (S) CARS 8004	3.50	5.25	7.00

ORPHEUS

TITLE	LABEL & NO.	GOOD	VERY GOOD	NEAR MINT
ASCENDING	MGM (S) SE 4569	3.50	5.25	7.00

OLDFIELD, Mike

TITLE	LABEL & NO.	GOOD	VERY GOOD	NEAR MINT
HERGEST RIDGE	Virgin (S) 13-109	3.50	5.25	7.00
OMMADAWN	Virgin (S) PZ 33913	4.00	6.00	8.00
OMMADAWN	Virgin (Q) PZQ-33913	3.50	5.25	7.00
TUBULAR BELLS	Virgin (S) QD-13-105	3.00	4.50	6.00

OLDHAM, Andrew, Orchestra

TITLE	LABEL & NO.	GOOD	VERY GOOD	NEAR MINT
EAST MEETS WEST	Parrot (M) PA 61003	3.00	6.00	9.00
EAST MEETS WEST	Parrot (S) PAS 71003	3.50	7.00	10.50
ROLLING STONES SONGBOOK, THE	London (M) LL 3457	3.00	6.00	9.00
ROLLING STONES SONGBOOK, THE	London (S) PS 457	3.50	7.00	10.50

OLENN, Johnny

TITLE	LABEL & NO.	GOOD	VERY GOOD	NEAR MINT
JUST ROLLIN'	Liberty (M) LRP 3029	6.00	12.00	18.00

OLIVER AND THE TWISTERS

TITLE	LABEL & NO.	GOOD	VERY GOOD	NEAR MINT
LOOK WHO'S TWISTIN' EVERYBODY	Colpix (M) CP 423	2.00	4.00	6.00

OLLIE AND THE NIGHTINGALES

TITLE	LABEL & NO.	GOOD	VERY GOOD	NEAR MINT
OLLIE AND THE NIGHTINGALES	Stax (S) STS 2021	3.50	5.25	7.00

OL' PAINT

TITLE	LABEL & NO.	GOOD	VERY GOOD	NEAR MINT
OL' PAINT	GWP (S) ST 2034	2.00	3.00	4.00

OLSSON, Nigel

TITLE	LABEL & NO.	GOOD	VERY GOOD	NEAR MINT
DRUMMERS CAN SING TOO! A PERSONAL MUSIC DIALOGUE WITH NIGEL OLSSON	Rocket (S) PIG 1932	4.50	6.75	9.00
NIGEL OLSSON	Rocket (S) PIG 2158	3.50	5.25	7.00
NIGEL OLSSON'S DRUM ORCHESTRA AND CHORUS	UNI (M) 73113	4.00	6.00	8.00

OLYMPIC RUNNERS

TITLE	LABEL & NO.	GOOD	VERY GOOD	NEAR MINT
OUT IN FRONT	London (S) PS-658	2.50	3.75	5.00
PUT THE MUSIC WHERE YOUR MOUTH IS	London (S) PS-653	2.50	3.75	5.00

OLYMPICS

TITLE	LABEL & NO.	GOOD	VERY GOOD	NEAR MINT
DANCE BY THE LIGHT OF THE MOON	Arvee (M) A 424	3.00	6.00	9.00
DOIN' THE HULLY GULLY	Arvee (M) A 423	3.00	6.00	9.00
DOIN' THE HULLY GULLY	Arvee (EP) A-423	1.50	3.00	4.50
DO THE BOUNCE	Tri-Disc (M) 1001	2.50	5.00	7.50
OLYMPICS SING	Post (M) 8000	3.00	4.50	6.00
PARTY TIME	Arvee (M) A 429	3.00	6.00	9.00
SOMETHING OLD, SOMETHING NEW	Mirwood (M) MW 7003	2.50	3.75	5.00

ONE

TITLE	LABEL & NO.	GOOD	VERY GOOD	NEAR MINT
ONE	Grunt (S) FTR 1008	3.50	5.25	7.00

ONES

TITLE	LABEL & NO.	GOOD	VERY GOOD	NEAR MINT
ONES, THE	Ashwood House (M) AH 1105	7.00	10.50	14.00

107-34-8933

TITLE	LABEL & NO.	GOOD	VERY GOOD	NEAR MINT
NUMBERS	Narco (M) NR 101	6.00	9.00	12.00

ONO, Yoko

TITLE	LABEL & NO.	GOOD	VERY GOOD	NEAR MINT
APPROXIMATELY INFINITE UNIVERSE	Apple (S) SVBB 3399	3.00	5.00	6.00
FEELING THE SPACE	Apple (S) SW 3412	2.00	3.00	4.00
FLY	Apple (S) SVBB 3380	3.00	5.00	6.00
PLASTIC ONO BAND	Apple (S) SW 3373	2.00	3.00	4.00
YOKO ONO AND THE PLASTIC ONO BAND	Apple (S) SW 3373	3.00	4.50	6.00

(Also see LENNON, John)

ORANGE COLORED SKY

TITLE	LABEL & NO.	GOOD	VERY GOOD	NEAR MINT
ORANGE COLORED SKY	UNI (S) 73031	3.00	4.50	6.00

ORBISON, Roy

TITLE	LABEL & NO.	GOOD	VERY GOOD	NEAR MINT
ALL TIME GREATEST HITS OF ROY ORBISON	Monument (M) KZG 31484	3.00	4.50	6.00
CLASSIC ROY ORBISON	MGM (M) E 4379	3.00	4.50	6.00
CLASSIC ROY ORBISON	MGM (S) SE 4379	4.00	6.00	8.00

(M) Mono (S) Stereo (EP) Extended Play (Q) Quad (RI) Re-issued

TITLE	LABEL & NO.	GOOD	VERY GOOD	NEAR MINT
JOYFUL	MGM (S) SE 4599	3.50	5.25	7.00
ORPHEUS	MGM (M) E 4524	3.00	4.50	6.00
ORPHEUS	MGM (S) SE 4524	3.50	5.25	7.00
ORPHEUS	Bell (S) 6061	4.00	6.00	8.00

OSIBISA

TITLE	LABEL & NO.	GOOD	VERY GOOD	NEAR MINT
HAPPY CHILDREN	Warner Bros. (S) B-2732	3.50	5.25	7.00
HEADS	Decca (S) 75368	4.00	6.00	8.00
OSIBIROCK	Warner Bros. (S) B-2802	3.50	5.25	7.00
OSIBISA	Decca (S) 75285	5.00	7.50	10.00
SUPER FLY T.N.T.	Buddah (S) 5136	4.00	6.00	8.00
WOYAYA	Decca (S) 75327	4.00	6.00	8.00

OSMOND BROTHERS

TITLE	LABEL & NO.	GOOD	VERY GOOD	NEAR MINT
NEW SOUND OF THE OSMOND BROTHERS	MGM (M) E-4291	3.50	5.25	7.00
NEW SOUND OF THE OSMOND BROTHERS	MGM (S) SE-4291	4.50	6.75	9.00
PREVIEW: THE OSMOND BROTHERS	MGM (M) PM-7	3.00	4.50	6.00
SONGS WE SANG ON THE ANDY WILLIAMS SHOW	MGM (M) E 4146	4.00	6.00	8.00
SONGS WE SANG ON THE ANDY WILLIAMS SHOW	MGM (S) SE 4146	5.00	7.50	10.00
WE SING YOU A MERRY CHRISTMAS	MGM (M) E-4187	4.00	6.00	8.00
WE SING YOU A MERRY CHRISTMAS	MGM (S) SE-4187	5.00	7.50	10.00
WE SING YOU A MERRY CHRISTMAS	Metro (M) M-543	3.50	5.25	7.00
WE SING YOU A MERRY CHRISTMAS	Metro (S) MS-543	4.50	6.75	9.00

OSMOND, Donny

TITLE	LABEL & NO.	GOOD	VERY GOOD	NEAR MINT
DONNY	MGM/Kolob (S) M3G-4978	2.50	3.75	5.00
DONNY OSMOND ALBUM	MGM (S) 4782	3.00	4.50	6.00
MY BEST TO YOU	MGM/Kolob (S) 4872	2.50	3.75	5.00
PORTRAIT OF DONNY	MGM (S) 4820	3.00	4.50	6.00
TIME FOR US	MGM/Kolob (S) 4930	2.50	3.75	5.00
TOO YOUNG	MGM/Kolob (S) 4854	2.50	3.75	5.00
TO YOU WITH LOVE	MGM (S) 4797	3.00	4.50	6.00

OSMOND, Donny & Marie

TITLE	LABEL & NO.	GOOD	VERY GOOD	NEAR MINT
I'M LEAVING IT ALL UP TO YOU	MGM/Kolob (S) M3G-4968	2.50	3.75	5.00
MAKE THE WORLD GO AWAY	MGM/Kolob (S) M3G-4996	2.50	3.75	5.00

OSMOND, Little Jimmy

TITLE	LABEL & NO.	GOOD	VERY GOOD	NEAR MINT
KILLER JOE	MGM/Kolob (S) 4855	3.00	4.50	6.00

OSMOND, Marie

TITLE	LABEL & NO.	GOOD	VERY GOOD	NEAR MINT
IN MY LITTLE CORNER OF THE WORLD	MGM/Kolob (S) M3G-4944	2.00	3.00	4.00
WHO'S SORRY NOW	MGM/Kolob (S) M3G-4979	2.00	3.00	4.00

OSMONDS

TITLE	LABEL & NO.	GOOD	VERY GOOD	NEAR MINT
AROUND THE WORLD LIVE IN CONCERT	MGM/Kolob M3JB-5012	3.00	4.50	6.00
CRAZY HORSES	MGM/Kolob (S) 4851	2.00	3.00	4.00
HOMEMADE	MGM (S) 4770	2.50	3.75	5.00
LOVE ME FOR A REASON	MGM/Kolob (S) M3G-4939	2.00	3.00	4.00
OSMONDS	MGM (S) 4724	2.50	3.75	5.00
OSMONDS "LIVE"	MGM (S) 4826	2.50	3.75	5.00
PHASE—III	MGM (S) 4796	2.50	3.75	5.00
PROUD ONE, THE	MGM/Kolob (S) M3G-4993	2.00	3.00	4.00

OTHER HALF

TITLE	LABEL & NO.	GOOD	VERY GOOD	NEAR MINT
OTHER HALF, THE	Acta (M) A 38004	5.00	7.50	10.00

OTIS, Johnny

TITLE	LABEL & NO.	GOOD	VERY GOOD	NEAR MINT
COLD SHOT	Kent (M) KST 534	3.00	4.50	6.00
GREAT RHYTHM AND BLUES OLDIES VOL. 3	Blues Spectrum (M) BS 103	2.50	3.75	5.00
JOHNNY OTIS	Capitol (EP) EAP-1-1134	2.50	6.25	10.00
JOHNNY OTIS SHOW, THE	Capitol (M) T940	5.00	10.00	15.00
LIVE AT MONTEREY	Epic (M) EG 30474	3.00	4.50	6.00
ROCK AND ROLL HIT PARADE	Dig (M) LP104	9.00	22.50	36.00

OTIS, Shuggie

TITLE	LABEL & NO.	GOOD	VERY GOOD	NEAR MINT
HERE COMES SHUGGIE OTIS	Epic (S) BN 26511	5.00	7.50	10.00
INSPIRATION INFORMATION	Epic (S) KE-33059	3.50	5.25	7.00

OTTY, John

TITLE	LABEL & NO.	GOOD	VERY GOOD	NEAR MINT
CAKES AND PIES	Mumm (M) 103	3.00	4.50	6.00
THIS IS JOHN OTTY	Mumm (M) 102	3.00	4.50	6.00

OUTLAW BLUES BAND

TITLE	LABEL & NO.	GOOD	VERY GOOD	NEAR MINT
OUTLAW BLUES BAND, THE	Blues Way (S) BLS 6021	3.00	4.50	6.00

OUTSIDERS

TITLE	LABEL & NO.	GOOD	VERY GOOD	NEAR MINT
ALBUM #2	Capitol (M) T 2568	3.00	4.50	6.00
ALBUM #2	Capitol (S) ST 2568	4.00	6.00	8.00
HAPPENING LIVE	Capitol (M) T 2745	4.00	6.00	8.00
HAPPENING LIVE	Capitol (S) ST 2745	5.00	7.50	10.00
IN	Capitol (M) T 2636	4.00	6.00	8.00
IN	Capitol (S) ST 2636	5.00	7.50	10.00
TIME WON'T LET ME	Capitol (M) T 2501	4.00	6.00	8.00
TIME WON'T LET ME	Capitol (S) ST 2501	5.00	7.50	10.00

OVATIONS

TITLE	LABEL & NO.	GOOD	VERY GOOD	NEAR MINT
HAVING A PARTY	MGM (S) SE 4945	3.00	4.50	6.00
HOOKED ON A FEELING	MGM/Sounds of Memphis (S) SOM 7001	3.00	4.50	6.00

OWEN-B

TITLE	LABEL & NO.	GOOD	VERY GOOD	NEAR MINT
OWEN-B	Musicol (M) 101209	4.00	6.00	8.00

OWEN, Reg

TITLE	LABEL & NO.	GOOD	VERY GOOD	NEAR MINT
CUDDLE UP A LITTLE CLOSER	RCA (M) LPM-1914	2.00	3.00	4.00
CUDDLE UP A LITTLE CLOSER	RCA (S) LSP-1914	2.50	3.75	5.00
FIORELLO	Palette (M) LPZ-1018	2.50	3.75	5.00
FIORELLO	Palette (S) SPZ-37018	3.00	4.00	6.00
GIRLS WERE MADE TO TAKE CARE OF BOYS	RCA (M) LPM-1908	2.00	3.00	4.00
GIRLS WERE MADE TO TAKE CARE OF BOYS	RCA (S) LSP-1908	2.50	3.75	5.00
I'LL SING YOU A 1000 LOVE SONGS	RCA (M) LPM-1906	2.00	3.00	4.00
I'LL SING YOU A 1000 LOVE SONGS	RCA (S) LSP-1906	2.50	3.75	5.00
MANHATTAN SPIRITUAL	Palette (M) LPZ-1001	2.50	3.75	5.00
MANHATTAN SPIRITUAL	Palette (S) SPZ-1001	3.00	4.00	6.00
UNDER PARIS SKIES	Decca (M) DL-8859	3.00	4.50	6.00
UNDER PARIS SKIES	Decca (S) DL-78859	3.50	5.25	7.00

OWENS, Bonnie

TITLE	LABEL & NO.	GOOD	VERY GOOD	NEAR MINT
DON'T TAKE ADVANTAGE OF ME	Capitol (M) T-2403	2.00	3.00	4.00
DON'T TAKE ADVANTAGE OF ME	Capitol (S) ST-2403	2.00	3.00	4.00
JUST BETWEEN THE TWO OF US	Capitol (M) T-2453	2.00	3.00	4.00
JUST BETWEEN THE TWO OF US	Capitol (S) ST-2453	2.00	3.00	4.00

OWENS, Buck

TITLE	LABEL & NO.	GOOD	VERY GOOD	NEAR MINT
AIN'T IT AMAZING, GRACIE	Capitol (S) SMAS-11180	2.00	3.00	4.00
BEST OF BUCK OWENS	Capitol (M) T-2105	2.00	3.00	4.00
BEST OF BUCK OWENS	Capitol (S) ST-2105	2.00	3.00	4.00
BEST OF BUCK OWENS	Capitol (S) ST-11273	2.50	3.75	5.00
BUCK OWENS	Capitol (M) T-1489	3.00	4.50	6.00
BUCK OWENS	Capitol (S) ST 1489	3.00	4.50	6.00
BUCK OWENS SINGS HARLAN HOWARD	Capitol (M) T-1482	3.00	4.50	6.00
BUCK OWENS SINGS HARLAN HOWARD	Capitol (S) ST-1482	3.00	4.50	6.00
BUCK OWENS SINGS TOMMY COLLINS	Capitol (M) T-1989	2.50	3.75	5.00
BUCK OWENS SINGS TOMMY COLLINS	Capitol (S) ST-1989	2.50	3.75	5.00
CARNEGIE HALL CONCERT	Capitol (M) T-2556	2.00	3.00	4.00
CARNEGIE HALL CONCERT	Capitol (S) ST-2556	2.00	3.00	4.00
CHRISTMAS WITH BUCK OWENS	Capitol (M) T-2396	2.00	3.00	4.00
CHRISTMAS WITH BUCK OWENS	Capitol (S) ST-2396	2.00	3.00	4.00
DUST ON MOTHER'S BIBLE	Capitol (M) T-2497	2.00	3.00	4.00
DUST ON MOTHER'S BIBLE	Capitol (S) ST-2497	2.00	3.00	4.00
FABULOUS COUNTRY MUSIC SOUND OF BUCK OWENS	Starday (M) S-324	2.00	3.00	4.00
FOOLIN' AROUND	Capitol (EP) EAP-1-1550	1.00	1.50	2.00
FOUR BY BUCK OWENS	Capitol (EP) R-5446	1.50	2.25	3.00
I DON'T CARE	Capitol (M) T-2186	2.00	3.00	4.00
I DON'T CARE	Capitol (S) ST-2186	2.00	3.00	4.00
IN THE PALM OF YOUR HAND	Capitol (S) ST-11136	2.00	3.00	4.00
IT TAKES PEOPLE LIKE YOU (TO MAKE PEOPLE LIKE ME)	Capitol (M) T-2841	2.00	3.00	4.00
IT TAKES PEOPLE LIKE YOU (TO MAKE PEOPLE LIKE ME)	Capitol (S) ST-2841	2.00	3.00	4.00
I'VE GOT A TIGER BY THE TAIL	Capitol (M) T-2283	2.00	3.00	4.00
I'VE GOT A TIGER BY THE TAIL	Capitol (S) ST-2283	2.00	3.00	4.00
MONSTERS HOLIDAY	Capitol (S) ST-11332	3.00	4.50	6.00
ON THE BANDSTAND	Capitol (M) T-1879	2.50	3.75	5.00
ON THE BANDSTAND	Capitol (S) ST 1879	2.50	3.75	5.00
ROLL OUT THE RED CARPET	Capitol (M) T-2443	2.00	3.00	4.00
ROLL OUT THE RED CARPET	Capitol (S) ST-2443	2.00	3.00	4.00
TOGETHER AGAIN (& MY HEART SKIPS A BEAT)	Capitol (M) T-2135	2.00	3.00	4.00
TOGETHER AGAIN (& MY HEART SKIPS A BEAT)	Capitol (S) ST-2135	2.00	3.00	4.00
WEEKEND DADDY	Capitol (S) ST-11390	2.00	3.00	4.00
YOU'RE FOR ME	Capitol (M) T-1777	2.50	3.75	5.00
YOU'RE FOR ME	Capitol (S) ST-1777	2.50	3.75	5.00

OWENS, Gary

TITLE	LABEL & NO.	GOOD	VERY GOOD	NEAR MINT
PUT YOUR HEAD ON MY FINGER	Pride (S) 0002	2.50	3.75	5.00

OXPETALS

TITLE	LABEL & NO.	GOOD	VERY GOOD	NEAR MINT
OXPETALS, THE	Mercury (S) SR 61289	3.00	4.50	6.00

OZARK MOUNTAIN DAREDEVILS

TITLE	LABEL & NO.	GOOD	VERY GOOD	NEAR MINT
CAR OVER THE LAKE ALBUM	A&M (S) 4549	2.00	3.00	4.00
DON'T LOOK DOWN	A&M (S) SP 4662	2.00	3.00	4.00
IT'LL SHINE WHEN IT SHINES	A&M (S) 3654	2.00	3.00	4.00
MEN FROM EARTH	A&M (S) SP 4601	2.00	3.00	4.00
OZARK MOUNTAIN DAREDEVIL	A&M (S) 4411	2.00	3.00	4.00

P

PABLO CRUISE

TITLE	LABEL & NO.	GOOD	VERY GOOD	NEAR MINT
PABLO CRUISE	A&M (S) 4528	2.00	3.00	4.00

PACIFIC DRIFT

TITLE	LABEL & NO.	GOOD	VERY GOOD	NEAR MINT
FEELIN' FREE	Deram (S) DES 18040	3.00	4.50	6.00

(M) Mono (S) Stereo (EP) Extended Play (Q) Quad (RI) Re-issued

TITLE	LABEL & NO.	GOOD	VERY GOOD	NEAR MINT
PARAGONS				
PARAGONS MEET THE JESTERS	Jubilee (M) JLP-1098	4.00	10.00	16.00
PARAGONS VS. THE HARP-TONES	Musicnote (M) M8001	4.00	10.00	16.00
SIMPLY THE PARAGONS	Rare Bird (M) 8002	5.00	10.00	15.00
PARIS PILOT				
PARIS PILOT	Hip (S) HIS 7004	3.50	5.25	7.00
PARIS SISTERS				
EVERYTHING UNDER THE SUN	Reprise (M) R 6259	5.00	7.50	10.00
GLASS HOUSE, THE	Unifilms (M) ULP 505	4.00	6.00	8.00
GOLDEN HITS OF THE PARIS SISTERS	Sidewalk (M) T 5906	5.00	7.50	10.00
PARKER, Fess				
DAVY CROCKETT AT THE ALAMO	Columbia (M) CL 666	4.00	6.00	8.00
DAVY CROCKETT AT THE ALAMO	Columbia (EP) B 2033	2.00	3.00	4.00
DAVY CROCKETT GOES TO CONGRESS	Columbia (M) CL 666	4.00	6.00	8.00
DAVY CROCKETT GOES TO CONGRESS	Columbia (EP) 2032	2.00	3.00	4.00
DAVY CROCKETT INDIAN FIGHTER	Columbia (M) CL 666	4.00	6.00	8.00
DAVY CROCKETT INDIAN FIGHTER	Columbia (EP) B 2031	2.00	3.00	4.00
FESS PARKER SINGS (ABOUT DANIEL BOONE, DAVEY CROCKETT, ABE LINCOLN)	RCA (M) LPM-2973	2.50	3.75	5.00
FESS PARKER SINGS (ABOUT DANIEL BOONE, DAVY CROCKETT, ABE LINCOLN)	RCA (S) LSP-2973	2.50	3.75	5.00
PARKER, Junior				
BEST OF JUNIOR PARKER, THE	Duke (M) DLP 83	2.50	3.75	5.00
DRIVING WHEEL	Duke (M) DLP 76	2.50	3.75	5.00
JUNIOR PARKER	Blues Way (S) BLS 6066	3.00	4.50	6.00
OUTSIDE MAN, THE	Capitol (S) ST 564	3.00	4.50	6.00
PARKER, Robert				
BAREFOOTIN'	Nola (M) LP 1001	4.00	8.00	12.00
PARKS, Michael				
CLOSING THE GAP	MGM (S) SE 4646	2.50	3.75	5.00
PARKS, Van Dyke				
CLANG OF THE YANKEE REAPER	Warner Brothers (S) BS-2878	2.50	3.75	9.00
DISCOVER AMERICA	Warner Brothers (S) BS 2589	3.00	4.50	6.00
SONG CYCLE	Warner Brothers (M) 1727	4.00	6.00	8.00
PARLIAMENT				
CHOCOLATE CITY	Casablanca (S) 7014	2.00	3.00	4.00
UP FOR THE DOWN STROKE	Casablanca (S) 9003	3.00	4.50	6.00
PARRISH AND GURVITZ				
PARRISH AND GURVITZ	Decca (S) DL7-5336	4.00	6.00	8.00
PARRISH, Paul				
FOREST OF MY MIND, THE	Music Factory (S) MFS 12,001	3.00	4.50	6.00
PARSONS, Gram				
GP	Reprise (S) 2123	3.50	5.25	7.00
PARTON, Dolly				
BARGAIN STORE	RCA (S) APL1-0950	2.50	3.75	5.00
BEST OF DOLLY PARTON	RCA (S) APL1-1117	2.50	3.75	5.00
BUBBLING OVER	RCA (S) APL1-0286	2.50	3.75	5.00
DOLLY PARTON SINGS	RCA (S) LSP-4762	3.50	5.25	7.00
HELLO, I'M DOLLY/ AS LONG AS I LOVE	Monument (S) BZ-33876	3.00	4.50	6.00
JOLENE	RCA (S) APL1-0473	2.50	3.75	5.00
JOSHUA	RCA (S) LSP 4507	3.00	4.50	6.00
LOVE IS LIKE A BUTTERFLY	RCA (S) APL1-0712	2.50	3.75	5.00
MY BLUE RIDGE MOUNTAIN BOY	RCA (S) LSP 4188	3.00	4.50	6.00
MY TENNESSEE MOUNTAIN HOME	RCA (Q) APD1-0033	3.00	4.50	6.00
A REAL LIVE DOLLY	RCA (S) LSP 4387	3.00	4.50	6.00
WORLD OF DOLLY PARTON	Monument (S) KZG-31913	3.00	4.50	6.00
PARTRIDGE FAMILY				
AT HOME WITH THEIR GREATEST HITS	Bell (S) 1107	2.00	3.00	4.00
BULLETIN BOARD	Bell (S) 1137	2.00	3.00	4.00
CROSS WORD PUZZLE	Bell (S) 1122	2.00	3.00	4.00
PARTRIDGE FAMILY ALBUM	Bell (S) 6050	2.00	3.00	4.00
PARTRIDGE FAMILY CHRISTMAS CARD	Bell (S) 6066	2.00	3.00	4.00
PARTRIDGE FAMILY NOTEBOOK, THE	Bell (S) 1111	2.00	3.00	4.00
SHOPPING BAG	Bell (S) 6072	2.00	3.00	4.00
SOUND MAGAZINE	Bell (S) 6064	2.00	3.00	4.00
UP TO DATE	Bell (S) 6059	2.00	3.00	4.00
WORLD OF THE PARTRIDGE FAMILY, THE	Bell (S) 1319	2.00	3.00	4.00
PASSING FANCY				
PASSING FANCY, THE	Boo (S) BST 6801	4.00	6.00	8.00
PATTERSON, Brenda				
BRENDA PATTERSON	Playboy (S) 109	2.50	3.75	5.00
LIKE GOOD WINE	Disc Reet (S) 2211	2.50	3.75	5.00
PATTON, Jimmy				
MAKE ROOM FOR THE BLUES	Moon (M) 101	7.00	17.50	28.00

(M) Mono (S) Stereo (EP) Extended Play (Q) Quad (RI) Re-issued

TITLE	LABEL & NO.	GOOD	VERY GOOD	NEAR MINT
PACIFIC GAS AND ELECTRIC				
ARE YOU READY	Columbia (S) CS 1017	3.00	4.50	6.00
BEST	Columbia (S) KC 32019	2.50	3.75	5.00
GET IT ON	Bright Orange (S) BO 701	5.00	7.50	10.00
GET IT ON	Kent (S) KST 547	3.00	4.50	6.00
GET IT ON!	United Superior (M) 7762	3.00	4.50	6.00
PACIFIC, GAS, AND ELECTRIC	Columbia (S) CS 9900	3.00	4.50	6.00
P,G, AND E	Columbia (S) CS 30362	2.50	3.75	5.00
PACKERS				
HOLE IN THE WALL	Pure Soul (M) PS 1001	4.00	6.00	8.00
PAGE, Gene				
BLACULA	RCA (S) LSP-4806	2.00	3.00	4.00
HOT CITY	Atlantic (S) 18111	2.50	3.75	5.00
LOVELOCK	Atlantic (S) 18161	2.50	3.75	5.00
PAGE, Patti				
FAVORITES FROM TV	Mercury (M) MG-20398	3.00	4.50	6.00
FAVORITES FROM TV	Mercury (S) SR-60025	3.50	5.25	7.00
GENTLE ON MY MIND	Columbia (S) CS-9666	2.50	3.75	5.00
GOLDEN HITS	Mercury (M) MG-20495	3.00	4.00	6.00
GOLDEN HITS OF THE BOYS	Mercury (M) MG-20712	3.00	4.50	6.00
HUSH, HUSH, SWEET CHARLOTTE	Columbia (M) CL-2353	2.50	3.75	5.00
HUSH, HUSH, SWEET CHARLOTTE	Columbia (S) CS-9153	3.00	4.50	6.00
I'LL REMEMBER APRIL	Mercury (M) MG-20406	2.50	3.75	5.00
I'LL REMEMBER APRIL	Mercury (S) SR-60081	3.00	4.50	6.00
INDISCRETION	Mercury (M) MG-20405	2.50	3.75	5.00
JUST A CLOSER WALK WITH THEE	Mercury (M) MG-20573	2.00	3.00	4.00
JUST A CLOSER WALK WITH THEE	Mercury (S) SR-60233	2.50	3.75	5.00
LET'S GET AWAY FROM IT ALL	Mercury (S) SR60010	3.50	5.25	7.00
SAY WONDERFUL THINGS	Columbia (M) CL-2049	2.00	3.00	4.00
SAY WONDERFUL THINGS	Columbia (S) CS-8849	2.50	3.75	5.00
THREE LITTLE WORDS	Mercury (M) MG-20417	3.00	4.50	6.00
THREE LITTLE WORDS	Mercury (S) SR-60037	3.50	5.25	7.00
WALTZES BRING MEMORIES	Mercury (S) SR-60049	3.00	4.50	6.00
PAGE, Ricky				
HARPER VALLEY PTA	Spar (M) 3011	3.00	4.50	6.00
PAINTER				
PAINTER	Elektra (S) EKS 75071	4.00	6.00	8.00
PAISLEYS				
COSMIC MIND AT PLAY	Audio City (M) 70	7.00	10.50	14.00
PALMER, Bruce				
BRUCE PALMER	Verve/Forecast (S) FTS 3086	4.00	6.00	8.00
CYCLE IS COMPLETE	Verve/Forecast (M) 3086	3.00	4.50	6.00
PALMER, Earl				
DRUMSVILLE	Liberty (S) LST 7201	3.00	6.00	9.00
PERCOLATOR TWIST	Liberty (M) LRP 3227	3.00	6.00	9.00
PALMER, Robert				
PRESSURE DROP	Island (S) 9372	2.50	3.75	5.00
SNEAKIN' SALLY THROUGH THE ALLEY	Island (S) 9294	2.50	3.75	5.00
PAN	Columbia (M) KC 32062	5.00	7.50	10.00
PANAMA LIMITED JUG BAND				
PANAMA LIMITED JUG BAND	Harvest (S) SKAO 387	5.00	7.50	10.00
PANICS				
DISCOTHEQUE DANCE PARTY	Philips (M) PHM 200-159	2.00	4.00	6.00
DISCOTHEQUE DANCE PARTY	Philips (S) PHS 600-159	2.50	5.00	7.50
PAPER LACE				
PAPER LACE	Mercury (S) SRM-1-1008	4.50	6.75	9.00

TITLE	LABEL & NO.	GOOD	VERY GOOD	NEAR MINT
PAUL, Billy				
EBONY WOMAN	Neptune (S) 201	5.00	7.50	10.00
GOING EAST	Philadelphia Int'l. (S) 30580	4.00	6.00	8.00
GOT MY HEAD ON STRAIGHT	Philadelphia Int'l (S) KZ-33157	2.00	3.00	4.00
LIVE IN EUROPE	Philadelphia Int'l (S) KZ-32952	2.00	3.00	4.00
LIVE IN EUROPE	Philadelphia Int'l (Q) ZQ-32952	3.00	4.50	6.00
360 DEGREES OF BILLY PAUL	Philadelphia Int'l (S) KZ-31793	3.00	4.50	6.00
360 DEGREES OF BILLY PAUL	Philadelphia Intl (Q) ZQ-31793	3.00	4.50	6.00
WAR OF THE GODS	Philadelphia Int'l (S) KZ-32409	2.50	3.75	5.00
WAR OF THE GODS	Philadelphia Int'l (Q) ZQ-32409	3.00	4.50	6.00
WHEN LOVE IS NEW	Philadelphia Int'l (S) PZ-33843	2.00	3.00	4.00
PAUL & PAULA				
HOLIDAY FOR TEENS	Philips (M) PHM-200101	3.00	4.50	6.00
HOLIDAY FOR TEENS	Philips (S) PHS-600101	3.50	5.25	7.00
PAUL & PAULA SING FOR YOUNG LOVERS	Philips (M) PHM 200078	3.00	4.50	6.00
PAUL & PAULA SING FOR YOUNG LOVERS	Philips (S) PHS 600078	4.00	6.00	8.00
PAUL, LES & MARY FORD				
BYE BYE BLUES	Capitol (M) T 356	5.00	10.00	15.00
HIT MAKERS, THE	Capitol (M) T 416	5.00	10.00	15.00
HITS OF LES & MARY	Capitol (M) T 1476	3.00	4.50	6.00
LES AND MARY	Capitol (M) T 577	5.00	7.50	10.00
NEW SOUND—Volume 1	Capitol (M) T 226	5.00	10.00	15.00
NEW SOUND—Volume 2	Capitol (M)T 286	5.00	10.00	15.00
PAUL, Louis				
REFLECTIONS OF THE WAY IT REALLY IS	Enterprise (S) ENS 1034	2.00	3.00	4.00
PAULSEN, Pat				
PAT PAULSEN FOR PRESIDENT	Mercury (S) 61179	3.00	4.50	6.00
PAUPERS				
ELLIS ISLAND	Verve/Forecast (S) FTS 3051	3.00	4.50	6.00
MAGIC PEOPLE	Verve/Forecast (S) FTS 3026	3.00	4.50	6.00
PAVLOV'S DOG				
PAMPERED MENIAL	ABC (S) ABCD 866	4.00	6.00	8.00
PAMPERED MENIAL	Columbia (S) PC-33552	2.50	3.75	5.00
PAVONE, Rita				
RITA PAVONE	RCA (M) LPM-2900	4.00	6.00	8.00
RITA PAVONE	RCA (S) LSP-2900	5.00	7.50	10.00
SMALL WONDER	RCA (M) LPM-2996	3.00	4.00	6.00
SMALL WONDER	RCA (S) LSP-2996	4.00	6.00	8.00
PAXTON, Tom				
HOW COME THE SUN	Reprise (S) 6443	2.50	3.75	5.00
NEW SONGS FROM OLD FRIENDS	Reprise (S) 2144	2.00	3.00	4.00
PAXTON BROS	Anchor (S) 2012	2.50	3.75	5.00
PEACE WILL COME	Reprise (S) 2096	2.00	3.00	4.00
SOMETHING IN MY LIFE	Private Stock (S) 2002	2.00	3.00	4.00
THINGS I NOTICE NOW	Elektra (S) 74043	2.50	3.75	5.00
TOM PAXTON 6	Elektra (S) 74066	2.50	3.75	5.00
PAYCHECK, Johnny				
JOHNNY PAYCHECK'S GREATEST HITS	Epic (S) KE-33091	2.00	3.00	4.00
LOVING YOU BEATS ALL I'VE EVER SEEN	Epic (S) KE-33354	2.50	3.75	5.00
SONG & DANCE MAN	Epic (S) KE-32570	2.50	3.75	5.00
PAYNE, Freda				
BAND OF GOLD	Invictus (S) ST-7301	3.00	4.50	6.00
BEST OF FREDA PAYNE	Invictus (S) ST-9804	3.00	4.50	6.00
CONTACT	Invictus (S) ST-7307	3.00	4.50	6.00
FREDA PAYNE (GOLDEN ARCHIVE SERIES)	MGM (M) GAS 128	3.00	4.50	6.00
OUT OF PAYNE COMES LOVE	ABC (S) ABCS 901	2.00	3.00	4.00
PAYNE AND PLEASURE	Dunhill (S) DSX 50176	2.00	3.00	4.00
REACHING OUT	Invictus (S) KZ 32493	2.50	3.75	5.00
STARES AND WHISPERS	Capitol (S) ST-11700	2.00	3.00	4.00
PEACHES				
PICK OF THE CROP	Capricorn (M) PRO 588	4.00	6.00	8.00
PICK OF THE CROP VOL. 2	Capricorn (M) PRO 605	4.00	6.00	8.00
PEACHES & HERB				
GOLDEN DUETS	Date (M) 3007	2.00	3.00	4.00
GOLDEN DUETS	Date (S) 4007	2.50	3.75	5.00
PEACHES & HERB'S GREATEST HITS	Date (S) 4012	2.50	3.75	5.00
PEANUT BUTTER CONSPIRACY				
FOR CHILDREN OF ALL AGES	Challenge (M) 2000	5.00	7.50	10.00
GREAT CONSPIRACY, THE	Columbia (M) CL 2790	3.50	5.25	7.00
GREAT CONSPIRACY, THE	Columbia (S) CS 9590	4.50	6.75	9.00
PEANUT BUTTER CONSPIRACY IS SPREADING	Columbia (M) CL 2654	3.50	5.25	7.00
PEANUT BUTTER CONSPIRACY IS SPREADING	Columbia (S) CS 9454	4.50	6.75	9.00
PEARLS BEFORE SWINE				
BALAKLAVA	ESP (M) 1075	4.00	6.00	8.00
BEAUTIFUL LIES YOU COULD LIVE IN	Reprise (M) 6467	2.50	3.75	5.00
PEARLS BEFORE SWINE	ESP (M) 1054	4.00	6.00	8.00
THESE THINGS TOO	Reprise (M) 6364	3.00	4.50	6.00
USE OF ASHES, THE	Reprise (M) 6405	3.00	4.50	6.00
PEDDLERS				
THREE IN A CELL	Epic (S) BN 26458	3.00	4.50	6.00
PEEBLES, Ann				
ANN PEEBLES TELLIN' IT	Hi (S) SHL 32091	2.50	3.75	5.00
I CAN'T STAND THE RAIN	Hi (S) SHL 32079	3.00	4.50	6.00
STRAIGHT FROM THE HEART	Hi (S) SHL 32065	2.50	3.75	5.00
PEEL, David & The Lower East Side				
AMERICAN REVOLUTION, THE	Elektra (S) EKS 74069	4.00	6.00	8.00
HAVE A MARIJUANA	Elektra (S) EKS 74032	4.00	6.00	8.00
POPE SMOKES DOPE, THE	Apple (S) SW 3391	6.00	9.00	12.00
PENGUINS				
COOL COOL PENGUINS	Dooto (M) DTL 242	8.00	12.00	16.00
COOL COOL PENGUINS	Dooto (EP) DTE 241	2.50	3.75	5.00
COOL COOL PENGUINS	Dooto (EP) DTE 243	2.50	3.75	5.00
COOL COOL PENGUINS	Dooto (EP) DTE 244	2.50	3.75	5.00
MEDALLIONS	Dooto (EP) 101	3.00	4.00	6.00
MEDALLIONS	Dooto (EP) LP 204	3.00	4.00	6.00
PENGUINS	Dooto (EP) EPD 201	3.00	4.00	6.00
PENN, Dan				
NOBODY'S FOOL	Bell (M) 1127	2.00	3.00	4.00
PEOPLE				
BOTH SIDES OF PEOPLE	Capitol (S) ST 151	4.00	6.00	8.00
I LOVE YOU	Capitol (S) ST 2924	4.50	6.75	9.00
THERE ARE PEOPLE AND THERE ARE PEOPLE	Paramount (S) PAS 5013	3.50	5.25	7.00
PEOPLE'S CHOICE				
BOOGIE DOWN, U.S.A.	TSOP (S) KZ-33154	2.50	3.75	5.00
PEOPLES VICTORY ORCHESTRA AND CHORUS				
SCHOOL, THE	Peoples Music (M) PM W 2	4.00	6.00	8.00
PEPPER, Billy & The Pepperpots				
MERSEYMANIA		6.00	12.00	18.00
PEPPERMINT, Danny				
DANNY PEPPERMINT	Carlton (M) LP 20001	3.00	6.00	9.00
PEPPERMINT RAINBOW				
WILL YOU BE STAYING AFTER SUNDAY	Decca (M) DL 75129	4.00	6.00	8.00
PEPPER TREE				
YOU'RE MY PEOPLE	Capitol (S) ST 848	2.00	3.00	4.00
PERICOLI, Emilio				
EMILIO PERICOLI GOLDEN HITS OF ITALY	Warner Brothers (M) W 1489	2.00	3.00	4.00
EMILIO PERICOLI GOLDEN HITS OF ITALY	Warner Brothers (S) WS 1489	2.00	3.00	4.00
PERKINS, Carl				
BEST OF CARL PERKINS	Trip (M) 8503	2.50	3.75	5.00
BLUE SUEDE SHOES	Sun (S) 112	4.00	6.00	8.00
BROWN EYED HANDSOME MAN	Harmony (S) H 31179	3.00	4.50	6.00
COUNTRY BOY'S DREAM	Dollie (M) 4001	5.00	10.00	15.00
DANCE ALBUM	Sun (M) LP 1225	30.00	75.00	120.00
DANCE ALBUM	Sun (EP) SEP 115	3.00	7.50	12.00
GREATEST HITS OF CARL PERKINS	Harmony (S) KH 31792	3.00	4.50	6.00
MY KIND OF COUNTRY	Mercury (S) SRM 1 691	2.50	3.75	5.00
OL' BLUE SUEDE'S BACK	Jet (S) JT-LA856	4.00	6.00	8.00
ORIGINAL GOLDEN HITS	Sun (S) 111	4.00	6.00	8.00
TEEN BEAT-THE BEST OF CARL PERKINS (RE-PACKAGE OF "DANCE ALBUM")	Sun (M) LP 1225	12.00	30.00	48.00
TENNESSEE	Design (M) DLP 611	5.00	10.00	15.00
WHOLE LOTTA SHAKIN	Columbia (M) CL 1234	14.00	35.00	56.00
WHOLE LOTTA SHAKIN'	Columbia (EP) B 12341	4.00	10.00	16.00
Sun 100 series are late 60's issues.				
PEPPERMINT TROLLEY				
PEPPERMINT TROLLEY COMPANY, THE	Acta (M) A 38007	5.00	7.50	10.00
PERKINS, Tony				
FROM MY HEART	RCA (M) LPM 1679	3.00	4.00	6.00
FROM MY HEART	RCA (S) LSP 1679	3.00	4.00	6.00
ON A RAINY AFTERNOON	RCA (M) LPM 1853	2.50	3.75	5.00
TONY PERKINS	Epic (M) LN 3394	2.00	3.00	4.00

(M) Mono (S) Stereo (EP) Extended Play (Q) Quad (RI) Re-issued

TITLE	LABEL & NO.	GOOD	VERY GOOD	NEAR MINT
PERRINE, Pep				
LIVE AND IN PERSON	Hideout (M) 1003	6.00	9.00	12.00
PERRY, Greg				
ONE FOR THE ROAD	Casablanca (S) 7009	2.50	3.75	5.00
PERSUADERS				
SURFER'S NIGHTMARE	Saturn (M) SAT 5000	4.00	8.00	12.00
PERSUADERS (Black Group)				
BEST THING THAT EVER HAPPENED TO ME	Atco (S) 7046	3.00	4.50	6.00
PERSUADERS	Atco (S) 7021	3.00	4.50	6.00
THIN LINE BETWEEN LOVE & HATE	Win Or Lose (S) SD 33-387	3.50	5.25	7.00
PERSUASIONS				
I JUST WANT TO SING WITH MY FRIENDS	A&M (S) 3656	2.50	3.75	5.00
MORE THAN BEFORE	A&M (S) 3635	2.50	3.75	5.00
SPREAD THE WORD	Capitol (S) 11101	2.50	3.75	5.00
STREET CORNER SYMPHONY	Capitol (S) 872	3.00	4.50	6.00
WE CAME TO PLAY	Capitol (S) 791	3.00	4.50	6.00
WE STILL AIN'T GOT NO BAND	MCA (S) 326	2.50	3.75	5.00
PETER AND GORDON				
A WORLD WITHOUT LOVE	Capitol (M) T 2115	4.00	8.00	12.00
A WORLD WITHOUT LOVE	Capitol (S) ST 2115	5.00	10.00	15.00
BEST OF PETER AND GORDON, THE	Capitol (M) T 2549	4.50	6.75	9.00
BEST OF PETER AND GORDON, THE	Capitol (S) ST 2549	5.00	7.50	10.00
HOT COLD AND CUSTARD	Capitol (M) T 2882	3.50	5.25	7.00
HOT COLD AND CUSTARD	Capitol (S) ST 2882	4.50	6.75	9.00
I DON'T WANT TO SEE YOU AGAIN	Capitol (M) T 2220	4.00	8.00	12.00
I DON'T WANT TO SEE YOU AGAIN	Capitol (S) ST 2220	5.00	10.00	15.00
I GO TO PIECES	Capitol (M) T 2324	4.00	8.00	12.00
I GO TO PIECES	Capitol (S) ST 2324	5.00	10.00	15.00
IN LONDON FOR TEA	Capitol (M) T 2747	3.50	5.25	7.00
IN LONDON FOR TEA	Capitol (S) ST 2747	4.50	6.75	9.00
KNIGHT IN RUSTY ARMOUR	Capitol (M) T 2729	3.00	4.50	6.00
KNIGHT IN RUSTY ARMOUR	Capitol (S) ST 2729	4.00	6.00	8.00
LADY GODIVA	Capitol (M) T 2664	3.00	4.50	6.00
LADY GODIVA	Capitol (S) ST 2664	4.00	6.00	8.00
PETER AND GORDON SING AND PLAY THE HITS OF NASHVILLE TENNESSEE	Capitol (M) T 2430	5.00	10.00	15.00
PETER AND GORDON SING AND PLAY THE HITS OF NASHVILLE TENNESSEE	Capitol (S) ST 2430	6.00	12.00	18.00
TRUE LOVE WAYS	Capitol (M) T 2368	4.00	8.00	12.00
TRUE LOVE WAYS	Capitol (S) ST 2368	5.00	10.00	15.00
WOMAN	Capitol (M) T 2477	4.00	6.00	8.00
WOMAN	Capitol (S) ST 2477	5.00	7.50	10.00
PETER PAN POP BAND AND SINGERS				
SNOOPY VERSUS THE RED BARON	Peter Pan (M) 8054	2.00	3.00	4.00
PETER, PAUL, AND MARY				
ALBUM 1700	Warner Brothers (M) 1700	2.00	3.00	4.00
ALBUM 1700	Warner Brothers (S) WS 1700	2.50	3.75	5.00
IN CONCERT	Warner Brothers (M) 1555	2.00	3.00	4.00
IN CONCERT	Warner Brothers (S) WS 1555	2.50	3.75	5.00
IN THE WIND	Warner Brothers (M) 1507	2.00	4.00	6.00
IN THE WIND	Warner Brothers (S) WS 1507	2.50	5.00	7.50
LATE AGAIN	Warner Brothers (S) WS 1751	2.50	3.75	5.00
MOVING	Warner Brothers (M) 1473	2.00	4.00	6.00
MOVING	Warner Brothers (S) WS 1473	2.50	5.00	7.50
PETER, PAUL AND MARY	Warner Brothers (M) 1449	2.00	4.00	6.00
PETER, PAUL AND MARY	Warner Brothers (S) WS 1449	2.50	5.00	7.50
PETER, PAUL AND MARY ALBUM	Warner Brothers (M) 1648	2.00	3.00	4.00
PETER, PAUL AND MARY ALBUM	Warner Brothers (S) WS 1648	2.50	3.75	5.00
PETER, PAUL AND MOMMY	Warner Brothers (S) WS 1785	2.50	3.75	5.00
SEE WHAT TOMORROW BRINGS	Warner Brothers (M) 1615	2.00	3.00	4.00
SEE WHAT TOMORROW BRINGS	Warner Brothers (S) WS 1615	2.50	3.75	5.00
A SONG WILL RISE	Warner Brothers (M) 1589	2.00	3.00	4.00
A SONG WILL RISE	Warner Brothers (S) WS 1589	2.50	3.75	5.00
10 YEARS TOGETHER-THE BEST OF PETER, PAUL AND MARY	Warner Brothers (S) BS 2552	3.00	4.50	6.00
PETERSON, Paul				
LOLLIPOPS AND ROSES	Colpix (M) CP 429	3.00	6.00	9.00
LOLLIPOPS AND ROSES	Colpix (S) SCP 429	4.00	8.00	12.00
MY DAD	Colpix (M) CP 442	3.00	6.00	9.00
MY DAD	Colpix (S) SCP 442	4.00	8.00	12.00
PETERSON, Ray				
OTHER SIDE OF RAY PETERSON	MGM (M) E-4277	2.00	3.00	4.00
OTHER SIDE OF RAY PETERSON	MGM (S) SE 4277	2.50	3.75	5.00
RAY PETERSON COUNTRY	Decca (M) 75307	2.00	3.00	4.00
TELL LAURA I LOVE HER	RCA (M) LPM 2297	5.00	10.00	15.00
TELL LAURA I LOVE HER	RCA (S) LSP 2297	7.00	14.00	21.00
VERY BEST OF RAY PETERSON, THE	MGM (M) E 4250	3.00	4.50	6.00
VERY BEST OF RAY PETERSON, THE	MGM (S) SE 4250	4.00	6.00	8.00
P.F.M.				
P.F.M. COOK	Manticore (S) MA6-502	2.50	3.75	5.00
PHANTOM				
DIVINE COMEDY	Capitol (S) ST-11313	4.00	6.00	8.00
PHANTOM OF THE ORGAN	Electric Lemon (S) 1909	4.50	6.75	9.00
PHILAMORE LINCOLN				
NORTH WIND BLEW SOUTH, THE	Epic (S) BN 26497	4.50	6.75	9.00
PHILLIPS, Esther ("Little Esther")				
ALONE AGAIN, NATURALLY	Kudu (M) 09	2.00	3.00	4.00
AND I LOVE HIM	Atlantic (M) 8102	4.00	8.00	12.00
BURNIN'.	Atlantic (S) SD 1565	5.00	7.50	10.00
COUNTRY SIDE OF ESTHER PHILLIPS	Atlantic (M) 8130	3.00	6.00	9.00
COUNTRY SIDE OF ESTHER PHILLIPS	Atlantic (S) SD 8130	3.50	7.00	10.50
ESTHER	Atlantic (M) 8122	3.00	6.00	9.00
ESTHER	Atlantic (S) SD 8122	3.50	7.00	10.50
ESTHER PHILLIPS	Crown (M)	3.50	3.75	14.00
FROM A WHISPER TO A SCREAM	Kudu (M) 05	2.00	3.00	4.00
MELODY LANE	King (M) 395-622	5.00	10.00	15.00
PERFORMANCE	Kudu (M) 18	2.00	3.00	4.00
RELEASE ME	Lenox (M) 227	5.00	10.00	15.00
PHILLIPS, Gene				
GENE PHILLIPS AND THE ROCKERS	Crown (M) CLP 5375	4.00	10.00	16.00
PHILLIPS, Shawn				
COLLABORATION	A&M (S) SP 4324	2.50	3.75	5.00
CONTRIBUTION	A&M (S) SP 4241	2.50	3.75	5.00
DO YOU WONDER	A&M (S) SP 4539	2.50	3.75	5.00
FACES	A&M (S) SP 4363	2.00	3.00	4.00
FURTHERMORE	A&M (S) SP 3662	2.50	3.75	5.00
SECOND CONTRIBUTION	A&M (S) SP 4282	2.00	3.00	4.00
SHAWN PHILLIPS	A&M (S) SP 4402	2.50	3.75	5.00
SPACED	A&M (S) SP 4650	2.00	3.00	4.00
RUMPLESTILTSKIN'S RESOLVE	A&M (S) SP 4582	2.00	3.00	4.00
PHILLIPS, Warren & The Rockets				
ROCKED OUT	Parrot (S) PAS 71044	6.00	9.00	12.00
PHLUPH				
PHLUPH	Verve (M) V6-5054	4.50	6.75	9.00
PHOENIX				
PHOENIX	ABC (S) ABCS 703	3.00	4.50	6.00
PIANO RED ("Dr. Feelgood")				
ALL ALONE WITH HIS PIANO	Arhoolie (M) 1064	3.50	5.25	7.00
HAPPINESS IS PIANO RED	King (M) 1117	4.50	6.75	9.00
JUMP MAN JUMP	Groove (M) LG 1001	6.00	12.00	18.00
JUMP MAN JUMP	Groove (EP) EGA3	3.00	6.00	9.00
PIANO RED IN CONCERT	Groove (M) LG 1002	6.00	12.00	18.00
PIANO RED IN CONCERT	Groove (EP) EG 10026	3.00	6.00	9.00
PIANO RED IN CONCERT	Groove (EP) EG 10027	3.00	6.00	9.00
PIANO RED IN CONCERT	Groove (EP) EG 10028	3.00	6.00	9.00
ROCKIN' WITH RED	RCA (EP) EPA 587	3.00	6.00	9.00
ROCKIN' WITH RED	RCA (EP) EPA-5091	3.00	6.00	9.00
PICKETT, Bobby (Boris) & The Crypt Kickers				
MONSTER MASH	Garpax (M) GPX 57001	4.00	8.00	12.00
MONSTER MASH	Garpax (S) SGP 67001	5.00	10.00	15.00
ORIGINAL MONSTER MASH	Parrot (S) XPAS 71063	3.00	4.50	6.00
PICKETT, Wilson				
BEST OF WILSON PICKETT	Atlantic (S) SD 8151	4.00	6.00	8.00
BEST OF WILSON PICKETT VOL. 2	Atlantic (S) SD 8290	3.50	5.25	7.00
DON'T KNOCK MY LOVE	Atlantic (S) SD 8300	3.50	5.25	7.00
EXCITING WILSON PICKETT, THE	Atlantic (M) 8129	4.00	6.00	8.00
GREAT HITS (RED COVER)	Wand (S) WDS 672	4.00	6.00	8.00
GREAT HITS (PHOTO COVER)	Wand (M) W 672	3.00	4.50	6.00
GREAT HITS (PHOTO COVER)	Wand (S) SW 672	2.50	3.75	5.00
HEY JUDE	Atlantic (S) SD 8215	4.00	6.00	8.00
I'M IN LOVE	Atlantic (S) SD 8175	4.00	6.00	8.00
IN PHILADELPHIA	Atlantic (S) SD 8270	3.50	5.25	7.00
IN THE MIDNIGHT HOUR	Atlantic (S) SD 8114	4.00	6.00	8.00
IT'S TOO LATE	Double-L (M) DL 2300	4.00	8.00	12.00
JOIN ME & LET'S BE FREE	RCA (S) APL1-0856	2.00	3.00	4.00
KEEP THE DREAM ALIVE	RCA (S) VPSX-6093	2.00	3.00	4.00
MIDNIGHT MOVER	Atlantic (S) SD 8183	4.00	6.00	8.00
RIGHT ON	Atlantic (S) SD 8250	3.50	5.25	7.00
SOUND OF WILSON PICKETT, THE	Atlantic (S) SD 8145	4.00	6.00	8.00
TONIGHT I'M MY BIGGEST AUDIENCE	RCA (S) LSP-4858	2.00	3.00	4.00
WICKED PICKETT	Atlantic (M) 8138	4.00	6.00	8.00
WILSON PICKETT'S GREATEST HITS	Atlantic (S) 2-501	3.00	4.50	6.00
PICKETTYWITCH				
PICKETTYWITCH	Janus (S) JLS 3015	3.50	5.25	7.00
PIDGEON				
PIDGEON	Decca (S) DL 75103	2.50	3.75	5.00
PIERCE, Webb				
BEST OF WEBB PIERCE	MCA (S) 2-4087	2.50	3.75	5.00
BOW THY HEAD	Decca (M) DL 4384	2.00	3.00	4.00
BOW THY HEAD	Decca (S) DL7-4384	2.00	3.00	4.00
COUNTRY CHURCH	Decca (EP) ED 2355	1.00	1.50	2.00

(M) Mono (S) Stereo (EP) Extended Play (Q) Quad (RI) Re-issued

TITLE	LABEL & NO.	GOOD	VERY GOOD	NEAR MINT
COUNTRY MUSIC TIME	Decca (M) DL-4659	2.00	3.00	4.00
COUNTRY MUSIC TIME	Decca (S) DL7-4659	2.00	3.00	4.00
COW TOWN	Decca (EP) ED-2751	1.00	1.50	2.00
CRAZY WILD DESIRE	Decca (EP) ED-2734	1.00	1.50	2.00
CROSS COUNTRY	Decca (M) DL-4294	2.00	3.00	4.00
CROSS COUNTRY	Decca (S) DL7-4294	2.00	3.00	4.00
FALLEN ANGEL	Decca (M) DL-4144	2.00	3.00	4.00
FALLEN ANGEL	Decca (S) DL7-4144	2.00	3.00	4.00
FALLEN ANGEL	Decca (EP) ED-2748	1.00	1.50	2.00
FOOL, FOOL, FOOL	Decca (M) 4964	2.00	3.00	4.00
FOOL, FOOL, FOOL	Decca (S) 7-4964	2.00	3.00	4.00
HIDEAWAY HEART	Decca (M) DL-4218	2.00	3.00	4.00
HIDEAWAY HEART	Decca (S) DL7-4218	2.00	3.00	4.00
I'VE GOT A NEW HEARTACHE	Decca (M) DL 4358	2.00	3.00	4.00
I'VE GOT A NEW HEARTACHE	Decca (S) DL7 4358	2.00	3.00	4.00
JUST IMAGINATION	Decca (M) DL 8728	3.00	4.50	6.00
JUST IMAGINATION	Decca (EP) ED 2581	1.50	2.25	3.00
LOVING YOU THEN LOSING YOU	Decca (EP) ED-2799	1.00	1.50	2.00
MEMORY NO. 1	Decca (M) DL-4604	2.00	3.00	4.00
MEMORY NO. 1	Decca (S) DL7-4604	2.00	3.00	4.00
NOBODY'S DARLIN' BUT MINE	Decca (EP) ED-2785	1.00	1.50	2.00
SANDS OF GOLD	Decca (M) DL-4486	2.00	3.00	4.00
SANDS OF GOLD	Decca (S) DL7-4486	2.00	3.00	4.00
SOUND FOR THE KINGDOM	Decca (M) DL-8889	3.00	4.50	6.00
SOUND FOR THE KINGDOM	Decca (S) DL-78889	3.00	4.50	6.00
SWEET MEMORIES	Decca (M) DL 4739	2.00	3.00	4.00
SWEET MEMORIES	Decca (S) DL 74739	2.00	3.00	4.00
WALKING THE STREETS	Decca (M) DL-4079	2.00	3.00	4.00
WALKING THE STREETS	Decca (S) DL7-4079	2.00	3.00	4.00
WALKING THE STREETS	Decca (EP) ED-2685	1.00	1.50	2.00
WEBB	Decca (M) DL 8899	3.00	4.50	6.00
WEBB	Decca (S) DL-78899	3.00	4.50	6.00
WEBB	Decca (EP) EPD-2653	1.00	1.50	2.00
WEBB	Decca (SEP) ED1-72653	1.50	2.25	3.00
WEBB PIERCE	Decca (EP) ED 2241	1.50	2.25	3.00
WEBB PIERCE	Decca (EP) ED-2668	1.00	1.50	2.00
WEBB PIERCE	Decca (SEP) ED7-2668	1.00	1.50	2.00
WEBB PIERCE	Decca (EP) ED-2694	1.00	1.50	2.00
WEBB PIERCE	Decca (EP) ED-2709	1.00	1.50	2.00
WEBB PIERCE	Decca (EP) ED-2715	1.00	1.50	2.00
WEBB PIERCE	Decca (M) DL 8129	4.00	6.00	8.00
WEBB PIERCE	King (S) 648	4.00	6.00	8.00
WEBB PIERCE GOLDEN FAVORITES	Decca (M) DL-4110	2.00	3.00	4.00
WEBB PIERCE'S GREATEST HITS	Decca (M) 4999	2.00	3.00	4.00
WEBB PIERCE'S GREATEST HITS	Decca (S) 7-4999	2.00	3.00	4.00
WEBB PIERCE'S GREATEST HITS (RI)	MCA (S) 120	2.00	3.00	4.00
WEBB PIERCE STORY	Decca (M) DXB-181	4.00	6.00	8.00
WEBB PIERCE STORY	Decca (S) DXSB7-181	4.00	6.00	8.00
WEBB'S CHOICE	Decca (M) 4782	2.00	3.00	4.00
WEBB'S CHOICE	Decca (S) 7-4782	2.00	3.00	4.00
WEBB WITH A BEAT	Decca (M) DL-4015	2.00	3.00	4.00
WEBB WITH A BEAT	Decca (S) DL74015	2.00	3.00	4.00
WITHOUT YOU	Coral (S) 20025	2.50	3.75	5.00
WONDERING BOY, THE	Decca (M) DL 5536	4.00	6.00	8.00
WONDERING BOY, THE	Decca (EP) ED 2144	1.50	2.25	3.00
WONDERING BOY, THE	Decca (EP) ED 2145	1.50	2.25	3.00

PIGEONS
PIGEONS, THE	Wand	3.00	4.50	6.00

PILOT
PILOT	EMI (S) ST-11368	3.00	4.50	6.00
POINT OF VIEW	RCA (S) LSP-4825	3.50	5.25	7.00

PINK FAIRIES
KINGS OF OBLIVION	Polydor (S) PD 5537	4.00	6.00	8.00

PINK FLOYD
ANIMALS	Columbia (S) 34474	2.00	3.00	4.00
ATOM HEART MOTHER	Harvest (S) 382	3.00	4.50	6.00
DARK SIDE OF THE MOON	Harvest SMAS-11163	2.00	3.00	4.00
MEDDLE	Harvest SMAS 832	3.00	4.50	6.00
MORE	Harvest SW 11198	2.50	3.75	5.00

(M) Mono (S) Stereo (EP) Extended Play (Q) Quad (RI) Re-issued

TITLE	LABEL & NO.	GOOD	VERY GOOD	NEAR MINT
NICE PAIR	Harvest SABB-11257	2.50	3.75	5.00
OBSCURED BY CLOUDS	Harvest ST-11078	2.50	3.75	5.00
OMAY YAD	TAKRL (M) 1830	5.00	7.50	10.00
PINK FLOYD	Tower (M) T 5093	4.50	6.75	9.00
PINK FLOYD	Tower (S) ST 5093	5.00	7.50	10.00
RELICS	Harvest SW-759	3.00	4.50	6.00
A SAUCERFUL OF SECRETS	Tower (S) ST 5131	5.00	7.50	10.00
UMMAGUMMA	Harvest (S) 388	3.00	4.50	6.00
WISH YOU WERE HERE	Columbia (S) PC 33453	2.00	3.00	4.00
WISH YOU WERE HERE	Columbia (Q) PCQ 33453	2.50	3.75	5.00

PINKINY CANANDY
PINKINY CANANDY	Uni (M) 73049	3.50	5.25	7.00

PIPKINS
GIMME DAT DING	Capitol (S) ST 483	3.00	4.50	6.00

PIRANHAS
SOMETHIN' FISHY	Custom Fidelity (M) CF 1452	6.50	13.00	19.50

PITNEY, Gene
BABY I NEED YOUR LOVIN'	Music Disc (S) MDS 1014	3.00	4.50	6.00
BACKSTAGE (I'M LONELY)	Musicor (M) MM 2095	2.00	3.00	4.00
BACKSTAGE (I'M LONELY)	Musicor (S) MS 3095	2.50	3.75	5.00
BEING TOGETHER (WITH MELBA MONTGOMERY)	Musicor (M) MM 2077	2.00	3.00	4.00
BEING TOGETHER (WITH MELBA MONTGOMERY)	Musicor (S) MS 3077	2.50	3.75	5.00
BIG SIXTEEN VOL. 3	Musicor (M) MM 2085	2.00	3.00	4.00
BIG SIXTEEN VOL. 3	Musicor (S) MS 3085	2.50	3.75	5.00
BLUE GENE	Musicor (M) MM 2006	2.50	5.00	7.50
BLUE GENE	Musicor (S) MS 3006	3.00	6.00	9.00
GENE ITALIANO	Musicor (M) MM 2015	2.00	3.00	4.00
GENE ITALIANO	Musicor (S) MS 3015	2.50	3.75	5.00
GENE PITNEY	Musicor (M) MM 2104	2.00	3.00	4.00
GENE PITNEY	Musicor (S) MS 3104	2.50	3.75	5.00
GENE PITNEY ESPANOL	Musicor (M) MM 2072	2.00	3.00	4.00
GENE PITNEY ESPANOL	Musicor (S) MS 3072	2.50	3.75	5.00
GENE PITNEY MEETS THE FAIR YOUNG LADIES OF FOLKLAND	Musicor (M) MM 2007	2.50	5.00	7.50
GENE PITNEY MEETS THE FAIR YOUNG LADIES OF FOLKLAND	Musicor (S) MS 3007	3.00	6.00	9.00
GENE PITNEY'S BIG SIXTEEN	Musicor (M) MM 2008	2.50	5.00	7.50
GENE PITNEY'S BIG SIXTEEN	Musicor (S) MS 3008	3.00	6.00	9.00
GENE PITNEY SINGS BURT BACHARACH	Musicor (S) MS 3161	2.50	3.75	5.00
GENE PITNEY SINGS JUST FOR YOU	Musicor (M) MM 2004	2.50	5.00	7.50
GENE PITNEY SINGS JUST FOR YOU	Musicor (S) MS 3004	3.00	6.00	9.00
GENE PITNEY'S MORE BIG SIXTEEN Vol. 2	Musicor (M) MM 2043	3.00	4.50	6.00
GENE PITNEY'S MORE BIG SIXTEEN Vol. 2	Musicor (S) MS 3043	4.00	6.00	8.00
GENE PITNEY STORY	Musicor (M) M2M 2148	2.00	3.00	4.00
GENE PITNEY STORY	Musicor (S) M2S 3148	2.50	3.75	5.00
GEORGE JONES AND GENE PITNEY	Musicor (M) MM 2044	2.00	3.00	4.00
GEORGE JONES AND GENE PITNEY	Musicor (S) MS 3044	2.50	3.75	5.00
GOLDEN GREATS	Musicor (S) MS 3134	2.50	3.75	5.00
GREATEST HITS OF ALL TIMES	Musicor (M) MM 2102	2.00	3.00	4.00
GREATEST HITS OF ALL TIMES	Musicor (S) MS 3102	2.50	3.75	5.00
I MUST BE SEEING THINGS	Musicor (M) MM 2056	2.00	3.00	4.00
I MUST BE SEEING THINGS	Musicor (S) MS 3056	2.50	3.75	5.00
IT HURTS TO BE IN LOVE	Musicor (M) MM 2019	2.00	3.00	4.00
IT HURTS TO BE IN LOVE	Musicor (S) MS 3019	2.50	3.75	5.00
IT'S COUNTRY TIME AGAIN (WITH GEORGE JONES)	Musicor (M) MM 2065	2.00	3.00	4.00
IT'S COUNTRY TIME AGAIN (WITH GEORGE JONES)	Musicor (S) MS 3065	2.50	3.75	5.00
JUST ONE SMILE	Musicor (M) MM 2117	2.00	3.00	4.00
JUST ONE SMILE	Musicor (S) MS 3117	2.50	3.75	5.00
LOOKING THROUGH THE EYES OF LOVE	Musicor (M) MM 2069	2.00	6.00	4.00
LOOKING THROUGH THE EYES OF LOVE	Musicor (S) MS 3069	2.50	3.75	5.00
MANY SIDES OF GENE PITNEY	Musicor (M) MM2001	2.50	5.00	7.50
MANY SIDES OF GENE PITNEY	Musicor (S) MS 3001	3.00	6.00	9.00
ONLY LOVE CAN BREAK A HEART	Musicor (M) MM 2003	2.50	5.00	7.50
ONLY LOVE CAN BREAK A HEART	Musicor (S) MS 3003	3.00	6.00	9.00
PITNEY ESPANOL	Musicor (S) MS 3154	2.50	3.75	5.00

TITLE	LABEL & NO.	GOOD	VERY GOOD	NEAR MINT
SHE'S A HEARTBREAKER	Musicor (S) MS 3164	2.50	3.75	5.00
TEN YEARS AFTER	Musicor (S) MS 3206	2.50	3.75	5.00
THIS IS GENE PITNEY	Musicor (S) P2S 5026	2.50	3.75	5.00
TOWN WITHOUT PITY	Music Disc (S) MDS 1005	3.00	4.50	6.00
WORLD WIDE WINNERS	Musicor (M) MM 2005	2.50	5.00	7.50
YOUNG AND WARM AND WONDERFUL	Musicor (M) MM 2108	2.00	3.00	4.00
YOUNG AND WARM AND WONDERFUL	Musicor (S) MS 3108	2.50	3.75	5.00

PITNEY, Gene & The Newcastle Trio
SPOTLIGHT ON GENE PITNEY	Design (M) DLP 160	2.00	4.00	6.00

PIXIES THREE
PARTY WITH THE PIXIES THREE	Mercury (M) MG 20912	4.00	8.00	12.00
PARTY WITH THE PIXIES THREE	Mercury (S) SR 60912	5.00	10.00	15.00

PLANT AND SEE
PLANT AND SEE	White Whale (S) WWS 7120	3.00	4.50	6.00

PLASTIC COW
PLASTIC COW GOES MOOOOOOG, THE	Dot (S) DLP 25961	3.50	5.25	7.00

PLASTIC ONO BAND
See LENNON, John

PLASTER CASTERS, THE
PLASTER CASTER BLUES BAND	Bluestime (M) 9001	4.00	8.00	12.00

PLATTERS
CHRISTMAS WITH THE PLATTERS	Mercury (M) MG-20841	3.00	4.50	6.00
CHRISTMAS WITH THE PLATTERS	Mercury (S) SR-60841	3.00	4.50	6.00
ENCORE OF BROADWAY GOLDEN HITS	Mercury (M) MG-20613	3.00	4.50	6.00
ENCORE OF BROADWAY GOLDEN HITS	Mercury (S) SR-60613	3.00	4.50	6.00
ENCORE OF GOLDEN HITS	Mercury (M) MG 20472	3.00	6.00	9.00
ENCORE OF GOLDEN HITS	Mercury (S) SR 60243	3.00	6.00	9.00
ENCORE OF GOLDEN HITS	Mercury (EP) 1-4029	2.00	3.00	4.00
ENCORE OF GOLDEN HITS	Mercury (EP) 1-4030	2.00	3.00	4.00
ENCORE OF GOLDEN HITS OF THE GROUPS	Mercury (M) MG-20693	3.00	4.50	6.00
ENCORE OF GOLDEN HITS OF THE GROUPS	Mercury (S) SR-60893	3.00	4.50	6.00
ENCORES (Wing Re-issue)	Mercury/Wing (M) MGW 12112	2.00	3.00	4.00
ENCORES (Wing Re-issue)	Mercury/Wing (S) SRW 16112	2.00	3.00	4.00
FLYING PLATTERS, THE	Mercury (M) MG 20298	3.00	6.00	9.00
FLYING PLATTERS (Wing Re-issue)	Mercury/Wing (M) MGW-12226	2.00	3.00	4.00
FLYING PLATTERS (Wing Re-issue)	Mercury/Wing (S) SRW-16226	2.00	3.00	4.00
FLYING PLATTERS AROUND THE WORLD	Mercury (M) MG 20366	3.00	6.00	9.00
FLYING PLATTERS AROUND THE WORLD	Mercury (S) SR-60043	3.00	6.00	9.00
GOING BACK TO DETROIT	Musicor (M) MM 2125	2.00	3.00	4.00
GOING BACK TO DETROIT	Musicor (S) MS 3125	2.00	3.00	4.00
I GET THE SWEETEST FEELING	Musicor (S) 3171	2.00	3.00	4.00
I LOVE YOU 1,000 TIMES	Musicor (M) 2091	2.50	3.75	5.00
I LOVE YOU 1,000 TIMES	Musicor (S) 3091	2.50	3.75	5.00
IN THE STILL OF THE NIGHT	Pickwick (S) 3120	2.00	3.00	4.00
MOONLIGHT MEMORIES	Mercury (M) MG 20759	3.00	4.50	6.00
MOONLIGHT MEMORIES	Mercury (S) SR 60759	3.00	4.50	6.00
MORE ENCORE OF GOLDEN HITS	Mercury (M) MG 20591	3.00	6.00	9.00
MORE ENCORE OF GOLDEN HITS	Mercury (S) SR 60252	3.00	6.00	9.00
NEW GOLDEN HITS OF THE PLATTERS	Musicor (S) MS 2141	2.50	3.75	5.00
NEW SOUL OF THE PLATTERS	Mercury (M) MG-20983	2.50	3.75	5.00
NEW SOUL OF THE PLATTERS	Mercury (S) SR-60983	2.50	3.75	5.00
PLATTERS	King (M) LP 549	4.00	10.00	16.00
PLATTERS	King (EP) EP 651	2.00	3.00	4.00
PLATTERS	King (EP) EP 378	2.00	3.00	4.00
PLATTERS	Federal (M) 549	8.00	20.00	32.00
PLATTERS, THE	Mercury (EP) EP 1 3344	2.00	3.00	4.00
PLATTERS, THE	Mercury (M) MG 20146	6.00	12.00	18.00
PLATTERS, THE	Mercury (M) MG-20589	3.00	4.50	6.00
PLATTERS, THE	Mercury (S) SR-60245	3.00	4.50	6.00
PLATTERS, THE VOL. 2	Mercury (M) MG 20216	4.00	8.00	12.00
PLATTERS HAVE THE MAGIC TOUCH	Musicor (M) MM 2111	2.00	3.00	4.00
PLATTERS HAVE THE MAGIC TOUCH	Musicor (S) MS 3111	2.00	3.00	4.00
PLATTERS SING ALL TIME MOVIE HITS	Mercury (M) MG-20782	3.00	4.50	6.00
PLATTERS SING ALL TIME MOVIE HITS	Mercury (S) SR-60782	3.00	4.50	6.00
PLATTERS SING LATINO	Mercury (M) MG 20808	3.00	4.50	6.00
PLATTERS SING LATINO	Mercury (S) SR 60808	3.00	4.50	6.00
REFLECTIONS	Mercury (M) MG-20481	3.00	4.50	6.00
REFLECTIONS	Mercury (S) MG 20481	3.00	4.50	6.00
REFLECTIONS (WING REISSUE)	Mercury (M) MGW-16272	2.00	3.00	4.00
REFLECTIONS (WING REISSUE)	Mercury (S) SRW-16272	2.00	3.00	4.00
REMEMBER WHEN	Mercury (M) MG 20410	3.00	6.00	9.00
REMEMBER WHEN	Mercury (S) SR 60087	4.00	8.00	12.00
SONG FOR THE LONELY	Mercury (M) MG-20669	3.00	4.50	6.00
SONG FOR THE LONELY	Mercury (S) SR-60669	3.00	4.50	6.00
SUPER HITS	Pickwick (S) 3236	2.00	3.00	4.00
SWEET, SWEET LOVIN'	Musicor (M) MM 2156	2.00	3.00	4.00
SWEET, SWEET LOVIN'	Musicor (S) MS 3156	2.00	3.00	4.00
TWILIGHT TIME	Mercury (EP) EP 13393	1.50	2.25	3.00

PLAYMATES
AT PLAY WITH THE PLAYMATES	Roulette (M) R 25043	4.00	6.00	8.00
BROADWAY SHOW STOPPERS	Roulette (M) R-25084	2.50	3.75	5.00
BROADWAY SHOW STOPPERS	Roulette (S) SR-25084	2.50	3.75	5.00
CALYPSO	Roulette (M) R 25001	4.00	6.00	8.00
CUTTIN' CAPERS	Roulette (M) R-25068	3.00	4.50	6.00
CUTTIN' CAPERS	Roulette (S) SR-25068	3.00	4.50	6.00
PLAYMATES VISIT THE WEST INDIES	Forum (M) F-16001	3.00	4.50	6.00
PLAYMATES VISIT THE WEST INDIES	Forum (S) SF-16001	3.50	5.25	7.00
ROCK & ROLL RECORD HOP	Roulette (M) R-25059	4.00	6.00	8.00
WAIT FOR ME	Roulette (M) R-25139	3.00	4.50	6.00
WAIT FOR ME	Roulette (S) SR-25139	3.00	4.50	6.00

PLUS
THE SEVEN DEADLY SINS	Probe (S) CPLP-4513	5.00	7.50	10.00

POE
THROUGH THE SPIRAL STAIRCASE	Uni (M) 73099	4.00	6.00	8.00

POET & THE ONE MAN BAND
POET & THE ONE MAN BAND	Paramount (S) PAS-5010	4.00	6.00	8.00

POINTER SISTERS
LIVE AT THE OPERA HOUSE	Blue Thumb (S) 8002	4.00	6.00	8.00
POINTER SISTERS	Blue Thumb (S) 48	3.50	5.25	7.00
STEPPIN'	Blue Thumb (S) 6021	3.00	4.50	6.00
THAT'S A PLENTY	Blue Thumb (S) 6009	3.00	4.50	6.00

POLLUTION (Dobie Gray Group)
POLLUTION	Prophesy (S) 6057	3.50	5.25	7.00

Also see GRAY, Dobie

POMERANZ, David
TIME TO FLY	Decca (S) 75329	2.50	3.75	5.00

POOLE, Brian & The Tremeloes
TREMELOES ARE HERE, THE	Audio Fidelity (M) AFLP 2177	4.50	9.00	13.50

POPPIES
LULLABY OF LOVE	Epic (M) LN 24200	3.00	4.50	6.00
LULLABY OF LOVE	Epic (S) BN 24200	3.00	4.50	6.00

POPPY FAMILY
POPPY FAMILY, THE	London (S) PS 574	3.00	4.50	6.00
POPPY SEEDS	London (S) PS-599	2.50	3.75	5.00

PORTER, David
GRITTY, GROOVY, AND GETTIN' IT	Enterprise (S) ENS 1009	2.00	3.00	4.00
INTO A REAL THING	Enterprise (S) ENS 1012	2.00	3.00	4.00
SWEAT AND LIVE	Enterprise (S) ENS 1026	2.00	3.00	4.00
VICTIM OF A JOKE	Enterprise (S) ENS 1019	2.00	3.00	4.00

PORTER, Jerry
DON'T BOTHER ME	Mirror (M) 122	3.00	6.00	9.00

POSEY, Sandy
BORN A WOMAN	MGM (M) 4418	2.00	3.00	4.00
BORN A WOMAN	MGM (S) 4418	2.00	3.00	4.00

POT LIQUOR
LEVEE BLUES	Janus (S) JLS 3033	3.00	4.50	6.00
LOUISIANA ROCK & ROLL	Janus (S) JLS 3036	2.50	3.75	5.00

POTTER ST. CLOUD
POTTER ST. CLOUD	Mediarts (M) 41-7	6.00	9.00	12.00
JIMMY POWELL	Decca (S) DL 75216	4.00	6.00	8.00

POWER, Duffy
DUFFY POWER	GSF (S) GSF-S-1005	3.50	5.25	7.00

POWER PLANT
GOLDEN DAWN, THE	International Artists (M) 1A LP 4	6.00	12.00	18.00

POWERS, Joey
MIDNIGHT MARY	Amy (M) AMY 8001	4.00	8.00	12.00

POWERS OF BLUE
FLIPOUT	MTA (M) MTA 1002	3.00	4.50	6.00
FLIPOUT	MTA (S) STS 5002	3.50	5.25	7.00

POZO SECO SINGERS
I CAN MAKE IT WITH YOU	Columbia (M) 2600	3.00	4.50	6.00
SHADES OF TIME	Columbia (S) CS-9656	2.50	3.75	5.00
TIME	Columbia (M) 2512	3.00	4.50	6.00

PRADO, Perez
POPS & PRADO	RCA (M) LPM-2028	2.00	4.00	6.00
PRADO PARADE	RCA (EP) EPA-5106	1.50	2.25	3.00
"PREZ"	RCA (M) LPM 1556	3.00	6.00	9.00

PRATT, Andy
ANDY PRATT	Columbia (M) KC 31722	2.50	3.75	5.00

(M) Mono   (S) Stereo   (EP) Extended Play   (Q) Quad   (RI) Re-issued

ELVIS!

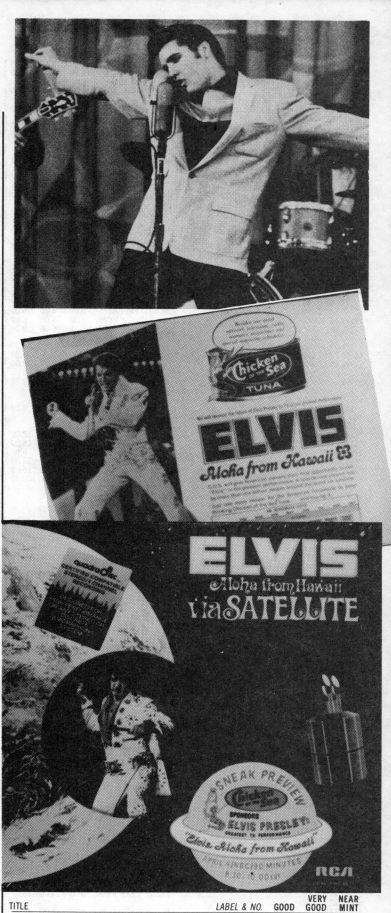

TITLE	LABEL & NO.	GOOD	VERY GOOD	NEAR MINT
ALMOST IN LOVE	RCA (S) Camden CAS 2440	2.00	3.00	4.00
ANYWAY YOU WANT ME	RCA (EP) EPA 965	5.00	10.00	15.00
Black Label-Dog on top				
ANYWAY YOU WANT ME	RCA (EP) EPA 965	3.00	6.00	9.00
Black Label-Dog on side				
ANYWAY YOU WANT ME	RCA (EP) EPA 965	2.00	4.00	6.00
Orange Label				
BACK IN MEMPHIS	RCA (S) LSP 4429	2.50	3.75	5.00
Now in single sleeve, this LP made up half of LSP 6020 (From Vegas to Memphis)				
*BLUE HAWAII	RCA (M) LPM 2436	6.00	12.00	18.00
*BLUE HAWAII	RCA (S) LSP 2436	6.00	12.00	18.00
BRIGHTEST STARS OF CHRISTMAS	RCA (M) DLP1-0086	5.00	10.00	15.00
Special Christmas album sold only by J.C. Penny stores, contains 1 song by Elvis Presley ("Here Comes Santa Claus")				
BURNING LOVE AND HITS FROM HIS MOVIES				
VOL. 2	RCA (S) Camden CAS 2595	2.00	3.00	4.00
CHRISTMAS WITH ELVIS	RCA (EP) EPA 4340	6.00	12.00	18.00
Black-Dog on top				
CHRISTMAS WITH ELVIS	RCA (EP) EPA 4340	4.00	8.00	12.00
Black-Dog on side				
CHRISTMAS WITH ELVIS	RCA (EP) EPA 4340	3.00	6.00	9.00
Orange Label				
*CLAMBAKE	RCA (M) LPM 3893	20.00	40.00	60.00
*CLAMBAKE	RCA (S) LSP 3893	8.00	16.00	24.00
C'MON EVERYBODY	RCA (M) Camden CAL 2518	2.00	3.00	4.00
CURRENT AUDIO MAGAZINE ("ELVIS-FIRST AND ONLY PRESS CONFERENCE")	CM (M) BOL 1 NO. 1 0249	6.00	12.00	18.00
*A DATE WITH ELVIS	RCA (M) LPM 2011	20.00	45.00	80.00
Double pocket-with pictures of Elvis in the Army inside and a 1960 calendar on the back cover.				
*A DATE WITH ELVIS	RCA (M) LPM 2011	10.00	20.00	30.00
Single pocket				
*A DATE WITH ELVIS	RCA (S) LSP 2011	3.00	6.00	9.00
DEALER'S PREVUE (EP)	RCA SDS S7-39	60.00	120.00	180.00
(Disc only) Contains excerpts (not complete versions) of "Jailhouse Rock" and "Treat Me Nice".				
DEALER'S PREVUE (WITH SPECIAL PICTURE ENVELOPE (EP)	RCA SDS S7-39	150.00	300.00	450.00
DEALER'S PREVUE (EP)	RCA SDS-57-24	200.00	400.00	600.00
(Contains complete version of "Teddy Bear" and edited version of "Loving You")				
DOUBLE TROUBLE	RCA (M) LPM-3787	11.00	22.00	33.00
(Cover reads, "Special Bonus—Full Color Photo Of Elvis")				
DOUBLE TROUBLE	RCA (M) LPM 3787	10.00	20.00	30.00
("Section where "Bonus Photo" was printed now reads "Double Trouble")				
DOUBLE TROUBLE	RCA (S) LSP-3787	8.00	12.00	24.00
EASY COME, EASY GO	RCA (EP) EPA 4387	5.00	10.00	15.00
Black-Dog on top				
EASY COME, EASY GO	RCA (EP) EPA 4387	3.00	6.00	9.00
Black-Dog on side				
EASY COME, EASY GO	RCA (EP) EPA 4387	2.00	4.00	6.00
Orange Label				
EASY COME, EASY GO	RCA (EPA-4387)	7.00	14.00	21.00
(White label promo)				
ELVIS	RCA (M) RCA-1382	20.00	40.00	60.00
With pictures of other RCA albums on back cover (may read "Band 1", "Band 2" etc on label)				
ELVIS	RCA (M) RCA-1382	15.00	30.00	45.00
With only liner notes on back—no pictures of other LP's				
ELVIS	RCA (S) RCA LSP-1382	5.00	10.00	15.00
ELVIS	Brookville (M) DPL2-0056	3.00	6.00	9.00
Double LP-single pocket set-offered via mail order on T.V.				
ELVIS	RCA (M) APL1-0283	3.00	6.00	9.00
ELVIS VOL. 1	RCA (EP) EPA 992	5.00	10.00	15.00
Black Label-Dog on top				
ELVIS VOL. 1	RCA (EP) EPA 992	3.00	6.00	9.00
Black Label-Dog on side				
ELVIS VOL. 1	RCA (EP) EPA 992	2.00	4.00	6.00
Orange Label				
ELVIS VOL. 2	RCA (EP) EPA 993	5.00	10.00	15.00
Black Label-Dog on Top				
ELVIS VOL. 2	RCA (EP) EPA 993	3.00	6.00	9.00
Black Label-Dog on side				
ELVIS VOL. 2	RCA (EP) EPA 993	2.00	4.00	6.00
Orange Label				
ELVIS-VOL. 1-A LEGENDARY PERFORMER	RCA (S) CPL1-0341	2.00	4.00	6.00
ELVIS-VOL. 2-A LEGENDARY PERFORMER	RCA (S) CPL1-1349	2.00	4.00	6.00
ELVIS ALOHA FROM HAWAII VIA SATELLITE	RCA (S) VPSX 6089	3.00	6.00	9.00
Double pocket-quadradisc.				
ELVIS, ALOHA FROM HAWAII VIA SATELLITE	RCA R-213736	5.00	10.00	15.00
Issued through RCA record club. Released in stereo instead of quad				
ELVIS, ALOHA FROM HAWAII VIA SATELLITE	RCA (EP) DTFO 2006	6.00	12.00	18.00
"Stereo Album EP" contains 6 songs-designed for jukebox play.				
ELVIS, ALOHA FROM HAWAII VIA SATELITE	VPSX-6089 (RCA)	450.00	675.00	900.00
Sneak preview LP made in very limited quantity for executives at 'Chicken Of The Sea' Tuna Co, who sponsored the "Aloha From Hawaii" T.V. broadcast, April 4, 1973. This LP had a special 'Chicken Of The Sea' insignia on the front of the album cover and came with a printed insert which contained ad schedules for the company for 1973...as well as a picture of Elvis.				

(M) Mono   (S) Stereo   (EP) Extended Play   (Q) Quad   (RI) Re-issued

TITLE	LABEL & NO.	GOOD	VERY GOOD	NEAR MINT
ELVIS AS RECORDED AT MADISON SQUARE GARDEN	RCA (S) LSP 4776	2.00	4.00	6.00
ELVIS AS RECORDED AT MADISON SQUARE GARDEN	RCA (S) LSP 4776 (SPS 33-571-1)	100.00	150.00	200.00
Special 2 record set double-pocket banded for radio station convenience-blank plain white cover.				

TITLE	LABEL & NO.	GOOD	VERY GOOD	NEAR MINT
ELVIS CHRISTMAS ALBUM	RCA (M) Camden CAL 2428	2.00	3.00	4.00
ELVIS CHRISTMAS ALBUM	RCA (M) LOC 1035	40.00	80.00	120.00
Double pocket package with ten pages of photos-opens up book style.				
ELVIS CHRISTMAS ALBUM	RCA (M) LPM 1951	11.00	22.00	33.00
Black-Dog on top				
ELVIS CHRISTMAS ALBUM	RCA (S) LSP 1951	5.00	10.00	15.00
Black-Dog on top				
ELVIS COUNTRY "I'M 10,000 YEARS OLD"	RCA (S) LSP 4460	2.00	4.00	6.00
ELVIS DOUBLE DYNAMITE	RCA (M) Pickwick DL2-5001	3.00	4.50	6.00
Repackage of former Camden LP's in double pocket, 2 disc set.				
ELVIS, EXCLUSIVE LIVE PRESS CONFERENCE-MEMPHIS, TENNESSEE-February 1961	Green Valley GV-2001	5.00	10.00	15.00
Contains complete 1961 Memphis press conference—First pressings were packaged in soft style. European-like cover				
ELVIS, EXCLUSIVE LIVE PRESS CONFERENCE-MEMPHIS, TENNESSEE-February 1961	Green Valley GV-2001	2.00	4.00	6.00
Second pressing had regular stiff-cardboard style cover				
*ELVIS FOR EVERYONE	RCA (M) LPM 3450	6.00	12.00	15.00
*ELVIS FOR EVERYONE	RCA (S) LSP 3450	5.00	10.00	15.00
*ELVIS GOLDEN RECORDS	RCA (M) LPM-1707	20.00	40.00	60.00
(LP title is printed in light blue color... no song titles on front cover)				
ELVIS GOLDEN RECORDS	RCA (M) LPM-1707	12.00	24.00	36.00
(LP title is printed in white...song titles appear on front cover)				
ELVIS GOLDEN RECORDS	RCA (S) LSP-1707	5.00	10.00	15.00
*ELVIS GOLDEN RECORDS VOL. 3	RCA (M) LPM 2765	6.00	12.00	18.00
*ELVIS GOLDEN RECORDS VOL. 3	RCA (S) LSP 2765	6.00	12.00	18.00
*ELVIS GOLD RECORDS VOL. 4	RCA (M) LPM 3921	25.00	50.00	75.00
*ELVIS GOLD RECORDS VOL. 4	RCA (S) LSP 3921	5.00	10.00	15.00
ELVIS-GOOD TIMES	RCA (S) CPL1-0475	2.00	4.00	6.00
ELVIS-HE TOUCHED ME	RCA (S) LSP 4690	2.00	4.00	6.00
ELVIS-HIS SONGS OF INSPIRATION	RCA DML-1-0264	3.00	6.00	9.00
RCA Special Products, issued as a bonus LP with the Candelite Box set "The Elvis Presley Story"				
ELVIS-I GOT LUCKY	RCA (S) Camden CAS 2611	2.00	3.00	4.00
ELVIS IN CONCERT	RCA APL 2-2587	3.00	6.00	9.00
2-record set double-pocket				
ELVIS IN HOLLYWOOD	RCA DLP 2-0168	4.00	8.00	12.00
RCA Special Products-2 record set, single pocket-Brookville TV marketed				
ELVIS IN PERSON AT THE INTERNATIONAL HOTEL LAS VEGAS, NEVADA	RCA (S) LSP 4428	2.00	4.00	6.00
Now in single sleeve, this LP made up half of LSP 6020 (From Memphis to Vegas)				
*ELVIS IS BACK	RCA (M) LPM 2231	6.00	12.00	18.00
*ELVIS IS BACK	RCA (S) LSP 2231	6.00	12.00	18.00
ELVIS NOW	RCA (S) LSP 4671	2.00	4.00	6.00
*ELVIS PRESLEY	RCA (M) LPM 1254	11.00	22.00	33.00
*ELVIS PRESLEY	RCA (S) LSP 1254	5.00	10.00	15.00
ELVIS PRESLEY	RCA (EP) EPB 1254	40.00	80.00	120.00
2 records in double pocket jacket-containing 8 songs (note: there were two variations of this issue, one with pictures of other RCA product on the back cover and one with writing about Elvis. There doesn't seem to be any significant variance in value).				
ELVIS PRESLEY	SPD (EP) 22	75.00	150.00	225.00
(Offered as a give-a-way bonus with RCA Victrola purchase)—Same front cover as EPB 1254 but blank inside. 8 songs-double pocket-back cover liner notes from LSP 1382.				
ELVIS PRESLEY	RCA (EP) SPD 23	100.00	200.00	300.00
(Offered as a give-a-way bonus with RCA Victrola purchase)—Triple EP, same front cover as SPD 22, blank inside, liner notes on back-contains 8 songs from LSP 1254 plus 4 songs from single releases.				
ELVIS PRESLEY	RCA (EP) EPA 830	5.00	10.00	15.00
Black Label-Dog on top				
ELVIS PRESLEY	RCA (EP) EPA 830	3.00	6.00	9.00
Black Label-Dog on side				
ELVIS PRESLEY	RCA (EP) EPA 830	2.00	4.00	6.00
Orange Label				
ELVIS PRESLEY— "THE MOST TALKED ABOUT NEW PERSONALITY IN THE LAST TEN YEARS OF MUSIC"	RCA LPM-1254/EPB-1254/EPA-747	150.00	300.00	450.00
Two 45RPM discs with six songs on each disc-(containing all 12 songs from LSP 1254) Issued with special paper sleeve.				
ELVIS PRESLEY STORY	RCA DML 5-0263	9.00	18.00	27.00
Five-LP Box set-RCA Special Products/Candelite Music (Special 2 record—ep)				
ELVIS PRESLEY VOL. 1	RCA (EPA-747)	20.00	40.00	60.00
Price for EP and special, temporary, white sleeve wherein EP is titled "Blue Suede Shoes"				
ELVIS PRESLEY VOL. 1	RCA (EP) EPA 747	5.00	10.00	15.00
Black Label-Dog on top				
ELVIS PRESLEY VOL. 1	RCA (EP) EPA 747	4.00	8.00	12.00
Black Label-Dog on side				
ELVIS PRESLEY VOL. 1	RCA (EP) EPA 747	3.00	6.00	9.00
Orange Label				
ELVIS-PROMISED LAND	RCA (M) APL1-0873	2.00	4.00	6.00
ELVIS-PURE GOLD	RCA (M) ANL1-0971	2.00	3.00	4.00
ELVIS-RAISED ON ROCK	RCA (M) APL1-0388	2.00	4.00	6.00
ELVIS RECORDED LIVE ON STAGE IN MEMPHIS	RCA (S) CPL1-0606	3.00	6.00	9.00
ELVIS RECORDED LIVE ON STAGE IN MEMPHIS Quad issue	RCA APD-0606	20.00	40.00	60.00
ELVIS SAILS	RCA (EP) EPA 4325	10.00	20.00	30.00
(1959 Calendar on back) Black-Dog on top				
ELVIS SAILS	RCA (EP) EPA 4325	5.00	10.00	15.00
Black-Dog on side				
ELVIS SAILS	RCA (EP) EPA 4325	4.00	8.00	12.00
Orange Label				
ELVIS SAILS	RCA (EP) EPA 5157 (reissue of EPA 4325)	20.00	40.00	60.00
Maroon Label				

(M) Mono (S) Stereo (EP) Extended Play (Q) Quad (RI) Re-issued

TITLE	LABEL & NO.	GOOD	VERY GOOD	NEAR MINT
ELVIS SAILS	RCA (EP) EPA 5157 (reissue of EPA 4325)	5.00	10.00	15.00
Black-Dog on top				
ELVIS SAILS	RCA (EP) EPA 5157 (reissue of EPA 4325)	4.00	8.00	12.00
Black-Dog on side				
ELVIS SAILS	RCA (EP) EPA 5157 (reissue of EPA 4325)	3.00	6.00	9.00
Orange Label				
ELVIS-SEPARATE WAYS	RCA (S) Camden CAS 2611	2.00	3.00	4.00
ELVIS SINGS CHRISTMAS SONGS	RCA (EP) EPA 4108	6.00	12.00	18.00
Black-Dog on top				
ELVIS SINGS CHRISTMAS SONGS	RCA (EP) EPA 4108	4.00	8.00	12.00
Black-Dog on side				
ELVIS SINGS CHRISTMAS SONGS	RCA (EP) EPA 4108	3.00	6.00	9.00
Orange Label				
ELVIS SINGS FLAMING STAR	RCA (S) Camden CAS 2304	2.00	3.00	4.00
Repackage of the Singer (PRS 279) LP.				
ELVIS SINGS HITS FROM HIS MOVIES VOL. 1	RCA (S) Camden CAS 2567	2.00	3.00	4.00
ELVIS SINGS THE WONDERFUL WORLD OF CHRISTMAS	RCA (S) LSP 4579	2.50	3.75	5.00
ELVIS TAPES	Great Northwest Music Company GNW-4005	2.50	5.00	7.50
Contains complete Vancouver, 1957, Press Conference				
ELVIS: THAT'S THE WAY IT IS	RCA (S) LSP 4445	2.00	4.00	6.00
ELVIS-THE OTHER SIDES-WORLDWIDE GOLD AWARD HITS, VOL. 2	RCA (M) LPM 6402	4.00	8.00	12.00
Four LP box set-All recordings in mono				
ELVIS, THE SUN SESSIONS	RCA AMP-1-1675	2.00	4.00	6.00
ELVIS SPEAKS	Green Valley 2003	4.50	6.75	9.00
(2 records, double pocket, one disc is GV2001)				
ELVIS TODAY	RCA (M) APL1-1039	2.00	4.00	6.00
ELVIS TODAY Quad Issue	RCA APD-1039	20.00	40.00	60.00
ELVIS (T.V. SPECIAL)	RCA LPM 4088 (Partially in Stereo)	2.50	3.75	5.00
ELVIS (YOU'LL NEVER WALK ALONE)	RCA (M) Camden CALX 2472	2.00	3.00	4.00
E-Z Country Programmers 10" and 12" promotional discs, issued as a special series containing either one or two Elvis songs	RCA	30.00	60.00	90.00
Not issued with special sleeve				
E-Z Pop Programmers 10" and 12" promotional discs, issued as a special series containing either one or two Elvis songs	RCA	30.00	60.00	90.00
Not issued with special sleeve				
50,000,000 Elvis Fans Can't Be Wrong-Elvis Gold Records Vol. 2	RCA (M) RCA 2075	75.00	150.00	225.00
With black cover instead of white				

TITLE	LABEL & NO.	GOOD	VERY GOOD	NEAR MINT
*50,000,000 ELVIS FANS CAN'T BE WRONG, ELVIS GOLD RECORDS VOL. 2	RCA (M) LPM 2075	11.00	22.00	33.00
*50,000,000 ELVIS FANS CAN'T BE WRONG, ELVIS GOLD RECORDS VOL. 2	RCA (S) LSP 2075	5.00	10.00	15.00
FLAMING STAR	RCA (EP) LPC 128	10.00	20.00	30.00
33 1/3 RPM EP-				
FOLLOW THAT DREAM	RCA (EP) EPA 4368	4.00	8.00	12.00
Black-Dog on top				
FOLLOW THAT DREAM	RCA (EP) EPA 4368	3.00	6.00	9.00
Black-Dog on side				
FOLLOW THAT DREAM	RCA (EP) EPA 4368	2.00	4.00	6.00
Orange Label				
FOLLOW THAT DREAM	RCA (EP) 4368	40.00	80.00	120.00
(Promotional 33 1/3 Jukebox EP, with cover.)				
*FOR LP FANS ONLY	RCA (M) LPM 1990	11.00	22.00	33.00
*FOR LP FANS ONLY	RCA (S) LSP 1990	5.00	10.00	15.00
*FRANKIE AND JOHNNY	RCA (M) LPM 3553	9.00	18.00	27.00
*FRANKIE AND JOHNNY	RCA (S) LSP 3553	9.00	18.00	27.00
FRANKIE & JOHNNY	Pickwick ACL-7007	2.00	3.00	4.00
Contains all but two of the songs on RCA LPM/LSP 3553				
FROM ELVIS IN MEMPHIS	RCA (S) LSP 4155	2.00	4.00	6.00
FROM ELVIS PRESLEY BOULEVARD, MEMPHIS, TENNESSEE	RCA APL-1-1506	2.00	4.00	6.00

TITLE	LABEL & NO.	GOOD	VERY GOOD	NEAR MINT
FROM ELVIS PRESLEY BOULEVARD, MEMPHIS, TENNESSEE Quad Issue	RCA APD-1-1506	30.00	60.00	90.00
FROM ELVIS WITH LOVE	RCA (R234340)	6.00	9.00	12.00
(RCA Record Club issue only—2 record set)				
FROM MEMPHIS TO VEGAS/ FROM VEGAS TO MEMPHIS	RCA (S) LSP 6020	4.00	8.00	12.00
Double pocket-2 record set.				
*FUN IN ACAPULCO	RCA (M) LPM 2756	5.00	10.00	15.00
*FUN IN ACAPULCO	RCA (S) LSP 2756	5.00	10.00	15.00
*G.I. BLUES	RCA (M) LPM 2256	5.00	10.00	15.00
*G.I. BLUES	RCA (S) LSP 2256	5.00	10.00	15.00
*GIRL HAPPY	RCA (M) LPM 3338	5.00	10.00	15.00
*GIRL HAPPY	RCA (S) LSP 3338	5.00	10.00	15.00
*GIRLS! GIRLS! GIRLS!	RCA (M) LPM 2621	5.00	10.00	15.00
*GIRLS! GIRLS! GIRLS!	RCA (S) LSP 2621	5.00	10.00	15.00
GOOD TIMES Quad Issue	RCA APD-0475	20.00	40.00	60.00
GREAT COUNTRY/WESTERN HITS Price including all ten discs and box	RCA (SPD-26)	100.00	200.00	300.00
GREAT COUNTRY/WESTERN HITS Price of Elvis EP only	RCA (SPD-26)	20.00	40.00	60.00
This box set contains 10 individual EP's. One of the ten (599-9141) contains "Mystery Train". "Milkcow Blues". "Blue Moon Of Kentucky" and "Love Me Tender" by Elvis.				
*HARUM SCARUM	RCA (M) LPM 3468	9.00	18.00	27.00
*HARUM SCARUM	RCA (S) LSP 3468	9.00	18.00	27.00
HAVING FUN WITH ELVIS ON STAGE	Boxcar (No #)	10.00	20.00	30.00
Sold only at Elvis personal appearances-at souvenir stand.				
HAVING FUN WITH ELVIS ON STAGE	RCA (S) Camden CPM1-0818	2.00	3.00	4.00
Commercial release of the Boxcar LP.				
HEARTBREAK HOTEL	RCA (EP) EPA 821	5.00	10.00	15.00
Black Label-Dog on top				
HEARTBREAK HOTEL	RCA (EP) EPA 821	3.00	6.00	9.00
Black Label-Dog on side				
HEARTBREAK HOTEL	RCA (EP) EPA 821	2.00	4.00	6.00
Orange Label				
HE WALKS BESIDE ME	RCA AFL1-2772	2.00	4.00	6.00
*HIS HAND IN MINE	RCA (M) LPM 2328	5.00	10.00	15.00
*HIS HAND IN MINE	RCA (S) LSP 2328	5.00	10.00	15.00
HIS HAND IN MINE	RCA ANL-1-1319	2.00	4.00	6.00
Reissue of LPM/LSP 2328-Different cover than the original issue				
*HOW GREAT THOU ART	RCA (M) LPM 3758	5.00	10.00	15.00
*HOW GREAT THOU ART	RCA (S) LSP 3758	5.00	10.00	15.00
INTERNATIONAL HOTEL PRESENTS ELVIS 1970	RCA	150.00	300.00	450.00
Limited edition box set issued by the International Hotel (now the Las Vegas Hilton) to certain invited guests. Box contained; special menu. Elvis calendar, Elvis record catalog, souvenir photo album. Latest single "Kentucky Rain" and the double-LP "Vegas To Memphis to Vegas" LSP-6020 (price includes box and contents)				
*IT HAPPENED AT THE WORLD'S FAIR	RCA (M) LPM 2697	9.00	18.00	27.00
*IT HAPPENED AT THE WORLD'S FAIR	RCA (S) LSP 2697	9.00	18.00	27.00
JAILHOUSE ROCK	RCA (EP) EPA 4114	5.00	10.00	15.00
Black-Dog on top				
JAILHOUSE ROCK	RCA (EP) EPA 4114	3.00	6.00	9.00
Black-Dog on side				
JUST FOR YOU	RCA (EP) EPA 4041	5.00	10.00	15.00
Black-Dog on top				
JUST FOR YOU	RCA (EP) EPA 4041	3.00	6.00	9.00
Black-Dog on side				
JUST FOR YOU	RCA (EP) EPA 4041	2.00	4.00	6.00
Orange Label				
KID GALAHAD	RCA (EP) EPA 4371	5.00	10.00	15.00
Black-Dog on top				
KID GALAHAD	RCA (EP) EPA 4371	3.00	6.00	9.00
Black-Dog on side				
KID GALAHAD	RCA (EP) EPA 4371	2.00	4.00	6.00
Orange Label				
*KING CREOLE	RCA (M) LPM 1884	11.00	22.00	33.00
*KING CREOLE	RCA (S) LSP 1884	5.00	10.00	15.00
KING CREOLE VOL. 1	RCA (EP) EPA 4319	5.00	10.00	15.00
Black-Dog on top				
KING CREOLE VOL. 1	RCA (EP) EPA 4319	3.00	6.00	9.00
Black-Dog on side				
KING CREOLE VOL. 1	RCA (EP) EPA 4319	2.00	4.00	6.00
Orange Label				
KING CREOLE VOL. 1	RCA (EP) EPA 5122 (reissue of EPA 4319)	20.00	40.00	60.00
Maroon Label				
KING CREOLE VOL. 1	RCA (EP) EPA 5122 (reissue of EPA 4319)	5.00	10.00	15.00
Black-Dog on top				
KING CREOLE VOL. 1	RCA (EP) EPA 5122 (reissue of EPA 4319)	3.00	6.00	9.00
Black-Dog on side				
KING CREOLE VOL. 1	RCA (EP) EPA 5122 (reissue of EPA 4319)	2.00	4.00	6.00
Orange Label				
KING CREOLE VOL. 2	RCA (EP) EPA 4321	5.00	10.00	15.00
Black-Dog on top				
KING CREOLE VOL. 2	RCA (EP) EPA 4321	3.00	6.00	9.00
Black-Dog on side				
KING CREOLE VOL. 2	RCA (EP) EPA 4321	2.00	4.00	6.00
Orange Label				
*KISSIN' COUSINS	RCA (M) LPM 2894	5.00	10.00	15.00
*KISSIN' COUSINS	RCA (S) LSP 2894	5.00	10.00	15.00
LET'S BE FRIENDS	RCA (S) Camden CAS 2408	2.00	3.00	4.00
LOVE LETTERS FROM ELVIS	RCA (S) LSP 4530	2.00	4.00	6.00
LOVE ME TENDER	RCA (EP) EPA 4006	5.00	10.00	15.00
Black Label-Dog on top				
LOVE ME TENDER	RCA (EP) EPA 4006	3.00	6.00	9.00
Black Label-Dog on side				
LOVE ME TENDER	RCA (EP) EPA 4006	2.00	4.00	6.00
Orange Label				
*LOVING YOU	RCA (M) LPM 1515	11.00	22.00	33.00
*LOVING YOU	RCA (S) LSP 1515	5.00	10.00	15.00

(M) Mono (S) Stereo (EP) Extended Play (Q) Quad (RI) Re-issued

TITLE	LABEL & NO.	GOOD	VERY GOOD	NEAR MINT
LOVING YOU VOL. 1	RCA (EP) EPA 1-1515	5.00	10.00	15.00
Black Label-Dog on top				
LOVING YOU VOL. 1	RCA (EP) EPA 1-1515	3.00	6.00	9.00
Black Label-Dog on side				
LOVING YOU VOL. 1	RCA (EP) EPA 1-1515	2.00	4.00	6.00
Orange Label				
LOVING YOU VOL. 2	RCA (EP) EPA 2-1515	5.00	10.00	15.00
Black Label-Dog on top				
LOVING YOU VOL. 2	RCA (EP) EPA 2-1515	3.00	6.00	9.00
Black Label-Dog on side				
LOVING YOU VOL. 2	RCA (EP) EPA 2-1515	2.00	4.00	6.00
Orange Label				
MOODY BLUE	RCA AFLI-2428	2.00	4.00	6.00
(Issued on blue vinyl)				
MOODY BLUE	RCA AFLI-2428	40.00	60.00	80.00
(Black vinyl-Promotional copy) (Foreign pressings are also black vinyl) Original "Moody Blue" album cover				

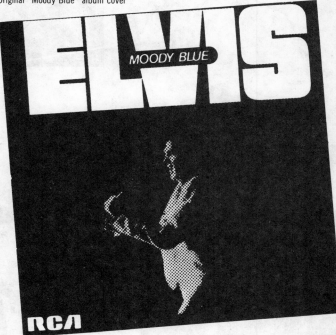

TITLE	LABEL & NO.	GOOD	VERY GOOD	NEAR MINT
OCTOBER CHRISTMAS SAMPLER	RCA (S) SPS 33-54	25.00	67.50	100.00
(Promotional use only contains one Elvis song "Blue Christmas") (Issued in 1959)				
ON STAGE: FEBRUARY 1970	RCA (S) LSP 4362	2.00	4.00	6.00
*PARADISE HAWAIIAN STYLE	RCA (M) LPM 3643	5.00	10.00	15.00
*PARADISE HAWAIIAN STYLE	RCA (S) LSP 3643	5.00	10.00	15.00
PEACE IN THE VALLEY	RCA (EP) EPA 4054	5.00	10.00	15.00
Black-Dog on top				
PEACE IN THE VALLEY	RCA (EP) EPA 4054	3.00	6.00	9.00
Black-Dog on side				
PEACE IN THE VALLEY	RCA (EP) EPA 4054	2.00	4.00	6.00
Orange Label				
PEACE IN THE VALLEY	RCA (EP) EPA 5121 (reissue of EPA 4054)	20.00	40.00	60.00
Maroon Label				
PEACE IN THE VALLEY	RCA (EP) EPA 5121 (reissue of EPA 4054)	4.00	8.00	12.00
Black-Dog on top				
PEACE IN THE VALLEY	RCA (EP) EPA 5121 (reissue of EPA 4054)	3.00	6.00	9.00
Black-Dog on side				
PEACE IN THE VALLEY	RCA (EP) EPA 5121 (reissue of EPA 4054)	2.00	4.00	6.00
Orange Label				
PERFECT FOR PARTIES	RCA (EP) SPA 737	20.00	40.00	60.00
Special RCA product offer through mail order, for 25¢ contains 'Love Me' by Elvis along with other (5) RCA artists, Elvis does the spoken introduction to each song. Black Dog on top only. Issued with picture sleeve.				
*POT LUCK	RCA (M) LPM 2523	5.00	10.00	15.00
*POT LUCK	RCA (S) LSP 2523	5.00	10.00	15.00
PROMISED LAND Quad Issue	RCA APD-0873	20.00	40.00	60.00
REAL ELVIS	RCA (EP) EPA 940	7.00	14.00	21.00
Black Label-Dog on top				
REAL ELVIS	RCA (EP) EPA 5120 (reissue of EPA 940)	20.00	40.00	60.00
Maroon Label				
REAL ELVIS	RCA (EP) EPA 5120 (reissue of EPA 940)	5.00	10.00	15.00
Black-Dog on top				
REAL ELVIS	RCA (EP) EPA 5120 (reissue of EPA 940)	4.00	8.00	12.00
Orange Label				
REAL HISTORY OF ROCK N' ROLL FEATURING ELVIS Narration by Wayne Stierle tracing Elvis career, issued on Gold Plastic		9.00	18.00	27.00
RCA PROMOTIONAL EP (UNTITLED-CONTAINS TWO ELVIS SONGS ON ONE SIDE. "LOVE ME TENDER" & "ANYWAY YOU WANT ME"	RCA (DJ-7)	15.00	30.00	45.00
Not issued with cover (Flip side has two songs by Jean Chapel)				

(list continued on page 134)

FOREIGN RELEASES

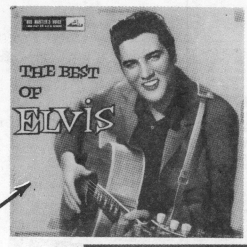

To list every valuable and collectible Elvis release, from around the world, would be a monumental undertaking...and would take up dozens of pages. It is just not practical to consider such a project. On the other hand, there are a significant number of foreign releases that are among the most valuable of all Elvis records. Collectors should know which ones are the most sought-after and their values. We have therefore decided to list only those releases that have a near-mint value of $50.00 or higher. As with the entire Price Guide, we welcome information on any that we may have missed for this section. Overseas readers can be particularly helpful in this area. Thank you!

BEST OF ELVIS..........................HMV England (DLP-1159) 30.00 60.00 90.00
(10" LP containing 10 songs)
BEST OF ELVIS....................PS Records Malaysia NTLP-237 20.00 40.00 60.00
(12" LP containing 14 songs-hits of 1969-1972)
ELVIS AS RECORDED LIVE AT MADISON
  SQUARE GARDEN................PS Records Malaysia (NTLP-238) 18.00 36.00 54.00
(Has Elvis photo on label)
ELVIS CHRISTMAS ALBUM ....RCA England (RD-27052) 25.00 50.00 75.00
ELVIS CHRISTMAS ALBUM ....RCA Brazil (LOC 1035) 100.00 200.00 300.00
(Different picture cover than U.S. release)
ELVIS GOLDEN RECORDS ....RCA England (RB-16069) 40.00 80.00 120.00
(RCA Red Seal label)
(Issued with photo booklet bound in jacket-as was our U.S. LOC-1035)
ELVIS, NOW & BEFORE ....Holy Hawk China (HH7009) 50.00 100.00 150.00
(Elvis hits-1956-1972 10 disc set)
ELVIS PRESLEY ....RCA Chile (CML-3012) 150.00 300.00 450.00
(Issued in 1956 only-10" LP-10 songs)
ELVIS PRESLEY NO. 2..................HMV England (CLP-1105) 25.00 50.00 75.00
ELVIS PRESLEY, PANEL DELUXE............RCA Japan (RP-9201-2) 70.00 140.00 210.00
(Two records in a deluxe 12" x 18" box-set. Includes a special
booklet)
ELVIS PRESLEY-ROCK 'N' ROLL...........HMV England (CLP-1093) 20.00 40.00 60.00
ELVIS PRESLEY'S GOLDEN HITS .....PS Records Malaysia (NTLP-264) 17.00 34.00 51.00
(24 songs)
ELVIS PRESLEY'S GREATEST HITS...........RCA England (GELV-6A) 35.00 70.00 105.00
(Special Reader's Digest seven-record box set)
ELVIS PRESLEY'S 23 GOLDEN HITS .. PS Records Malaysia (NTLP-264) 18.00 36.00 54.00
ELVIS PRESLEY-Y SU CONJUNTO ....RCA Chile (CML-3009) 150.00 300.00 450.00
(Issued in 1956 only-10" LP-10 songs)-issued with two different
covers-one like U.S. EPA 747 and one like EPA 830)
50 GOLD AWARD HITS ....RCA Yugoslavia (LS-RCA-70851-4) 30.00 60.00 90.00
(Has picture of Elvis on cover instead of gold records)
GOLDEN BOY ELVIS...................Hor Zu Germany (SHZT 521) 80.00 160.00 240.00
(Available only for a few months in 1965, then removed from the
market)
GOOD ROCKIN' TONIGHT ....RCA France (130-252) 200.00 400.00 600.00
(First issue-Has 1956 shot of Elvis from "Love Me Tender" on cover)
GOOD ROCKIN' TONIGHT ....RCA France (130-252) 40.00 80.00 120.00
(Second issue-Has photo of Elvis on cover wearing white jacket)
HITS & HITBOUNDS-MAY 1973.................RCA SP CS-33-118 25.00 50.00 75.00
(Not issued with special jacket contains "Steamroller Blues".
Canadian release...there were several others, with Elvis cuts,
in this series.)
JAILHOUSE ROCK ....RCA South Africa (31-126) 40.00 80.00 120.00
(First issue-1957-black albel)
JANIS & ELVIS..................RCA South Africa (T-31-077) 400.00 800.00 1200.00
(10" LP with four songs by Janis Martin on one side and four by
Elvis on the other side)
KING OF THE WHOLE WIDE WORLD ....RCA South Africa (31-673) 150.00 300.00 450.00
LOS DISCOS DE ORO DE ELVIS...........RCA Argentina (LPM-1707) 17.00 34.00 51.00
LOVE ME TENDER ....(EPA 4006) Belgium 50.00 100.00 150.00
(Different cover picture than any other Elvis cover-anywhere)
LOVING YOU............................RCA England (RCA-24001) 18.00 36.00 54.00
MAGICAL ROCKIN' SOUND OF
  ELVIS PRESLEY ....Jubilee Cambodia (MLP-1956) 17.00 34.00 51.00
ON STAGE/ELVIS GOLDEN RECORDS .Lyou Fang Japan (LF 2361-2370) 50.00 100.00 150.00
(Issued in conjunction with Reader's Digest-contains 10 discs. Cover
is similar to U.S. "Elvis Golden Records Vol. 1")
PERFECT FOR PARTIES.................(RCA Germany) SPA 7-37 100.00 200.00 300.00
(Has one different cut-by Tony Cabot "Ring Out Then You're Hoiahs"
instead of "Anchors Away")
ROCK IS BACK, ELVIS IS KING ....RCA South Africa (32,384) 20.00 30.00 60.00
(Original 1967 issue-black label)
TICKLE ME ....RCA South Africa (32-049) 80.00 160.00 240.00
VANCOUVER'S OFFICIAL ELVIS PRESLEY
  PRESS CONFERENCE ....(Kellys-no number) 30.00 60.00 90.00
Contains excerpts from Vancouver Press Conference-Issued with
special picture sleeve

Note: There are a number of Elvis releases from the Orient, Korea and U.S.S.R. and other countries where neither the LP title or the songs are in English, therefore making it impossible to print the information in this book. In most cases these issues are quite valuable, and their ommission from this guide should not be interpeted as an indication that their value is below the $50 minimum.

RCA PROMOTIONAL EP (UNTITLED-CONTAINS TWO ELVIS SONGS ON ONE SIDE. "TOO MUCH" & PLAYING FOR KEEPS") .. RCA (DJ-56) — 15.00 / 30.00 / 45.00
Not issued with cover (Flip side contains two songs by Dinah Shore)

RCA Promotional LP (Untitled-contains one Elvis song. "King Creole") .... RCA (SP 33-10-P) — 60.00 / 120.00 / 180.00
Not issued with jacket.

RCA SPD 15 RCA ten record boxed set. Has one Elvis EP -599-9089), the rest are by other RCA artists, and all the discs have gray labels. (56) — 150.00 / 300.00 / 450.00

RCA SPD-19 RCA eight record EP boxed set, has one Elvis EP, the rest are by other artists. (56) — 200.00 / 400.00 / 600.00

*ROUSTABOUT .... RCA (M) LPM 2999 — 5.00 / 10.00 / 15.00

*ROUSTABOUT .... RCA (S) LSP 2999 — 5.00 / 10.00 / 15.00

SAVE-ON RECORDS EP .... RCA SPA 7-27 — 150.00 / 300.00 / 450.00
(This special EP was issued so that the record buyer could sample some of the songs and artists that RCA was releasing new product by, during the spring and early summer of 1956. This particular EP (for the month of June) offered an excerpt from Elvis' "I'm Gonna Sit Right Down And Cry". Issued with a special cover, which did not picture any of the artists...the above price range reflects both disc and cover. The cover is extremely rare, and without it the disc itself would be valued at 30% - 50% of above prices.)

SINGER PRESENTS ELVIS SINGING FLAMING STAR AND OTHERS .... RCA (S) PRS 279 — 10.00 / 20.00 / 30.00
This album was sold only in Singer Sewing Machine Centers in conjunction with the '68 T.V. special.

*SOMETHING FOR EVERYBODY .... RCA (M) LPM 2370 — 5.00 / 10.00 / 15.00

*SOMETHING FOR EVERYBODY .... RCA (S) LSP 2370 — 5.00 / 10.00 / 15.00

SPECIAL PALM SUNDAY PROGRAMMING ..... RCA SP-33-461 — 40.00 / 80.00 / 120.00
Issued in 1967...used by radio stations to present special ½ hour Palm Sunday program. Contains songs from "How Great Thou Art" LP. Issued without special jacket. This disc has been bootlegged...but boots can be distinguished by inferior label printing.

*SPEEDWAY .... RCA (M) LPM 3989 — 40.00 / 80.00 / 120.00

*SPEEDWAY .... RCA (S) LSP 3989 — 5.00 / 10.00 / 15.00

*SPINOUT .... RCA (M) LPM 3702 — 9.00 / 18.00 / 27.00

*SPINOUT .... RCA (S) LSP 3702 — 9.00 / 18.00 / 27.00

STRICTLY ELVIS .... RCA (EP) EPA 994 — 5.00 / 10.00 / 15.00
Black-Dog on top

STRICTLY ELVIS .... RCA (EP) EPA 994 — 3.00 / 6.00 / 9.00
Black-Dog on side

STRICTLY ELVIS .... RCA (EP) EPA 994 — 2.00 / 4.00 / 6.00
Orange Label

SUN YEARS (INTERVIEWS & MEMORIES) ..... Sun 1001 — 3.00 / 6.00 / 9.00
Dark Yellow cover with brown printing. Label is standard SSS with four target/circles

SUN YEARS (INTERVIEWS & MEMORIES) ..... Sun 1001 — 8.00 / 16.00 / 24.00
Light yellow, or cream cover with brown printing. Label is old style Sun label, without target/circles

SUN YEARS (INTERVIEWS & MEMORIES) ..... Sun 100 — 5.00 / 10.00 / 15.00
White cover with brown printing

SUN YEARS (INTERVIEWS & MEMORIES) ..... Sun 1001 — 15.00 / 30.00 / 45.00
White cover with black printing

THAT'S THE WAY IT IS (Soundtrack) ...... RCA (S) LSP4445 — 3.00 / 6.00 / 9.00

TICKLE ME .... RCA (EP) EPA 4383 — 4.00 / 8.00 / 12.00
Black-Dog on top

TICKLE ME .... RCA (EP) EPA 4383 — 3.00 / 6.00 / 9.00
Black-Dog on side

TICKLE ME .... RCA (EP) EPA 4383 — 2.00 / 4.00 / 6.00
Orange Label

TO ELVIS: LOVE STILL BURNING .... Fotoplay FSP 1001 — 7.50 / 11.25 / 15.00
World's first commercially released picture record—features a full color print of Elvis pressed into the record. Contains 11 Elvis tribute songs by various artists.

A TOUCH OF GOLD VOL. 1 .... RCA (EP) EPA 5088 — 11.00 / 22.00 / 33.00
Maroon Label

A TOUCH OF GOLD VOL. 1 .... RCA (EP) EPA 5088 — 4.00 / 8.00 / 12.00
Black-Dog on top

A TOUCH OF GOLD VOL. 1 .... RCA (EP) EPA 5088 — 3.00 / 6.00 / 9.00
Black-Dog on side

A TOUCH OF GOLD VOL. 1 .... RCA (EP) EPA 5088 — 2.00 / 4.00 / 6.00
Orange Label

A TOUCH OF GOLD VOL. 2 .... RCA (EP) EPA 5101 — 11.00 / 22.00 / 33.00
Maroon Label

A TOUCH OF GOLD VOL. 2 .... RCA (EP) EPA 5101 — 4.00 / 8.00 / 12.00
Black-Dog on top

A TOUCH OF GOLD VOL. 2 .... RCA (EP) EPA 5101 — 3.00 / 6.00 / 9.00
Black-Dog on side

A TOUCH OF GOLD VOL. 2 .... RCA (EP) EPA 5101 — 2.00 / 4.00 / 6.00
Orange Label

A TOUCH OF GOLD VOL. 3 .... RCA (EP) EPA 5141 — 11.00 / 22.00 / 33.00
Maroon Label

A TOUCH OF GOLD VOL. 3 .... RCA (EP) EPA 5141 — 4.00 / 8.00 / 12.00
Black-Dog on top

A TOUCH OF GOLD VOL. 3 .... RCA (EP) EPA 5141 — 3.00 / 6.00 / 9.00
Black-Dog on side

A TOUCH OF GOLD VOL. 3 .... RCA (EP) EPA 5141 — 2.00 / 4.00 / 6.00
Orange Label

TV GUIDE PRESENTS ELVIS PRESLEY ... RCA Custom (EP) G8-MW-8705 — Est. $3500

This is a package containing a one-sided EP with four spoken responses by Elvis that were exerpted from an interview conducted by a **TV Guide** reporter in Lakeland, Florida in 1956. These "answers" are only 19, 34, 54 and 44 seconds long, respectively. The estimated value listed is for the complete package (which we have never documented as having been sold) of the record and two paper inserts all in near mint condition. The value of any part of the package would be negotiable according to condition and assessment by the parties involved as to the desirability and relative worth of the record by itself, which is scarce; the "suggested continuity" insert, which is probably twice as rare (it was offered as a guide to anyone, such as a radio station disc jockey, who wanted to "ask" Elvis the questions he answered on the disc); and the second insert that tells the story behind the interview, which is much rarer than either of the other two.

(**Note:** the record has been bootlegged, but is easy to identify. The serial, or matrix number of the record has been scratched by hand lettering into the vinyl between the last band and the label, whereas on the original it has been pressed into the vinyl by a stamper. Also, the bootleg "tracks through," meaning that all four bands play one after the other with a pause between each. On the original, the bands are "locked," which means that after each response has been played, the needle has to be picked up and moved over by hand to the next track.)

VIVA LAS VEGAS .... RCA (EP) EPA 4382 — 4.00 / 8.00 / 12.00
Black-Dog on top

VIVA LAS VEGAS .... RCA (EP) EPA 4382 — 3.00 / 6.00 / 9.00
Black-Dog on side

VIVA LAS VEGAS .... RCA (EP) EPA 4382 — 2.00 / 4.00 / 6.00
Orange Label

WELCOME TO MY WORLD .... RCA APL 1-2274 — 2.00 / 4.00 / 6.00

WORLDWIDE GOLD HITS PARTS 1 & 2 ..... RCA R-213690 — 15.00 / 30.00 / 45.00
2-record set in single pocket-Issued by RCA record club.

WORLDWIDE 50 GOLD AWARDS HITS VOL. 1 ... RCA (M) LPM 6401 — 5.00 / 10.00 / 15.00
A four LP box set-with all recordings in Mono.

*Black-Dog on top
Note: Several of the albums previously deleted by RCA were reissued after the singer's death, in 1977. All of these carried new release numbers and thus cannot be confused with the original counterparts. The reissues also had the orange RCA label as compared to the black originals.

(M) Mono (S) Stereo (EP) Extended Play (Q) Quad (RI) Re-issued

TITLE	LABEL & NO.	GOOD	VERY GOOD	NEAR MINT
PRESTON, Billy				
BILLY PRESTON	A&M (S) SP 4587	2.00	3.00	4.00
BILLY PRESTON'S "LIVE EUROPEAN TOUR"	A&M (S) SP 3637	3.00	4.50	6.00
ENCOURAGING WORDS	Apple (S) ST 3370	4.00	6.00	8.00
EVERYBODY LIKES SOME KIND OF MUSIC	A&M (S) SP 3526	2.00	3.00	4.00
GOSPEL IN MY SOUL	Peacock (S) 179	2.00	4.00	6.00
I WROTE A SIMPLE SONG	A&M (S) SP 3507	2.00	3.00	4.00
IT'S A WHOLE NEW THING	A&M (S) SP 4532	2.00	3.00	4.00
IT'S MY PLEASURE	A&M (S) SP 4532	2.00	3.00	4.00
KIDS & ME	A&M (S) SP 3645	2.00	3.00	4.00
MOST EXCITING ORGAN EVER	Vee Jay (S) 1123	2.50	5.00	7.50
MUSIC IS MY LIFE	A&M (S) SP 3516	2.00	3.00	4.00
SOUL'D OUT	GNP/Crescendo (S) GNPS-2-2071	3.00	4.50	6.00
THAT'S THE WAY GOD PLANNED IT	Apple (S) ST 3359	4.00	6.00	8.00
WILDEST ORGAN IN TOWN	Capitol (M) T 2532	2.00	4.00	6.00
WILDEST ORGAN IN TOWN	Capitol (S) ST 2532	2.00	4.00	6.00
PRESTON, Johnny				
COME ROCK WITH ME	Mercury (M) MG 20609	7.50	18.75	30.00
COME ROCK WITH ME	Mercury (S) SR 60609	8.00	20.00	32.00
RUNNING BEAR	Mercury (M) MG-20592	9.00	22.50	36.00
RUNNING BEAR	Mercury (S) SR-60250	10.00	25.00	40.00
RUNNING BEAR	Mercury (EP) 3397	2.00	4.00	6.00
RUNNING BEAR	Mercury/Wing (M) MGW 12246	4.00	6.00	8.00
RUNNING BEAR	Mercury/Wing (S) SRW 16246	4.00	6.00	8.00
PRETTY PEOPLE				
PRETTY PEOPLE BY THE PRETTY PEOPLE, THE	Crestview (S) CRS 3056	4.00	6.00	8.00
PRETTY THINGS				
FREEWAY MADNESS	Warner Brothers (S) BS 2680	4.00	6.00	8.00
PARACHUTE	Rare Earth (S) RS 515	4.00	6.00	8.00
PRETTY THINGS, THE	Fontana (M) MGF 27544	6.00	9.00	12.00
PRETTY THINGS, THE	Fontana (S) SRF 67544	7.00	10.50	14.00
SAVAGE EYE	Swan (S) 8414	3.00	4.50	6.00
S.F. SORROW	Rare Earth (S) RS 506	5.00	7.50	10.00
SILK TORPEDO	Swan Song (S) 8411	3.00	4.50	6.00

TITLE	LABEL & NO.	GOOD	VERY GOOD	NEAR MINT
PRICE, Alan				
PRICE IS RIGHT, THE	Parrot (M) PA 61018	3.00	4.50	6.00
PRICE IS RIGHT, THE	Parrot (S) PAS 71018	3.50	5.25	7.00
PRICE, Lloyd				
COME TO ME	Guest Star (M) G 1910	2.50	3.75	5.00
EXCITING LLOYD PRICE, THE	ABC/Paramount (M) ABC 277	4.00	8.00	12.00
EXCITING LLOYD PRICE, THE	ABC (S) ABCS-277	2.00	4.00	6.00
FANTASTIC LLOYD PRICE	ABC (M) ABC-346	3.00	6.00	9.00
FANTASTIC LLOYD PRICE	ABC (S) ABCS 346	2.00	4.00	6.00
15 HITS	ABC (S) ABCS 324	4.00	8.00	12.00
LLOYD PRICE	Specialty (S) SP-2105	6.00	12.00	18.00
LLOYD PRICE COOKIN'	ABC (M) ABC-382	3.00	4.50	6.00
LLOYD PRICE COOKIN'	ABC (S) ABCS-382	3.00	4.50	6.00
LLOYD PRICE ORCHESTRA	Double L (M) D-2301	3.00	4.50	6.00
LLOYD PRICE ORCHESTRA	Double L (S) S-8301	3.00	6.00	9.00
LLOYD PRICE SINGS THE MILLION SELLERS	ABC (M) ABC-366	3.00	6.00	9.00
LLOYD PRICE SINGS THE MILLION SELLERS	ABC (S) ABCS-366	2.00	4.00	6.00
LLOYD SWINGS FOR SAMMY	Monument (M) MLP 8032	2.50	3.75	5.00
MR. PERSONALITY	ABC/Paramount (M) ABC 297	4.00	8.00	12.00
MR. PERSONALITY	ABC/Paramount (M) ABC 297	2.50	3.75	5.00
MR. PERSONALITY'S BIG 15	ABC (M) ABC-324	4.00	8.00	12.00
MR. PERSONALITY SINGS THE BLUES	ABC/Paramount (M) ABC 315	3.00	6.00	9.00
MR. PERSONALITY SINGS THE BLUES	ABC/Paramount (EP) A 315	3.00	4.50	6.00
MR. RHYTHM AND BLUES	Grand Prix (M) K 422	2.50	3.75	5.00
MISTY	Double L (S) SDL 8303	3.00	4.50	6.00
MISTY	Up Front (M) UPF 126	2.00	3.00	4.00
NOW	Jad (M) 1002	3.00	4.50	6.00
NOW	Turntable (M) 5001	2.50	3.75	5.00
16 GREATEST HITS	ABC (S) ABCX 763	2.50	3.75	5.00
PRICE, Ray				
ANOTHER BRIDGE TO BURN	Columbia (M) CL-2528	3.00	6.00	9.00
ANOTHER BRIDGE TO BURN	Columbia (S) CS-9328	3.00	6.00	9.00
BURNING MEMORIES	Columbia (M) CL-2289	3.00	4.50	6.00
BURNING MEMORIES	Columbia (S) CS-9089	3.00	4.50	6.00

TITLE	LABEL & NO.	GOOD	VERY GOOD	NEAR MINT
COLLECTORS' CHOICE	Harmony (M) HL 7372	2.50	3.75	5.00
COLLECTORS' CHOICE	Harmony (S) HS 11172	2.50	3.75	5.00
DANNY BOY	Columbia (M) CL 2677	2.50	3.75	5.00
DANNY BOY	Columbia (S) CS 9477	2.50	3.75	5.00
FAITH	Columbia (M) CL-1494	3.00	4.50	6.00
FAITH	Columbia (S) CS-8285	3.00	4.50	6.00
FAITH	Columbia (EP) B-14941	1.50	2.25	3.00
FAITH	Columbia (EP) B-14942	1.50	2.25	3.00
FAITH	Columbia (EP) B-14943	1.50	2.25	3.00
FOR THE GOOD TIMES	Columbia (S) C 30106	2.50	3.75	5.00
FOR THE GOOD TIMES	Columbia (Q) CQ 30106	2.50	3.75	5.00
FOR THE GOOD TIMES/ I WON'T MENTION IT AGAIN	Columbia (S) CG-33633	2.00	3.00	4.00
FOUR HITS BY RAY PRICE	Columbia (EP) B 2118	2.00	3.00	4.00
I FALL TO PIECES	Harmony (S) HS 11373	2.50	3.75	5.00
IF YOU EVER CHANGE YOU MIND	Columbia (S) KC-33560	2.00	3.00	4.00
I WON'T MENTION IT AGAIN	Columbia (S) 30510	2.50	3.75	5.00
LIKE OLD TIMES AGAIN	ABC (S) 871	3.00	4.50	6.00
LIKE OLD TIMES AGAIN	Myrrh (S) 6538	3.50	5.25	7.00
LONESOMEST LONESOME	Columbia (S) 31546	2.00	3.00	4.00
LOVE LIFE	Columbia (M) CL-2189	3.00	4.50	6.00
LOVE LIFE	Columbia (S) CS-8989	3.00	4.50	6.00
MAKE THE WORLD GO AWAY	Harmony (S) KH 30272	3.00	4.50	6.00
NIGHT LIEE	Columbia (M) CL-1971	3.00	6.00	9.00
NIGHT LIFE	Columbia (S) CS-8771	3.00	6.00	9.00
OTHER WOMAN, THE	Columbia (M) CL 2382	3.00	6.00	9.00
OTHER WOMAN, THE	Columbia (S) CS 9182	3.00	6.00	9.00
RAY PRICE	Columbia (EP) 2809	2.00	3.00	4.00
RAY PRICE	Columbia (EP) B 2812	2.00	3.00	4.00
RAY PRICE GREATEST HITS	Columbia (M) CL-1566	3.00	4.50	6.00
RAY PRICE GREATEST HITS	Columbia (S) CS 8866	2.00	3.00	4.00
RAY PRICE GREATEST HITS VOL. 2	Columbia (M) CL 2670	3.00	4.50	6.00
RAY PRICE GREATEST HITS VOL. 2	Columbia (S) CS 9470	3.00	4.50	6.00
RAY PRICE'S ALL TIME GREATEST HITS	Columbia (S) 31364	2.00	3.00	4.00
RAY PRICE SINGS FOUR HITS	Columbia (EP) B 2137	2.00	3.00	4.00
RAY PRICE SINGS HEART SONGS	Columbia (M) CL 1015	4.00	8.00	12.00
RAY PRICE SINGS HEART SONGS	Columbia (EP) B 10051	2.00	4.00	6.00
RAY PRICE SINGS HEART SONGS	Columbia (EP) B 10052	2.00	4.00	6.00
RAY PRICE SINGS HEART SONGS	Columbia (EP) B 10053	2.00	4.00	6.00
RAY PRICE SINGS SAN ANTONIO ROSE	Columbia (M) CL-1756	3.00	6.00	9.00
RAY PRICE SINGS SAN ANTONIO ROSE	Columbia (S) CS-8556	3.00	6.00	9.00
RELEASE ME	Harmony (S) KH-30919	2.50	3.75	5.00
SAY I DO	Dot (S) DOSD-2037	2.50	3.75	5.00
TALK TO YOUR HEART	Columbia (M) CL 1148	5.00	7.50	10.00
TALK TO YOUR HEART	Columbia (M) CL 1148	4.00	8.00	12.00
TALK TO YOUR HEART	Columbia (EP) B 11481	2.00	3.00	4.00
TOUCH MY HEART	Columbia (M) CL 2606	3.00	4.50	6.00
TOUCH MY HEART	Columbia (S) CS 9406	3.00	4.50	6.00
VOCAL SELECTIONS WITH STRING BAND	Columbia (EP) H 1786	2.00	3.00	4.00
WELCOME TO MY WORLD	Columbia (S) 30878	2.00	3.00	4.00
WESTERN STRINGS	Columbia (M) CL-2339	3.00	6.00	9.00
WESTERN STRINGS	Columbia (S) CS-9139	3.00	6.00	9.00
YOU'RE THE BEST THING THAT EVER HAPPENED TO ME	Columbia (S) KC-32777	2.00	3.00	4.00
PRIDE, Charley				
AMAZING LOVE	RCA (S) APL1-0397	2.00	3.00	4.00
BEST OF CHARLEY PRIDE	RCA (S) LPS 4223	2.50	3.75	5.00
BEST OF CHARLEY PRIDE, VOL. II	RCA (S) LPS 4682	2.50	3.75	5.00
BEST OF CHARLEY PRIDE, VOL. 3	RCA (S) APL1-2023	2.00	3.00	4.00
CHARLEY PRIDE IN PERSON	RCA (S) LPS 4094	2.50	3.75	5.00
CHARLEY PRIDE SINGS HEART SONGS	RCA (S) LPS 4617	2.50	3.75	5.00
CHARLEY PRIDE'S 10TH ALBUM	RCA (S) LPS 4367	2.50	3.75	5.00
COUNTRY CHARLEY PRIDE	RCA (M) LPM 3645	3.50	5.25	7.00
COUNTRY CHARLEY PRIDE	RCA (S) LPS 3645	3.00	4.50	6.00
COUNTRY FEELIN'	RCA (S) APL1-0534	2.00	3.00	4.00
COUNTRY WAY	RCA (M) LPM 3895	3.50	5.25	7.00
COUNTRY WAY	RCA (S) LPS 3895	3.00	4.50	6.00
DID YOU THINK TO PRAY	RCA (S) LPS 4513	2.50	3.75	5.00
FROM ME TO YOU	RCA (S) LPS 4468	2.50	3.75	5.00
I'M JUST ME	RCA (S) LPS 4560	2.50	3.75	5.00
JUST PLAIN CHARLEY	RCA (S) LPS 4290	2.50	3.75	5.00
HAPPINESS OF HAVING YOU	RCA (S) APL1-1241	2.00	3.00	4.00
HAPPINESS OF HAVING YOU	RCA (Q) APD1-1241	2.50	3.75	5.00
PRIDE OF AMERICA	RCA (Q) APD1-0757	2.00	3.00	4.00
PRIDE OF COUNTRY MUSIC	RCA (M) LPM 3775	3.50	5.25	7.00
PRIDE OF COUNTRY MUSIC	RCA (S) LPS 3775	3.00	4.50	6.00
SENSATIONAL CHARLEY PRIDE	RCA (S) LPS 4153	2.50	3.75	5.00
SHE'S JUST AN OLD LOVE TURNED MEMORY	RCA (S) APL1-2261	2.00	3.00	4.00
SOMEONE LOVES YOU HONEY	RCA (S) APL1-2478	2.00	3.00	4.00
SONG OF LOVE	RCA (S) LSP-4837	2.50	3.75	5.00
SONGS OF PRIDE	RCA (S) LPS 4041	3.50	5.25	7.00
A SUNSHINY DAY	RCA (S) LPS 4742	2.50	3.75	5.00
SWEET COUNTRY	RCA (Q) APD1-0217	2.50	3.75	5.00
SWEET COUNTRY	RCA (S) APL1-0217	2.00	3.00	4.00
PRINCE BUSTER				
TEN COMMANDMENTS	RCA (M) LPM 3792	3.00	6.00	9.00
TEN COMMANDMENTS	RCA (S) LSP 3792	4.00	8.00	12.00
PRINCIPAL EDWARDS MAGIC THEATER				
PRINCIPAL EDWARDS MAGIC THEATER	Dandealion (M) D9-103	5.00	7.50	10.00
PRINE, John				
DIAMONDS IN THE ROUGH	Atlantic (S) SD 7240	3.00	4.50	6.00
JOHN PRINE	Atlantic (S) SD 8296	3.50	5.25	7.00
SWEET REVENGE	Atlantic (S) SD 7274	3.00	4.50	6.00

(M) Mono (S) Stereo (EP) Extended Play (Q) Quad (RI) Re-issued

PRINZE, Freddie
LOOKING GOOD	Columbia (S) PC-33562	2.50	3.75	5.00

PRISCILLA
PRISCILLA LOVES BILLY	Happy Tiger (M) HT 1002	3.00	6.00	9.00
PRISCILLA SINGS HERSELF	York (M) 4005	4.00	8.00	12.00

PRIVILEGE
PRIVILEGE	T-Neck (S) TNS 3003	2.50	3.75	5.00

PROBY, P.J.
ENIGMA	Liberty (M) LRP 3497	3.00	4.50	6.00
ENIGMA	Liberty (S) LST 7497	4.00	6.00	8.00
P.J. PROBY	Liberty (M) LRP 3421	3.00	6.00	9.00
P.J. PROBY	Liberty (S) LST 7421	4.00	8.00	12.00
SOMEWHERE	Liberty (M) LRP3406	3.00	4.50	6.00
SOMEWHERE	Liberty (S) LST7406	4.00	6.00	8.00
WHAT'S WRONG IN MY WORLD	Liberty (M) LRP 3561	3.00	4.50	6.00
WHAT'S WRONG IN MY WORLD	Liberty (S) LST 7561	4.00	6.00	8.00

PROCESSION
PROCESSION	Smash (S) SRS 67122	4.50	6.75	9.00

PROCOL HARUM
BEST OF PROCOL HARUM	A&M (S) SP 4401	2.00	3.00	4.00
BROKEN BARRICADES	A&M (S) SP 4294	2.00	3.00	4.00
HOME	A&M (S) SP 4261	2.50	3.75	5.00
LIVE IN CONCERT WITH THE EDMONTON SYMPHONY ORCHESTRA	A&M (S) SP 4335	2.00	3.00	4.00
PROCOL HARUM	Deram (M) DE 16008	3.00	4.50	6.00
PROCOL HARUM	Deram (S) DES 18008	4.00	6.00	8.00
PROCOL HARUM LIVES (A CONSUMERS GUIDE TO PROCOL HARUM) Includes an Interview	A&M (S) SP 8053	8.00	12.00	16.00
PROCOL'S NINTH	Chrysalis (S) 1080	3.00	4.50	6.00
SHINE ON BRIGHTLY	A&M (S) SP 4151	2.50	3.75	5.00
A SALTY DOG	A&M (S) SP 4179	2.00	3.00	4.00
WHITER SHADE OF PALE	A&M (S) SP 4373	2.50	3.75	5.00

PROTHEROE, Brian
PICK-UP	Chrysalis (S) 1090	2.00	3.00	4.00
PINBALL	Chrysalis (S) 1065	2.00	3.00	4.00

PRYOR, Richard
THAT NIGGER IS CRAZY	Partee (S) 2404	4.00	6.00	8.00
THAT NIGGER'S CRAZY	Reprise (S) MS 2241	3.00	4.50	6.00

PRYOR, Snooky
DO IT IF YOU WANT	Bluesway (M) 6076	2.00	3.00	4.00

PRYSOCK, Red
BEAT, THE	Mercury (M) MG 20307	4.00	10.00	16.00
ROCK N' ROLL	Mercury (M) MG 20086	4.00	10.00	16.00

PUCKETT, Gary & The Union Gap
INCREDIBLE	Columbia (S) CS 9715	2.00	3.00	4.00
NEW GARY PUCKETT AND THE UNION GAP	Columbia (S) CS 9935	2.00	3.00	4.00
WOMAN, WOMAN	Columbia (S) CS 9612	2.25	3.50	4.50
YOUNG GIRL	Columbia (S) CS 9664	2.25	3.50	4.50

PUFF
PUFF	MGM (S) SE 4622	4.00	6.00	8.00

PUGH
JA, DA A DA	Vault (M) 137	3.50	5.25	7.00

PUGSLEY MUNION
JUST LIKE YOU	J&S (S) SLP 0001	6.00	9.00	12.00

PULLEN, Whitey
WHITEY PULLEN	Crown (M) CLP 5332	6.00	15.00	24.00

PULSE
PULSE	Poison Ring (M) 2237	5.00	7.50	10.00

PURE PRAIRIE LEAGUE
TWO LANE HIGHWAY	RCA (S) APL1-0933	2.50	3.75	5.00
TWO LANE HIGHWAY	RCA (Q) APD1-0933	2.50	3.75	5.00

PURIFY, James & Bobby
PURE SOUND OF JAMES & BOBBY PURIFY, THE	Bell (M) 6010	2.50	3.75	5.00

PURPLE GANG
PURPLE GANG STRIKES, THE	Sire (M) 97006	5.00	7.50	10.00

PURPLE IMAGE
PURPLE IMAGE	Map (M) 3015	4.00	6.00	8.00

(M) Mono   (S) Stereo   (EP) Extended Play   (Q) Quad   (RI) Re-issued

PUZZLE
PUZZLE	ABC (M) 671	3.00	4.50	6.00
PUZZLE	Motown (S) 768	2.50	3.75	5.00
SECOND ALBUM	Motown (S) 807	2.50	3.75	5.00

PYRAMIDS
PENETRATION	Best (M) LPM 1001	5.00	10.00	15.00

PYTHON LEE JACKSON
IN A BROKEN DREAM	GNP-Crescendo (S) GNPS 2066	4.00	6.00	8.00
Also see STEWART, Rod				

QUATRAIN
QUATRAIN	Tetragrammaton (S) T-5002	2.50	3.75	5.00

QUATRO, Michael
DANCERS, ROMANCERS, DREAMERS & SCHEMERS	United Artists (S) UA-LA587	3.50	5.25	7.00
DANCERS, ROMANCERS, DREAMERS & SCHEMERS (RI OF UA 587)	Prodigal (S) P6-10010	3.00	4.50	6.00
IN COLLABORATION WITH THE GODS	United Artists (S) UA-LA420	2.00	3.00	4.00
LOOK DEEPLY INTO THE MIRROR	Evolution (M) 3021	4.00	6.00	8.00
PAINTINGS	Evolution (M) 3011	4.00	6.00	8.00
(Evolution entries shown as "Mike Quatro Jam Band")				

QUATRO, Suzi
QUATRO	Bell (S) 1313	3.00	4.50	6.00
SUZI QUATRO	Bell (S) 1302	3.00	4.50	6.00
YOUR MAMA WON'T LIKE ME	Arista (S) AL 4035	2.50	3.75	5.00

QUEEN
DAY AT THE RACES	Elektra (S) 6E-101	2.50	3.75	5.00
NEWS OF THE WORLD	Elektra (S) 6E-112	2.50	3.75	5.00
NIGHT AT THE OPERA	Elektra (S) 7E-1053	2.50	3.75	5.00
QUEEN	Elektra (S) EKS 75064	3.50	5.25	7.00
QUEEN	Elektra (Q) EQ 5064	3.00	4.50	6.00
QUEEN 2	Elektra (S) 75082	3.50	5.25	7.00
SHEER HEART ATTACK	Elektra (S) 7E-1026	2.50	3.75	5.00

QUESTION MARK & THE MYSTERIANS
ACTION	Cameo (M) C 2006	4.50	6.75	9.00
ACTION	Cameo (S) SC 2006	5.50	7.75	11.00
96 TEARS	Cameo (M) C 2004	4.00	6.00	8.00
96 TEARS	Cameo (S) CS 2004	5.00	7.50	10.00

QUICKSILVER
ANTHOLOGY	Capitol (S) SVBB-11165	3.00	4.50	6.00
COMIN' THROUGH	Capitol (S) 11002	2.50	3.75	5.00
HAPPY TRAILS	Capitol (S) 120	3.00	4.50	6.00
JUST FOR LOVE	Capitol (S) 498	3.00	4.50	6.00
QUICKSILVER	Capitol (S) 819	3.00	4.50	6.00
QUICKSILVER MESSENGER SERVICE	Capitol (S) ST-2904	4.00	6.00	8.00
SHADY GROVE	Capitol (S) 391	3.00	4.50	6.00
SOLID SILVER	Capitol (S) ST-11462	2.50	3.75	5.00
WHAT ABOUT ME	Capitol (S) 630	3.00	4.50	6.00
(Capitol 2904 & 120 shown as "QUICKSILVER MESSENGER SERVICE")				

QUILL
QUILL	Cotillion (S) SD 9017	3.00	4.50	6.00

QUINTET
FUTURE TENSE	United Artists (S) UAS 5514	2.50	3.75	5.00

QUIVER
GONE IN THE MORNING	Warner Brothers (S) BS 2630	3.00	4.50	6.00
QUIVER	Warner Brothers (S) 1939	4.00	6.00	8.00

R

RABBIT 1
RABBIT 1	Bell (S) 6057	3.00	4.50	6.00

Also see FIVE AMERICANS

RABON, Michael & Choctaw
MICHAEL RABON AND CHOCTAW	Uni (S) 73102	4.00	6.00	8.00

RACKET SQUAD
CORNERS OF YOUR MIND	Jubilee (S) JGS 8026	5.00	7.50	10.00
RACKET SQUAD, THE	Jubilee (S) JGS 8015	4.00	6.00	8.00

RADHA KRISHNA TEMPLE
RADHA KRISHNA TEMPLE LONDON, THE	Apple (S) SKAO 3376	4.00	6.00	8.00

RAEBURN, Boyd
TEEN ROCK	Columbia (M) CL-1073	5.00	10.00	15.00

RAELETTS
SOULED OUT (With Ike & Tina Turner)	TRC (S) TRCS 1511	3.00	4.50	6.00
YESTERDAY, TODAY, TOMORROW	TRC (S) 1515	3.00	4.50	6.00

RAFFERTY, Gerry
CAN I HAVE MY MONEY BACK	Blue Thumb (S) BTS 58	4.00	6.00	9.00

RAICEVIC, Nik
BEYOND THE END . . . ETERNITY	Narco (S) NR 102	5.00	7.50	10.00

RAIDERS
TWISTIN' THE COUNTRY CLASSICS	Liberty (M) LRP-3225	2.00	4.00	6.00
TWISTIN' THE COUNTRY CLASSICS	Liberty (S) LST-7225	2.50	5.00	7.50

RAINBOW
LONG LIVE ROCK 'N' ROLL	Polydor (S) PD-1-6143	2.00	3.00	4.00
RAINBOW RISING	Oyster (S) 1601	3.00	4.50	6.00

(Listed as "Blackmore's Rainbow")
Also see BLACKMORE, Ritchie & DEEP PURPLE

RAINBOW BAND
RAINBOW BAND, THE	Elektra (S) EKS 74092	2.00	3.00	4.00

RAINBOW PRESS
SUNDAY PRESS	Mr. G (S) G 9004	4.50	6.75	9.00

RAINBOX
AFTER THE STORM	GNP/Crescendo (S) GNPS 2049	4.00	6.00	8.00

RAINDROPS
RAINDROPS	Jubilee (M) J-5023	4.00	8.00	12.00
RAINDROPS	Jubilee (S) SJ-5023	5.00	10.00	15.00

RAINWATER, Marvin
GONNA FIND ME A BLUEBIRD	MGM (M) E 4046	10.00	20.00	30.00
SONGS BY MARVIN RAINWATER	MGM (M) E 3534	10.00	20.00	30.00
SONGS BY MARVIN RAINWATER	MGM (EP) X 1464	1.50	2.25	3.00

WITH A HEART—WITH A BEAT	MGM (M) E3721	10.00	20.00	30.00

RAINY DAZE
THAT ACAPULCO GOLD	Uni (M) 3002	3.00	4.50	6.00
THAT ACAPULCO GOLD	Uni (S) 73002	3.50	5.25	7.00

RAITT, Bonnie
STREETLIGHTS	Warner Bros. (S) BS-2818	2.00	3.00	4.00
TAKIN' MY TIME	Warner Bros. (S) BS-2729	2.00	3.00	4.00

RAITT, John
UNDER OPEN SKIES	Capitol (M) T 1058	3.00	6.00	9.00

(John Raitt is one of Broadway's most successful lead singers, having starred in "Carousel," "The Pajama Game," and others. See Original Casts and Soundtracks section.)

RAMBEAU, Eddie
CONCRETE & CLAY	Dyno Voice (M) 9001	2.50	3.75	5.00

RAM, Buck
MAGIC TOUCH, THE	Mercury (M) MG-20392	3.00	4.50	6.00
MAGIC TOUCH, THE	Mercury (S) SR-60067	3.00	4.50	6.00
ROCK'N RAM WITH BUCK RAM	Camden (EP) CAE 435	1.00	1.50	2.00

Also see PLATTERS

RAMONES
LEAVE HOME	Sire (S) 7528	2.50	3.75	5.00
LEAVE HOME ('77 RI)	Sire (S) SRK 6031	2.00	3.00	4.00
RAMONES	Sire (S) 7520	2.50	3.75	5.00
RAMONES ('77 RI)	Sire (S) SRK 6020	2.00	3.00	4.00
ROCKET TO RUSSIA	Sire (S) SRK 6042	2.00	3.00	4.00

RANDAZZO, Teddy
BIG WIDE WORLD	Colpix (M) 445	3.00	6.00	9.00
I'M CONFESSIN	VIK (M) LX 1121	6.00	15.00	24.00
I'M CONFESSIN	VIK (EP) EXA 281	2.00	5.00	8.00
JOURNEY TO LOVE	ABC/Paramount (M) ABC 352	2.50	5.00	7.50
JOURNEY TO LOVE	ABC/Paramount (S) ABCS 352	3.00	6.00	9.00
MISTER ROCK AND ROLL	VIK (EP) EXA 300	2.00	5.00	8.00
MISTER ROCK AND ROLL	VIK (EP) EXA 301	2.00	5.00	8.00
TNT	ABC/Paramount (M) ABC 421	2.50	5.00	7.50
TNT	ABC/Paramount (S) ABCS 421	3.00	6.00	9.00

RANDOLPH, Boots
MORE YAKETY SAX!	Monument (M) 8037	3.00	4.50	6.00
MORE YAKETY SAX!	Monument (S) 18037	3.50	5.25	7.00
YAKETY SAX	Monument (M) 8002	2.00	4.00	6.00
YAKETY SAX	Monument (S) 18002	3.00	5.25	7.50

RANKIN, Kenny
INSIDE	Little David (S) 1009	3.00	4.50	6.00
SILVER MORNING	Little David (S) 3000	2.50	3.75	5.00

RARE BIRD
AS YOUR MIND FLIES BY	ABC (S) 716	3.00	4.50	6.00
BORN AGAIN	Polydor (S) 6506	2.50	3.75	5.00
EPIC FOREST	Polydor (S) 5530	2.50	3.75	5.00
RARE BIRD	Probe (S) 4514	4.00	6.00	8.00
SOMEBODY'S WATCHING	Polydor (S) 6502	2.50	3.75	5.00

RARE EARTH
BAND TOGETHER	Prodigal (S) P7-10025	2.00	3.00	4.00
DREAMS/ANSWERS	Verve (S) V6 5066	4.00	6.00	8.00
ECOLOGY	Rare Earth 514	3.50	5.25	7.00
GET READY	Rare Earth (S) 507	3.50	5.25	7.00
MIDNIGHT LADY	Rare Earth (S) R6-550	3.00	4.50	6.00
ONE WORLD	Rare Earth 520	3.00	4.50	6.00
RARE EARTH	Prodigal (S) P6-10019	2.00	3.00	4.00
RARE EARTH	Rare Earth 546	3.00	4.50	6.00
RARE EARTH IN CONCERT	Rare Earth 534	3.00	4.50	6.00
WILLIE REMEMBERS	Rare Earth 543	3.00	4.50	6.00

(M) Mono   (S) Stereo   (EP) Extended Play   (Q) Quad   (RI) Re-issued

TITLE	LABEL & NO.	GOOD	VERY GOOD	NEAR MINT
RASPBERRIES				
FRESH	Capitol (S) ST11123	3.00	4.50	6.00
RASPBERRIES	Capitol (S) 11036	3.00	4.50	6.00
RASPBERRIES' BEST	Capitol (S) ST 11524	2.50	3.75	5.00
(Featuring Eric Carmen)				
SIDE 3	Capitol (S) SMAS 11220	3.00	4.50	6.00
STARTING OVER	Capitol (S) ST 11329	3.00	4.50	6.00
Also see CARMEN, Eric				
RASPUTIN & THE MONKS				
SUN OF MY SOUL	Trans Radio (M) TR 968	8.00	12.00	16.00
RASPUTIN'S STASH				
RASPUTIN'S STASH	Cotillion (S) 9046	3.00	4.50	6.00
RASPUTIN STASH	Gemigo (S) 5500	4.00	6.00	8.00
RATIONALS				
RATIONALS, THE	Crewe (M) CR 1334	6.00	9.00	12.00
RATTLES				
GREATEST HITS	Mercury (M) MG 21127	5.00	7.50	10.00
GREATEST HITS	Mercury (S) SR 61127	6.00	9.00	12.00
RAVEN				
LIVE AT THE INFERNO	Discovery (M) 36133	3.00	4.50	6.00
RAVENS				
RAVENS	Harlem Hit Parade (M) HHPS007	3.00	4.50	6.00
RAVENS, THE	King (EP) EP 310	3.00	7.50	12.00
WRITE ME A LETTER	Regent (M) MG6062	5.00	10.00	15.00
RAW HOLLY				
RAW HOLLY	Coral (S) CRL 757515	4.00	6.00	8.00
RAY, Dave				
FINE SOFT LAND	Elektra (M) EKL 319	2.50	3.75	5.00
FINE SOFT LAND	Elektra (S) EKS 7319	3.00	4.50	6.00
SNAKER'S HERE	Elektra (M) EKL 284	2.50	3.75	5.00
SNAKER'S HERE	Elektra (S) EKS 7284	3.00	4.50	6.00
RAY, Diane				
EXCITING YEARS, THE	Mercury (M) MG 20903	4.00	8.00	12.00
EXCITING YEARS, THE	Mercury (S) SR 60903	5.00	10.00	15.00
RAY, James				
JAMES RAY	Caprice (M) 1002	3.00	4.50	6.00
JAMES RAY	Caprice (S) 1002	4.00	6.00	8.00
RAY, Johnnie				
BIG BEAT, THE	Columbia (M) CL 961	2.50	3.75	5.00
BIG BEAT, THE	Columbia (EP) B 9611	1.50	2.25	3.00
BIG BEAT, THE	Columbia (EP) B 9612	1.50	2.25	3.00
I CRY FOR YOU	Columbia (M) CL 2510	3.00	4.50	6.00
JOHNNIE RAY (10")	Columbia (M) CL 6199	2.50	3.75	5.00
JOHNNIE RAY	Columbia (EP) B 288	1.00	1.50	2.00
JOHNNIE RAY	Columbia (EP) B 2536	1.00	1.50	2.00
JOHNNIE RAY	Columbia (EP) B 2595	1.00	1.50	2.00
JOHNNIE RAY	Epic (M) LN 1120	3.50	5.25	7.00
JOHNNIE RAY AND THE FOUR LADS	Epic (EP) PG 9003	2.00	3.00	4.00
JOHNNIE RAY GREATEST	Epic (EP) EG 7021	1.00	1.50	2.00
JOHNNIE RAY GREATEST HITS	Columbia (M) CL 1227	4.00	6.00	8.00
JOHNNIE RAY ON THE TRAIL	Columbia (EP) B-13787	1.00	1.50	2.00
JOHNNIE RAY ON THE TRAIL	Columbia (M) CL-1385	3.00	4.50	6.00
JOHNNIE RAY ON THE TRAIL	Columbia (S) CS-8180	3.50	5.25	7.00
JOHNNIE RAY WITH THE FOUR LADS	Columbia (EP) B 2566	1.00	1.50	2.00
JUST WALKING IN THE RAIN	Columbia (EP) B 2113	1.50	2.25	3.00
PAJAMA GAME	Columbia (EP) B 1863	1.00	1.50	2.00
RAY SPOTLITE	Columbia (EP) B 1635	1.00	1.50	2.00

TITLE	LABEL & NO.	GOOD	VERY GOOD	NEAR MINT
'TIL MORNING	Columbia (S) CS-8034	3.50	5.25	7.00
YOU DON'T OWE ME A THING	Columbia (EP) B 2123	1.50	2.25	3.00
RAYE, Jerry				
MANY SIDES OF JERRY RAYE	De Ville (M) LP101	6.00	9.00	12.00
RAYS				
RAYS, THE	Chess (EP) EP 5120	2.00	4.00	6.00
REBECCA & THE SUNNY BROOK FARMERS				
REBECCA AND THE SUNNY BROOK FARMERS	Musicor (M) MS 3176	4.00	6.00	8.00
REDDING, Otis				
BEST OF OTIS REDDING, THE	Atco (M) 2-801	4.00	6.00	8.00
DICTIONARY OF SOUL	Volt (M) 415	3.00	4.50	6.00
DICTIONARY OF SOUL	Volt (S) 415	3.50	5.25	7.00
DOCK OF THE BAY	Volt (M) 419	2.50	3.75	5.00
DOCK OF THE BAY	Volt (S) 419	3.00	4.50	6.00
GREAT OTIS REDDING SINGS SOUL BALLADS	Volt (M) 411	3.00	4.50	6.00
GREAT OTIS REDDING SINGS SOUL BALLADS	Volt (S) 411	3.50	5.25	7.00
HISTORY OF OTIS REDDING	Volt (M) M418	3.00	4.50	6.00
HISTORY OF OTIS REDDING	Volt (S) S 418	3.50	5.25	7.00
IMMORTAL OTIS REDDING	Atco (M) 252	3.00	4.50	6.00
IN PERSON AT THE WHISKEY A-GO-GO	Atco (M) 265	3.00	4.50	6.00
LIVE IN EUROPE	Volt (S) S 416	3.50	5.25	7.00
LIVE IN EUROPE	Volt (M) M 416	3.00	4.50	6.00
LOVE MAN	Atco (S) 289	3.00	4.50	6.00
OTIS BLUE	Volt (M) M 412	3.50	5.25	7.00
OTIS BLUE	Volt (S) S 412	4.00	6.00	8.00
PAIN IN MY HEART	Atco (M) 161	3.00	4.50	6.00
PAIN IN MY HEART	Atco (S) 161	3.50	5.25	7.00
SOUL ALBUM	Volt (M) 413	3.00	4.50	6.00
SOUL ALBUM	Volt (S) 413	3.50	4.50	7.00
TELL THE TRUTH	Atco (S) SD 33-333	4.00	6.00	8.00
REDDING, Otis & Little Joe Curtis				
HERE COMES SOME SOUL FROM OTIS REDDING AND LITTLE JOE CURTIS	Somerset (M) SF 29200	5.00	7.50	10.00
SOUL AS SUNG BY OTIS REDDING AND LITTLE JOE CURTIS	Alshire (S) S 5082	5.00	7.50	10:00
REDDING, Otis & Carla Thomas				
KING AND QUEEN	Stax (S) S 716	3.00	4.50	6.00
REDDING, Otis & The Jimi Hendrix Experience				
HISTORIC PERFORMANCES RECORDED AT THE MONTEREY INTERNATIONAL POP FESTIVAL	Reprise (S) RS 2029	2.50	3.75	5.00
REDDY, Helen				
EAR CANDY	Capitol (S) SO 11640	2.00	3.00	4.00
FREE & EASY	Capitol (S) ST 11348	2.50	3.75	5.00
HELEN REDDY	Capitol (S) ST 857	3.00	4.50	6.00
HELEN REDDY'S GREATEST HITS	Capitol (S) ST-11467	2.00	3.00	4.00
I AM WOMAN	Capitol (S) ST 11068	2.50	3.75	5.00
I DON'T KNOW HOW TO LOVE HIM	Capitol (S) ST762	3.00	4.50	6.00
LONG HARD CLIMB	Capitol (S) SMAS 11213	2.50	3.75	5.00
LOVE SONG FOR JEFFREY	Capitol (S) SO-11284	2.50	3.75	5.00
MUSIC, MUSIC	Capitol (S) ST 11547	2.00	3.00	4.00
NO WAY TO TREAT A LADY	Capitol (S) ST 11418	2.00	3.00	4.00
WE'LL SING IN THE SUNSHINE	Capitol (S) SW-11759	2.00	3.00	4.00
RED HOOK (The Echoes)				
RED HOOK	Red Hook (M) 523	5.00	7.50	10.00
RED HOOK AS THE DUKES	Blue Lion (M) 101	5.00	7.50	10.00
RED KRAYOLA				
GOD BLESS THE RED KRAYOLA AND ALL WHO SAIL WITH IT	International Artists (M) 1A LP 7	6.00	12.00	18.00
PARABLE OF ARABLE LAND, THE	International Artists (M) 1A LP 2	6.00	12.00	18.00
(With the Familiar Ugly)				
REDNOW, Eivets-see WONDER, Stevie				
REDWING				
BEYOND THE SUN & STARS	Fantasy (S) F 9438	3.00	4.50	6.00
DEAD OR ALIVE	Fantasy (S) F-9459	3.00	4.50	6.00
REDWING	Fantasy (S) F-8409	3.00	4.50	6.00
TAKE ME HOME	Fantasy (S) F-9439	3.00	4.50	6.00
WHAT THIS COUNTRY NEEDS	Fantasy (S) F 9405	3.00	4.50	6.00
REED, Jerry				
GOOD WOMAN'S LOVE	RCA (S) APL1-0544	2.50	3.75	5.00
HOT A' MIGHTY	RCA (S) LSP-4838	3.00	4.50	6.00
LORD, MR. FORD	RCA (S) APL1-0238	2.50	3.75	5.00
LORD, MR. FORD	RCA (Q) APD1-0238	2.50	3.75	5.00
MIND YOUR LOVE	RCA (S) APL1-0787	2.50	3.75	5.00
NASHVILLE UNDERGROUND	RCA (M) LPM 3978	3.00	4.50	6.00
NASHVILLE UNDERGROUND	RCA (S) LSP 3978	3.00	4.50	6.00
RED HOT PICKER	RCA (S) APL1-1226	2.50	3.75	5.00
UNBELIEVABLE GUITAR & VOICE	RCA (M) LPM 3756	4.00	6.00	8.00
UNBELIEVABLE GUITAR & VOICE	RCA (S) LSP 3756	4.00	6.00	8.00
UPTOWN POKER CLUB	RCA (S) APL1-0356	2.50	3.75	5.00

(M) Mono (S) Stereo (EP) Extended Play (Q) Quad (RI) Re-issued

TITLE	LABEL & NO.	GOOD	VERY GOOD	NEAR MINT
REED, Jimmy				
AS JIMMY IS	Roker (M) 4001	2.00	3.00	4.00
BEST OF JIMMY REED, THE	Vee Jay (M) LP 1039	5.00	10.00	15.00
BEST OF JIMMY REED, THE	Exodus (M) 308	2.00	3.00	4.00
BEST OF THE BLUES, THE	Vee Jay (M) VJ 1072	4.00	8.00	12.00
BIG BOSS MAN	Bluesway (M) BL 6015	4.00	6.00	8.00
BOSS MAN OF THE BLUES, THE	Vee Jay (M) VJ 1080	4.00	8.00	12.00
DOWN IN VIRGINIA	Bluesway (M) 6024	2.50	3.75	5.00
FOUND LOVE	Vee Jay (M) LP 1022	5.00	10.00	15.00
I AIN'T FROM CHICAGO	Bluesway (M) 6054	2.50	3.75	5.00
I AIN'T FROM CHICAGO	Blues Way (S) BLS 6054	4.00	6.00	8.00
I'M JIMMY REED	Vee Jay (M) LP 1004	5.00	10.00	15.00
JIMMY REED	Everest (M) 234	2.50	3.75	5.00
JIMMY REED AT CARNEGIE HALL	Vee Jay (M) 1035	2.00	3.00	4.00
JIMMY REED AT CARNEGIE HALL	Exodus (M) EX 2 307	3.50	5.25	7.00
JIMMY REED AT SOUL CITY	Vee Jay (M) VJ,1095	3.00	6.00	9.00
JIMMY REED SINGS THE BEST OF THE BLUES	Exodus (M) 311	2.00	3.00	4.00
JUST JIMMY REED	Vee Jay (M) LP 1050	4.00	8.00	12.00
JUST JIMMY REED	Exodus (M) 310	2.50	3.75	5.00
JUST JIMMY REED	Buddah (M) 4003	2.50	3.75	5.00
LEGEND-THE MAN	Vee Jay (S) VJS 8501	3.50	5.25	7.00
LET THE BOSSMAN SPEAK	Blues on Blues (M) 10001	2.00	3.00	4.00
NOW APPEARING	Vee Jay (M) LP 1025	5.00	10.00	15.00
ROCKIN WITH REED	Vee Jay (M) LP1008	5.00	10.00	15.00
SOULIN	Bluesway (M) 6009	2.50	3.75	5.00
T'AINT NO BIG THING, BUT HE IS JIMMY REED	Vee Jay (M) LP 1067	4.00	8.00	12.00
ULTIMATE, THE	Bluesway (M) 6067	2.00	3.00	4.00
WAILIN' THE BLUES	Tradition (M) 2069	2.50	3.75	5.00
REED, Lou				
CONEY ISLAND BABY	RCA (S) APL1-0915	3.00	4.50	6.00
CONEY ISLAND BABY ('77 RI)	RCA (S) ANL1-2480	2.00	3.00	4.00
LOU REED	RCA LSP-4701	5.00	7.50	10.00
LOU REED & THE VELVET UNDERGROUND	Pride 0022	2.50	3.75	5.00
1969 VELVET UNDERGROUND LIVE	Mercury (S) SRM-2-7504	3.00	4.50	6.00
(Shown as LOU REED & THE VELVET UNDERGROUND)				
ROCK & ROLL HEART	Arista (S) 4100	2.00	3.00	4.00
ROCK 'N' ROLL ANIMAL	RCA APL1-0472	3.00	4.50	6.00
SALLY CAN'T DANCE	RCA (S) CPL1-0611	3.00	4.50	6.00
STREET HASSLE	Arista (S) 4169	3.00	4.50	6.00
TRANSFORMER	RCA (S) LSP-4807	4.00	6.00	8.00
WALK ON THE WILD SIDE (The Best of Lou Reed)	RCA (S) APL1-2001	2.50	3.75	5.00
REED, Lulu				
BLUE & MOODY	King (M) 604	5.00	12.50	20.00
REESE, Della				
DELLA	RCA (M) LPM-2157	2.00	4.00	6.00
DELLA	RCA (S) LSP-2157	2.50	5.00	7.50
DELLA BY STARLIGHT	RCA (M) LPM-2204	2.00	4.00	6.00
DELLA BY STARLIGHT	RCA (S) LSP-2204	2.50	5.00	7.50
DON'T YOU KNOW	RCA (EP) EPA 4349	1.50	3.00	4.50
LET ME IN YOUR LIFE	LMI (S) 1002	2.50	3.75	5.00
WHAT DO YOU KNOW ABOUT LOVE	Jubilee (M) 1109	3.00	6.00	9.00
REEVES, Jim				
AM I LOSING YOU	RCA (EP) EPA-5145	1.00	1.50	2.00
BIMBO	RCA (M) LPM 1410	4.00	6.00	8.00
BIMBO	RCA (EP) EPA 1-1410	2.00	3.00	4.00
FOUR WALLS	RCA (EP) EPA 406	1.50	2.25	3.00
GENTLEMAN JIM	RCA (M) LPM 2605	2.00	3.00	4.00
GENTLEMAN JIM	RCA (S) LSP 2605	2.00	3.00	4.00
GIRLS I HAVE KNOWN	RCA (M) LPM 165	4.00	6.00	8.00
GOD BE WITH YOU	RCA (M) LPM-1950	2.50	3.75	5.00
GOD BE WITH YOU	RCA (S) LSP-1950	2.50	3.75	5.00
HE'LL HAVE TO GO	RCA (M) LPM-2223	2.50	3.75	5.00
HE'LL HAVE TO GO	RCA (S) LSP-2223	2.50	3.75	5.00
HE'LL HAVE TO GO	RCA (EP) EPA-4357	1.50	2.25	3.00
I'D FIGHT THE WORLD	RCA (S) APL1-0537	2.00	3.00	4.00
JIM REEVES	RCA (M) LPM 157	4.00	6.00	8.00
JIM REEVES	RCA (EP) EPA 1-157	1.50	2.25	3.00
JIM REEVES HITS	RCA (EP) EPA-5124	1.00	1.50	2.00
JIM REEVES SINGS	Abbott (M) LP 5001	6.00	12.00	18.00
MY ROUGH & ROWDY WAYS	RCA (M) LPM-2112	2.50	3.75	5.00
MY ROUGH & ROWDY WAYS	RCA (S) LSP-2112	2.50	3.75	5.00
SINGING DOWN THE LANE	RCA (M) LPM 1256	5.00	7.50	10.00
SINGING DOWN THE LANE	RCA (EP) EPA 757	2.00	3.00	4.00
SONGS TO WARM THE HEART	RCA (M) LPM-2001	2.50	3.75	5.00
SONGS TO WARM THE HEART	RCA (S) LSP-2001	2.50	3.75	5.00
STORY OF THE BLUES	Jubilee (M) 1095	5.00	12.50	20.00
TALKIN' TO YOUR HEART	RCA (M) LPM-2339	2.00	3.00	4.00
TALKIN' TO YOUR HEART	RCA (S) LSP-2339	2.00	3.00	4.00
TALL TALES & SHORT TEMPERS	RCA (M) LPM-2284	2.00	3.00	4.00
TALL TALES & SHORT TEMPERS	RCA (S) LSP-2284	2.00	3.00	4.00
TALL TALES & SHORT TEMPERS	RCA (EP) LPC-133	1.00	1.50	2.00
TOUCH OF VELVET	RCA (M) LPM-2487	2.00	3.00	4.00
TOUCH OF VELVET	RCA (S) LSP-2487	2.00	3.00	4.00
REFLECTIONS				
JUST LIKE ROMEO AND JULIET	Golden World (M) LPM 300	5.00	7.50	10.00
REFUGEE				
REFUGEE	Charisma (S) 6066	3.00	4.50	6.00

TITLE	LABEL & NO.	GOOD	VERY GOOD	NEAR MINT
REGENTS				
BARBARA-ANN	Gee (M) G-706	7.00	14.00	21.00
BARBARA-ANN	Gee (S) SG-706	8.00	16.00	24.00
DISCOTHEQUE	Capitol (S) SKAO 2153	3.00	6.00	9.00
REID, Terry				
BANG, BANG, YOU'RE TERRY REID	Epic (S) BN 26427	4.00	6.00	8.00
RIVER	Atlantic (S) SD 7259	2.50	3.75	5.00
TERRY REID	Epic (S) BN 26477	3.00	4.50	6.00
REJOICE				
REJOICE	Dunhill (S) DS 50049	2.50	3.75	5.00
REMAINS				
REMAINS, THE	Epic (M) LN 24214	5.00	7.50	10.00
RENAISSANCE				
ASHES ARE BURNING	Capitol (S) ST-11216	3.50	5.25	7.00
PROLOGUE	Capitol (S) SMAS-11116	3.50	5.25	7.00
RENAISSANCE	Elektra (S) EKS 74068	4.00	6.00	8.00
TURN OF THE CARDS	Sire (S) 7502	3.00	4.50	6.00
RENAY, Diane				
NAVY BLUE	20th Century (M) TFM 3133	4.00	8.00	12.00
RENBOURN, John				
FARO ANNIE	Reprise (S) 2082	3.00	4.50	6.00
JOHN RENBOURN	Reprise (S) 2-6482	4.00	6.00	8.00
LADY AND THE UNICORN	Reprise (M) 6407	3.00	4.50	6.00
RENE, Googie, Combo				
FLAPJACKS	Class (M) LP 200	3.00	6.00	9.00
ROMESVILLE	Class (S) CS LP 5003	3.00	6.00	9.00
REPAIRS				
ALREADY A HOUSEHOLD WORD	Rare Earth (S) 532	3.00	4.50	6.00
REPAIRS	Mowest (S) 121	3.00	4.50	6.00
REPARATA & THE DELRONS				
ROCK AND ROLL REVOLUTION	Avco Embassy (M) AVE 33008	4.00	6.00	8.00
WHENEVER A TEENAGER CRIES	World Artists (M) WAM 2006	5.00	10.00	15.00
RESEARCH 1 6 12				
IN RESEARCH	Flick City (M) FC 5001	5.00	7.50	10.00
RESIDENTS				
MEET THE RESIDENTS	Ralph (M) RR 0274	4.00	6.75	8.00
RESTIVO, Johnny				
OH JOHNNY	RCA (M) 2149	6.00	12.00	18.00
REVELS				
REVELS ON A RAMPAGE	Impact (M) LPM No 1	9.00	18.00	27.00

(M) Mono (S) Stereo (EP) Extended Play (Q) Quad (RI) Re-issued

REVERE, Paul & The Raiders

TITLE	LABEL & NO.	GOOD	VERY GOOD	NEAR MINT
ALIAS PINK PUZZ	Columbia (S) CS 9905	6.00	9.00	12.00
ALL TIME GREATEST HITS	Columbia (M) KG 31464	4.00	6.00	8.00
A CHRISTMAS PRESENT AND PAST	Columbia (M) CL 2755	5.00	7.50	10.00
A CHRISTMAS PRESENT AND PAST	Columbia (S) CS 9555	5.50	6.75	11.00
COLLAGE (Shown as The RAIDERS)	Columbia (S) CS 9964	5.00	7.50	10.00
COUNTRY WINE	Columbia (M) KC 31196	4.00	6.00	8.00
FROM THE AIR FORCE ACADEMY FEATURING THE FALCONAIRES WITH MARK LINDSAY, STEVE ALAIMO, KEITH ALLISON, JEFF THOMAS	Mutual (M) 70-3	15.00	22.50	30.00
GOIN TO MEMPHIS	Columbia (M) 2805	4.50	6.75	9.00
GOIN TO MEMPHIS	Columbia (S) CS 9605	5.00	7.50	10.00
GOOD THING	Harmony (M) KH 30975	3.00	4.50	6.00
GREATEST HITS	Columbia (M) KCL 2662	4.00	6.00	8.00
GREATEST HITS	Columbia (S) KCS 9462	4.50	6.75	9.00
GREATEST HITS VOL 2	Columbia (S) C 30386	4.50	6.75	9.00
HARD AND HEAVY WITH MARSHMALLOW	Columbia (S) CS 9753	6.00	9.00	12.00
HERE THEY COME	Columbia (M) CL 2307	4.00	6.00	8.00
HERE THEY COME	Columbia (S) CS 9107	4.50	6.75	9.00
INDIAN RESERVATION (Shown as The RAIDERS)				
JUST LIKE US	Columbia (M) CL 2451	4.00	6.00	8.00
JUST LIKE US	Columbia (S) CS 9251	4.50	6.75	9.00
LIKE LONG HAIR	Gardena (M) LP G1000	15.00	37.50	60.00
MIDNIGHT RIDE	Columbia (M) CL 2508	4.00	6.00	8.00
MIDNIGHT RIDE	Columbia (S) CS 9308	4.50	6.75	9.00
MOVIN' ON	Harmony (M) KH-31183	3.00	4.50	6.00
PAUL REVERE & THE RAIDERS	Sande (M) 1001	20.00	50.00	80.00
PAUL REVERE AND THE RAIDERS	Sears (S) SPS 493	16.00	24.00	32.00
PAUL REVERE AND THE RAIDERS	Columbia (M) GP 12	5.00	7.50	10.00
PAUL REVERE AND THE RAIDERS	Pickwick (S) SPC 3176	4.00	6.00	8.00
PAUL REVERE AND THE RAIDERS FEATURING MARK LINDSAY	Harmony (M) H 30089	3.00	4.50	6.00
REVOLUTION	Columbia (M) CL 2721	4.00	6.00	8.00
REVOLUTION	Columbia (S) CS 9521	4.50	6.75	9.00
SOMETHING HAPPENING	Columbia (S) CS 9665	5.00	7.50	10.00
SPIRIT OF '67, THE	Columbia (M) CL2595	4.00	6.00	8.00
SPIRIT OF '67, THE	Columbia (S) CS 9395	4.50	6.75	9.00
Also see LINDSAY, Mark & WELLER, Freddy				

REVOLUTIONARY BLUES BAND

TITLE	LABEL & NO.	GOOD	VERY GOOD	NEAR MINT
REVOLUTIONARY BLUES BAND	Coral (S) CRL 757506	3.00	4.50	6.00

REYNOLDS, Burt

TITLE	LABEL & NO.	GOOD	VERY GOOD	NEAR MINT
ASK ME WHAT I AM	Mercury (S) SRM-1-693	3.50	5.25	7.00

REYNOLDS, Debbie

TITLE	LABEL & NO.	GOOD	VERY GOOD	NEAR MINT
AM I THAT EASY TO FORGET	Dot (M) DLP-3295	2.50	3.75	5.00
AM I THAT EASY TO FORGET	Dot (S) DLP-25295	3.00	4.50	6.00
DEBBIE	Dot (M) DLP-3191	2.50	3.75	5.00
DEBBIE	Dot (S) DLP-25191	3.00	4.50	6.00
FROM DEBBIE WITH LOVE	MGM (M) E-3806	2.00	3.00	4.00
FROM DEBBIE WITH LOVE	MGM (S) SE-3806	2.50	3.75	5.00
MILLION DOLLAR VAUDEVILLE SHOW	Lion (M) L-70089	2.50	3.75	5.00

RHODES, Emitt

TITLE	LABEL & NO.	GOOD	VERY GOOD	NEAR MINT
AMERICAN DREAM, THE	A&M (S) SP 4254	3.50	5.25	7.00
EMITT RHODES	Dunhill (S) DS 50089	3.00	4.50	6.00
FAREWELL TO PARADISE	Dunhill (S) DSX 50122	2.50	3.75	5.00
MIRROR	Dunhill (S) DSX 50111	3.00	4.50	6.00

RHODES, Todd

TITLE	LABEL & NO.	GOOD	VERY GOOD	NEAR MINT
TODD RHODES PLAYS HIS HITS (10")	King (M) 295 88	9.00	22.50	36.00

RHYTHM MAKERS

TITLE	LABEL & NO.	GOOD	VERY GOOD	NEAR MINT
SOUL ON YOUR SIDE	Vigor (S) 7002	2.00	3.00	4.00

RICH, Charlie

TITLE	LABEL & NO.	GOOD	VERY GOOD	NEAR MINT
BIG BOSS MAN	RCA (M) LPM-3537	3.00	4.00	6.00
BIG BOSS MAN	RCA (S) LSP-3537	3.50	5.25	7.00
CHARLIE RICH	Smash (M) 27078	4.00	6.00	8.00
CHARLIE RICH	Smash (S) 67078	4.50	6.75	9.00
CHARLIE RICH	Groove (M) GM-1000	3.00	4.50	6.00
CHARLIE RICH	Groove (S) GS-1000	3.50	5.25	7.00
CHARLIE RICH SINGS COUNTRY & WESTERN	HI (M) 32037	3.00	4.50	6.00
LONELY WEEKENDS	Phillips (M) PLP1970	10.00	25.00	40.00
LONELY WEEKENDS (SONGS FROM PHILLIPS LP)	Sun (M) 110	2.00	3.00	4.00
MANY NEW SIDES OF CHARLIE RICH	Smash (M) MGS-27070	4.00	6.00	8.00
MANY NEW SIDES OF CHARLIE RICH	Smash (S) SRS-67070	4.00	6.00	8.00
THAT'S RICH	RCA (M) LPM-3352	3.00	4.00	6.00
THAT'S RICH	RCA (S) LSP-3352	3.50	5.25	7.00
THERE WON'T BE ANYMORE	Power-Pack (M) 241	2.00	3.00	4.00
A TIME FOR TEARS	Sun (M) 123	2.00	3.00	4.00

RICHARD, Cliff

TITLE	LABEL & NO.	GOOD	VERY GOOD	NEAR MINT
EVERY FACE TELLS A STORY	Rocket (S) 2268	3.00	4.50	6.00
HITS FROM THE ORIGINAL SOUND TRACK OF SUMMER HOLIDAY	Epic (M) LN 24063	3.00	6.00	9.00
HITS FROM THE ORIGINAL SOUND TRACK OF SUMMER HOLIDAY	Epic (S) BN 26063	4.00	8.00	12.00
I'M NEARLY FAMOUS	Rocket (S) 2210	3.00	4.50	6.00
IT'S ALL IN THE GAME	Epic (M) LN 24089	3.00	6.00	9.00
IT'S ALL IN THE GAME	Epic (S) BN 26089	4.00	8.00	12.00
SWINGERS PARADISE	Epic (S) 26145	5.00	10.00	15.00
WONDERFUL TO BE YOUNG	Dot (M) 3474	5.00	10.00	15.00

RICHARD, Cliff & The Shadows

TITLE	LABEL & NO.	GOOD	VERY GOOD	NEAR MINT
CLIFF RICHARD IN SPAIN WITH THE SHADOWS	Epic (M) LN 24115	3.00	6.00	9.00
CLIFF RICHARD IN SPAIN WITH THE SHADOWS	Epic (S) BN 26115	4.00	8.00	12.00
CLIFF'S HIT ALBUM	Columbia (M) OSX 1512	4.00	10.00	16.00
Australian Import				
Also see SHADOWS				
CLIFF SINGS	ABC/Paramount (M) ABC 321	3.00	6.00	9.00
CLIFF SINGS	ABC/Paramount (S) ABCS 321	5.00	10.00	15.00
LISTEN TO CLIFF	ABC/Paramount (M) ABC 391	3.00	6.00	9.00
LISTEN TO CLIFF	ABC/Paramount (S) ABCS 391	4.00	8.00	12.00

RIGHTEOUS BROTHERS

TITLE	LABEL & NO.	GOOD	VERY GOOD	NEAR MINT
BACK TO BACK	Philles (M) 4009	4.50	6.75	9.00
BEST OF THE RIGHTEOUS BROTHERS	Moonglow (M) 1004	4.00	6.00	8.00
GIVE IT TO THE PEOPLE	Haven (S) ST 9201	2.00	3.00	4.00
GO AHEAD AND CRY	Verve (M) V 5004	2.50	3.75	5.00
GO AHEAD AND CRY	Verve (S) V6 5004	3.00	4.50	6.00
GREATEST HITS	Moonglow (EP) 1004	2.00	4.00	6.00
GREATEST HITS VOL 2	Verve (M) 5071	2.50	3.75	5.00
HISTORY OF THE RIGHTEOUS BROTHERS	MGM (M) 4885	2.00	3.00	4.00
JUST ONCE IN MY LIFE	Philles (M) PHLP 4008	5.00	7.50	10.00
ONE FOR THE ROAD	Verve (S) V6 5058	3.00	4.50	6.00
RIGHTEOUS BROTHERS GREATEST HITS	Verve (M) 5020	2.50	3.75	5.00
RIGHTEOUS BROTHERS STANDARDS	Verve (S) V 6-5051	2.50	3.75	5.00
RIGHT NOW	Moonglow (M) 1001	5.00	7.50	10.00
SAYIN' SOMETHIN'	Verve (S) V6 5010	2.50	3.75	5.00
SOME BLUE EYED SOUL	Moonglow (M) 1002	5.00	7.50	10.00
SONS OF MRS. RIGHTEOUS	Haven (S) ST 9203	2.00	3.00	4.00
SOULED OUT	Verve (M) 5031	2.50	3.75	5.00
THIS IS NEW!	Moonglow (M) 1003	4.00	6.00	8.00
YOU'VE LOST THAT LOVIN' FEELIN	Philles (M) PHLP 4007	5.00	7.50	10.00

RILEY, Billy Lee

TITLE	LABEL & NO.	GOOD	VERY GOOD	NEAR MINT
BIG HARMONICA SPECIAL	Mercury (M) MG-20965	2.00	4.00	6.00
BIG HARMONICA SPECIAL	Mercury (S) SR-60965	2.50	5.00	7.50
BILLY LEE RILEY IN ACTION	Crescendo (M) 2028	4.00	6.00	8.00
BILLY LEE RILEY IN ACTION	Crescendo (S) 2028	4.50	6.75	9.00
FUNK HARMONICA	Crescendo (M) 2020	4.00	6.00	8.00
FUNK HARMONICA	Crescendo (S) 2020	4.50	6.75	9.00
HARMONICA AND THE BLUES	Crown (M) CLP 5277	3.00	6.00	9.00
HARMONICA BEATLEMANIA	Mercury (M) MG-20974	4.00	8.00	12.00
HARMONICA BEATLEMANIA	Mercury (S) SR-60974	4.50	9.00	13.50
SOUTHERN SOUL	Majo (M) 1933	6.00	12.00	18.00
WHISKEY A-GO-GO PRESENTS BILLY LEE RILEY	Mercury (M) MG 20985	3.00	4500	6.00
WHISKEY A-GO-GO PRESENTS BILLY LEE RILEY	Mercury (S) SR 60985	3.50	5.25	7.00

RINCON SURFSIDE BAND

TITLE	LABEL & NO.	GOOD	VERY GOOD	NEAR MINT
SURFING SONGBOOK	Dunhill (M) 50001	4.00	8.00	12.00

RIOPELLE, Jerry

TITLE	LABEL & NO.	GOOD	VERY GOOD	NEAR MINT
JERRY RIOPELLE	Capitol ST-732	3.50	5.25	7.00
SAVING GRACE	ABC (S) 827	3.00	4.50	6.00
SECOND ALBUM	Capitol (S) ST-863	3.50	5.25	7.00

RIOT

TITLE	LABEL & NO.	GOOD	VERY GOOD	NEAR MINT
WELCOME TO THE WORLD OF RIOT	Motown (M) M6 806 S1	2.00	3.00	4.00

RIP CHORDS

TITLE	LABEL & NO.	GOOD	VERY GOOD	NEAR MINT
HEY LITTLE COBRA	Columbia (M) CL 2151	4.00	8.00	12.00
HEY LITTLE COBRA	Columbia (S) CS 8951	5.00	10.00	15.00
THREE WINDOW COUPE	Columbia (M) CL 2216	4.00	8.00	12.00
THREE WINDOW COUPE	Columbia (S) CS 9016	5.00	10.00	15.00

RIPERTON, Minnie

TITLE	LABEL & NO.	GOOD	VERY GOOD	NEAR MINT
ADVENTURES IN PARADISE	Epic (S) PE-33454	2.00	3.00	4.00
ADVENTURES IN PARADISE	Epic (Q) PEQ 33454	2.00	3.00	4.00
PERFECT ANGEL	Epic (S) KE 32561	2.00	3.00	4.00
STAY IN LOVE	Epic (S) PE 34191	2.00	3.00	4.00

RIPPLE BLAST SINGERS AND BAND

TITLE	LABEL & NO.	GOOD	VERY GOOD	NEAR MINT
RHYTHM AND BLUES HITS OF '64	Power (S) S 9001	3.00	6.00	9.00

RISERS

TITLE	LABEL & NO.	GOOD	VERY GOOD	NEAR MINT
SHE'S A BAD MOTORCYCLE	Imperial (M) LP 9269	3.00	6.00	9.00
SHE'S A BAD MOTORCYCLE	Imperial (S) LP 12269	4.00	8.00	12.00

RISING STORM

TITLE	LABEL & NO.	GOOD	VERY GOOD	NEAR MINT
CALM BEFORE RISING STORM	Remnant (M) BBA 3571	2.00	3.00	4.00

RITTER, Tex

TITLE	LABEL & NO.	GOOD	VERY GOOD	NEAR MINT
AN AMERICAN LEGEND	Capitol (S) SKC-11241	2.00	3.00	4.00
BLOOD ON THE SADDLE	Capitol (M) T-1292	2.50	3.75	5.00
BLOOD ON THE SADDLE	Capitol (S) ST-1292	2.50	3.75	5.00
BLOOD ON THE SADDLE	Capitol (EP) EAP-1-1292	1.00	1.50	2.00
BLOOD ON THE SADDLE	Capitol (M) EAP-2-1292	1.00	1.50	2.00
BLOOD ON THE SADDLE	Capitol (EP) EAP-3-1292	1.00	1.50	2.00
BORDER AFFAIR	Capitol (M) T-1910	2.00	3.00	4.00
BORDER AFFAIR	Capitol (S) ST-1910	2.00	3.00	4.00
COWBOY FAVORITES	Capitol (M) H 4004	4.00	6.00	8.00

(M) Mono (S) Stereo (EP) Extended Play (Q) Quad (RI) Re-issued

TITLE	LABEL & NO.	GOOD	VERY GOOD	NEAR MINT
FALL AWAY	Capitol (S) ST-11351	2.00	3.00	4.00
PSALMS	Capitol (M) T 1100	2.50	3.75	5.00
PSALMS	Capitol (EP) EAP 1-1100	1.00	1.50	2.00
RITTER SINGS	Capitol (EP) EAP 1-431	1.50	2.25	3.00
SONGS FROM THE WESTERN SCREEN	Capitol (M) T 971	3.50	5.25	7.00

RIVERS, Johnny

AND I KNOW YOU WANNA DANCE	Imperial (M) LP 9307	3.00	4.50	6.00
AND I KNOW YOU WANNA DANCE	Imperial (S) LP 12307	3.50	5.25	7.00
CHANGES	Imperial (M) LP 9334	2.50	3.75	5.00
CHANGES	Imperial (S) LP 12334	3.00	4.50	6.00
DISCOTHEQUE AU GO GO	Design (M) DLP 194	3.00	6.00	9.00
GO GO	Custom (M) CM 2019	3.00	6.00	9.00
GO GO	Custom (S) CS 1019	2.00	4.00	6.00
GO, JOHNNY, GO	United Artists (M) UAL 3386	5.00	10.00	15.00
GOLDEN HITS	Imperial (M) LP 9324	3.00	4.50	6.00
GOLDEN HITS	Imperial (S) LP 12324	3.50	5.25	7.00
HERE WE A GO GO AGAIN	Imperial (M) LP 9274	3.00	4.50	6.00
HERE WE A GO GO AGAIN	Imperial (S) LP 12274	3.50	5.25	7.00
IF YOU WANT IT I GOT IT	Pickwick (S) SPC 3191	3.00	4.50	6.00
JOHNNY RIVERS	Sunset (M) SUM 1157	3.00	6.00	9.00
JOHNNY RIVERS	Sunset (S) SUS 5157	2.00	4.00	6.00
JOHNNY RIVERS	United Artists (S) UXS 93	3.00	4.50	6.00
JOHNNY RIVERS	Guest Star (M) 1482	3.00	6.00	9.00
JOHNNY RIVERS AT THE WHISKEY A GO GO	Imperial (M) LP 9264	3.00	4.50	6.00
JOHNNY RIVERS AT THE WHISKEY A GO GO	Imperial (S) LP 12264	3.50	5.25	7.00
JOHNNY RIVERS IN ACTION	Imperial (S) LP 12280	3.50	5.25	7.00
MEANWHILE BACK AT THE WHISKEY A GO GO	Imperial (M) LP 9284	3.00	4.50	6.00
MEANWHILE BACK AT THE WHISKEY A GO GO	Imperial (S) LP 12284	3.50	5.25	7.00
MR. TEENAGE	Sears (M) SP 417	3.00	6.00	9.00
MR. TEENAGE	Sears (S) SPS 417	2.00	4.00	6.00
REALIZATION	Imperial (M) LP 12372	3.00	4.50	6.00
REWIND	Imperial (M) LP 9341	2.50	3.75	5.00
REWIND	Imperial (S) LP 12341	3.00	4.50	6.00
RIVERS ROCKS THE FOLK	Imperial (M) LP 9293	3.00	4.50	6.00
RIVERS ROCKS THE FOLK	Imperial (S) LP 12293	3.50	5.25	7.00
SENSATIONAL JOHNNY RIVERS, THE	Capitol (M) 2161	6.00	12.00	18.00
SLIM SLO SLIDER	Imperial (M) LP 16001	2.50	3.75	5.00
A TOUCH OF GOLD	Imperial (M) LP 12427	3.00	4.50	6.00

RIVIERAS

CAMPUS PARTY	Riviera (M) LP 701	8.00	16.00	24.00
LET'S HAVE A PARTY	USA (M) LP 102	5.00	10.00	15.00

RIVIERAS

RIVIERAS SING, THE	Post (M) 2000	3.00	4.50	6.00

RIVINGTONS

DOIN' THE BIRD	Liberty (M) LRP 3282	4.00	8.00	12.00
DOIN' THE BIRD	Liberty (S) LST 7282	5.00	10.00	15.00

RIZZI, Tony

SURFIN' PACIFIC	MORhythm (M) 010	2.00	3.00	4.00

ROAD

COGNITION	Kama Sutra (S) KSBS 2032	3.50	5.25	7.00
ROAD, THE	Kama Sutra (S) 2012	3.50	5.25	7.00

ROAD RUNNERS

NEW MUSTANG, THE	London (M) LL 3381	5.00	10.00	15.00
NEW MUSTANG, THE	London (S) PS 381	6.00	12.00	18.00

ROBBER, Robby & The Hi Jackers

TWIST, THE	Spinorama (M) M76	2.00	4.00	6.00

ROBBINS, Marty

CARL, LEFTY, AND MARTY	Columbia (M) CL 2544	4.00	6.00	8.00
DEVIL WOMAN	Columbia (M) CL 1918	3.00	4.50	6.00
DEVIL WOMAN	Columbia (S) CS 8718	3.00	4.50	6.00
DRIFTER, THE	Columbia (M) CL-2527	2.50	3.75	5.00
DRIFTER, THE	Columbia (S) CS9327	2.50	3.75	5.00
GUN FIGHTER BALLADS	Columbia (M) CL-1349	2.50	3.75	5.00
GUN FIGHTER BALLADS	Columbia (S) CS-8158	2.50	3.75	5.00
GUN FIGHTER BALLADS	Columbia (EP) B-13491	1.50	2.25	3.00
GUN FIGHTER BALLADS	Columbia (EP) B-13492	1.50	2.25	3.00
GUN FIGHTER BALLADS	Columbia (EP) B-13493	1.50	2.25	3.00
HAWAII'S CALLING ME	Columbia (M) CL-2040	3.00	4.00	6.00
HAWAII'S CALLING ME	Columbia (S) CS-8840	3.00	4.00	6.00
ISLAND WOMAN	Columbia (M) CL-2167	2.50	3.75	5.00
ISLAND WOMAN	Columbia (S) CS-8976	2.50	3.75	5.00
JUST A LITTLE SENTIMENTAL	Columbia (M) CL-1666	3.00	4.50	6.00
JUST A LITTLE SENTIMENTAL	Columbia (S) CS-8466	3.00	4.50	6.00
MARTY ROBBINS	Columbia (M) CL 1189	4.00	6.00	8.00
MARTY ROBBINS	Columbia (EP) B 11891	2.00	3.00	4.00
MARTY ROBBINS	Columbia (EP) B 2814	2.00	3.00	4.00
MARTY ROBBINS AFTER MIDNIGHT	Columbia (M) CL-1801	3.00	4.50	6.00
MARTY ROBBINS AFTER MIDNIGHT	Columbia (S) CS-8601	3.00	4.50	6.00
MARTY'S GREATEST HITS	Columbia (S) CS-8639	2.50	3.75	5.00
MORE GREATEST HITS	Columbia (M) CL-1635	2.50	3.75	5.00
MORE GREATEST HITS	Columbia (S) CS-8435	2.50	3.75	5.00

TITLE	LABEL & NO.	GOOD	VERY GOOD	NEAR MINT
MORE GUNFIGHTER BALLADS (& TRAIL SONGS)	Columbia (EP) B-14811	1.50	2.25	3.00
MORE GUNFIGHTER BALLADS (& TRAIL SONGS)	Columbia (M) CL-1481	2.50	3.75	5.00
MORE GUNFIGHTER BALLADS (& TRAIL SONGS)	Columbia (S) CS-8272	2.50	3.75	5.00
PORTRAIT OF MARTY	Columbia (M) CL-1855	3.00	4.50	6.00
PORTRAIT OF MARTY	Columbia (S) CS-8655	3.00	4.50	6.00
RETURN OF THE GUNFIGHTER	Columbia (M) CL-2072	2.50	3.75	5.00
RETURN OF THE GUNFIGHTER	Columbia (S) CS-8872	2.50	3.75	5.00
R.F.D.	Columbia (M) CL-2220	2.50	3.75	5.00
R.F.D.	Columbia (S) CS-9020	2.50	3.75	5.00
ROCK AND ROLL 'N ROBBINS	Columbia (M) CL 2601	22.50	56.25	90.00
SINGING THE BLUES	Columbia (EP) B 2116	2.50	3.75	5.00
SINGING THE BLUES	Harmony (S) HS 11338	2.00	3.00	4.00
SONG OF ROBBINS	Columbia (M) CL 976	4.00	6.00	8.00
SONG OF ROBBINS	Columbia (EP) B 9761	2.00	3.00	4.00
SONG OF ROBBINS	Columbia (EP) B 9762	2.00	3.00	4.00
SONG OF ROBBINS	Columbia (EP) B 9763	2.00	3.00	4.00
TURN THE LIGHTS DOWN LOW	Columbia (M) CL-2304	2.50	3.75	5.00
TURN THE LIGHTS DOWN LOW	Columbia (S) CS-9104	2.50	3.75	5.00
WHAT GOD HAS DONE	Columbia (M) CL-2448	2.50	3.75	5.00
WHAT GOD HAS DONE	Columbia (S) CS-9248	2.50	3.75	5.00
WHITE SPORT COAT	Columbia (EP) B 2134	2.00	3.00	4.00

ROBBS

ROBBS, THE	Mercury (S) SR 61130	5.00	7.50	10.00

ROBERTS, Andy

HOME GROWN	Ampex (S) 10120	3.00	4.50	6.00

ROBERTS, Rocky & The Airedales

RICKY ROBERTS AND THE AIREDALES	Brunswick (M) BL54133	4.00	6.00	8.00

ROBINS

BEST OF THE ROBINS	Crescendo (S) 9034	4.00	6.00	8.00
ROCK' ROLL WITH THE ROBINS	Whippett (M) WLP 703	12.00	30.00	48.00

ROBINSON, Fenton

MONDAY MORNING BLUES 'N' BOOGIE	Seventy 7 (M) 2001	2.00	3.00	4.00
MONDAY MORNING BOOGIE 'N' BLUES	Seventy 7 (M) ¼72001	3.50	5.25	7.00
SOMEBODY LOAN ME A DIME	Alligator (M) 4705	4.00	6.00	8.00

ROBINSON, Floyd

FLOYD ROBINSON	RCA (M) LPM-2162	3.00	4.50	6.00
FLOYD ROBINSON	RCA (S) LSP-2162	5.00	7.50	10.00
MAKIN' LOVE	RCA (EP) EPA-4350	2.00	3.00	4.00

ROBINSON, Freddy

AT THE DRIVE IN	Enterprise (S) ENS 1025	2.00	3.00	4.00

ROBINSON, L.C.

HOUSE CLEANIN BLUES	Bluesway (M) 6082	2.00	3.00	4.00

ROBINSON, J.C.

GOOD ROCKIN'	Arhoolie (M) 1062	4.00	6.00	8.00

ROBINSON, Smokey

PURE SMOKEY	Tamla (S) 331	2.00	3.00	4.00
QUIET STORM	Tamla (S) T6-337	2.00	3.00	4.00
SMOKEY	Tamla (S) 328	2.00	3.00	4.00

ROCK-A-TEENS

WOO-HOO	Roulette (M) R-25109	10.00	25.00	40.00
WOO-HOO	Roulette (S) SR-25109	12.00	30.00	48.00

ROCKETS

ROCKETS, THE	White Whale (S) WWS 7116	6.00	9.00	12.00

ROCK FLOWERS

NATURALLY	Wheel (S) WLS 1002	2.50	3.75	5.00
ROCK FLOWERS	Wheel (S) WLS 1001	2.50	3.75	5.00

(M) Mono (S) Stereo (EP) Extended Play (Q) Quad (RI) Re-issued

TITLE	LABEL & NO.	GOOD	VERY GOOD	NEAR MINT
ROCKINGFOO				
ROCKIN FOO	Uni (M) 73115	3.00	4.50	6.00
ROCKIN FOO	Hobbit (M) HB 5001	4.00	6.00	8.00
ROCKIN' REBELS				
WILD WEEKEND	Swan (M) SLP 509	6.00	12.00	18.00
ROCK SHOP				
ROCK SHOP	Lee MO (M) No.1	4.00	6.00	8.00
ROCKY FELLERS				
KILLER JOE	Scepter (M) 512	3.00	6.00	9.00
ROD AND THE COBRAS				
ROD AND THE COBRAS AT A DRAG RACE AT SURF CITY	Somerset (M) SF 20500	3.00	6.00	9.00
RODGERS, Eileen				
BLUE SWING	Columbia (M) CL 1096	3.00	4.50	6.00
BLUE SWING	Columbia (S) CS 8029	3.50	5.25	7.00
BLUE SWING	Columbia (EP) B 10961	1.00	1.50	2.00
MIRACLE OF LOVE	Columbia (EP) B 2117	1.50	2.25	3.00
RODGERS, Jimmie				
BEST OF JIMMIE RODGERS FOLK SONGS	Roulette (M) R 25160	2.50	3.75	5.00
BEST OF JIMMIE RODGERS FOLK SONGS	Roulette (S) SR 25160	2.50	3.75	5.00
15 MILLION SELLERS	Roulette (M) R 25179	2.50	3.75	5.00
15 MILLION SELLERS	Roulette (S) SR 25179	2.50	3.75	5.00
FOLK SONGS & READINGS	Roulette (M) R 25020	3.00	4.50	6.00
FOLK SONGS & READINGS	Roulette (EP) EPR 1-303	1.00	1.50	2.00
FOLK SONG WORLD OF JIMMIE RODGERS	Roulette (M) R 25150	2.50	3.75	5.00
FOLK SONG WORLD OF JIMMIE RODGERS	Roulette (S) SR 25150	2.50	3.75	5.00
HIS GOLDEN YEAR	Roulette (M) R-25057	3.00	4.50	6.00
IT'S CHRISTMAS ONCE AGAIN	Roulette (M) R-25095	3.00	4.50	6.00
IT'S CHRISTMAS ONCE AGAIN	Roulette (S) SR-25095	3.00	4.50	6.00
JIMMIE RODGERS FOLK SONGS	Roulette (M) R 25199	2.00	3.00	4.00
JIMMIE RODGERS FOLK SONGS	Roulette (S) SR 25199	2.00	3.00	4.00
JIMMIE RODGERS SINGS FOLK SONGS	Roulette (M) R 25042	3.00	4.50	6.00
NUMBER ONE BALLADS	Roulette (M) R 25033	3.00	4.50	6.00
TV FAVORITES	Roulette (M) R-25071	3.00	4.50	6.00
TV FAVORITES	Roulette (S) SR-25071	3.00	4.50	6.00
TWILIGHT ON THE TRAIL	Roulette (M) R-25081	3.00	4.50	6.00
TWILIGHT ON THE TRAIL	Roulette (S) SR-25081	3.00	4.50	6.00
WHEN THE SPIRIT MOVES YOU	Roulette (M) R-25103	2.50	3.75	5.00
WHEN THE SPIRIT MOVES YOU	Roulette (S) SR-25103	2.50	3.75	5.00
ROE, Tommy & Bobby Lee Trammell				
TOMMY ROE AND BOBBY LEE	Crown (M) CLP 5323	5.00	10.00	15.00
ROE, Tommy				
BEGINNINGS	ABC (S) ABCS 732	2.00	3.00	4.00
DIZZY	ABC (S) ABCS 683	3.50	5.25	7.00
ENERGY	Monument (M) PZ 34182	2.00	3.00	4.00
IT'S NOW WINTERS DAY	ABC (M) ABC 594	3.50	5.25	7.00
IT'S NOW WINTERS DAY	ABC (S) ABCS 594	4.50	6.75	9.00
PHANTASY	ABC (M) 610	3.50	5.25	7.00
SHEILA	ABC/Paramount (M) ABC 432	4.00	8.00	12.00
SHEILA	ABC/Paramount (S) ABCS 423	5.00	10.00	15.00
SOMETHING FOR EVERYBODY	ABC/Paramount (M) ABC 467	4.00	8.00	12.00
SOMETHING FOR EVERYBODY	ABC/Paramount (S) ABCS 467	5.00	10.00	15.00
SWEET PEA	ABC (M) ABC 575	4.00	6.00	8.00
SWEET PEA	ABC (S) ABCS 575	3.50	5.25	7.00
TOMMY ROE'S 16 GREATEST HITS	ABC (S) ABCX 762	2.50	3.75	5.00
12 IN A ROE	ABC (S) ABCS 700	3.50	5.25	7.00
WE CAN MAKE MUSIC	ABC (S) ABCS 714	3.00	4.50	6.00
WHIRLING WITH TOMMY ROE	Diplomat (S) DS 6-68	3.00	4.50	6.00
ROGERS, Julie				
JULIE ROGERS	Mercury (M) MG-20981	2.50	3.75	5.00
JULIE ROGERS	Mercury (S) SR-60981	2.50	3.75	5.00
ROGERS, Kenny & The First Edition				
BALLAD OF CALICO	Reprise (S) 2XS 6476	2.25	3.50	4.50
FIRST EDITION '69, THE	Reprise (S) 6328	2.50	3.75	5.00
FIRST EDITION, THE	Reprise (M) 6276	3.00	4.50	6.00
FIRST EDITION, THE	Reprise (S) 6276	2.50	3.75	5.00
GREATEST HITS	Reprise (S) 6437	2.50	3.75	5.00
MONUMENTAL	Jolly Rogers (S) 5004	2.00	3.00	4.00
ROLLIN'	Jolly Rogers (S) 5003	2.00	3.00	4.00
RUBY, DON'T TAKE YOUR LOVE TO TOWN	Reprise (S) 6352	2.25	3.50	4.50
SOMETHINGS BURNING	Reprise (S) 6385	2.25	3.50	4.50
TELL IT ALL BROTHER	Reprise (S) 6412	2.25	3.50	4.50
TRANSITION	Reprise (S) 2039	2.00	3.00	4.00
(Reprise 6276 & 6328 shown only as THE FIRST EDITION) Also see NEW CHRISTY MINSTRELS				
ROGERS, Roy				
HAPPY TRAILS TO YOU	20th Century (S) 467	2.50	3.75	5.00
HYMNS OF FAITH	RCA (M) LPM 3168	2.00	3.00	4.00
HYMNS OF FAITH	RCA (EP) EPB 3168	1.00	1.50	2.00
LORE OF THE WEST	Camden (M) CAL-1074	2.50	3.75	5.00
LORE OF THE WEST	Camden (S) CAS-1074	2.50	3.75	5.00

TITLE	LABEL & NO.	GOOD	VERY GOOD	NEAR MINT
PECOS BILL	RCA (EP) EYA 5	1.50	2.25	3.00
ROGERS ROUNDUP	RCA (EP) EPA 253	1.50	2.25	3.00
ROGERS SOUVENIR	RCA (M) LPM 3041	2.00	3.00	4.00
ROGERS SOUVENIR	RCA (EP) P 215	1.00	1.50	2.00
SWEET HOUR OF PRAYER	RCA (M) LPM 1439	2.00	3.00	4.00
SWEET HOUR OF PRAYER	RCA (EP) EPA 1-1439	1.00	1.50	2.00
SWEET HOUR OF PRAYER	RCA (EP) EPA 2-1439	1.00	1.50	2.00
ROKES				
CHE MONDO STRANO	RCA International (M) FPM 185	7.00	14.00	21.00
ROLLING STONES				
AFTERMATH	London (M) LL 3476	5.00	10.00	15.00
AFTERMATH	London (S) PS 476	2.00	4.00	6.00
AN INTERVIEW WITH M. JAGGER BY TOM DONAHUE APRIL 1971	Rolling Stone ST-PR-B-164 PR	10.00	15.00	20.00
BATTLE (STONES VERSUS THE BEATLES) BATTLE	RP-24	7.00	10.50	14.00
BEGGARS BANQUET	London (S) PS 539	4.00	6.00	8.00
BETWEEN THE BUTTONS	London (M) LL 3499	5.00	10.00	15.00
BETWEEN THE BUTTONS	London (S) PS 499	2.00	4.00	6.00
BIG HITS	London (M) NP-1	5.00	10.00	15.00
BIG HITS	London (S) NPS-1	2.00	4.00	6.00
BLACK & BLUE	Rolling Stones (S) 79104	2.50	3.75	5.00
DECEMBER'S CHILDREN	London (M) LL 3451	5.00	10.00	15.00
DECEMBER'S CHILDREN	London (S) PS 451	2.00	4.00	6.00
EXILE ON MAIN ST.	Rolling Stones (S) COC 2900	3.50	5.25	7.00
FLOWERS	London (M) LL 3509	5.00	10.00	15.00
FLOWERS	London (S) PS 509	2.00	4.00	6.00
'GET YER YA-YA'S OUT!'	London (S) NPS-5	3.00	4.50	6.00
GOATSHEAD SOUP	Rolling Stones (S) 59101	3.00	4.50	6.00
GOT LIVE IF YOU WANT IT	London (M) LL 3493	5.00	10.00	15.00
GOT LIVE IF YOU WANT IT	London (S) PS 493	2.00	4.00	6.00
HOT ROCKS 1964-1971	London (S) 2PS 606/7	4.00	6.00	8.00
IT'S HERE LUV!!! 1965 EXCLUSIVE TALK ALBUM (ED RUDY INTERVIEW LP) 0	INS Radio (M) LL-1003	8.00	16.00	24.00
JAMMING WITH EDWARD	Rolling Stone (M) COC 39100	3.00	4.50	6.00
LET IT BLEED	London (S) NPS-4	3.00	4.50	6.00
LIVER THAN YOU'LL EVER BE	Oakland (M) Acorn 1	5.00	7.50	10.00
LOVE YOU LIVE	Rolling Stones (S) 2-9001	3.00	4.50	6.00
MADE IN THE SHADE	Rolling Stones 79102	2.50	3.75	5.00
METAMORPHOSIS	ABKCO ANA-1	3.00	4.50	6.00
MORE HOT ROCKS	London (S) 2PS 626/7	4.00	6.00	8.00
OUT OF OUR HEADS	London (M) LL 3429	5.00	10.00	15.00
OUT OF OUR HEADS	London (S) PS 429	2.00	4.00	6.00
ROLLING STONES, THE	London (M) LL 3375	5.00	10.00	15.00
ROLLING STONES, THE	London (S) PS 375	2.00	4.00	6.00
ROLLING STONES, THE (White label, promotional copy)	London (M) 3375	11.00	22.00	33.00
ROLLING STONES NOW, THE	London (M) LL 3420	6.00	9.00	12.00
STICKY FINGERS	Rolling Stones (S) COC 59100	3.00	4.50	6.00
THEIR SATANIC MAJESTIES REQUEST	London (S) NPS-2	3.00	4.50	6.00
THEIR SATANIC MAJESTIES REQUEST (With 3-D photograph cover)	London (S) NPS-2	8.00	12.00	16.00
THROUGH THE PAST DARKLY	London (S) NPS-3	3.00	4.50	6.00
12 X 5	London (M) LL 3402	5.00	10.00	15.00
12 X 5	London (S) PS 402	2.00	4.00	6.00
ROMANCERS				
LET'S DO THE SWIM	Selma (M) S 1501	4.00	8.00	12.00
ROMEOS				
PRECIOUS MEMORIES	Mark II (M ⅛??⅛	½_??	—_??	⅛¼_??
PRECIOUS MEMORIES	Mark II (M) 1001	5.00	10.00	15.00
RONDO, Don				
HAVE YOU MET DON RONDO	Jubilee (M) JLP 1081	2.00	3.00	4.00
RONDO	Jubilee (M) JLP 1052	2.00	3.00	4.00
RONETTES				
PRESENTING THE FABULOUS RONETTES FEATURING VERONICA	Philles (M) PHLP 4006	20.00	40.00	60.00
PRESENTING THE FABULOUS RONETTES FEATURING VERONICA	Philles (S) 4006	25.00	50.00	75.00
RONETTES FEATURING VERONICA	Colpix (M) CP 486	6.00	12.00	18.00

(M) Mono (S) Stereo (EP) Extended Play (Q) Quad (RI) Re-issued

TITLE	LABEL & NO.	GOOD	VERY GOOD	NEAR MINT
RONNIE & THE DAYTONAS				
GTO	Mala (M) 4001	5.00	10.00	15.00
SANDY	Mala (M) 4002	4.00	8.00	12.00
RONNIE AND THE DEADBEATS				
GROOVIN' WITH RONNIE AND THE DEADBEATS	Check (M) 103	5.00	7.50	10.00
RONNIE & THE POMONA CASUALS				
EVERYBODY JERK	Donna (M) DO 2112	3.00	6.00	9.00
RONSTADT, Linda				
DIFFERENT DRUM	Capitol (S) ST-11269	2.00	3.00	4.00
DON'T CRY NOW	Asylum 5064	2.50	3.75	5.00
GREATEST HITS	Asylum (S) 7E-1092	2.50	3.75	5.00
GREATEST HITS	Asylum (S) 6E-106	2.00	3.00	4.00
(RI of Asylum 1092)				
HASTEN DOWN THE WIND	Asylum (S) 7E-1072	2.00	3.00	4.00
HEART LIKE A WHEEL	Capitol ST-11358	2.00	3.00	4.00
LINDA RONSTADT	Capitol SMAS-635	3.00	4.50	6.00
PRISONER IN DISGUISE	Asylum 7E-1045	2.00	3.00	4.00
RETROSPECTIVE, A	Capitol (S) SKBB-11629	3.00	4.50	6.00
SILK PURSE	Capitol ST-407	3.50	5.25	7.00
SIMPLE DREAMS	Asylum (S) 6E-104	2.00	3.00	4.00
Also see STONE PONEYS				
ROOFTOP SINGERS				
RAINY RIVER	Vanguard (M) VRS-9190	2.50	3.75	5.00
RAINY RIVER	Vanguard (S) VSD7-9190	2.50	3.75	5.00
ROOFTOP SINGERS-WALK RIGHT IN	Vanguard (M) VRS 9123	3.00	4.50	6.00
ROOFTOP SINGERS-WALK RIGHT IN	Vanguard (S) VSD 2136	3.00	4.50	6.00
ROSE, Biff				
BIFF ROSE	Buddah (S) BDS 5069	2.50	3.75	5.00
CHILDREN OF LIGHT	Buddah (S) BDS 5076	2.50	3.75	5.00
HALF LIVE AT THE BITTER END	Buddah (S) BDS 5078	2.50	3.75	5.00
THORN IN MRS. ROSE'S SIDE	Tetragrammaton (M) T-103	2.50	3.75	5.00
UNCLE JESUS ANTY CHRIST	United Artists (S) UA-LA009-F	2.50	3.75	5.00
ROSE GARDEN				
ROSE GARDEN	Atco (S) SD 33-225	3.00	4.50	6.00
ROSE, Tim				
LOVE, A KIND OF HATE STORY	Capitol (S) ST 673	2.50	3.75	5.00
TIM ROSE	Columbia (M) CL 2777	3.00	4.50	6.00
TIM ROSE	Columbia (S) CS 9577	4.00	6.00	8.00
TIM ROSE	Playboy (M) 101	2.00	3.00	4.00
ROSIE				
LONELY BLUE NIGHTS	Brunswick (M) BL 54102	5.00	10.00	15.00
ROSS, Diana				
BABY, IT'S ME	Motown (S) 890	2.00	3.00	4.00
DIANA ROSS	Motown (S) 711	2.50	3.75	5.00
DIANA ROSS	Motown (S) 861	2.00	3.00	4.00
DIANA ROSS' GREATEST HITS	Motown (S) 869	2.00	3.00	4.00
DIANA ROSS, LIVE	Motown (S) 801	2.50	3.75	5.00
AN EVENING WITH DIANA ROSS	Motown (S) 877	2.00	3.00	4.00
EVERYTHING IS EVERYTHING	Motown (S) 724	2.50	3.75	5.00
LAST TIME I SAW HIM	Motown (S) 812	2.50	3.75	5.00
SURRENDER	Motown (S) 723	2.50	3.75	5.00
TOUCH ME IN THE MORNING	Motown (S) 772	2.50	3.75	5.00
Also see SUPREMES				
ROSS, Jack				
CINDERELLA	Dot (M) DLP-3429	2.50	3.75	5.00
ROSS, Jackie				
FULL BLOOM	Chess (M) 1489	3.00	6.00	9.00
FULL BLOOM	Chess (S) 1489	3.50	7.00	10.50

TITLE	LABEL & NO.	GOOD	VERY GOOD	NEAR MINT
ROTARY CONNECTION				
PEACE	Cadet Concept (S) 318	2.50	3.75	5.00
ROTARY CONNECTION	Cadet Concept (M) 312	3.00	4.50	6.00
ROTARY CONNECTION	Cadet Concept (S) 312	2.50	3.75	5.00
ALADDIN	Cadet Concept (S) 317	2.50	..75	5.00
ROUND ROBIN				
GREATEST DANCE HITS SLAUSON STYLE	Domain (M) 101	5.00	7.50	10.00
LLOYD THAXTON PRESENTS THE LAND OF 1000 DANCES FEATURING ROUND ROBIN	Challenge (M) LP 620	4.50	6.75	9.00
ROUTERS				
CHARGE	Warner Brothers (M) W 1559	2.50	5.00	7.50
CHARGE	Warner Brothers (S) WS 1559	2.00	4.00	6.00
LET'S GO WITH THE ROUTERS	Warner Brothers (M) W 1490	2.50	5.00	7.50
LET'S GO WITH THE ROUTERS	Warner Brothers (S) WS 1490	3.00	6.00	9.00
ROUTERS GO GO GO WITH THE CHUCK BERRY SONG BOOK	Warner Brothers (M) W 1595	3.00	6.00	9.00
ROUTERS GO GO GO WITH THE CHUCK BERRY SONG BOOK	Warner Brothers (S) WS 1595	2.50	5.00	7.50
ROUTERS PLAY 1963's GREAT INSTRUMENTAL HITS	Warner Brothers (M) W 1524	2.50	5.00	7.50
ROUTERS PLAY 1963's GREAT INSTRUMENTAL HITS	Warner Brothers (S) WS 1524	2.00	4.00	6.00
SUPERBIRD	Mercury (S) SRM-1-682	2.50	3.75	5.00
ROWAN BROTHERS				
ROWAN BROTHERS	Columbia (S) KC 31297	3.00	4.50	6.00
ROXY				
ROXY	Elektra (S) EKS 74063	4.00	6.00	8.00
ROXY MUSIC				
COUNTRY LIFE	Atco (S) SD 36-106	3.50	5.25	7.00
FOR YOUR PLEASURE	Warner Bros. (S) BS-2696	4.00	6.00	8.00
FOR YOUR PLEASURE	Atco (S) SD 36-134	3.50	5.25	7.00
(RI of Warner Bros. 2696)				
GREATEST HITS	Atco (S) SD 38-103	2.50	3.75	5.00
ROXY MUSIC	Atco (S) SD 36-133	3.50	5.25	7.00
ROXY MUSIC	Reprise (S) 2114	4.00	6.00	8.00
SIREN	Atco (S) SD 36-127	3.50	5.25	7.00
STRANDED	Atco (S) 7045	3.00	4.50	6.00
VIVA, ROXY MUSIC	Atco (S) SD 36-139	3.50	5.25	7.00
(Live Roxy Music Album)				
Also see FERRY, Bryan				
ROYALETTES				
ELEGANT SOUND OF THE ROYALETTES	MGM (M) E 4366	2.00	4.00	6.00
ELEGANT SOUND OF THE ROYALETTES	MGM (S) SE 4366	2.50	5.00	7.50
IT'S GONNA TAKE A MIRACLE	MGM (M) E 4332	2.50	5.00	7.50
IT'S GONNA TAKE A MIRACLE	MGM (S) SE 4332	3.00	6.00	9.00
ROYAL GUARDSMEN				
RETURN OF THE RED BARON, THE	Laurie (S) SLP 2039	3.00	4.50	6.00
SNOOPY AND HIS FRIENDS	Laurie (S) SLLP 2042	4.00	6.00	8.00
SNOOPY FOR PRESIDENT	Laurie (S) SLP 2046	4.00	6.00	8.00
SNOOPY VERSUS THE RED BARON	Laurie (M) LLP 2038	3.00	4.50	6.00
ROYAL JOKERS				
ROCK & ROLL SPECTACULAR	Dawn (M) 1119	6.00	12.00	18.00
ROYAL PLAYBOYS				
SPIRITUALS AND JUBILEES (10")	Waldorf Music Hall (M) 33 136	6.00	15.00	24.00
ROYAL TEENS				
MUSIC GEMS FROM THE ROYAL TEENS	Tru-Gems (M) TG 1001	3.00	4.50	6.00
NEWIES BUT OLDIES	Musicor (M) MS 3186	4.00	6.00	8.00
RUBBER BAND				
CREAM SONGBOOK	GRT (M) 1000	3.00	4.50	6.00
JIM HENDRIX SONGBOOK	GRT (S) GRT 10007	3.00	4.50	6.00
RUBY & THE ROMANTICS				
GREATEST HITS ALBUM	Kapp (M) KL-1458	2.00	4.00	6.00
GREATEST HITS ALBUM	Kapp (S) KS-3458	2.50	5.00	7.50
MORE THAN YESTERDAY	ABC (S) 638	2.50	3.75	5.00
OUR DAY WILL COME	Kapp (M) KL 1323	2.00	4.00	6.00
OUR DAY WILL COME	Kapp (S) KS 3323	2.50	5.00	7.50
TILL THEN	Kapp (M) KL-1341	2.00	4.00	6.00
TILL THEN	Kapp (S) KS-3341	2.50	5.00	7.50
RUFUS (Featuring Chaka Khan)				
RAGS TO RUFUS	ABC (S) ABCX-809	2.50	3.75	5.00
RAGS TO RUFUS	Command (Q) QD-40024	2.50	3.75	5.00
RUFUS	ABC (S) ABCX-783	2.50	3.75	5.00
RUFUS FEATURING CHAKA KHAN	ABC (S) ABCD-909	2.00	3.00	4.00
RUFUSIZED	ABC (S) ABCD-837	2.50	3.75	5.00
REFUSIZED	Command (Q) QD-40023	2.50	3.75	5.00
STREET PLAYER	ABC (S) AA 1049	2.00	3.00	4.00
STREET PLAYER (Picture record)	ABC (S) AA 1049	12.00	18.00	24.00

(M) Mono   (S) Stereo   (EP) Extended Play   (Q) Quad   (RI) Re-issued

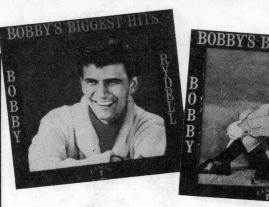

TITLE	LABEL & NO.	GOOD	VERY GOOD	NEAR MINT
RUGBYS				
RUGBYS HOT CARGO	Amazon (M) 1000	4.00	6.00	8.00
RUMBLERS				
BOSS!	Downey (M) DLP 1001	5.00	10.00	15.00
BOSS!	Downey (S) DLPS 1001	6.00	12.00	18.00
BOSS!	Dot (M) DLP 3509	4.00	8.00	12.00
BOSS!	Dot (S) DLPS 25509	4.50	9.00	13.50
RUMPLESTILTSKIN				
RUMPLESTILTSKIN	Bell (M) 6047	4.00	6.00	8.00
RUNAWAYS				
QUEENS OF NOISE	Mercury (S) SRM-1-1126	2.50	3.75	5.00
RUNAWAYS, THE	Mercury SRM-1-1090	2.50	3.75	5.00
WAITIN' FOR THE NIGHT	Mercury (S) SRM-1-3705	2.50	3.75	5.00
RUNDGREN, Todd				
ANOTHER LIVE	Bearsville 6961	2.50	3.75	5.00
FAITHFUL	Bearsville (S) 6963	2.50	3.75	5.00
FROM HERE TO UTOPIA	Little John Todd (S) 1	4.00	6.00	8.00
HERMIT OF MINK HOLLOW	Bearsville (S) BRK 6981	2.00	3.00	4.00
INITIATION	Bearsville 6957	2.50	3.75	5.00
OOPS, WRONG PLANET	Bearsville 6970	2.00	3.00	4.00
RA	Bearsville 6965	2.00	3.00	4.00
RUNT	Ampex (S) A 10105	5.00	7.50	10.00
RUNT: THE BALLAD OF TODD RUNDGREN	Ampex (S) A 10116	5.00	7.50	10.00
SOMETHING/ANYTHING?	Bearsville (S) 2066	3.00	4.50	6.00
TODD	Bearsville (S) 2B-6952	3.00	4.50	6.00
TODD RUNDGREN RADIO SHOW	Bearsville (S) PRO 524	8.00	12.00	16.00
TODD RUNDGREN'S UTOPIA	Bearsville 6954	2.50	3.75	5.00
WIZARD, A TRUE STAR	Bearsville (S) 2133	3.00	4.50	6.00
(Listed as "RUNT" on Ampex LP'S)				
(LP's 6954, 6961, 6965 & 6970 shown as TODD RUNDGREN'S UTOPIA)				
Also see NAZZ				
RUSHING, Jimmy				
LIVIN' THE BLUES	Blues Way (S) BLS 6017	4.00	6.00	8.00
SENT FOR YOU YESTERDAY	Blues Way (S) BLS 6057	4.00	6.00	8.00
RUSH, Merrilee				
ANGEL OF THE MORNING	Bell (M) 6020	4.50	6.75	9.00
RUSH, Otis				
BLUES MASTERS VOL. 2	Blue Horizon (M) 54602	2.00	3.00	4.00
BLUES MASTERS VOL. 2	Blue Horizon (S) BM 4602	4.50	6.75	9.00
MOURNING IN THE MORNING	Cotillion (S) SD 9006	4.00	6.00	8.00
RUSH, Tom				
BEST OF TOM RUSH	Columbia (S) PC-33907	2.00	3.00	4.00
BLUES, SONGS, AND BALLADS	Prestige (M) 7374	4.00	8.00	12.00
GOT A MIND TO RAMBLE	Prestige (M) 14003	4.00	6.00	8.00
LADIES LOVE OUTLAWS	Columbia (S) KC-33054	2.50	3.75	5.00
TOM RUSH AT THE UNICORN	Ly Cornu (M) SA-70-2	5.00	10.00	15.00
RUSSELL, Bobby				
WORDS, MUSIC, LAUGHTER & TEARS	Elf (S) 9500	2.50	3.75	5.00
RUSSELL, Leon				
ASYLUM CHOIR 2 (With Marc Benno)	Shelter (S) 8910	5.00	7.50	10.00
ASYLUM CHOIR 2 (With Marc Benno) (RI of Shelter 8910)	Shelter (S) 2120	3.00	4.50	6.00
ASYLUM CHOIR 2 (With Marc Benno) (RI of Shelter 2120)	Shelter (S) 52010	2.00	3.00	4.00
BEST OF LEON RUSSELL	Shelter (S) 52004	2.00	3.00	4.00
CARNEY	Shelter (S) SW-8911	4.00	6.00	8.00
CARNEY (RI of Shelter 8911)	Shelter 2121	3.00	4.50	6.00
CARNEY (RI of Shelter 2121)	Shelter (S) 52011	2.00	3.00	4.00
LEON LIVE	Shelter (S) STCO 8917	5.00	7.50	10.00
LEON RUSSELL	Shelter (S) 1001	6.00	9.00	12.00
LEON RUSSELL (RI of Shelter 2118)	Shelter (S) 2118	3.00	4.50	6.00

(M) Mono (S) Stereo (EP) Extended Play (Q) Quad (RI) Re-issued

TITLE	LABEL & NO.	GOOD	VERY GOOD	NEAR MINT
LEON RUSSELL (RI of Shelter 2118)	Shelter (S) 52007	2.00	3.00	4.00
LEON RUSSELL & THE SHELTER PEOPLE	Shelter (S) 8903	5.00	7.50	10.00
LEON RUSSELL & THE SHELTER PEOPLE (WITH THE SHELTER PEOPLE) (RI of Shelter 8903)	Shelter (S) 2119	3.00	4.50	6.00
LEON RUSSELL & THE SHELTER PEOPLE (With the Shelter People) (RI of Shelter 2119)	Shelter (S) 52008	2.00	3.00	4.00
LOOKING BACK	Olympic (M) 7112	4.00	6.00	8.00
STOP ALL THAT JAZZ	Shelter 2108	3.00	4.50	6.00
WILL O' THE WISP	Shelter (S) 2138	3.00	4.50	6.00
WILL O' THE WISP (RI of Shelter 2138)	Shelter (S) 52020	2.00	3.00	4.00
RUSSELL, Leon & Mary				
MAKE LOVE TO THE MUSIC	Paradise (S) 3066	2.50	3.75	5.00
WEDDING ALBUM	Paradise (S) 2943	2.50	3.75	5.00
RUSTIX				
COME ON PEOPLE	Rare Earth (S) RS 513	3.00	4.50	6.00
RYAN, Charlie				
HOT ROD	King (M) 751	5.00	12.50	20.00
HOT ROD LINCOLN DRAGS AGAIN	Hilltop (M) JM 6006	4.00	10.00	16.00
RYDELL, Bobby				
ALL THE HITS BY BOBBY RYDELL	Cameo (M) C 1019	2.50	3.75	5.00
ALL THE HITS BY BOBBY RYDELL VOL. 2	Cameo (M) C 1040	2.50	3.75	5.00
BIGGEST HITS VOL. 2	Cameo (M) C 1028	2.50	3.75	5.00
BOBBY'S BIGGEST HITS (Fold-out cover)	Cameo (M) C 1009	5.00	10.00	15.00
BOBBY'S BIGGEST HITS	Cameo (M) C 1009	4.00	8.00	12.00
BOBBY RYDELL SALUTES THE GREAT ONES	Cameo (M) C 1010	3.00	6.00	9.00
BOBBY RYDELL SINGS	Strand (S) SLS 1120	5.00	10.00	15.00
BOBBY SINGS	Cameo (M) LP 1007	4.00	8.00	12.00
BYE BYE BIRDIE	Cameo (M) C 1043	2.50	3.75	5.00
18 GOLDEN HITS	Cameo (M) C 2001	3.50	5.25	7.00
18 GOLDEN HITS	Cameo (S) SC 2001	2.50	3.75	5.00
ERA REBORN, AN	Cameo (M) C 4017	2.50	3.75	5.00
ERA REBORN, AN	Cameo (S) SC 4017	2.00	3.00	4.00
FORGET HIM	Cameo (M) C 1080	2.50	3.75	5.00
FORGET HIM	Cameo (S) SC 1080	2.50	3.75	5.00
RYDELL AT THE COPA	Cameo (M) C 1011	3.00	4.50	6.00
SOMEBODY LOVES YOU	Capitol (S) ST 2281	3.00	4.50	6.00
SOMEBODY LOVES YOU	Capitol (EP) EP 2281	2.00	3.00	4.00
STARRING BOBBY RYDELL	Spinorama (S) S 143	3.00	6.00	9.00
TOP HITS OF '63 SUNG BY BOBBY RYDELL	Cameo (M) C 1070	2.50	3.75	5.00
TOP HITS OF '63 SUNG BY BOBBY RYDELL	Cameo (S) SC 1070	2.50	3.75	5.00
WE GOT LOVE	Cameo (M) LP 1006	5.00	10.00	15.00
WILD (WOOD) DAYS	Cameo (M) C 1055	3.00	4.50	6.00
WILD (WOOD) DAYS	Cameo (S) SC 1055	3.00	4.50	6.00
RYDELL, Bobby & Chubby Checker				
BOBBY RYDELL, AND CHUBBY CHECKER	Cameo (M) C 1013	3.00	4.50	6.00
RYDER, John & Anne				
I STILL BELIEVE IN TOMORROW	Decca (M) DL 75167	2.25	3.50	4.50
RYDER, Mitch				
ALL THE HEAVY HITS	Crewe (S) 1335	5.00	7.50	10.00
DETROIT MEMPHIS EXPERIMENT	Dot (S) DLP 25963	3.50	5.25	7.00
MITCH RYDER SINGS THE HITS	New Voice (S) 2005	4.50	6.75	9.00
WHAT NOW MY LOVE	Dyno Voice (M) DY 1901	4.50	6.75	9.00
WHAT NOW MY LOVE	Dyno Voice (M) DY 31901	5.00	7.50	10.00
RYDER, Mitch & The Detroit Wheels				
ALL MITCH RYDER HITS	New Voice (M) NV 2004	4.00	6.00	8.00
ALL MITCH RYDER HITS	New Voice (S) NVS 2004	4.50	6.75	9.00
BREAKOUT	New Voice (M) 2002	4.50	6.75	9.00
BREAKOUT (WITH "DEVIL WITH A BLUE DRESS" ADDED)	New Voice (M) 2002	4.00	6.00	8.00
BREAKOUT (WITH "DEVIL WITH A BLUE DRESS" ADDED)	New Voice (S) 2002-S	4.50	6.75	9.00
MITCH RYDER & DETROIT WHEELS GREATEST HITS	Virgo (S) 12001	3.00	4.50	6.00

TITLE	LABEL & NO.	GOOD	VERY GOOD	NEAR MINT
SOCK IT TO ME!	New Voice (N) NV 2003	4.00	6.00	8.00
SOCK IT TO ME!	New Voice (S) NVS 2003	4.50	6.75	9.00
TAKE A RIDE	New Voice (M) 2000	4.00	6.00	8.00
TAKE A RIDE	New Voice (S) 2000-S	4.50	6.75	9.00

RHYTHM ROCKERS
SOUL SURFIN	Challenge (M) CH 617	4.00	8.00	12.00

S

SACRED MUSHROOM
SACRED MUSHROOM, THE	Parallax (M) P 4001	5.50	8.00	11.00

SADLER, S./SGT. Barry
BALLADS OF THE GREEN BERETS	RCA (M) LPM-3547	3.00	4.50	6.00
BALLADS OF THE GREEN BERETS	RCA (S) LSP-3547	3.50	5.25	7.00
S/SGT. BARRY S. SADLER	RCA (M) LPM-3605	2.50	3.75	5.00
S/SGT. BARRY S. SADLER	RCA (S) LSP-3605	3.00	4.50	6.00

SAGITTARIUS
BLUE MARBLE, THE	Together (S) STT 1002	6.00	9.00	12.00
PRESENT TENSE	Columbia (S) CS 9644	5.50	8.25	11.00

SAIN, Oliver
BUS STOP	Abet (M) ABET 406	2.50	3.75	5.00
MAIN MAN	Abet (M) ABET 404	2.50	3.75	5.00

ST. JOHN, Bridget
ASK ME NO QUESTIONS	Dandelion (M) D9 101	4.50	6.75	9.00
SONGS FOR THE GENTLEMAN	Elektra (S) EKS 74104	4.00	6.00	8.00

ST. JOHN, Green
ST. JOHN GREEN	Flick Disc (S) FLS 45, 001	4.50	6.75	9.00

ST. LOUIS, Jimmy
GOIN' DOWN SLOW	Prestige/Bluesville (M) BV 1028	5.00	10.00	15.00

ST. PETERS, Crispian
PIED PIPER, THE	Jamie (M) JLPM 3027	4.00	8.00	12.00

SAINT STEVEN
SAINT STEVEN	Probe (M) CPLP 4506	3.50	5.25	7.00

SAKAMOTO, Kyu
SUKIYAKI	Capitol (M) T 10349	3.00	6.00	9.00
SUKIYAKI	Capitol (S) DT 10349	4.00	8.00	12.00

SALES, Soupy
SOUPY SALES SEZ DO THE MOUSE	ABC (M) ABC 517	2.00	3.00	4.00
SOUPY SALES SEZ DO THE MOUSE	ABC (S) ABCS 512	2.00	3.00	4.00
SOUPY SALES SHOW	Reprise (M) R-6010	3.00	4.00	6.00
SOUPY SALES SHOW	Reprise (S) R9-6010	3.50	5.25	7.00
SPY WITH A PIE	ABC (M) ABC 503	2.00	3.00	4.00
SPY WITH A PIE	ABC (S) ABCS 503	2.00	3.00	4.00
UP IN THE AIR	Reprise (M) R-6052	2.00	3.00	4.00
UP IN THE AIR	Reprise (S) R9-6052	2.50	3.75	5.00

SALLYANGIE
CHILDREN OF THE SUN	Warner Brothers (M) 1783	5.00	7.50	10.00

SALVATION
SALVATION	ABC (M) ABC 623	4.00	6.00	8.00
SALVATION	ABC (S) ABCS 623	5.00	7.50	10.00
SALVATION GYPSY CARNIVAL CARAVAN	ABC (S) ABCS 653	6.00	9.00	12.00

SAM AND DAVE
BACK AT 'CHA	United Artists (S) UA-LA262	2.00	3.00	4.00
BACK AT 'CHA!	United Artists (S) UA LA 524 G	2.00	3.00	4.00
DOUBLE DYNAMITE	Stax (M) 712	4.00	6.00	8.00
HOLD ON I'M COMIN'	Stax (M) 708	4.00	6.00	8.00
SAM AND DAVE	Roulette (S) SR 25323	6.00	9.00	12.00
SOUL MEN	Stax (S) 725	5.00	7.50	10.00

SAM APPLE PIE
SAM APPLE PIE	Sire (S) SES 97020	4.00	6.00	8.00

SAM THE SHAM & THE PHARAOHS
BEST OF SAM THE SHAM AND THE PHARAOHS	MGM (M) E 4422	3.50	5.25	7.00
BEST OF SAM THE SHAM AND THE PHARAOHS	MGM (S) SE 4422	4.00	6.00	8.00
HARD AND HEAVY	Atlantic (S) SD 8271	2.00	3.00	4.00
LIL RED RIDING HOOD	MGM (M) E 4407	3.50	5.25	7.00
LIL RED RIDING HOOD	MGM (S) SE 4407	4.00	6.00	8.00
NEFERTITI	MGM (S) SE 4479	4.00	6.00	8.00
ON TOUR	MGM (M) E 4347	3.50	5.25	7.00
ON TOUR	MGM (S) SE 4347	4.00	6.00	8.00
SAM THE SHAM REVUE ("Nefertiti" Re-titled)	MGM (S) SE 4479	3.00	4.50	6.00
TEN OF PENTACLES	MGM (S) SE 4526	3.00	4.50	6.00
THEIR SECOND ALBUM	MGM (M) E 4314	3.50	5.25	7.00
THEIR SECOND ALBUM	MGM (S) SE 4314	4.00	6.00	8.00
WOOLY BULLY	MGM (M) E 4297	3.50	5.25	7.00
WOOLY BULLY	MGM (S) SE 4297	4.00	6.00	8.00

SAM, Washboard
FEELING LOWDOWN	RCA (M) 577	2.00	3.00	4.00

SANCTUARY
SANCTUARY	Veritas (S) VS 92072	2.50	3.75	5.00

SANDALWOOD
SANDALWOOD	Bell (S) 1134	2.00	3.00	4.00

SANDELLS
SCRAMBLERS	World Pacific (M) 1818	3.00	6.00	9.00

SANDI AND THE STYLERS
DO ME	NJ (M) 1003	3.50	4.25	7.00

SANDS, Evie
ANY WAY THAT YOU WANT ME	A&M (S) SP 4239	3.50	5.25	7.00

SANDS, Tommy
DREAM WITH ME	Capitol (M) T-1426	2.50	3.75	5.00
DREAM WITH ME	Capitol (S) ST-1426	2.50	3.75	5.00
SANDS AT THE SANDS	Capitol (M) T 1364	3.00	6.00	9.00
SANDS AT THE SANDS	Capitol (S) ST 1364	3.50	7.00	10.50
SANDS STORM	Capitol (M) T 1081	5.00	10.00	15.00
SING BOY SING	Capitol (EP) EAP-1-929	2.00	3.00	4.00
SING BOY SING	Capitol (EP) EAP-2-929	2.00	3.00	4.00
SING BOY SING	Capitol (EP) EAP-3-929	2.00	3.00	4.00
STEADY DATE WITH TOMMY SANDS	Capitol (M) T 848	5.00	10.00	15.00
STEADY DATE WITH TOMMY SANDS	Capitol (EP) EAP 2 848	2.00	3.00	4.00
STEADY DATE WITH TOMMY SANDS	Capitol (EP) EAP 1 848	2.00	3.00	4.00
STEADY DATE WITH TOMMY SANDS	Capitol (EP) EAP 3 848	2.00	3.00	4.00
TEENAGE CRUSH	Capitol (EP) EAP 1-851	2.00	3.00	4.00
TEENAGE ROCK	Capitol (M) 1009	4.00	8.00	12.00
THIS THING CALLED LOVE	Capitol (M) T-1123	2.50	3.75	5.00
THIS THING CALLED LOVE	Capitol (S) ST-1123	2.50	3.75	5.00
THIS THING CALLED LOVE	Capitol (EP) EAP-1-1123	1.50	2.25	3.00
WHEN I'M THINKING OF YOU	Capitol (M) T 1239	3.00	6.00	9.00
WHEN I'M THINKING OF YOU	Capitol (S) ST 1239	3.50	7.00	10.50

SANTA FE
SANTA FE	Ampex (M) A 10135	3.00	4.50	6.00

SANTANA
ABRAXAS	Columbia (S) KC-30130	2.50	3.75	5.00
ABRAXAS	Columbia (Q) CQ-30130	2.50	3.75	5.00
AMIGOS	Columbia (S) 33576	2.00	3.00	4.00
AMIGOS	Columbia (Q) PCQ 33576	2.00	3.00	4.00
BORBOLETTA	Columbia (S) PC-33135	3.00	4.50	6.00
BORBOLETTA	Columbia (Q) PCQ-33135	2.50	3.75	5.00
CARAVANSERAI	Columbia (S) KC-31610	3.00	4.50	6.00
CARAVANSERAI	Columbia (Q) CQ-31610	2.50	3.75	5.00
FESTIVAL	Columbia (S) PC 34423	2.00	3.00	4.00
FESTIVAL	Columbia (Q) PCQ 34423	2.00	3.00	4.00
ILLUMINATIONS (WITH ALICE COLTRANE)	Columbia (S) PC-32900	3.00	4.50	6.00
ILLUMINATIONS (WITH ALICE COLTRANE)	Columbia (Q) PCQ-32900	2.50	3.75	5.00
MOONFLOWER	Columbia (S) C2-34914	3.00	4.50	6.00
SANTANA	Columbia (S) CS 9781	3.00	4.50	6.00
SANTANA	Columbia (Q) PCQ 32964	2.50	3.75	5.00
SANTANA	Columbia (S) KC 30595	2.50	3.75	5.00
SANTANA	Columbia (Q) CQ-30595	2.50	3.75	5.00
SANTANA'S GREATEST HITS	Columbia (S) 33050	2.00	3.00	4.00
SANTANA'S GREATEST HITS	Columbia (Q) PCQ 53050	2.00	3.00	4.00
WELCOME	Columbia (S) PC-32445	3.00	4.50	6.00
WELCOME	Columbia (Q) PCQ-32445	2.50	3.75	5.00

SANTO AND JOHNNY
BEATLES GREATEST HITS	Canadian American (M) CA-1017	4.00	6.00	8.00
BEATLES GREATEST HITS	Canadian American (S) SC 1017	5.00	7.50	10.00
BEST THAT COULD HAPPEN	Imperial (S) LP 12435	3.50	5.25	7.00
COME ON IN	Canadian American (M) CA-1006	3.00	6.00	9.00
COME ON IN	Canadian American (S) SC-1006	4.00	8.00	12.00
ENCORE	Canadian American (M) CALP 1002	3.00	6.00	9.00
ENCORE	Canadian American (S) SCA 1002	4.00	8.00	12.00
GOLDEN GUITARS	Imperial (S) 12366	3.50	5.25	7.00
HAWAII	Canadian American (M) CA-1004	3.00	6.00	9.00
HAWAII	Canadian American (S) SCA-1004	4.00	8.00	12.00
IN THE STILL OF THE NIGHT	Canadian American (M) CALP 1014	3.00	6.00	9.00
IN THE STILL OF THE NIGHT	Canadian American (S) SCA 1014	4.00	8.00	12.00
MUCHO	Canadian American (M) SCALP 1018	2.50	5.00	7.50
MUCHO	Canadian American (S) SCA 1018	3.50	7.00	10.50
OFF SHORE	Canadian American (M) CALP 1011	3.00	6.00	9.00

(M) Mono (S) Stereo (EP) Extended Play (Q) Quad (RI) Re-issued

TITLE	LABEL & NO.	GOOD	VERY GOOD	NEAR MINT
OFF SHORE	Canadian American (S) SCA 1011	4.00	8.00	12.00
ON THE ROADS AGAIN	Imperial (S) 12418	3.00	4.50	6.00
SANTO AND JOHNNY	Canadian American (M) CALP 1001	5.00	10.00	15.00
WISH YOU WERE HERE	Canadian American (M) CALP 1016	3.00	6.00	9.00
WISH YOU WERE HERE	Canadian American (S) SCA 1016	4.00	8.00	12.00

SANTOS, Larry
DON'T LET THE MUSIC STOP	Casablanca (S) 7061	2.50	3.75	5.00

SAPPHIRES
WHO DO YOU LOVE	Swan (M) LP 513	5.00	10.00	15.00

SAPPHIRE THINKERS
FROM WITHIN	Hobbit (M) H.B. 5003	2.50	3.75	5.00

SARIDIS, Saverio
LOVE IS THE SWEETEST THING	Warner Brothers (M) W-1450	2.50	3.75	5.00
LOVE IS THE SWEETEST THING	Warner Brothers (S) WS-1450	2.50	3.75	5.00

SAROFEEN AND SMOKE
SAROFEEN AND SMOKE	GWP (S) ST 2029	2.25	2.50	4.50

SARSTEDT, Clive
CLIVE SARSTEDT	RCA (S) LSP 4375	3.00	4.50	6.00
FREEWAY GETAWAY	RCA (S) LSP 4509	3.00	4.50	6.00

SARSTEDT, Peter
AS THOUGH IT WERE A MOVIE	World Pacific (S) WPS 21899	4.00	8.00	12.00
EVERY WORD YOU SAY IS WRITTEN DOWN	United Artists (S) 5558	5.00	10.00	15.00
WHERE DO YOU GO TO MY LOVELY	World Pacific (S) WPS 218 95	4.00	8.00	12.00

SARSTEDT, Richard
ANOTHER DAY PASSES BY	Evolution (M) 2022	4.00	6.00	8.00

SAVAGE GRACE
SAVAGE GRACE	Reprise (S) RS 6399	3.00	4.50	6.00
SAVAGE GRACE 2	Reprise (S) RS 6484	3.00	4.50	6.00

SAVAGE RESURRECTION
SAVAGE RESURRECTION, THE	Mercury (S) SR 61156	3.50	5.25	7.00

SAVAGE ROSE
IN THE PLAIN	Polydor (M) 24 6001	3.50	5.50	7.50
REFUGEE	Gregar (M) GG 104	4.00	6.00	8.00
YOUR DAILY GIFT	Gregar (M) GG 103	4.00	6.00	8.00

SAVAGE SONS OF YA HO WA
I'M GONNA TAKE YOU HOME	Higher Key (M) HKR 3309	2.00	3.00	4.00
SAVAGE SONS OF YA HO WA	Higher Key (M) HKR 3306	2.00	3.00	4.00

SAVOY BROWN
BLUE MATTER	Parrot (S) 71027	3.50	5.25	7.00
BOOGIE BROHERS	London (S) 638	2.50	3.75	5.00
HELLBOUND TRAIN	Parrot (S) 71052	3.00	4.50	6.00
JACK THE TOAD	Parrot (S) 71059	3.00	4.50	6.00
LION'S SHARE	Parrot (S) 71057	3.00	4.50	6.00
LOOKING IN	Parrot (S) 71042	3.50	5.25	7.00
RAW SIENNA	Parrot (S) 71036	3.50	5.25	7.00
STEP FURTHER, A	Parrot (S) 71029	3.50	5.25	7.00
STREET CORNER TALKING	Parrot (S) 71047	3.50	5.25	7.00
WIRE FIRE	London (S) 659	2.50	3.75	5.00

Also see FOGHAT

SAYER, Leo
ENDLESS FLIGHT	Warner Bros. (S) BS 2962	2.00	3.00	4.00
JUST A BOY	Warner Bros. (S) BS 2836	3.00	4.50	6.00
THUNDER IN MY HEART	Warner Bros. (S) BSK 3089	2.00	3.00	4.00

SCAFFOLD
THANK U VERY MUCH	Bell (M) 6018	4.00	6.00	8.00

SCAGGS, Boz
BOZ SCAGGS & BAND	Columbia (S) 30796	3.50	5.25	7.00
MOMENTS	Columbia (S) 30454	3.00	4.50	6.00
MY TIME	Columbia (S) 31384	3.00	4.50	6.00
SILK DEGREES	Columbia (S) JC 33920	2.00	3.00	4.00
SLOW DANCER	Columbia (S) KC-32760	2.50	3.75	5.00

SCHATZ, Warren
WARREN SCHATZ	Columbia (M) C 30685	2.00	3.00	4.00

SCHILLER, Lawrence
LSD	Capitol (M) TAO-2574	4.00	6.00	8.00
LSD	Capitol (S) STAO-2574	5.00	7.50	10.00

SCHOOLBOYS
BEATLE MANIA	Palace (M) 778	4.00	8.00	12.00

SCHWARTZ, Bernie
WHEEL, THE	Co Burt (M) CO 1001	2.00	3.00	4.00

SCHWARZ, Brinsley
BRINSLEY SCHWARZ	Capitol (S) ST 589	3.00	4.50	6.00
DESPITE IT ALL	Capitol (S) ST 744	3.00	4.50	6.00
NERVOUS ON THE ROAD	United Artists (S) UAS 5647	2.50	3.75	5.00
SILVER PISTOL	United Artists (S) UAS 29217	2.50	3.75	5.00

SCORPIONS
LONESOME CROW	Billingsgate (M) 1004	2.50	3.75	5.00

SCOTT, Calvin
I'M NOT BLIND I JUST CAN'T SEE	Stax (S) STS 2046	2.00	3.00	4.00

SCOTT, Esther Mae
MAMA AIN'T NOBODY'S FOOL	Bomp (M) 1	2.50	3.75	5.00

SCOTT, Freddie
ARE YOU LONELY FOR ME	Shout (S) SLPS 501	4.50	6.75	9.00
EVERYTHING I HAVE IS YOURS	Columbia (M) CL-2258	2.50	3.75	5.00
EVERYTHING I HAVE IS YOURS	Columbia (S) CS-90058	3.00	4.50	6.00
FREDDIE SCOTT SINGS	Colpix (M) CP 461	3.50	5.25	7.00
FREDDIE SCOTT SINGS	Colpix (S) SCP 461	4.00	6.00	8.00
I SHALL BE RELEASED	Probe (M) CPLP 451	3.00	4.50	6.00

SCOTT, Jack
BURNING BRIDGES	Capitol (M) T 2035	7.00	17.50	28.00
BURNING BRIDGES	Capitol (S) ST 2035	10.00	25.00	40.00
I REMEMBER HANK WILLIAMS	Top Rank (M) RM-319	9.00	22.50	36.00
I REMEMBER HANK WILLIAMS	Top Rank (S) RS-619	10.00	25.00	40.00
JACK SCOTT	Carlton (M) LP 12/107	10.00	25.00	40.00
JACK SCOTT	Carlton (S) STLP 12/107	14.00	35.00	56.00
JACK SCOTT SINGS	Carlton (EP) EP7/1072	2.00	5.00	8.00
PRESENTING JACK SCOTT	Carlton (EP) EP7/1070	2.00	5.00	8.00
PRESENTING JACK SCOTT	Carlton (EP) EP7/1071	2.00	5.00	8.00
SPIRIT MOVES ME, THE (WITH THE CHANTONES)	Top Rank (M) RM 348	10.00	25.00	40.00
STARRING JACK SCOTT	Carlton (EP) EP7/1073	2.00	5.00	8.00
WHAT AM I LIVING FOR	Carlton (M) LP 12/122	14.00	35.00	56.00
WHAT IN THE WORLD'S COME OVER YOU	Top Rank (M) RM-326	9.00	22.50	36.00
WHAT IN THE WORLD'S COME OVER YOU	Top Rank (S) RS-626	10.00	25.00	40.00

SCOTT, Jimmy
FABULOUS SONGS OF JIMMY SCOTT	Savoy (M) MG 12150	3.00	7.50	12.00

SCOTT, Linda
GREAT SCOTT- HER GREATEST HITS	Canadian American (M) CALP 1007	4.00	8.00	12.00
HEY, LOOK AT ME NOW	Kapp (M) KL 1424	3.50	5.25	7.00
STARLIGHT-STARBRIGHT	Canadian American (M) CA-1005	3.50	7.00	10.50
STARLIGHT-STARBRIGHT	Canadian American (S) SC-1005	4.50	9.00	13.50

SCOTTI, Tony
PRESENTING	Liberty (M) LRP 3528	2.00	3.00	4.00
PRESENTING	Liberty (S) LST 7528	2.00	3.00	4.00

SCRA
SHIP ALBUM, THE	Atlantic (S) SD7235	2.25	3.50	4.50

SCRAMBLERS
CYCLE PSYCHOS	Crown (S) CST 384	4.00	8.00	12.00
LITTLE HONDA	Wyncote (S) W 9048	3.00	6.00	9.00

SEA DOG
SEA DOG	Buddah (S) BDS5104	2.00	3.00	4.00

SEALS, Son, Blues Band
SON SEALS BLUES BAND, THE	Alligator (M) 4703	3.00	4.50	6.00

SEALS & CROFTS
DIAMOND GIRL	Warner Bros. BS2699	2.00	3.00	4.00
DIAMOND GIRL	Warner Bros. (Q) BS4-2699	2.50	3.75	5.00
DOWN HOME	T.A. (S) 5004	5.00	7.50	10.00
I'LL PLAY FOR YOU	Warner Bros. BS 2848	2.00	3.00	4.00
I'LL PLAY FOR YOU	Warner Bros. (Q) BS4-2848	2.50	3.75	5.00
SEALS & CROFT'S GREATEST HITS	Warner Bros. (S) BS 2886	2.00	3.00	4.00
SEALS & CROFTS 1 & 2.	Warner Bros. 2WS-2809	3.00	4.50	6.00
SUMMER BREEZE	Warner Bros. BS2629	2.00	3.00	4.00
SUMMER BREEZE	Warner Bros. (Q) BS4-2629	2.50	3.75	5.00
TAKIN' IT EASY	Warner Bros. (S) BSK 3163	2.00	3.00	4.00
UNBORN CHILD	Warner Bros. 2761	2.00	3.00	4.00
YEAR OF SUNDAY	Warner Bros. BS 2568	2.50	3.75	5.00

SEARCHERS
HEAR! HEAR!	Mercury (M) MG 20914	4.00	8.00	12.00
HEAR! HEAR!	Mercury (S) SR 60914	5.00	10.00	15.00

(M) Mono   (S) Stereo   (EP) Extended Play   (Q) Quad   (RI) Re-issued

TITLE	LABEL & NO.	GOOD	VERY GOOD	NEAR MINT
MEET THE SEARCHERS	Kapp (S) KS 3363	3.50	7.00	10.50
NEW SEARCHERS LP	Kapp (S) KS 3412	3.50	7.00	10.50
SEARCHERS MEET THE RATTLES	Mercury (M) MG 20994	4.00	8.00	12.00
SEARCHERS MEET THE RATTLES	Mercury (S) SR 60994	5.00	10.00	15.00
SEARCHERS NO. 4	Kapp (M) KL 1449	3.00	6.00	9.00
TAKE ME FOR WHAT I'M WORTH	Kapp (M) KL 1477	3.00	6.00	9.00
THIS IS US	Kapp (M) KL 1409	3.00	6.00	9.00
THIS IS US	Kapp (EP) KS 3409	3.00	6.00	9.00

SEBASTIAN, John
CHEAPO-CHEAPO PRODUCTIONS PRESENTS

TITLE	LABEL & NO.	GOOD	VERY GOOD	NEAR MINT
REAL LIVE JOHN SEBASTIAN	Reprise (S) 2036	2.50	3.75	5.00
FOUR OF US, THE	Reprise (S) 2041	2.50	3.75	5.00
JOHN B. SEBASTIAN	Reprise (S) 6379	3.00	4.50	6.00
JOHN B. SEBASTIAN	MGM (S) SE 4654	4.00	6.00	8.00
JOHN SEBASTIAN LIVE!	MGM (S) SE 4720	4.00	6.00	8.00
TARZANA KID	Reprise (S) 2187	2.50	3.75	5.00
WELCOME BACK	Reprise (S) 2249	2.50	3.75	5.00

Also see LOVIN' SPOONFUL

SECOND COMING

TITLE	LABEL & NO.	GOOD	VERY GOOD	NEAR MINT
SECOND COMING, THE	Mercury (S) SR 61299	4.50	6.75	9.00

SEDAKA, Neil

TITLE	LABEL & NO.	GOOD	VERY GOOD	NEAR MINT
BREAKING UP IS HARD TO DO	Camden (S) ACL 7006	4.00	6.00	8.00
CIRCULATE	RCA (M) LPM 2317	5.00	10.00	15.00
CIRCULATE	RCA (S) LSP 2317	6.00	12.00	18.00
HUNGRY YEARS, THE	Rocket (S) PIG 2157	2.00	3.00	4.00
I GO APE	RCA (EP) EPA-4334	2.00	4.00	6.00
ITALIANO	RCA (S) 10140	6.00	12.00	18.00
LITTLE DEVIL	RCA (M) LPM2421	5.00	10.00	15.00
LITTLE DEVIL	RCA (S) LSP 2421	6.00	12.00	18.00
NEIL'S BEST	RCA (S) LPC-105	6.00	9.00	12.00
NEIL'S BEST	RCA (EP) LPC 105	2.00	4.00	6.00
NEIL SEDAKA (ROCK WITH SEDAKA)	RCA (m) LPM 2035	6.00	12.00	18.00
NEIL SEDAKA (ROCK WITH SEDAKA)	RCA (S) LSP-2035	10.00	20.00	30.00
NEIL SEDAKA SINGS HIS GREATEST HITS	RCA (M) LPM 2627	4.00	8.00	12.00
NEIL SEDAKA SINGS HIS GREATEST HITS	RCA (S) LSP 2627	5.00	10.00	15.00
OH, CAROL	RCA (S) ANL1 0879	3.00	4.50	6.00
OH, CAROL	RCA (EP) EPA-4353	2.00	4.00	6.00
SEDAKA'S BACK	Rocket (S) 463	2.00	3.00	4.00
SINGS HIS GREATEST HITS	RCA (S) APL1 0928	3.00	4.50	6.00
SMILE	RCA (M) LPM-10181	5.00	7.50	10.00
SMILE	United Artists (S) UA-LA-467-G	3.00	4.50	6.00
SOLITAIRE	Kirshner (S) KES 117	5.00	7.50	10.00
STEPPIN' OUT	Rocket (S) PIG 2195	2.00	3.00	4.00

SEDAKA, Neil and The Tokens

TITLE	LABEL & NO.	GOOD	VERY GOOD	NEAR MINT
NEIL SEDAKA AND THE TOKENS	Guest Star (M) G 1448	3.00	6.00	9.00
NEIL SEDAKA AND THE TOKENS AND COINS	Crown (M) CLP 5366	3.00	6.00	9.00
NEIL SEDAKA WITH THE TOKENS	Vernon (M) 518	4.00	8.00	12.00

SEEDS

TITLE	LABEL & NO.	GOOD	VERY GOOD	NEAR MINT
FUTURE	GNP/Crescendo (M) GNP 2038	2.50	3.75	5.00
RAW AND ALIVE	GNP/Crescendo (S) GNPS 2043	4.00	6.00	8.00
SEEDS, THE	GNP/Crescendo (M) GNP 2023	3.00	4.50	6.00
SKY SAXON BLUES BAND	GNP/Crescendo (M) GNP 2040	4.00	6.00	8.00
A WEB OF SOUND	GNP/Crescendo (M) GNP 2033	3.00	4.50	6.00

SEEGER, Pete

TITLE	LABEL & NO.	GOOD	VERY GOOD	NEAR MINT
BANKS OF MARBLE	Folkways (S) 31040	2.00	3.00	4.00
CHAMPLAIN VALLEY SONGBAG	Folkways (M) FH-5210	2.00	3.00	4.00
GAZETTE	Folkways (M) FN-2501	2.00	3.00	4.00
HOOTENANNY AT CARNEGIE HALL	Folkways (M) FN-2512	2.00	3.00	4.00
PETE SEEGER SINGS FOLK MUSIC OF THE WORLD	Tradition (S) 2107	2.00	3.00	4.00
WE SHALL OVERCOME	Columbia (M) CL 2101	5.00	7.50	10.00
WORLD OF PETE SEEGER	Columbia (S) KG-31949	2.50	3.75	5.00

SEEKERS

TITLE	LABEL & NO.	GOOD	VERY GOOD	NEAR MINT
BEST OF THE SEEKERS, THE	Capitol (S) ST 2746	4.00	6.00	8.00
GEORGY GIRL	Capitol (M) T 2431	2.50	5.00	7.50
GEORGY GIRL	Capitol (S) ST 2431	3.00	6.00	9.00
NEW SEEKERS, THE	Capitol (M) T 2319	2.50	5.00	7.50
NEW SEEKERS, THE	Capitol (S) ST 2319	3.00	6.00	9.00
SEEKERS, THE	Marvel (M) 2060	3.00	6.00	9.00
SEEKERS, THE	Marvel (S) 3060	4.00	8.00	12.00
SEEKERS SEEN IN GREEN	Capitol (S) SKAO-2821	3.00	6.00	9.00
A WORLD OF OUR OWN	Capitol (M) T 2369	2.50	5.00	7.50
A WORLD OF OUR OWN	Capitol (S) ST2369	3.00	6.00	9.00

SEEMON AND MARIJKE

TITLE	LABEL & NO.	GOOD	VERY GOOD	NEAR MINT
SON OF AMERICA	A&M (S) SP 4309	4.00	6.00	8.00

SEGER, Bob System

TITLE	LABEL & NO.	GOOD	VERY GOOD	NEAR MINT
BACK IN '72	Palladium (S) MS 2126	4.00	6.00	8.00
BRAND NEW DAY	Capitol (S) ST 731	3.00	4.50	6.00
'LIVE' BULLET (With the Silver Bullet Band)	Capitol (S) SKBB-11523	3.00	4.50	6.00
MONGREL	Capitol (S) SCAO 499	3.00	4.50	6.00
NIGHT MOVES (With Silver Bullet Band)	Capitol (S) ST 11557	2.00	3.00	4.00
NOAH	Capitol (S) ST 236	3.00	4.50	6.00
RAMBLIN' GAMBLIN' MAN	Capitol (S) ST 172	3.00	4.50	6.00
SEVEN ('77 RI, listed as Bob Seger only)	Capitol ST-11748	2.00	3.00	4.00
SMOKIN' O.P.'s	Palladium (S) P-1006	4.00	6.00	8.00
SMOKIN' O.P.'s ('77 RI, listed as Bob Seger only)	Capitol (S) ST 11746	2.00	3.00	4.00
STRANGER IN TOWN (With Silver Bullet Band)	Capitol (S) SW 11698	2.00	3.00	4.00

SELAH JUBILEE QUARTETTE, THE
SPIRITUALS BY THE SELAH JUBILEE QUARTETTE

TITLE	LABEL & NO.	GOOD	VERY GOOD	NEAR MINT
(10")	Remington (M) RLP 1023	8.00	20.00	32.00

SELF, Ronnie

TITLE	LABEL & NO.	GOOD	VERY GOOD	NEAR MINT
AIN'T I'M A DOG	Columbia (EP) EP-B-2149	4.00	10.00	16.00

SELVIDGE, Sid

TITLE	LABEL & NO.	GOOD	VERY GOOD	NEAR MINT
PORTRAIT	Enterprise (S) ENS 1003	2.00	3.00	4.00

SENSATIONS

TITLE	LABEL & NO.	GOOD	VERY GOOD	NEAR MINT
LET ME IN	Argo (M) LP 4022	4.50	11.25	18.00

SENTINALS

TITLE	LABEL & NO.	GOOD	VERY GOOD	NEAR MINT
BIG SURF	Del Fi (M) DFLP 1232	3.50	7.00	10.50
BIG SURF	Del Fi (S) DFST 1232	4.00	8.00	12.00
SURFER GIRL	Del Fi (M) DFLP 1241	3.50	7.00	10.50
SURFER GIRL	Del Fi (S) DFST 1241	4.00	8.00	12.00
VEGAS GO GO	Sutton (M) SU 338	3.00	6.00	9.00

SERFS

TITLE	LABEL & NO.	GOOD	VERY GOOD	NEAR MINT
EARLYBIRD CAFE	Capitol (S) SKAO 207	3.50	5.25	7.00

SERPENT POWER

TITLE	LABEL & NO.	GOOD	VERY GOOD	NEAR MINT
SERPENT POWER, THE	Vanguard (S) VSD 79252	5.00	7.50	10.00

SEVEN
SONG IS SONG, THE ALBUM

TITLE	LABEL & NO.	GOOD	VERY GOOD	NEAR MINT
IS ALBUM	Thunderbird (S) THS 9006	3.00	4.50	6.00

SEVENTH SONS

TITLE	LABEL & NO.	GOOD	VERY GOOD	NEAR MINT
SEVENTH SONS	ESP (M) 1078	3.50	5.25	7.00

SEVILLE, David

TITLE	LABEL & NO.	GOOD	VERY GOOD	NEAR MINT
MUSIC OF DAVID SEVILLE	Liberty (M) LRP 3073	4.00	8.00	12.00
WITCH DOCTOR	Liberty (M) LRP 3092	4.00	8.00	12.00
WITCH DOCTOR	Liberty (EP) LSX 1003	2.00	4.00	6.00

SEWARD, Alec

TITLE	LABEL & NO.	GOOD	VERY GOOD	NEAR MINT
CREEPIN' BLUES	Prestige/Bluesville (M) BV 1076	4.00	6.00	8.00

SEX PISTOLS
NEVER MIND THE BOLLOCKS

TITLE	LABEL & NO.	GOOD	VERY GOOD	NEAR MINT
(Here's The Sex Pistols)	Warner Bros. (S) BSK-3147	2.00	3.00	4.00

SHACKLEFORDS

TITLE	LABEL & NO.	GOOD	VERY GOOD	NEAR MINT
SHACKLEFORDS	Mercury (M) MG 20806	2.00	3.00	4.00
SHACKLEFORDS	Mercury (S) SR 60806	3.00	4.50	6.00

SHADES OF BLUE

TITLE	LABEL & NO.	GOOD	VERY GOOD	NEAR MINT
HAPPINESS IS THE SHADES OF BLUE	Impact (M) IM 101	4.50	6.75	9.00

SHADOWS

TITLE	LABEL & NO.	GOOD	VERY GOOD	NEAR MINT
SHADOWS KNOW, THE	Atlantic (M) 8097	4.00	8.00	12.00
SURFING WITH THE SHADOWS	Atlantic (M) 8089	4.00	8.00	12.00

Also see RICHARD, Cliff & The Shadows

SHADOWS OF KNIGHT

TITLE	LABEL & NO.	GOOD	VERY GOOD	NEAR MINT
BACK DOOR MEN	Dunwich (M) 667	5.00	7.50	10.00
BACK DOOR MEN	Dunwich (S) S 667	6.00	9.00	12.00
GLORIA	Dunwich (M) 666	5.00	7.50	10.00
GLORIA	Dunwich (S) S 666	6.00	9.00	12.00
SHADOWS OF KNIGHT	Super K (S) SKS 6002	5.00	7.50	10.00
VOICES OF VISTA (With other Artists)	No. 30 ABC	7.00	10.50	14.00

SHAGGS

TITLE	LABEL & NO.	GOOD	VERY GOOD	NEAR MINT
PHILOSOPHY OF THE WORLD	Third World (M) 3001	5.00	7.50	10.00

SHAKEY JAKE

TITLE	LABEL & NO.	GOOD	VERY GOOD	NEAR MINT
BLUES MAKERS (With The All Stars)	World Pacific (S) WPS 21886	4.00	8.00	12.00
SHAKEY JAKE	Bluesville (M) 1008	5.00	7.50	10.00

SHAKEY VICK

TITLE	LABEL & NO.	GOOD	VERY GOOD	NEAR MINT
LITTLE WOMAN YOU'RE SO SWEET	Janus (S) JLS 3000	3.50	5.25	7.00

SHA NA NA

TITLE	LABEL & NO.	GOOD	VERY GOOD	NEAR MINT
FROM THE STREETS OF NEW YORK	Kama Sutra (S) 2075	2.50	3.75	5.00

(M) Mono (S) Stereo (EP) Extended Play (Q) Quad (RI) Re-issued

TITLE	LABEL & NO.	GOOD	VERY GOOD	NEAR MINT
HOT SOX	Kama Sutra (S) 2600	2.50	3.75	5.00
NIGHT IS STILL YOUNG, THE	Kama Sutra (S) 2050	2.50	3.75	5.00
ROCK & ROLL IS HERE TO STAY!	Kama Sutra (S) 2010	2.50	3.75	5.00
SHANANA	Kama Sutra (S) 2034	2.50	3.75	5.00
SHA NA NA (ROCK & ROLL) IS HERE TO STAY	Kama Sutra (S) 2077	2.50	3.75	5.00
SHANANOW	Kama Sutra (S) 2605	2.50	3.75	5.00

SHANGRI-LAS
TITLE	LABEL & NO.	GOOD	VERY GOOD	NEAR MINT
GOLDEN HITS OF THE SHANGRI-LAS	Mercury (M) MG 21099	3.50	5.25	7.00
GOLDEN HITS OF THE SHANGRI-LAS	Mercury (S) SR 61099	4.00	6.00	8.00
I CAN NEVER GO HOME ANYMORE (Shangri-Las '65 re-titled, with "I Can Never Go Home Anymore" replacing "The Dum Dum Ditty" track)	Red Bird (M) RB 20 104	6.00	9.00	12.00
LEADER OF THE PACK	Red Bird (M) RB 20 101	5.00	7.50	10.00
SHANGRI-LAS SING, THE	Post (M) 4000	4.00	6.00	8.00
SHANGRI-LAS '65	Red Bird (M) 20 104	9.00	13.50	18.00

SHANKAR, Ravi
TITLE	LABEL & NO.	GOOD	VERY GOOD	NEAR MINT
IN CONCERT 1972	Apple (S) SVBB 3396	6.00	9.00	12.00
RAVI SHANKAR IN NEW YORK	World Pacific (M) 1441	4.00	6.00	8.00
RAVI SHANKAR IN NEW YORK	World Pacific (S) 21441	4.50	6.75	9.00
RAVI SHANKAR IN SAN FRANCISCO	World Pacific (S) 21449	4.50	6.75	9.00
RAVI SHANKAR AT THE MONTEREY INTERNATIONAL POP FESTIVAL	World Pacific (S) 21442	4.50	6.75	9.00
RAVI SHANKAR AT THE MONTEREY INTERNATIONAL POP FESTIVAL	World Pacific (M) 1442	4.00	6.00	8.00
SHANKAR FAMILY & FRIENDS	Dark Horse (S) 22002	4.50	6.75	9.00

SHANNON, Del
TITLE	LABEL & NO.	GOOD	VERY GOOD	NEAR MINT
BEST OF DEL SHANNON	Dot (M) DLP 3824	4.50	6.75	9.00
BEST OF DEL SHANNON	Dot (S) DLP 25824	3.50	5.25	7.00
DEL SHANNON SINGS	Post (M) 9000	4.00	6.00	8.00
DEL SHANNON SINGS HANK WILLIAMS	Amy (M) 8004	4.00	6.00	8.00
DEL SHANNON SINGS HANK WILLIAMS	Amy (S) S 8004	5.00	7.50	10.00
FURTHER ADVENTURES OF CHARLES WESTOVER	Liberty (S) LST 7539	4.00	6.00	8.00
HANDY MAN	Amy (M) 8003	4.00	6.00	8.00
HANDY MAN	Amy (S) S 8003	5.00	7.50	10.00
LITTLE TOWN FLIRT	Big Top (M) 12-1308	6.00	12.00	18.00
LIVE IN ENGLAND	United Artists (S) UALA 151	3.00	4.50	6.00
ONE THOUSAND SIX HUNDRED SIXTY ONE SECONDS	Amy (M) 8006	3.50	5.25	7.00
ONE THOUSAND SIX HUNDRED SIXTY ONE SECONDS	Amy (S) S 8006	4.50	6.75	9.00
RUNAWAY	Big Top (M) 12-1303	7.00	14.00	21.00
THIS IS MY BAG	Liberty (M) LRP 3453	3.50	5.25	7.00
THIS IS MY BAG	Liberty (S) LST 7452	4.50	6.75	9.00
TOTAL COMMITMENT	Liberty (M) LRP 3479	3.50	5.25	7.00
TOTAL COMMITMENT	Liberty (S) LST 7479	4.50	6.75	9.00
VINTAGE YEARS	Sire (S) SASH 3708-2	3.50	5.25	7.00

SHAPIRO, Helen
TITLE	LABEL & NO.	GOOD	VERY GOOD	NEAR MINT
A TEENAGER IN LOVE	Epic (M) LN 24075	4.00	8.00	12.00
A TEENAGER IN LOVE	Epic (S) BN 26075	5.00	10.00	15.00

SHARON, Ralph
TITLE	LABEL & NO.	GOOD	VERY GOOD	NEAR MINT
MODERN INNOVATIONS ON COUNTRY AND WESTERN THEMES	Gordy (M) 903	4.00	8.00	12.00

SHARP, Dee Dee
TITLE	LABEL & NO.	GOOD	VERY GOOD	NEAR MINT
ALL THE HITS	Cameo (M) 1027	2.50	5.00	7.50
ALL THE HITS BY DEE DEE SHARP	Cameo (M) C-1032	2.00	4.00	6.00
ALL THE HITS BY DEE DEE SHARP	Cameo (S) SC-1032	3.00	6.00	9.00
BIGGEST HITS	Cameo (M) C 1062	2.00	4.00	6.00
DO THE BIRD	Cameo (M) C-1050	2.00	4.00	6.00
DO THE BIRD	Cameo (S) SC-1050	3.00	6.00	9.00
DOWN MEMORY LANE	Cameo (M) C 1074	2.50	3.75	5.00
18 GOLDEN HITS	Cameo (M) C 2002	3.00	3.75	6.00
18 GOLDEN HITS	Cameo (S) SC 2002	2.50	3.75	5.00
HAPPY 'BOUT THE WHOLE THING	Philadelphia Int'l (S) PZ-33839	2.50	3.75	5.00
IT'S MASHED POTATO TIME	Cameo (M) C 1018	2.50	5.00	7.50
SONGS OF FAITH	Cameo (M) C 1022	2.50	5.00	7.50

SHAW BROTHERS
TITLE	LABEL & NO.	GOOD	VERY GOOD	NEAR MINT
FOLLOW ME	RCA (S) APL1-0511	2.00	3.00	4.00

SHAW, Robert
TITLE	LABEL & NO.	GOOD	VERY GOOD	NEAR MINT
TEXAS BARRELHOUSE PIANO	Almanac (M) AM 10	4.00	6.00	8.00

SHAW, Sandie
TITLE	LABEL & NO.	GOOD	VERY GOOD	NEAR MINT
ME	Reprise (M) R 6191	3.00	6.00	9.00
ME	Reprise (S) SR 6191	4.00	8.00	12.00
SANDIE SHAW	Reprise (M) R 6166	3.00	6.00	9.00
SANDIE SHAW	Reprise (S) RS 6166	4.00	8.00	12.00

SHELLS
TITLE	LABEL & NO.	GOOD	VERY GOOD	NEAR MINT
GREATEST HITS OF THE SHELLS	Johnson (M) 1619	4.00	6.00	8.00

SHELTON, Roscoe
TITLE	LABEL & NO.	GOOD	VERY GOOD	NEAR MINT
ROSCOE SHELTON	Excello (M) 8002	4.00	8.00	12.00

SHEP & THE LIMELITES
TITLE	LABEL & NO.	GOOD	VERY GOOD	NEAR MINT
OUR ANNIVERSARY	Roulette (M) R 25350	5.00	12.50	20.00

SHEPARD, Jean
TITLE	LABEL & NO.	GOOD	VERY GOOD	NEAR MINT
COUNTRY BALLADS	Capitol (EP) EAP 1-687	1.00	1.50	2.00
JEAN SHEPARD (WITH FERLIN HUSKY)	Capitol (EP) EAP 1-609	1.00	1.50	3.00
SONGS OF A LOVE AFFAIR	Capitol (M) T 728	2.50	3.75	5.00
SONGS OF A LOVE AFFAIR	Capitol (EP) EAP 1-728	1.00	1.50	2.00
SONGS OF A LOVE AFFAIR	Capitol (EP) EAP-2-728	1.00	1.50	2.00
SONGS OF A LOVE AFFAIR	Capitol (EP) EAP 3-728	1.00	1.50	2.00
THIS IS JEAN SHEPARD	Capitol (M) T-1253	2.50	3.75	5.00
THIS IS JEAN SHEPARD	Capitol (EP) EAP-1-1253	1.00	1.50	2.00
THIS IS JEAN SHEPARD	Capitol (EP) EAP-2-1253	1.00	1.50	2.00
THIS IS JEAN SHEPARD	Capitol (EP) EAP-3-1253	1.00	1.50	2.00

SHEPPARDS
TITLE	LABEL & NO.	GOOD	VERY GOOD	NEAR MINT
SHEPPARDS, THE VOL. IV	Constellation (M) CS 4	5.00	10.00	15.00

SHERMAN, Allan
TITLE	LABEL & NO.	GOOD	VERY GOOD	NEAR MINT
FOR SWINGIN' LOVERS ONLY	Warner Brothers (M) W-1569	2.00	3.00	4.00
FOR SWINGIN' LOVERS ONLY	Warner Brothers (S) WS-1569	2.50	3.75	5.00
MY NAME IS ALLAN	Warner Brothers (M) W-1604	2.00	3.00	4.00
MY NAME IS ALLAN	Warner Brothers (S) WS-1604	2.50	3.50	5.00
MY SON, THE CELEBRITY	Warner Brothers (M) W 1487	2.00	3.00	4.00
MY SON, THE CELEBRITY	Warner Brothers (S) WS 1487	2.50	3.75	5.00
MY SON THE FOLK SINGER	Warner Brothers (M) W-1475	2.50	3.75	5.00
MY SON THE FOLK SINGER	Warner Brothers (S) WS-1475	3.00	4.50	6.00
MY SON, THE NUT	Warner Brothers (M) W 1501	2.00	3.00	4.00
MY SON, THE NUT	Warner Brothers (S) WS-1501	2.50	3.25	5.00
PETER & THE COMMISSAR (& OTHERS)	RCA (M) LM-2773	2.00	3.00	4.00
PETER & THE COMMISSAR (& OTHERS)	RCA (S) LSC-2773	2.50	3.75	5.00

SHERMAN, Bobby
TITLE	LABEL & NO.	GOOD	VERY GOOD	NEAR MINT
BOBBY	Metromedia (S) PM 1	2.00	3.00	4.00
BOBBY SHERMAN	Metromedia (S) MD 1014	2.00	3.00	4.00
CHRISTMAS ALBUM	Metromedia (S) MD 1038	2.00	3.00	4.00
GETTING TOGETHER	Metromedia (S) MD 1045	2.00	3.00	4.00
GREATEST HITS VOL. 1	Metromedia (S) MD 1048	2.00	3.00	4.00
HERE COMES BOBBY	Metromedia (S) MD 1028	2.00	3.00	4.00
JUST FOR YOU	Metromedia (S) MD 1060	2.00	3.00	4.00
PORTRAIT OF BOBBY	Metromedia (S) MD 1040	2.00	3.00	4.00
WITH LOVE, BOBBY	Metromedia (S) MD 1032	2.00	3.00	4.00

SHERRYS
TITLE	LABEL & NO.	GOOD	VERY GOOD	NEAR MINT
AT THE HOP WITH THE SHERRYS	Guyden (M) GLP 503	5.00	10.00	15.00

SHILOH
TITLE	LABEL & NO.	GOOD	VERY GOOD	NEAR MINT
SHILOH	Amos (M) AAS 7015	5.00	7.50	10.00

SHINES, Johnny
TITLE	LABEL & NO.	GOOD	VERY GOOD	NEAR MINT
BLUES MASTERS	Blue Horizon (M) BM 4607	4.50	6.75	9.00

SHIRELLES
TITLE	LABEL & NO.	GOOD	VERY GOOD	NEAR MINT
BABY IT'S YOU	Scepter (M) S 504	5.00	10.00	15.00
FOOLISH LITTLE GIRL	Scepter (M) S 511	4.00	8.00	12.00
GREATEST HITS	Scepter (M) S 507	4.00	8.00	12.00
GREATEST HITS VOL. 2	Scepter (M) S 560	3.00	4.50	6.00
GREATEST HITS VOL. 2	Scepter (S) SPS 560	3.50	5.25	7.00
HAPPY AND IN LOVE	RCA (S) LSP 4581	2.50	3.75	5.00
REMEMBER WHEN	Scepter (S) SPS 2-599	3.00	4.50	6.00
SHIRELLES AND KING CURTIS GIVE A TWIST PARTY	Scepter (M) S 505	4.00	8.00	12.00
SHIRELLES SING THE GOLDEN 1 OLDIES	Scepter (M) S 516	3.00	6.00	9.00
SHIRELLES SING TO TRUMPETS AND STRINGS	Scepter (M) S 502	4.00	8.00	12.00
SING THEIR SONGS IN THE GREAT MOVIE IT'S A MAD, MAD, MAD, MAD WORLD AND OTHERS	Scepter (M) S 514	3.00	6.00	9.00
SPONTANEOUS COMBUSTION	Scepter (S) SPS 562	3.50	5.25	7.00
SWING THE MOST	Pricewise (M) P 4001	4.00	8.00	12.00
TONIGHT'S THE NIGHT	Scepter (M) S 501	6.00	12.00	18.00
VERY BEST OF THE SHIRELLES, THE	United Artists (S) UA-LA340	2.00	3.00	4.00

SHIRLEY AND LEE
TITLE	LABEL & NO.	GOOD	VERY GOOD	NEAR MINT
LEGENDARY MASTERS— SHIRLEY & LEE	United Artists (S) UA-LA026-G2	5.00	7.50	10.00
LET THE GOOD TIMES ROLL	Aladdin (M) 807	14.00	35.00	56.00
LET THE GOOD TIMES ROLL	Score (M) SLP 4023	10.00	20.00	30.00
LET THE GOOD TIMES ROLL	Warwick (M) 2028	9.00	22.50	36.00
LET THE GOOD TIMES ROLL	Imperial (M) A-9179	8.00	20.00	32.00

SHIVA'S HEADBAND
TITLE	LABEL & NO.	GOOD	VERY GOOD	NEAR MINT
COMING TO A HEAD	Armadillo no #	6.00	9.00	12.00
TAKE ME TO THE MOUNTAINS	Capitol (S) ST 538	4.50	6.75	9.00

SHOCKING BLUE
TITLE	LABEL & NO.	GOOD	VERY GOOD	NEAR MINT
SHOCKING BLUE	Colosssus (S) CS 1000	3.00	4.50	6.00

SHONDELL, Troy
TITLE	LABEL & NO.	GOOD	VERY GOOD	NEAR MINT
MANY SIDES OF TROY SHONDELL	Everest (M) BR 5206	3.50	7.00	10.50
MANY SIDES OF TROY SHONDELL	Everest (S) SD 1206	4.50	9.00	12.50

SHONDELLS
TITLE	LABEL & NO.	GOOD	VERY GOOD	NEAR MINT
SHONDELLS AT THE SATURDAY HOP	La Louisiane (M) LL 109	6.00	15.00	24.00

SHOOT
TITLE	LABEL & NO.	GOOD	VERY GOOD	NEAR MINT
ON THE FRONTIER	EMI (S) SMAS 11229	3.00	4.50	6.00

(M) Mono (S) Stereo (EP) Extended Play (Q) Quad (RI) Re-issued

TITLE	LABEL & NO.	GOOD	VERY GOOD	NEAR MINT
SHORE, Kurt & Jim Stanton				
DIALOGUE	DM (M) 68425	4.00	6.00	8.00
SHORTY				
SHORTY	Epic (S) BN 26563	4.00	6.00	8.00
SHOTGUNS				
30 DANCE HITS	Wyncote (M) W 9094	2.00	4.00	6.00
30 DANCE HITS	Wyncote (S) WS 9094	2.50	5.00	7.50
SICKNIKS				
SICK #2	Amy (M) 2	4.00	8.00	12.00
SIDEKICKS				
SIDEKICKS FIRST ALBUM FOR YOU	RCA (M) LPM 3712	3.00	4.50	6.00
SIDEKICKS FIRST ALBUM FOR YOU	RCA (S) LSP 3712	3.50	5.25	7.00
SIDEWINDERS				
SIDEWINDERS	RCA (S) LSP 4696	5.00	7.50	10.00
SIGLER, Bunny				
KEEP SMILIN'	Philadelphia Int'l (S) KZ-33249	2.50	3.75	5.00
LET THE GOOD TIMES ROLL	Parkway (M) P 50,000	3.00	4.50	6.00
LET THE GOOD TIMES ROLL	Parkway (S) PS 50,000	4.00	6.00	8.00
THAT'S HOW LONG I'LL BE LOVING YOU	Philadelphia Int'l (S) KZ-32859	2.50	3.75	5.00
SILHOUETTES				
GET A JOB	Goodway (M) GLP 100	8.00	16.00	24.00

TITLE	LABEL & NO.	GOOD	VERY GOOD	NEAR MINT
SILHOUETTES				
CONVERSATIONS WITH THE SILOUETTES	Segue (M) SEG 1001	2.50	3.75	5.00
SILK				
SMOOTH AS RAW SILK	ABC (S) ABCS 694	3.00	4.50	6.00
SILKIE				
YOU'VE GOT TO HIDE YOUR LOVE AWAY	Fontana (M) MGF 27548	3.00	6.00	9.00
YOU'VE GOT TO HIDE YOUR LOVE AWAY	Fontana (S) SRF 67548	4.00	8.00	12.00
SILLY SURFERS				
SOUNDS OF SILLY SURFERS	Mercury (S) SR 60977	4.00	8.00	12.00
SILVER APPLES				
CONTACT	Kapp (S) KS 3584	3.00	4.00	6.00
SILVER APPLES	Kapp (S) KS 3562	3.00	4.00	6.00
SILVER CONVENTION				
GOLDEN GIRLS	Midsong Int'l (S) BKL1-2296	2.50	3.75	5.00
LOVE IN A SLEEPER	Midsong Int'l (S) 3038	2.00	3.00	4.00
MADHOUSE	Midland Int'l (S) BKL1-1824	2.50	3.75	5.00
SAVE ME	Midland Int'l (S) BKL1-1129	2.50	3.75	5.00
SILVER CONVENTION	Midland Int'l (S) BKL1-1369	2.50	3.75	5.00
SILVERHEAD				
SILVERHEAD	Signpost (S) SP 8407	3.00	4.00	6.00
SILVERHEAD	MCA (S) 306	2.50	3.75	5.00
SIXTEEN AND SAVAGE	MCA (S) 391	2.50	3.75	5.00
SILVER METRE				
SILVER METRE	National General (M) NG 2000	4.00	6.00	8.00
SIMMONS, Gene				
JUMPIN' GENE SIMMONS	Hi (M) HL 12018	3.00	6.00	9.00
JUMPIN' GENE SIMMONS	Hi (S) SHL 32018	4.00	8.00	12.00
SIMMONS, Jeff				
LUCILLE HAS MESSED MY MIND UP	Straight (S) STS 1057	4.00	6.00	8.00

(M) Mono (S) Stereo (EP) Extended Play (Q) Quad (RI) Re-issued

TITLE	LABEL & NO.	GOOD	VERY GOOD	NEAR MINT
SIMON, Carly				
ANTICIPATION	Elektra (S) 75016	3.00	4.50	6.00
BEST OF CARLY SIMON	Elektra 7E-1048	2.00	3.00	4.00
BOYS IN THE TREES	Elektra (S) 6E-128	2.00	3.00	4.00
CARLY SIMON	Elektra 74082	3.00	4.50	6.00
CARLY SIMON	Elektra (Q) EQ-4082	2.50	3.75	5.00
HOTCAKES	Elektra 7E-1002	2.00	3.00	4.00
NO SECRETS	Elektra (Q) EQ-5049	2.50	3.75	5.00
NO SECRETS	Elektra (S) 75049	2.50	3.75	5.00
PLAYING POSSUM	Elektra 7E-1033	2.00	3.00	4.00
SIMON, Joe				
CHOKIN' KIND	Sound Stage (M) SSS15006	2.00	3.00	4.00
CHOKIN' KIND BETTER THAN EVER	Sound Stage 7 (S) BZ-33879	2.50	3.75	5.00
DROWNING IN THE SEA OF LOVE	Spring (M) 5702	2.00	3.00	4.00
GET DOWN, GET DOWN	Spring (S) 6706	2.50	3.75	5.00
JOE SIMON'S GREATEST HITS	Sound Stage 7 (S) B-2663	2.00	3.00	4.00
MOOD, HEART, AND SOUL	Spring (S) SPR 6702	2.50	3.75	5.00
MY SAD SONGS	Sound Stage 7 (M) 15004	2.00	3.00	4.00
POWER OF JOE SIMON	Spring (S) 5704	2.00	3.00	4.00
SIMON COUNTRY	Spring (M) 5705	2.00	3.00	4.00
SOUNDS OF SIMON	Spring (M) SPR 4701	2.50	3.75	5.00
TODAY	Spring (M) SP 1 6710	2.50	3.75	5.00
WORLD OF JOE SIMON	Sound Stage 7 (M) KZG 32536	2.00	3.00	4.00
SIMON, Paul				
GREATEST HITS, ETC	Columbia (S) JC 35032	2.00	3.00	4.00
LIVE RHYMIN'	Columbia (S) PC32855	2.25	3.50	4.50
PAUL SIMON	Columbia (S) KC30750	2.00	3.00	4.00
PAUL SIMON	Columbia (Q) CQ-30750	2.50	3.75	5.00
STILL CRAZY AFTER ALL THESE YEARS	Columbia (S) PC 33540	2.00	3.00	4.00
STILL CRAZY AFTER ALL THESE YEARS	Columbia (Q) PCQ-33540	2.50	3.75	5.00
THERE GOES RHYMIN' SIMON	Columbia (S) KC32280	2.00	3.00	4.00
SIMON AND GARFUNKEL				
BOOKENDS	Columbia (S) KCS 9529	2.50	3.75	5.00
BRIDGE OVER TROUBLED WATER	Columbia (S) CS 9914	2.50	3.75	5.00
BRIDGE OVER TROUBLED WATER	Columbia (Q) CQ 30995	2.50	3.75	5.00
HIT SOUNDS OF SIMON & GARFUNKEL	Pickwick (S) 3059	3.50	5.25	7.00
(Simon & Garfunkel were known as "Tom & Jerry" on the "Big" label. This album is a re-issue of material originally on the "Big" label.)				
PARSLEY, SAGE, ROSEMARY & THYME	Columbia (M) CL 2563	3.00	4.50	6.00
PARSLEY, SAGE, ROSEMARY & THYME	Columbia (S) CS 9363	2.50	3.75	5.00
SIMON & GARFUNKEL	Sears (S) 435	4.00	6.00	8.00
(Another re-issue of "Big" label material)				
SIMON & GARFUNKEL'S GREATEST HITS	Columbia (S) KC 31350	2.00	3.00	4.00
SOUNDS OF SILENCE	Columbia (M) CL 2469	3.00	4.50	6.00
SOUNDS OF SILENCE	Columbia (S) CS 9269	2.50	3.75	5.00
WEDNESDAY MORNING, 3 A.M.	Columbia (M) CL 2249	3.00	4.50	6.00
WEDNESDAY MORNING, 3 A.M.	Columbia (S) CS 9049	2.50	3.75	5.00
SIMON SISTERS (Lucy & Carly)				
SIMON SISTERS	Kapp (M) KL 1359	4.50	6.75	9.00
SIMON SISTERS SING FOR CHILDREN	Columbia (S) CR-21539	4.00	6.00	8.00
SIMS, Frankie Lee				
LUCY MAE BLUES	Specialty (S) SPS 2124	4.00	6.00	8.00
SIN SAY SHUNS				
I'LL BE THERE	Venett (M) V 940	2.50	5.00	7.50
I'LL BE THERE	Venett (S) VS 940	3.00	6.00	9.00
SINATRA, Frank				
ADVENTURES OF THE HEART	Columbia (M) CL 953	2.50	3.75	5.00
ADVENTURES OF THE HEART	Columbia (EP) B 9531	1.00	1.50	2.00
ADVENTURES OF THE HEART	Columbia (EP) B 9532	1.00	1.50	2.00
ADVENTURES OF THE HEART	Columbia (EP) B 9533	1.00	1.50	2.00
CAROUSEL	Columbia (EP) B 1620	1.00	1.50	2.00
CHRISTMAS DREAMING	Columbia (M) CL 1032	2.50	3.75	5.00
CHRISTMAS SONGS BY SINATRA (10")	Columbia (M) CL 6019	2.50	6.25	10.00
CHRISTMAS WITH SINATRA	Columbia (M) CL 2542	2.50	3.75	5.00
CLOSE TO YOU	Capitol (M) W 789	2.50	3.75	5.00
CLOSE TO YOU	Capitol (EP) EAP 1-789	1.00	1.50	2.00
CLOSE TO YOU	Capitol (EP) EAP 2-789	1.00	1.50	2.00
CLOSE TO YOU	Capitol (EP) EAP 3-789	1.00	1.50	2.00
CLOSE TO YOU	Capitol (EP) EAP 4-789	1.00	1.50	2.00
COME FLY WITH ME	Capitol (M) W 920	2.50	3.75	5.00
COME FLY WITH ME	Capitol (EP) EAP 1-920	1.00	1.50	2.00
COME FLY WITH ME	Capitol (EP) EAP 2-920	1.00	1.50	2.00
COME FLY WITH ME	Capitol (EP) EAP 4-920	1.00	1.50	2.00
DEDICATED TO YOU (10")	Columbia (M) CL 6096	3.00	7.50	12.00
DEDICATED TO YOU	Columbia (EP) B 197	1.00	1.50	2.00
FABULOUS FRANKIE	RCA (M) LPT 3063	2.50	3.75	5.00
FABULOUS FRANKIE	RCA (EP) EPBT 3063	1.00	1.50	2.00
FRANKIE	Columbia (M) CL 606	2.50	3.75	5.00
FRANKIE	Columbia (EP) B 1984	1.00	1.50	2.00
FRANKIE & TOMMY	RCA (M) LPM 1569	2.50	3.75	5.00
FRANKIE & TOMMY	RCA (EP) EPA 5014	1.00	1.50	2.00
FRANKLY SENTIMENTAL SINATRA (10")	Columbia (M) CL 6059	3.00	7.50	12.00
FRANK SINATRA	Columbia (EP) B 2515	1.00	1.50	2.00
FRANK SINATRA	Columbia (EP) B 2516	1.00	1.50	2.00
FRANK SINATRA	Columbia (EP) B 2517	1.00	1.50	2.00
FRANK SINATRA	Columbia (EP) B 2559	1.00	1.50	2.00
FRANK SINATRA	Columbia (EP) B 2589	1.00	1.50	2.00
FRANK SINATRA	Capitol (EP) EAP 1013	1.00	1.50	2.00

TITLE	LABEL & NO.	GOOD	VERY GOOD	NEAR MINT
FRANK SINATRA SINGS FOR ONLY THE LONELY	Capitol (M) W 1053	2.50	3.75	5.00
FRANK SINATRA SINGS FOR ONLY THE LONELY	Capitol (EP) EAP 1-1053	1.00	1.50	2.00
FRANK SINATRA STORY, THE	Columbia (M) C2L 6	3.00	4.50	6.00
FRANK SINATRA WITH HARRY JAMES & PEARL BAILEY	Columbia (EP) B 2542	1.00	1.50	2.00
FRANK SINATRA WITH KEN LANE SINGERS	Columbia (EP) B 2564	1.00	1.50	2.00
GET HAPPY	Columbia (M) CL 2521	2.50	3.75	5.00
HEY JEALOUS LOVER	Capitol (EP) EAP 1-800	1.00	1.50	2.00
IN THE WEE SMALL HOURS	Capitol (M) W 581	2.50	3.75	5.00
IN THE WEE SMALL HOURS	Capitol (EP) EAP 1-581	1.00	1.50	2.00
IN THE WEE SMALL HOURS	Capitol (EP) EAP 2-581	1.00	1.50	2.00
IN THE WEE SMALL HOURS	Capitol (EP) EAP 3-581	1.00	1.50	2.00
IN THE WEE SMALL HOURS	Capitol (EP) EAP 4-581	1.00	1.50	2.00
I'VE GOT A CRUSH ON YOU (10")	Columbia (M) CL 6290	2.50	6.25	10.00
I'VE GOT A CRUSH ON YOU	Columbia (M) CL 2539	2.50	3.75	5.00
I'VE GOT A CRUSH ON YOU	Columbia (EP) B 419	1.00	1.50	2.00
A JOLLY CHRISTMAS	Capitol (M) W 894	2.50	3.75	5.00
A JOLLY CHRISTMAS	Capitol (EP) EAP 1-894	1.00	1.50	2.00
A JOLLY CHRISTMAS	Capitol (EP) EAP 2-894	1.00	1.50	2.00
A JOLLY CHRISTMAS	Capitol (EP) EAP 3-894	1.00	1.50	2.00
KING AND I HITS, THE	Columbia (M) B 2109	1.00	1.50	2.00
MELODY OF LOVE	Capitol (EP) EAP 1-590	1.00	1.50	2.00
NEW ORLEANS (10")	Columbia (M) CL 6268	3.00	7.50	10.00
NEW ORLEANS	Columbia (EP) B 342	1.00	1.50	2.00
OUR TOWN	Capitol (EP) EAP 1-673	1.00	1.50	2.00
PUT YOUR DREAMS AWAY	Columbia (M) CL 1136	2.50	3.75	5.00
SESSION WITH SINATRA	Capitol (EP) EAP 1-629	1.00	1.50	2.00
SINATRA SINGS BERLIN	Columbia (EP) B 1524	1.00	1.50	2.00
SINATRA SINGS GERSHWIN	Columbia (EP) B 1673	1.00	1.50	2.00
SINATRA SINGS KERN	Columbia (EP) B 1702	1.00	1.50	2.00
SINATRA SINGS PORTER	Columbia (EP) B 1815	1.00	1.50	2.00
SINATRA SINGS RODGERS & HART	Columbia (EP) B 1872	1.00	1.50	2.00
SING AND DANCE WITH SINATRA (10")	Columbia (M) CL 6143	3.00	7.50	10.00
SING AND DANCE WITH SINATRA	Columbia (EP) B 218	1.00	1.50	2.00
SONGS BY SINATRA, Vol. 1 (10")	Columbia (M) CL 6087	3.00	7.50	12.00
SONGS FOR SWINGIN' LOVERS	Capitol (M) W 653	2.50	3.75	5.00
SONGS FOR SWINGIN' LOVERS	Capitol (EP) EAP 1-653	1.00	1.50	2.00
SONGS FOR SWINGIN' LOVERS	Capitol (EP) EAP 2-653	1.00	1.50	2.00
SONGS FOR SWINGIN' LOVERS	Capitol (EP) EAP 3-653	1.00	1.50	2.00
SONGS FOR SWINGIN' LOVERS	Capitol (EP) EAP 4-653	1.00	1.50	2.00
SONGS FOR YOUNG LOVERS	Capitol (M) W 587	2.50	3.75	5.00
SONGS FOR YOUNG LOVERS	Capitol (EP) EAP 1-587	1.00	1.50	2.00
SONGS FOR YOUNG LOVERS	Capitol (EP) EAP 2-587	1.00	1.50	2.00
SOUTH PACIFIC AND OKLAHOMA HITS	Columbia (EP) B 1608	1.00	1.50	2.00
SWING EASY	Capitol (M) W 528	2.50	3.75	5.00
SWING EASY	Capitol (EP) EAP 1-528	1.00	1.50	2.00
SWING EASY	Capitol (EP) EAP 2-528	1.00	1.50	2.00
A SWINGIN AFFAIR	Capitol (M) W803	2.50	3.75	5.00
A SWINGIN AFFAIR	Capitol (EP) EAP 1-803	1.00	1.50	2.00
A SWINGIN AFFAIR	Capitol (EP) EAP 2-803	1.00	1.50	2.00
A SWINGIN AFFAIR	Capitol (EP) EAP 3-803	1.00	1.50	2.00
A SWINGIN AFFAIR	Capitol (EP) EAP 4-803	1.00	1.50	2.00
THAT OLD FEELING	Columbia (M) CL 902	2.50	3.75	5.00
THAT OLD FEELING	Columbia (EP) B 9021	1.00	1.50	2.00
THAT OLD FEELING	Columbia (EP) B 9022	1.00	1.50	2.00
THAT OLD FEELING	Columbia (EP) B 9023	1.00	1.50	2.00
THIS IS SINATRA	Capitol (M) T768	2.50	3.75	5.00
THIS IS SINATRA VOL 2	Capitol (M) W 982	2.50	3.75	5.00
THIS IS SINATRA VOL 2	Capitol (EP) EAP 1-982	1.00	1.50	2.00
THIS IS SINATRA VOL 2	Capitol (EP) EAP 2-982	1.00	1.50	2.00
THIS IS SINATRA VOL 2	Capitol (EP) EAP 3-982	1.00	1.50	2.00
THIS IS SINATRA VOL 2	Capitol (EP) EAP 4-982	1.00	1.50	2.00
THREE COINS IN THE FOUNTAIN	Capitol (EP) EAP 1-542	1.00	1.50	2.00
TONE POEMS OF COLOR	Capitol W 735	2.50	3.75	5.00
VOICE OF SINATRA (10")	Columbia (M) CL 6001	3.00	7.50	12.00
VOICE OF SINATRA	Columbia (EP) B 7431	1.00	1.50	2.00
VOICE OF SINATRA	Columbia (EP) B 7432	1.00	1.50	2.00
VOICE OF SINATRA	Columbia (EP) B 7433	1.00	1.50	2.00
WE THREE	RCA (M) LPM 1632	2.50	3.75	5.00
WHERE ARE YOU	Capitol (M) W 855	2.50	3.75	5.00
WHERE ARE YOU	Capitol (EP) EAP 1-855	1.00	1.50	2.00
WHERE ARE YOU	Capitol (EP) EAP 2-855	1.00	1.50	2.00
WHERE ARE YOU	Capitol (EP) EAP 3-855	1.00	1.50	2.00
WHERE ARE YOU	Capitol (EP) EAP 4-855	1.00	1.50	2.00
WILDER MUSIC	Columbia (M) M 4271	2.50	3.75	5.00
YOUNG AT HEART	Capitol (M) H 9117	2.50	3.75	5.00
YOUNG AT HEART	Capitol (EP) EAP 1-9117	1.00	1.50	2.00
YOUNG AT HEART	Capitol (EP) EAP 1-510	1.00	1.50	2.00
YOUNG AT HEART	Capitol (EP) EAP 1-571	1.00	1.50	2.00
YOUNG AT HEART (10")	Columbia (M) CL 6339	3.00	7.50	12.00
YOUNG AT HEART	Columbia (EP) B 455	1.00	1.50	2.00

SINATRA, Nancy

TITLE	LABEL & NO.	GOOD	VERY GOOD	NEAR MINT
BOOTS	Reprise (M) R 6202	2.50	3.75	5.00
BOOTS	Reprise (S) RS 6202	2.50	3.75	5.00
COUNTRY MY WAY	Reprise (S) RS 6251	2.50	3.75	5.00
GREATEST HITS	Reprise (S) RS 6409	2.50	3.75	5.00
HOW DOES THAT GRAB YOU	Reprise (S) RS 6207	2.50	3.75	5.00
MOVIN WITH NANCY	Reprise (S) RS 6277	2.50	3.75	5.00
NANCY	Reprise (S) RS 6333	2.50	3.75	5.00
NANCY IN LONDON	Reprise (M) R 6221	2.50	3.75	5.00
NANCY IN LONDON	Reprise (S) RS 6221	2.50	3.75	5.00
SUGAR	Reprise (M) R 6239	2.50	3.75	5.00
SUGAR	Reprise (S) RS 6239	2.50	3.75	5.00
THIS IS NANCY SINATRA	RCA (S) VPS 6078	2.50	3.75	5.00
WOMAN	RCA (S) LSP 4774	2.50	3.75	5.00

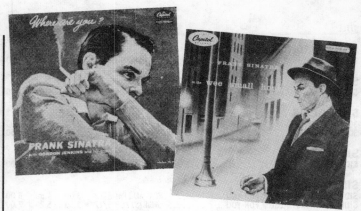

TITLE	LABEL & NO.	GOOD	VERY GOOD	NEAR MINT
SINATRA, Nancy & Lee Hazelwood				
NANCY & LEE	Reprise (S) 6273	2.50	3.75	5.00
SIR DOUGLAS QUINTET				
ALL AMERICAN HITS	Parrot (S) 71023	2.50	3.75	5.00
BEST OF SIR DOUGLAS QUINTET	Tribe (M) TR 37001	4.00	6.00	8.00
BEST OF SIR DOUGLAS QUINTET	Tribe (S) TRS 47001	5.00	7.50	10.00
HONKEY BLUES	Smash (S) SRS 67108	2.50	3.75	5.00
MENDICINO	Smash (S) SRS 67115	2.50	3.75	5.00
1 PLUS 1 PLUS 1 EQUALS 4	Philips (M) 600 344	2.75	3.75	5.50
ROUGH EDGES	Mercury (S) SRM 1 655	2.50	3.75	5.00
TOGETHER AFTER FIVE	Smash (S) SRS 67130	2.50	3.75	5.00
SIREN				
SIREN	Dandelion (S) D9-104	3.00	4.50	6.00
STRANGE LOCOMOTION	Elektra (S) EKS 74087	3.00	4.50	6.00
SIR LORD BALTIMORE				
SIR LORD BALTIMORE	Mercury (S) SR 61328	3.00	4.50	6.00
SKUNKS				
SKUNKS	Teentown (M)	7.00	14.00	21.00
SKY				
SAILORS DELIGHT	RCA (S) LSP 4514	3.00	4.50	6.00
SKY	RCA (S) 4457	2.50	3.75	5.00
SKYLINERS				
ONCE UPON A TIME	Kama Sutra (S) KSBS 2026	2.50	3.75	5.00
SINCE I DON'T HAVE YOU	Original Sound (M) OSR LPM 5010	4.00	8.00	12.00
SKY LINERS	Calico (M) LP 3000	12.00	24.00	36.00
SLADE				
AMBROSE SLADE	Fontana (S) SRF 67598	6.00	12.00	18.00
PLAY IT LOUD	Cotillion (S) SD 9035	5.00	7.50	10.00
SLADE ALIVE!	Polydor (S) PD 5508	3.00	4.50	6.00
SLADE IN FLAME	Warner Bros. (S) BS-2865	2.50	3.75	5.00
SLADEST	Reprise (S) 2173	3.00	4.50	6.00
SLAYED	Polydor (S) PD 5524	3.00	4.50	6.00
STOMP YOUR HANDS, CLAP YOUR FEET	Warner Bros. (S) BS-2770	2.50	3.75	5.00
SLEDGE, Percy				
BEST OF PERCY SLEDGE	Atlantic (S) SD 8180	3.00	4.50	6.00
BEST OF PERCY SLEDGE	Atlantic (S) SD 8210	3.00	4.50	6.00
I'LL BE YOUR EVERYTHING	Capricorn (S) 0147	2.00	3.00	4.00
PERCY SLEDGE WAY	Atlantic (M) 8146	2.50	3.75	5.00
PERCY SLEDGE WAY	Atlantic (S) SD 8146	3.00	4.50	6.00
WARM AND TENDER	Atlantic (S) SD 8132	3.00	4.50	6.00
WHEN A MAN LOVES A WOMAN	Atlantic (M) 8125	2.50	3.75	5.00
WHEN A MAN LOVES A WOMAN	Atlantic (S) SD 8125	3.00	4.50	6.00
SLEEPY HOLLOW				
SLEEPY HOLLOW	Family Productions (S) FPS 2708	4.50	6.75	9.00
SLICK, Grace				
CONSPICUOUS ONLY IN IT'S ABSENCE (& THE GREAT SOCIETY)	Columbia (S) CS 9624	5.00	7.50	10.00
MANHOLE	Grunt (S) BFL1-0347	3.50	5.25	7.00
Also see JEFFERSON AIRPLANE				
SLIM, Harmonica				
RETURN OF HARMONICA SLIM	Bluestime (M) 9005	2.50	4.00	5.00
SLOAN, P.F.				
MEASURE OF PLEASURE	Atco (S) SD 33-268	4.00	6.00	8.00
RAISED ON RECORDS	Mums (M) KZ 31260	2.50	3.75	5.00
SONGS OF OUR TIMES	Dunhill (S) D 50004	4.50	6.75	9.00
TWELVE MORE TIMES	Dunhill (M) D 50007	4.50	6.75	9.00

(M) Mono   (S) Stereo   (EP) Extended Play   (Q) Quad   (RI) Re-issued

TITLE	LABEL & NO.	GOOD	VERY GOOD	NEAR MINT

SLY & THE FAMILY STONE

TITLE	LABEL & NO.	GOOD	VERY GOOD	NEAR MINT
A WHOLE NEW THING	Epic (M) LN 24324	4.00	6.00	8.00
A WHOLE NEW THING	Epic (S) BN 26324	5.00	7.50	10.00
DANCE TO THE MUSIC	Epic (M) LN 24371	4.00	6.00	8.00
DANCE TO THE MUSIC	Epic (S) BN 26371	5.00	7.50	10.00
DANCE TO THE MUSIC (RI)	Epic (S) E 30334	2.00	3.00	4.00
GREATEST HITS	Epic (S) KE 30325	2.50	3.75	5.00
HIGH ON YOU	Epic (S) PE-33835	2.00	3.00	4.00
HIGH ON YOU	Epic (Q) PEQ-33835	2.50	3.75	5.00
LIFE	Epic (S) BN 26397	5.00	7.50	10.00
LIFE (RI)	Epic (S) E 30333	2.00	3.00	4.00
SMALL TALK	Epic (S) PE-32930	2.00	3.00	4.00
SMALL TALK	Epic (Q) PEQ-32930	2.50	3.75	5.00
STAND!	Epic (S) BN 26456	3.50	5.25	7.00
THERE'S A RIOT GOIN' ON	Epic (S) 30986	2.50	3.75	5.00
WHOLE NEW THING, A (RI)	Epic (S) E 30335	2.00	3.00	4.00

SMALL FACES

TITLE	LABEL & NO.	GOOD	VERY GOOD	NEAR MINT
ARCHETYPES: THE SMALL FACES	MGM (S) M3F 4955	2.50	3.75	5.00
EARLY FACES	Pride (S) 0001	3.00	4.50	6.00
HISTORY OF THE SMALL FACES	Pride (S) 0014	3.00	4.50	6.00
IMMEDIATE STORY	Sire (S) 3709	3.50	5.25	7.00
OGDEN'S NUT GONE FLAKE	Immediate (S) Z12 52 008	5.00	7.50	10.00
SMALL FACES—FIRST STEP	Warner Bros. (S) WS 1851	4.50	6.75	9.00
THERE ARE BUT FOUR SMALL FACES	Immediate (M) A12 52 001	5.00	7.50	10.00
THERE ARE BUT FOUR SMALL FACES	Immediate (S) Z12 52 002	5.00	7.50	10.00

Also see STEWART, Rod

SMALL, Millie

TITLE	LABEL & NO.	GOOD	VERY GOOD	NEAR MINT
MY BOY LOLLIPOP	Smash (M) MGS 27055	4.00	8.00	12.00
MY BOY LOLLIPOP	Smash (S) SRS 67055	5.00	10.00	15.00

SMITH

TITLE	LABEL & NO.	GOOD	VERY GOOD	NEAR MINT
A GROUP CALLED SMITH	Dunhill (S) DS 50056	2.50	3.75	5.00
MINUS-PLUS	Dunhill (S) DS 50081	2.50	3.75	5.00

SMITH, Bessie

TITLE	LABEL & NO.	GOOD	VERY GOOD	NEAR MINT
BESSIE SMITH STORY	Columbia (M) ML 4807	4.00	6.00	8.00
SMITH STORY VOL. 1	Columbia (M) ML 4807	4.00	6.00	8.00
SMITH STORY VOL. 1	Columbia (EP) G 5 403	2.00	3.00	4.00
SMITH STORY VOL. 2	Columbia (M) ML 4808	4.00	6.00	8.00
SMITH STORY VOL. 2	Columbia (EP) G 6 504	2.00	3.00	4.00
SMITH STORY VOL. 3	Columbia (M) ML 4809	4.00	6.00	8.00
SMITH STORY VOL. 3	Columbia (EP) G 7 505	2.00	3.00	4.00
SMITH STORY VOL. 4	Columbia (M) ML 4810	4.00	6.00	8.00
SMITH STORY VOL. 4	Columbia (EP) G 8 506	2.00	3.00	4.00

SMITH, Bob

TITLE	LABEL & NO.	GOOD	VERY GOOD	NEAR MINT
HOWDY DOODY AND YOU	RCA (EP) EYA 41	3.00	4.50	6.00
HOWDY DOODY'S MAGIC JUKE BOX	RCA (EP) EYA 42	3.00	4.50	6.00

SMITH, Carl

TITLE	LABEL & NO.	GOOD	VERY GOOD	NEAR MINT
CARL SMITH	Columbia (M) CL 2579	2.50	3.75	5.00
CARL SMITH	Columbia (EP) B 2810	1.00	1.50	2.00
CARL SMITH	Columbia (EP) B-2821	1.00	1.50	2.00
GIRL I LOVE	Hickory (S) H3G-4522	2.00	3.00	4.00
LET'S LIVE A LITTLE	Columbia (M) CL 1172	2.50	3.75	5.00
LET'S LIVE A LITTLE	Columbia (EP) B 11721	1.00	1.50	2.00
SENTIMENTAL SONGS	Columbia (M) HL 9023	2.50	3.75	5.00
SMITH'S THE NAME	Columbia (M) CL 1022	2.50	3.75	5.00
SMITH'S THE NAME	Columbia (EP) B 10221	1.00	1.50	2.00
SMITH'S THE NAME	Columbia (EP) B 10222	1.00	1.50	2.00
SMITH'S THE NAME	Columbia (EP) B 10223	1.00	1.50	2.00
SOFTLY AND TENDERLY	Columbia (M) HL 9026	2.50	3.75	5.00
SUNDAY DOWN SOUTH	Columbia (M) CL 959	2.50	3.75	5.00
WAY I LOSE MY MIND	Hickory (S) 4518	2.00	3.00	4.00

SMITH, Connie

TITLE	LABEL & NO.	GOOD	VERY GOOD	NEAR MINT
CONNIE SMITH	RCA (M) LPM 3341	3.00	4.50	6.00
CONNIE SMITH	RCA (S) LPS 3341	3.00	4.50	6.00
CONNIE SMITH NOW	RCA (S) APL1-0607	2.50	3.75	5.00
DREAM PAINTER	RCA (S) APL1-0188	2.50	3.75	5.00
GOT MY BABY ON MY MIND (RETITLED)	Columbia (S) KC 33375	2.00	3.00	4.00
I GOT A LOT OF HURTIN' DONE TODAY	Columbia (S) KC-33375	2.50	3.75	5.00
I NEVER KNEW (WHAT THAT SONG MEANT BEFORE)	Columbia (S) KC-33055	2.00	3.00	4.00
JOY TO THE WORLD	Columbia (S) C-33553	2.00	3.00	4.00
LADY NAMED SMITH	Columbia (S) KC-32185	2.50	3.75	5.00
LOVE IS THE LOOK YOU'RE LOOKING FOR	RCA (S) LSP-4840	2.50	3.75	5.00
NEW HORIZONS	Monument (S) MG 7624	2.00	3.00	4.00
THAT'S THE WAY LOVE GOES	Columbia (S) KC-32581	2.00	3.00	4.00

SMITH, George

TITLE	LABEL & NO.	GOOD	VERY GOOD	NEAR MINT
GEORGE SMITH OF THE BLUES	Bluesway (M) 6029	2.00	3.00	4.00
A TRIBUTE TO LITTLE WALKER	World Pacific (M) 21887	2.00	3.00	4.00

SMITH, George "Harmonica"

TITLE	LABEL & NO.	GOOD	VERY GOOD	NEAR MINT
ARKANSAS TRAP	Deram (M) 18059	4.00	6.00	8.00
BLUES WITH A FEELING	World Pacific (M) 21887	5.00	7.50	10.00

SMITH, Huey "Piano"

TITLE	LABEL & NO.	GOOD	VERY GOOD	NEAR MINT
FOR DANCING	Ace (M) LP 1015	12.00	30.00	48.00
HAVING A GOOD TIME	Ace (M) LP 1004	8.00	20.00	32.00

(M) Mono (S) Stereo (EP) Extended Play (Q) Quad (RI) Re-issued

HAVING FUN WITH HUEY "PIANO" SMITH	Ace (EP) 104	2.00	5.00	8.00
HUEY "PIANO" SMITH	Grand Prix (S) KS 418	6.00	12.00	18.00
ROCK N' ROLL REVIVAL	Ace (M) 2021	6.00	9.00	12.00
TWAS THE NIGHT BEFORE CHRISTMAS	Ace (M) LP 1027	8.00	20.00	32.00

SMITH, Patti

TITLE	LABEL & NO.	GOOD	VERY GOOD	NEAR MINT
EASTER	Arista (S) AS 4171	2.00	3.00	4.00
HORSES	Arista (S) 4066	2.00	3.00	4.00

SMITH, Ray

TITLE	LABEL & NO.	GOOD	VERY GOOD	NEAR MINT
RAY SMITH GREATEST HITS	Columbia (M) CL 1737	3.00	4.50	6.00
RAY SMITH GREATEST HITS	Columbia (S) CS 8737	3.00	4.50	6.00
TRAVELIN' WITH RAY	Judd (M) JLPA 701	15.00	37.50	60.00

SMITH, Ray and Patt Cupp

TITLE	LABEL & NO.	GOOD	VERY GOOD	NEAR MINT
RAY SMITH AND PATT CUPP	Crown (M) CLP 5364	5.00	10.00	15.00

SMITH, Roger

TITLE	LABEL & NO.	GOOD	VERY GOOD	NEAR MINT
BEACH ROMANCE	Warner Brothers (M) W-1305	3.00	6.00	9.00
BEACH ROMANCE	Warner Brothers (S) WS-1305	3.50	7.00	10.50

SMITH, Sylvia

TITLE	LABEL & NO.	GOOD	VERY GOOD	NEAR MINT
WOMAN OF THE WORLD	ABC (S) ABCD 876	2.00	3.00	4.00

SMITH, Tiger B.

TITLE	LABEL & NO.	GOOD	VERY GOOD	NEAR MINT
WE'RE THE TIGER BUNCH	Janus (S) JXS 7007	2.50	3.75	5.00

SMITH, Verdelle

TITLE	LABEL & NO.	GOOD	VERY GOOD	NEAR MINT
IN MY ROOM	Capitol (M) T-2476	2.50	3.75	5.00
IN MY ROOM	Capitol (S) ST-2476	2.50	3.75	5.00

SMITH, Warren

TITLE	LABEL & NO.	GOOD	VERY GOOD	NEAR MINT
FIRST COUNTRY COLLECTION OF WARREN SMITH	Liberty (M) LRP-3199	3.00	4.00	6.00
FIRST COUNTRY COLLECTION OF WARREN SMITH	Liberty (S) LST-7199	4.00	6.00	8.00

SMITH, Whispering

TITLE	LABEL & NO.	GOOD	VERY GOOD	NEAR MINT
WHISPERING SMITH	Excello (M) 8020	3.00	6.00	9.00

SMITHER, Chris

TITLE	LABEL & NO.	GOOD	VERY GOOD	NEAR MINT
DON'T IT DRAG ON	Poppy (S) 5704	2.00	3.00	4.00

SMOKE

TITLE	LABEL & NO.	GOOD	VERY GOOD	NEAR MINT
AT GEORGES COFFEE SHOP	Uni (M) 73065	4.00	6.00	8.00
SMOKE, THE	Sidewalk (S) ST 5912	3.00	4.50	6.00
SMOKE	Uni (M) 73052	3.50	5.25	7.00

SMOKESTACK LIGHTNIN'

TITLE	LABEL & NO.	GOOD	VERY GOOD	NEAR MINT
OFF THE WALL	Bell (M) 6026	4.50	6.75	9.00

SMOKEY AND HIS SISTER

TITLE	LABEL & NO.	GOOD	VERY GOOD	NEAR MINT
SMOKEY AND HIS SISTER	Warner Brothers (S) WS 1763	4.00	6.00	8.00

SMOKEY BABE

TITLE	LABEL & NO.	GOOD	VERY GOOD	NEAR MINT
BLUES OF SMOKEY BABE, THE	Bluesville (M) 1063	5.00	7.50	10.00
HOT BLUES	Arhoolie (M) 2019	2.00	3.00	4.00

SMOKEY HOGG

TITLE	LABEL & NO.	GOOD	VERY GOOD	NEAR MINT
SMOKEY HOGG	United (M) 7745	2.00	3.00	4.00

SMOTHERS BROTHERS

TITLE	LABEL & NO.	GOOD	VERY GOOD	NEAR MINT
AESOP'S FABLES THE SMOTHERS BROTHERS WAY	Mercury (M) MG 20989	3.50	5.25	7.00
AESOP'S FABLES THE SMOTHERS BROTHERS WAY	Mercury (S) SR 60989	3.00	4.50	6.00
CURB YOUR TONGUE, KNAVE!	Mercury (M) MG 20862	3.50	7.00	10.50
CURB YOUR TONGUE, KNAVE!	Mercury (S) SR 60862	3.00	6.00	9.00
GOLDEN HITS OF THE SMOTHERS BROTHERS	Mercury (M) MG 21089	3.50	5.25	7.00
GOLDEN HITS OF THE SMOTHERS BROTHERS	Mercury (S) SR 61089	3.00	4.50	6.00
IT MUST HAVE BEEN SOMETHING I SAID!	Mercury (M) MG 20904	3.50	7.00	10.50
IT MUST HAVE BEEN SOMETHING I SAID!	Mercury (S) SR 60904	3.00	6.00	9.00
MOM ALWAYS LIKED YOU BEST!	Mercury (M) MG 21051	3.50	5.25	7.00
MOM ALWAYS LIKED YOU BEST!	Mercury (S) SR 61051	3.00	4.50	6.00
SMOTHERS COMEDY BROTHERS HOUR	Mercury (S) SR 61193	3.00	4.50	6.00
SONGS AND COMEDY OF THE SMOTHERS BROTHERS AT THE PURPLE ONION	Mercury (M) MG 20611	3.50	7.00	10.50
SONGS AND COMEDY OF THE SMOTHERS BROTHERS AT THE PURPLE ONION	Mercury (S) SR 60611	3.00	6.00	9.00
THINK ETHNIC!	Mercury (M) MG 20777	3.50	7.00	10.50
THINK ETHNIC!	Mercury (S) SR 60777	3.00	6.00	9.00
TOUR DE FARCE AMERICAN HISTORY	Mercury (M) MG 20948	3.50	7.00	10.50
TOUR DE FARCE AMERICAN HISTORY	Mercury (S) SR 60948	3.00	6.00	9.00
TWO SIDES OF THE SMOTHERS BROTHERS	Mercury (M) MG 20675	3.50	7.00	10.50
TWO SIDES OF THE SMOTHERS BROTHERS	Mercury (S) SR 60675	3.00	6.00	9.00

SMOTHERS, Dick

TITLE	LABEL & NO.	GOOD	VERY GOOD	NEAR MINT
SATURDAY NIGHT AT THE WORLD	Mercury (M) MG 21134	2.50	3.75	5.00
SATURDAY NIGHT AT THE WORLD	Mercury (S) SR 61134	3.00	4.50	6.00

SMUBBS
TITLE	LABEL & NO.	GOOD	VERY GOOD	NEAR MINT
THIS IS THE END OF THE NIGHT	Monument (S) SLP 1 8112	2.00	3.00	4.00

SNELL, Tony
| MEDIEVAL AND LATTER DAY LAYS | ESP (S) 3004 | 3.50 | 5.25 | 7.00 |

SNOW, Hank
TITLE	LABEL & NO.	GOOD	VERY GOOD	NEAR MINT
BEST OF HANK SNOW, VOL. 2	RCA (S) LSP-4798	2.00	3.00	4.00
CANADIAN FAVORITES OF SNOW	RCA (EP) EPA 443	1.50	2.25	3.00
COUNTRY AND WESTERN JAMBOREE	RCA (M) LPM 1419	4.00	6.00	8.00
COUNTRY AND WESTERN JAMBOREE	RCA (EP) EPA 1-1419	1.50	2.25	3.00
COUNTRY AND WESTERN JAMBOREE	RCA (EP) EPA 2-1419	1.50	2.25	3.00
COUNTRY CHRISTMAS	RCA (EP) EPA 472	1.50	2.25	3.00
COUNTRY CLASSICS	RCA (M) LPM 1233	4.00	6.00	8.00
COUNTRY CLASSICS	RCA (EP) EPA 794	1.50	2.25	3.00
COUNTRY GUITAR	RCA (M) LPM 3267	4.00	6.00	8.00
COUNTRY GUITAR	RCA (EP) EPA 582	1.50	2.25	3.00
COUNTRY PICKIN	RCA (EP) EPA 546	1.50	2.25	3.00
GOD'S LITTLE CANDLES	RCA (EP) EPA 591	1.50	2.25	3.00
GOLDEN ROCKET	RCA (EP) EPA-5086	1.00	1.50	2.00
HANK SNOW COUNTRY GUITAR VOL. 2	RCA (M) LPM 1435	3.50	5.25	7.00
HANK SNOW COUNTRY GUITAR VOL. 2	RCA (EP) EPA 1-1435	1.50	2.25	3.00
HANK SNOW SINGS JIMMIE RODGERS SONGS	RCA (M) LPM-2043	2.50	3.75	5.00
HANK SNOW SINGS JIMMIE RODGERS SONGS	RCA (S) LSP-2043	2.50	3.75	5.00
HANK SNOW SINGS SACRED SONGS	RCA (M) LPM 1638	3.00	4.50	6.00
HANK SNOW SINGS SACRED SONGS	RCA (EP) EPA 4158	1.00	1.50	2.00
HELLO LOVE	RCA (S) APL1-0441	2.00	3.00	4.00
I'VE BEEN EVERYWHERE	RCA (M) LPM-2675	2.00	3.00	4.00
JUST KEEP A MOVIN	RCA (M) LPM 1113	4.00	6.00	8.00
OLD DOC BROWN	RCA (M) LPM 1156	4.00	6.00	8.00
RAILROADING SONGS	RCA (EP) EPA 310	1.50	2.25	3.00
SNOW FAVORITES	RCA (EP) EPA 295	1.50	2.25	3.00
SNOW SALUTES JIMMIE RODGERS	RCA (M) LPM 3131	4.00	6.00	8.00
SNOW SINGS	RCA (EP) EPA 3070	1.50	2.25	3.00
THAT'S YOU & ME	RCA (S) APL1-0608	2.00	3.00	4.00
THESE THINGS SHALL PASS	RCA (EP) EPA 503	1.50	2.25	3.00
THIS IS MY STORY	RCA (M) LPM-6014	4.50	6.75	9.00
THIS IS MY STORY	RCA (S) LSP-6014	4.00	6.00	8.00
WHEN TRAGEDY STRUCK	RCA (M) LPM-1861	2.50	3.75	5.00
YOU'RE EASY TO LOVE	RCA (S) APL1-0908	2.00	3.00	4.00

SNOW, Phoebe
IT LOOKS LIKE SNOW	Columbia (S) PC 34387	2.00	3.00	4.00
NEVER LETTING GO	Columbia (S) JC 34875	2.00	3.00	4.00
PHOEBE SNOW	Shelter (S) 2109	3.00	4.50	6.00
SECOND CHILDHOOD	Columbia (S) PC 33952	2.00	3.00	4.00
SECOND CHILDHOOD	Columbia (S) PCQ 33952	2.00	3.00	4.00

SOCIETY OF SEVEN
| HOW HAS YOUR LOVE LIFE BEEN | Silver Sword (M) 7012 | 3.00 | 4.50 | 6.00 |

SOD
| SOD | Decca (S) 75316 | 2.50 | 3.75 | 5.00 |

SOEUR SOURIRE
| SINGING NUN, THE | Philips (M) PCC-203 | 2.00 | 3.00 | 4.00 |
| SINGING NUN, THE | Philips (S) PCC-603 | 2.50 | 3.75 | 5.00 |

SOFT MACHINE
SIX	Columbia (S) KG-32260	2.50	3.75	5.00
SOFT MACHINE, THE	Probe (S) 4500	3.50	5.25	7.00
SOFT MACHINE SEVEN	Columbia (S) KC-32716	2.50	3.75	5.00

SOMMERS, Joanie
COME ALIVE	Columbia (M) CL 2495	2.00	4.00	6.00
COME ALIVE	Columbia (S) CS 9295	2.50	5.00	7.50
JOHNNY GET ANGRY	Warner Brothers (M) 1470	3.00	6.00	9.00
JOHNNY GET ANGRY	Warner Brothers (S) WS 1470	3.50	7.00	10.50
LET'S TALK ABOUT LOVE	Warner Brothers (M) 1474	3.00	6.00	9.00
LET'S TALK ABOUT LOVE	Warner Brothers (S) WS 1474	3.50	7.00	10.50
POSITIVELY THE MOST	Warner Brothers (M) W 1346	4.00	8.00	12.00

SONG
| SONG ALBUM | MGM (S) SE 4714 | 5.00 | 7.50 | 10.00 |

SONICS
EXPLOSIVES	Buckshot (M) BSR 001	4.00	6.00	8.00
HERE ARE THE SONICS	Etiquette (M) ET LP 024	8.00	12.00	16.00
INTRODUCING THE SONICS	Jerden (M) JRL 7007	7.00	10.50	14.00
INTRODUCING THE SONICS	Jerden (S) JRLS 7007	8.00	12.00	16.00
SONICS BOOM, THE	Etiquette (S) ET ALBS 027	7.00	10.50	14.00

SONNY AND CHER
ALL I EVER NEED IS YOU	Kapp (S) 3660	2.00	3.00	4.00
ALL I EVER NEED IS YOU (RI)	MCA (S) 2021	2.00	3.00	4.00
BABY DON'T GO	Reprise (M) 6177	5.00	7.50	10.00
BABY DON'T GO	Reprise (S) 6177	3.50	5.00	7.50
BABY DON'T GO	Reprise (EP) 6177	2.50	3.75	5.00
BEAT GOES ON, THE	Atco (S) SD 11000	2.50	3.75	5.00
BEST OF SONNY AND CHER	Atco (S) SD 33-219	4.00	6.00	8.00

(M) Mono (S) Stereo (EP) Extended Play (Q) Quad (RI) Re-issued

---

GOOD TIMES (Soundtrack)	Atco (S) SD 33 214	4.00	6.00	8.00
GREATEST HITS	MCA (S) 2117	2.00	3.00	4.00
IN CASE YOU'RE IN LOVE	Atco (S) SD 33-203	3.00	4.50	6.00
LIVE	Kapp (S) KS 3654	2.50	3.75	5.00
LOOK AT US	Atco (S) SD 33-177	4.00	6.00	8.00
SONNY AND CHER LIVE IN LAS VEGAS VOL. 2	MCA (S) 2-8004	2.00	3.00	4.00
TWO OF US, THE	Atco (S) SD 2-804	4.00	6.00	8.00
WONDROUS WORLD OF SONNY AND CHER	Atco (S) SD 33-183	3.00	4.50	6.00

SONS OF CHAMPLIN
LOOSEN UP NATURALLY	Capitol (S) 200	4.00	6.00	8.00
SONS, THE	Capitol (S) 332	3.00	4.50	6.00
SONS OF CHAMPLIN	Ariola America (S) ST-50002	2.50	3.75	5.00
WELCOME TO THE DANCE	Columbia (S) KC-32341	3.00	4.50	6.00

SONS OF THE PIONEERS
COOL WATER	RCA (M) LPM-2118	2.50	3.75	5.00
COOL WATER	RCA (S) LSP-2118	3.00	4.50	6.00
COOL WATER	RCA (EP) EPA-5116	1.00	1.50	2.00
COWBOY CLASSICS	RCA (M) LPM 3032	2.50	3.75	5.00
COWBOY CLASSICS	RCA (EP) P 168	1.00	1.50	2.00
COWBOY HYMNS AND SPIRITUALS	RCA (M) LPM 3095	2.00	3.00	4.00
COWBOY HYMNS AND SPIRITUALS	RCA (EP) P 229	1.00	1.50	2.00
FAVORITE COWBOY SONGS	RCA (M) LPM 1130	2.50	3.75	5.00
FAVORITE COWBOY SONGS	RCA (EP) EPA 650	1.00	1.50	2.00
FAVORITE COWBOY SONGS	RCA (EP) EPA 651	1.00	1.50	2.00
FAVORITE COWBOY SONGS	RCA (EP) EPA 652	1.00	1.50	2.00
GARDEN OF ROSES	RCA (EP) EPA 309	1.00	1.50	2.00
SONS OF THE PIONEERS SING FRED ROSE SONGS	RCA (EP) EPA 4218	1.00	1.50	2.00
WESTERN CLASSICS	RCA (M) LPM 3162	2.50	3.75	5.00
WESTERN FAVORITES	RCA (EP) EPA 422	1.00	1.50	2.00

SOPHOMORES
| SOPHOMORES, THE | Seeco (M) CELP 451 | 7.00 | 17.50 | 28.00 |

SOPWITH CAMEL
MIRACULOUS HUMP RETURNS FROM THE MOON	Reprise (S) MS 2108	2.50	3.75	5.00
SOPWITH CAMEL, THE	Kama Sutra (M) KLP 8060	3.00	4.50	6.00
SOPWITH CAMEL, THE	Kama Sutra (S) KLPS 8060	4.00	6.00	8.00
SOPWITH CAMEL IN HELLO HELLO	Kama Sutra (S) KSBS 2063	3.00	4.50	6.00

SOUL, Jimmy
| IF YOU WANNA BE HAPPY | S.P.Q.R. (M) E 16001 | 4.00 | 8.00 | 12.00 |

SOUL, Jimmy & The Belmonts
| JIMMY SOUL AND THE BELMONTS | Spinorama (M) 125 | 3.00 | 6.00 | 9.00 |

SOUL CHILDREN
BEST OF TWO WORLDS	Stax (S) STS 2043	2.00	3.00	4.00
FRICTION	Stax (S) 5507	2.00	3.00	4.00
GENESIS	Stax (S) STS 3003	2.00	3.00	4.00
SOUL CHILDREN, THE	Stax (S) STS 2018	2.50	3.75	5.00

SOUL SISTERS
| I CAN'T STAND IT | Sue (M) LP 1022 | 4.00 | 8.00 | 12.00 |

SOUL SOCIETY
| SATISFACTION | Dot (S) 25842 | 2.50 | 3.75 | 5.00 |

SOUL STIRRERS
GOSPEL SOUL OF SAM COOKE AND THE SOUL STIRRERS	Specialty (S) SPS 2116	4.00	6.00	8.00
GOSPEL SOUL OF SAM COOKE AND THE SOUL STIRRERS VOL. 2	Specialty (S) SPS 2128	4.00	6.00	8.00
SOUL STIRRERS FEATURING SAM COOKE	Specialty (M) SP 2106	4.00	6.00	8.00
THAT'S HEAVEN TO ME	Specialty (S) SPS 2146	4.00	6.00	8.00

SOUL SURVIVORS
| SOUL SURVIVORS | TSOP (S) KZ-33186 | 2.50 | 3.75 | 5.00 |
| WHEN THE WHISTLE BLOWS ANYTHING GOES WITH THE SOUL SURVIVORS | Crimson (M) LP 502 | 3.50 | 5.25 | 7.00 |

SOUNDS OF MODIFICATION
| SOUNDS OF MODIFICATION | Jubilee (S) JGS 8013 | 2.00 | 3.00 | 4.00 |

SOUNDS ORCHESTRAL
CAST YOUR FATE TO THE WIND	Parkway (M) 7046	3.00	4.50	6.00
IMPRESSIONS OF JAMES BOND	Parkway (M) 7050	2.50	3.75	5.00
IMPRESSIONS OF JAMES BOND	Parkway (S) 7050	3.00	4.50	6.00

SOUP
| SOUP ALBUM, THE | Big Tree (S) 2007 | 4.00 | 6.00 | 8.00 |

SOUTH, Joe
DON'T IT MAKE YOU WANT TO GO HOME	Capitol (S) ST 392	2.00	3.00	4.00
INTROSPECT	Capitol (S) 108	3.00	4.50	6.00
JOE SOUTH	Capitol (S) 845	2.00	3.00	4.00
JOE SOUTH GREATEST HITS	Capitol (S) 450	2.00	3.00	4.00
JOE SOUTH STORY, THE	Mine (S) MSG 1100	2.00	3.00	4.00

TITLE	LABEL & NO.	GOOD	VERY GOOD	NEAR MINT
LOOK INSIDE	Capitol (S) 11074	2.00	3.00	4.00
MIDNIGHT RAINBOWS	Island (S) 9328	2.00	3.00	4.00
WALKIN' SHOES	Mine (S) MSG 1100	2.00	3.00	4.00

SOUTH CENTRAL AVENUE MUNICIPAL BLUES BAND

TITLE	LABEL & NO.	GOOD	VERY GOOD	NEAR MINT
SOUL OF BONNY AND CLYDE	Blues Way (S) BLS 6018	2.00	3.00	4.00

SOUTHER, HILLMAN, FURAY BAND

TITLE	LABEL & NO.	GOOD	VERY GOOD	NEAR MINT
SOUTHER-HILLMAN-FURAY BAND	Asylum (S) 7E-1006	2.00	3.00	4.00
TROUBLE IN PARADISE	Asylum (S) 7E-1036	2.00	3.00	4.00

SOUTH 40

TITLE	LABEL & NO.	GOOD	VERY GOOD	NEAR MINT
SOUTH 40 LIVE AT THE SOMEPLACE ELSE	Metrobeat (S) MBS 1000	8.00	12.00	16.00

SOUTHWEST F.O.B. (England Dan & John Ford Coley)

TITLE	LABEL & NO.	GOOD	VERY GOOD	NEAR MINT
SMELL OF INCENSE	Hip (S) HIS 7001	6.00	12.00	18.00

SOUTHWIND

TITLE	LABEL & NO.	GOOD	VERY GOOD	NEAR MINT
READY TO RIDE	Blue Thumb (S) BTS 13	4.00	6.00	8.00
SOUTHWIND	Venture (S) VTS 4002	4.00	6.00	8.00
WHAT A PLACE TO LAND	Blue Thumb (S) BTS 26	3.00	4.50	6.00

SOUVENIRS

TITLE	LABEL & NO.	GOOD	VERY GOOD	NEAR MINT
EVERYBODY'S DOIN' IT	Reprise (M) R 6027	2.50	3.75	5.00

SOXX, Bob B & The Blue Jeans

TITLE	LABEL & NO.	GOOD	VERY GOOD	NEAR MINT
ZIP A DEE DOO DAH	Philles (M) PHLP 4002	6.00	12.00	18.00

SPACE ARK

TITLE	LABEL & NO.	GOOD	VERY GOOD	NEAR MINT
SPACE ARK	Color World (M) CW 1001	5.00	7.50	10.00

SPANA, Lucille

TITLE	LABEL & NO.	GOOD	VERY GOOD	NEAR MINT
BEFORE I GO	Bluesway (M) 6070	2.00	3.00	4.00

SPANIELS

TITLE	LABEL & NO.	GOOD	VERY GOOD	NEAR MINT
GOODNITE, IT'S TIME TO GO	Vee Jay (M) LP 1002	8.00	20.00	32.00
HITS OF THE SPANIELS	Up Front (M) UPF 131	3.00	4.50	6.00
SPANIELS, THE	Vee Jay (M) LP 1024	8.00	20.00	32.00
SPANIELS	Lost Nite (M) LP 137	7.00	10.50	14.00

SPANKY AND OUR GANG

TITLE	LABEL & NO.	GOOD	VERY GOOD	NEAR MINT
CHANGE	Epic (S) PE 33580	3.00	4.50	6.00
LIKE TO GET TO KNOW YOU	Mercury (S) SR 61161	2.50	3.75	5.00
SPANKY AND OUR GANG	Mercury (M) MG 21124	2.00	3.00	4.00
SPANKY AND OUR GANG	Mercury (S) SR 61124	2.50	3.75	5.00
SPANKY AND OUR GANG LIVE	Mercury (S) SR 61326	2.50	3.75	5.00
SPANKY'S GREATEST HITS	Mercury (S) SR 61227	3.00	4.50	6.00
WITHOUT RHYME OR REASON	Mercury (S) SR 61183	2.50	3.75	5.00

SPANN, Otis

TITLE	LABEL & NO.	GOOD	VERY GOOD	NEAR MINT
BLUES NEVER DIE, THE	Prestige (M) 7719	6.00	9.00	12.00
BLUES NEVER DIE	Prestige (M) 7391	5.00	7.50	10.00
BOTTOM OF THE BLUES, THE	Blues Way (M) BL 6013	4.00	6.00	8.00
BOTTOM OF THE BLUES, THE	Blues Way (S) BLS 6013	5.00	7.50	10.00
HEART LOADED WITH TROUBLE	Blues Way (S) BLS 6063	5.00	7.50	10.00
OTIS SPANN	Everest (M) 216	2.50	4.00	5.00
OTIS SPANN IS THE BLUES	Barnaby (M) Z 30246	3.00	4.50	6.00

SPARK PLUGS

TITLE	LABEL & NO.	GOOD	VERY GOOD	NEAR MINT
CRAZY BEAT	Sutton (S) SSU 322	4.50	9.00	13.50

SPARKS, Randy

TITLE	LABEL & NO.	GOOD	VERY GOOD	NEAR MINT
RANDY SPARKS	Verve (M) GV 2103	2.50	3.75	5.00
RANDY THREE SPARKS	Verve (M) MGV 2143	2.00	3.00	4.00
RANDY THREE SPARKS	Verve (S) MGVS6-2143	2.50	3.75	5.00

Also see NEW CHRISTY MINSTRELS

SPARROWS

TITLE	LABEL & NO.	GOOD	VERY GOOD	NEAR MINT
MERSEY SOUND, THE	Elkay (M) 3009	4.00	8.00	12.00

SPATS

TITLE	LABEL & NO.	GOOD	VERY GOOD	NEAR MINT
COOKIN WITH THE SPATS	ABC/Paramount (M) ABC 502	3.00	4.50	6.00
COOKIN WITH THE SPATS	ABC/Paramount (S) ABCS 502	3.50	5.25	7.00

SPEAR, Roger Ruskin

TITLE	LABEL & NO.	GOOD	VERY GOOD	NEAR MINT
ELECTRIC SHOCKS	United Artists (S) UA-LA 097	2.50	3.75	5.00

SPENCE, Alexander

TITLE	LABEL & NO.	GOOD	VERY GOOD	NEAR MINT
OAR	Columbia (S) CS 9831	5.00	7.50	10.00

SPENCER, Jeremy & The Children

TITLE	LABEL & NO.	GOOD	VERY GOOD	NEAR MINT
JEREMY SPENCER AND THE CHILDREN	Columbia (M) KC 31990	3.00	4.50	6.00

SPIDERS

TITLE	LABEL & NO.	GOOD	VERY GOOD	NEAR MINT
I DIDN'T WANNA DO IT	Imperial (M) LP 9140	8.00	20.00	32.00

(M) Mono (S) Stereo (EP) Extended Play (Q) Quad (RI) Re-issued

---

SPINNERS

TITLE	LABEL & NO.	GOOD	VERY GOOD	NEAR MINT
BEST OF THE SPINNERS	Atlantic (S) SD 19179	2.00	3.00	4.00
BEST OF THE SPINNERS	Motown 769	2.50	3.75	5.00
MIGHTY LOVE	Atlantic (S) SD 7296	2.00	3.00	4.00
NEW & IMPROVED	Atlantic (S) 18118	2.00	3.00	4.00
NEW & IMPROVED	Atlantic (Q) QD-18118	2.50	3.75	5.00
THE ORIGINAL SPINNERS	Motown (M) 639	4.00	6.00	8.00
THE ORIGINAL SPINNERS	Motown 639	5.00	7.50	10.00
PARTY-MY PAD	Time (M) 52092	3.50	7.00	10.50
PICK OF THE LITTER	Atlantic (S) 18141	2.00	3.00	4.00
SECOND TIME AROUND	V.I.P. 405	3.50	5.25	7.00
SPINNERS	Atlantic (S) 7256	2.50	3.75	5.00
SPINNERS	Atlantic (Q) QD-7256	2.50	3.75	5.00
SPINNERS LIVE, THE	Atlantic (S) SD 2-910	3.00	4.50	6.00

SPIRIT

TITLE	LABEL & NO.	GOOD	VERY GOOD	NEAR MINT
CLEAR SPIRIT	Ode (S) Z12 44016	4.00	6.00	8.00
FAMILY THAT PLAYS TOGETHER	Ode (S) Z12 44014	5.00	7.50	10.00
SON OF SPIRIT	Mercury (S) SRM-1-1053	2.50	3.75	5.00
SPIRIT	Epic (S) KEG-31457	2.50	3.75	5.00
SPIRIT	Ode (M) A12 44003	5.00	7.50	10.00
SPIRIT	Ode (S) Z 12 44004	6.00	9.00	12.00
SPIRIT OF '76	Mercury (S) SRM-2-804	3.00	4.50	6.00

Also see FERGUSON, Jay, Jo Jo Gunne

SPLINTER

TITLE	LABEL & NO.	GOOD	VERY GOOD	NEAR MINT
PLACE I LOVE	Dark Horse (S) 22001	4.00	6.00	8.00

Splinter

SPLIT LEVEL

TITLE	LABEL & NO.	GOOD	VERY GOOD	NEAR MINT
SPLIT LEVEL, THE	Dot (M)	4.00	6.00	8.00

SPOKESMEN

TITLE	LABEL & NO.	GOOD	VERY GOOD	NEAR MINT
DAWN OF CORRECTION	Decca (M) DL 74712	4.00	6.00	8.00

SPOOKY TOOTH

TITLE	LABEL & NO.	GOOD	VERY GOOD	NEAR MINT
CEREMONY	A&M (S) SP 4225	2.50	3.75	5.00
LAST PUFF, THE	A&M (S) SP 4266	2.50	3.75	5.00
MIRROR, THE	Island (S) 9292	2.00	3.00	4.00
SPOOKY TWO	A&M (S) SP 4194	2.50	3.75	5.00
TOBACCO ROAD	A&M (S) SP 4300	2.50	3.75	5.00
WITNESS	Island (S) SW 9337	2.00	3.00	4.00
WITNESS (RI)	Island (S) 9255	3.00	4.50	6.00
YOU BROKE MY HEART, SO I BUSTED YOUR JAW	A&M (S) SP 4385	2.50	3.75	5.00

SPREADEAGLE

TITLE	LABEL & NO.	GOOD	VERY GOOD	NEAR MINT
PIECE OF PAPER	Charisma (S) CAS 1055	4.00	6.00	8.00

SPRING

TITLE	LABEL & NO.	GOOD	VERY GOOD	NEAR MINT
SPRING	United Artists (S) UAS 5571	6.00	9.00	12.00

SPRINGFIELD, Dusty

TITLE	LABEL & NO.	GOOD	VERY GOOD	NEAR MINT
A BRAND NEW ME	Atlantic (S) SD 8249	3.00	4.50	6.00
CAMEO	Dunhill (S) DSX 50128	3.50	5.25	7.00
DUSTY	Philips (S) PHM 200-156	4.00	6.00	8.00
DUSTY	Philips (S) PHS 600-156	5.00	7.50	10.00
DUSTY IN MEMPHIS	Atlantic (S) SD 8214	3.00	4.50	6.00
DUSTY SPRINGFIELD'S GOLDEN HITS	Philips (M) PHM200-220	3.00	4.50	6.00
DUSTY SPRINGFIELD'S GOLDEN HITS	Philips (S) PHS 600-220	4.00	6.00	8.00
EVERYTHING'S COMING UP	Philips (M) PHM 303	3.00	4.50	6.00
LOOK OF LOVE, THE	Philips (M) PHM 200-256	3.00	4.50	6.00
LOOK OF LOVE, THE	Philips (S) PHS 600-256	4.00	6.00	8.00
OOOOOO WEEEE!!!	Philips (M) PHM 200-174	4.00	6.00	8.00
OOOOOO WEEEE!!!	Philips (S) PHS 600-174	5.00	7.50	10.00
STAY AWHILE/I ONLY WANT TO BE WITH YOU	Philips (M) PHM 200-133	4.00	6.00	8.00
STAY AWHILE/I ONLY WANT TO BE WITH YOU	Philips (S) PHS 600-133	5.00	7.50	10.00
STAY AWHILE/I ONLY WANT TO BE WITH YOU	Mercury/Wing (S) SRW 16353	2.50	3.75	5.00

TITLE	LABEL & NO.	GOOD	VERY GOOD	NEAR MINT
YOU DON'T HAVE TO SAY YOU LOVE ME	Philips (M) PHM 200-210	3.00	4.50	6.00
YOU DON'T HAVE TO SAY YOU LOVE ME	Philips (S) PHS 600-210	4.00	6.00	8.00

SPRINGFIELD, Rick
COMIC BOOK HEROES	Capitol (S) SMAS 11206	2.50	3.75	5.00
COMIC BOOK HEROES	Columbia (S) KC-32704	2.00	3.00	4.00
RICK SPRINGFIELD BEGINNINGS	Capitol (S) SMAS 11047	2.50	3.75	5.00

SPRINGFIELD REVIVAL
SPRINGFIELD REVIVAL	MGM (S) SE-4905	2.50	3.75	5.00

SPRINGFIELD RIFLE
SPRINGFIELD RIFLE	Burdette (S) ST 5159	7.00	10.50	14.00

SPRINGFIELDS
FOLK SONGS FROM THE HILLS	Philips (M) PHM 200-076	3.00	4.00	6.00
FOLK SONGS FROM THE HILLS	Philips (S) PHS 600-076	4.00	6.00	8.00
SILVER THREADS AND GOLDEN NEEDLES	Philips (M) PHM200-052	3.00	6.00	9.00
SILVER THREADS AND GOLDEN NEEDLES	Philips (S) PHS600-052	4.00	8.00	12.00

SPRINGSTEEN, Bruce
BORN TO RUN	Columbia (S) PC-33795	2.00	3.00	4.00
DARKNESS ON THE EDGE OF TOWN	Columbia (S) JC 35318	2.00	3.00	4.00
GREETINGS FROM ASBURY PARK, N.J.	Columbia (S) KC-31903	2.50	3.75	5.00
WILD, THE INNOCENT & STREET SHUFFLE, THE	Columbia (S) KC-32432	2.50	3.75	5.00

SRC
MILESTONES	Capitol (S) ST 134	6.00	9.00	12.00
SRC	Capitol (S) ST 2991	7.00	10.50	14.00
TRAVELERS TALE	Capitol (S) SKAO 273	7.00	10.50	14.00

STAFFORD, Jo
BALLAD OF THE BLUES	Columbia (M) CL-1332	3.00	4.50	6.00
BALLAD OF THE BLUES	Columbia (S) CS-8139	3.50	5.25	7.00
I'LL BE SEEING YOU	Columbia (M) CL-1262	3.00	4.50	6.00
I'LL BE SEEING YOU	Columbia (S) CS-8080	3.50	5.25	7.00
JO STAFFORD	Columbia (EP) B-2619	1.00	1.50	2.00
JO STAFFORD & FRANKIE LAINE	Columbia (EP) B-2629	1.00	1.50	2.00
JO'S GREATEST HITS	Columbia (M) CL 1228	3.00	4.50	6.00

STAFFORD, Terry
SAY, HAS ANYBODY SEEN MY SWEET GYPSY ROSE	Atlantic (S) SD 7282	2.50	3.75	5.00
SUSPICION!	Crusader (M) CLP 1001	4.00	8.00	12.00
SUSPICION!	Crusader (S) SC 1001	5.00	10.00	15.00

STAINED GLASS
AURORA	Capitol (S) ST 242	4.50	6.75	9.00
CRAZY HORSE ROADS	Capitol (S) ST 154	4.50	6.75	9.00

STAIRSTEPS
STAIRSTEPS	Buddah (S) BDS 5079	2.00	3.00	4.00

STAMPLEY, Joe
BILLY, GET ME A WOMAN	Epic (S) KE-33546	2.00	3.00	4.00
I'M STILL LOVING YOU	Dot (S) 26020	2.50	3.75	5.00
JOE STAMPLEY	Epic (S) KE-33356	2.00	3.00	4.00
JOE STAMPLEY'S GREATEST HITS	Dot (S) DOSD-2023	2.00	3.00	4.00
SOUL SONG	Dot (S) 26007	2.50	3.75	5.00
TAKE ME HOME TO SOMEWHERE	Dot (S) DOSD-2006	2.00	3.00	4.00

STANDELLS
DIRTY WATER	Tower (M) T 5027	5.00	7.50	10.00
DIRTY WATER	Tower (S) ST 5027	6.00	9.00	12.00
HOT ONES	Tower (M) T 5049	5.00	7.50	10.00
HOT ONES	Tower (S) ST 5049	6.00	9.00	12.00
LIVE AND OUT OF SIGHT	Sunset (M) SUM 1186	4.00	8.00	12.00
LIVE AND OUT OF SIGHT	Sunset (S) SUS 5136	4.50	9.00	13.50
STANDELLS IN PERSON AT P.J.'S	Liberty (M) LRP 3384	4.50	9.00	13.50
STANDELLS IN PERSON AT P.J.'S	Liberty (S) LST 7384	5.00	10.00	15.00
TRY IT	Tower (M) T 5098	5.00	7.50	10.00
TRY IT	Tower (S) ST 5098	6.00	9.00	12.00
WHY PICK ON ME	Tower (M) T 5044	5.00	7.50	10.00
WHY PICK ON ME	Tower (S) ST 5044	6.00	9.00	12.00

STANDLEY, Johnny
IT'S IN THE BOOK	Capitol (EP) EAP 1-697	3.00	4.50	6.00

STANLEY, Michael
MICHAEL STANLEY (With J. Walsh, T. Rundgren, & R. Derringer'	Tumbleweed (M) 106	4.00	6.00	8.00

STANLEY, Michael, Band
FRIENDS & LEGENDS	MCA (S) 372	2.00	3.00	4.00
LADIES' CHOICE	Epic (S) 33917	2.00	3.00	4.00
STAGE PASS	Epic (S) 34661	2.00	3.00	4.00
YOU BREAK IT, YOU BOUGHT IT	Epic (S) PE-33492	2.00	3.00	4.00

STAPLE SINGERS
BEALTITUDE: RESPECT YOURSELF	Stax (S) STS 3002	2.00	3.00	4.00

TITLE	LABEL & NO.	GOOD	VERY GOOD	NEAR MINT
BEST OF THE STAPLE SINGERS	Stax (S) 5523	2.00	3.00	4.00
BE WHAT YOU ARE	Stax (S) STS 3015	2.00	3.00	4.00
CITY IN THE SKY	Stax (S) 5515	2.00	3.00	4.00
FILET OF SOUL	Stax (S) 3023	2.00	3.00	4.00
FOR WHAT IT'S WORTH	Epic (M) LN 24332	2.00	3.00	4.00
FOR WHAT IT'S WORTH	Epic (S) BN 26332	2.00	3.00	4.00
GREAT DAY	Milestone (M) 47028	4.00	6.00	8.00
HAMMER AND NAILS	Riverside (M) 3501	5.00	7.50	10.00
SOUL FOLK IN ACTION	Stax (S) STS 2004	2.50	3.75	5.00
STAPLE SINGERS	Creed (S) 3042	2.50	3.75	5.00
STAPLE SWINGERS, THE	Stax (S) STS 2034	2.00	3.00	4.00
TELL IT LIKE IT IS	Harmony (S) KH-31775	2.00	3.00	4.00
USE WHAT YOU GOT	Fantasy (S) 9423	2.00	3.00	4.00
WE'LL GET OVER	Stax (S) STS 2016	2.00	3.00	4.00
WILL THE CIRCLE BE UNBROKEN	Vee Jay (M) LP 5008	4.50	6.75	9.00

STAPLES, Mavis
MAVIS STAPLES	Volt (S) VOS 6007	2.00	3.00	4.00
ONLY FOR THE LONELY	Volt (S) VOS 6010	2.00	3.00	4.00

STARDRIVE (Robert Mason)
INTERGALACTIC TROT	Elektra (S) 75058	2.50	3.75	5.00
INTERGALACTIC TROT	Elektra (Q) EQ-5058	3.00	4.50	6.00

STARFIRES
TEENBEAT A GO GO	La Brea (S) LS 8018	4.00	8.00	12.00

STARK NAKED
STARK NAKED	RCA (S) LSP 4592	2.00	3.00	4.00

STARR, Edwin
HELL UP IN HARLEM	Motown (S) 802	2.00	3.00	4.00
INVOLVED	Gordy (S) 956	2.00	3.00	4.00
SOUL MASTER	Gordy (S) 931	2.00	3.00	4.00
25 MILES	Gordy (S) 940	2.00	3.00	4.00
WAR AND PEACE	Gordy (S) GS 948	2.00	3.00	4.00

STARR, Kay
ALL STARR HITS	Capitol (M) T-1468	3.00	4.50	6.00
HITS OF KAY STARR	Capitol (M) T 415	4.00	6.00	8.00

STARR, Ringo
BAD BOY	Portrait (S) JR 35378	2.00	3.00	4.00
BEAUCOUPS OF BLUES	Apple (S) 3368	5.00	7.50	10.00
BEAUCOUPS OF BLUES	Apple (S) SMAS 3368	2.00	3.00	4.00
BLAST FROM YOUR PAST	Apple (S) SW 3422	2.00	3.00	4.00
GOODNIGHT VIENNA	Apple (S) SW 3417	2.00	3.00	4.00
RINGO	Apple (S) SW 3413	2.00	3.00	4.00
RINGO	Apple (S) SWAL-3413	4.00	6.00	8.00
RINGO IV	Atlantic (S) SD 19108	2.00	3.00	4.00
ROTOGRAVURE	Atlantic (S) SD 18193	2.00	3.00	4.00
SENTIMENTAL JOURNEY	Apple (S) 3365	5.00	7.50	10.00
SENTIMENTAL JOURNEY	Apple (S) SW3365	2.00	3.00	4.00

Also see BEATLES

STATLER BROTHERS
BED OF ROSE'S	Mercury (S) SR 61317	2.50	3.75	5.00
BEST OF THE STATLER BROS., THE	Mercury (S) SRM-1-1037	2.00	3.00	4.00
ENTERTAINERS... ON AND OFF THE RECORD	Mercury (S) SRM-1-5007	2.00	3.00	4.00
FLOWERS ON THE WALL	Columbia (M) CL-2449	2.50	3.75	5.00
FLOWERS ON THE WALL	Columbia (S) CS-9249	2.50	3.75	5.00
PICTURES OF MOMENTS TO REMEMBER	Mercury (S) SR 61349	2.50	3.75	5.00
SONS OF THE MOTHERLAND	Mercury (S) SRM-1-1019	2.00	3.00	4.00
STATLER BROS. SING (COUNTRY SYMPHONIES IN E MAJOR)	Mercury (S) 61374	2.50	3.75	5.00
THANK YOU WORLD	Mercury (S) SRM-1-707	2.00	3.00	4.00

STATON, Candi
CANDI	Warner Bros. (S) BS-2830	2.00	3.00	4.00
CANDI STATON	Fame (S) FAS 1800	2.00	3.00	4.00
STAND BY YOUR MAN	Fame (S) 4202	2.00	3.00	4.00

STATUS QUO
DOG OF TWO HEADS	Pye (M) 3301	3.00	4.50	6.00
HELLO!	A&M (S) SP 4408	3.00	4.50	6.00
HELLO! (RI)	A&M (S) 3615	2.00	3.00	4.00
MA KELLY'S GREASY SPOON	Janus (S) JLS 3018	3.00	4.50	6.00
MESSAGES FROM THE STATUS QUO	Cadet Concept (S) LPS 315	4.00	6.00	8.00
ON THE LEVEL	Capitol (S) ST-11381	2.50	3.75	5.00
PILEDRIVER	A&M (S) SP 4381	2.00	3.00	4.00
QUO	A&M (S) SP 3649	2.00	3.00	4.00

STAYMER, Hans, Band
HANS STAYMER BAND, THE	CSF (M) CSF S 1004	3.00	4.50	6.00

STEALERS WHEEL
FERGUSLIE PARK	A&M (S) 4419	2.00	3.00	4.00
RIGHT OR WRONG	A&M (S) 4517	2.00	3.00	4.00
STEALERS WHEEL	A&M (S) 4377	2.00	3.00	4.00

STEAM
STEAM	Mercury (S) SR 61254	3.00	4.50	6.00

(M) Mono (S) Stereo (EP) Extended Play (Q) Quad (RI) Re-issued

Ringo Starr

TITLE	LABEL & NO.	GOOD	VERY GOOD	NEAR MINT
STEAMHAMMER				
REFLECTION	Epic (S) BN 26490	4.00	6.00	8.00
STEELE, Tommy				
EVERYTHINGS COMING UP BROADWAY	Liberty (M) LRP 3426	4.00	6.00	8.00
EVERYTHINGS COMING UP BROADWAY	Liberty (S) LST 7426	5.00	7.50	10.00
ROCK AROUND THE WORLD (SONGS FROM THE FILM)	London (S) LL 1770 (M)	5.00	12.50	20.00
SIXPENNY MILLIONARE	Liberty (S) LST 7566	4.50	6.75	9.00
STEELEYE SPAN				
ALL AROUND MY HAT	Chrysalis (S) 1091	2.00	3.00	4.00
BELOW THE SALT	Chrysalis (S) 1008	2.00	3.00	4.00
PARCEL OF ROGUES	Chrysalis (S) 1046	2.00	3.00	4.00
STEELY DAN				
AJA	ABC (S) 1006	2.00	3.00	4.00
CAN'T BUY A THRILL	ABC 758	2.00	3.00	4.00
CAN'T BUY A THRILL	Command (Q) QD-40009	2.50	3.75	5.00
COUNTDOWN TO ECSTASY	ABC 779	2.00	3.00	4.00
COUNTDOWN TO ECSTASY	Command (Q) QD-40010	2.50	3.75	5.00
KATTY LIED	ABC 646	3.00	4.50	6.00
PRETZEL LOGIC	ABC 808	2.00	3.00	4.00
PRETZEL LOGIC	Command (Q) QD-40015	2.50	3.75	5.00
STEIN, Frankie & His Ghouls				
GHOUL MUSIC	Power (M) 340	3.00	4.50	6.00
MONSTER MELODIES	Power (S) S 341	3.00	4.50	6.00
MONSTER SOUNDS AND DANCE MUSIC	Power (M) 342	3.00	4.50	6.00
MONSTER SOUNDS AND DANCE MUSIC	Power (S) S 342	3.00	4.50	6.00
SHOCK! TERROR! FEAR!	Power (M) 339	3.00	4.50	6.00
STEINBERG, David				
BOOGA, BOOGA	Columbia (S) KC-32563	2.00	3.00	4.00
DISGUISED AS A NORMAL PERSON	Elektra (S) EKS 74065	3.00	4.50	6.00
GOODBYE TO THE 70's	Columbia (S) PC-33399	2.00	3.00	4.00
STEPHENS, Leigh				
RED WEATHER	Philips (S) PHS 600-294	5.00	7.50	10.00
STEPPENWOLF				
AT YOUR BIRTHDAY PARTY	Dunhill (S) 50053	3.00	4.50	6.00
EARLY STEPPENWOLF	Dunhill (S) 50060	3.00	4.50	6.00
FOR LADIES ONLY	Dunhill (S) 50110	3.00	4.50	6.00
HOUR OF THE WOLF	Epic PE-33583	3.00	4.50	6.00
MONSTER	Dunhill (S) 50066	3.00	4.50	6.00
SIXTEEN GREATEST HITS	Dunhill (S) 50135	2.50	3.75	5.00
16 GREAT PERFORMANCES	ABC 4011	2.50	3.75	5.00
SLOW FLUX	Mums PZ-33093	2.50	3.75	5.00
STEPPENWOLF	Dunhill (S) 50029	3.00	4.50	6.00
STEPPENWOLF GOLD— THEIR GREATEST HITS	Dunhill (S) 50099	3.00	4.50	6.00
STEPPENWOLF 'LIVE'	Dunhill 50075	3.00	4.50	6.00
STEPPENWOLF 1967-1972/REST IN PEACE	Dunhill (S) 50124	2.50	3.75	5.00
STEPPENWOLF 7	Dunhill (S 50090	3.00	4.50	6.00
STEPPENWOLF THE SECOND	Dunhill (S) 50037	3.00	4.50	6.00
STEVENS, April				
APRIL STEVENS	King (EP) EP 300	2.00	4.00	6.00
TEACH ME TIGER	Imperial (S) 9118	4.50	9.00	13.50
TORRID TUNES	Audio Lab (M) AL-1534	5.00	10.00	15.00
Also see TEMPO, Nino & April Stevens				
STEVENS, Cat				
BUDDHA & THE CHOCOLATE BOX	A&M (S) 3623	2.00	3.00	4.00
BUDDHA & THE CHOCOLATE BOX	A&M (Q) QU-53623	2.00	3.00	4.00
CAT STEVENS GREATEST HITS	A&M (S) 4519	2.00	3.00	4.00
CAT STEVENS' GREATEST HITS	A&M (Q) QU 54519	2.50	3.75	5.00
CATCH BULL AT FOUR	A&M (S) 4365	2.00	3.00	4.00
CATCH BULL AT FOUR	A&M (Q) QU54365	2.50	3.75	5.00
FOREIGNER	A&M (S) 4391	2.00	3.00	4.00
FOREIGNER	A&M (Q) QU-54391	2.00	3.00	4.00
IZITSO	A&M (S) 4702	2.00	3.00	4.00

(M) Mono (S) Stereo (EP) Extended Play (Q) Quad (RI) Re-issued

TITLE	LABEL & NO.	GOOD	VERY GOOD	NEAR MINT
MATTHEW AND SON/NEW MASTERS	Deram (S) 18005	4.00	6.00	8.00
MONA BONE JAKON	A&M (S) 4260	2.00	3.00	4.00
NUMBERS	A&M (S) 4555	2.00	3.00	4.00
TEA FOR THE TILLERMAN	A&M (S) 4280	2.00	3.00	4.00
TEA FOR THE TILLERMAN	A&M (Q) QU 54280	2.50	3.75	5.00
TEASER AND THE FIRECAT	A&M (S) 4313	2.00	3.00	4.00
TEASER AND THE FIRECAT	A&M (Q) QU 54313	2.50	3.75	5.00
VERY YOUNG AND EARLY SONGS	Deram (S) 18061	4.00	6.00	8.00
STEVENS, Connie				
CONCHETTA	Warner Brothers (M) W 1208	5.00	10.00	15.00
CONNIE STEVENS	Warner Brothers (M) W-1431	4.00	8.00	12.00
CONNIE STEVENS	Warner Brothers (S) WS-1431	5.00	10.00	15.00
CONNIE STEVENS (AS CRICKET)	Warner Brothers (M) W-1382	4.00	8.00	12.00
CONNIE STEVENS (AS CRICKET)	Warner Brothers (S) WS-1382	5.00	10.00	15.00
HANK WILLIAMS SONG BOOK	Warner Brothers (M) W-1460	3.50	7.00	10.50
HANK WILLIAMS SONG BOOK	Warner Brothers (S) WS-1460	4.50	9.00	13.50
STEVENS, Dodie				
DODIE STEVENS	Dot (M) DLP-3212	4.00	8.00	12.00
DODIE STEVENS	Dot (S) DLP-25212	5.00	10.00	15.00
OVER THE RAINBOW	Dot (M) DLP-3323	2.50	5.00	7.50
OVER THE RAINBOW	Dot (S) DLP-25323	3.50	7.00	10.50
PINK SHOELACES	Dot (M) DLP-3371	4.00	8.00	12.00
PINK SHOELACES	Dot (S) DLP-25371	5.00	10.00	15.00
STEVENS, Even				
EVEN STEVENS	Dakar (S) 76905	3.00	4.50	6.00
STEVENS, Ray				
AHAB THE ARAB	Mercury (M) MG 20732	3.00	6.00	9.00
AHAB THE ARAB	Mercury (S) SR 60732	4.00	8.00	12.00
BEST OF RAY STEVENS	Mercury (S) 61272	2.50	3.75	5.00
BEST OF RAY STEVENS	Mercury/Wing (S) 16377	2.00	3.00	4.00
BEST OF RAY STEVENS	Barnaby (S) 6018	2.00	3.00	4.00
BOOGITY, BOOGITY, BOOGITY	Barnaby (S) 6003	2.00	3.00	4.00
1837 SECONDS OF HUMOR	Mercury (M) MG-20732	4.00	8.00	12.00
1837 SECONDS OF HUMOR	Mercury (S) SR-60732	4.00	8.00	12.00
EVEN STEVENS	Monument (S) 18102	2.00	3.00	4.00
EVERYTHING IS BEAUTIFUL	Barnaby (S) 35005	2.00	3.00	4.00
GITARZAN	Monument (S) 18115	3.00	4.50	6.00
MISTY	Barnaby (S) 6012	2.00	3.00	4.00
NASHVILLE	Barnaby (S) 15007	2.00	3.00	4.00
1,837 SECONDS OF HUMOR (Original Title)	Mercury (M) MG 20732	6.00	12.00	18.00
RAY STEVENS	Barnaby (S) KZ-32139	2.00	3.00	4.00
RAY STEVEN'S GREATEST HITS	Barnaby (S) 5004	2.00	3.00	4.00
RAY STEVENS GREATEST HITS	Barnaby (Q) ZQ-30770	2.50	3.75	5.00
THIS IS RAY STEVENS	Mercury (S) MG20828	3.00	6.00	9.00
THIS IS RAY STEVENS	Mercury (S) SR 60828	4.00	8.00	12.00
TURN YOUR RADIO ON	Barnaby (S) 30809	2.00	3.00	4.00
UNREAL	Barnaby (S) 30092	2.00	3.00	4.00
STEWART, Al				
EARLY YEARS	Janus (S) 7026	3.50	5.25	7.00
MODERN TIMES	Janus (S) 7012	3.00	4.50	6.00
PAST, PRESENT & FUTURE	Janus (S) 3063	4.00	6.00	8.00
YEAR OF THE CAT	Janus (S) 7022	2.50	3.75	5.00
STEWART, Andy				
SCOTTISH SOLDIER, A	Warwick (M) W-2043	2.50	3.75	5.00
SCOTTISH SOLDIER, A	Warwick (S) WST-3043	2.50	3.75	5.00
STEWART, Billy				
CROSS MY HEART	Chess (S) CH 50059	3.00	4.50	6.00
I DO LOVE YOU	Chess (M) LP 1496	4.00	6.00	8.00
I DO LOVE YOU	Chess (S) LPS 1496	5.00	7.50	10.00
UNBELIEVABLE	Chess (M) LP 1499	4.00	6.00	8.00
UNBELIEVABLE	Chess (S) LPS 1499	5.00	7.50	10.00
STEWART, John				
CALIFORNIA BLOODLINES	Capitol (S) 203	5.00	7.50	10.00
CANNONS IN THE RAIN	RCA (S) LSP-4827	3.00	4.50	6.00
FIRE IN THE WIND	RSO (S) RS-1-3027	2.00	3.00	4.00
LONESOME PICKER RIDES AGAIN	Warner Brothers (S) 1948	2.50	3.75	5.00
PHOENIX CONCERTS	RCA (S) CPL2-0265	3.50	5.25	7.00
SIGNALS THROUGH THE GLASS	Capitol (S) SM-2975	3.00	4.50	6.00
WILLARD	Capitol ST-540	5.00	7.50	10.00
WINGLESS ANGELS	RCA APL1-0816	3.00	4.50	6.00
Also see KINGSTON TRIO				
STEWART, John & Scott Engel				
JOHN STEWART AND SCOTT ENGEL/I ONLY CAME TO DANCE WITH YOU	Tower (M) T 5026	4.00	6.00	8.00
STEWART, Rod				
ATLANTIC CROSSING	Warner Bros. (S) BS 2875	2.50	3.75	5.00
ATLANTIC CROSSING ('77 RI)	Warner Bros. BSK-3108	2.00	3.00	4.00
EVERY PICTURE TELLS A STORY	Mercury (S) SRM-1-609	3.00	4.50	6.00
FOOT LOOSE & FANCY FREE	Warner Bros. BSK 3092	2.00	3.00	4.00
GASOLINE ALLEY	Mercury 61264	3.50	5.25	7.00
NEVER A DULL MOMENT	Mercury SRM-1-646	3.00	4.50	6.00
ROD STEWART ALBUM, THE	Mercury (S) SR 61237	4.00	6.00	8.00
ROD STEWART & FACES LIVE	Mercury (S) SRM-1-697	3.50	5.25	7.00
(Shown as Rod Stewart & Faces)				

TITLE	LABEL & NO.	GOOD	VERY GOOD	NEAR MINT
SHOT OF RHYTHM AND BLUES, A	Private Stock (S) 2021	3.00	4.50	6.00
SING IT AGAIN ROD	Mercury SRM-1-680	3.00	4.50	6.00
SMILER	Mercury (S) SRM-1-1017	3.00	4.50	6.00

Also see FACES, PYTHON LEE JACKSON

STEWART, Sandy
SANDY STEWART (MY COLORING BOOK)	Colpix (M) CP 441	2.00	4.00	6.00
SANDY STEWART (MY COLORING BOOK)	Colpix (S) SCP 441	3.00	6.00	9.00

STIDHAM, Arbee
ARBEE STIDHAM	Bluesville (M) 1021	5.00	7.50	10.00
TIRED OF WANDERING	Prestige (M) BV-1021	4.00	8.00	12.00

STILL ROCK
STILL ROCK	Enterprise (S) ENS 1016	2.50	3.75	5.00

STILLS, Stephen
DOWN THE ROAD	Atlantic 7250	2.50	3.75	5.00
ILLEGAL STILLS	Columbia (S) PC 34148	2.00	3.00	4.00
MANASSAS	Atlantic 2-903	3.00	4.50	6.00
STEPHEN STILLS	Atlantic 7202	2.50	3.75	5.00
STEPHEN STILLS LIVE	Atlantic 18156	2.00	3.00	4.00
STEPEHN STILLS 2	Atlantic (S) 7206	2.50	3.75	5.00
STILLS	Columbia PC 33575	2.00	3.00	4.00
STILLS	Columbia (Q) PCQ 33575	2.00	3.00	4.00

Also see CROSBY, STILLS, NASH & YOUNG

STITES, Gary
LONELY FOR YOU	Carlton (M) LP 12/120	4.00	8.00	12.00
LONELY FOR YOU	Carlton (S) STLP 120	5.00	10.00	15.00

STOECKLEIN, Val
GREY LINE	Dot (M) DLP 25904	3.00	4.50	6.00

STOKES, Simon & The Night Hawks
INCREDIBLE SIMON STOKES AND THE BLACK WHIP THRILL BAND	Spindizzy (S) KZ 32075	2.50	3.75	5.00
SIMON STOKES AND THE NIGHTHAWKS	MGM (S) SE 4677	3.00	4.50	6.00

STONE CIRCUS
STONE CIRCUS, THE	Mainstream (S) S/6119	4.50	6.75	9.00

STONEGROUND
FLAT OUT	Flat Out (M) FOR 101	3.00	4.50	6.00
STONEGROUND	Warner Brothers (S) 1895	5.00	7.50	10.00
STONEGROUND FAMILY ALBUM	Warner Brothers (S) 2ZS 1956	6.00	9.00	12.00
STONEGROUND 3	Warner Brothers (S) BS 2645	4.00	6.00	8.00

STONE PONEYS
BEGINNINGS, THE (SHOWN AS LINDA RONSTADT & THE STONE PONEYS)	Capitol (S) ST-11383	5.00	7.50	10.00
DIFFERENT DRUM	Capitol (S) ST 11269	4.00	6.00	8.00
EVERGREEN VOL. 2	Capitol (S) ST 2763	4.00	6.00	8.00
STONE PONEYS, THE	Capitol (S) ST 2666	4.50	6.75	9.00
STONE PONEYS FEATURING LINDA RONSTADT (RETITLED)	Capitol (S) ST-11383	2.00	3.00	4.00
STONEY END	Pickwick (S) SPO 3298	3.00	4.50	6.00

Also see RONSTADT, Linda

STONE, Roland
JUST A MOMENT	Ace (M) LP 1018	4.00	10.00	16.00

STOOGES
FUN HOUSE	Elektra (S) EKS 74071	6.00	9.00	12.00
RAW POWER	Columbia (S) KC 32111	3.00	4.50	6.00
STOOGES, THE	Elektra (S) EKS 74051	5.00	7.50	10.00

Also see IGGY & THE STOOGES

STOOKEY, Paul
NOEL	Warner Brothers (S) BS2674	2.50	3.75	5.00

STORM, Billy
BILLY STORM	Buena Vista (M) BV 3315	3.50	7.00	10.50

STORM, Billy & The Valiants
THIS IS THE NIGHT	Famous (M) F 504	4.00	8.00	12.00

STORM, Gale
GALE STORM	Dot (M) DLP 3011	4.50	9.00	13.50
GALE STORM	Dot (EP) DEP 1050	1.50	3.00	4.50
GALE STORM	Dot (EP) DEP 1051	1.50	3.00	4.50
GALE STORM	Dot (EP) DEP 1052	1.50	3.00	4.50
GALE STORM HITS	Dot (M) DLP 3098	4.00	8.00	12.00
GALE'S GREAT HITS	Dot (EP) DEP 1074	1.50	3.00	4.50
SENTIMENTAL ME	Dot (M) DLP 3017	3.50	7.00	10.50
SOFTLY & TENDERLY	Dot (M) DLP-3197	3.00	6.00	9.00
SOFTLY & TENDERLY	Dot (S) DLP-25197	4.00	8.00	12.00

STOVALL, Babe
BABE STOVALL	Verve (M) VPM 1	5.00	10.00	15.00

STRANGE
TRANSLUCENT WORLD	Outer Galaxie (M) TW 1000	7.00	10.50	14.00

STRANGE CREEK SINGERS
STRANGE CREEK SINGERS	Arhoolie (M) 4004	3.00	4.50	6.00

STRANGELOVES
I WANT CANDY	Bang (M) 211	5.00	7.50	10.00

STRAWBERRY ALARM CLOCK
BEST OF THE STRAWBERRY ALARM CLOCK	Uni (S) 73074	3.00	4.50	6.00
CHANGES	Vocalion (S) 73915	4.00	6.00	8.00
GOOD MORNING STARSHINE	Uni (S) 73054	3.00	4.50	6.00
INCENSE AND PEPPERMINTS	Uni (S) 73014	3.00	4.50	6.00
WAKE UP IT'S TOMORROW	Uni (S) 73025	3.00	4.50	6.00
WORLD IN A SEA SHELL, THE	Uni (S) 73035	3.00	4.50	6.00

STRAWBS
BURSTING AT THE SEAMS	A&M (S) SP 4383	2.00	3.00	4.00
DEADLINES	Arista (S) AB 4172	2.00	3.00	4.00
FROM THE WITCHWOOD	A&M (S) SP 4304	2.00	3.00	4.00
GHOSTS	A&M (S) SP 4506	2.00	3.00	4.00
GRAVE NEW WORLD	A&M (S) SP 4344	2.00	3.00	4.00
HERO & HEROINE	A&M (S) SP 3607	2.00	3.00	4.00
JUSTA COLLECTION OF ANTIQUES AND CURIOS	A&M (S) SP 4288	2.00	3.00	4.00
NOMADNESS	A&M (S) SP 4544	2.00	3.00	4.00

STREET
STREET	Verve/Forecast (S) FTS 3057	3.00	4.50	6.00

STREET PEOPLE, THE
JENNIFER TOMKINS	Musicor (S) MS 3189	2.00	3.00	4.00

STREISAND, Barbra
BARBRA JOAN STREISAND	Columbia (S) 30792	2.00	3.00	4.00
BARBRA JOAN STREISAND	Columbia (Q) 30792	2.00	3.00	4.00
BARBRA STREISAND ALBUM, THE	Columbia (M) CL 2007	2.00	4.00	6.00
BARBRA STREISAND ALBUM, THE	Columbia (S) CS 8807	2.00	4.00	6.00
BARBRA STREISAND & OTHER MUSICAL INSTRUMENTS	Columbia (S) KC 32655	2.50	3.75	5.00
BARBRA STREISAND'S GREATEST HITS	Columbia (S) CS 9968	2.00	3.00	4.00
BUTTERFLY	Columbia (S) PC 33005	2.00	3.00	4.00
BUTTERFLY	Columbia (Q) PCQ 33005	2.00	3.00	4.00
CLASSICAL BARBRA	Columbia (S) M 33452	2.00	3.00	4.00
COLOR ME BARBRA	Columbia (M) CL 2478	2.50	3.75	5.00
COLOR ME BARBRA	Columbia (S) CS 9278	2.50	3.75	5.00
HAPPENING IN CENTRAL PARK, A	Columbia (S) CS 9710	2.00	3.00	4.00
JE M'APPELLE BARBRA	Columbia (M) CL 2547	2.50	3.75	5.00
JE M'APPELLE BARBRA	Columbia (S) CS 9347	2.50	3.75	5.00
LAZY AFTERNOON	Columbia (Q) PCQ 33815	2.00	3.00	4.00
LAZY AFTERNOON	Columbia (S) PC 33815	2.00	3.00	4.00
LIVE IN CONCERT AT THE FORUM	Columbia (Q) 31760	2.00	3.00	4.00
LIVE IN CONCERT AT THE FORUM	Columbia (S) 31760	2.00	3.00	4.00
MY NAME IS BARBRA	Columbia (M) CL 2336	2.50	3.75	5.00
MY NAME IS BARBRA	Columbia (S) CS 9136	2.50	3.75	5.00
MY NAME IS BARBRA, TWO	Columbia (M) CL 2409	2.50	3.75	5.00
MY NAME IS BARBRA, TWO	Columbia (S) CS 9209	2.50	3.75	5.00
PEOPLE	Columbia (M) CL 2215	2.00	4.00	6.00
PEOPLE	Columbia (S) CS 9015	2.00	4.00	6.00
SECOND BARBRA STREISAND ALBUM, THE	Columbia (M) CL 2054	2.00	4.00	6.00
SECOND BARBRA STREISAND ALBUM, THE	Columbia (S) CS 8854	2.00	4.00	6.00
SIMPLY STREISAND	Columbia (M) CL 2682	2.50	3.75	5.00
SIMPLY STREISAND	Columbia (S) CS 9482	2.00	3.00	4.00
STONEY END	Columbia (Q) 30378	2.00	3.00	4.00
STONEY END	Columbia (S) 30378	2.00	3.00	4.00
SUPERMAN	Columbia (S) JC 34830	2.00	3.00	4.00
THIRD BARBRA STREISAND ALBUM, THE	Columbia (M) CL 2154	2.00	4.00	6.00
THIRD BARBRA STREISAND ALBUM, THE	Columbia (S) CS 8954	2.00	4.00	6.00
WAY WE WERE, THE (Soundtrack)	Columbia (Q) PCQ 32801	2.00	3.00	4.00
WAY WE WERE, THE (Soundtrack)	Columbia (S) PC 32801	2.00	3.00	4.00
WHAT ABOUT TODAY?	Columbia (S) CS 9816	2.50	3.75	5.00

STRICKLAND, William R.
IS ONLY THE NAME	Deram (S) DES 18031	3.00	4.50	6.00

STRICKLIN, Brother Al
WANTED: ALIVE	Texas Re-Cord Co. (S) LP-1004	2.50	3.75	5.00

STRING-A-LONGS
MATILDA	Dot (M) DLP-3463	3.00	6.00	9.00
MATILDA	Dot (S) DLP-25463	4.00	8.00	12.00
PICK A HIT	Warwick (M) W-2036	3.00	6.00	9.00
PICK A HIT	Warwick (S) WST-2036	4.00	8.00	12.00

STRONG, Barrett
STRONGHOLD	Capitol (S) ST-11376	2.50	3.75	5.00

STRONG, Nolan & The Diablos
FORTUNE OF HITS	Fortune (M) 8010	6.00	15.00	24.00
FORTUNE OF HITS VOL. 2	Fortune (M) LP 8012	6.00	9.00	12.00
MIND OVER MATTER	Fortune (M) LP 8015	6.00	9.00	12.00

(M) Mono   (S) Stereo   (EP) Extended Play   (Q) Quad   (RI) Re-issued

STYLISTICS
		GOOD	VERY GOOD	NEAR MINT
HEAVY	Avco (S) 69004	2.00	3.00	4.00
LET'S PUT IT ALL TOGETHER	Avco (S) 69001	2.00	3.00	4.00
ROCKIN' ROLL BABY	Avco (S) 11010	3.00	4.50	6.00
ROUND 2	Avco Embassy (S) 11006	3.00	4.50	6.00
STYLISTICS, THE	Avco Embassy (S) 33023	3.00	4.50	6.00
THANK YOU BABY	Avco (S) 69008	2.00	3.00	4.00
YOU ARE BEAUTIFUL	Avco (S) 69010	2.00	3.00	4.00

STYX
		GOOD	VERY GOOD	NEAR MINT
CRYSTAL BALL	A&M (S) SP 4604	2.00	3.00	4.00
EQUINOX	A&M (S) 4559	2.00	3.00	4.00
GRAND ILLUSION, THE	A&M (S) SP 4637	2.00	3.00	4.00
MAN OF MIRACLES	Wooden Nickel (S) BWL1-0638	2.00	3.00	4.00
SERPENT IS RISING	Wooden Nickel (S) SWL1-0287	2.00	3.00	4.00
STYX 2	Wooden Nickel (S) 1012	3.50	5.25	7.00

SUGAR BEARS
		GOOD	VERY GOOD	NEAR MINT
INTRODUCING THE SUGAR BEARS	Big Tree (S) BTS 2009	2.50	3.75	5.00

SULLIVAN, Big Jim
		GOOD	VERY GOOD	NEAR MINT
SITAR BEAT	Mercury (M) MG 21137	2.50	3.75	5.00
SITAR BEAT	Mercury (S) SR 61137	3.00	4.50	6.00

SUMMER, Donna
		GOOD	VERY GOOD	NEAR MINT
FOUR SEASONS OF LOVE	Casablanca (S) NBLP 7038	2.00	3.00	4.00
I REMEMBER YESTERDAY	Casablanca (S) NBLP 7056	2.00	3.00	4.00
LOVE TO LOVE YOU BABY	Oasis (S) 5001	2.50	3.75	5.00
LOVE TRILOGY	Oasis (S) 5004	2.50	3.75	5.00
ONCE UPON A TIME	Casablanca (S) NBLP 7078	3.00	4.50	6.00

SUM PEAR
		GOOD	VERY GOOD	NEAR MINT
SUM PEAR	Jubilee (S) EST 1	3.00	4.50	6.00

SUNDAY FUNNIES
		GOOD	VERY GOOD	NEAR MINT
BENEDICTION	Rare Earth (S) RS 538	3.00	4.50	6.00
SUNDAY FUNNIES	Rare Earth (S) RS 526	3.00	4.50	6.00

SUNDOWNERS
		GOOD	VERY GOOD	NEAR MINT
CAPTAIN NEMO AND THE SUNDOWNERS	Decca (S) DL 75036	4.00	6.00	8.00

SUNNY & The Sunliners
		GOOD	VERY GOOD	NEAR MINT
LIVE IN HOLLYWOOD	Key Loc (M) KL 3003	3.00	6.00	9.00
SKY HIGH	Key Loc (M) KL 3009	3.00	6.00	9.00
SMILE NOW CRY LATER	Key Loc (M) KY 3001	3.00	6.00	9.00
TALK TO ME	Teardrop (M) LPM 2000	4.00	8.00	12.00
THIS IS MY BAND	Key-Loc (M) KL 3006	4.50	6.75	9.00

SUNNYLAND SLIM
		GOOD	VERY GOOD	NEAR MINT
BLUES MASTERS VOL. 8	Blue Horizon (M) BM 4608	4.50	6.75	9.00
SLIM'S GOT HIS THING GOIN' ON	World Pacific (S) WPS 21890	4.50	6.75	9.00
SUNNYLAND SLIM PLAYS RAGTIME BLUES	Bluesway (M) 6068	2.50	4.00	5.00

SUNRAYS
		GOOD	VERY GOOD	NEAR MINT
ANDREA	Tower (M) T 5017	4.00	8.00	12.00

SUNSET STRINGS
		GOOD	VERY GOOD	NEAR MINT
SUNSET STRINGS PLAY ROY ORBISON	Liberty (M) LRP-3395	2.50	3.75	5.00
SUNSET STRINGS PLAY ROY ORBISON	Liberty (S) LST-7395	3.00	4.50	6.00

SUNSET SURF
		GOOD	VERY GOOD	NEAR MINT
SUNSET SURF	Capitol (M) T 1915	2.50	5.00	7.50
SUNSET SURF	Capitol (S) ST 1915	3.00	6.00	9.00

SUNSETS
		GOOD	VERY GOOD	NEAR MINT
SURFING WITH THE SUNSETS	Palace (M) 752	3.50	7.00	10.50

(M) Mono (S) Stereo (EP) Extended Play (Q) Quad (RI) Re-issued

SUNSHINE COMPANY
		GOOD	VERY GOOD	NEAR MINT
HAPPY IS THE SUNSHINE COMPANY	Imperial (M) LP 12359	3.00	4.50	6.00
SUNSHINE AND SHADOWS	Imperial (M) LP 12399	3.00	4.50	6.00
SUNSHINE COMPANY, THE	Imperial (M) LP 12368	3.00	4.50	6.00

SUPERFINE DANDELION
		GOOD	VERY GOOD	NEAR MINT
SUPERFINE DANDELION	Mainstream (M) 56102	3.00	4.50	6.00
SUPERFINE DANDELION	Mainstream (S) S/6102	3.50	5.25	7.00

SUPERSISTER
		GOOD	VERY GOOD	NEAR MINT
SUPERSISTER	Dwarf (M) PDLP 2001	2.50	3.75	5.00

SUPER STOCKS
		GOOD	VERY GOOD	NEAR MINT
SCHOOL IS A DRAG	Capitol (M) T 2190	4.00	8.00	12.00
SCHOOL IS A DRAG	Capitol (S) ST 2190	5.00	10.00	15.00
SURF ROUTE 101	Capitol (M) T 2113	4.00	8.00	12.00
SURF ROUTE 101	Capitol (S) ST 2113	5.00	10.00	15.00
THUNDER ROAD	Capitol (M) T 2060	4.00	8.00	12.00
THUNDER ROAD	Capitol (S) ST 2060	5.00	10.00	15.00

SUPERTRAMP
		GOOD	VERY GOOD	NEAR MINT
SUPERTRAMP	A&M (S) SP 4665	2.00	3.00	4.00
CRIME OF THE CENTURY	A&M (S) SP 3647	2.00	3.00	4.00
CRISIS? WHAT CRISIS?	A&M (S) SP 4560	2.00	3.00	4.00
EVEN IN THE QUIETEST MOMENTS	A&M (S) SP 4634	2.00	3.00	4.00
INDELIBLY STAMPED	A&M (S) SP 4311	2.00	3.00	4.00

SUPREMES
		GOOD	VERY GOOD	NEAR MINT
AT THE COPA	Motown (M) 636	2.00	3.00	4.00
AT THE COPA	Motown (S) 636	2.50	3.75	5.00
BIT OF LIVERPOOL	Motown (M) MLP 623	3.00	4.50	6.00
CREAM OF THE CROP	Motown (S) 694	2.00	3.00	4.00
DIANA ROSS & THE SUPREMES' ANTHOLOGY	Motown (S) 794	3.50	5.25	7.00
FAREWELL	Motown (S) 708	2.00	3.00	4.00
FLOY JOY	Motown (S) 751	2.00	3.00	4.00
FUNNY GIRL	Motown (S) 672	2.50	3.75	5.00
GREATEST HITS	Motown (M) 2-663	2.50	3.75	5.00
GREATEST HITS	Motown (S) 663	3.00	4.50	6.00
GREATEST HITS VOL. 3	Motown (S) 702	2.00	3.00	4.00
HIGH ENERGY	Motown (S) 863	2.00	3.00	4.00
I HEAR A SYMPHONY	Motown (M) 643	2.00	3.00	4.00
I HEAR A SYMPHONY	Motown (S) 643	2.50	3.75	5.00
LET THE SUNSHINE IN	Motown (S) 689	2.00	3.00	4.00
LIVE AT LONDONS TALK OF THE TOWN	Motown (S) 676	2.50	3.75	5.00
MARY, SCHERRIE & SUSAYE	Motown (S) 873	2.00	3.00	4.00
MEET THE SUPREMES (ORIGINAL WITH GIRLS SITTING ON STOOLS)	Motown (M) MLP 606	9.00	22.50	36.00
MEET THE SUPREMES (LATER PRESSING WITH GIRLS FACES ON COVER)	Motown (M) MLP 606	3.00	6.00	9.00
MERRY CHRISTMAS	Motown (M) 638	2.50	3.00	5.00
MERRY CHRISTMAS	Motown (S) 638	3.00	4.50	5.00
MORE HITS BY THE SUPREMES	Motown (M) 627	2.50	3.75	5.00
MORE HITS BY THE SUPREMES	Motown (S) 627	3.00	4.50	6.00
NEW WAYS, BUT LOVE STAYS	Motown (S) 720	2.00	3.00	4.00
REFLECTIONS	Motown (M) 665	2.00	3.00	4.00
REFLECTIONS	Motown (S) 665	2.50	3.75	5.00
RIGHT ON	Motown (S) 705	2.00	3.00	4.00
SUPREMES	Motown (S) 756	2.00	3.00	4.00
SUPREMES	Motown (S) 828	2.00	3.00	4.00
SUPREMES A-GO-GO	Motown (M) 649	2.00	3.00	4.00
SUPREMES A-GO-GO	Motown (S) 649	2.50	3.75	5.00
SUPREMES SING COUNTRY, WESTERN, AND POP	Motown (M) 625	2.50	3.75	5.00
SUPREMES SING COUNTRY, WESTERN, AND POP	Motown (S) 625	3.00	4.50	6.00
SUPREMES SING ROGERS AND HART	Motown (M) 659	2.00	3.00	4.00
SUPREMES SING ROGERS AND HART	Motown (S) 659	2.50	3.75	5.00
TOUCH	Motown (S) 737	2.00	3.00	4.00
WE REMEMBER SAM COOKE	Motown (M) 629	2.50	3.75	5.00
WE REMEMBER SAM COOKE	Motown (S) 629	3.00	4.50	6.00
WHERE DID OUR LOVE GO	Motown (M) MLP 621	4.00	6.00	8.00
WHERE DID OUR LOVE GO	Motown (EP) EPS 621	2.50	3.75	5.00

(Motown 663 thru 708 except 705 shown as Diana Ross & The Supremes)
Also see ROSS, Dianna

SUPREMES & THE TEMPTATIONS
		GOOD	VERY GOOD	NEAR MINT
DIANA ROSS AND THE SUPREMES JOIN THE TEMPTATIONS	Motown (S) 679	2.50	3.75	5.00
ON BROADWAY	Motown (S) 699	2.00	3.00	4.00
TCB	Motown (S) 682	2.00	3.00	4.00
TOGETHER	Motown (S) 692	2.00	3.00	4.00

SUPREMES & THE FOUR TOPS
		GOOD	VERY GOOD	NEAR MINT
DYNAMITE	Motown (S) 745	2.00	3.00	4.00
MAGNIFICENT 7, THE	Motown (S) 717	2.00	3.00	4.00
RETURN OF THE MAGNIFICENT 7, THE	Motown (S) 736	2.00	3.00	4.00

SURFARIS
		GOOD	VERY GOOD	NEAR MINT
FUN CITY U.S.A.	Decca (M) DL 4560	3.00	6.00	9.00
HIT CITY '64	Decca (M) DL 4487	3.00	6.00	9.00
HIT CITY '65	Decca (M) DL 4614	3.00	6.00	9.00
IT AIN'T ME BABE	Decca (M) DL 4683	3.00	6.00	9.00
SURFARIS PLAY, THE	Decca (M) DL 4470	3.00	6.00	9.00
WHEELS	Diplomat (M) D 2309	2.50	5.00	7.50
WIPE OUT	Dot (M) DLP 3535	3.00	6.00	9.00
WIPE OUT	Dot (S) DLP 25535	3.50	7.00	10.50

157

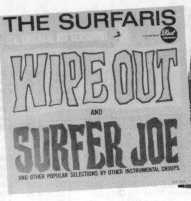

TITLE	LABEL & NO.	GOOD	VERY GOOD	NEAR MINT
SURFERS				
HIGH TIDE	High Fidelity (M) R-411	2.00	4.00	6.00
HIGH TIDE	High Fidelity (S) SR-411	2.50	5.00	7.50
SURFERS "LIVE & WELL"	Daybreak (S) 2001	2.50	5.00	7.50
SURFERS (SING HIT MOVIE SONGS FROM EXOTIC ISLANDS)	Warner Brothers (M) W 1493	2.00	4.00	6.00
SURFERS (SING HIT MOVIE SONGS FROM EXOTIC ISLANDS)	Warner Brothers (S) WS 1493	2.50	5.00	7.50
TAHITI	High Fidelity (M) R-417	2.00	4.00	6.00
TAHITI	High Fidelity (S) SR-417	2.50	5.00	7.50
SURFRIDERS				
SURFBEAT	Vault (M) V-105	3.00	6.00	9.00
SURFBEAT	Vault (S) VS-105	3.50	7.00	10.50
SURF STOMPERS				
ORIGINAL SURFER STOMP	Del Fi (M) DF-1236	3.00	6.00	9.00
ORIGINAL SURFER STOMP	Del Fi (S) DFS-1236	4.00	8.00	12.00
SURF TEENS				
SURF MANIA	Sutton (M) 339	4.00	8.00	12.00
SURPRISE PACKAGE				
FREE UP	LHI (S) S 12005	3.50	5.25	7.00
SWAMP DOGG				
HAVE YOU HEARD THIS STORY?	Island (S) 9299	2.00	3.00	4.00
TOTAL DESTRUCTION TO YOUR MIND	Canyon (M) LP 7706	4.00	6.00	8.00
SWAMPWATER				
SWAMPWATER	RCA (S) LSP-4572	2.00	3.00	4.00
SWAN, Billy				
FOUR	Columbia/Monument (S) PZ-34473	2.00	3.00	4.00
I CAN HELP	Monument (S) KZ-33279	2.50	3.75	5.00
ROCK N' ROLL MOON	Monument (S) PZ-33805	2.00	3.00	4.00
YOU'RE OK, I'M OK	A&M (S) SP 4686	2.00	3.00	4.00
SWANN, Bettye				
MAKE ME YOURS	A-Bet (S) 405	3.50	5.25	7.00
MAKE ME YOURS	Money (S) 1103	4.00	6.00	8.00
SOUL VIEW NOW, THE	Capitol (S) ST 190	2.50	3.75	5.00
SWEET				
DESOLATION BOULEVARD	Capitol (S) ST 11395	2.00	3.00	4.00
GIVE US A WINK	Capitol (S) ST 11496	2.00	3.00	4.00
LEVEL HEADED	Capitol (S) SKAO 11744	2.00	3.00	4.00
OFF THE RECORD	Capitol (S) TAO 11636	2.00	3.00	4.00
SWEET (FEATURING LITTLE WILLY AND BLOCKBUSTER)	Bell (S) 1125	3.00	4.50	6.00
SWEET INSPIRATIONS				
ESTELLE, MYRNA, AND SYLVIA	Stax (S) STS 3017	2.00	3.00	4.00
SWEET INSPIRATIONS	Atlantic (M) 8155	2.00	3.00	4.00
SWEET, SWEET SOUL	Atlantic (M) 8253	2.00	3.00	4.00
WHAT THE WORLD NEEDS NOW IS LOVE	Atlantic (M) 8201	2.00	3.00	4.00
SWEET MARIE				
STUCK IN PARADISE	Yard Bird (S) YDBS 771	4.00	6.00	8.00
SWEET MARIE 1	Yard Bird (S) YDBS 770	3.50	5.25	7.00
SWEET PAIN				
ENGLAND'S HEAVY BLUES SUPER SESSION	Mercury (S) SR 61231	4.00	6.00	8.00
SWEET PAIN	United Artists (S) UAS 6793	2.50	3.75	5.00
SWEET PIE & BILL MALONEY				
PLEASURE PUDDING	Rug (M) 2004	2.50	3.75	5.00
SWEET THURSDAY				
SWEET THURSDAY	Tetragrammation (S) T-112	4.00	6.00	8.00

(M) Mono (S) Stereo (EP) Extended Play (Q) Quad (RI) Re-issued

TITLE	LABEL & NO.	GOOD	VERY GOOD	NEAR MINT
SWEETWATER				
MELON	Reprise (S) 6473	3.00	4.50	6.00
SWEETWATER	Reprise (S) 6313	3.00	4.50	6.00
SWINGING BLUE JEANS				
HIPPY HIPPY SHAKE	Imperial (M) LP 9261	6.00	9.00	12.00
HIPPY HIPPY SHAKE	Imperial (S) LP 12261	7.00	10.50	14.00
SWINGIN MEDALLIONS				
DOUBLE SHOT	Smash (M) MGS 27083	3.50	5.25	7.00
DOUBLE SHOT	Smash (S) SRS 67083	4.50	6.75	9.00
SWORDSMEN, THE				
WHAT'S IT ALL ABOUT WORLD	RCA (S) LSP-4544	2.00	3.00	4.00
SYKES, Keith				
KEITH SYKES	Vanguard (S) VSD 6548	2.50	3.75	5.00
SYKES, Roosevelt				
DIRTY DOUBLE MOTHER	Bluesway (M) 6077	2.50	4.00	6.00
RETURN OF ROOSEVELT SYKES	Prestige/Bluesville (M) 1006	4.00	8.00	12.00
ROOSEVELT SYKES SINGS THE BLUES	United (M) 7792	2.50	4.00	5.00
ROOSEVELT SYKES SINGS THE BLUES	Crown (M) CL 5287	4.00	10.00	16.00
SYLVERS				
SYLVERS	Pride (S) 0007	2.00	3.00	4.00
SYLVERS 2	Pride (S) 0026	2.00	3.00	4.00
SYLVERS 3	MGM (S) M3G-4940	2.00	3.00	4.00
SYLVERS, Foster				
FOSTER SYLVERS	Pride (S) 0027	2.00	3.00	4.00
SYLVIA (of MICKY & SYLVIA)				
PILLOW TALK	Vibration (S) 126	2.50	3.75	5.00
SYNDICATE OF SOUND				
LITTLE GIRL	Bell (M) LP 6001	5.00	7.50	10.00
LITTLE GIRL	Bell (S) SLP 6001	6.00	9.00	12.00

T

TITLE	LABEL & NO.	GOOD	VERY GOOD	NEAR MINT
TAJ MAHAL				
GIANT STEP	Columbia (S) 18	3.50	5.25	7.00
HAPPY JUST TO BE LIKE I AM	Columbia (S) 30767	2.00	3.00	4.00
MO' ROOTS	Columbia (S) KC-33051	2.00	3.00	4.00
MUSIC KEEPS ME TOGETHER	Columbia (S) PC-33801	2.00	3.00	4.00
NATCH'L BLUES	Columbia (S) CS 9698	4.00	6.00	8.00
REAL THING, THE	Columbia (S) 30619	2.00	3.00	4.00
RECYCLING THE BLUES & OTHER RELATED STUFF	Columbia (S) 31605	2.00	3.00	4.00
TALBERT, Wayne				
LORD HAVE MERCY ON MY FUNKY SOUL	Pulsar (M) AR-10607	4.00	6.00	8.00
TAMS				
HEY GIRL DON'T BOTHER ME	ABC/Paramount (M) ABC499	4.00	6.00	8.00
PORTRAIT OF THE TAMS, A	ABC/Paramount (S) ABCS 673	4.00	6.00	8.00
PRESENTING THE TAMS	ABC/aramount (M) ABC 481	3.00	4.50	6.00
TIME FOR THE TAMS	ABC (M) ABC 596	3.00	4.50	6.00
TIME FOR THE TAMS	ABC (S) ABCS 596	3.00	4.50	6.00
TANEGA, Norma				
WALKIN' MY CAT NAMED DOG	New Voice (M) 2001	3.25	5.00	6.50

TANGERINE ZOO

TITLE	LABEL & NO.	GOOD	VERY GOOD	NEAR MINT
OUTSIDE LOOKING IN	Mainstream (S) S/6116	4.50	6.75	9.00
TANGERINE ZOO	Mainstream (M) 56107	4.00	6.00	8.00
TANGERINE ZOO	Mainstream (S) S/6107	4.50	6.75	9.00

TANGO

TANGO	A&M (S) SP 3612	2.00	3.00	4.00

TANYET

TANYET	Vault (M) LP 117	5.00	7.50	10.00

TARRIERS (Featuring Vince Martin)

HARD TRAVELIN'	United Artists (M) UAL-4033	2.50	3.75	5.00
HARD TRAVELIN'	United Artists (S) USL-5033	3.00	4.50	6.00
TARRIERS	Glory (M) GLP 1200	4.00	8.00	12.00

TASTE

ON THE BOARDS	Atco (S) SD 33-322	4.00	6.00	8.00
TASTE	Atco (S) SD 33-296	4.00	6.00	8.00

TATE, Howard

GET IT WHILE YOU CAN	Verve (M) V 5022	3.00	4.50	6.00
GET IT WHILE YOU CAN	Verve (S) V6-5022	3.50	5.25	7.00
HOWARD TATE	Atlantic (S) SD 8303	2.25	3.50	4.50

TAUPIN, Bernie

BERNIE TAUPIN	Elektra (S) 75020	4.00	6.00	8.00

Also see JOHN, Elton

TAVARES

FUTURE BOUND	Capitol (S) SW 11719	2.00	3.00	4.00
HARD CORE POETRY	Capitol (S) ST-11316	2.00	3.00	4.00
IN THE CITY	Capitol (S) ST-11396	2.00	3.00	4.00

TAVENER, John

WHALE, THE	Apple (S) SMAS 3369	4.00	6.00	8.00

TAYLOR, Bobby

TAYLOR MADE SOUL	Gordy (S) GS 942	3.00	4.50	6.00

TAYLOR, Bobby and The Vancouvers

BOBBY TAYLOR AND THE VANCOUVERS	Gordy (M) G 930	3.50	5.25	7.00

TAYLOR, Chip

CHIP TAYLOR'S LAST CHANCE	Warner Bros. (S) BS-2718	2.00	3.00	4.00
GASOLINE	Buddah (S) 5118	2.00	3.00	4.00
SOME OF US	Warner Bros. (S) BS-2824	2.00	3.00	4.00

TAYLOR, Hound Dog & The Houserockers

NATURAL BOOGIE	Alligator (S) 4704	3.50	5.25	7.00

TAYLOR, James

GORILLA	Warner Bros. (S) BS2866	2.50	3.75	5.00
GORILLA	Warner Bros. (Q) BS4-2866	2.50	3.75	5.00
JAMES TAYLOR	Apple (S) SKAO 3352	4.50	6.75	9.00
JAMES TAYLOR & THE ORIGINAL FLYING MACHINE	Euphoria (S) 2	5.00	7.50	10.00
JAMES TAYLOR'S GREATEST HITS	Warner Bros. (S) BSK-3113	2.00	3.00	4.00
JT	Columbia (S) JC 34811	2.00	3.00	4.00
MUD SLIDE SLIM & THE BLUE HORIZON	Warner Bros. (S) BS 2561	2.50	3.75	5.00
ONE MAN DOG	Warner Bros. (S) BS 2660	2.50	3.75	5.00
SWEET BABY JAMES	Warner Bros. (S) WS 1843	2.50	3.75	5.00
WALKING MAN	Warner Bros. (S) BS 2794	2.50	3.75	5.00

Also see FLYING MACHINE

TAYLOR, Johnnie

BEST OF JOHNNIE TAYLOR	Stax (S) STS 5522	2.00	3.00	4.00
GREATEST HITS	Stax (S) 2032	2.00	3.00	4.00
JOHNNIE TAYLOR PHILOSOPHY CONTINUES	Stax (S) STS 2023	2.00	3.00	4.00
ONE STEP BEYOND	Stax (S) STS 2030	2.00	3.00	4.00
RARE STAMPS	Stax (S) STS 2012	2.00	3.00	4.00
RAW BLUES	Stax (S) STS 2008	2.00	3.00	4.00
SUPER TAYLOR	Stax (S) STS 5509	2.00	3.00	4.00
TAYLORED IN SILK	Stax (S) STS 3014	2.00	3.00	4.00
WANTED: ONE SOUL SINGER	Stax (M) 715	3.00	4.50	6.00
WHO'S MAKING LOVE	Stax (S) STS 2005	2.00	3.00	4.00
WANTED: ONE SOUL SIGER	Stax (S) 715	3.50	5.25	7.00

TAYLOR, Kingsize & The Dominoes

REAL GONK MAN	Midnight (M) HLP 2101	5.00	10.00	15.00
REAL GONK MAN	Midnight (S) HST 2101	5.50	11.00	16.50

TAYLOR, Koko

I GOT WHAT IT TAKES	Alligator (S) 4706	3.00	4.50	6.00
KOKO TAYLOR	Chess (S) LPS 1532	3.50	5.25	7.00

TAYLOR, Little Johnny

EVERYBODY KNOWS ABOUT MY GOOD THING	Ronn (S) LPS 7530	2.50	3.75	5.00
LITTLE JOHNNY TAYLOR	Galaxy (M) 203	3.00	4.50	6.00
LITTLE JOHNNY TAYLOR	Galaxy (S) 8-203	3.50	5.25	7.00

TAYLOR, Little Johnny & Ted

TITLE	LABEL & NO.	GOOD	VERY GOOD	NEAR MINT
SUPER TAYLORS, THE	Ronn (S) LPS 7533	2.25	3.50	4.50

TAYLOR, Ted

BE EVER WONDERFUL	Okeh (M) OKM 12104	4.00	6.00	8.00
BE EVER WONDERFUL	Okeh (S) OKS 14104	4.50	6.75	9.00
GREATEST HITS	Okeh (M) OKM 12113	4.00	6.00	8.00
GREATEST HITS	Okeh (S) OKS 14113	4.50	6.75	9.00
TAYLOR MADE	Ronn (S) LPS 7531	2.50	3.75	5.00
YOU CAN DIG IT	Ronn (S) LPS 7529	2.50	3.75	5.00

T-BONES

BOSS DRAG	Liberty (M) LRP 3346	3.00	4.50	6.00
BOSS DRAG	Liberty (S) LST 7346	3.50	5.25	7.00
BOSS DRAG AT THE BEACH	Liberty (M) LRP 3363	3.00	4.50	6.00
BOSS DRAG AT THE BEACH	Liberty (S) LST 7363	3.50	5.25	7.00
DOIN THE JERK	Liberty (M) LRP 3404	3.00	4.50	6.00
DOIN THE JERK	Liberty (S) LST 7404	3.50	5.25	7.00
EVERYONE'S GONE TO THE MOON	Liberty (M) LRP 3471	3.00	4.50	6.00
EVERYONE'S GONE TO THE MOON	Liberty (S) LST 7471	3.50	5.25	7.00
SIPPIN' AND CHIPPIN	Liberty (M) LRP 3446	3.00	4.50	6.00
SIPPIN' AND CHIPPIN	Liberty (S) LST 7446	3.50	5.25	7.00

T.C. ATLANTIC

T.C. ATLANTIC	Dove (M) LP 4459	8.00	12.00	16.00

TEA COMPANY

COME AND HAVE SOME TEA WITH THE TEA COMPANY	Smash (S) SRS 67105	3.50	5.25	7.00

TEARDROPS

TEARDROPS AT TRINCHI'S, THE	20th Century (M) FXG 5011	3.00	4.50	6.00

TEAR GAS

PIGGY GO GETTER	Paramount (S) PAS 5029	3.00	4.50	6.00

TEA SET

MA BELLE AMIE	Colossus (S) CCS 1001	2.50	3.75	5.00

TEDDY BEARS (Featuring Phil Spector)

TEDDY BEARS SING!	Imperial (S) LP-9067	19.00	47.50	76.00
TEDDY BEARS SING!	Imperial (S) LP-12010	11.00	27.50	44.00

TEDDY & DARREL

THESE ARE THE HITS, YOU SILLY SAVAGE	Mira (M) LP 10,000	5.00	7.50	10.00

TEDDY & THE PANDAS

BASIC MAGNETISM	Tower (S) ST 5125	4.50	6.75	9.00

TEE, Willie

I'M ONLY A MAN	Capitol (S) ST 199	2.50	3.75	5.00

TEEGARDEN & VAN WINKLE

AN EVENING AT HOME WITH TEEGARDEN & VAN WINKLE	Atco (S) 33-272	4.00	6.00	8.00
BUT, ANYHOW	Westbound (S) 2003	3.00	4.50	6.00
ON OUR WAY	Westbound (S) 2010	3.00	4.50	6.00

TEEMATES

TEEMATES	Audio Fidelity (S)	5.00	10.00	15.00

TEENAGERS (Featuring Frankie Lymon)

JERRY BLAVAT PRESENTS TEENAGERS FEATURING FRANKIE LYMON	Roulette (M) R 25250	6.00	12.00	18.00
TEENAGERS FEATURING FRANKIE LYMON, THE	Gee (M) GLP 701	10.00	25.00	40.00
(Red label)				
TEENAGERS FEATURING FRANKIE LYMON, THE	Gee (S) GLP 701	4.00	10.00	16.00
(Gray label)				

TEEN QUEENS

TITLE	LABEL & NO.	GOOD	VERY GOOD	NEAR MINT
EDDIE, MY LOVE	Crown (M) CLP 5022	6.00	15.00	24.00
TEEN QUEENS	Crown (M) CST 373	5.00	12.50	20.00

TEMPESTS

WOULD YOU BELIEVE	Smash (M) MGS 27098	3.00	4.50	6.00
WOULD YOU BELIEVE	Smash (S) SRS 67098	3.50	5.25	7.00

TEMPO, Nick

ROCK 'N ROLL BEACH PARTY	Liberty (M) LRP 3023	2.25	4.50	6.75

TEMPO, Nino & April Stevens

DEEP PURPLE	Atco (M) 156	3.00	4.50	6.00
DEEP PURPLE	Atco (S) 156	4.00	6.00	8.00
HEY BABY	Atco (M) 180	2.50	3.75	5.00
HEY BABY	Atco (S) 180	3.00	4.50	6.00
NINO & APRIL SING THE GREAT SONGS	Atco (M) 162	3.00	4.50	6.00
NINO & APRIL SING THE GREAT SONGS	Atco (S) 162	3.50	5.25	7.00
TEMPO, NINO, APRIL STEVENS PROGRAM	Camden (M) CAL-824	2.50	3.75	5.00
TEMPO, NINO, APRIL STEVENS PROGRAM	Camden (S) CAS-824	3.00	4.50	6.00

TEMPREES

LOVE MAZE	We Produce (S) XPS 1903	2.00	3.00	4.00
LOVEMEN	We Produce (S) XPS 1901	2.00	3.00	4.00
THREE	We Produce (S) XPS 1905	2.00	3.00	4.00

TEMPTATIONS

ALL DIRECTIONS	Gordy (S) 962	2.00	3.00	4.00
CLOUD NINE	Gordy (S) 939	2.50	3.75	5.00
GETTIN' READY	Gordy (M) 918	3.50	5.25	7.00
GETTIN' READY	Gordy (S) 918	4.00	6.75	8.00
GREATEST HITS	Gordy (M) 919	3.50	5.25	7.00
GREATEST HITS	Gordy (S) 919	4.00	6.75	8.00
GREATEST HITS VOL. 2	Gordy (S) 954	2.50	3.75	5.00
HOUSE PARTY	Gordy (S) 973	2.00	3.00	4.00
IN A MELLOW MOOD	Gordy (M) 924	2.50	3.75	5.00
IN A MELLOW MOOD	Gordy (S) 924	3.00	4.50	6.00
LIVE	Gordy (M) 921	3.00	4.50	6.00
LIVE	Gordy (S) 921	3.50	5.25	7.00
LIVE AT LONDON'S TALK OF THE TOWN	Gordy (S) 953	2.50	3.75	5.00
LIVE AT THE COPA	Gordy (S) 938	2.50	3.75	5.00
MASTERPIECE	Gordy (S) 965	2.00	3.00	4.00
MEET THE TEMPTATIONS	Gordy (M) 911	4.00	6.00	8.00
MEET THE TEMPTATIONS	Gordy (S) 911	5.00	7.50	10.00
PSYCHEDELIC SHACK	Gordy (S) 947	2.50	3.75	5.00
PUZZLE PEOPLE	Gordy (S) 949	2.50	3.75	5.00
SKY'S THE LIMIT	Gordy (S) 957	2.00	3.00	4.00
SOLID ROCK	Gordy (S) 961	2.00	3.00	4.00
SONG FOR YOU	Gordy (S) 969	2.00	3.00	4.00
TEMPTATIONS' ANTHOLOGY, THE/10th ANNIVERSARY SPECIAL (3 record set)	Motown (S) 782	3.50	5.25	7.00
TEMPTATIONS SING SMOKEY	Gordy (M) 912	4.00	6.75	8.00
TEMPTATIONS SING SMOKEY	Gordy (S) 912	5.00	7.50	10.00
TEMPTATIONS WISH IT WOULD RAIN	Gordy (M) 927	2.50	3.75	5.00
TEMPTATIONS WISH IT WOULD RAIN	Gordy (S) 927	3.00	4.50	6.00
TEMPTIN' TEMPTATIONS	Gordy (M) 914	3.50	5.25	7.00
TEMPTIN' TEMPTATIONS	Gordy (S) 914	4.00	6.00	8.00
TV SHOW	Gordy (S) 933	2.50	3.75	5.00
WITH A LOT O' SOUL	Gordy (M) 922	3.00	4.50	6.00
WITH A LOT O' SOUL	Gordy (S) 922	3.50	5.25	7.00

10CC

100 C.C.	UK (S) 53110	4.00	6.00	8.00
SHEET MUSIC	UK (S) 53107	4.00	6.00	8.00
10 C.C.	UK (S) 53105	4.00	6.00	8.00

TEN WHEEL DRIVE

BRIEF REPLIES	Polydor (S) 4024	2.50	3.75	5.00
CONSTRUCTION #1	Polydor (S) 4008	2.50	3.75	5.00
PECULIAR FRIENDS	Polydor (S) 4062	2.50	3.75	5.00
TEN WHEEL DRIVE	Capitol (S) ST-11199	2.00	3.00	4.00

TEN YEARS AFTER

ALVIN LEE & COMPANY	Deram (S) 18064	4.00	6.00	8.00
CRICKLEWOOD GREEN	Deram (S) 18038	4.00	6.00	8.00
GOIN' HOME	Deram (S) 18072	3.00	4.50	6.00
POSITIVE VIBRATIONS	Columbia (S) PC 32851	2.00	3.00	4.00
ROCK & ROLL MUSIC TO THE WORLD	Columbia (S) KC 31779	2.50	3.75	5.00
SPACE IN TIME, A	Columbia (S) 30801	2.50	3.75	5.00
SSSH	Deram (S) 18029	4.00	6.00	8.00
STONEHOUSE	Deram (S) 18021	4.00	6.00	8.00
TEN YEARS AFTER RECORDED LIVE	Columbia (S) C2X 32288	2.00	3.00	4.00
UNDEAD	Deram (S) 18016	4.50	6.75	5.00
WATT	Deram (S) 18050	4.00	6.00	8.00

Also see LEE, Alvin

TERRELL, Tammi

IRRESISTIBLE	Motown (S) MS 652	3.00	4.50	6.00

TERRY, Dewey

CHIEF	Tumble weed (S) TWS 104	2.50	3.75	5.00

TERRY, Sonny

SONNY TERRY	Everest (M) 206	2.50	3.75	5.00

(M) Mono (S) Stereo (EP) Extended Play (Q) Quad (RI) Re-issued

TEX, Joe

TITLE	LABEL & NO.	GOOD	VERY GOOD	NEAR MINT
BEST OF JOE TEX	Atlantic (S) 8144	2.50	3.75	5.00
BEST OF JOE TEX	King (M) 935	4.00	8.00	12.00
BEST OF JOE TEX	Parrot (M) 61002	2.50	3.75	5.00
BEST OF JOE TEX	Parrot (S) 71002	3.00	4.50	6.00
BUYING A BOOK	Atlantic (S) SD 8231	2.00	3.00	4.00
HISTORY OF JOE TEX	Pride (S) PRD 0020	2.50	3.75	5.00
HOLD ON	Checker (M) 2993	3.00	6.00	9.00
HOLD WHAT YOU'VE GOT	Atlantic (M) 8106	3.00	4.50	6.00
HOLD WHAT YOU'VE GOT	Atlantic (S) SD 8106	3.50	5.25	7.00
I GOTCHA	Dial (S) 6002	2.25	3.50	4.50
I'VE GOT TO DO A LITTLE BETTER	Atlantic (M) 8133	2.50	3.75	5.00
I'VE GOT TO DO A LITTLE BETTER	Atlantic (S) SD 8133	3.00	4.50	6.00
JOE TEX SPILLS THE BEANS	Dial (S) DL 6004	2.00	3.00	4.00
LIVE AND LIVELY	Atlantic (M) 8156	2.50	3.75	5.00
LIVE AND LIVELY	Atlantic (S) SD 8156	3.00	4.50	6.00
LOVE YOU SAVE, THE	Atlantic (S) 8124	2.50	3.75	5.00
NEW BOSS	Atlantic (M) 8115	2.50	3.75	5.00
NEW BOSS	Atlantic (S) 8115	3.00	4.50	6.00
SOUL COUNTRY	Atlantic (S) SD 8187	2.50	3.75	5.00

THAXTON, Lloyd

LLOYD THAXTON PRESENTS	Decca (M) DL-4594	2.50	3.75	5.00
LLOYD THAXTON PRESENTS	Decca (S) DL7-4594	3.00	4.50	6.00

THEE MIDNITERS

GIANTS	Whittier (S) WS 5002	4.00	6.00	8.00
LOVE SPECIAL DELIVERY	Whittier (S) WS 5000	5.00	7.50	10.00
THEE MIDNITERS	Chattahoochee (M) C 1001	4.50	6.75	9.00
UNLIMITED	Whittier (M) W 5001	4.00	6.00	8.00

THEE PROPHETS

PLAYGIRL	Kapp (S) KS 3596	2.25	3.50	4.50

THEM

NOW AND THEM	Tower (S) ST 5104	3.50	5.25	7.00
THEM	Happy Tiger (S) HT 1004	4.50	6.75	9.00
THEM (FEATURING "HERE COMES THE NIGHT)	Parrot (M) PA 61005	5.00	10.00	15.00
THEM (FEATURING "HERE COMES THE NIGHT")	Parrot (S) PAS 71005	4.00	8.00	12.00
THEM AGAIN	Parrot (M) PA 61008	4.50	6.75	9.00
THEM AGAIN	Parrot (S) PAS 71008	4.00	6.00	8.00
THEM IN REALITY	Happy Tiger (S) HT 1012	4.50	6.75	9.00
TIME OUT! TIME IN FOR THEM	Tower (S) ST5116	3.50	5.25	7.00

Also see MORRISON, Van

THINK

ENCOUNTER	Laurie (S) SLP 2052	4.00	6.00	8.00

THIN LIZZY

FIGHTING	Vertigo (S) 2005	3.50	5.25	7.00
JAILBREAK	Mercury (S) SRM-1-1081	2.50	3.75	5.00
NIGHT LIFE	Vertigo (S) 2002	3.50	5.25	7.00
VAGABONDS OF THE WESTERN WORLD	London (S) XPS 636	2.50	3.75	5.00

THIRD POWER

BELIEVE	Vanguard (S) 6554	5.00	7.50	10.00

THIRD RAIL

ID MUSIC	Epic (M) LN 24327	4.00	6.00	8.00
ID MUSIC	Epic (S) BN 26327	4.50	6.75	9.00

13th FLOOR ELEVATORS

BULL OF THE WOODS	International Artists (M) IALP9	5.00	10.00	15.00
EASTER EVERYWHERE	International Artists (M) IALP 5	7.00	17.50	28.00
LIVE	International Artists (M) IALP8	5.00	10.00	15.00
PSYCHEDELIC SOUNDS	International Artists (M) LP 1	7.00	17.50	28.00

THOMAS, B.J.

B.J. THOMAS COUNTRY	Scepter (S) 5108	2.00	3.00	4.00
B.J. THOMAS SONGS	Paramount (S) 6052	3.00	4.50	6.00
I'M SO LONESOME I COULD CRY	Scepter (M) 535	3.50	5.25	7.00
I'M SO LONESOME I COULD CRY	Scepter (S) 535	4.00	6.00	8.00
EVERYBODY'S OUT OF TOWN	Scepter (S) SPS 582	2.50	3.75	5.00
GREATEST ALL TIME HITS	Scepter (S) 2-5112	3.00	4.50	6.00
GREATEST HITS	Scepter (S) SPS 578	2.50	3.75	5.00
HELP ME MAKE IT TO MY ROCKIN' CHAIR	ABC (S) 912	2.00	3.00	4.00
I'M SO LONESOME I COULD CRY	Pacemaker (M) PLP 3001	5.00	7.50	10.00
LONGHORNS & LONDONBRIDGES	Paramount (S) 1020	3.00	4.50	6.00
ON MY WAY	Scepter (S) SPS 570	2.50	3.75	5.00
RAINDROPS KEEP FALLIN' ON MY HEAD	Scepter (S) SPS 580	3.00	4.50	6.00
TOMORROW NEVER COMES	Scepter (M) SRM 556	2.00	3.00	4.00
TOMORROW NEVER COMES	Scepter (S) SPS 556	2.50	3.75	5.00
VERY BEST OF B.J. THOMAS	Hickory (S) LPS 133	3.00	4.50	6.00
VERY BEST OF B.J. THOMAS	United Artists (S) UA-LA389	2.00	3.00	4.00

THOMAS, Carla

BEST OF CARLA THOMAS	Atlantic (S) SD 8232	3.00	4.50	6.00
CARLA	Stax (M) 709	3.00	4.50	6.00
CARLA	Stax (S) 709	3.50	5.25	7.00
COMFORT ME	Stax (S) 706	3.00	4.50	6.00
GEE WHIZ	Atlantic (M) 8057	4.00	6.00	8.00
LOVE MEANS CARLA THOMAS	Stax (S) STS 2044	2.75	3.00	5.50

TITLE	LABEL & NO.	GOOD	VERY GOOD	NEAR MINT
MEMPHIS QUEEN	Stax (S) STS 2019	2.75	3.00	5.50
QUEEN ALONE, THE	Stax (M) 718	2.50	3.75	5.00

THOMAS, Henry

TITLE	LABEL & NO.	GOOD	VERY GOOD	NEAR MINT
HENRY THOMAS SINGS THE TEXAS BLUES	Origin (M) OJL 3	4.00	6.00	8.00

THOMAS, Irma

TITLE	LABEL & NO.	GOOD	VERY GOOD	NEAR MINT
IN BETWEEN TEARS	Fungus (M) FB 25150	2.50	3.75	5.00
IRMA THOMAS & MAXINE BROWN	Grand Prix (S) KS 426	2.50	3.75	5.00
TAKE A LOOK	Imperial (M) 9302	3.50	5.25	7.00
TAKE A LOOK	Imperial (S) LP 12302	4.00	6.00	8.00
WISH SOMEONE WOULD CARE	Imperial (M) LP 9266	4.00	6.00	8.00
WISH SOMEONE WOULD CARE	Imperial (S) LP 12266	4.50	6.75	9.00

THOMAS, Rufus

TITLE	LABEL & NO.	GOOD	VERY GOOD	NEAR MINT
CROWN PRINCE OF DANCE	Stax (S) STS 3008	3.00	4.50	6.00
DID YOU HEARD ME	Stax (S) STS 3004	3.00	4.50	6.00
DOING THE PUSH AND PULL LIVE AT P.J's	Stax (S) STS 2039	3.00	4.50	6.00
DO THE FUNKY CHICKEN	Stax (S) STS 2028	3.00	4.50	6.00
MAY I HAVE YOUR TICKET PLEASE	Stax (S) STS 2022	3.00	4.50	6.00
WALKING THE DOG	Stax (M) 704	3.50	7.00	10.50

THOMAS, Timmy

TITLE	LABEL & NO.	GOOD	VERY GOOD	NEAR MINT
WHY CAN'T WE LIVE TOGETHER	Glades (S) 6501	2.50	3.75	5.00

THOMPSON, Don

TITLE	LABEL & NO.	GOOD	VERY GOOD	NEAR MINT
JUPITER	Sunday (S) KS 5101	2.50	3.75	5.00

THOMPSON, Hank

TITLE	LABEL & NO.	GOOD	VERY GOOD	NEAR MINT
BEST OF HANK THOMPSON	Capitol (M) T-1878	2.50	3.75	5.00
BEST OF HANK THOMPSON	Capitol (S) ST-1878	2.50	3.75	5.00
BEST OF HANK THOMPSON VOL. 2	Capitol (M) T 2661	2.00	3.00	4.00
BEST OF HANK THOMPSON VOL. 2	Capitol (S) ST 2661	2.00	3.00	4.00
BREAKIN' IN ANOTHER HEART	Capitol (M) T-2274	2.00	3.00	4.00
BREAKIN' IN ANOTHER HEART	Capitol (S) ST-2274	2.00	3.00	4.00
BREAKIN' THE RULES	Capitol (M) T-2575	2.00	3.00	4.00
BREAKIN' THE RULES	Capitol (S) DT-2575	2.00	3.00	4.00
DANCE RANCH	Capitol (M) T 975	4.00	6.00	8.00
DANCING WESTERN STYLE	Capitol (EP) EAP 1-705	2.00	3.00	4.00
FAVORITE WALTZES	Capitol (M) T-1111	3.00	4.50	6.00
FAVORITE WALTZES	Capitol (EP) EAP-1-1111	1.50	2.25	3.00
GOLDEN COUNTRY HITS	Capitol (M) T-2089	2.50	3.75	5.00
GOLDEN COUNTRY HITS	Capitol (S) ST-2089	2.50	3.75	5.00
HANK	Capitol (M) T 826	4.00	6.00	8.00
HANK	Capitol (EP) EAP 1-826	2.00	3.00	4.00
HANK	Capitol (EP) EAP 2-826	2.00	3.00	4.00
HANK	Capitol (EP) EAP 3-826	2.00	3.00	4.00
HANK THOMPSON	Capitol (EP) EAP 1-601	2.00	3.00	4.00
HANK THOMPSON ALL TIME HITS	Capitol (M) T 729	5.00	7.50	10.00
HANK THOMPSON ALL TIME HITS	Capitol (EP) EAP 1-729	2.00	3.00	4.00
HANK THOMPSON ALL TIME HITS	Capitol (EP) EAP 2-729	2.00	3.00	4.00
HANK THOMPSON ALL TIME HITS	Capitol (EP) EAP 3-729	2.00	3.00	4.00
HANK THOMPSON AT THE GOLDEN NUGGET	Capitol (M) T-1632	3.00	4.50	6.00
HANK THOMPSON AT THE GOLDEN NUGGET	Capitol (S) ST-1632	3.00	4.50	6.00
HANK THOMPSON'S GREATEST HITS	Dot (S) 26004	2.00	3.00	4.00
HANK THOMPSON SINGS THE HITS OF NAT "KING" COLE	Dot (S) DOSD-2032	2.00	3.00	4.00
IT'S CHRISTMAS TIME	Capitol (M) T-2154	2.50	3.75	5.00
IT'S CHRISTMAS TIME	Capitol (S) ST-2154	2.50	3.75	5.00
JUST AN OLD FLAME	Capitol (M) T 2826	2.00	3.00	4.00
JUST AN OLD FLAME	Capitol (S) ST 2826	2.00	3.00	4.00
KINDLY KEEP IT COUNTRY	Dot (S) 26015	2.00	3.00	4.00
LUCKIEST HEARTACHE IN TOWN	Capitol (M) T 2342	2.00	3.00	4.00
LUCKIEST HEARTACHE IN TOWN	Capitol (S) ST 2342	2.00	3.00	4.00
MOST OF ALL	Capitol (M) T-1360	3.00	4.50	6.00
MOST OF ALL	Capitol (S) ST-1360	3.00	4.50	6.00
MOST OF ALL	Capitol (EP) EAP-1-1360	1.50	2.25	3.00
MOVIN' ON	Dot (S) DOSD-2003	2.00	3.00	4.00
NO. 1 COUNTRY & WESTERN BAND	Capitol (M) T-1741	2.50	3.75	5.00
NO. 1 COUNTRY & WESTERN BAND	Capitol (S) ST-1741	2.50	3.75	5.00
NORTH OF THE RIO GRANDE	Capitol (M) T 618	5.00	7.50	10.00
NORTH OF THE RIO GRANDE	Capitol (EP) EAP 1-618	2.00	3.00	4.00
NORTH OF THE RIO GRANDE	Capitol (EP) EAP 2-618	2.00	3.00	4.00
NORTH OF THE RIO GRANDE	Capitol (EP) EAP 3-618	2.00	3.00	4.00
OLD LOVE AFFAIR	Capitol (M) T-1544	3.00	4.50	6.00
OLD LOVE AFFAIR	Capitol (S) ST-1544	3.00	4.50	6.00
SIX PACK TO GO	Capitol (M) T-2460	2.00	3.00	4.00
SIX PACK TO GO	Capitol (S) ST-2460	2.00	3.00	4.00
SIX PACK TO GO	Dot (S) 2-1041	2.00	3.00	4.00
SONGS FOR ROUNDERS	Capitol (M) T-1246	3.00	4.50	6.00
SONGS FOR ROUNDERS	Capitol (S) ST-1246	3.00	4.50	6.00
SONGS FOR ROUNDERS	Capitol (EP) EAP-1-1246	1.50	2.25	3.00
SONGS FOR ROUNDERS	Capitol (EP) EAP-2-1246	1.50	2.25	3.00
SONGS FOR ROUNDERS	Capitol (EP) EAP-3-1246	1.50	2.25	3.00
SONGS OF BRAZOS VALLEY (10")	Capitol (M) H 418	5.00	7.50	10.00
STATE FAIR OF TEXAS	Capitol (M) T-1955	2.50	3.75	5.00
STATE FAIR OF TEXAS	Capitol (S) ST-1955	2.50	3.75	5.00
THIS BROKEN HEART OF MINE	Capitol (M) T-1469	2.50	3.75	5.00
THIS BROKEN HEART OF MINE	Capitol (S) ST-1469	2.50	3.75	5.00
THOMPSON FAVORITES (10")	Capitol (M) H 9111	5.00	7.50	10.00
WHERE IS THE CIRCUS	Warner Brothers (M) 1664	2.00	3.00	4.00
WHERE IS THE CIRCUS	Warner Brothers (S) 1664	2.00	3.00	4.00

THOMPSON, Mayo

TITLE	LABEL & NO.	GOOD	VERY GOOD	NEAR MINT
CORKY'S DEBT TO HIS FATHER	Texas Revolution (S) CFS 2270	6.00	9.00	12.00

(M) Mono (S) Stereo (EP) Extended Play (Q) Quad (RI) Re-issued

THOMPSON, Sonny

TITLE	LABEL & NO.	GOOD	VERY GOOD	NEAR MINT
BLUES SELECTIONS	King (EP) EP 209	2.00	5.00	8.00
SONNY THOMPSON INSTRUMENTALS	King (EP) KEP 273	2.00	5.00	8.00

THORINSHIELD

TITLE	LABEL & NO.	GOOD	VERY GOOD	NEAR MINT
THORINSHIELD	Philips (M) PHM 200-251	2.50	3.75	5.00
THORINSHIELD	Philips (S) PHS 600 251	3.00	4.50	6.00

THORNTON, Big Mama

TITLE	LABEL & NO.	GOOD	VERY GOOD	NEAR MINT
BIG MAMA THRONTON IN EUROPE	Arhoolie (M) 1028	3.00	4.50	6.00
JAIL	Vanguard (S) VSD 79351	3.50	5.25	7.00
SASSY MAMA	Vanguard (S) VSD 79354	3.50	5.25	7.00
SAVED	Pentagram (M) PE 10,005	3.00	4.50	6.00
SHE'S BACK	Back Beat (M) BLP 68	5.00	12.50	20.00
STRONGER THAN DIRT	Mercury (M) 61225	3.00	4.50	6.00

THREE CHUCKLES

TITLE	LABEL & NO.	GOOD	VERY GOOD	NEAR MINT
THREE CHUCKLES	RCA (M) LX 1067	7.00	14.00	21.00
THREE CHUCKLES	RCA (EP) EXA 192	2.50	3.00	5.00
THREE CHUCKLES	RCA (EP) EXA 193	2.50	3.00	5.00
THREE CHUCKLES	RCA (EP) EXA 194	2.50	3.00	5.00
THREE CHUCKLES	RCA (EP) DJ4	3.00	6.00	9.00

THREE DEGREES

TITLE	LABEL & NO.	GOOD	VERY GOOD	NEAR MINT
INTERNATIONAL	Philadelphia Int'l (S) KZ-33162	2.50	3.75	5.00
MAYBE	Roulette (S) SR 42050	4.50	9.00	13.50
SO MUCH LOVE	Roulette (S) 3015	3.00	4.00	6.00
THREE DEGREES	Philadelphia Int'l (S) KZ-32406	3.00	4.50	6.00
THREE DEGREES LIVE	Philadelphia Int'l (S) PZ-33840	2.50	3.75	5.00

THREE DOG NIGHT

TITLE	LABEL & NO.	GOOD	VERY GOOD	NEAR MINT
AROUND THE WORLD WITH THREE DOG NIGHT	Dunhill (S) 50138	2.50	3.75	5.00
COMING DOWN YOUR WAY	ABC (S) 888	2.00	3.00	4.00
COMING DOWN YOUR WAY	Command (Q) QD-40018	2.00	3.00	4.00
GOLDEN BISQUITS	Dunhill (S) 50098	2.50	3.75	5.00
HARD LABOR	Dunhill (S) 50168	2.50	3.75	5.00
HARD LABOR	Command (Q) QD 40014	2.50	3.75	5.00
HARMONY	Dunhill (S) 50108	2.50	3.75	5.00
IT AIN'T EASY	Dunhill (S) 50078	3.00	4.50	6.00
NATURALLY	Dunhill (S) 50088	3.00	4.50	6.00
SEVEN SEPARATE FOOLS	Dunhill (S) 50118	2.50	3.75	5.00
SUITABLE FOR FRAMING	Dunhill (S) 50058	3.00	4.50	6.00
THREE DOG NIGHT	Dunhill (S) 50048	3.00	4.50	6.00
THREE DOG NIGHT WAS CAPTURED LIVE AT THE FORUM	Dunhill (S) 50068	3.00	4.50	6.00

Also see HUTTON, Danny

3'S A CROWD

TITLE	LABEL & NO.	GOOD	VERY GOOD	NEAR MINT
CHRISTOPHER'S MOVIE MATINEE	Dunhill (M) D 50030	3.50	5.25	7.00

THRILLERS, THE

TITLE	LABEL & NO.	GOOD	VERY GOOD	NEAR MINT
ELIZABETH (10")	Big Town (M) 1001	20.00	50.00	80.00

THUNDER, Johnny

TITLE	LABEL & NO.	GOOD	VERY GOOD	NEAR MINT
LOOP DE LOOP	Diamond (M) D 5001	4.00	6.00	8.00
LOOP DE LOOP	Diamond (S) SD 5001	4.50	6.75	9.00

THUNDERBIRDS

TITLE	LABEL & NO.	GOOD	VERY GOOD	NEAR MINT
MEET THE FABULOUS THUNDERBIRDS	Red Feather (M) RF TH 1	6.00	12.00	18.00

THUNDERTONES

TITLE	LABEL & NO.	GOOD	VERY GOOD	NEAR MINT
CLOUDBURST	Aurora (M) ALM 920	4.00	8.00	12.00

TIDBITS

TITLE	LABEL & NO.	GOOD	VERY GOOD	NEAR MINT
GREETINGS FROM JAMAICA	Family Productions (S) FPS 2714	2.50	3.75	5.00

TIDE

TITLE	LABEL & NO.	GOOD	VERY GOOD	NEAR MINT
ALMOST LIVE	Mouth (S) 7237	4.00	6.00	8.00

TIDES

TITLE	LABEL & NO.	GOOD	VERY GOOD	NEAR MINT
SURF CITY AND OTHER FAVORITES	Wing (M) MGW 12265	3.50	5.25	7.00

TIEKEN, Freddie & The Rockers

TITLE	LABEL & NO.	GOOD	VERY GOOD	NEAR MINT
BY POPULAR DEMAND	IT (M) 2301	6.00	12.00	18.00
LIVE	IT (M) 2304	6.00	12.00	18.00

TILLIS, Mel

TITLE	LABEL & NO.	GOOD	VERY GOOD	NEAR MINT
BEST OF MEL TILLIS	MCA (S) 2-4091	3.00	4.50	6.00
I AIN'T NEVER/NEON ROSE	MGM (S) 4870	2.50	3.75	5.00
MEL TILLIS & THE STATESIDERS	MGM (S) M3G-4987	2.00	3.00	4.00
MEL TILLIS & THE STATESIDERS ON STAGE	MGM (S) 4889	2.00	3.00	4.00
MEL TILLIS GREATEST HITS	MCA (S) 66	2.00	3.00	4.00
MEL TILLIS' GREATEST HITS	MGM (S) M3G-4970	2.00	3.00	4.00
M-M-MEL	MGM (S) M3G-5002	2.00	3.00	4.00
SAWMILL	MGM (S) 4907	2.50	3.75	5.00
STOMP THEM GRAPES	MGM (S) M3G-4960	2.00	3.00	4.00

TILLOTSON, Johnny

TITLE	LABEL & NO.	GOOD	VERY GOOD	NEAR MINT
BEST OF JOHNNY TILLOTSON	MGM (M) 4532	3.00	4.50	6.00

TITLE	LABEL & NO.	GOOD	VERY GOOD	NEAR MINT
BEST OF JOHNNY TILLOTSON	MGM (S) 4532	3.00	4.50	6.00
CHRISTMAS TOUCH	MGM (M) 4402	2.00	3.00	4.00
CHRISTMAS TOUCH	MGM (S) 4402	2.50	3.75	5.00
DREAMY EYES	Cadence (EP) EP 114	1.50	3.00	4.50
IT KEEPS RIGHT ON A-HURTIN'	Cadence (M) 3058	4.00	8.00	12.00
IT KEEPS RIGHT ON A-HURTIN'	Cadence (S) 25058	5.00	10.00	15.00
JOHNNY SINGS TILLOTSON	Metro (M) M-561	2.00	3.00	4.00
JOHNNY SINGS TILLOTSON	Metro (S) MS-561	2.00	3.00	4.00
JOHNNY TILLOTSON'S BEST	Cadence (M) 3052	6.00	12.00	18.00
JOHNNY TILLOTSON'S BEST	Cadence (S) 25052	8.00	16.00	24.00
JOHNNY TILLOTSON SINGS	MGM (M) E 4328	4.00	6.00	8.00
JOHNNY TILLOTSON SINGS	MGM (S) SE 4328	4.50	6.75	9.00
NO LOVE AT ALL	MGM (M) 4395	2.00	3.00	4.00
NO LOVE AT ALL	MGM (S) 4395	2.50	3.75	5.00
OUR WORLD	MGM (M) E-4328	2.00	3.00	4.00
OUR WORLD	MGM (S) SE-4328	2.50	3.75	5.00
PRINCESS PRINCESS	Cadence (EP) EP 2	1.50	3.00	4.50
SHE UNDERSTANDS ME	MGM (M) E-4270	4.00	6.00	8.00
SHE UNDERSTANDS ME	MGM (S) SE-4270	4.50	5.25	9.00
TALK BACK TREMBLING LIPS	MGM (M) E 4188	4.00	8.00	12.00
TALK BACK TREMBLING LIPS	MGM (S) SE 4188	5.00	10.00	15.00
TILLOTSON TOUCH, THE	MGM (M) E-4224	4.00	6.00	8.00
TILLOTSON TOUCH, THE	MGM (S) SE-4224	4.50	5.25	9.00
VERY BEST OF JOHNNY TILLOTSON	MGM (S) 4814	3.00	4.50	6.00
YOU CAN NEVER STOP ME LOVING YOU	Cadence (M) CLP 3067	4.00	8.00	12.00
YOU CAN NEVER STOP ME LOVING YOU	Cadence (S) 25067	5.00	10.00	15.00

T.I.M.E.

TITLE	LABEL & NO.	GOOD	VERY GOOD	NEAR MINT
SMOOTH BALL	Liberty (S) LST 7605	3.50	5.25	7.00
TIME	Liberty (S) LST 7558	3.00	4.50	6.00

TINGLING BROTHERS CIRCUS

A CIRCUS OF THE MIND	Musicor (S) MS 3167	3.00	4.50	6.00

TIN TIN

ASTRAL TAXI	Atco (S) SD 33-370	3.50	5.00	7.00
TIN TIN	Atco (S) SD 33-350	4.00	6.00	8.00

TINY TIM

FOR ALL MY LITTLE FRIENDS	Reprise (S) 6351	3.00	4.50	6.00
GOD BLESS TINY TIM	Reprise (S) 6292	3.00	4.50	6.00
LOVE AND KISSES FROM TINY TIM	Bouquet (S) SLP 711	2.50	3.75	5.00
TINY TIM'S SECOND ALBUM	Reprise (S) 6323	3.00	4.50	6.00

TIR NA NOG

TEAR & A SMILE	Chrysalis (S) 1006	3.00	4.50	6.00

TITANS

DO THE TWIST	MGM	3.00	6.00	9.00
TODAY'S TEEN BEAT	MGM (M) E 3992	3.00	6.00	9.00
TODAY'S TEEN BEAT	MGM (S) SE 3992	3.50	7.00	10.50

TITUS GROAN

TITUS GROAN	Janus (S) JLS 3024	3.00	4.50	6.00

TOAD HALL

TOAD HALL	Liberty (S) LST 7580	3.00	4.50	6.00

TODD, Art & Dotty

BLACK VELVET EYES	Dart (S) D-444	3.00	4.50	6.00

TOE FAT

TOE FAT	Rare Earth (S) RS 511	4.50	6.75	9.00
TOE FAT TWO	Rare Earth (S) 525	6.00	9.00	12.00

TOKENS

BOTH SIDES NOW	Buddah (S) BDS 5059	3.00	4.50	6.00
DECEMBER 5TH	BT Puppy (M) 1014	5.00	7.50	10.00
GREATEST MOMENTS	BT Puppy (M) 1012	4.00	6.00	8.00
I HEAR TRUMPETS BLOW	BT Puppy (M) BTP 1000	3.00	4.50	6.00
I HEAR TRUMPETS BLOW	BT Puppy (S) BTPS 1000	3.50	5.25	7.00
INTERCOURSE	BT Puppy (M) 1027	5.00	7.50	10.00
IT'S A HAPPENING WORLD	Warner Brothers (M) 1685	3.00	4.50	6.00
KINGS OF THE HOT RODS	Diplomat (M) D 2308	3.00	6.00	9.00
KINGS OF THE HOT RODS	Diplomat (S) DS 2308	2.50	5.00	7.50
LION SLEEPS TONIGHT, THE	RCA (M) LPM 2514	6.00	12.00	18.00
LION SLEEPS TONIGHT, THE	RCA (S) LSP 2514	7.00	14.00	21.00
TOKENS AGAIN, THE	RCA (M) LPM 3685	5.00	10.00	15.00
TOKENS AGAIN, THE	RCA (S) LSP 3685	6.00	12.00	18.00
TOKENS OF GOLD	BT Puppy (M) 1006	4.00	6.00	8.00
VERY BEST	BT Puppy (M) 1028	5.00	7.50	10.00
WE SING FOLK	RCA (M) LPM 2631	5.00	10.00	15.00
WE SING FOLK	RCA (S) LSP 2631	6.00	12.00	18.00
WHEELS	RCA (M) LPM 2886	5.00	10.00	15.00
WHEELS	RCA (S) LSP 2886	6.00	12.00	18.00

TOKENS & The Happenings

BACK TO BACK (6 SELECTIONS BY EACH GROUP)	BT Puppy (M) BTP 1002	2.50	3.75	5.00
BACK TO BACK (6 SELECTIONS BY EACH GROUP)	BT Puppy (S) BTPS 1002	3.00	4.50	6.00

TOM AND JERRY

SURFIN' HOOTENANNY	Mercury (M) MG 20842	3.00	6.00	9.00

TITLE	LABEL & NO.	GOOD	VERY GOOD	NEAR MINT
SURFIN' HOOTENANNY	Mercury (S) SR 60842	3.50	7.00	10.50

Also see SIMON & GARFUNKEL

TOMLIN, Lily

AND THAT'S THE TRUTH	Polydor (S) 5023	2.50	3.75	5.00
MODERN SCREAM	Polydor (S) 6051	2.50	3.75	5.00
THIS IS A RECORDING	Polydor (S) 4055	2.50	3.75	5.00

TOMORROW

TOMORROW	Sire (S) SES 97012	6.00	9.00	12.00

TOMPALL & THE GLASER BROTHERS

GREAT HITS FROM 2 DECADES	MGM (S) 4888	2.00	3.00	4.00

TONGUE AND GROOVE (Featuring Lynne Hughes)

GROOVE	Fontana (S) SRF 67593	4.50	6.75	9.00

TONICS

HIT PARADE	Polydor (S) 184003	3.00	4.50	6.00

TONTOS EXPANDING HEAD BAND

ZERO TIME	Embryo (S) SD 732	4.00	6.00	8.00

TONY, Vic & Manuel

A GO GO HOLLYWOOD NIGHT LIFE	Reprise (M) R 6139	4.00	8.00	12.00

TONY'S TIGERS

TONY'S TIGERS	Teen Town	7.00	14.00	21.00

TORMENTORS

HANGING ROUND	Royal (S) RLP 111	4.00	8.00	12.00

TORNADOES

BUSTIN' SURFBOARDS	Josie (M) 4005	5.00	10.00	15.00
TELSTAR	London (M) LL 3279	5.00	10.00	15.00

TOROK, Mitchell

CARIBBEAN	Guyden (M) G-502	5.00	10.00	15.00
CARIBBEAN	Guyden (S) ST-502	6.00	12.00	18.00
GUITAR COURSE	Reprise (M) 6223	2.50	3.75	5.00

TORQUES

LIVE	Lemco (M) 604	5.00	10.00	15.00
ZOOM	WA (M) 64-010	6.00	12.00	18.00

TOUCH

TOUCH	Coliseum (S) DS 51004	4.50	6.75	9.00

TOUCHSTONE

TAROT	United Artists (S) UAS 5563	3.00	4.50	6.00

TOWER OF POWER

BACK TO OAKLAND	Warner Bros. (S) BS-2749	2.50	3.75	5.00
BUMP CITY	Warner Bros. (S) 2616	2.50	3.75	5.00
EAST BAY GREASE	San Francisco (S) 204	4.00	6.00	8.00
TOWER OF POWER	Warner Bros. (S) BS 2681	2.50	3.75	5.00
URBAN RENEWAL	Warner Bros (S) BS 2834	2.50	3.75	5.00
WE CAME TO PLAY	Columbia (S) JC 34906	2.00	3.00	4.00

TOWNSHEND, Peter

WHO CAME FIRST	Decca/Track (S) 79189	3.00	4.50	6.00

Also see WHO

TOYS

LOVERS CONCERTO, A/ATTACK	Dyno Voice (M) 9002	3.50	5.25	7.00

TRADEWINDS

EXCURSIONS	Kama Sutra (M) KLP 8057	4.00	6.00	8.00
EXCURSIONS	Kama Sutra (S) KLPS 8057	4.50	6.75	9.00

(M) Mono   (S) Stereo   (EP) Extended Play   (Q) Quad   (RI) Re-issued

TITLE	LABEL & NO.	GOOD	VERY GOOD	NEAR MINT
TRAFFIC				
BEST OF TRAFFIC	United Artists (S) UAS 5500	3.00	4.50	6.00
HEAVY TRAFFIC	United Artists (S) UA-LA421	2.00	3.00	4.00
JOHN BARLEYCORN MUST DIE	United Artists (S) UAS 5504	3.00	4.50	6.00
JOHN BARLEYCORN MUST DIE (RI)	United Artists (S) UA-LA202	2.00	3.00	4.00
LAST EXIT	United Artists (S) UAS 6702	3.00	4.50	6.00
LOW SPARK OF HIGH HEELED BOYS, THE	Island (S) SW 9306	3.00	4.50	6.00
LOW SPARK OF HIGH HEELED BOYS, THE ('75 RI)	Island (S) 9180	2.00	3.00	4.00
MR. FANTASY	United Artists (M) UAL 3651	3.50	5.25	7.00
MR. FANTASY	United Artists (S) UAS 6651	3.00	4.50	6.00
MORE HEAVY TRAFFIC	United Artists (S) UA-LA526	2.00	3.00	4.00
SHOOT OUT AT THE FANTASY FACTORY	Island (S) SW 9323	3.00	4.50	6.00
SHOOT OUT AT THE FANTASY FACTORY ('75 RI)	Island (S) 9224	2.00	3.00	4.00
TRAFFIC	United Artists (S) UAS 6676	3.00	4.50	6.00
TRAFFIC ON THE ROAD	Island (S) 2	3.00	4.50	6.00
WELCOME TO THE CANTEEN	United Artists (S) UAS 5550	3.00	4.50	6.00
TRAMMELL, Bobby Lee				
ARKANSAS TWIST	Atlanta (M) LPM 1503	10.00	25.00	40.00
LOVE ISN'T LOVE	Souncot (S) CS 1141	6.50	9.75	13.00
TRAMMPS				
LEGENDARY ZING ALBUM FEATURING THE FABULOUS TRAMMPS, THE	Buddah (S) BDS 5641	2.00	3.00	4.00
TRAMMPS	Golden Fleece (S) KZ 33163	2.00	3.00	4.00
TRASHMEN				
SURFIN' BIRD	Garrett (M) GA 200	5.00	10.00	15.00
SURFIN' BIRD	Garrett (S) GAS 200	6.00	12.00	18.00
TRAVEL AGENCY				
TRAVEL AGENCY, THE	Viva (M) V 36017	6.00	9.00	12.00
TRAVERS, Mary				
ALL MY CHOICES	Warner Brothers (S) B-2677	2.50	3.75	5.00
CIRCLES	Warner Brothers (S) B-2795	2.50	3.75	5.00
MARY (OF PETER, PAUL & MARY)	Warner Brothers (M) 1907	2.50	3.75	5.00
MORNING GLORY	Warner Brothers (M) 2609	2.50	3.75	5.00
TREMELOES				
EVEN THE BAD TIMES ARE GOOD	Epic (M) LN 24326	3.00	4.50	6.00
EVEN THE BAD TIMES ARE GOOD	Epic (S) BN 26326	4.00	6.00	8.00
HERE COMES MY BABY	Epic (M) LN 24310	3.00	4.50	6.00
HERE COMES MY BABY	Epic (S) BN 26310	4.00	6.00	8.00
SUDDENLY YOU LOVE ME	Epic (M) LN 24363	3.00	4.50	6.00
SUDDENLY YOU LOVE ME	Epic (S) BN 26363	4.00	6.00	8.00
WORLD EXPLOSION '58/68	Epic (S) BN 26388	4.00	6.00	8.00
TRENIERS				
GO, GO, GO	Epic (M) LG3125	5.00	12.50	20.00
T. REX (Tyrannosaurus Rex)				
A BEARD OF STARS	Blue Thumb (S) BTS 18	3.00	4.50	6.00
AN INTERVIEW WITH MARC BOLAN OF T REX BY MIKE CUSCUNA	Reprise (S) PRO 511	6.00	9.00	12.00
ELECTRIC WARRIOR	Reprise (S) RS 6466	2.50	3.75	5.00
LIGHT OF LOVE	Casablanca (S) NBLP 9006	2.50	3.75	5.00
SLIDER, THE	Reprise (S) MS 2095	2.50	3.75	5.00
TANX	Reprise (S) MS 2132	2.50	3.75	5.00
T-REX (FEATURING RIDE A WHITE SWAN)	Reprise (S) RS 6440	3.00	4.50	6.00
TYRANNOSAURUS REX-A BEGINNING	A&M (S) SP 3514	4.00	6.00	8.00
(Combines LP's "My People Were Fair" and "Prophets, Seers & Sages")				
TRIALS AND TRIBULATIONS				
TRIALS AND TRIBULATIONS	Vanguard (S) VSD 6565	3.00	4.50	6.00
TRIANGLE				
HOW NOW BLUE COW	Amaret (S) 5001	3.00	4.50	6.00
TRIBESMEN				
BAREFOOTIN'	Hanna Barbera (M) HLP 8507	2.50	3.75	5.00
BAREFOOTIN'	Hanna Barbera (S) HST 9507	3.00	4.50	6.00
TRICE, Willie				
BLUE AND RAG'D	Trix (M) 3305	2.50	3.75	5.00
TRIPSICHORD MUSIC BOX				
TRIPSICHORD	Janus (S) JLS 3016	5.00	7.50	10.00
TROGGS				
LOVE IS ALL AROUND	Fontana (S) SRF 67576	5.00	7.50	10.00
TROGGS, THE	Pye (S) 12112	3.00	4.50	6.00
WILD THING	Atco (M) 33-193	6.00	9.00	12.00
WILD THING	Atco (S) SD 33-193	7.00	10.50	14.00
WILD THING	Fontana (S) SRF 67556	6.00	9.00	12.00
TROLL				
ANIMATED MUSIC	Smash (S) SRS 67114	5.00	7.50	10.00
TROUT				
TROUT, THE	MGM (S) SE 4592	2.00	3.00	4.00
TROWER, Robin				
FOR EARTH BELOW	Chrysalis (S) 1073	2.50	3.75	5.00
ROBIN TROWER IN CITY DREAMS	Chrysalis (S) 1148	2.00	3.00	4.00
TWICE REMOVED FROM YESTERDAY	Chrysalis (S) 1039	2.50	3.75	5.00
TROY, Doris				
DORIS TROY	Apple (S) ST 3371	7.00	10.50	14.00
JUST ONE LOOK	Atlantic (M) 8088	3.00	4.50	6.00
TRUMPETEERS				
MILKY WHITE WAY (VERY RARE!)	Score (M) 4021	15.00	37.50	60.00
T. SWIFT & THE ELECTRIC BAG				
ARE YOU EXPERIENCED	Custom (S) CS 1115	2.25	3.50	4.50
T.2.				
T.2.	London (S) PS 583	2.50	3.75	5.00
TUBES				
NOW	A&M (S) SP 4632	2.00	3.00	4.00
TUBES, THE	A&M (S) SP 4534	2.00	3.00	4.00
WHAT DO YOU WANT FROM LIVE!	A&M (S) SP 6003	3.00	4.50	6.00
YOUNG & RICH	A&M (S) SP 4580	2.00	3.00	4.00
TUCKER, Tanya				
DELTA DAWN	Columbia (S) 31742	2.00	3.00	4.00
TANYA TUCKER'S GREATEST HITS	Columbia (S) KC-33355	2.00	3.00	4.00
WHAT'S YOUR MAMA'S NAME	Columbia (S) KC-32272	2.00	3.00	4.00
WOULD YOU LAY WITH ME (IN A FIELD OF STONE)	Columbia (S) KC-32744	2.00	3.00	4.00
TUCKER, Tommy				
HI HEEL SNEAKERS	Checker (M) 2990	3.50	7.00	10.50
TUFANO & GIAMMARESE BAND				
TUFANO & GIAMMARESE	Ode (S) 77017	3.50	5.25	7.00
TUFANO & GIAMMARESE BAND	Ode (S) 77032	3.50	5.25	7.00
TUFF JACK				
TWANGY, SHOUTIN', FANTASTIC BIG BAND SOUNDS OF TUFF JACK	Capitol (M) T 1727	2.00	3.00	4.00
TURNER, Ike				
BLACK MAN'S SOUL, A (& The Kings of Rhythm)	Pompii (S) SD 6003	3.00	4.50	6.00
BLUES ROOTS	United Artists (S) UAS 5576	2.00	3.00	4.00
IKE TURNER ROCKS THE BLUES	Crown (S) CST 367	5.00	12.50	20.00
TURNER, Ike and Tina				
BEST OF IKE & TINA TURNER	Blue Thumb (S) 49	2.50	3.75	5.00
COME TOGETHER	Liberty (S) LST 7637	2.50	3.75	5.00
DANCE	Sue (M) LP 2003	6.00	12.00	18.00
DON'T PLAY ME CHEAP	Sue (M) LP 2005	6.00	12.00	18.00
DYNAMITE	Sue (M) LP 2004	6.00	12.00	18.00
FESTIVAL OF LIVE PERFORMANCES	Kent (S) KST 538	5.00	7.50	10.00
GET IT GET IT	Cenco (M) LP 104	5.00	10.00	15.00
GOSPEL ACCORDING TO IKE & TINA	United Artists (S) UA-LA203-G	1.50	2.25	3.00
GREATEST HITS	Warner Brothers (S) WS 1810	4.00	6.00	8.00
GREATEST HITS OF IKE AND TINA TURNER	Sue (M) 1038	5.00	7.50	10.00
HER MAN HIS WOMAN	Capitol (S) ST 571	3.00	4.50	6.00
HUNTER, THE	Blue Thumb (M) 11	2.50	3.75	5.00
IKE & TINA GREATEST HITS	United Artists (S) 5667	2.00	3.00	4.00
IN PERSON	Minit (M) 24018	4.00	6.00	8.00
IT'S GONNA WORK OUT FINE	Sue (M) LP 2007	5.00	10.00	15.00
LET ME TOUCH YOUR MIND	United Artists (S) UAS 5660	2.00	3.00	4.00
LIVE	Kent (M) KLMP 5014	4.50	6.75	9.00
LIVE	Loma (M) 5904	4.00	6.00	8.00
LIVE	Loma (S) 5904	5.00	7.50	10.00
LIVE	Warner Bros. (M) 1579	3.50	5.25	7.00
LIVE	Warner Brothers (S) WS 1579	4.00	6.00	8.00
NUTBUSH CITY LIMITS	United Artists (S) UALA 180F	1.50	2.25	3.00
NUFF SAID	United Artists (S) 5530	1.50	2.25	3.00
OUTTA SEASON	Blue Thumb (M) 5	2.50	3.75	5.00
PLEASE PLEASE PLEASE	Kent (M) 550	4.50	6.75	9.00
RIVER DEEP, MOUNTAIN HIGH	Philles (M) 4011	20.00	30.00	40.00
RIVER DEEP, MOUNTAIN HIGH ('70 RI)	A&M (S) 4178	4.00	6.00	8.00
16 GREAT PERFORMANCES- IKE & TINA TURNER	ABC (S) BTD-4014	2.00	3.00	4.00
SO FINE	Pompeii (S) SD 6000	3.00	4.50	6.00
SOUL OF IKE AND TINA, THE	Kent (M) 5019	4.50	6.75	9.00
SOUL OF IKE AND TINA, THE	Kent (S) KS519	5.00	7.50	10.00
SOUND OF IKE AND TINA TURNER, THE	Sue (M) LP 2001	6.00	12.00	18.00
SWEET RHODE ISLAND RED	United Artists (S) UA-LA312-G	2.50	3.75	5.00
WHAT YOU HEAR IS WHAT YOU GET	United Artists (M) 9953	2.00	3.00	4.00
WORKIN' TOGETHER	Liberty (M) 7650	2.50	3.75	5.00
WORLD OF IKE AND TINA LIVE	United Artists (S) UALA064 G2	2.50	3.75	5.00

(M) Mono (S) Stereo (EP) Extended Play (Q) Quad (RI) Re-issued

TURNER, Joe

TITLE	LABEL & NO.	GOOD	VERY GOOD	NEAR MINT
BEST OF JOE TURNER	Atlantic (M) 8081	5.00	7.50	10.00
BIG JOE IS HERE	Atlantic (M) 8033	5.00	12.50	20.00
BIG JOE RIDES AGAIN	Atlantic (M) 1332	5.00	12.50	20.00
BIG JOE RIDES AGAIN	Atlantic (S) SD-1332	6.00	15.00	24.00
BOSS OF THE BLUES	Atlantic (M) 1234	5.00	12.50	20.00
BOSS OF THE BLUES	Atlantic (S) SD 1234	6.00	15.00	24.00
CARELESS LOVE	Savoy (M) MG 14016	5.00	12.50	20.00
GREAT R&B OLDIES	Blues Spectrum (M) 104	2.00	3.00	4.00
HIS GREATEST RECORDINGS	Atco (M) 376	2.50	4.00	8.00
HIS GREATEST RECORDINGS	Atco (S) SD 33-376	4.00	6.00	8.00
JOE TURNER	Atlantic (M) 8005	5.00	7.50	10.00
JOE TURNER	Atlantic (EP) EP 565	2.00	5.00	8.00
JOE TURNER	Savoy (M) MG 14012	5.00	12.50	20.00
JOE TURNER AND JIMMY NELSON	Crown (S) CST 383	3.50	8.75	14.00
JOE TURNER (WITH RED NELSON)	Crown (M) 5295	3.50	8.75	14.00
JUMPIN THE BLUES	Arhoolie (M) R 2004	4.00	6.00	8.00
ROCKIN THE BLUES	Atlantic (M) 8023	5.00	7.50	10.00
ROCK WITH JOE TURNER	Atlantic (EP) EP 606	2.00	5.00	8.00
ROLL EM	Bluesway (M) 6060	2.50	4.00	5.00
ROLL 'EM	Blues Way (S) BLS 6060	5.00	7.50	10.00
SINGING THE BLUES	Bluesway (M) 6006	2.50	4.00	5.00
SINGS	Atlantic (EP) EP 536	2.00	5.00	8.00
STILL BOSS OF THE BLUES	United (M) 7790	2.00	3.00	4.00
TURNS ON THE BLUES	United (M) 7759	2.00	3.00	4.00

TURNER, Sammy

TITLE	LABEL & NO.	GOOD	VERY GOOD	NEAR MINT
LAVENDER BLUE MOODS	Bigtop (M) 1301	5.00	10.00	15.00
LAVENDER BLUE MOODS	Bigtop (S) 1301	6.00	12.00	18.00

TURNER, Tina

TITLE	LABEL & NO.	GOOD	VERY GOOD	NEAR MINT
ACID QUEEN	United Artists (S) UA-LA495 G	2.00	3.00	4.00
TINA TURNER TURNS THE COUNTRY ON	United Artists (S) UA-LA200G	2.00	3.00	4.00

TURNER, Titus

TITLE	LABEL & NO.	GOOD	VERY GOOD	NEAR MINT
SOUND OFF	Jamie (M) JLP 3018	5.00	10.00	15.00

TURTLES

TITLE	LABEL & NO.	GOOD	VERY GOOD	NEAR MINT
GOLDEN HITS	White Whale (M) WW 115	3.00	4.50	6.00
GOLDEN HITS	White Whale (S) WWS 115	3.50	5.25	7.00
HAPPY TOGETHER	White Whale (M) WW 114	3.00	4.50	6.00
HAPPY TOGETHER	White Whale (S) WWS 7114	3.50	5.25	7.00
HAPPY TOGETHER AGAIN	Sire (S) H-3703	3.00	4.50	6.00
IT AIN'T ME BABE	White Whale (M) WW 111	3.50	5.25	7.00
IT AIN'T ME BABE	White Whale (S) WWS 7111	4.00	6.00	8.00
MORE GOLDEN HITS	White Whale (S) WWS 7127	4.00	6.00	8.00
TURTLE SOUP	White Whale (S) WWS 7124	3.50	5.25	7.00
TURTLES PRESENT THE BATTLE OF THE BANDS	White Whale (S) WWS 7118	3.50	5.25	7.00
WOODEN HEAD	White Whale (S) WWS 7133	4.00	6.00	8.00
YOU BABY	White Whale (M) WW 112	3.50	5.25	7.00
YOU BABY	White Whale (S) WWS 7112	4.00	6.00	8.00

Also see FLO & EDDIE

TWENTIETH CENTURY ZOO

TITLE	LABEL & NO.	GOOD	VERY GOOD	NEAR MINT
THUNDER ON A CLEAR DAY	Vault (M) 122	4.00	6.00	8.00

TWIN TONES

TITLE	LABEL & NO.	GOOD	VERY GOOD	NEAR MINT
JIM AND JOHN	RCA (EP) EPA 4107	1.50	3.75	6.00

TWINS, (Jim and John)

TITLE	LABEL & NO.	GOOD	VERY GOOD	NEAR MINT
TEENAGERS LOVE	RCA (M) LPM 1708	4.00	10.00	16.00
TEENAGERS LOVE	RCA (EP) EPA 4237	1.50	3.75	6.00

TWINK

TITLE	LABEL & NO.	GOOD	VERY GOOD	NEAR MINT
THINK PINK	Sire (S) SES 97022	8.00	12.00	16.00

TWISTIN KINGS

TITLE	LABEL & NO.	GOOD	VERY GOOD	NEAR MINT
TWISTIN' THE WORLD AROUND	Motown (M) MLP 601	4.00	8.00	12.00

TWITTY, Conway

TITLE	LABEL & NO.	GOOD	VERY GOOD	NEAR MINT
CONWAY TWITTY COUNTRY	Decca (M) DL 4913	3.00	4.50	6.00
CONWAY TWITTY COUNTRY	Decca (S) DL 74913	3.00	4.50	6.00
CONWAY TWITTY'S GREATEST HITS	MGM (M) E-3849	4.00	8.00	12.00
CONWAY TWITTY'S GREATEST HITS	MGM (S) SE-3849	5.00	10.00	15.00
CONWAY TWITTY'S GREATEST HITS, Vol. I	Decca (S) DL 75352	3.00	4.50	6.00
CONWAY TWITTY'S GREATEST HITS, Vol. I (RI)	MCA (S) 52	2.50	3.75	5.00
CONWAY TWITTY'S GREATEST HITS, Vol. I ('78 RI)	MCA (S) 2345	2.00	3.00	4.00
CONWAY TWITTY'S GREATEST HITS, Vol. II	MCA (S) 2235	2.00	3.00	4.00
CONWAY TWITTY'S HONKY TONK ANGEL	MCA (S) 406	2.00	3.00	4.00
CONWAY TWITTY SINGS	Decca (M) DL 4724	3.00	4.50	6.00
CONWAY TWITTY SINGS	Decca (S) DL 74724	3.00	4.50	6.00
CONWAY TWITTY SINGS	MGM (M) E 3744	5.00	12.50	20.00
CONWAY TWITTY SINGS	MGM (S) SE 3744	9.00	22.50	36.00
CONWAY TWITTY SINGS	MGM (EP) X-1640	2.00	5.00	8.00
CONWAY TWITTY SINGS	MGM (EP) X-1641	2.00	5.00	8.00
CONWAY TWITTY SINGS	MGM (EP) X-1642	2.00	5.00	8.00
CONWAY TWITTY SINGS (PORTRAIT OF A FOOL & OTHERS)	MGM (M) E-4019	7.50	18.75	30.00
CONWAY TWITTY SINGS (PORTRAIT OF A FOOL & OTHERS)	MGM (S) SE-4019	4.00	8.00	12.00
CONWAY TWITTY SINGS THE BLUES	MGM (S) 4837	3.00	4.50	6.00
CONWAY TWITTY TOUCH	MGM (M) E-3943	7.50	18.75	30.00
CONWAY TWITTY TOUCH	MGM (S) SE-3943	5.00	10.00	15.00
DARLING, YOU KNOW I WOULDN'T LIE	Decca (S) DL 75105	3.00	4.50	6.00
FIFTEEN YEARS AGO	Decca (S) DL 75248	3.00	4.50	6.00
FIFTEEN YEARS AGO (RI)	MCA (S) 22	2.00	3.00	4.00
GEORGIA KEEPS PULLING ON MY RING	MCA (S) 2328	2.00	3.00	4.00
GOLDEN ARCHIVE SERIES	MGM (M) GAS 110	3.00	4.50	6.00
HELLO DARLIN'	Decca (S) DL 75209	3.00	4.50	6.00
HELLO DARLIN' (RI)	MCA (S) 19	2.00	3.00	4.00
HERE'S CONWAY TWITTY (& HIS LONELY BLUE BOYS)	Decca (M) DL 4990	3.00	4.50	6.00
HERE'S CONWAY TWITTY (& HIS LONELY BLUE BOYS)	Decca (S) DL 74990	3.00	4.50	6.00
HIGH PRIEST OF COUNTRY MUSIC, THE	MCA (S) 2144	2.00	3.00	4.00
HITS	MGM (S) SE 4799	3.00	4.50	6.00
HITS THE ROAD	MGM (M) E-4217	4.00	8.00	12.00
HITS THE ROAD	MGM (S) SE-4217	5.00	10.00	15.00
HOW MUCH MORE CAN SHE STAND	Decca (S) DL 75276	3.00	4.50	6.00
HOW MUCH MORE CAN SHE STAND (RI)	MCA (S) 30	3.00	3.00	4.00
I CAN'T SEE ME WITHOUT YOU	Decca (S) DL 75335	3.00	4.50	6.00
I CAN'T SEE ME WITHOUT YOU (RI)	MCA (S) 46	2.00	3.00	4.00
I LOVE YOU MORE TODAY	Decca (S) DL 75131	3.00	4.50	6.00
I LOVE YOU MORE TODAY (RI)	MCA (S) 130	2.00	3.00	4.00
I'M NOT THROUGH LOVING YOU YET	MCA (S) 441	2.00	3.00	4.00
IT'S ONLY MAKE BELIEVE	Metro (M) 512	5.00	7.50	10.00
I'VE ALREADY LOVED YOU IN MY MIND	MCA (S) 2293	2.00	3.00	4.00
I WONDER WHAT SHE'LL THINK OF ME	Decca (S) DL 75292	3.00	4.50	6.00
LINDA ON MY MIND	MCA (S) 469	2.00	3.00	4.00
LONELY BLUE BOY	MGM (M) E 3818	7.50	18.75	30.00
LONELY BLUE BOY	MGM (S) SE 3818	5.00	12.50	20.00
LONELY BLUE BOY	MGM (EP) X-1701	2.00	5.00	8.00
LOOK INTO MY TEARDROPS	Decca (M) DL 4828	3.00	4.50	6.00
LOOK INTO MY TEARDROPS	Decca (S) DL 74828	3.00	4.50	6.00
LOOK INTO MY TEARDROPS (RI)	MCA (S) 112	2.00	3.00	4.00
NEXT IN LINE	Decca (S) DL 75062	3.00	4.50	6.00
NEXT IN LINE (RI)	MCA (S) 123	2.00	3.00	4.00
NOW AND THEN	MCA (S) 2206	2.00	3.00	4.00
PLAY, GUITAR PLAY	MCA (S) 2262	2.00	3.00	4.00
R&B '63	MGM (M) E 4089	4.00	6.00	8.00
R&B '63	MGM (S) SE 4089	5.00	7.50	10.00
ROCK AND ROLL STORY	MGM (M) E 3907	4.00	10.00	16.00
ROCK AND ROLL STORY	MGM (S) SE 3907	5.00	12.50	20.00
SATURDAY NIGHT WITH CONWAY TWITTY	MGM (M) E 3786	7.50	18.75	30.00
SATURDAY NIGHT WITH CONWAY TWITTY	MGM (S) SE 3786	5.00	12.50	20.00
SATURDAY NIGHT WITH CONWAY TWITTY	MGM (EP) X-1678	2.00	5.00	8.00
SATURDAY NIGHT WITH CONWAY TWITTY	MGM (EP) X-1679	2.00	5.00	8.00
SATURDAY NIGHT WITH CONWAY TWITTY	MGM (EP) X-1680	2.00	5.00	8.00
SHAKE IT UP	Pickwick (M) SPC 3360	4.00	6.00	8.00
SHE NEEDS SOMEONE TO HOLD HER	MCA (S) 303	2.00	3.00	4.00
TO SEE AN ANGEL CRY	Decca (S) DL 75172	3.00	4.50	6.00
TO SEE AN ANGEL CRY/THAT'S WHEN SHE STARTED TO STOP LOVING YOU (RI)	MCA (S) 18	2.00	3.00	4.00
20 GREAT HITS	MGM (M) 2 SES 4884	3.00	4.50	6.00
TWITTY	MCA (S) 2176	2.00	3.00	4.00
YOU'VE NEVER BEEN THIS FAR BEFORE/ BABY'S GONE	MCA (S) 359	2.00	3.00	4.00

TWITTY, Conway & Loretta Lynn

TITLE	LABEL & NO.	GOOD	VERY GOOD	NEAR MINT
COUNTRY PARTNERS	MCA (S) 427	2.00	3.00	4.00
COUNTRY PARTNERS ('78 RI)	MCA (S) 2354	2.00	3.00	4.00
DYNAMIC DUO	MCA (S) 2278	2.00	3.00	4.00
FEELINS'	MCA (S) 2143	2.00	3.00	4.00
LEAD ME ON	Decca (S) DL 75326	2.50	3.75	5.00
LEAD ME ON (RI)	MCA (S) 9	2.00	3.00	4.00
LOUISIANA WOMAN, MISSISSIPPI MAN	MCA (S) 335	2.00	3.00	4.00
UNITED TALENT	MCA (S) 2209	2.00	3.00	4.00
WE ONLY MAKE BELIEVE	Decca (S) DL 75251	2.50	3.75	5.00
WE ONLY MAKE BELIEVE (RI)	MCA (S) 8	2.00	3.00	4.00

TYLER, Red and The Gyros

TITLE	LABEL & NO.	GOOD	VERY GOOD	NEAR MINT
ROCKIN' AND ROLLIN'	Ace (M) LP 1006	4.00	10.00	16.00

TYMES

TITLE	LABEL & NO.	GOOD	VERY GOOD	NEAR MINT
BEST OF TYMES	ABKCO (S) 4228	3.00	4.50	6.00
PEOPLE	Columbia (S) CS 9778	2.00	3.00	4.00
SOMEWHERE	Parkway (M) 7039	3.00	4.50	6.00
SOMEWHERE	Parkway (S) 7039	4.00	6.00	8.00
SOUND OF THE WONDERFUL TYMES	Parkway (M) 7038	3.00	4.50	6.00
SOUND OF THE WONDERFUL TYMES	Parkway (S) 7038	4.00	6.00	8.00
TRUSTMAKER	RCA (S) APL1-0727	2.00	3.00	4.00

(M) Mono (S) Stereo (EP) Extended Play (Q) Quad (RI) Re-issued

U

TITLE	LABEL & NO.	GOOD	VERY GOOD	NEAR MINT
ULTIMATE SPINACH				
BEHOLD AND SEE	MGM (S) SE 4570	4.00	6.00	8.00
ULTIMATE SPINACH	MGM (S) SE 4518	4.00	6.00	8.00
ULTIMATE SPINACH	MGM (S) SE 4600	4.00	6.00	8.00
UNBEETABLES				
LIVE AT PALISADES PARK	Dawn (M) LP 5050	7.00	14.00	21.00
UNDERGROUND ALL-STARS				
EXTREMELY HEAVY	Dot (M) DLP 25964	5.00	7.50	10.00
UNDERGROUND SUNSHINE				
LET THERE BE LIGHT	Interpid (M) IT 74003	3.50	5.25	7.00
UNDERWOOD, Charlie, Glide Band				
BIRTH OF A SOUND	Warner Brothers (M) W 1675	2.50	3.75	5.00
UNDISPUTED TRUTH				
COSMIC TRUTH	Gordy (S) 970	2.50	3.75	5.00
DOWN TO EARTH	Gordy (S) 968	2.50	3.75	5.00
FACE TO FACE WITH THE TRUTH	Gordy (S) 959	3.00	4.50	6.00
LAW OF THE LAND	Gordy (S) 963	2.50	3.75	5.00
METHOD TO THE MADNESS	Whitfield (S) 2967	2.00	3.00	4.00
UNDISPUTED TRUTH, THE	Gordy (S) 955	3.00	4.50	6.00
UNIQUES (Features Joe Stampley)				
GOLDEN HITS	Paula (S) LPS 2208	4.50	6.75	9.00
HAPPENING NOW	Paula (M) LP 2194	4.00	6.00	8.00
HAPPENING NOW	Paula (S) LPS 2194	5.00	7.50	10.00
PLAYTIME	Paula (M) LP 2199	4.00	6.00	8.00
PLAYTIME	Paula (S) LPS 2199	5.00	7.50	10.00
UNIQUELY YOURS	Paula (M) LP 2190	4.00	6.00	8.00
UNIQUELY YOURS	Paula (S) LPS 2190	5.00	7.50	10.00
UNIQUES	Paula (S) LPS 2204	4.50	6.75	9.00

Also see STAMPLEY, Joe

TITLE	LABEL & NO.	GOOD	VERY GOOD	NEAR MINT
UNITED STATES OF AMERICA				
UNITED STATES OF AMERICA	Columbia (S) CS 9619	5.00	7.50	10.00
UNIT 4 PLUS 2				
UNIT 4 PLUS 2 (FEATURING CONCRETE AND CLAY)	London (M) LL 3427	4.00	6.00	8.00
UNIT 4 PLUS 2 (FEATURING CONCRETE AND CLAY)	London (S) PS 427	5.00	7.50	10.00
UNIVERSALS				
ACAPELLA SHOWCASE	Relic (M) 5006	4.00	6.00	8.00
UNSPOKEN WORD				
TUESDAY, APRIL 19TH	Ascot (S) AS 16028	3.00	4.50	6.00
UNSPOKEN WORD	Atco (S) SD 33335	2.50	3.75	5.00
UPCHURCH, Phil				
TWIST, THE-BIG HIT DANCES	United Artists (M) UAL 3175	3.00	6.00	9.00
TWIST, THE-BIG HIT DANCES	United Artists (S) UAS 6175	3.50	7.00	10.50
YOU CAN'T SIT DOWN	Boyd (M) B 398	4.00	8.00	12.00
YOU CAN'T SIT DOWN PART 2	United Artists (M) UAL 3162	3.00	6.00	9.00
YOU CAN'T SIT DOWN PART 2	United Artists (S) UAS 6162	3.50	7.00	10.50
UPSETTERS (Featuring Jimmy Wess)				
WE REMEMBER OTIS	ABC (S) ABCS 651	3.00	4.50	6.00
URIAH HEEP				
DEMONS AND WIZARDS	Mercury (S) SRM-1-630	3.00	4.50	6.00
LOOK AT YOURSELF	Mercury (S) SRM-1-614	3.00	4.50	6.00
MAGICIAN'S BIRTHDAY, THE	Mercury (S) SRM-1-652	3.00	4.50	6.00
RETURN TO FANTASY	Warner Bros. (S) BS-2869	2.50	3.75	5.00
SALISBURY	Mercury (S) SR 61319	3.50	5.25	7.00
URIAH HEEP	Mercury (S) SR 61294	3.50	5.25	7.00
URIAH HEEP LIVE	Mercury (S) SRM-2-7503	3.50	5.25	7.00
WONDERWORLD	Warner Bros. (S) BS 2800	2.50	3.75	5.00
URSA MAJOR				
URSA MAJOR	RCA (S) LSP 4777	3.00	4.50	6.00
USSERY				
USSERY	Mercury (S) SRM 1 671	2.50	3.75	5.00

(M) Mono (S) Stereo (EP) Extended Play (Q) Quad (RI) Re-issued

V

TITLE	LABEL & NO.	GOOD	VERY GOOD	NEAR MINT
VALE, Jerry				
ALONE AGAIN (NATURALLY)	Columbia (S) 31716	2.00	3.00	4.00
ARRIVEDERCI, ROMA	Columbia (M) CL 1955	2.00	3.00	4.00
BE MY LOVE	Columbia (M) CL 2181	2.00	3.00	4.00
BE MY LOVE	Columbia (S) CS 8991	2.50	3.75	5.00
FREE AS THE WIND	Columbia (S) KC-32829	2.00	3.00	4.00
GREAT ITALIAN HITS	Columbia (S) 31938	2.00	3.00	4.00
GREAT MOMENTS ON BROADWAY	Columbia (M) CL 2489	2.00	3.00	4.00
GREAT MOMENTS ON BROADWAY	Columbia (S) CS 9289	2.00	3.00	4.00
HAVE YOU LOOKED INTO YOUR HEART	Columbia (M) CL 2313	2.00	3.00	4.00
HAVE YOU LOOKED INTO YOUR HEART	Columbia (S) CS 9113	2.50	3.75	5.00
I HAVE BUT ONE HEART	Columbia (M) CL 1797	2.00	3.00	4.00
I HEAR A RHAPSODY	Columbia (S) CS 9634	2.00	3.00	4.00
IMPOSSIBLE DREAM, THE	Columbia (M) CL 2583	2.00	3.00	4.00
IMPOSSIBLE DREAM, THE	Columbia (S) CS 9383	2.00	3.00	4.00
I REMEMBER BUDDY	Columbia (S) CS-8069	2.00	4.00	6.00
ITALIAN ALBUM/ ARRIVEDERCI, ROMA	Columbia (S) CG-33615	2.00	3.00	4.00
IT'S MAGIC	Columbia (M) CL 2444	2.00	3.00	4.00
IT'S MAGIC	Columbia (S) CS 9244	2.50	3.75	5.00
JERRY VALE	Columbia (EP) B-2154	1.00	1.50	2.00
JERRY VALE'S ALL-TIME GREATEST HITS	Columbia (S) 31543	2.00	3.00	4.00
JERRY VALE SINGS THE GREAT LOVE SONGS	Columbia (S) KG-32083	2.00	3.00	4.00
JERRY VALE SINGS THE GREAT NAT "KING" COLE	Columbia (S) 31147	2.00	3.00	4.00
JERRY VALE'S WORLD	Columbia (S) KC-32454	2.00	3.00	4.00
LANGUAGE OF LOVE, THE	Columbia (M) CL 2043	2.00	3.00	4.00
LET IT BE	Columbia (S) 1021	2.00	3.00	4.00
SAME OLD MOON	Columbia (M) CL-1380	2.00	3.00	4.00
SAME OLD MOON	Columbia (S) CS-8175	2.50	3.75	5.00
16 GREATEST HITS OF THE 60'S	Columbia (S) CS 9982	2.00	3.00	4.00
STANDING OVATION!	Columbia (M) CL 2273	2.00	3.00	4.00
STANDING OVATION!	Columbia (S) CS 9073	2.50	3.75	5.00
THERE GOES MY HEART	Columbia (M) CL 2387	2.00	3.00	4.00
THERE GOES MY HEART	Columbia (S) CS 9187	2.50	3.75	5.00
THIS GUY'S IN LOVE WITH YOU	Columbia (S) CS 9694	2.00	3.00	4.00
TILL	Columbia (S) CS 9757	2.00	3.00	4.00
TILL THE END OF TIME	Columbia (M) CL 2116	2.00	3.00	4.00
TILL THE END OF TIME	Columbia (S) CS 8916	2.50	3.75	5.00
TIME ALONE WILL TELL	Columbia (M) CL 2684	2.00	3.00	4.00
TIME ALONE WILL TELL	Columbia (S) CS 9484	2.00	3.00	4.00
WHERE'S THE PLAYGROUND SUSIE?	Columbia (S) CS 9838	2.00	3.00	4.00
WITH LOVE	Columbia (S) GP 16	2.00	3.00	4.00
YOU DON'T HAVE TO SAY YOU LOVE ME	Columbia (M) CL 2774	2.00	3.00	4.00
YOU DON'T HAVE TO SAY YOU LOVE ME	Columbia (S) CS 9574	2.00	3.00	4.00
VALE, Ricky and His Surfers				
EVERYBODY'S SURFIN'	Strand (M) SL 1104	3.00	6.00	9.00
EVERYBODY'S SURFIN'	Strand (S) SLS 1104	3.50	7.00	10.50
VALENS, Ritchie				
GREATEST HITS VOL. 2	Del Fi (S) 1247	10.00	25.00	40.00
HIS GREATEST HITS	Del Fi (M) DFLP 1225	8.00	20.00	32.00
IN CONCERT AT PACOIMA JR. HIGH	Del Fi (M) DFLP 1214	12.00	30.00	48.00
ORIGINAL LA BAMBA	Guest Star (S) GS 1484	4.00	8.00	12.00
ORIGINAL RITCHIE VALENS	Guest Star (M) G 1469	5.00	10.00	15.00
RITCHIE	Del Fi (M) DFLP 1206	7.00	17.50	28.00
RITCHIE VALENS	Del Fi (M) DFLP 1201	7.00	17.50	28.00
RITCHIE VALENS	Del Fi (EP) DFEP-111	2.00	5.00	8.00
RITCHIE VALENS AND JERRY KOLE	Crown (M) CLP 5336	5.00	10.00	15.00
RITCHIE VALENS AND JERRY KOLE	Crown (S) CST 336	4.00	8.00	12.00

VALENTE, Dino
Title	Label & No.	Good	Very Good	Near Mint
DINO VALENTE	Epic (S) BN 26335	4.00	6.00	8.00

VALENTINE, Hilton
ALL IN YOUR HEAD	Capitol (S) ST 330	6.00	9.00	12.00

VALENTINO, Mark
MARK VALENTINO	Swan (M) LP 508	6.00	12.00	18.00

VALHALLA
VALHALLA	United Artists (S) UAS 6730	3.00	4.50	6.00

VALINO, Joe
GARDEN OF EDEN	Vik (EP) EXA 223	2.00	3.00	4.00

VALJEAN
MASHIN' THE CLASSICKS	Carlton (M) 146	2.50	3.75	5.00
MASHIN' THE CLASSICKS	Carlton (S) 146	2.50	3.75	5.00

VALLEY, Jim With Don and The Good Times
HARPO	Panorama (M) 104	5.00	10.00	15.00

VALLI, Frankie
CLOSEUP	Private Stock (S) PS 2000	2.00	3.00	4.00
DO IT YOURSELF WEDDING ALBUM	Mercury (M) MG-20463	4.00	6.00	8.00
FRANKIE VALLI GOLD	Private Stock (S) PS 2001	2.00	3.00	4.00
HITS	Private Stock (S) PS 7012	2.00	3.00	4.00
INSIDE YOU	Motown (S) M6-852	1.50	3.00	4.00
LADY PUT THE LIGHT OUT	Private Stock (S) PS 7002	2.00	3.00	4.00
OUR DAY WILL COME	Private Stock (S) PS 2006	2.00	3.00	4.00
SOLO	Philips (M) PHM 200-247	10.00	15.00	20.00
SOLO	Philips (S) PHS600-247	3.00	6.00	8.00
TIMELESS	Philips (S) PHS 600-274	3.00	6.00	9.00
VALLI	Private Stock (S) PS 2017	2.00	3.00	4.00

Also see FOUR SEASONS

VANCE, Joel
WHAT I DID ON MY VACATION	Cadet Concept (S) LPS 325	2.00	3.00	4.00

VAN DYKE, LeRoy
AUCTIONEER	Dot (M) DLP 3693	3.00	4.50	6.00
GREATEST HITS	MCA (S) 145	2.00	3.00	4.00
(RI of Kapp releases)				
GREAT HITS OF LEROY VAN DYKE	Mercury (M) MG-20802	2.00	3.00	4.00
GREAT HITS OF LEROY VAN DYKE	Mercury (S) SR-60802	2.00	3.00	4.00
MOVIN' GOES VAN DYKE	Mercury/Wing (M) MGW 12322	2.00	3.00	4.00
MOVIN' GOES VAN DYKE	Mercury/Wing (S) SRW 16322	2.00	3.00	4.00
MOVIN' VAN DYKE	Mercury (M) MG-20716	2.00	3.00	4.00
MOVIN' VAN DYKE	Mercury (S) SR-60716	2.00	3.00	4.00
OUT OF LOVE	Mercury/Wing (M) MGW-12302	2.00	3.00	4.00
OUT OF LOVE	Mercury/Wing (S) SRW-16302	2.00	3.00	4.00
WALK ON BY	Mercury (M) MG-20682	2.00	3.00	4.00
WALK ON BY	Mercury (S) SR-60682	2.00	3.00	4.00

VAN DYKES
TELLIN' IT LIKE IT IS	Bell (M) 6004	3.00	4.50	6.00

VAN EATON, Lon and Derek
BROTHER	Apple (S) SMAS 3390	4.50	6.75	9.00

VANILLA FUDGE
BEAT GOES ON, THE	Atco (S) SD 33-237	2.50	3.75	5.00
NEAR THE BEGINNING	Atco (S) SD 33-278	3.00	4.50	6.00
RENAISSANCE	Atco (S) SD 33-244	3.00	4.50	6.00
ROCK N' ROLL	Atco (S) SD 33-303	2.50	3.75	5.00
VANILLA FUDGE	Atco (M) 33-224	2.50	3.75	5.00
VANILLA FUDGE	Atco (S) SD 33-224	3.00	4.50	6.00

VANITY FARE
EARLY IN THE MORNING	Page One (S) 2502	3.00	4.50	6.00

VANNELLI, Gino
CRAZY LIFE	A&M (S) SP 4395	2.50	3.75	5.00
GIST OF THE GEMINI, THE	A&M (S) SP 4596	2.00	3.00	4.00
PAUPER IN PARADISE, A	A&M (S) SP 4664	2.00	3.00	4.00
POWERFUL PEOPLE	A&M (S) SP 3630	2.00	3.00	4.00
STORM AT SUNUP	A&M (S) SP 4533	2.00	3.00	4.00

VAN PEEBLES, Melvin
AS SERIOUS AS A HEART ATTACK	A&M (S) SP 4326	1.50	2.25	3.00
DON'T PLAY US CHEAP	Stax (S) STS 2-3006	2.00	3.00	4.00
SWEET SWEETBACK'S BAADASSS SONG	Stax (S) STS 3001	2.00	3.00	4.00

VAN ZANDT, Townes
LATE GREAT TOWNES VAN ZANDT, THE	Poppy (M) PP-LA004	3.00	4.50	6.00

VARTAN, Sylvie
GIFT WRAPPED FROM PARIS	RCA (S) 3438	4.50	6.75	9.00
SYLVIE-A-NASHVILLE	RCA (S) 430154	4.00	6.00	8.00

(M) Mono (S) Stereo (EP) Extended Play (Q) Quad (RI) Re-issued

VAUGHAN, Sarah
BEST OF SARAH VAUGHAN	Scepter (S) 18029	2.00	3.00	4.00
DIVINE SARAH VAUGHAN	Mercury (M) MG-20540	3.00	4.50	6.00
DIVINE SARAH VAUGHAN	Mercury (S) SR-60255	3.00	4.50	6.00
DREAMY	Roulette (M) R-52046	2.50	3.75	5.00
DREAMY	Roulette (S) SR-52046	2.50	3.75	5.00
MAGIC OF SARAH VAUGHAN	Mercury (M) MG-20438	3.00	4.50	6.00
MAGIC OF SARAH VAUGHAN	Mercury (S) SR-60110	3.00	4.50	6.00
MORE SARAH VAUGHAN FROM JAPAN	Mainstream (S) 419	2.50	3.75	5.00
NO COUNT SARAH	Mercury (M) MG-20441	3.00	4.50	6.00
NO COUNT SARAH	Mercury (S) SR-60116	3.00	4.50	6.00
SARAH VAUGHAN	Mercury (EP) 1-3396	1.50	2.25	3.00
SARAH VAUGHAN (& Jimmy Rowles Quintet)	Mainstream (S) 404	2.50	3.75	5.00
SARAH VAUGHAN, GREAT SONGS FROM HIT SHOWS	Mercury (M) MG-20244	3.00	4.50	6.00
SARAH VAUGHAN, GREAT SONGS FROM HIT SHOWS	Mercury (S) SR-60041	3.00	4.50	6.00
SARAH VAUGHAN'S GOLDEN HITS	Mercury (M) MG-20645	2.50	3.75	5.00
SARAH VAUGHAN'S GOLDEN HITS	Mercury (S) SR-60645	2.50	3.75	5.00
VAUGHAN & VIOLINS	Mercury (M) MG-20370	3.00	4.50	6.00
VAUGHAN & VIOLINS	Mercury (S) SR-60038	3.00	4.50	6.00

VAUGHN, Billy
GREAT GOLDEN HITS	Dot (M) DLP-3288	2.00	3.00	4.00
GREAT GOLDEN HITS	Dot (S) DLP-25288	2.00	3.00	4.00
SAIL ALONG SILV'RY MOON	Dot (M) DLP 3100	2.50	3.75	5.00
SAIL ALONG SILV'RY MOON	Dot (EP) DEP 1072	1.00	1.50	2.00
SWINGIN' SAFARI	Dot (M) DLP-3458	2.00	3.00	4.00
SWINGIN' SAFARI	Dot (S) DLP-25458	2.00	3.00	4.00

VAUGHT, Bob and The Renegades
SURF CRAZY	GNP/Crescendo (M) GNP 83	4.00	8.00	12.00

VEE, Bobby
BOBBY VEE	Liberty (M) LRP 3181	4.00	8.00	12.00
BOBBY VEE	Liberty (S) LST 7181	5.00	10.00	15.00
BOBBY VEE	Sunset (M) SUM 1111	2.50	3.75	5.00
BOBBY VEE	Sunset (S) SUS 5111	3.00	4.50	6.00
BOBBY VEE MEETS THE CRICKETS	Liberty (M) LRP 3228	3.00	4.50	6.00
BOBBY VEE MEETS THE CRICKETS	Liberty (S) LST 7228	4.00	6.00	8.00
BOBBY VEE MEETS THE VENTURES	Liberty (M) LRP 3289	3.00	4.50	6.00
BOBBY VEE MEETS THE VENTURES	Liberty (S) LST 7289	4.00	6.00	8.00
A BOBBY VEE RECORDING SESSION	Liberty (M) LRP 3232	3.00	4.50	6.00
A BOBBY VEE RECORDING SESSION	Liberty (S) LST 7232	4.00	6.00	8.00
BOBBY VEE'S GOLDEN GREATS	Liberty (M) LRP 3245	3.00	4.50	6.00
BOBBY VEE'S GOLDEN GREATS	Liberty (S) LST 7245	4.00	6.00	8.00
BOBBY VEE'S GOLDEN GREATS VOL. 2	Liberty (M) LRP 3464	3.00	4.50	6.00
BOBBY VEE'S GOLDEN GREATS VOL. 2	Liberty (S) LST 7464	4.00	6.00	8.00
BOBBY VEE'S HITS	Liberty (EP) LSX 1010	1.50	3.00	4.50
BOBBY VEE SINGS THE NEW SOUND FROM ENGLAND	Liberty (M) LRP 3352	4.00	6.00	8.00
BOBBY VEE SINGS THE NEW SOUND FROM ENGLAND	Liberty (S) LST 7352	4.50	6.75	9.00
COME BACK WHEN YOU GROW UP	Liberty (M) LRP 3534	2.50	3.75	5.00
COME BACK WHEN YOU GROW UP	Liberty (S) LST 7534	3.00	4.50	6.00
DEVIL OR ANGEL	Liberty (M) LRP 3165	4.00	8.00	12.00
DEVIL OR ANGEL	Liberty (S) LST 7165	5.00	10.00	15.00
DO WHAT YOU GOTTA DO	Liberty (S) LST 7592	3.00	4.50	6.00
A FOREVER KIND OF LOVE	Sunset (M) SUM 1162	2.50	3.75	5.00
A FOREVER KIND OF LOVE	Sunset (S) SUS 5162	3.00	4.50	6.00
GATES, GRILLS, AND RAILINGS	Liberty (S) LST 7612	3.00	4.50	6.00
HITS OF THE ROCKIN' 50's	Liberty (M) LRP 3205	3.00	6.00	9.00
HITS OF THE ROCKIN' 50's	Liberty (S) LST 7205	4.00	8.00	12.00
I REMEMBER BUDDY HOLLY	Liberty (M) LRP 3336	3.50	5.25	7.00
I REMEMBER BUDDY HOLLY	Liberty (S) LST 7336	4.50	6.75	9.00
JUST TODAY	Liberty (S) LSR 7554	3.00	4.50	6.00
LEGENDARY MASTERS—BOBBY VEE	United Artists (S) UA-LA025	2.50	3.75	5.00
LIVE ON TOUR	Liberty (M) LRP 3393	3.00	4.50	6.00
LIVE ON TOUR	Liberty (S) LST 7393	4.00	6.00	8.00
LOOK AT ME GIRL	Liberty (M) LRP 3480	2.75	3.50	5.50
LOOK AT ME GIRL	Liberty (S) LST 7482	3.25	4.25	6.50
MERRY CHRISTMAS FROM BOBBY VEE	Liberty (M) LRP 3267	3.00	4.50	6.00
MERRY CHRISTMAS FROM BOBBY VEE	Liberty (S) LST 7267	4.00	6.00	8.00
NIGHT HAS A THOUSAND EYES, THE	Liberty (M) LRP 3285	3.00	4.50	6.00
NIGHT HAS A THOUSAND EYES, THE	Liberty (S) LST 7285	4.00	6.00	8.00
ROBERT THOMAS VELLINE NOTHIN' LIKE A SUNNY DAY	United Artists (EP) SP 85	1.50	2.25	3.00
TAKE GOOD CARE OF MY BABY	Liberty (M) LRP 3211	3.00	6.00	9.00
TAKE GOOD CARE OF MY BABY	Liberty (S) LST 7211	4.00	8.00	12.00
30 BIG HITS FROM THE 60's	Liberty (M) LRP 3385	3.00	4.50	6.00
30 BIG HITS FROM THE 60's	Liberty (S) LST 7385	4.00	6.00	8.00
VERY BEST OF BOBBY VEE	United Artists (S) UA LA 332	2.00	3.00	4.00
WITH STRINGS AND THINGS	Liberty (M) LRP 3186	3.00	6.00	9.00
WITH STRINGS AND THINGS	Liberty (S) LST 7186	4.00	8.00	12.00

VEGAS, Pat & Lolly (Redbone)
AT THE HAUNTED HOUSE	Mercury (M) MG 21059	3.50	7.00	10.50
AT THE HAUNTED HOUSE	Mercury (S) SR 61059	4.00	8.00	12.00

VELEBNY, Karel
She	ESP (M) 1080	3.00	4.50	6.00

VELVET, Jimmy
A TOUCH OF VELVET	United Artists (S) UAS 6653	3.00	6.00	9.00
A TOUCH OF VELVET	Velvetone (S) 101	4.50	9.00	13.50

TITLE	LABEL & NO.	GOOD	VERY GOOD	NEAR MINT
VELVET UNDERGROUND				
ARCHETYPES	MGM (S) M3F 4950	2.50	3.75	5.00
LIVE AT MAX'S KANSAS CITY	Cotillion (S) SD 9500	3.00	4.50	6.00
LOADED	Cotillion (S) SD 9034	4.00	6.00	8.00
LOU REED AND THE VELVET UNDERGROUND	Pride (S) PRD 0022	3.00	4.50	6.00
1969	Mercury (S) SRM 2 7504	3.00	4.50	6.00
VELVET UNDERGROUND AND NICO	Verve (M) 5008	3.00	4.50	6.00
VELVET UNDERGROUND AND NICO	Verve (S) V6-5008	4.00	6.00	8.00
VELVET UNDERGROUND (WITH BANANA INTACT)	MGM (S) SE 4617	4.00	6.00	8.00
WHITE LIGHT, WHITE HEAT	Verve (M) V 5046	3.00	4.50	6.00
WHITE LIGHT, WHITE HEAT	Verve (S) V6-5046	4.00	6.00	8.00
Also see REED, Lou				
VENET, Nick				
FLIPPIN'	RCA (EP) EPA 4100	3.00	6.00	9.00
VENT, Joanne				
BLACK AND WHITE OF IT IS BLUES, THE	A&M (S) SP 4165	3.00	4.50	6.00
VENTURAS				
HERE THEY ARE, THE VENTURAS	Drum Boy (M) DB-1003	4.00	8.00	12.00
HERE THEY ARE, THE VENTURAS	Drum Boy (S) DBS-1003	4.50	9.00	13.50
VENTURES				
ANOTHER SMASH	Dolton (M) BLP 2006	4.00	6.00	8.00
ANOTHER SMASH	Dolton (S) BST 8006	5.00	7.50	10.00
BATMAN THEME	Dolton (M) BLP 2042	2.50	3.75	5.00
("Ventures" LP retitled)				
BATMAN THEME	Dolton (S) BST 8042	3.00	4.50	6.00
("Ventures" LP retitled)				
BOBBY VEE MEETS THE VENTURES	Liberty (M) LRP 3289	3.00	4.50	6.00
BOBBY VEE MEETS THE VENTURES	Liberty (S) LST 7289	4.00	6.00	8.00
COLORFUL VENTURES	Dolton (M) BLP 2008	4.00	6.00	8.00
COLORFUL VENTURES	Dolton (S) BST 8008	5.00	7.50	10.00
CHRISTMAS ALBUM	Dolton (M) BLP 2038	3.00	4.50	6.00
CHRISTMAS ALBUM	Dolton (S) BST 8038	4.00	6.00	8.00
DANCE!	Dolton (M) BLP 2010	3.00	4.50	6.00
("Twist with the Ventures" LP retitled)				
DANCE!	Dolton (S) BST 8010	4.00	6.00	8.00
("Twist with the Ventures" LP retitled)				
DANCE WITH THE VENTURES	Dolton (M) BLP 2014	3.00	4.50	6.00
("Ventures' Twist Party, Vol. 2" LP retitled)				
DANCE WITH THE VENTURES	Dolton (S) BST 8014	4.00	6.00	8.00
("Ventures' Twist Party, Vol. 2" LP retitled)				
FABULOUS VENTURES	Dolton (M) BLP 2029	2.50	3.75	5.00
FABULOUS VENTURES	Dolton (S) BSP 8029	3.00	4.50	6.00
FLIGHTS OF FANTASY	Liberty (M) LRP 2055	2.50	3.75	5.00
FLIGHTS OF FANTASY	Liberty (S) LST 8055	3.00	4.50	6.00
GOING TO THE VENTURES DANCE PARTY!	Dolton (M) BLP 2017	4.00	6.00	8.00
GOING TO THE VENTURES DANCE PARTY!	Dolton (S) BST 8017	5.00	7.50	10.00
GOLDEN GREATS BY THE VENTURES	Liberty (M) LRP 2053	2.50	3.75	5.00
GOLDEN GREATS BY THE VENTURES	Liberty (S) LST 8053	3.00	4.50	6.00
GO WITH THE VENTURES!	Dolton (M) BLP 2045	3.00	4.50	6.00
GO WITH THE VENTURES!	Dolton (S) BST 8045	4.00	6.00	8.00
GUITAR FREAKOUT	Dolton (M) BLP 2050	2.50	3.75	5.00
GUITAR FREAKOUT	Dolton (S) BST 8050	3.50	5.25	7.00
HAWAII FIVE-O	Liberty (S) LST 8061	3.00	4.50	6.00
HORSE, THE	Liberty (S) LST 8057	3.00	4.50	6.00
JIM CROCE SONGBOOK	United Artists (S) UA-LA 217	2.00	3.00	4.00
JOY—THE VENTURES PLAY THE CLASSICS	United Artists (S) UAS 5575	2.00	3.00	4.00
LET'S GO!	Dolton (M) BLP 2024	3.00	4.50	6.00
LET'S GO!	Dolton (S) BST 8024	4.00	6.00	8.00
MASHED POTATOES AND GRAVY	Dolton (M) BLP 2016	4.00	6.00	8.00
MASHED POTATOES AND GRAVY	Dolton (S) BST 8016	5.00	7.50	10.00
MORE GOLDEN GREATS	Liberty (S) LST 8060	3.00	4.50	6.00
$1,000,000.00 WEEKEND	Liberty (S) LST 8054	3.50	5.25	7.00
ONLY HITS	United Artists (S) UA-LA147-G2	2.00	3.00	4.00
ON STAGE	Dolton (M) BLP 2035	3.00	4.50	6.00
ON STAGE	Dolton (S) BST 8035	4.00	6.00	8.00
PLAY GUITAR WITH THE VENTURES	Dolton (M) BLP 16501	3.00	4.50	6.00
PLAY GUITAR WITH THE VENTURES	Dolton (S) BST 17501	4.00	6.00	8.00
PLAY GUITAR WITH THE VENTURES VOL. 2	Dolton (M) BLP 16502	3.00	4.50	6.00
PLAY GUITAR WITH THE VENTURES, Vol. 2	Dolton (S) BST 17502	4.00	6.00	8.00
PLAY GUITAR WITH THE VENTURES VOL. 3	Dolton (M) BLP16503	2.50	3.75	5.00
PLAY GUITAR WITH THE VENTURES VOL. 3	Dolton (S) BST17503	3.00	4.50	6.00
PLAY GUITAR WITH THE VENTURES, Vol. 4 (Learn The Electric Bass)	Dolton (M) BLP 16504	3.00	4.50	6.00
PLAY GUITAR WITH THE VENTURES, Vol. 4 (Learn The Electric Bass)	Dolton (S) BST 17504	4.00	6.00	8.00
ROCK AND ROLL FOREVER	United Artists (S) UAS 5649	2.00	3.00	4.00
ROCKY ROAD	United Artists (S) UA LA 586	2.00	3.00	4.00
RUNNIN STRONG	Sunset (M) 1116	2.00	3.00	4.00
RUNNIN STRONG	Sunset (S) 5116	2.50	3.75	5.00
SUPER PSYCHEDELICS	Liberty (M) LRP 8052	2.50	3.75	5.00
SUPER PSYCHEDELICS	Liberty (S) LST 8052	3.00	4.50	6.00
SURFING	Dolton (M) BLP 2022	4.00	6.00	8.00
SURFING	Dolton (S) BST 8022	5.00	7.50	10.00
SWAMP ROCK	Liberty (S) LST 8062	3.00	4.50	6.00
THEME FROM "SHAFT"	United Artists (S) UAS 5547	2.50	3.75	5.00
TWIST WITH THE VENTURES	Dolton (M) BLP 2010	4.00	6.00	8.00
TWIST WITH THE VENTURES	Dolton (S) BST 8010	5.00	7.50	10.00
UNDERGROUND FIRE	Liberty (S) LST 8059	3.00	4.50	6.00
VENTURES A GO-GO	Dolton (M) BLP 2037	3.00	4.50	6.00
VENTURES A GO-GO	Dolton (S) BST 8037	4.00	6.00	8.00
VENTURES, THE	Dolton (M) BLP 2004	4.00	6.00	8.00

(M) Mono (S) Stereo (EP) Extended Play (Q) Quad (RI) Re-issued

TITLE	LABEL & NO.	GOOD	VERY GOOD	NEAR MINT
VENTURES, THE	Dolton (S) BST 8004	5.00	7.50	10.00
VENTURES	Dolton (M) BLP 2042	3.00	4.50	6.00
VENTURES	Dolton (S) BST 8042	4.00	6.00	8.00
VENTURES	United Artists (S) UXS 80	3.00	4.50	6.00
VENTURES BEACH PARTY	Dolton (M) BLP 2016	3.00	4.50	6.00
("Mashed Potatoes and Gravy" LP retitled)				
VENTURES BEACH PARTY	Dolton (S) BST 8016	4.00	6.00	8.00
("Mashed Potatoes and Gravy" LP retitled)				
VENTURES IN SPACE	Dolton (M) BLP 2027	3.50	5.25	7.00
VENTURES IN SPACE	Dolton (S) BST-8027	4.50	6.75	9.00
VENTURES KNOCK ME OUT!	Dolton (M) BLP 2033	3.00	4.50	6.00
VENTURES KNOCK ME OUT!	Dolton (S) BST 8033	4.00	6.00	8.00
VENTURES PLAY TELSTAR, THE LONELY BULL	Dolton (M) BLP 2019	4.00	6.00	8.00
VENTURES PLAY TELSTAR, THE LONELY BULL	Dolton (S) BST 8019	5.00	7.50	10.00
VENTURES PLAY THE COUNTRY CLASSICS	Dolton (M) BLP 2023	3.00	4.50	6.00
VENTURES PLAY THE COUNTRY CLASSICS	Dolton (S) BST 8023	4.00	6.00	8.00
VENTURES 10TH ANNIVERSARY ALBUM	Liberty (S) LST 35000	3.50	5.25	7.00
VENTURES TWIST PARTY VOL. 2	Dolton (M) BLP 2014	4.00	6.00	8.00
VENTURES TWIST PARTY VOL. 2	Dolton (S) BST 8014	5.00	7.50	10.00
VERY BEST OF THE VENTURES	United Artists (S) UA LA 331	2.00	3.00	4.00
WALK, DON'T RUN	Dolton (M) BLP 2003	4.00	6.00	8.00
WALK, DON'T RUN	Dolton (S) BST 8003	5.00	7.50	10.00
WALK, DON'T RUN VOL. 2	Dolton (M) BLP 2031	3.00	4.50	6.00
WALK, DON'T RUN VOL. 2	Dolton (S) BST 8031	4.00	6.00	8.00
WHERE THE ACTION IS!	Dolton (M) BLP 2040	3.00	4.50	6.00
WHERE THE ACTION IS!	Dolton (S) BST 8040	4.00	6.00	8.00
WILD THINGS	Dolton (M) BLP 2047	2.50	3.75	5.00
WILD THINGS	Dolton (S) BST 8047	3.50	5.25	7.00
VERA, Billy				
WITH PEN IN HAND	Atlantic (S) SD 8197	2.50	3.75	5.00
VERA, Billy & Judy Clay				
STORYBOOK CHILDREN	Atlantic (M) 8174	2.00	3.00	4.00
STORYBOOK CHILDREN	Atlantic (S) 8174	2.50	3.75	5.00
VERNE, Larry				
MISTER LARRY VERNE	Era (M) EL 104	3.50	7.00	10.50
VERNON, Mike				
MOMENT OF MADNESS	Sire (S) SAS 7410	3.00	4.50	6.00
VERSATONES				
VERSATONES, THE	RCA (M) 1538	3.00	6.00	9.00
VETTES				
REV-UP	MGM (M) E 4193	3.00	6.00	9.00
REV-UP	MGM (S) SE 4193	3.50	7.00	10.50
VIBRATIONS				
WATUSI	Checker (M) 2978	3.00	6.00	9.00
VICEROYS				
VICEROYS AT GRANNY'S PAD, THE	Bolo (M) BLP 8000	5.00	10.00	15.00
VICKERY, Mack				
MACK VICKERY LIVE AT THE ALABAMA WOMEN'S PRISON (INCLUDING LIVE ELVIS IMPERSONATION)	Mega (S) 1002	4.00	6.00	8.00
VICTIMS OF CHANCE				
VICTIMS OF CHANCE, THE	Crestview (S) CRS 3052	3.00	4.50	6.00
VIGRASS AND OSBORNE				
QUEUES	Uni (S) 73129	4.00	6.00	8.00
STEPPIN OUT	Epic (S) KE 33077	2.50	3.75	5.00
VILLAGE PEOPLE				
MACHO MAN	Casablanca (S) NBLP 7096	2.00	3.00	4.00
VILLAGE PEOPLE	Casablanca (S) NBLP 7064	2.00	3.00	4.00
VINCENT, Gene				
BLUEJEAN BOP	Capitol (M) T 764	20.00	50.00	80.00
BLUEJEAN BOP	Capitol (EP) EPA 1-764	5.00	10.00	15.00
BLUEJEAN BOP	Capitol (EP) EPA 2-764	5.00	10.00	15.00
BLUEJEAN BOP	Capitol (EP) EPA 3-764	5.00	10.00	15.00
CRAZY TIMES	Capitol (M) T 1342	12.50	31.75	50.00
CRAZY TIMES	Capitol (S) ST-1342	10.00	25.00	40.00
DANCE TO THE BOP	Capitol (EP) PRO-438	4.00	8.00	12.00
DAY THE WORLD TURNED BLUE, THE	Kama Sutra (S) KSBS 2027	4.00	6.00	8.00
GENE VINCENT	Kama Sutra (S) KSBS 2019	4.00	6.00	8.00
GENE VINCENT AND THE BLUE CAPS	Capitol (M) T 811	19.00	47.50	76.00
GENE VINCENT AND HIS BLUE CAPS ('70's RI)	Capitol (S) ST 11287	5.00	7.50	10.00
GENE VINCENT AND HIS BLUE CAPS	Capitol (EP) EPA 1-811	4.00	8.00	12.00
GENE VINCENT AND HIS BLUE CAPS	Capitol (EP) EPA 2-811	4.00	8.00	12.00
GENE VINCENT AND HIS BLUE CAPS	Capitol (EP) EPA 3-811	4.00	8.00	12.00
A GENE VINCENT RECORD DATE	Capitol (M) T 1059	15.00	37.50	60.00
A GENE VINCENT RECORD DATE	Capitol (EP) EPA 1-1059	4.00	8.00	12.00
A GENE VINCENT RECORD DATE	Capitol (EP) EPA 2-1059	4.00	8.00	12.00
A GENE VINCENT RECORD DATE	Capitol (EP) EPA 3-1059	4.00	8.00	12.00
GENE VINCENT ROCKS AND THE BLUE CAPS ROLL	Capitol (M) T 970	15.00	37.50	60.00
GENE VINCENT ROCKS AND THE BLUE CAPS ROLL	Capitol (EP) EAP 1-970	4.00	8.00	12.00

VISCOUNTS

TITLE	LABEL & NO.	GOOD	VERY GOOD	NEAR MINT
HARLEM NOCTURNE	Amy (M) 8008	4.00	8.00	12.00
HARLEM NOCTURNE	Amy (S) S-8008	3.50	7.00	10.50
VISCOUNTS, THE	Madison (M) MA LP 1001	5.00	12.50	20.00

VOGUES

FIVE O'CLOCK WORLD	CO & CE (M) LP 1230	3.50	5.25	7.00
FIVE O'CLOCK WORLD	CO & CE (S) CS 1230	4.00	6.00	8.00
GREATEST HITS	Reprise (M) 6371	3.00	4.50	6.00
GREATEST HITS	Reprise (S) 6371	3.00	4.50	6.00
MEET THE VOGUES	CO & CE (M) LP 1229	4.00	6.00	8.00
YOU'RE THE ONE	CO & CE (M) C-1229	4.00	6.00	8.00
YOU'RE THE ONE	CO & CE (S) CS 1229	4.50	6.75	9.00

VYTO B

TRICENTENNIAL 2076	Clay Pigeon (S) CPS 3012	3.00	4.50	6.00

TITLE	LABEL & NO.	GOOD	VERY GOOD	NEAR MINT

WACKERS

HOT WACKS	Elektra (S) EKS 75025	3.00	4.50	6.00
SHREDDER	Elektra (S) EKS 75046	3.00	4.50	6.00
WACKERS	Elektra (S) EKS 74098	3.00	4.50	6.00

WADE, Adam

ADAM & EVENING	Coed (M) C-903	3.00	6.00	9.00
ADAM & EVENING	Coed (S) CS-903	3.50	7.00	10.50
ADAM WADE GREATEST HITS	Epic (M) LN-24019	3.00	6.00	9.00
ADAM WADE GREATEST HITS	Epic (S) BN-26019	3.50	7.00	10.50
AND THEN CAME ADAM	Coed (M) LPC 902	3.00	6.00	9.00
ONE IS A LONELY NUMBER	Epic (M) LN-24026	2.00	3.00	4.00
ONE IS A LONELY NUMBER	Epic (S) BN-26026	2.00	3.00	4.00
A VERY GOOD YEAR FOR GIRLS	Epic (M) LN 24056	2.00	3.00	4.00
WHAT KIND OF FOOL AM I (& MY OTHER FAVORITE SONGS)	Epic (M) LN 24044	2.00	3.00	4.00
WHAT KIND OF FOOL AM I (& MY OTHER FAVORITE SONGS)	Epic (S) BN 26044	2.00	3.00	4.00

WAGONER, Porter

COMPANY'S COMIN'	RCA (EP) EPA 937	1.00	1.50	2.00
COMPANY'S COMIN'	RCA (EP) EPA 938	1.00	1.50	2.00
SATISFIED MIND	RCA (M) LPM 1358	3.00	4.50	6.00
SATISFIED MIND	RCA (EP) EPA 937	1.00	1.50	2.00

WAIKIKIS

HAWAII HONEYMOON	Kapp (M) KL-1432	2.00	3.00	4.00
HAWAII HONEYMOON	Kapp (S) KS-3432	2.00	3.00	4.00
HAWAII KAI	Kapp (M) KL-1366	2.00	3.00	4.00
HAWAII KAI	Kapp (S) KS-3366	2.50	3.75	5.00
MERRY CHRISTMAS IN HAWAII	Kapp (M) KL-1444	2.00	3.00	4.00
MERRY CHRISTMAS IN HAWAII	Kapp (S) KS-3444	2.00	3.00	4.00

WAILERS

FABULOUS WAILERS (1st Cover)	Golden Crest (M) CR 3075	7.00	14.00	21.00
FABULOUS WAILERS AT THE CASTLE	Etiquette (M) ET ALB 1	5.00	10.00	15.00
MERRY CHRISTMAS FROM THE WAILERS/ THE SONICS/THE GALAXIES	Etiquette (M) ET ALB 02	10.00	20.00	30.00
OUT BURST	United Artists (M) UAL 3557	4.00	6.00	8.00
OUT BURST	United Artists (S) UAS 6557	4.50	6.75	9.00
OUT OF OUR TREE	Etiquette (M) ET ALB 026	4.50	6.75	9.00
TALL COOL ONE	Imperial (M) LP 9262	4.00	6.00	8.00
TALL COOL ONE	Imperial (S) LP 12262	4.50	6.75	9.00
WAILERS AND COMPANY	Etiquette (M) 022	4.50	9.00	13.50
WAILERS WAIL, THE (2nd Cover)	Golden Crest (M) CR 3075	4.00	8.00	12.00
WAILERS, WAILERS, EVERYWHERE	Etiquette (M) ET ALB 023	5.00	7.50	10.00
WALK THRU THE PEOPLE	Bell (M) 6016	4.00	6.00	8.00

WAINWRIGHT, Loudon, III

ALBUM 3	Columbia (S) KC-31462	3.00	4.50	6.00
ATTEMPTED MUSTACHE	Columbia (S) KC-32710	2.50	3.75	5.00
LOUDON WAINWRIGHT III ("Album 3" retitled)	Columbia (S) C 31462	2.00	3.00	4.00
UNREQUITED	Columbia (S) PC-33369	2.00	3.00	4.00

WAITS, Tom

CLOSING TIME	Asylum (S) 5061	2.50	3.75	5.00

WAKEMAN, Rick

JOURNEY TO THE CENTRE OF THE EARTH	A&M (S) SP 3621	2.00	3.00	4.00

TITLE	LABEL & NO.	GOOD	VERY GOOD	NEAR MINT

GENE VINCENT ROCKS AND THE BLUE CAPS ROLL	Capitol (EP) EAP 2-970	4.00	8.00	12.00
GENE VINCENT ROCKS AND THE BLUE CAPS ROLL	Capitol (EP) EAP 3-970	4.00	8.00	12.00
GENE VINCENT'S GREATEST	Capitol (S) DKAO 380	4.00	8.00	12.00
HOT ROD GANG	Capitol (EP) EAP1-985	4.00	8.00	12.00
I'M BACK AND I'M PROUD	Dandelion (M) D9 102	5.00	7.50	10.00
SOUNDS LIKE GENE VINCENT	Capitol (M) T1207	12.50	31.75	50.00

VINSON, Eddie "Cleanhead"

BACKDOOR BLUES	Riverside (M) Z3502	4.00	8.00	12.00
CHERRY RED	King (M) 1087	4.00	6.00	8.00
SINGS	Aamco (M) 312	5.00	10.00	15.00

VINTON, Bobby

BLUE VELVET	Epic (M) LN-24068	2.00	3.00	4.00
BLUE VELVET	Epic (S) BN-26068	2.50	3.75	5.00
BOBBY VINTON'S ALL-TIME GREATEST HITS	Epic (S) 31487	2.00	3.00	4.00
BOBBY VINTON'S GREATEST HITS	Epic (M) LN-24098	2.00	3.00	4.00
BOBBY VINTON'S GREATEST HITS	Epic (S) BN-26098	2.00	3.00	4.00
BOBBY VINTON'S GREATEST HITS OF LOVE	Epic (S) BN-26517	2.00	3.00	4.00
BOBBY VINTON SHOW	ABC (S) 924	2.00	3.00	4.00
BOBBY VINTON SINGS THE BIG ONES	Epic (M) LN-24035	2.00	3.00	4.00
BOBBY VINTON SINGS THE BIG ONES	Epic (S) BN-26035	2.50	3.75	5.00
BOBBY VINTON (YOUNG MAN WITH A BIG BAND)	Epic (M) LN-3780	3.00	4.00	6.00
BOBBY VINTON (YOUNG MAN WITH A BIG BAND)	Epic (S) BN-597	4.00	6.00	8.00
COUNTRY BOY	Epic (M) LN 24188	2.00	3.00	4.00
COUNTRY BOY	Epic (S) BN 26188	2.00	3.00	4.00
DANCING AT THE HOP	Epic (M) LN-3727	3.00	4.50	6.00
DANCING AT THE HOP	Epic (S) BN-579	4.00	6.00	8.00
EV'RY DAY OF MY LIFE	Epic (S) 31286	2.00	3.00	4.00
FOUR SONGS OF CHRISTMAS	Epic (EP) EG-7125	1.00	1.50	2.00
GOLDEN DECADE OF LOVE, THE	Epic (S) 33468	2.00	3.00	4.00
GREATEST HITS/ GREATEST HITS OF LOVE	Epic (S) BG-33767	2.00	3.00	4.00
HEART OF HEARTS	ABC (S) 891	2.00	3.00	4.00
I LOVE HOW YOU LOVE ME	Epic (S) BN-26437	2.00	3.00	4.00
LIVE AT THE COPA	Epic (M) LN 24203	2.00	3.00	4.00
LIVE AT THE COPA	Epic (S) BN 26203	2.00	3.00	4.00
LONELY NIGHTS	Epic (M) LN-24154	2.00	3.00	4.00
LONELY NIGHTS	Epic (S) BN-26154	2.00	3.00	4.00
MELODIES OF LOVE	ABC (S) 851	2.50	3.75	5.00
MR. LONELY	Epic (M) LN-24136	2.00	3.00	4.00
MR. LONELY	Epic (S) BN-26136	2.00	3.00	4.00
MORE OF BOBBY'S GREATEST HITS	Epic (M) LN 24187	2.00	3.00	4.00
MORE OF BOBBY'S GREATEST HITS	Epic (S) BN 26187	2.00	3.00	4.00
MY ELUSIVE DREAMS	Epic (S) BN-26540	2.00	3.00	4.00
PLEASE LOVE ME FOREVER	Epic (M) LN-24341	2.00	3.00	4.00
PLEASE LOVE ME FOREVER	Epic (S) BN-26341	2.00	3.00	4.00
ROSES ARE RED	Epic (M) LN-24020	2.00	3.00	4.00
ROSES ARE RED	Epic (S) BN-26020	2.50	3.75	5.00
SATIN PILLOWS	Epic (M) LN-24182	2.00	3.00	4.00
SATIN PILLOWS	Epic (S) BN-26182	2.00	3.00	4.00
SEALED WITH A KISS	Epic (S) 31642	2.00	3.00	4.00
TAKE GOOD CARE OF MY BABY	Epic (S) BN-26382	2.00	3.00	4.00
TELL ME WHY	Epic (M) LN-24113	2.00	3.00	4.00
TELL ME WHY	Epic (S) BN-26113	2.00	3.00	4.00
THERE! I'VE SAID IT AGAIN	Epic (M) LN-24081	2.00	3.00	4.00
THERE! I'VE SAID IT AGAIN	Epic (S) BN-26081	2.50	3.75	5.00
THERE! I'VE SAID IT AGAIN	Epic (EP) 26081	1.00	1.50	2.00
VERY MERRY CHRISTMAS	Epic (M) LN-24122	2.00	3.00	4.00
VERY MERRY CHRISTMAS	Epic (S) BN-26122	2.00	3.00	4.00
VINTON	Epic (S) BN-26471	2.00	3.00	4.00
WITH LOVE	Epic (S) PE-32921	2.00	3.00	4.00

VIOLINAIRES

PLEASE ANSWER THIS PRAYER	Checker (M) 2CK 10065	3.50	5.25	7.00

VIRGIN INSANITY

ILLUSIONS OF THE MAINTENANCE MAN	Funky (M) 72411	8.00	12.00	16.00

VIRTUES

GUITAR BOOGIE SHUFFLE	Strand (M) SL 1061	4.00	10.00	16.00
GUITAR BOOGIE SHUFFLE	Strand (S) SL 1061	4.50	11.25	18.00
GUITAR BOOGIE SHUFFLE	Wynne (M) WLP 111	3.00	6.00	9.00

(M) Mono (S) Stereo (EP) Extended Play (Q) Quad (RI) Re-issued

TITLE	LABEL & NO.	GOOD	VERY GOOD	NEAR MINT
JOURNEY TO THE CENTRE OF THE EARTH	A&M (Q) QU 53621	2.50	3.75	5.00
MYTHS AND LEGENDS OF KING ARTHUR AND THE KNIGHTS OF THE ROUND TABLE	A&M (S) SP 4515	2.00	3.00	4.00
MYTHS AND LEGENDS OF KING ARTHUR AND THE KNIGHTS OF THE ROUND TABLE	A&M (Q) QU 54515	2.50	3.75	5.00
NO EARTHLY CONNECTION	A&M (S) SP 4583	2.00	3.00	4.00
RICK WAKEMAN'S CRIMINAL RECORD	A&M (S) SP 4660	2.00	3.00	4.00
SIX WIVES OF HENRY VIII	A&M (S) SP 4361	2.00	3.00	4.00
SIX WIVES OF HENRY VIII, THE	A&M (Q) QU 54361	2.50	3.75	5.00

Also see YES

WALKER, Jerry Jeff

TITLE	LABEL & NO.	GOOD	VERY GOOD	NEAR MINT
JERRY JEFF WALKER	Decca (S) 75384	3.00	4.50	6.00
VIVA TERLINGUA	MCA (S) 382	2.50	3.75	5.00

WALKER, Jimmy and Erwin Helfer

TITLE	LABEL & NO.	GOOD	VERY GOOD	NEAR MINT
ROUGH AND READY	Testament (M) 2202	4.00	6.00	8.00

WALKER, Johnny Big Moose

TITLE	LABEL & NO.	GOOD	VERY GOOD	NEAR MINT
RAMBLING WOMAN	Bluesway (M) 6036	2.00	3.00	4.00

WALKER, Junior and The All Stars

TITLE	LABEL & NO.	GOOD	VERY GOOD	NEAR MINT
ANTHOLOGY	Motown (S) 786	4.00	6.00	8.00
A GASSSSS	Soul (S) 726	2.50	3.75	5.00
GREATEST HITS	Soul (M) 718	3.00	4.50	6.00
GREATEST HITS	Soul (S) 718	3.50	5.25	7.00
HOME COOKIN'	Soul (M) 710	3.00	4.50	6.00
HOME COOKIN'	Soul (S) 710	3.50	5.25	7.00
LIVE	Soul (M) 705	4.00	6.00	8.00
LIVE	Soul (S) 705	5.00	7.50	10.00
MOODY JR.	Soul (S) 733	2.00	3.00	4.00
PEACE AND UNDERSTANDING IS HARD TO FIND	Soul (S) 738	2.00	3.00	4.00
RAINBOW FUNK	Soul (S) 732	2.00	3.00	4.00
ROAD RUNNER	Soul (M) 703	4.00	6.00	8.00
ROAD RUNNER	Soul (S) 703	5.00	7.50	10.00
SHOTGUN	Soul (M) 701	4.00	6.00	8.00
SHOTGUN	Soul (S) 701	5.00	7.50	10.00
SOUL SESSION	Soul (M) 702	4.00	6.00	8.00
SOUL SESSION	Soul (S) 702	5.00	7.50	10.00
WHAT DOES IT TAKE TO WIN YOUR LOVE	Soul (M) 721	3.00	4.50	6.00
WHAT DOES IT TAKE TO WIN YOUR LOVE	Soul (S) 721	3.50	5.25	7.00

WALKER, Lucille

TITLE	LABEL & NO.	GOOD	VERY GOOD	NEAR MINT
BEST OF LUCILLE WALKER, THE	Checker (M) 1428	5.00	7.50	10.00

WALKER, Scott

TITLE	LABEL & NO.	GOOD	VERY GOOD	NEAR MINT
ALONER	Smash (M) MGS 27099	2.25	2.50	4.50
ALONER	Smash (S) SRS 67099	2.75	3.50	5.50
SCOTT, VOL. 2	Smash (S) SRS 67106	3.00	4.50	6.00
3	Smash (S) SRS 67121	3.00	4.50	6.00

WALKER, T-Bone

TITLE	LABEL & NO.	GOOD	VERY GOOD	NEAR MINT
BLUE ROCKS	Bluestime (M) 29010	4.00	6.00	8.00
CLASSICS IN JAZZ	Capitol (M) T 370	3.00	4.50	6.00
DIRTY MISTREATER	Blues Way (S) BLS 6058	4.00	6.00	8.00
FLY WALKER AIRLINES	Polydor (S) PD 5521	3.00	4.50	6.00
FUNKY TOWN	Blues Way (M) BL 6014	4.00	6.00	8.00
FUNKY TOWN	Blues Way (S) BLS 6014	4.50	6.75	9.00
GREAT BLUES VOCALS & GUITARS OF T-BONE WALKER, THE	Capitol (M) 1958	10.00	15.00	20.00
I GET SO WEARY	Imperial (M) 9146	5.00	12.50	20.00
I WANT A LITTLE GIRL	Delmark (S) DS 633	5.00	7.50	10.00
SINGING THE BLUES	Imperial (M) 9116	5.00	10.00	15.00
SINGIN' THE BLUES	Imperial (M) LP 12397	3.00	6.00	9.00
STORMY MONDAY BLUES	Wet Soul (M) 1002	3.00	4.50	6.00
T-BONE BLUES (Original 50's release)	Atlantic (M) 8020	5.00	7.50	10.00
T-BONE BLUES (70 release)	Atalntic (S) SD 8256	2.50	3.75	5.00
T-BONE WALKER	Blue Note (M) BNLA 533	2.00	3.00	4.00
T BONE WALKER SINGS THE BLUES	Imperial (M) 9098	5.00	12.50	20.00
VERY RARE	Reprise (S) 2XS 6483	3.00	4.50	6.00

WALKER BROTHERS

TITLE	LABEL & NO.	GOOD	VERY GOOD	NEAR MINT
INTRODUCING THE WALKER BROTHERS	Smash (M) MGS 27076	3.50	5.25	7.00
INTRODUCING THE WALKER BROTHERS	Smash (S) SRS 67076	4.00	6.00	8.00
SUN AIN'T GONNA SHINE ANYMORE, THE	Smash (M) MGS 27082	3.50	5.25	7.00
SUN AIN'T GONNA SHINE ANYMORE, THE	Smash (S) SRS 67082	4.00	6.00	8.00

WALLACE, Jerry

TITLE	LABEL & NO.	GOOD	VERY GOOD	NEAR MINT
IN THE MISTY MOONLIGHT	Challenge (M) CHL-619	3.00	6.00	9.00
IN THE MISTY MOONLIGHT	Challenge (S) CHS-619	3.50	7.00	10.50
JUST JERRY	Challenge (M) CHL-606	6.00	12.00	18.00
SHUTTERS & BOARDS	Challenge (M) CHL-616	3.00	6.00	9.00
SHUTTERS & BOARDS	Challenge (S) CHS-616	3.50	7.00	10.50
THERE SHE GOES	Challenge (M) CHL-612	5.00	10.00	15.00
THERE SHE GOES	Challenge (S) CHS 612	6.00	12.00	18.00

WALLACE BROTHERS

TITLE	LABEL & NO.	GOOD	VERY GOOD	NEAR MINT
SOUL, SOUL, SOUL	Sims (M) 128	4.00	6.00	8.00

WALLACE COLLECTION

TITLE	LABEL & NO.	GOOD	VERY GOOD	NEAR MINT
WALLACE COLLECTION	Capitol (S) ST 350	4.50	6.75	9.00

(M) Mono (S) Stereo (EP) Extended Play (Q) Quad (RI) Re-issued

WALLER, Gordon

TITLE	LABEL & NO.	GOOD	VERY GOOD	NEAR MINT
AND GORDON	ABC (S) X-749	4.00	6.00	8.00

Also see PETER & GORDON

WALLER, Jim and The Deltas

TITLE	LABEL & NO.	GOOD	VERY GOOD	NEAR MINT
SURFIN' WILD	Arvee (M) 432	4.50	9.00	13.50

WALSH, Joe

TITLE	LABEL & NO.	GOOD	VERY GOOD	NEAR MINT
BARNSTORM	Dunhill (S) 50130	3.00	4.50	6.00
BEST OF THE JAMES GANG & JOE WALSH	ABC (S) 774	2.50	3.75	5.00
SMOKER YOU DRINK, THE PLAYER YOU GET	Command (Q) QD-40016	2.50	3.75	5.00
SMOKER YOU DRINK, THE PLAYER YOU GET	Dunhill (S) 50140	3.00	4.50	6.00
SO WHAT	Command (Q) QD-40017	2.50	3.75	5.00
SO WHAT	Dunhill (S) 50171	3.00	4.50	6.00

Also see JAMES GANG

WAR

TITLE	LABEL & NO.	GOOD	VERY GOOD	NEAR MINT
ALL DAY MUSIC	United Artists (S) UAS 5546	3.00	4.50	6.00
DELIVER THE WORD	United Artists (S) UA-LA 128	2.50	3.75	5.00
GALAXY	MCA (S) 3030	2.00	3.00	4.00
WAR	United Artists (S) UAS 5508	3.50	5.25	7.00
WAR LIVE	United Artists (S) UA-LA193	3.00	4.50	6.00
WORLD IS A GHETTO, THE	United Artists (S) UAS 5652	3.00	4.50	6.00

WARD, Billy & Dominoes

TITLE	LABEL & NO.	GOOD	VERY GOOD	NEAR MINT
ALL TIME HIT STANDARDS	King (EP) EP-212	3.00	4.50	6.00
ALL TIME HIT STANDARDS	King (EP) EP-262	2.00	3.00	4.00
ALL TIME HIT STANDARDS	King (EP) EP-269	2.00	3.00	4.00
BILLY WARD & HIS DOMINOES	Federal (M) 548	30.00	75.00	120.00
BILLY WARD AND HIS DOMINOES (10")	Federal (M) 295 94	90.00	225.00	360.00
(One of the rarest and most sought-after 10" LP's. Price may vary widely.)				
BILLY WARD AND HIS DOMINOES	King (M) LP 548	4.00	6.00	8.00
BILLY WARD & HIS DOMINOES	King (M) 733	3.00	6.00	9.00
BILLY WARD AND THE DOMINOES (FEATURES JACKIE WILSON LEAD ON SOME TRACKS)	Decca (M) DL 8621	10.00	25.00	60.00
BILLY WARD AND THE DOMINOES (FEATURES JACKIE WILSON LEAD ON SOME TRACKS)	Decca (EP) ED 2549	2.00	3.00	4.00
CLYDE MCPHATTER WITH BILLY WARD	King (M) LP 559	5.00	12.50	20.00
CLYDE MCPHATTER WITH THE DOMINOES	Federal (M) 559	15.00	22.50	60.00
GOLDEN HITS	Hallmark (M) 7021	4.00	10.00	16.00
PAGAN LOVE SONG	Liberty (M) LRP-3113	2.50	5.00	7.50
PAGAN LOVE SONG	Liberty (S) LST-7113	3.00	6.00	9.00
SEA OF GLASS	Liberty (M) LRP 3056	3.00	6.00	9.00
YOURS FOREVER	Liberty (M) LRP 3083	3.00	6.00	9.00

WARD, Robin

TITLE	LABEL & NO.	GOOD	VERY GOOD	NEAR MINT
WONDERFUL SUMMER	Dot (M) 25555	6.00	12.00	18.00

WARREN, Rusty

TITLE	LABEL & NO.	GOOD	VERY GOOD	NEAR MINT
BANNED IN BOSTON	Jubilee (M) JGM 2049	4.00	8.00	12.00
KNOCKERS UP!	Jubilee (M) JGM 2029	5.00	10.00	15.00
MORE KNOCKERS UP!	Jubilee (M) JGM 2059	5.00	7.50	10.00
RUSTY WARREN BOUNCES BACK	Jubilee (M) JGM 2039	4.00	8.00	12.00
RUSTY WARREN IN ORBIT	Jubilee (M) JGM 2044	4.00	8.00	12.00
SINSATIONAL	Jubilee (M) JGM 2034	4.00	8.00	12.00
SONGS FOR SINNERS	Jubilee (M) JGM 2024	4.00	8.00	12.00

WARWICK, Dee Dee

TITLE	LABEL & NO.	GOOD	VERY GOOD	NEAR MINT
I WANT TO BE WITH YOU	Mercury (M) MG 21100	3.00	6.00	9.00
I WANT TO BE WITH YOU	Mercury (S) SR 61100	3.50	7.00	10.50

WARWICK, Dionne

TITLE	LABEL & NO.	GOOD	VERY GOOD	NEAR MINT
ANYONE WHO HAD A HEART	Scepter (M) 517	3.00	4.50	6.00
ANYONE WHO HAD A HEART	Scepter (S) S 517	3.50	5.25	7.00
DIONNE	Scepter (S) P2S 5140	2.00	3.00	4.00
DIONNE	Warner Bros. (S) BS 2585	2.00	3.00	4.00
DIONNE WARWICK IN PARIS	Scepter (M) 534	2.50	3.75	5.00
DIONNE WARWICK IN PARIS	Scepter (S) S 534	3.00	4.50	6.00

TITLE	LABEL & NO.	GOOD	VERY GOOD	NEAR MINT
DIONNE WARWICK ON STAGE AND IN THE MOVIES	Scepter (M) 559	2.50	3.75	5.00
DIONNE WARWICK ON STAGE AND IN THE MOVIES	Scepter (S) 559	3.00	4.50	6.00
DIONNE WARWICK'S GOLDEN HITS-PART ONE	Scepter (M) SRM 565	2.00	3.00	4.00
DIONNE WARWICK'S GOLDEN HITS-PART ONE	Scepter (S) SPS 565	2.00	3.00	4.00
DIONNE WARWICK'S GOLDEN HITS— PART TWO	Scepter (S) 577	2.00	3.00	4.00
DIONNE WARWICK'S GREATEST MOTION PICTURE HITS	Scepter (S) 575	2.00	3.00	4.00
DIONNE WARWICK STORY	Scepter (S) 2-596	2.00	3.00	4.00
FOREVER OLD	Scepter (S) 2-5110	3.00	4.50	6.00
FROM WITHIN	Scepter (S) 2-598	2.00	3.00	4.00
HERE I AM	Scepter (M) 531	2.50	3.75	5.00
HERE I AM	Scepter (S) SS-531	3.00	4.50	6.00
HERE, WHERE THERE IS LOVE	Scepter (M) 555	2.50	3.75	5.00
HERE, WHERE THERE IS LOVE	Scepter (S) 555	3.00	4.50	6.00
I'LL NEVER FALL IN LOVE AGAIN	Scepter (S) 581	2.00	3.00	4.00
JUST BEING MYSELF	Warner Bros. (S) BS2658	2.00	3.00	4.00
LOVE AT FIRST SIGHT	Warner Bros. (S) BS 3119	2.00	3.00	4.00
MAGIC OF BELIEVING	Scepter (S) 567	2.00	3.00	4.00
MAKE WAY FOR DIONNE WARWICK	Scepter (M) S-523	2.50	3.75	5.00
MAKE WAY FOR DIONNE WARWICK	Scepter (S) SS-523	3.00	4.50	6.00
PRESENTING DIONNE WARWICK	Scepter (S) S-508	4.00	6.00	8.00
PROMISES, PROMISES	Scepter (S) 571	2.00	3.00	4.00
SENSITIVE SOUND OF DIONNE WARWICK	Scepter (M) S-528	3.00	4.50	6.00
SENSITIVE SOUND OF DIONNE WARWICK	Scepter (S) SS-528	3.50	5.25	7.00
SOULFUL	Scepter (S) 573	2.00	3.00	4.00
THEN CAME YOU	Warner Bros. (S) BS2846	2.00	3.00	4.00
THEN CAME YOU	Warner Bros. (Q) BS4-2846	2.50	3.75	5.00
TRACK OF THE CAR	Warner Bros. (S) BS2893	2.00	3.00	4.00
VALLEY OF THE DOLLS	Scepter (M) 568	2.00	3.00	4.00
VALLEY OF THE DOLLS	Scepter (S) 568	2.00	3.00	4.00
VERY BEST OF DIONNE WARWICK	United Artists (S) UA-LA388	2.00	3.00	4.00
VERY DIONNE	Scepter (S) 587	2.00	3.00	4.00
WINDOWS OF THE WORLD, THE	Scepter (M) 563	2.50	3.75	5.00
WINDOWS OF THE WORLD, THE	Scepter (S) 563	3.00	4.50	6.00

WASHINGTON, Baby

TITLE	LABEL & NO.	GOOD	VERY GOOD	NEAR MINT
ONLY THOSE IN LOVE	Sue (M) 1042	4.00	8.00	12.00
THAT'S HOW HEARTACHES ARE MADE	Sue (M) LP 1014	4.00	8.00	12.00

WASHINGTON, Dinah

TITLE	LABEL & NO.	GOOD	VERY GOOD	NEAR MINT
SEPTEMBER IN THE RAIN	Mercury (M) MG 20638	3.00	6.00	9.00
UNFORGETTABLE	Mercury (M) MG 20572	3.00	6.00	9.00
WHAT A DIFFERENCE A DAY MAKES	Mercury (M) MG 20479	3.00	6.00	9.00
WHAT A DIFFERENCE A DAY MAKES	Mercury (S) SR60158	4.00	8.00	12.00

WASHINGTON, Gino

TITLE	LABEL & NO.	GOOD	VERY GOOD	NEAR MINT
RAM JAM BAND	Kapp (M) 1515	4.00	8.00	12.00

WATERS, Muddy

TITLE	LABEL & NO.	GOOD	VERY GOOD	NEAR MINT
AT NEWPORT	Chess (M) LP 1449	5.00	10.00	15.00
BEST OF MUDDY WATERS	Chess (M) LP 1427	5.00	10.00	15.00
CANT GET NO GRINDIN	Chess (M) 50023	2.00	3.00	4.00
DOWN ON STOVALL'S PLANTATION	Testament (M) T 2210	6.00	12.00	18.00
FOLK SINGER	Chess (M) LP 1483	5.00	10.00	15.00
LIVE	Chess (M) CH 50012	4.00	6.00	8.00
LONDON SESSIONS	Chess (M) 60013	2.50	4.00	5.00
MCKINLEY MORGANFIELD AKA MUDDY WATERS	Chess (M) 2CH 600006	4.00	6.00	8.00
MORE REAL FOLK BLUES	Chess (M) LP 1511	5.00	10.00	15.00
MORE REAL FOLK BLUES	Chess (S) LPS 1511	3.50	7.00	10.50
MUDDY, BRASS & THE BLUES	Chess (M) 1507	5.00	10.00	15.00
MUDDY, BRASS & THE BLUES	Chess (S) 1507	3.50	7.00	10.50
MUDDY WATERS AT WOODSTOCK	Chess (S) 60035	3.00	4.50	6.00
REAL FOLK BLUES	Chess (M) LP 1501	5.00	10.00	15.00
SAIL ON	Chess (M) LP 1539	5.00	10.00	15.00
SINGS BIG BILL BROONZY	Chess (M) LP 1444	5.00	10.00	15.00
THEY CALL ME MUDDY WATERS	Chess (M) CH 1553	5.00	10.00	15.00
UNK IN FUNK	Chess (S) 60031	2.50	3.75	5.00

WATSON, Doc

TITLE	LABEL & NO.	GOOD	VERY GOOD	NEAR MINT
BEST OF DOC WATSON	Vanguard (S) VSD-45/46	3.50	5.25	7.00

WATSON, Doc & Merle

TITLE	LABEL & NO.	GOOD	VERY GOOD	NEAR MINT
THEN & NOW	Poppy (S) PP-LA022-F	2.00	3.00	4.00
TWO DAYS IN NOVEMBER	Poppy (S) PP-LA210-G	2.00	3.00	4.00

WATSON, Johnny Guitar

TITLE	LABEL & NO.	GOOD	VERY GOOD	NEAR MINT
I DON'T WANT TO BE ALONE STRANGER	Fantasy (S) 9484	2.00	3.00	4.00
JOHNNY GUITAR WATSON	King (M) 857	4.00	8.00	12.00

WAVE CRESTS

TITLE	LABEL & NO.	GOOD	VERY GOOD	NEAR MINT
SURFTIME USA	Viking (M) VK 606	3.00	6.00	9.00

WAYNE, James

TITLE	LABEL & NO.	GOOD	VERY GOOD	NEAR MINT
JAMES WAYNE	Time (M) 2	5.00	10.00	15.00
JAMES WAYNE	Time (M) 4	5.00	10.00	15.00

WAYNE, John

TITLE	LABEL & NO.	GOOD	VERY GOOD	NEAR MINT
AMERICA, WHY I LOVE HER	RCA (S) LSP-4828	2.00	3.00	4.00

WAYNE, Thomas

TITLE	LABEL & NO.	GOOD	VERY GOOD	NEAR MINT
TRAGEDY	Fernwood	6.00	15.00	24.00

WAYNE, Wee Willie

TITLE	LABEL & NO.	GOOD	VERY GOOD	NEAR MINT
TRAVELIN' MOOD	Imperial (M) LP 9144	6.00	15.00	24.00

WEASELS

TITLE	LABEL & NO.	GOOD	VERY GOOD	NEAR MINT
LIVERPOOL BEAT, THE	Mercury/Wing (M) 12282	3.00	6.00	9.00

WEAVERS

TITLE	LABEL & NO.	GOOD	VERY GOOD	NEAR MINT
BEST OF THE WEAVERS	Decca (M) DL-8893	3.00	6.00	9.00
BEST OF THE WEAVERS	Decca (M) DXB-173	3.00	4.50	6.00
BEST OF THE WEAVERS	Decca (S) DXB7-173	3.00	4.50	6.00
FOLK SONGS AROUND THE WORLD	Decca (M) DL-8909	2.50	5.00	7.50
TRAVELING ON WITH THE WEAVERS	Vanguard (M) VRS-9043	3.50	5.25	7.00
TRAVELING ON WITH THE WEAVERS	Vanguard (S) VSD-2022	4.00	6.00	8.00
WEAVERS AT CARNEGIE HALL, THE	Vanguard (M) VRS 9010	3.50	5.25	7.00
WEAVERS AT CARNEGIE HALL Vol. 2, THE	Vanguard (M) VRS 9075	3.50	5.25	7.00

WEB

TITLE	LABEL & NO.	GOOD	VERY GOOD	NEAR MINT
FULLY INTERLOCKING	Deram (S) DES 18018	2.50	3.75	5.00

WEBB, T.S. Henry

TITLE	LABEL & NO.	GOOD	VERY GOOD	NEAR MINT
YOU ARE A STAR	Dharma (M) D 803	2.50	3.75	5.00

WEBER, Joan

TITLE	LABEL & NO.	GOOD	VERY GOOD	NEAR MINT
JOAN WEBER	Columbia (EP) B 2018	1.00	1.50	2.00

WEDGES

TITLE	LABEL & NO.	GOOD	VERY GOOD	NEAR MINT
SURFIN WITH THE WEDGES	Time (M) S/2090	3.00	6.00	9.00

WE FIVE

TITLE	LABEL & NO.	GOOD	VERY GOOD	NEAR MINT
CATCH THE WIND	Vault (M) 136	3.50	5.25	7.00
MAKE SOMEONE HAPPY	A&M (M) LP 138	3.50	5.25	7.00
MAKE SOMEONE HAPPY	A&M (S) SP 4138	3.00	4.50	6.00
RETURN OF WE FIVE	A&M (S) SP 4168	3.00	4.50	6.00
YOU WERE ON MY MIND	A&M (M) LP 111	3.50	5.25	7.00
YOU WERE ON MY MIND	A&M (S) SP 4111	2.50	3.75	5.00

WEISBERG, Tim

TITLE	LABEL & NO.	GOOD	VERY GOOD	NEAR MINT
DREAMSPEAKER	A&M (S) SP 3045	2.50	3.75	5.00
4	A&M (S) SP 3658	2.50	3.75	5.00
HURTWOOD EDGE	A&M (S) SP 4352	2.50	3.75	5.00
LISTEN TO THE CITY	A&M (S) SP 4545	2.50	3.75	5.00
LIVE AT LAST	A&M (S) SP 4600	2.50	3.75	5.00
ROTATIONS	United Artists (S) UA-LA857	2.00	3.00	4.00
TIM WEISBERG	A&M (S) SP 3039	2.00	3.00	4.00

WELCH, Bob

TITLE	LABEL & NO.	GOOD	VERY GOOD	NEAR MINT
FRENCH KISS	Capitol (S) SW 11663	2.50	3.75	5.00

Also see FLEETWOOD MAC

WELCH, Lenny

TITLE	LABEL & NO.	GOOD	VERY GOOD	NEAR MINT
LENNY	Kapp (M) KL 1517	2.00	3.00	4.00
LENNY	Kapp (S) KS 3517	2.50	3.75	5.00
RAGS TO RICHES	Kapp (M) 1481	2.00	3.00	4.00
RAGS TO RICHES	Kapp (S) 3481	2.50	3.75	5.00
SINCE I FELL FOR YOU	Cadence (M) 3068	2.00	4.00	6.00
SINCE I FELL FOR YOU	Cadence (S) 25068	3.00	6.00	9.00
SINCE I FELL FOR YOU	Columbia (M) CL-2430	2.50	3.75	5.00
SINCE I FELL FOR YOU	Columbia (S) CS-9230	3.00	4.50	6.00
TWO DIFFERENT WORLDS	Kapp (M) KL-1457	2.00	3.00	4.00
TWO DIFFERENT WORLDS	Kapp (S) KS-3457	2.50	3.75	5.00

WELK, Lawrence

TITLE	LABEL & NO.	GOOD	VERY GOOD	NEAR MINT
A-ONE A-TWO, THIS IS LAWRENCE WELK (2 12")	Coral CX-3	3.00	4.50	6.00
BABY ELEPHANT WALK	Dot (M) 3457	2.00	3.00	4.00
BABY ELEPHANT WALK	Dot (S) 25457	2.50	3.75	5.00
BEST OF LAWRENCE WELK	Decca (S) KXSE-7208	3.00	4.50	6.00
CALCUTTA!	Dot (M) 3359	2.00	3.00	4.00
CALCUTTA!	Dot (S) 25359	2.50	3.75	5.00
IN ACAPULCO	Coral (EP) EC-81183	1.00	1.50	2.00
IN ACAPULCO	Coral (SEP) EC-781183	1.50	2.25	3.00
LAST DATE	Dot (M) 3350	2.00	3.00	4.00
LAST DATE	Dot (S) 25350	2.50	3.75	5.00
LAWRENCE WELK'S MOST REQUESTED TV FAVORITES	Ranwood (S) 8140	2.00	3.00	4.00
MR. MUSIC MAKER	Dot (M) DLP-3164	2.00	3.00	4.00
MR. MUSIC MAKER	Dot (S) DLP-25164	2.00	3.00	4.00
MR. MUSIC MAKER	Dot (EP) DEP-1079	1.00	1.50	2.00
MR. MUSIC MAKER	Dot (SEP) DEP-21079	1.00	1.50	2.00
MR. MUSIC MAKER	Dot (EP) DEP-1080	1.00	1.50	2.00
MR. MUSIC MAKER	Dot (SEP) DEP-21080	1.00	1.50	2.00
MOON RIVER	Dot (M) 3412	2.00	3.00	4.00
MOON RIVER	Dot (S) 25412	2.50	3.75	5.00
SWEET & LOVELY	Dot (M) DLP-3296	2.00	3.00	4.00
SWEET & LOVELY	Dot (S) DLP-25296	2.50	3.75	5.00
T.V. WESTERN THEME SONGS	Coral (M) CRL-76267	2.00	3.00	4.00
T.V. WESTERN THEME SONGS	Coral (S) CRL-757267	2.50	3.75	5.00
T.V. WESTERN THEME SONGS	Coral (EP) EC-81181	1.00	1.50	2.00
T.V. WESTERN THEME SONGS	Coral (SEP) EC-781181	1.50	2.25	3.00
YELLOW BIRD	Dot (M) 3389	2.00	3.00	4.00
YELLOW BIRD	Dot (S) 25389	2.50	3.75	5.00

(M) Mono (S) Stereo (EP) Extended Play (Q) Quad (RI) Re-issued

WELLS, Junior

TITLE	LABEL & NO.	GOOD	VERY GOOD	NEAR MINT
IT'S MY LIFE BABY	Vanguard (S) VSD 79231	3.00	4.50	6.00
JUNIOR WELLS SINGS LIVE AT THE GOLDEN BEAR	Blue Rock (S) SRB 64003	3.00	4.50	6.00
YOU'RE TUFF ENOUGH	Blue Rock (S) SRB 64002	3.00	4.50	6.00

WELLS, Junior, Chicago Blues Band

TITLE	LABEL & NO.	GOOD	VERY GOOD	NEAR MINT
HOODOO MAN BLUES	Delmark (S) DS 9612	3.50	5.25	7.00

WELLS, Mary

TITLE	LABEL & NO.	GOOD	VERY GOOD	NEAR MINT
BYE BYE BABY (I DON'T WANT TO TAKE A CHANCE)	Motown (M) 600	5.00	10.00	15.00
LIVE ON STAGE	Motown (M) 611	3.50	5.25	7.00
LIVE ON STAGE	Motown (S) 611	4.00	6.00	8.00
LOVE SONGS TO THE BEATLES	20th Century (M) TFM-3178	4.00	6.00	8.00
LOVE SONGS TO THE BEATLES	20th Century (S) RFS-4178	5.00	7.50	10.00
MARY WELLS	20th Century (M) TFM 3171	3.00	4.50	6.00
MARY WELLS GREATEST HITS	Motown (M) 616	4.00	6.00	8.00
MARY WELLS SINGS MY GUY	Motown (M) 617	4.00	6.00	8.00
ONE WHO REALLY LOVES YOU	Motown (M) 605	5.00	10.00	15.00
OOH	Movietone (M) 71010	3.50	5.25	7.00
OOH	Movietone (S) 72010	4.50	6.75	9.00
SERVIN UP SOME SOUL	Jubilee (S) JGS 8018	4.50	6.75	9.00
TWO LOVERS	Motown (M) 607	3.50	5.25	7.00
TWO LOVERS	Motown (S) 607	4.00	6.00	8.00
TWO SIDES OF MARY WELLS	Atco (S) SD 33-199	3.00	4.50	6.00
VINTAGE STOCK	Motown (M) 653	3.00	4.50	6.00
VINTAGE STOCK	Motown (S) 653	3.50	5.25	7.00

WELLS, Orson

TITLE	LABEL & NO.	GOOD	VERY GOOD	NEAR MINT
BEGATTING OF THE PRESIDENT, THE	Mediarts (S) 41-2	4.00	6.00	8.00
COMPULSION	20th Century Fox (EP) FEP-101	3.00	6.00	9.00

WESS, Frank

TITLE	LABEL & NO.	GOOD	VERY GOOD	NEAR MINT
WESS TO MEMPHIS	Enterprise (S) ENS 5001	2.00	3.00	4.00

WEST

TITLE	LABEL & NO.	GOOD	VERY GOOD	NEAR MINT
BRIDGES	Epic (S) BN 26433	3.50	5.25	7.00
WEST	Epic (S) BN 26380	3.50	5.25	7.00

WEST, Clint & The Boogie Kings

TITLE	LABEL & NO.	GOOD	VERY GOOD	NEAR MINT
CLINT WEST & THE BOOGIE KINGS	Jin (M) 4003	4.00	6.00	8.00
CLINT WEST & THE BOOGIE KINGS	Jin (M) 4004	4.00	6.00	8.00

WEST COAST POP ART EXPERIMENTAL BAND

TITLE	LABEL & NO.	GOOD	VERY GOOD	NEAR MINT
A CHILD'S GUIDE TO GOOD AND EVIL	Reprise (S) RS 6298	4.50	6.75	9.00
PART ONE	Reprise (S) RS 6247	4.50	6.75	9.00
VOL. 2	Reprise (S) RS 6270	4.50	6.75	9.00
WHERE'S MY DADDY	Amos (S) AAS 7004	5.00	7.50	10.00

WEST, Mae

TITLE	LABEL & NO.	GOOD	VERY GOOD	NEAR MINT
FABULOUS MAE WEST	Decca (M) DL9016	3.00	6.00	9.00
FABULOUS MAE WEST	Decca (EP) EP 838	1.00	1.50	2.00
GREAT BALLS OF FIRE	MGM (M) 4869	3.00	4.50	6.00
GREAT BALLS OF FIRE	MGM (S) SE 4869	3.50	5.25	7.00
WAY OUT WEST	Tower (S) ST 5028	3.50	5.25	7.00
WILD CHRISTMAS	Dogonet (M) 4	3.00	6.00	9.00
WILD CHRISTMAS	Dagonet (S) 4	3.50	7.00	10.50

WEST, Tommy

TITLE	LABEL & NO.	GOOD	VERY GOOD	NEAR MINT
HOME TOWN FROLICS	Lifesong (S) 6003	2.50	3.75	5.00

WESTERN, Johnny

TITLE	LABEL & NO.	GOOD	VERY GOOD	NEAR MINT
HAVE GUN, WILL TRAVEL	Columbia (M) CL-1788	2.50	3.75	5.00
HAVE GUN, WILL TRAVEL	Columbia (S) CS-8588	2.50	3.75	5.00

WESTON, Kim

TITLE	LABEL & NO.	GOOD	VERY GOOD	NEAR MINT
KIM KIM KIM	Volt (S) VOS 6014	2.00	3.00	4.00

WET WILLIE

TITLE	LABEL & NO.	GOOD	VERY GOOD	NEAR MINT
DIXIE ROCK	Capricorn (S) 0149	2.50	3.75	5.00
DRIPPIN' WET LIVE	Capricorn (S) 0113	3.00	4.50	6.00
KEEP ON SMILIN'	Capricorn (S) 0128	3.00	4.50	6.00
MANORISMS	Epic (S) JE 34983	2.00	3.00	4.00
WET WILLIE	Capricorn (S) 0138	2.50	3.75	5.00
WET WILLIE II	Capricorn (S) 0109	3.00	4.50	6.00

WHEATSTRAW & Chuck McDermott

TITLE	LABEL & NO.	GOOD	VERY GOOD	NEAR MINT
LAST STRAW	Back Door (M) BDF 7474	2.50	3.75	5.00

WHEELER, Clarence and The Enforcers

TITLE	LABEL & NO.	GOOD	VERY GOOD	NEAR MINT
THE LOVE I'VE BEEN LOOKING FOR	Atlantic (S) SD 1585	3.00	4.50	6.00

WHISTLER, Chaucer, Detroit, and Greenhill

TITLE	LABEL & NO.	GOOD	VERY GOOD	NEAR MINT
UNWRITTEN WORKS OF GEOFFREY, THE	Uni (S) 73034	2.50	3.75	5.00

WHITCOMB, Ian

TITLE	LABEL & NO.	GOOD	VERY GOOD	NEAR MINT
IAN WHITCOMBS MOD, MOD, MUSIC HALL	Tower (M) T 5042	4.50	6.75	9.00
ROCK ME SOME ROCK	Tower (S) ST 5100	4.50	6.75	9.00
UNDER THE RAGTIME MOON	United Artists (M) UALA 021	3.00	4.50	6.00

(M) Mono (S) Stereo (EP) Extended Play (Q) Quad (RI) Re-issued

TITLE	LABEL & NO.	GOOD	VERY GOOD	NEAR MINT
YELLOW UNDERGROUND	Tower (M) 5071	4.50	6.75	9.00
YOU TURN ME ON	Tower (M) DT 5004	4.50	6.75	9.00
YOU TURN ME ON	Tower (M) T 5004	4.50	6.75	9.00

WHITE, Barry

TITLE	LABEL & NO.	GOOD	VERY GOOD	NEAR MINT
BARRY WHITE'S GREATEST HITS	20th Century (S) 493	2.00	3.00	4.00
BARRY WHITE SINGS FOR SOMEONE YOU LOVE	20th Century (S) 543	2.00	3.00	4.00
CAN'T GET ENOUGH	20th Century (S) 444	2.00	3.00	4.00
IS THIS WHATCHA WONT?	20th Century (S) 516	2.00	3.00	4.00
I'VE GOT SO MUCH TO GIVE	20th Century (S) 407	2.00	3.00	4.00
JUST ANOTHER WAY TO SAY I LOVE YOU	20th Century (S) 466	2.00	3.00	4.00
LET THE MUSIC PALY	20th Century (S) 502	2.00	3.00	4.00
STONE GON'	20th Century (S) 423	2.00	3.00	4.00

WHITE, Buhla

TITLE	LABEL & NO.	GOOD	VERY GOOD	NEAR MINT
SHY SONGS VOL. 1	Arhoolie (M) 1019	2.50	3.75	5.00
SHY SONGS VOL. 2	Arhoolie (M) 1020	2.50	3.75	5.00

WHITE, Bukka

TITLE	LABEL & NO.	GOOD	VERY GOOD	NEAR MINT
BLUES MASTERS VOL. 4	Blue Horizon (M) BM 4604	4.00	6.00	8.00
MISSISSIPPI BLUES	Takoma (M) B 1001	3.50	5.25	7.00
SIC 'EM DOGS ON ME	Herwin (M) 201	4.50	6.75	9.00

WHITE CLOUD

TITLE	LABEL & NO.	GOOD	VERY GOOD	NEAR MINT
WHITE CLOUD	Good Medicine (M) GM-LP-3500	2.50	3.75	5.00

WHITE DUCK

TITLE	LABEL & NO.	GOOD	VERY GOOD	NEAR MINT
IN SEASON	Uni (S) 73140	2.50	3.75	5.00
WHITE DUCK	Uni (S) 73122	2.50	3.75	5.00

WHITEHEAD, Charlie and The Swamp Dogg Band

TITLE	LABEL & NO.	GOOD	VERY GOOD	NEAR MINT
CHARLIE WHITEHEAD	Fungus (M) FB 25145	3.50	5.25	7.00

WHITE LIGHT

TITLE	LABEL & NO.	GOOD	VERY GOOD	NEAR MINT
WHITE LIGHT	Century (M) 39955	3.00	4.50	6.00

WHITE PLAINS

TITLE	LABEL & NO.	GOOD	VERY GOOD	NEAR MINT
MY BABY LOVES LOVING	Deram (S) DES 18045	3.00	4.50	6.00

WHITESIDE, Bobby

TITLE	LABEL & NO.	GOOD	VERY GOOD	NEAR MINT
BITTERSWEET STORIES	Curtom (S) CRS 8603	2.50	3.75	5.00

WHITMAN, Slim

TITLE	LABEL & NO.	GOOD	VERY GOOD	NEAR MINT
COOL WATER	Imperial (M) 9156	2.00	3.00	4.00
COOL WATER	Imperial (S) 12156	2.00	3.00	4.00
COUNTRY HITS	Imperial (M) 9003	2.00	3.00	4.00
COUNTRY HITS	Imperial (S) 12100	2.00	3.00	4.00
COUNTRY HITS	Imperial (M) 9026	2.00	3.00	4.00
COUNTRY HITS	Imperial (S) 12104	2.00	3.00	4.00
EVERYTHING LEADS BACK TO YOU	United Artists (S) UA-LA513	2.00	3.00	4.00
FAVORITES	Imperial (M) 9252	2.00	3.00	4.00
FAVORITES	Imperial (S) 12252	2.00	3.00	4.00
FOREVER	Imperial (M) 9171	2.00	3.00	4.00
FOREVER	Imperial (S) 12171	2.00	3.00	4.00
GOD'S HAND IN MINE	Imperial (M) 9308	2.00	3.00	4.00
GOD'S HAND IN MINE	Imperial (S) 12308	2.00	3.00	4.00
HAPPY ANNIVERSARY	United Artists (S) UA-LA319	2.00	3.00	4.00
HEART SONGS & LOVE SONGS	Imperial (M) 9209	2.00	3.00	4.00
HEART SONGS & LOVE SONGS	Imperial (S) 12209	2.00	3.00	4.00
I'LL NEVER STOP LOVING YOU	Imperial (M) 9135	2.00	3.00	4.00
I'LL NEVER STOP LOVING YOU	Imperial (S) 12135	2.00	3.00	4.00
I'LL SEE YOU WHEN	United Artists (S) UA-LA046	2.00	3.00	4.00
MORE THAN YESTERDAY	Imperial (M) 9303	2.00	3.00	4.00
MORE THAN YESTERDAY	Imperial (S) 12303	2.00	3.00	4.00
PORTRAIT	Imperial (M) 9137	2.00	3.00	4.00
PORTRAIT	Imperial (S) 12137	2.00	3.00	4.00
SLIM SINGS AND YODELS	RCA (M) LPM 3217	3.00	4.50	6.00
SLIM SINGS AND YODELS	RCA (EP) EPB 3217	1.00	1.50	2.00
SLIM WHITMAN	Imperial (M) LP 9056	2.50	3.75	5.00
SLIM WHITMAN FAVORITES	Imperial (M) LP 9003	3.00	4.50	6.00
SLIM WHITMAN SINGS	Imperial (M) LP 9026	3.00	4.50	6.00
SLIM WHITMAN SINGS	Imperial (S) 9194	3.00	4.50	6.00
SLIM WHITMAN SINGS	Imperial (S) 12194	2.00	3.00	4.00
SLIM WHITMAN SINGS MILLION RECORD HITS	Imperial (M) 9102	2.00	3.00	4.00
SLIM WHITMAN SINGS MILLION RECORD HITS	Imperial (S) 12102	2.00	3.00	4.00
SWEETER THAN THE FLOWERS	Imperial (M) 9163	2.50	3.75	5.00
SWEETER THAN THE FLOWERS	Imperial (S) 12077	2.50	3.75	5.00
TRAVELIN' MAN	Imperial (M) 9313	2.00	3.00	4.00
TRAVELIN' MAN	Imperial (S) 12313	2.00	3.00	4.00

WHO

TITLE	LABEL & NO.	GOOD	VERY GOOD	NEAR MINT
HAPPY JACK	Decca (M) DL 4892	6.00	9.00	12.00
HAPPY JACK	Decca (S) DL 74892	2.50	3.75	5.00
HAPPY JACK/WHO SELL OUT, THE (RI)	MCA (S) 2-4067	2.50	3.75	5.00
LIVE AT LEEDS	Decca (S) 79175	4.00	6.00	8.00
MAGIC BUS	Decca (S) DL 75064	2.50	3.75	5.00
MAGIC BUS/WHO SINGS MY GENERATION, THE (RI)	MCA (S) 2-4068	3.00	5.00	7.00
MEATY, BEATY, BIG & BOUNCY	Decca (S) 79184	4.00	6.00	8.00
QUADROPHENIA	MCA (S) 2-10004	3.50	5.25	7.00
TOMMY (Original Cast)	Decca (S) DXSW 7205	3.50	5.25	7.00

TITLE	LABEL & NO.	GOOD	VERY GOOD	NEAR MINT
TOMMY (Soundtrack)	Polydor (S) PD 2-9502	3.00	4.50	6.00
WHO BY NUMBERS	MCA (S) 2161	2.50	3.75	5.00
WHO SELL OUT, THE	Decca (M) DL 4950	8.00	12.00	16.00
WHO SELL OUT, THE	Decca (S) DL 74950	2.50	3.75	5.00
WHO SINGS MY GENERATION, THE	Decca (M) DL 4664	7.00	10.50	14.00
WHO SINGS MY GENERATION, THE	Decca (S) DL 74664	2.50	3.75	5.00
WHO'S NEXT	Decca 79182	4.00	6.00	8.00

WICHITA TRAIN WHISTLE
WICHITA TRAIN WHISTLE SINGS, THE	Dot (M) DLP 25861	2.50	3.75	5.00

WIGWAM
TOMBSTONE VALENTINE	Verve/Forecast (S) FTS 3089-2	4.50	6.75	9.00

WILD BUTTER
WILD BUTTER	United Artists (S) UAS 6766	3.00	4.50	6.00

WILDCATS
BANDSTAND RECORD HOP	United Artists (M) 3031	5.00	10.00	15.00

WILDE, Marty
BAD BOY	Epic (M) LN 3686	6.00	12.00	18.00
WILDE ABOUT MARTY	Epic (M) LN 3711	5.00	10.00	15.00
WILDE ABOUT MARTY	Epic (S) EPSP 575	7.00	14.00	21.00

WILDERNESS ROAD
SOLD FOR PREVENTION OF DISEASE ONLY	Reprise (S) MS 2125	2.50	3.75	5.00
THREE GENUINE TRANSPARENT	Reprise (EP) PRO 556	3.00	4.50	6.00
WILDERNESS ROAD	Columbia (M) C 31118	3.00	4.50	6.00

WILD MAGNOLIAS
WILD MAGNOLIAS, THE	Polydor (S) PD 6026	2.50	3.75	5.00

WILD ONES
ARTHUR SOUND, THE	United Artists (S) UAS 6450	4.50	6.75	9.00

WILD THING
PARTYIN'	Elektra (S) EKS 74059	4.00	6.00	8.00

WILDWEEDS
WILDWEEDS	Vanguard (S) VSD 6552	4.00	6.00	8.00

WILKINSON TRI-CYCLE
WILKINSON TRI-CYCLE	Date (S) TES 4016	3.00	4.50	6.00

WILLIAMS, Andy
ANDY WILLIAMS' BEST	Cadence (M) CLP 3054	3.00	6.00	9.00
ANDY WILLIAMS' BEST	Cadence (S) CLP 25054	4.00	8.00	12.00
ANDY WILLIAMS' GREATEST HITS, Vol. II	Columbia (S) KC-32384	2.00	3.00	4.00
ANDY WILLIAMS HITS	Dacence (M) 3002	6.00	12.00	18.00
ANDY WILLIAMS MILLION SELLER SONGS	Cadence (M) CLP-3061	2.50	3.75	5.00
ANDY WILLIAMS MILLION SELLER SONGS	Cadence (S) CLP 25061	3.00	4.50	6.00
BORN FREE	Columbia (M) CL 2680	2.00	3.00	4.00
BORN FREE	Columbia (S) CS 9480	2.50	3.75	5.00
CHRISTMAS PRESENT	Columbia (S) C-33191	2.00	3.00	4.00
DANNY BOY AND OTHER SONGS I LOVE TO SING	Columbia (S) CS 8551	3.00	4.50	6.00
DAYS OF WINE AND ROSES, THE	Columbia (S) CS 8679	3.00	4.50	6.00
DEAR HEART	Columbia (M) CL 2338	2.50	3.75	5.00
DEAR HEART	Columbia (S) CS 9138	3.00	4.50	6.00
HAWAIIAN WEDDING SONG	Columbia (M) CL 2323	2.00	3.00	4.00
HAWAIIAN WEDDING SONG	Columbia (S) CS 9123	2.00	3.00	4.00
HONEY	Columbia (S) CS 9662	2.00	3.00	4.00
LONELY STREET	Cadence (M) CLP-3030	4.00	8.00	12.00
LONELY STREET	Cadence (S) CLP 25030	4.50	9.00	13.50
LOVE, ANDY	Columbia (M) CL 2766	2.00	3.00	4.00
LOVE, ANDY	Columbia (S) CS 9566	2.50	3.75	5.00
LOVE STORY/BORN FREE	Columbia (S) CG-33597	2.00	3.00	4.00
MOON RIVER AND OTHER GREAT MOVIE THEMES	Columbia (S) CS 8609	3.00	4.50	6.00
MOON RIVER/DAYS OF WINE & ROSES	Columbia (S) CG-33600	2.00	3.00	4.00
OTHER SIDE OF ME, THE	Columbia (S) PC-33563	2.00	3.00	4.00
SOLITAIRE	Columbia (S) KC-32383	2.00	3.00	4.00
SONGS OF THE ISLANDS	Cadence (EP) CEP-120	1.00	1.50	2.00

(M) Mono (S) Stereo (EP) Extended Play (Q) Quad (RI) Re-issued

TITLE	LABEL & NO.	GOOD	VERY GOOD	NEAR MINT
TO YOU SWEETHEART ALOHA	Cadence (EP) CEP-119	1.00	1.50	2.00
UNDER PARIS SKIES	Cadence (M) CLP-3047	3.00	6.00	9.00
UNDER PARIS SKIES	Cadence (S) CLP-25047	3.50	7.00	10.50
VILLAGE OF ST. BERNADETTE	Cadence (M) CLP-3038	3.00	6.00	9.00
VILLAGE OF ST. BERNADETTE	Cadence (S) CLP-25038	3.50	7.00	10.50
WAY WE WERE, THE	Columbia (S) KC-32949	2.00	3.00	4.00
YOU LAY SO EASY ON MY MIND	Columbia (S) KC-33234	2.00	3.00	4.00
YOU'VE GOT A FRIEND	Columbia (Q) CQ-30797	2.00	3.00	4.00

WILLIAMS, Andy and David
MEET ANDY AND DAVID	Kapp (S) 3673	3.00	4.50	6.00
ONE MORE TIME	MCA (S) 346	2.00	3.00	4.00

WILLIAMS, Big Joe
BIG JOE WILLIAMS	Everest (M) 218	2.50	4.00	5.00
BIG JOE WILLIAMS	World Pacific (M) 21897	2.00	3.00	4.00
BLUES FROM THE MISSISSIPPI DELTA	Blues On Blue (M) 10003	2.00	3.00	4.00
DON'T YOUR . . . LOOK MELLOW	Blueway (M) 6080	2.50	4.00	5.00
HAND ME DOWN MY WALKING CANE	World Pacific (M) 21897	2.50	4.00	5.00
TOUGH TIMES	Arhoolie (M) 1002	2.50	4.00	5.00

WILLIAMS, Billy
BILLY WILLIAMS	Coral (M) CRL57184	4.00	10.00	16.00
BILLY WILLIAMS QUARTET	MGM (M) E 3400	3.00	7.50	12.00
BILLY WILLIAMS QUARTET	MGM (EP) X 1305	2.00	3.00	4.00
BILLY WILLIAMS QUARTET	MGM (EP) X 1306	2.00	3.00	4.00
BILLY WILLIAMS QUARTET	MGM (EP) X 1307	2.00	3.00	4.00
BILLY WILLIAMS REVUE	Coral (M) CRL 57343	3.00	7.50	12.00
HALF SWEET HALF BEAT	Coral (M) CRL-57251	3.00	7.50	12.00
HALF SWEET HALF BEAT	Coral (S) CRL7-57251	4.00	10.00	16.00
OH YEAH!	Mercury (M) MG 20317	3.00	6.00	9.00
TV FAVORITES	Mercury (EP) EP 1-3086	2.00	3.00	4.00
VIDEO VARIETY	Mercury (EP) EP 1-3219	2.00	3.00	4.00

WILLIAMS, Clarence
MAGIC CRYSTAL BALL	Accent (S) ACS 5057	3.00	4.50	6.00

WILLIAMS, Danny
EXCITING DANNY WILLIAMS	United Artists (M) UAL 3297	2.50	5.00	7.50
EXCITING DANNY WILLIAMS	United Artists (S) UAS 6297	3.00	6.00	9.00
MAGIC TOWN	United Artists (M) UAL3493	2.00	4.00	6.00
MAGIC TOWN	United Artists (S) UAS 6493	2.50	5.00	7.50
WHITE ON WHITE	United Artists (M) UAL 3359	2.50	5.00	7.50
WHITE ON WHITE	United Artists (S) UAS 6359	3.00	6.00	9.00
WITH YOU IN MIND	United Artists (M) UAL 3380	2.00	4.00	6.00
WITH YOU IN MIND	United Artists (S) UAS 6380	2.50	5.00	7.50

WILLIAMS, Hank
ARCHETYPES—HANK WILLIAMS	MGM (S) 4954	2.00	3.00	4.00
CRAZY HEART	MGM (EP) X 1014	3.00	4.50	6.00
FIRST, LAST & ALWAYS HANK WILLIAMS	MGM (M) E-3928	2.50	3.75	5.00
HANK WILLIAMS	MGM (M) 3-E 2	4.00	8.00	12.00
HANK WILLIAMS GREATEST HITS	MGM (M) E-3918	2.50	3.75	5.00
HANK WILLIAMS GREATEST HITS	MGM (S) SE 3918	2.50	3.75	5.00
HANK WILLIAMS LIVES AGAIN	MGM (M) E-3923	2.50	3.75	5.00
HANK WILLIAMS (LONESOME SOUND OF)	MGM (M) E-3803	3.00	4.50	6.00
HANK WILLIAMS (LONESOME SOUND OF)	MGM (EP) X-1698	1.50	2.25	3.00
HANK WILLIAMS (LONESOME SOUND OF)	MGM (EP) X-1699	1.50	2.25	3.00
HANK WILLIAMS (LONESOME SOUND OF)	MGM (EP) X-1700	1.50	2.25	3.00
HANK WILLIAMS SINGS (10")	MGM (M) E 107	8.00	20.00	32.00
HANK WILLIAMS SINGS	MGM (EP) X 1101	4.00	6.00	8.00
HANK WILLIAMS SINGS	MGM (EP) X 1102	4.00	6.00	8.00
HOME IN HEAVEN	MGM (S) M3G-4991	2.00	3.00	4.00
HONKY TONKIN' (10")	MGM (M) E 242	5.00	12.50	20.00
HONKY TONKIN	MGM (M) E 3412	4.00	8.00	12.00
HONKY TONKIN	MGM (EP) X 1317	3.00	4.50	6.00
HONKY TONKIN	MGM (EP) X 1318	3.00	4.50	6.00
HONKY TONKIN	MGM (EP) X 1319	3.00	4.50	6.00
HUMOROUS SONGS OF HANK WILLIAMS	MGM (M) E 4300	2.50	3.75	5.00
HUMOROUS SONGS OF HANK WILLIAMS	MGM (S) SE 4300	2.00	3.00	4.00
I'M BLUE INSIDE	MGM (M) E-3926	2.50	3.75	5.00
IMMORTAL HANK WILLIAMS	MGM (M) E 3605	5.00	10.00	15.00
IMMORTAL HANK WILLIAMS	MGM (EP) X 1554	3.00	4.50	6.00
IMMORTAL HANK WILLIAMS	MGM (EP) X 1555	3.00	4.50	6.00
IMMORTAL HANK WILLIAMS	MGM (EP) X 1556	3.00	4.50	6.00
I SAW THE LIGHT (10")	MGM (M) E 243	5.00	12.50	20.00
I SAW THE LIGHT	MGM (M) E 3331	4.00	8.00	12.00
I SAW THE LIGHT	MGM (EP) X 1218	3.00	4.50	6.00
LET ME SING A BLUE SONG	MGM (M) E-3924	2.50	3.75	5.00
LUKE THE DRIFTER (10")	MGM (M) E 203	5.00	12.50	20.00
LUKE THE DRIFTER	MGM (M) E 3267	4.00	8.00	12.00
LUKE THE DRIFTER	MGM (M) E-3927	2.50	3.75	5.00
LUKE THE DRIFTER	MGM (EP) X 1165	3.00	4.50	6.00
MEMORIAL ALBUM	MGM (M) E 3272	5.00	10.00	15.00
MEMORIAL ALBUM	MGM (EP) E 202	3.00	4.50	6.00
MOANIN' THE BLUES (10")	MGM (M) E 168	6.00	15.00	24.00
MOANIN' THE BLUES	MGM (M) E 3330	4.00	8.00	12.00
MOANIN' THE BLUES	MGM (EP) X168	3.00	4.50	6.00
MOANIN' THE BLUES	MGM (EP) X 1215	3.00	4.50	6.00
MOANIN' THE BLUES	MGM (EP) X 1216	3.00	4.50	6.00
MOANIN' THE BLUES	MGM (EP) X 1217	3.00	4.50	6.00
MOVE IT ON OVER	MGM (EP) X 1076	3.00	4.50	6.00
ON STAGE	MGM (M) E-3999	2.50	3.75	5.00
RAMBLIN' MAN (10")	MGM (M) E 291	5.00	12.50	20.00
RAMBLIN' MAN	MGM (M) E 3219	4.00	8.00	12.00
RAMBLIN' MAN	MGM (EP) X 291	3.00	4.50	6.00
RAMBLIN' MAN	MGM (EP) X 1135	3.00	4.50	6.00

TITLE	LABEL & NO.	GOOD	VERY GOOD	NEAR MINT
RAMBLIN' MAN	MGM (EP) X 1136	3.00	4.50	6.00
SING ME A BLUE SONG	MGM (M) E 3560	4.00	8.00	12.00
SING ME A BLUE SONG	MGM (EP) X 1491	3.00	4.50	6.00
SING ME A BLUE SONG	MGM (EP) X 1492	3.00	4.50	6.00
SING ME A BLUE SONG	MGM (EP) X 1493	3.00	4.50	6.00
THERE'LL BE NO TEARDROPS TONIGHT	MGM (EP) X 1082	3.00	4.50	6.00
UNFORGETTABLE	MGM (M) E-3733	3.00	6.00	9.00
WAIT FOR THE LIGHT TO SHINE	MGM (M) E-3850	3.00	4.50	6.00
WANDERIN' AROUND	MGM (M) E-3925	2.50	3.75	5.00

WILLIAMS, Hank, Jr.

TITLE	LABEL & NO.	GOOD	VERY GOOD	NEAR MINT
BALLADS OF THE HILLS & PLAINS	MGM (M) E 4316	3.00	4.50	6.00
BALLADS OF THE HILLS & PLAINS	MGM (S) SE 4316	3.50	5.25	7.00
BOCEPHUS	MGM (S) M3G-4988	2.50	3.75	5.00
JUST PICKIN'...NO SINGIN'	MGM (S) 4906	2.50	3.75	5.00
(With the Cheatin' Hearts)				
LAST LOVE SONG	MGM (S) 4936	2.50	3.75	5.00
LIVE AT COBO HALL, DETROIT	MGM (S) SE 4644	2.50	3.75	5.00
LIVING PROOF	MGM (S) M3G-4971	2.50	3.75	5.00
SEND ME SOME LOVIN'/				
WHOLE LOTTA LOVING	MGM (S) 4857	2.50	3.75	5.00
(With Lois Johnson)				
SONGS MY FATHER LEFT ME	MGM (S) SE 4621	2.50	3.75	5.00

WILLIAMS, Hank, Sr. & Jr.

TITLE	LABEL & NO.	GOOD	VERY GOOD	NEAR MINT
AGAIN	MGM (M) 4378	2.50	3.75	5.00
AGAIN	MGM (S) 4378	2.50	3.75	5.00
HANK WILLIAMS, SR. & HANK WILLIAMS, JR.	MGM (M) E-4276	2.50	3.75	5.00
(Singing Together in a Recording Miracle)				
HANK WILLIAMS, SR. & HANK WILLIAMS, JR.	MGM (S) SE-4276	2.50	3.75	5.00
(Singing Together in a Recording Miracle)				
LEGEND OF HANK WILLIAMS	MGM (S) 2SE-4865	3.00	4.50	6.00

WILLIAMS, Larry

TITLE	LABEL & NO.	GOOD	VERY GOOD	NEAR MINT
HERE'S LARRY WILLIAMS	Specialty (M) SP 2109	6.00	15.00	24.00
LARRY WILLIAMS GREATEST HITS	Okeh (M) OKM 12123	3.00	6.00	9.00

WILLIAMS, Maurice and The Zodiacs

TITLE	LABEL & NO.	GOOD	VERY GOOD	NEAR MINT
STAY	Herald (M) HLP 1014	8.00	20.00	32.00
STAY (RI)	Sphere Sound (S) SSR 7007	5.00	10.00	15.00

WILLIAMS, Mel

TITLE	LABEL & NO.	GOOD	VERY GOOD	NEAR MINT
ALL THROUGH THE NIGHT	Dig (M) 103	9.00	22.50	36.00

WILLIAMS, Otis

TITLE	LABEL & NO.	GOOD	VERY GOOD	NEAR MINT
OTIS WILLIAMS	Deluxe (EP) EP 385	2.00	3.00	4.00
OTIS WILLIAMS GREATEST HITS	Power Pak (S) 224	4.50	5.25	9.00

WILLIAMS, Otis and His Charms

TITLE	LABEL & NO.	GOOD	VERY GOOD	NEAR MINT
OTIS WILLIAMS AND HIS CHARMS				
SING THEIR ALL TIME HITS	Deluxe (M) 570	15.00	37.50	60.00
THIS IS OTIS WILLIAMS AND HIS CHARMS	King (M) 614	6.00	15.00	24.00

WILLIAMS, Paul

TITLE	LABEL & NO.	GOOD	VERY GOOD	NEAR MINT
CLASSICS	A&M (S) SP 4701	2.00	3.00	4.00
HERE COMES INSPIRATION	A&M (S) SP 4410	2.00	3.00	4.00
IN MEMORY OF ROBERT JOHNSON	King (M) K-1139	5.00	7.50	10.00
JUST AN OLD FASHIONED LOVE SONG	A&M (S) SP 4327	2.00	3.00	4.00
LIFE GOES ON	A&M (S) SP 4367	2.00	3.00	4.00
LITTLE BIT OF LOVE, A	A&M (S) SP 3655	2.00	3.00	4.00
ORDINARY FOOL	A&M (S) SP 4550	2.00	3.00	4.00

WILLIAMS, Robert Pete

TITLE	LABEL & NO.	GOOD	VERY GOOD	NEAR MINT
LOUISIANA BLUES	Takoma (M) B 1011	3.50	5.25	7.00

WILLIAMS, Robert Pete and Snooks Eaglin

TITLE	LABEL & NO.	GOOD	VERY GOOD	NEAR MINT
RURAL BLUES	Fantasy (M) 24716	3.50	5.25	7.00

WILLIAMS, Tony

TITLE	LABEL & NO.	GOOD	VERY GOOD	NEAR MINT
GIRL IS A GIRL IS A GIRL	Mercury (M) MG-20454	3.00	4.50	6.00
GIRL IS A GIRL IS A GIRL	Mercury (S) SR-60138	3.50	5.25	7.00
MAGIC TOUCH OF TONY	Philips (M) PHM-200051	2.50	3.75	5.00
MAGIC TOUCH OF TONY	Philips (S) PHS-600051	2.50	3.75	5.00
TONY WILLIAMS SINGS HIS GREATEST HITS	Reprise (M) R-6006	3.00	4.50	6.00
TONY WILLIAMS SINGS HIS GREATEST HITS	Reprise (S) R9-6006	3.50	5.25	7.00
Also see PLATTERS				

WILLIAMSON, Chris

TITLE	LABEL & NO.	GOOD	VERY GOOD	NEAR MINT
CHRIS WILLIAMSON	Ampex (S) 10134	2.00	3.00	4.00

WILLIAMSON, Sonny Boy

TITLE	LABEL & NO.	GOOD	VERY GOOD	NEAR MINT
DOWN AND OUT BLUES	Checker (EP) LP 1437	2.00	4.00	6.00
REAL FOLK BLUES, THE	Chess (M) 1503	5.00	7.50	10.00
SONNY BOY WILLIAMSON	Blues Classics (M) 9	2.50	4.00	5.00
THIS IS MY STORY	Chess (S) 2CH 50027	4.00	6.00	8.00
YARDBIRDS, THE	Mercury (M) MG 21071	4.00	6.00	8.00
YARDBIRDS, THE	Mercury (S) SR 61071	3.50	5.25	7.00

WILLIE & THE RED RUBBER BAND

TITLE	LABEL & NO.	GOOD	VERY GOOD	NEAR MINT
WILLIE & THE RED RUBBER BAND	RCA (S) LSP 4074	2.25	3.50	4.50

(M) Mono (S) Stereo (EP) Extended Play (Q) Quad (RI) Re-issued

WILLIS, Chuck

TITLE	LABEL & NO.	GOOD	VERY GOOD	NEAR MINT
CHUCK WILLIS SINGS THE BLUES	Epic (EP) EG 7070	4.00	10.00	16.00
HIS GREATEST RECORDINGS	Atco (S) SD 33-373	3.00	4.50	6.00
I REMEMBER CHUCK WILLIS	Atlantic (M) 8079	5.00	12.50	20.00
IT'S TOO LATE	Atlantic (EP) EP 591	2.00	5.00	8.00
KING OF THE SCROLL, THE	Atlantic (M) 8018	6.00	15.00	24.00
ROCK WITH CHUCK WILLIS	Atlantic (EP) EP 609	2.00	5.00	8.00
ROCK WITH CHUCK WILLIS	Atlantic (EP) EP 608	2.00	5.00	8.00
TRIBUTE TO CHUCK WILLIS	Epic (M) LN-3728	10.00	25.00	40.00
WAILS THE BLUES	Epic (M) LN 3425	10.00	25.00	40.00

WILLOWS

TITLE	LABEL & NO.	GOOD	VERY GOOD	NEAR MINT
CHURCH BELLS MAY RING	Melba (M) 102	25.00	62.50	100.00

WILLS, Bob & His Texas Playboys

TITLE	LABEL & NO.	GOOD	VERY GOOD	NEAR MINT
BEST OF BOB WILLS	MCA (S) 2-4092	2.50	3.75	5.00
BOB WILLS AND HIS TEXAS PLAYBOYS	Decca (M) DL 8727	4.00	6.00	8.00
BOB WILLS AND HIS TEXAS PLAYBOYS	Columbia	4.00	6.00	8.00
BOB WILLS AND HIS TEXAS PLAYBOYS	Columbia (EP) B 2805	1.50	2.25	3.00
BOB WILLS ANTHOLOGY, THE	Columbia (S) KG-32416	2.00	3.00	4.00
BOB WILLS PLAYS	MCA (S) 152	2.00	3.00	4.00
BOB WILLS SPECIAL	Harmony (M) HL 7036	4.00	6.00	8.00
DANCE-O-RAMA	Decca (M) DL 5562	4.00	6.00	8.00
DANCE-O-RAMA	Decca (EP) ED 2223	1.50	2.25	3.00
DANCE-O-RAMA	Decca (EP) ED 2224	1.50	2.25	3.00
HISTORY OF BOB WILLS & HIS				
TEXAS PLAYBOYS	MGM (S) 4866	2.00	3.00	4.00
RANCH HOUSE FAVORITES (RI)	MGM (M) E 91	5.00	10.00	15.00
RANCH HOUSE FAVORITES	MGM (M) E 3352	4.00	6.00	8.00
RANCH HOUSE FAVORITES	MGM (EP) X 1237	1.50	2.25	3.00
RANCH HOUSE FAVORITES	MGM (EP) X 1238	1.50	2.25	3.00
RANCH HOUSE FAVORITES	MGM (EP) X 1239	1.50	2.25	3.00
WILLS ROUND UP	Columbia (M) HL 9003	4.00	6.00	8.00

WILSON, Al

TITLE	LABEL & NO.	GOOD	VERY GOOD	NEAR MINT
LA LA PEACE SONG	Rocky Road (S) 3700	2.50	3.75	5.00
SEARCHING FOR THE DOLPHINS	Soul City (S) SCS-92006	3.50	5.25	7.00
SHOW & TELL	Rocky Road (S) 3601	2.50	3.75	5.00
WEIGHING IN	Rocky Road (S) 3600	2.50	3.75	5.00

WILSON, Dennis

TITLE	LABEL & NO.	GOOD	VERY GOOD	NEAR MINT
PACIFIC OCEAN BLUE	Caribou (S) PZ 34354	2.50	3.75	5.00
Also see BEACH BOYS				

WILSON, Flip

TITLE	LABEL & NO.	GOOD	VERY GOOD	NEAR MINT
COWBOYS & COLORED PEOPLE	Atlantic (M) 8149	3.00	4.50	6.00
COWBOYS & COLORED PEOPLE	Atlantic (S) SD 8149	3.00	4.50	6.00
FLIPPIN	Imperial (M) 9155	4.00	8.00	12.00
FLIPPIN	Minit (S) 24012	4.00	6.00	8.00
FLIP WILSON SHOW, THE	Little David (S) 2000	2.50	3.75	5.00
GERALDINE/				
DON'T FIGHT THE FEELING	Little David (S) 1001	2.50	3.75	5.00
"THE DEVIL MADE ME BUY				
THIS DRESS"	Little David (S) 1000	2.50	3.75	5.00
YOU DEVIL YOU	Atlantic (S) 8179	2.00	3.00	4.00

WILSON, Gary

TITLE	LABEL & NO.	GOOD	VERY GOOD	NEAR MINT
YOU THINK YOU REALLY KNOW ME	GW (S) 7042 N11	3.00	4.50	6.00

WILSON, Hank (Leon Russell)

TITLE	LABEL & NO.	GOOD	VERY GOOD	NEAR MINT
HANK WILSON'S BACK, Vol. 1	Shelter (S) SW-8923	3.50	5.25	7.00
HANK WILSON'S BACK, Vol. 1 (RI)	Shelter (S) 2131	3.00	4.50	6.00

WILSON, J. Frank and The Cavaliers

TITLE	LABEL & NO.	GOOD	VERY GOOD	NEAR MINT
LAST KISS	Josie (M) JGM 4006	4.00	8.00	12.00
LAST KISS	Josie (S) JS-4006	5.00	10.00	15.00

WILSON, Jackie

TITLE	LABEL & NO.	GOOD	VERY GOOD	NEAR MINT
AT THE COPA	Brunswick (M) BL 54108	3.00	4.50	6.00
AT THE COPA	Brunswick (S) 754108	3.50	5.25	7.00
BABY WORKOUT	Brunswick (M) 54110	3.50	5.25	7.00
BABY WORKOUT	Brunswick (S) 754110	4.00	6.00	8.00
BEAUTIFUL DAY	Brunswick (S) 754189	3.50	5.25	7.00
BODY AND SOUL	Brunswick (M) 54105	3.50	5.25	7.00
BODY AND SOUL	Brunswick (S) 754105	4.00	6.00	8.00
BODY AND SOUL	Brunswick (EP) EL 754105	2.00	4.00	6.00
BY SPECIAL REQUEST	Brunswick (M) 54101	4.00	6.00	8.00
BY SPECIAL REQUEST	Brunswick (S) 754101	4.50	6.75	9.00
DO YOUR THING	Brunswick (M) 54154	3.00	4.50	6.00
DO YOUR THING	Brunswick (S) 754154	3.50	5.25	7.00
GREATEST HITS	Brunswick (M) 54140	3.50	5.25	7.00
GREATEST HITS	Brunswick (S) 754140	4.00	6.00	8.00
HE'S SO FINE	Brunswick (M) BL 54042	5.00	10.00	15.00
HIGHER AND HIGHER	Brunswick (M) 54130	3.00	4.50	6.00
HIGHER AND HIGHER	Brunswick (S) 754130	3.50	5.25	7.00
I GET THAT SWEETEST FEELING	Brunswick (M) 54138	3.50	5.25	7.00
I GET THAT SWEETEST FEELING	Brunswick (S) 754138	4.00	6.00	8.00
IT'S ALL A PART OF LOVE	Brunswick (M) BL 754158	3.50	5.25	7.00
JACKIE SINGS THE BLUES	Brunswick (M) 54055	3.50	7.00	10.50
JACKIE SINGS THE BLUES	Brunswick (S) 754055	4.00	8.00	12.00
JACKIE WILSON	Brunswick (EP) EB 71048	2.00	4.00	6.00
JACKIE WILSON	Brunswick (EP) EB 71049	2.00	4.00	6.00
JACKIE WILSON GREATEST HITS	Brunswick (M) 54185	3.50	5.25	7.00
JACKIE WILSON GREATEST HITS	Brunswick (S) 754185	4.00	6.00	8.00

TITLE	LABEL & NO.	GOOD	VERY GOOD	NEAR MINT
JACKIE WILSON SINGS THE WORLD'S GREATEST MELODIES	Brunswick (M) 54106	3.50	5.25	7.00
JACKIE WILSON SINGS THE WORLD'S GREATEST MELODIES	Brunswick (S) 754106	4.00	6.00	8.00
LONELY TEARDROPS	Brunswick (M) BL 54045	5.00	10.00	15.00
MERRY CHRISTMAS FROM JACKIE WILSON	Brunswick (M) 54112	3.50	5.25	7.00
MERRY CHRISTMAS FROM JACKIE WILSON	Brunswick (S) 754112	4.00	6.00	8.00
MR. EXCITEMENT	Brunswick (EP) EB 71047	2.00	4.00	6.00
MY GOLDEN FAVORITES	Brunswick (M) BL 54058	4.50	9.00	13.50
MY GOLDEN FAVORITES	Brunswick (S) 754058	5.00	10.00	15.00
MY GOLDEN FAVORITES	Brunswick (M) 54115	3.50	5.25	7.00
MY GOLDEN FAVORITES	Brunswick (S) 754115	4.00	6.00	8.00
NOWSTALGIA	Brunswick (M) 54199	3.50	5.25	7.00
NOWSTALGIA	Brunswick (S) 754199	4.00	6.00	8.00
SOMETHIN' ELSE	Brunswick (M) BL-54117	3.50	5.25	7.00
SOMETHIN' ELSE	Brunswick (S) BL7-54117	4.00	6.00	8.00
SO MUCH	Brunswick (M) BL 54050	4.50	9.00	13.50
SO MUCH	Brunswick (S) 754050	5.00	10.00	15.00
SOUL GALORE	Brunswick (M) 54120	3.50	5.25	7.00
SOUL GALORE	Brunswick (S) 754120	4.00	6.00	8.00
SOUL TIME	Brunswick (M) BL-54118	3.50	5.25	7.00
SOUL TIME	Brunswick (S) BL7-54118	4.00	6.00	8.00
TALK THAT TALK	Brunswick (EP) EB 71046	2.00	4.00	6.00
WHISPERS	Brunswick (M) 54122	3.50	5.25	7.00
WHISPERS	Brunswick (S) 7-54122	4.00	6.00	8.00
A WOMAN, A LOVER, A FRIEND	Brunswick (M) BL 54059	4.50	9.00	13.50
A WOMAN, A LOVER, A FRIEND	Brunswick (S) 754059	5.00	10.00	15.00
YOU AIN'T HEARD NOTHIN' YET	Brunswick (M) BL 54100	4.00	6.00	8.00
YOU AIN'T HEARD NOTHIN' YET	Brunswick (S) 754100	4.50	6.75	9.00
YOU GOT ME WALKING	Brunswick (M) 54172	3.50	5.25	7.00
YOU GOT ME WALKING	Brunswick (S) 754172	4.00	6.00	8.00

WILSON, Jackie and Linda Hopkins

TITLE	LABEL & NO.	GOOD	VERY GOOD	NEAR MINT
MANUFACTURERS OF SOUL	Brunswick (M) 54134	3.50	5.25	7.00
MANUFACTURERS OF SOUL	Brunswick (S) 754134	4.00	6.00	8.00
SHAKE A HAND	Brunswick (M) BL 54113	3.50	5.25	7.00
SHAKE A HAND	Brunswick (S) 754113	4.00	6.00	8.00
SHAKE A HAND	Brunswick (EP) EB-71104	2.00	4.00	6.00

WIND IN THE WILLOWS

TITLE	LABEL & NO.	GOOD	VERY GOOD	NEAR MINT
WIND IN THE WILLOWS (1969 LP featured Deborah Harry, now of Blondie)	Capitol (S) SKAO 2956	10.00	15.00	20.00

WINGFIELD, Pete

TITLE	LABEL & NO.	GOOD	VERY GOOD	NEAR MINT
BREAKFAST SPECIAL	Island (S) 9333	3.00	4.50	6.00

Also see OLYMPIC RUNNERS

WINGS

TITLE	LABEL & NO.	GOOD	VERY GOOD	NEAR MINT
WINGS	Dunhill (S) 50046	3.00	4.50	6.00

WINNERS

TITLE	LABEL & NO.	GOOD	VERY GOOD	NEAR MINT
CHECKERED FLAG	Crown (M) CLP 5394	3.00	6.00	9.00
CHECKERED FLAG	Crown (S) CST 394	2.50	5.00	7.50

WINTER, Edgar, Group

TITLE	LABEL & NO.	GOOD	VERY GOOD	NEAR MINT
EDGAR WINTER GROUP WITH RICK DERRINGER	Blue Sky (S) PZ-33798	3.00	4.50	6.00
EDGAR WINTER GROUP WITH RICK DERRINGER	Blue Sky (Q) PZQ-33798	3.00	4.50	6.00
EDGAR WINTER'S WHITE TRASH	Epic (S) 30512	4.00	6.00	8.00
ENTRANCE	Epic (S) BN 26503	4.00	6.00	8.00
ENTRANCE/WHITE TRASH	Epic (S) BG-33770	3.50	5.25	7.00
JASMINE NIGHT DREAMS	Blue Sky (S) PZ 33483	2.50	3.75	5.00
ROADWORK	Epic (S) 31249	2.50	3.75	5.00
SHOCK TREATMENT	Epic (S) PE-32461	3.50	5.25	7.00
SHOCK TREATMENT	Epic (Q) PEQ-32461	3.00	4.50	6.00
THEY ONLY COME OUT AT NIGHT	Epic (S) KE-31584	2.50	3.75	5.00
THEY ONLY COME OUT AT NIGHT	Epic (Q) EQ-31584	3.00	4.50	6.00
TOGETHER—JOHNNY & EDGAR LIVE (With Johnny Winter)	Blue Sky (S) PZ-34033	3.00	4.50	6.00

Also see DERRINGER, Rick

WINTER, Johnny

TITLE	LABEL & NO.	GOOD	VERY GOOD	NEAR MINT
CAPTURED LIVE	Blue Sky (S) 33944	2.00	3.00	4.00
JOHN DAWSON WINTER III	Blue Sky (S) PZ-33292	2.00	3.00	4.00
JOHN DAWSON WINTER III	Blue Sky (Q) PZQ-33292	2.50	3.75	5.00
JOHNNY WINTER	Columbia (S) CS 9826	3.50	5.25	7.00
JOHNNY WINTER AND	Columbia (S) C 30221	3.00	4.50	6.00
JOHNNY WINTER AND/LIVE	Columbia (S) CG-33651	2.00	3.00	4.00
JOHNNY WINTER STORY, THE	GRT (S) 10010	4.50	6.75	9.00
LIVE	Columbia (S) C 30475	2.50	3.75	5.00
NOTHIN' BUT THE BLUES	Blue Sky (S) 34813	2.00	3.00	4.00
PROGRESSIVE BLUES EXPERIMENT, THE	Imperial (S) 12431	4.00	6.00	8.00
SAINTS & SINNERS	Columbia (S) KC-32715	2.50	3.75	5.00
SAINTS & SINNERS	Columbia (Q) CQ-32715	2.50	3.75	5.00
SECOND WINTER	Columbia (S) CS 9947	2.50	3.75	5.00
STILL ALIVE & WELL	Columbia (S) KC-32188	2.00	3.00	4.00
STILL ALIVE & WELL	Columbia (Q) CQ-32188	2.50	3.75	5.00
TEXAS AUSTIN	United Artists (S) UA-LA139	3.00	4.50	6.00
TOGETHER—JOHNNY AND EDGAR LIVE (With Edgar Winter)	Blue Sky (S) 34033	3.00	4.50	6.00

WINWOOD, Stevie

TITLE	LABEL & NO.	GOOD	VERY GOOD	NEAR MINT
WINWOOD	United Artists (S) UAS 9950	6.00	9.00	12.00
WINWOOD	United Artists (S) UAS 9964	4.00	6.00	8.00

(M) Mono (S) Stereo (EP) Extended Play (Q) Quad (RI) Re-issued

WIRTZ, Mark

TITLE	LABEL & NO.	GOOD	VERY GOOD	NEAR MINT
BALLOON	Capitol (S) ST 11155	3.00	4.50	6.00
HOTHOUSE SMILES	Capitol (S) ST 11208	3.00	4.50	6.00
SMOOTH AND EASY	Mardi Gras (M) LP 5034	5.00	7.50	10.00
SMOOTH AND EASY	Mardi Gras (S) SLP 5034	6.00	9.00	12.00
WIRTZ AND MUSIC	Mardi Gras (M) LP 5033	5.00	7.50	10.00
WIRTZ AND MUSIC	Mardi Gras (S) SLP 5033	6.00	9.00	12.00

WISEMAN, Mac

TITLE	LABEL & NO.	GOOD	VERY GOOD	NEAR MINT
MAC WISEMAN	Dot (EP) DEP 1027	1.00	1.50	2.00
16 GREAT COUNTRY SONGS	ABC (S) DP-4009	2.00	3.00	4.00
TIS SWEET TO BE REMEMBERED	Dot (M) DLP 3084	2.50	3.75	5.00

WISHBONE ASH

TITLE	LABEL & NO.	GOOD	VERY GOOD	NEAR MINT
AN EVENING PROGRAM WITH WISHBONE ASH	Decca (S) DL7-1919	4.00	6.00	8.00
ARGUS	Decca (S) 75437	3.50	5.25	7.00
LIVE DATES	MCA 2-6006	3.00	4.50	6.00
LIVE FROM EMMPHIS	Decca (S) DL 71922	4.00	6.00	8.00
PILGRIMAGE	Decca 75295	4.00	6.00	8.00
THERE'S THE RUB	MCA 464	2.50	3.75	5.00
WISHBONE ASH	Decca 75249	4.00	6.00	8.00
WISHBONE FOUR	MCA (S) 327	2.50	3.75	5.00

WISHFUL THINKING

TITLE	LABEL & NO.	GOOD	VERY GOOD	NEAR MINT
HIROSHIMA	Ampex (M) A10123	5.00	7.50	10.00

WITHERS, Bill

TITLE	LABEL & NO.	GOOD	VERY GOOD	NEAR MINT
BEST OF BILL WITHERS	Sussex (S) 8037	2.50	3.75	5.00
JUST AS I AM	Sussex (S) 7006	3.00	4.50	6.00
LIVE AT CARNEGIE HALL	Sussex (S) 7025-2	3.00	4.50	6.00
MAKING MUSIC	Columbia (S) PC-33704	2.00	3.00	4.00
+ 'JUSTMENTS	Sussex (S) 8032	3.00	4.50	6.00
STILL BILL	Sussex (S) 7014	3.00	4.50	6.00

WITHERSPOON, Jimmy

TITLE	LABEL & NO.	GOOD	VERY GOOD	NEAR MINT
BEST OF JIMMY WITHERSPOON	Blues Way (S) BLS 6051	4.00	6.00	8.00
BLUE BOX	Verve Folkways (M) 3011	3.50	5.25	7.00
BLUE BOX	Verve Folkways (S) 3011	4.00	6.00	8.00
BLUE SPOON	Prestige (M) PR-7327	4.00	8.00	12.00
BLUE SPOON	Prestige (S) PRS-7327	4.50	9.00	13,50
EVENIN' BLUES	Prestige (M) PR-7300	4.00	8.00	12.00
EVENIN' BLUES	Prestige (S) PRS-7300	4.50	9.00	13.50
GOIN' TO CHICAGO BLUES	Prestige (S) PR-7314	4.00	8.00	12.00
GOIN' TO CHICAGO BLUES	Prestige (S) PRS-7314	4.50	9.00	13.50
GOIN' TO KANSAS CITY BLUES	RCA (M) LPM 1639	4.00	8.00	12.00
HEY, MRS. JONES	Reprise (M) R-6012	3.50	5.25	7.00
HEY, MRS. JONES	Reprise (S) R9-6012	4.00	6.00	8.00
JIMMY WITHERSPOON	Crown (M) CLP 5156	4.50	11.25	18.00
JIMMY WITHERSPOON	King (M) 634	6.00	15.00	24.00
JIMMY WITHERSPOON (AT THE MONTEREY JAZZ FESTIVAL)	Hi Fi (M) R-421	4.00	8.00	12.00
JIMMY WITHERSPOON (AT THE MONTEREY JAZZ FESTIVAL)	Hi Fi (S) SR-421	5.00	10.00	15.00
JIMMY WITHERSPOON SINGS THE BLUES	Crown (M) CLP 5192	4.50	11.25	18.00
LOVE IS A FIVE LETTER WORD/SPOON	Capitol (S) ST-11360	3.00	4.50	6.00
ROOTS	Reprise (M) R-6057	3.50	5.00	7.00
ROOTS	Reprise (S) R9-6057	4.00	6.00	8.00
SINGIN' THE BLUES	World Pacific (M) WP-1267	4.00	8.00	12.00
SPOON	Reprise (M) R-2008	3.50	5.25	7.00
SPOON	Reprise (S) R9-2008	4.00	6.00	8.00
'SPOON CONCERTS, THE	Fantasy (M) 24701	4.00	6.00	8.00
A SPOONFUL OF BLUES	United (S) US 7715	3.00	6.00	9.00
SPOON IN LONDON	Prestige (M) PR-7418	3.50	7.00	10.50
SPOON IN LONDON	Prestige (S) PRS-7418	4.00	8.00	12.00
STORMY MONDAY AND OTHER BLUES	Sutton (S) SSU 316	3.00	6.00	9.00
THERE'S GOOD ROCKIN' TONIGHT	World Pacific (M) WP-1402	4.00	8.00	12.00

WITHERSPOON, Jimmy and Eric Burdon

TITLE	LABEL & NO.	GOOD	VERY GOOD	NEAR MINT
GUILTY	MGM (S) SE 4791	3.00	4.50	6.00

WITHERSPOON, Jimmy/Ben Webster

TITLE	LABEL & NO.	GOOD	VERY GOOD	NEAR MINT
JIMMY WITHERSPOON & BEN WEBSTER	Verve (S) V6-8835	3.50	5.25	7.00

WITHERSPOON, Jimmy and Groove Holmes

TITLE	LABEL & NO.	GOOD	VERY GOOD	NEAR MINT
BLUES FOR SPOON & GROOVE	Surrey (M) S-1006	3.50	7.00	10.50
BLUES FOR SPOON & GROOVE	Surrey (S) SS-1006	4.00	8.00	12.00
TAKE THIS HAMMER	Constellation (M) M-1422	5.00	10.00	15.00

WOLFE

TITLE	LABEL & NO.	GOOD	VERY GOOD	NEAR MINT
WOLFE	Rare Earth (M) R 541	3.50	5.25	7.00

WOLFMAN JACK

TITLE	LABEL & NO.	GOOD	VERY GOOD	NEAR MINT
WOLFMAN JACK & THE WOLF PACK	Bread (M) BD 0170	9.00	13.50	18.00

WOMACK, Bobby

TITLE	LABEL & NO.	GOOD	VERY GOOD	NEAR MINT
BOBBY WOMACK'S GREATEST HITS	United Artists (S) UA LA 346	2.00	3.00	4.00
BOBBY WOMACK UNDERSTANDING	United Artists (EP) SP 72	2.00	3.00	4.00
COMMUNICATION	United Artists (S) UAS 5539	2.50	3.75	5.00
FACTS OF LIFE	United Artists (S) UA LA 043	2.00	3.00	4.00
FLY ME TO THE MOON	Minit (S) LP 24014	3.50	5.25	7.00
I DON'T KNOW WHAT THE WORLD IS COMING TO	United Artists (S) UA-LA353	2.00	3.00	4.00
LOOKIN' FOR A LOVE AGAIN	United Artists (S) UA LA 199	2.00	3.00	4.00

TITLE	LABEL & NO.	GOOD	VERY GOOD	NEAR MINT
MY PRESCRIPTION	Minit (S) LP 24027	3.50	5.25	7.00
SAFETY ZONE	United Artists (S) UA-LA544	2.00	3.00	4.00
UNDERSTANDING	United Artists (S) UAS 5577	2.50	3.75	5.00
WOMACK "LIVE"	Liberty (S) LST 7645	4.00	6.00	8.00

WOMB

TITLE	LABEL & NO.	GOOD	VERY GOOD	NEAR MINT
OVERDUE	Dot (S) DLP 25959	4.50	6.75	9.00
WOMB	Dot (S) DLP 25933	4.00	6.00	8.00

WONDER, Stevie

TITLE	LABEL & NO.	GOOD	VERY GOOD	NEAR MINT
DOWN TO EARTH	Tamla (S) 272	3.00	4.50	6.00
EIVETS	Gordy (S) GS 932	4.00	8.00	12.00
FOR ONCE IN MY LIFE	Tamla (S) TS 291	2.50	3.75	5.00
FULFILLINGNESS' FIRST FINALE	Tamla (S) 332	2.00	3.00	4.00
GREATEST HITS	Tamla (S) 282	3.00	4.50	6.00
INNERVISIONS	Tamla (S) 326	2.00	3.00	4.00
I WAS MADE TO LOVE HER	Tamla (S) 279	3.00	4.50	6.00
I WAS MADE TO LOVE HER	Tamla (M) 279	3.50	5.25	7.00
JAZZ SOUL	Tamla (M) 233	8.00	12.00	16.00
LOOKING BACK	Motown (S) 804	4.00	6.00	8.00
MUSIC OF MY MIND	Tamla (S) 314	2.00	3.00	4.00
MY CHERIE AMOUR	Tamla (S) 296	2.50	3.75	5.00
SIGNED, SEALED & DELIVERED	Tamla (S) 304	2.50	3.75	5.00
SONGS IN THE KEY OF LIFE	Tamla (S) 340	3.50	5.25	7.00
STEVIE AT THE BEACH	Tamla (S) 255	4.00	6.00	8.00
STEVIE WONDER LIVE	Tamla (S) 298	2.50	3.75	5.00
STEVIE WONDER'S GREATEST HITS, Vol. 2	Tamla (S) 313	2.00	3.00	4.00
TALKING BOOK	Tamla (S) 319	2.00	3.00	4.00
TRIBUTE TO UNCLE RAY	Tamla (M) 232	8.00	12.00	16.00
12 YEAR OLD GENIUS	Tamla (M) 240	8.00	12.00	16.00
UP-TIGHT	Tamla (M) 268	4.00	6.00	8.00
UP-TIGHT	Tamla (S) 268	5.00	7.50	10.00
WHERE I'M COMING FROM	Tamla (S) 308	2.50	3.75	5.00
WITH A SONG IN MY HEART	Tamla (M) 250	4.00	6.00	8.00
WORKOUT STEVIE, WORKOUT	Tamla (M) TM-248	7.00	10.50	14.00

WOOD, Brenton

TITLE	LABEL & NO.	GOOD	VERY GOOD	NEAR MINT
BABY YOU GOT IT	Double Shot (M) DSM 1003	2.00	3.00	4.00
BABY YOU GOT IT	Double Shot (S) DSS 5003	2.50	3.75	5.00
OOGUM OOGUM	Double Shot (M) DSM 1002	2.00	3.00	4.00
OOGUM OOGUM	Double Shot (S) DSS 5002	2.50	3.75	5.00

WOODY'S TRUCK STOP

TITLE	LABEL & NO.	GOOD	VERY GOOD	NEAR MINT
WOODY'S TRUCK STOP	Smash (S) SRS 67111	4.00	6.00	8.00

WOOFERS

TITLE	LABEL & NO.	GOOD	VERY GOOD	NEAR MINT
DRAGSVILLE	Wyncote (M) W 9011	2.50	5.00	7.50

WOOL

TITLE	LABEL & NO.	GOOD	VERY GOOD	NEAR MINT
WOOL	ABC (S) ABCS 676	3.50	5.25	7.00

WOOLEY, Sheb

TITLE	LABEL & NO.	GOOD	VERY GOOD	NEAR MINT
IT'S A BIG LAND	MGM (M) E-4325	2.00	3.00	4.00
IT'S A BIG LAND	MGM (S) SE-4325	2.00	3.00	4.00
PURPLE PEOPLE EATER, THE	MGM (EP) X 1608	2.00	3.00	4.00
PURPLE PEOPLE EATER PLAYS EARTH MUSIC	MGM (EP) X 1607	2.00	3.00	4.00
SHEB WOOLEY	MGM (M) E 3299	4.00	6.00	8.00
SHEB WOOLEY	MGM (EP) X 1188	1.50	2.25	3.00
SHEB WOOLEY	MGM (EP) X 1189	1.50	2.25	3.00
SHEB WOOLEY	MGM (EP) X 1190	1.50	2.25	3.00
TALES OF HOW THE WEST WAS WON	MGM (M) E-4136	2.00	3.00	4.00
TALES OF HOW THE WEST WAS WON	MGM (S) SE-4136	2.00	3.00	4.00
THAT'S MY PA & THAT'S MY MA	MGM (EP) E-4026	2.50	3.75	5.00
THAT'S MY PA & THAT'S MY MA	MGM (S) SE-4026	2.50	3.75	5.00

WOOLIES

TITLE	LABEL & NO.	GOOD	VERY GOOD	NEAR MINT
BASIC ROCK	Split (M) 9645 2001	8.00	12.00	16.00
LIVE AT LIZARD'S	Spirit	7.00	10.50	14.00

WRAY, Link

TITLE	LABEL & NO.	GOOD	VERY GOOD	NEAR MINT
BE WHAT YOU WANT TO	Polydor (S) 5047	3.00	4.50	6.00
COUNTRY JUBILEE OF STARS WITH BILLY GRAMMER & JUDY LYNN	Guest Star (S) GS 1444	5.00	10.00	15.00
GREAT GUITAR HITS	Vermillion (M) 1924	10.00	15.00	20.00
LINK WRAY	Polydor (S) PD 24-4064	2.00	3.00	4.00
SINGS & PLAYS GUITAR	Vermillion (M) 1925	10.00	15.00	20.00
YESTERDAY AND TODAY	Record Factory (M) LP 1929	10.00	15.00	20.00

(M) Mono (S) Stereo (EP) Extended Play (Q) Quad (RI) Re-issued

TITLE	LABEL & NO.	GOOD	VERY GOOD	NEAR MINT

WRAY, Link and The Ray Men

TITLE	LABEL & NO.	GOOD	VERY GOOD	NEAR MINT
JACK THE RIPPER	Swan (M) SLP 510	5.00	12.50	20.00
LINK WRAY AND THE RAYMEN	Epic (M) LN 3661	6.00	15.00	24.00

WRAY, Vernon

TITLE	LABEL & NO.	GOOD	VERY GOOD	NEAR MINT
WASTED	Vermillion (M) V 1972	10.00	15.00	20.00

WRIGHT, Betty

TITLE	LABEL & NO.	GOOD	VERY GOOD	NEAR MINT
DANGER HIGH VOLTAGE	Alston (S) 4400	2.00	3.00	4.00
EXPLOSION	Alston (S) 4402	2.00	3.00	4.00
I LOVE THE WAY YOU LOVE	Alston (S) 388	2.00	3.00	4.00
MY FIRST TIME AROUND	Atco (S) 260	4.00	6.00	8.00

WRIGHT, Charles

TITLE	LABEL & NO.	GOOD	VERY GOOD	NEAR MINT
DOING WHAT COMES NATURALLY	Dunhill (S) D-30162	2.00	3.00	4.00
LIL' ENCOURAGEMENT	ABC (S) D-887	2.00	3.00	4.00

WRIGHT, Charles and The Watts 103rd Street Rhythm Band

TITLE	LABEL & NO.	GOOD	VERY GOOD	NEAR MINT
EXPRESS YOURSELF	Warner Brothers (S) WS 1864	2.00	3.00	4.00

WRIGHT, David

TITLE	LABEL & NO.	GOOD	VERY GOOD	NEAR MINT
ORIGINAL TIME BAND	Spun	2.50	3.75	5.00

WRIGHT, Gary

TITLE	LABEL & NO.	GOOD	VERY GOOD	NEAR MINT
DREAM WEAVER	Warner Bros. (S) BS 2868	2.00	3.00	4.00
EXTRACTION	A&M (S) SP 4277	3.50	5.25	7.00
FOOTPRINT	A&M (S) SP 4296	3.50	5.25	7.00

WRIGHT, O.V.

TITLE	LABEL & NO.	GOOD	VERY GOOD	NEAR MINT
A NICKLE AND A NAIL AND ACE OF SPADES	Back Beat (M) BBLP 70	3.00	4.50	6.00

WYATT, Robert

TITLE	LABEL & NO.	GOOD	VERY GOOD	NEAR MINT
ROCK BOTTOM	Virgin (S) VR 13-112	2.00	3.00	4.00

WYNETTE, Tammy

TITLE	LABEL & NO.	GOOD	VERY GOOD	NEAR MINT
ANOTHER LONELY SONG	Epic (S) KE-32745	2.00	3.00	4.00
BEDTIME STORY	Epic (S) 31285	2.00	3.00	4.00
D-I-V-O-R-C-E	Epic (S) BN 26392	2.00	3.00	4.00
FIRST LADY, THE	Epic (S) E 30213	2.50	3.75	5.00
FIRST SONGS OF THE FIRST LADY	Epic (S) EG-30358	2.50	3.75	5.00
I STILL BELIEVE IN FAIRY TALES	Epic (S) KE-33582	2.00	3.00	4.00
KIDS SAY THE DARNDEST THINGS	Epic (S) KE-31937	2.00	3.00	4.00
LET'S GET TOGETHER	Epic (S) PE 34694	2.00	3.00	4.00
ONE OF A KIND	Epic (S) KE 35044	2.00	3.00	4.00
STAND BY YOUR MAN	Epic (S) BN 26451	2.00	3.00	4.00
STAND BY YOUR MAN/BEDTIME STORY	Epic (S) BG-33773	2.00	3.00	4.00
TAMMY'S GREATEST HITS	Epic (S) BN 26486	2.00	3.00	4.00
TAMMY'S GREATEST HITS, Vol. II	Epic (S) E 30733	2.00	3.00	4.00
TAMMY'S GREATEST HITS, Vol. III	Epic (S) KE 33396	2.00	3.00	4.00
TAMMY'S TOUCH	Epic (S) BN 26549	2.50	3.75	5.00
TILL I CAN MAKE IT ON MY OWN	Epic (S) PE 34075	2.00	3.00	4.00
WAYS TO LOVE A MAN, THE	Epic (S) BN 26519	2.50	3.75	5.00
WE SURE CAN LOVE EACH OTHER	Epic (S) E 30658	2.50	3.75	5.00
WOMAN TO WOMAN	Epic (S) KE-33246	2.00	3.00	4.00
WORLD OF TAMMY WYNETTE, THE	Epic (S) EGP 503	3.00	4.50	6.00
YOU AND ME	Epic (S) PE 34289	2.00	3.00	4.00

Y

YANCEY, Jimmy and Mama

TITLE	LABEL & NO.	GOOD	VERY GOOD	NEAR MINT
CHICAGO PIANO VOL. 1	Atlantic (S) SD 7229	4.00	6.00	8.00

YANOVSKY, Zalman

TITLE	LABEL & NO.	GOOD	VERY GOOD	NEAR MINT
ALIVE AND WELL IN ARGENTINA	Buddah (S) BS 5019	4.00	6.00	8.00
ALIVE AND WELL IN ARGENTINA	Kama Sutra (S) KSBS 2030	3.00	4.50	6.00

YARBROUGH, Glenn

TITLE	LABEL & NO.	GOOD	VERY GOOD	NEAR MINT
BABY THE RAIN MUST FALL	RCA (M) LPM 3422	2.00	3.00	4.00
BABY THE RAIN MUST FALL	RCA (S) LSP 3422	3.00	4.50	6.00
COME SHARE MY LIFE	RCA (M) LPM 3301	2.00	3.00	4.00
COME SHARE MY LIFE	RCA (S) LSP 3301	2.50	3.75	5.00
EACH OF US ALONE (THE WORDS & MUSIC OF ROD McKUEN)	Warner Bros. (S) 1736	3.00	4.50	6.00
FOR EMILY, WHENEVER I MAY FIND HER	RCA (M) LPM 3801	2.00	3.00	4.00
FOR EMILY, WHENEVER I MAY FIND HER	RCA (S) LSP 3801	2.50	3.75	5.00
GLENN YARBROUGH (SINGS THE ROD McKUEN SONGBOOK)	RCA (S) VPS 6018	3.00	4.50	6.00
HONEY & WINE	RCA (M) LPM 3860	2.00	3.00	4.00
HONEY & WINE	RCA (S) LSP 3860	2.50	3.75	5.00
IT'S GONNA BE FINE	RCA (M) LPM 3472	2.50	3.75	5.00
IT'S GONNA BE FINE	RCA (S) LSP 3472	3.00	4.50	6.00
JUBILEE	Warner Bros. (S) 1876	2.00	3.00	4.00
LIVE AT THE HUNGRY I	RCA (M) LPM 3661	2.00	3.00	4.00
LIVE AT THE HUNGRY I	RCA (S) LSP 3661	2.50	3.75	5.00

175

TITLE	LABEL & NO.	GOOD	VERY GOOD	NEAR MINT
LONELY THINGS, THE	RCA (M) LPM 3539	2.00	3.00	4.00
LONELY THINGS, THE	RCA (S) LSP 3539	2.50	3.75	5.00
MY SWEET LADY	Stax (S) 5506	2.00	3.00	4.00
ONE MORE ROUND	RCA (M) LPM 2905	2.00	3.00	4.00
ONE MORE ROUND	RCA (S) LSP 2905	2.50	3.75	5.00
REUNION	Stax (S) 5513	2.00	3.00	4.00
SOMEHOW, SOMEWAY	Warner Bros. (S) 1782	2.00	3.00	4.00

YARDBIRDS

TITLE	LABEL & NO.	GOOD	VERY GOOD	NEAR MINT
FOR YOUR LOVE	Epic (M) LN 24167	5.00	15.00	25.00
FOR YOUR LOVE	Epic (S) BN 26167	9.00	18.00	27.00
HAVING A RAVE UP WITH THE YARDBIRDS	Epic (M) LN 24177	7.00	10.50	14.00
HAVING A RAVE UP WITH THE YARDBIRDS	Epic (S) BN 26177	8.00	12.00	16.00
LITTLE GAMES	Epic (M) LN 24313	4.00	6.00	8.00
LITTLE GAMES	Epic (S) BN 24313	5.00	7.50	10.00
LIVE YARDBIRDS FEATURING JIMMY PAGE	Epic (S) E 30615	15.00	22.50	30.00
OVER UNDER SIDEWAYS DOWN	Epic (M) LN 24210	7.00	10.50	14.00
OVER UNDER SIDEWAYS DOWN	Epic (S) BN 26210	8.00	12.00	16.00
SONNY BOY WILLIAMSON AND THE YARDBIRDS	Mercury (M) MG 21071	4.00	6.00	8.00
SONNY BOY WILLIAMSON AND THE YARDBIRDS	Mercury (S) SR 61071	3.50	5.25	7.00
YARDBIRDS FEATURING PERFORMANCES BY E. CLAPTON, J. BECK, J. PAGE	Epic (S) EG 30135	15.00	22.50	30.00

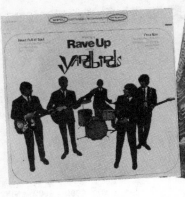 

YARROW, Peter

TITLE	LABEL & NO.	GOOD	VERY GOOD	NEAR MINT
HARD TIMES	Warner Brothers (S) B-2860	2.50	3.75	5.00
PETER	Warner Brothers (S) B-2599	2.50	3.75	5.00
PETER YARROW	Warner Brothers (S) B-2891	2.50	3.75	5.00
THAT'S ENOUGH FOR ME	Warner Brothers (S) B-2730	2.50	3.75	5.00

Also see PETER, PAUL & MARY

YELLOW BALLOON

TITLE	LABEL & NO.	GOOD	VERY GOOD	NEAR MINT
YELLOW BALLOON, THE	Canterbury (M) CLPM 1502	5.00	7.50	10.00

YELLOW PAYGES

TITLE	LABEL & NO.	GOOD	VERY GOOD	NEAR MINT
VOLUME 1	Uni (S) 73045	5.50	8.25	11.00

YES

TITLE	LABEL & NO.	GOOD	VERY GOOD	NEAR MINT
CLOSE TO THE EDGE	Atlantic (S) 7244	3.00	4.50	6.00
FRAGILE	Atlantic 7211	3.00	4.50	6.00
GOING FOR THE ONE	Atlantic 19106	2.00	3.00	4.00
RELAYER	Atlantic 18122	2.50	3.75	5.00
TALES FROM TOPOGRAPHIC OCEANS	Atlantic 2-908	3.50	5.25	7.00
TIME & WORD	Atlantic 8273	4.00	6.00	8.00
YES ALBUM, THE	Atlantic 8283	4.00	6.00	8.00
YESSONGS	Atlantic (S) 3-100	4.50	6.75	9.00
YESTERDAYS	Atlantic 18103	2.50	3.75	5.00

YESTERDAYS CHILDREN

TITLE	LABEL & NO.	GOOD	VERY GOOD	NEAR MINT
YESTERDAYS CHILDREN	Map (S) 3012	3.00	4.50	6.00

YESTERDAYS FOLK

TITLE	LABEL & NO.	GOOD	VERY GOOD	NEAR MINT
US 69	Buddah (S) BDS 5035	2.00	3.00	4.00

YOST, Dennis & Classics IV

TITLE	LABEL & NO.	GOOD	VERY GOOD	NEAR MINT
DENNIS YOST & CLASSICS IV	MGM (South) (S) 702	2.00	3.00	4.00

Also see 'Classics IV'

YOU KNOW WHO GROUP

TITLE	LABEL & NO.	GOOD	VERY GOOD	NEAR MINT
YOU KNOW WHO GROUP, THE	Int'l Allied (M) IA 420	5.00	10.00	15.00

YOUNG, Barry

TITLE	LABEL & NO.	GOOD	VERY GOOD	NEAR MINT
ONE HAS MY NAME	Dot (M) DLP-3672	2.00	3.00	4.00
ONE HAS MY NAME	Dot (S) DLP-25672	2.00	3.00	4.00

YOUNGBLOODS

TITLE	LABEL & NO.	GOOD	VERY GOOD	NEAR MINT
BEST OF THE YOUNGBLOODS	RCA (S) LSP 4399	2.50	3.75	5.00
EARTH MUSIC	RCA (M) LPM 3865	2.00	3.00	4.00
EARTH MUSIC	RCA LSP 3865	2.50	3.75	5.00
ELEPHANT MOUNTAIN	RCA (S) LSP 4150	2.50	3.75	5.00
GOOD AND DUSTY	Warner Brothers (S) BS 2566	2.00	3.00	4.00
HIGH ON A RIDGETOP	Warner Bros. (S) BS 2653	2.50	3.75	5.00
RIDE THE WIND	Warner Bros. (S) BS 2563	2.50	3.75	5.00
ROCK FESTIVAL	Warner Brothers (S) 1878	2.25	3.50	4.50
SUNLIGHT	RCA (S) LSP 4561	3.00	4.50	6.00
THIS IS THE YOUNGBLOODS	RCA (S) VPS 6051	3.00	4.50	6.00
YOUNGBLOODS, THE	RCA (M) LPM 3724	3.00	4.50	6.00
YOUNGBLOODS, THE	RCA (S) LSP 3724	3.50	5.25	7.00

Also see YOUNG, Jesse Colin

YOUNGBLOOD, Tommy

TITLE	LABEL & NO.	GOOD	VERY GOOD	NEAR MINT
SOUL OF TOMMY YOUNGBLOOD, THE	United Superior (M) 7758	3.00	4.50	6.00

YOUNG, Cathy

TITLE	LABEL & NO.	GOOD	VERY GOOD	NEAR MINT
A SPOONFUL OF CATHY YOUNG	Mainstream (S) S/6121	3.50	5.25	7.00

YOUNG, Faron

TITLE	LABEL & NO.	GOOD	VERY GOOD	NEAR MINT
ALL-TIME GREAT HITS OF FARON YOUNG	Capitol (M) T-1876	3.00	4.50	6.00
ALL-TIME GREAT HITS OF FARON YOUNG	Capitol (S) ST 1976	3.00	4.50	6.00
FALLING IN LOVE	Capitol (M) T-2307	2.50	3.75	5.00

TITLE	LABEL & NO.	GOOD	VERY GOOD	NEAR MINT
FALLING IN LOVE	Capitol (S) ST-2307	2.50	3.75	5.00
FAN CLUB FAVORITES	Capitol (M) T-1528	3.00	4.50	6.00
FAN CLUB FAVORITES	Capitol (S) ST-1528	3.00	4.50	6.00
FAN CLUB FAVORITES	Capitol (EP) EAP-1-1528	1.50	2.25	3.00
FARON YOUNG	Capitol (EP) EAP 1-611	2.00	3.00	4.00
FARON YOUNG MEMORY LANE	Capitol (M) T-2037	2.50	3.75	5.00
FARON YOUNG MEMORY LANE	Capitol (S) DT-2037	2.50	3.75	5.00
FARON YOUNG SINGS THE BEST OF FARON YOUNG	Capitol (M) T-1450	3.00	4.50	6.00
FARON YOUNG SINGS THE BEST OF JIM REEVES	Mercury (M) MG 21058	2.50	3.75	5.00
FARON YOUNG SINGS THE BEST OF JIM REEVES	Mercury (S) SR 61058	2.50	c.75	5.00
GOIN' STEADY	Capitol (EP) EAP 1-450	2.00	3.00	4.00
HELLO WALLS	Capitol (EP) EAP-1-1549	1.50	2.25	3.00
IF YOU AIN'T LOVIN' YOU AIN'T LIVIN'	Capitol (M) T-2536	2.50	3.75	5.00
IT'S A GREAT LIFE	Tower (M) 5022	2.50	3.75	5.00
IT'S A GREAT LIFE	Tower (S) 5022	2.50	3.75	5.00
JUST WHAT I HAD IN MIND	Mercury (S) SRM-1-674	2.00	3.00	4.00
MY GARDEN OF PRAYER	Capitol (M) T-1185	3.00	4.50	6.00
MY GARDEN OF PRAYER	Capitol (EP) EAP-1-1185	1.50	2.25	3.00
MY GARDEN OF PRAYER	Capitol (EP) EAP-2-1185	1.50	2.25	3.00
MY GARDEN OF PRAYER	Capitol (EP) EAP-3-1185	1.50	2.25	3.00
OBJECT OF MY AFFECTION, THE	Capitol (M) T 1004	4.00	6.00	8.00
OBJECT OF MY AFFECTION, THE	Capitol (S) ST-1004	5.00	7.50	10.00
SHRINE OF ST. CECILIA	Capitol (EP) EAP 1-869	2.00	3.00	4.00
SOME KIND OF A WOMAN	Mercury (S) SR-1-698	2.00	3.00	4.00
SWEETHEARTS OR STRANGERS	Capitol (M) T 778	5.00	7.50	10.00
SWEETHEARTS OR STRANGERS	Capitol (EP) EAP 1-778	2.00	3.00	4.00
SWEETHEARTS OR STRANGERS	Capitol (EP) EAP 2-778	2.00	3.00	4.00
SWEETHEARTS OR STRANGERS	Capitol (EP) EAP 3-778	2.00	3.00	4.00
TALK ABOUT HITS	Capitol (M) T-1245	3.00	4.50	6.00
TALK ABOUT HITS	Capitol (S) ST-1245	3.00	4.50	6.00
TALK ABOUT HITS	Capitol (EP) EAP-1-1245	1.50	2.25	3.00
TALK ABOUT HITS	Capitol (EP) EAP-2-1245	1.50	2.25	3.00
TALK ABOUT HITS	Capitol (EP) EAP-3-1245	1.50	2.25	3.00
THIS IS FARON YOUNG	Capitol (M) T 1096	4.00	6.00	8.00
THIS IS FARON YOUNG	Capitol (EP) EAP-1-1096	1.50	2.25	3.00
THIS IS FARON YOUNG	Capitol (EP) EAP-2-1096	1.50	2.25	3.00
THIS IS FARON YOUNG	Capitol (EP) EAP-3-1096	1.50	2.25	3.00
THIS TIME THE HURTIN'S ON ME	Mercury (S) 61376	2.00	3.00	4.00
YOUNG APPROACH	Capitol (M) T-1634	3.00	4.50	6.00
YOUNG APPROACH	Capitol (S) ST-1634	3.00	4.50	6.00

YOUNG, Jesse Colin

TITLE	LABEL & NO.	GOOD	VERY GOOD	NEAR MINT
JESSE COLIN YOUNG AND THE YOUNGBLOODS	Mercury (M) MG 21005	3.00	4.50	6.00
JESSE COLIN YOUNG AND THE YOUNGBLOODS	Mercury (S) SR 61005	4.00	6.00	8.00
LOVE ON THE WING	Warner Bros. (S) BS 3033	2.00	3.00	4.00
SONGBIRD	Warner Bros. (S) BS-2845	2.00	3.00	4.00
SONG FOR JULI	Warner Bros. (S) BS-2734	2.00	3.00	4.00
SOUL OF A CITY BOY	Capitol (M) T 2070	4.00	8.00	12.00
SOUL OF A CITY BOY	Capitol (S) ST 2070	5.00	10.00	15.00
SOUL OF A CITY BOY (RI)	Capitol (S) ST-11267	2.50	3.75	5.00
TOGETHER	Warner Bros. (S) BS 2588	3.00	4.50	6.00
YOUNGBLOOD	Mercury (M) MG 21005	5.00	7.50	10.00
YOUNGBLOOD	Mercury (S) SR 61005	6.00	9.00	12.00

Also see YOUNGBLOODS

YOUNG, Johnny

TITLE	LABEL & NO.	GOOD	VERY GOOD	NEAR MINT
BLUES MASTERS VOL. 9	Blue Horizon (M) BM 4609	4.50	6.75	9.00
I CAN'T KEEP MY FOOT FROM JUMPING	Bluesway (M) 6075	2.00	3.00	4.00
JOHNNY YOUNG & HIS CHICAGO BLUES BAND	Arhoolie (M) 1029	2.50	4.50	5.00

YOUNG, Kathy

TITLE	LABEL & NO.	GOOD	VERY GOOD	NEAR MINT
SOUND OF KATHY YOUNG	Indigo (M) IND LP 504	6.00	12.00	18.00

YOUNG, Kenny

TITLE	LABEL & NO.	GOOD	VERY GOOD	NEAR MINT
CLEVER DOGS CHASE THE SUN	Warner Brothers (S) BS 2579	3.00	4.50	6.00
LAST STAGE FOR SILVERWORLD	Warner Brothers (S) BS 2676	3.00	4.50	6.00

YOUNG, Lester

TITLE	LABEL & NO.	GOOD	VERY GOOD	NEAR MINT
LESTER YOUNG AND HIS TENOR SAX (10")	Aladdin (M) 706	8.00	20.00	32.00
LESTER YOUNG TRIO (10")	Aladdin (M) 705	8.00	20.00	32.00

Also see JACQUET, Illinois

(M) Mono (S) Stereo (EP) Extended Play (Q) Quad (RI) Re-issued

TITLE	LABEL & NO.	GOOD	VERY GOOD	NEAR MINT

YOUNG, Neil

TITLE	LABEL & NO.	GOOD	VERY GOOD	NEAR MINT
AFTER THE GOLD RUSH	Reprise 6383	3.00	4.50	6.00
AMERICAN STARS N' BARS	Reprise MS K-2261	2.00	3.00	4.00
DECADE	Reprise 3RS-2257	4.00	6.00	8.00
EVERYONE KNOWS THIS IS NOWHERE	Reprise (S) 6349	3.00	4.50	6.00
(With Crazy Horse)				
HARVEST	Reprise 2032	2.50	3.75	5.00
ON THE BEACH	Reprise (S) 2180	2.50	3.75	5.00
TIME FADES AWAY	Reprise (S) 2151	2.50	3.75	5.00
TONIGHT'S THE NIGHT	Reprise (S) 2221	2.50	3.75	5.00
ZUMA (With Crazy Horse)	Reprise (S) 2242	2.50	3.75	5.00

YOUNG RASCALS

TITLE	LABEL & NO.	GOOD	VERY GOOD	NEAR MINT
COLLECTIONS	Atlantic (M) 8134	3.00	4.50	6.00
COLLECTIONS	Atlantic (M) 8134	4.00	6.00	8.00
GROOVIN'	Atlantic (M) 8148	3.00	4.50	6.00
GROOVIN'	Atlantic (S) SD 8148	3.50	5.25	7.00
ONCE UPON A DREAM	Atlantic (S) 8169	3.50	5.25	7.00
TIME PEACE-GREATEST HITS	Atlantic (M) 8190	3.00	4.50	6.00
YOUNG RASCALS, THE	Atlantic (M) 8123	3.00	4.50	6.00
YOUNG RASCALS, THE	Atlantic (S) SD 8123	4.00	6.00	8.00
(Shown as "Rascals" beginning with Atlantic 8148)				

YOUR GANG

TITLE	LABEL & NO.	GOOD	VERY GOOD	NEAR MINT
IF YOU WANT TO BUY EM	Mercury (M) MG 21094	3.50	5.25	7.00
IF YOU WANT TO BUY EM	Mercury (S) SR 61094	4.50	6.75	9.00

YURO, Timi

TITLE	LABEL & NO.	GOOD	VERY GOOD	NEAR MINT
BEST OF TIMI YURO, THE	Liberty (M) LRP 3286	3.00	4.50	6.00
BEST OF TIMI YURO	Liberty (S) LSR 7286	3.50	6.00	7.00
HURT	Liberty (M) LRP 3208	4.00	6.00	8.00
HURT	Liberty (S) LST 7208	4.50	6.75	9.00
INTERLUDE	Colgems (S) 5007	2.00	3.00	4.00
LET ME CALL YOU SWEETHEART	Liberty (M) LRP-3234	3.50	5.25	7.00
LET ME CALL YOU SWEETHEART	Liberty (S) LST-7234	4.00	6.75	8.00
MAKE THE WORLD GO AWAY	Liberty (M) LRP 3319	3.00	4.50	6.00
MAKE THE WORLD GO AWAY	Liberty (S) LS 7319	3.50	6.00	7.00
SOUL	Liberty (M) LRP3212	4.00	6.75	8.00
SOUL	Liberty (S) LST 7212	3.50	5.25	7.00
TIMI YURO	Sunset (M) 1107	2.50	3.75	5.00
TIMI YURO	Sunset (S) 5107	3.00	4.50	6.00
VERY BEST OF TIMI YURO	United Artists (S) UA-LA429-E	1.50	2.25	3.00
WHAT'S A MATTER BABY	Liberty (M) LRP 3263	3.50	5.25	7.00
WHAT'S A MATTER BABY	Liberty (S) LST 7263	4.00	6.00	8.00

Z

TITLE	LABEL & NO.	GOOD	VERY GOOD	NEAR MINT

ZABACH, Florian

TITLE	LABEL & NO.	GOOD	VERY GOOD	NEAR MINT
HOT CANARY	Decca (M) DL 5367	2.00	3.00	4.00
HOT CANARY	Decca (EP) ED 2154	1.00	1.50	2.00

ZACHERLEY, John

TITLE	LABEL & NO.	GOOD	VERY GOOD	NEAR MINT
MONSTER MASH	Parkway (M) P 7018	7.00	17.50	28.00
SCARY TALES	Parkway (M) 7023	6.00	15.00	24.00
SPOOK ALONG WITH ZACHERLEY	Elektra (M) EKL-190	4.00	8.00	12.00
SPOOK ALONG WITH ZACHERLEY	Elektra (S) EKS-7190	5.00	10.00	15.00
ZACHERLEY'S MONSTER GALLERY	Crestview (M) CRV-803	6.00	15.00	24.00
ZACHERLEY'S MONSTER GALLERY	Crestview (S) CRS7-803	7.00	17.50	28.00

ZAGER AND EVANS

TITLE	LABEL & NO.	GOOD	VERY GOOD	NEAR MINT
EARLY, WRITINGS OF ZAGER AND EVANS AND OTHERS	White Whale (S) WW 7123	4.00	6.00	8.00
FOOD OF THE MIND	Vanguard (S) VSD 6568	3.00	4.50	6.00
IN THE YEAR 2525	RCA (S) 1077	2.50	3.75	5.00
2525 (EXORDIUM & TERMINUS)	RCA (S) LSP 4214	3.50	5.25	7.00

ZAPPA, Frank

TITLE	LABEL & NO.	GOOD	VERY GOOD	NEAR MINT
APOSTROPHE (')	Disc Reet DS 2175	3.50	5.25	7.00
APOSTROPHE (')	Disc Reet (Q) DS4-2175	3.00	4.50	6.00
APOSTROPHE (') ('77 RI)	Disc Reet DS K-2289	2.00	3.00	4.00
BONGO FURY	Disc Reet 2234	2.50	3.75	5.00
(With Capt. Beefheart & Mothers of Invention)				
CHUNGA'S REVENGE	Bizarre MS 2030	4.00	6.00	8.00
HOT RATS	Bizarre RS 6356	5.00	7.50	10.00
LUMPY GRAVY	Verve (M) V-8741	5.00	7.50	10.00
(Artist listed as Francis Vincent Zappa)				
LUMPY GRAVY	Verve (S) V6-8741	6.00	9.00	12.00
(Artist listed as Francis Vincent Zappa)				
ONE SIZE FITS ALL	Disc Reet (S) DS 2216	2.50	3.75	5.00
(With Mothers of Invention)				
ROXY & ELSEWHERE (With Mothers)	Disc Reet (S) 2DS-2202	3.00	4.00	6.00
200 MOTELS (Soundtrack)	United Artists 9956	4.00	6.00	8.00
WAKA/JAWAKA-HOT RATS	Bizarre MS 2094	4.00	6.00	8.00
ZAPPA IN NEW YORK	Disc Reet (S) 2D-2290	3.00	4.50	6.00
ZOOT ALLURES	Warner Bros. (S) BS 2970	4.00	6.00	8.00
Also see MOTHERS OF INVENTION				

ZAVARONI, Lena

TITLE	LABEL & NO.	GOOD	VERY GOOD	NEAR MINT
MA, HE'S MAKING EYES AT ME	Stax (S) 5511	2.00	3.00	4.00

ZEVON, Warren

TITLE	LABEL & NO.	GOOD	VERY GOOD	NEAR MINT
EXCITABLE BOY	Asylum (S) 6E-118	2.00	3.00	4.00
WANTED DEAD OR ALIVE	Imperial (S) LP 12456	3.00	4.50	6.00
(Shown as ZEVON)				
WARREN ZEVON	Asylum (S) 7E-1060	2.00	3.00	4.00

ZEPHYR

TITLE	LABEL & NO.	GOOD	VERY GOOD	NEAR MINT
GOING BACK TO COLORADO	Warner Brothers (M) 1897	2.50	3.75	5.00
ZEPHYR	Command/Probe (S) CPLP 4510	3.00	4.50	6.00

ZIG ZAG PEOPLE

TITLE	LABEL & NO.	GOOD	VERY GOOD	NEAR MINT
ZIG ZAG PEOPLE TAKE BUBBLE GUM MUSIC UNDERGROUND, THE	Decca (M) DL 75110	3.00	4.50	6.00

ZIP CODES

TITLE	LABEL & NO.	GOOD	VERY GOOD	NEAR MINT
MUSTANG	Liberty (M) LRP 3367	4.00	8.00	12.00

ZIPPERMAN, Stan

TITLE	LABEL & NO.	GOOD	VERY GOOD	NEAR MINT
EVERYHEAD: A ROCK OPERA	Stanza (S) ST 2 2001	3.00	4.50	6.00

ZODIACS

TITLE	LABEL & NO.	GOOD	VERY GOOD	NEAR MINT
ZODIACS AT THE BEACH	Snyder (M) 5586	4.00	8.00	12.00

ZOMBIES

TITLE	LABEL & NO.	GOOD	VERY GOOD	NEAR MINT
EARLY DAYS	London (S) PS 557	3.00	4.50	6.00
ODESSEY AND ORACLE	Date (S) TES 4013	5.00	7.50	10.00
TIME OF THE ZOMBIES	Epic (S) KEG 32861	3.50	5.25	7.00
ZOMBIES FEATURING SHE'S NOT THERE AND TELL HER NO	Parrot (M) PA 61001	4.00	6.00	8.00
ZOMBIES FEATURING SHE'S NOT THERE AND TELL HER NO	Parrot (S) PAS 71001	2.50	3.75	5.00

ZOO

TITLE	LABEL & NO.	GOOD	VERY GOOD	NEAR MINT
ZOO, THE	Mercury (S) SR 61300	3.50	5.25	7.00
ZOO PRESENTS CHOCOLATE MOUSE	Sunburst (M) 7500	4.50	6.75	9.00

ZWERLING, Andy

TITLE	LABEL & NO.	GOOD	VERY GOOD	NEAR MINT
SPIDERS IN THE NIGHT	Kama Sutra (S) KSBS 2036	3.50	5.25	7.00

ZZ TOP

TITLE	LABEL & NO.	GOOD	VERY GOOD	NEAR MINT
BEST OF Z Z TOP	London (S) PS 706	2.00	3.00	4.00
FANDANGO	London (S) PS 656	2.50	3.75	5.00
FIRST ALBUM	London (S) PS 584	2.50	3.75	5.00
RIO GRANDE MUD	London (S) PS 612	2.50	3.75	5.00
TEJAS	London (S) PS 680	2.50	3.75	5.00
TRES HOMBRES	London (S) XPS-631	2.50	3.75	5.00

(M) Mono (S) Stereo (EP) Extended Play (Q) Quad (RI) Re-issued

Original Casts and Soundtracks

The following Broadway Original Cast and motion picture soundtrack section is a disarmingly contagious, intriguing list that's far more than a compendium: it is comprehensive to the extent of offering more than a collector would likely be able to turn up in a lifetime of diligent search, is complete enough to offer the prices—or a guide of comparison—to almost any album of this type one should want to look up, and is interesting enough to provide long periods of informative reading.

At that, it is less than we'll want to include in Volume III, when we go back to press with our third edition, probably in the spring of 1980. The additional information we seek is primarily to fill in the significant artists, singers, narrators, or performers on soundtracks from movies that we already have listed. We already have the release dates of most of the movies that don't have that fact indicated, as our source came in too late to include this time around. We are **not** soliciting, or interested in, the names of the **stars** of the movie, even though their names are often listed on the cover of the album jacket. We are only interested in knowing who, of significance—that is, anyone whose appearance would be a determining factor in someone wanting to purchase the album—is actually recorded on at least one cut. This is especially significant on older records that had the name of a then unknown who has gone on to bigger things.

In 1950 an Original London Cast, for instance, starred Noel Coward and Lily Pons. Buried at the end of the list of secondary names (but the only other name we list) was Richard Burton! The same was true of a show a while back, which we'll let you discover on your own, that we've called attention to that buried the unknown's name of John Travolta! Do you know what big show from the late 60's featured a small part by Diane Keaton (you'll be less surprised by this now that you've seen her in "Looking for Mr. Goodbar")?

If you do send us any information, send us all you can. Less information than we need is sometimes worse than none at all. If you know for sure, and have an album in mono and we list only the stereo, drop us a line (or, obviously, vice versa). Be especially sure to indicate if it's re-channeled stereo. Though we've run into some differing opinions on this, the overwhelming consensus is that a stereo album is worth more than a mono, unless the stereo is re-channeled.

One of our biggest problems has been how to document the worth of first pressings of big-hit shows that have never gone out of print and are still being issued with the original number. Even though we know these early pressings to be of significant value, until we can document in each case how a collector can identify them, we're listing them at a minimum price. We've

pictured, for instance, under "South Pacific," two album jackets with different pictures—one, though obviously an early release, may or may not be a **first**—and they have the same record number. We're soliciting help in this area, but we do not want any guesses. We don't want to add to, or "correct" something unless we're positive our new information is unquestioned.

The minimum value that we've attached to a single release that is still in print is $4.00. A double album is $6.00. A triple album is $8.00. That does **not** mean that it might not cost you more to go in to a record store and pick up a copy. The retail prices of different records vary considerably when new, and even the same record, depending on where you buy it. The minimum price we've listed is for the purpose of standardization only, plus the assumption that as a "collector's item," its re-sale value would have to be less than the price a brand new copy would cost in a record store.

We've listed many shows that are still available in stores because we think their documentation is important. The following section is comprehensive enough we think it would be unthinkable to leave certain records out.

A date following the boldface listing of the title means that that is the date of the origin of the show, not necessarily when any of the records were made or released.

The date following the listing of a particular record is when it was issued, or re-issued. We tried, however, to avoid unnecessary repetition. The first recording listed under a title is usually the earliest known and no date follows if we know it to be within a year of the date of origin. Pre-1950 shows may mean, however, that we just don't know. When we have both a mono and stereo shown and list a date only after the former, it's because we felt it wasn't necessary to repeat the same date. In the case of re-channeled stereo, we often didn't know. Many shows are available and in print with different numbers than those assigned when originally released. In these cases we've not listed the re-issues at all.

We are especially interested in any documentation on 10" albums. They're showing signs of becoming one of the hottest collectibles.

We would like to thank the many collectors of this type material who have contributed with the input that's made this major section of our second edition possible. Particular thanks go to David Hummel and Ski Bowser. David has a book he edits on Original Casts that is one of the most definitive of its kind and highly recommended by us. It contains a wealth of information and detail (see the advertisement on it in the yellow portion of our book).

TITLE	LABEL & NO.	GOOD	VERY GOOD	NEAR MINT
AARON SLICK FROM PUNKIN CRICK (1951)				
Soundtrack (10")	RCA (M) LPM-3006	30.00	45.00	60.00
ABOMINABLE DR. PHIBES, THE (1971) (See: Dr. Phibes)				
ABSENT MINDED PROFESSOR (1961)				
Soundtrack (With Dialogue)	Disneyland (M) ST-1911	4.00	6.00	8.00
ADDAMS FAMILY, THE (1964)				
TV Soundtrack	RCA (M) LPM-3421	7.50	11.25	15.00
TV Soundtrack	RCA (S) LSP-3421	10.00	15.00	20.00
ADRIFT (1971)				
Soundtrack (Limited release)	(S) MPO 1001	12.00	18.00	24.00
ADVANCE TO THE REAR (1964)				
Soundtrack	Columbia (M) CL-2159	5.00	7.50	10.00
Soundtrack	Columbia (S) CS-8959	7.50	11.25	15.00
ADVENTURERS, THE (1970)				
Soundtrack	Paramount (S) 6001	3.00	4.00	6.00
ADVENTURES OF A YOUNG MAN (1962)				
Soundtrack	RCA (M) LOC-1074	18.00	27.00	36.00
Soundtrack	RCA (S) LSO-1074	25.00	37.50	50.00
ADVENTURES OF MARCO POLO (1956)				
TV Soundtrack	Columbia (M) ML-5111	10.00	15.00	20.00
ADVENTURES OF ROBIN HOOD, THE (1938)				
Soundtrack (1962)	Warner Bros. (M) W-1438	4.00	6.00	8.00
Soundtrack	Warner Bros. (S) WS-1438	5.00	7.50	10.00

(M) Mono (S) Stereo (EP) Extended Play (Q) Quad (RI) Re-issued

TITLE	LABEL & NO.	GOOD	VERY GOOD	NEAR MINT
ADVISE & CONSENT (1962)				
Soundtrack	RCA (M) LOC-1068	7.50	11.25	15.00
Soundtrack	RCA (S) LSO-1068	10.00	15.00	20.00
AFFAIR TO REMEMBER, AN (1957)				
Soundtrack	Columbia (M) CL-1013	15.00	22.50	30.00
AFRICA (1967)				
TV Soundtrack	MGM (M) E-4462	5.00	7.50	10.00
TV Soundtrack	MGM (S) SE-4462	7.50	11.25	15.00
AFRICA ADDIO (1967)				
Soundtrack	United Artists (M) 4141	7.00	11.00	15.00
Soundtrack	United Artists (S) 5141	10.00	15.00	20.00
AFTER THE FOX (1966)				
Soundtrack	United Artists (M) 4148	5.00	7.50	10.00
Soundtrack	United Artists (S) 5148	7.50	11.25	15.00
AGONY & THE ECSTASY, THE (1965)				
Soundtrack	Capitol (M) MAS-2427	10.00	15.00	20.00
Soundtrack	Capitol (S) SMAS-2427	15.00	22.50	30.00
AIN'T SUPPOSED TO DIE A NATURAL DEATH (1972)				
Original Cast (2 records)	A&M (S) SP 3510	10.00	15.00	20.00
Arthur French, Gloria Edwards, Ralph Wilcox.				
AIRBORNE SYMPHONY (1946)				
Original Cast	Columbia (S) M 34136	2.00	3.00	4.00
A 1976 recording with the original conductor, Leonard Bernstein, and the original Monitor, Orson Wells, with the New York Philharmonic and Choral Art Society.				
AIRPORT 1975				
Soundtrack	MCA (S) 2082	3.00	4.00	6.00
AIR POWER (1957)				
TV Soundtrack	Columbia (M) ML-5214	7.50	11.25	15.00
TV Soundtrack	Columbia (S) MS-6029	10.00	15.00	20.00
ALADDIN (1958)				
TV Soundtrack	Columbia (M) CL-1117	12.00	18.00	24.00
ALBERT PECKINGPAW'S REVENGE (1967)				
Soundtrack	Sidewalk (M) T-5907	4.00	6.00	8.00
Soundtrack	Sidewalk (S) ST-5907	5.00	7.50	10.00
ALAKAZAM THE GREAT (1961)				
Soundtrack	Vee Jay (M) LP-6000	12.00	18.00	24.00
ALEXANDER (1970)				
Soundtrack	Polydor (S) 24-7001	10.00	15.00	20.00
ALEXANDER THE GREAT (1956)				
Soundtrack	Mercury (M) MG-20148	40.00	60.00	80.00

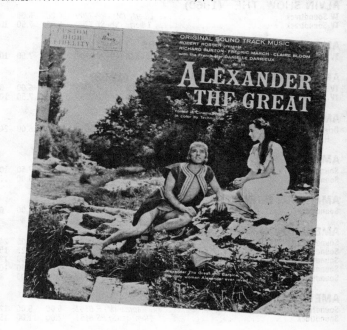

ALFIE
Soundtrack......................................Impulse (M) 9111	7.00	11.00	15.00
Soundtrack......................................Impulse (S) 9111	10.00	15.00	20.00

ALICE IN WONDERLAND (1952)
Soundtrack (1959).....................Disneyland (M) DQ-1208	6.00	9.00	12.00

ALICE THROUGH THE LOOKING GLASS (1966)
TV Soundtrack.............................RCA (M) LOC-1130	6.00	9.00	12.00
TV Soundtrack.............................RCA (S) LSO-1130	5.00	7.50	10.00

ALICE'S ADVENTURES IN WONDERLAND (1972)
Soundtrack........................Warner Bros. (S) BS-2671	7.50	11.25	15.00

ALIKI MY LOVE (1963)
Soundtrack...................................Fontana (M) 27523	5.00	7.50	10.00
Soundtrack...................................Fontana (S) 67523	7.50	11.25	15.00

ALL AMERICAN (1962)
Original Cast........................Columbia (M) KOL 5760	5.00	7.50	10.00
Ray Bolger, Eileen Herlie, Ron Husmann, Anita Gillette, Fritz Weaver.			
Original Cast........................Columbia (S) KOS 2160	10.00	15.00	20.00

ALL BY MYSELF (See: Anna Russell's Little Show)

ALLEGRO (1947)
Original Cast.........................RCA (M) LOC 1099	10.00	15.00	20.00
John Battles, Annamary Dickey, John Conte, Lisa Kirk.			
Original Cast.........................RCA (S) LSO 1099	10.00	15.00	20.00

ALL IN LOVE (1961)
Original Cast.....................Mercury (M) OCM 6204	10.00	15.00	20.00
David Atkinson, Lee Cass, Gaylea Byrne, Dom deLouise.			
Original Cast.....................Mercury (S) OCS 6204	12.00	18.00	24.00

ALL IN ONE (Featuring Trouble In Tahiti) (1952)
TV Soundtrack (1958).....................MGM (M) E 3646	10.00	15.00	20.00
Featuring the 1952 cast of Beverly Wolff, David Atkinson, Miriam Workman, Earl Rogers and Robert Bollinger, recorded in stereo, but released only in mono.			
TV Soundtrack (1966 Re-issue in mono)........Heliodor (M) H25020	4.00	6.00	8.00
TV Soundtrack (1966)........................Heliodor (S) H25020	6.00	9.00	12.00
First release in stereo of the 1952 cast recording of eight years earlier.			
Studio Cast (Conducted by Leonard Bernstein, composer)......................Columbia (S) KM 32597	2.00	3.00	4.00
Nancy Williams, Julian Patrick, Antonia Butler.			

ALL NIGHT LONG (1962)
Soundtrack.......................................Epic (M) LA-16032	7.50	11.25	15.00
Soundtrack.......................................Epic (S) BA-17032	10.00	15.00	20.00

ALL THE LOVING COUPLES (1969)
Soundtrack...........................GNP Crescendo (S) 2051	7.50	11.25	15.00

ALL THE RIGHT NOISES (1971)
Soundtrack..Buddah (S) BDS-5132	5.00	7.50	10.00

ALVIN SHOW, THE (1960)
TV Soundtrack.............................Liberty (M) LRP-3209	4.00	6.00	8.00
TV Soundtrack.............................Liberty (S) LST-7209	5.00	7.50	10.00

AMAHL AND THE NIGHT VISITORS (1951)
TV Soundtrack...........................RCA (M) LM-1701	5.00	7.50	10.00

AMAHL AND THE NIGHT VISITORS (1963)
TV Soundtrack...........................RCA (M) LM-2762	4.00	6.00	8.00
TV Soundtrack...........................RCA (S) LSC-2762	5.00	7.50	10.00

AMBASSADOR (1972)
Original London Cast...................RCA (S) SER 5618	12.00	18.00	24.00
Howard Keel, Danielle Darrieux, Margaret Courtenay.			

AMERICA, AMERICA (1963)
Soundtrack........................Warner Bros. (M) W-1527	5.00	7.50	10.00
Soundtrack........................Warner Bros. (S) WS-1527	6.00	9.00	12.00

AMERICAN DREAMER
Soundtrack...........................United Artists (S) 5219	3.00	4.00	6.00

AMERICAN IN PARIS, AN (1951)
Soundtrack (1951) (10")...........................MGM (M) E-93	12.00	18.00	24.00
Soundtrack (1955).................................MGM (M) E-3232	7.50	11.25	15.00
Soundtrack (1959).................................MGM (M) E-3767	6.00	9.00	12.00
Soundtrack (1966)...................................Metro (M) M-552	5.00	7.50	10.00
Soundtrack (Re-channeled stereo)...........Metro (S) M-552	4.00	6.00	8.00

AMERCANIZATION OF EMILY, THE
Soundtrack.....................................Reprise (M) R-6151	6.00	9.00	12.00
Soundtrack.....................................Reprise (S) RS-6151	7.00	11.00	15.00

AMOROUS ADVENTURES OF MOLL FLANDERS
Soundtrack...................................RCA (M) LOC-1113	12.00	18.00	24.00
Soundtrack...................................RCA (S) LSO-1113	15.00	22.50	30.00

ANASTASIA (1956)
Soundtrack...Decca (M) DL-8460	10.00	15.00	20.00

ANATOMY OF A MURDER (1969)
Soundtrack.....................................Columbia (M) CL-1360	7.50	11.25	15.00
Soundtrack.....................................Columbia (S) CS-8166	10.00	15.00	20.00

AND GOD CREATED WOMAN (1957)
Soundtrack (With dialogue)...................Decca (M) DL-8685	12.00	18.00	24.00

ANDROCLES AND THE LION (1967)
TV Soundtrack...............................RCA (M) LOC-1141	10.00	15.00	20.00
TV Soundtrack...............................RCA (S) LSO-1141	12.00	18.00	24.00

ANDY GRIFFITH SHOW, THE (1961)
TV Soundtrack..................................Capitol (M) T-1611	4.00	6.00	8.00
TV Soundtrack..................................Capitol (S) ST-1611	6.00	9.00	12.00

ANDROMEDA STRAIN, THE (1971)
Soundtrack...Kapp (S) 5513	10.00	15.00	20.00

ANGEL, ANGEL, DOWN WE GO
Soundtrack..Tower (S) 5161	5.00	7.00	10.00

ANGELS DIE HARD
Soundtrack...Uni (S) 73091	3.00	4.00	6.00

ANGELS FROM HELL
Soundtrack...Tower (S) ST-5128	5.00	7.00	10.00

ANKLES AWEIGH (1955)
Original Cast......................................Decca (M) DL 9025	20.00	30.00	40.00
Betty and Jane Kean, Lew Parker, Mark Dawson, Gabriel Dell, Betty George, Ray Mason.			

ANNA RUSSELL'S LITTLE SHOW (1953)
Original Cast..............................Columbia (M) ML 4594	10.00	15.00	20.00
Anna Russell, revised in 1964 as ;All By Myself.			
Original Cast (Re-issues, approximate equal values)..........Columbia (M) ML 4733, 4928, 5036, 5195, 5295	7.50	11.25	15.00

ANNE OF GREEN GABLES (1971)
Original London Cast...........................CBS (S) 70053	12.00	18.00	24.00
Polly James, Barbara Hamilton, Hiram Sherman.			

ANNE OF THE 1000 DAYS (1970)
Soundtrack.............................(S) Decca DL-79174	6.00	9.00	12.00

ANNIE (1977)
Original Cast................................Columbia (S) PS 34712	2.00	3.00	4.00
Andrea McArdle, Dorothy Loudon, Reid Shelton.			

ANNIE GET YOUR GUN (1946)
Original Cast (1949)..........................Decca (M) DL 8001	25.00	37.50	50.00
Ethel Merman, Ray Middleton, Robert Lenn.			
Original Cast (Re-issue) (1955)...................Decca (M) DL 9018	7.50	11.25	15.00
Original Cast (Re-channeled stereo).........Decca (S) DL 79018	7.50	11.25	15.00
Original German Cast (1963)......................Philips (S) 838900	12.00	18.00	24.00
Heidi Bruhl, Robert Trehy, Colette Warren.			
Original London Cast.............................Stanyan (M) 10069	2.00	3.00	4.00
Dolores Gray, Bill Johnson, Irving Davies.			
Original Revival Cast (1966)................RCA (M) LOC 1124	4.00	6.00	8.00
Ethel Merman, Bruce Yarnell, Benay Venuta.			
Soundtrack (From the 1950 film) (10")..........MGM (M) E 508	18.00	24.00	36.00
Betty Hutton, Howard Keel, Louis Calhern, Keenan Wynn.			
Soundtrack (1955 re-issue).........................MGM (M) E 3227	10.00	15.00	20.00
Soundtrack (1960 re-issue)..........................MGM (M) E 3768	5.00	7.50	10.00
Soundtrack (1965 re-issue)...........................Metro (M) 548	3.00	4.50	6.00
Soundtrack (Re-channeled stereo)...............Metro (S) 548	4.00	6.00	8.00
TV Soundtrack (1957).............................Capitol (M) W 913	12.00	18.00	24.00
A road show with Mary Martin and John Raitt televised by NBC.			
Studio Cast......................................Columbia (S) OS 2360	2.00	3.00	4.00
Doris Day, Robert Goulet, Leonard Stokes.			
Studio Cast (With the original Broadway star).....London (S) XPS 905	7.50	11.25	15.00
Ethel Merman, Neilson Taylor, Neil Howlett.			

ANOTHER TIME, ANOTHER PLACE (1958)
Soundtrack......................................Columbia (M) CL-1180	20.00	30.00	40.00

ANTHONY ADVERSE (1936)
Soundtrack (1962).........................Warner Bros. (M) W-1438	4.00	6.00	8.00

ANYA (1965)
Original Cast (Based on Rachmaninoff)...United Artists (M) UAL 4133	6.00	9.00	12.00
Constance Towers, Michael Karmoyan, Lillian Gish.			
Original Cast.............................United Artists (S) UAS 5133	7.50	11.25	15.00

TITLE	LABEL & NO.	GOOD	VERY GOOD	NEAR MINT

ANYONE CAN WHISTLE (1964)
Original Cast (1966) .... Columbia (M) KOL 6080		6.00	9.00	12.00
Lee Remick, Angela Lansbury, Harry Guardino.				
Original Cast .... Columbia (S) KOS 2480		7.50	11.25	15.00
Soundtrack .... Columbia (S) 32608		7.00	11.00	15.00

ANYTHING GOES (1934)
Original Revival Cast (1962) .... Epic (S) FLS 15100		2.00	3.00	4.00
Eileen Rodgers, Hal Linden, Mickey Deems.				
Soundtrack (From the 1956 film) .... Decca (M) DL 8318		12.00	18.00	24.00
Bing Crosby, Donald O'Connor, Jeanmaire, Mitzi Gaynor.				
Soundtrack (1962, partial re-issue) .... Decca (M) DL 4264		5.00	7.50	10.00
TV Soundtrack .... Larynx (M) 567		9.00	13.50	18.00
Ethel Merman, Bert Lahr, Frank Sinatra.				
Studio Cast .... Columbia (M) ML 4751		6.00	9.00	12.00
Mary Martin.				

ANY WEDNESDAY (1966)
Soundtrack .... Warner Bros. (M) 1669		4.00	6.00	8.00
Soundtrack .... Warner Bros. (S) 1669		5.00	7.50	10.00

APARTMENT, THE
Soundtrack .... United Artists (M) UAL 3105		7.00	11.00	15.00
Soundtrack .... United Artists (S) UAS 6105		10.00	15.00	20.00

APPLAUSE (1970)
Original Cast .... ABC (S) OCS 11		2.00	3.00	4.00
Lauren Bacall, Len Cariou, Robert Mandon.				

APPLE TREE (1966)
Original Cast .... Columbia (M) KOL 6620		7.50	11.25	15.00
Barbara Harris, Larry Blyden, Alan Alda.				
Original Cast .... Columbia (S) KOS 3020		10.00	15.00	20.00
Original Canadian Cast .... Trillium (S) TR 2000		12.00	18.00	24.00
Tom Kneebone, Dinah Christie.				

APRIL FOOLS
Soundtrack .... Columbia (S) OS 3340		3.00	4.00	6.00

APRIL LOVE (1957)
Soundtrack .... Dot (M) 9000		10.00	15.00	20.00

ARABESQUE (1966)
Soundtrack .... RCA (M) LPM-3623		4.00	6.00	8.00
Soundtrack .... RCA (S) LPS-3623		5.00	7.50	10.00

ARABIAN NIGHTS (1954)
Original Cast .... Decca (M) DL 9013		20.00	30.00	40.00
Lauritz Melchior, Helena Scott, Ralph Herbert.				
Studio Cast .... Decca (M) DL 5542		12.00	18.00	24.00
Orchestra conducted by the producer Guy Lombardo (composer				
Carmen Lombardo), Bill Flanagan, Kenny Gardner.				

ARCADIANS (1910)
London Studio Cast .... Columbia (S) TWO 233		10.00	15.00	20.00
June Bronhill, Ann Howard, Andy Cole.				

ARCHIES, THE (1968)
TV Soundtrack .... Calendar (S) KES-101		4.00	6.00	8.00

ARCHY AND MEHITABEL (1954) (See: Shinbone Alley)

(M) Mono (S) Stereo (EP) Extended Play (Q) Quad (RI) Re-issued

TITLE		LABEL & NO.	GOOD	VERY GOOD	NEAR MINT

ARMS & THE GIRL (1950)
Original Cast (10") .... Decca (M) DL 5200		40.00	60.00	80.00
Nanette Fabray, Georges Gustaray, Pearl Bailey, Florenz Ames.				

AROUND THE WORLD UNDER THE SEA
Soundtrack .... Monument (M) 8050		5.00	7.00	10.00
Soundtrack .... Monument (S) 18050		6.00	9.00	12.00

ARRANGEMENT, THE (1970)
Soundtrack .... Warner Bros. (S) WS-1824		5.00	7.50	10.00

ARRIVEDERCI, BABY (1966)
Soundtrack .... RCA (M) LOC-1132		7.50	11.25	15.00
Soundtrack .... RCA (S) LSO-1132		10.00	15.00	20.00

ART OF LOVE, THE (1965)
Soundtrack .... Capitol (M) T-2355		7.50	11.25	15.00
Soundtrack .... Capitol (S) ST-2355		10.00	15.00	20.00

ATHENA (1954)
Soundtrack (10") .... Mercury (M) MG-25202		30.00	45.00	60.00

ATHENIAN TOUCH (1964)
Original Cast .... Broadway East (M) OC 101		50.00	75.00	100.00
Marion Marlowe, Butterfly McQueen, Robert Cosden.				
Original Cast .... Broadway East (S) OCS 101		70.00	105.00	140.00

AT HOME AT THE PALACE (1967)
Original Cast .... ABC (S) S 620		5.00	7.50	10.00
Judy Garland, Joey and Lorna Luft.				

AT HOME WITH ETHEL WATERS (1951)
Original Cast .... Monmouth Evergreen (M) MES 6812		2.00	3.00	4.00
Ethel Waters.				

AT THE DROP OF A HAT (1957)
Original Cast (1960) .... Angel (M) 35797		7.50	11.25	15.00
Michael Flanders and Donald Swann.				
Original Cast .... Angel (S) S 35797		10.00	15.00	20.00
Original London Cast .... Angel (M) 65042		10.00	15.00	20.00
Michael Flanders and Donald Swann.				

AT THE DROP OF ANOTHER HAT (1966)
Original Cast .... Angel (M) 36388		4.00	6.00	8.00
Michael Flanders and Donald Swann.				
Original Cast .... Angel (S) S 36388		5.00	7.50	10.00

AUNTIE MAME (1958)
Soundtrack .... Warner Bros. (M) W-1242		12.00	18.00	24.00
Soundtrack .... Warner Bros. (S) WS-1242		18.00	27.00	36.00

B

BABES IN ARMS (1937)

Studio Cast .... Columbia (M) ML 4488 — 7.50 — 11.25 — 15.00
  Mary Martin, Mardi Bayne, Jack Cassidy.
Studio Cast (1 side) .... RCA (M) LPM 3152 — 10.00 — 15.00 — 20.00
  Lisa Kirk, William Tabbert, Sheila Bond.

BABES IN TOYLAND (1903)

Soundtrack (From the 1961 film) .... Buena Vista (M) BV 4022 — 5.00 — 7.50 — 10.00
  Ray Bolger, Henry Calvin, Tommy Sands, Annette, Ed Wynn.
Soundtrack .... Buena Vista (S) ST 4022 — 7.50 — 11.25 — 15.00
Studio Cast (Side 2, "The Red Mill") ...... Decca (M) DL 8458 — 7.50 — 11.25 — 15.00
  Kenny Baker, Karen Kemple.

BABY DOLL (1956)

Soundtrack .... Columbia (M) CL-958 — 7.50 — 11.25 — 15.00

BABY FACE NELSON (1957)

Soundtrack .... Jubilee (M) 2021 — 20.00 — 30.00 — 40.00

BABY MAKER

Soundtrack .... Ode '70 (S) 77002 — 3.00 — 4.00 — 6.00

BABY THE RAIN MUST FALL (1965)

Soundtrack .... Ava (M) A-53 — 7.50 — 11.25 — 15.00
Soundtrack .... Ava (S) AS-53 — 10.00 — 15.00 — 20.00
Soundtrack .... Mainstream 56056 — 7.50 — 11.25 — 15.00
Soundtrack .... Mainstream (S) S-6056 — 10.00 — 15.00 — 20.00

BACK STREET

Soundtrack .... Decca (M) DL 9097 — 15.00 — 22.50 — 30.00
Soundtrack .... Decca (S) DL7 9097 — 12.00 — 19.00 — 25.00

BAD SEED, THE (1956)

Soundtrack .... RCA (M) LPM-1395 — 30.00 — 45.00 — 60.00

BAJOUR (1964)

Original Cast .... Columbia (M) KOL 6300 — 7.50 — 11.25 — 15.00
  Chita Rivera, Nancy Dussault, Hershel Bernardi.
Original Cast .... Columbia (S) KOS 2700 — 10.00 — 15.00 — 20.00

BAKER STREET (1965)

Original Cast .... MGM (M) E 7000 — 5.00 — 7.50 — 10.00
  Fritz Weaver, Inga Swenson, Martin Gabel.
Original Cast .... MGM (S) SE 7000 — 6.00 — 9.00 — 12.00

BAKER'S WIFE (1976)

Original Cast .... T.H.T. (S) 772 — 2.00 — 3.00 — 4.00
  The show closed out of town and this would have been the cast to have
  opened on Broadway: Paul Sorvino, Patti Lupone, Kurt Peterson,
  Teri Ralson.
Original Cast (7" LP) .... T.H.T. (S) 773 — 2.00 — 3.00 — 4.00
  With original cast star Paul Sorvino, the composers Steven and
  Carol Schwartz and others.

BALLAD FOR BIMSHIRE (1963)

Original Cast .... London (M) AM 48002 — 12.00 — 18.00 — 24.00
  Frederick O'Neal, Christine Spencer, Jimmy Randolph.
Original Cast .... London (S) AMS 78002 — 15.00 — 22.50 — 30.00

BALLAD OF BABY DOE (1958)

Original Cast (3 records) .... Heliodor (S) 250 35 3 — 12.00 — 18.00 — 24.00
  New York City Opera Company and Beverly Sills, Walter Cassell,
  Frances Bible.

BAMBI (1942)

Soundtrack (1957) .... Disneyland (M) WDL-4009 — 7.50 — 11.25 — 15.00

BAND OF ANGELS (1957)

Soundtrack .... RCA (M) LPM-1557 — 35.00 — 52.50 — 70.00

BANDOLERO (1968)

Soundtrack .... Project 3 (S) 5026-SD — 6.00 — 9.00 — 12.00

BANDWAGON (1931)

Original Cast .... RCA (M) RD 7756 — 10.00 — 15.00 — 20.00
  Re-cast of original stars Fred and Adele Astaire and composer
  Arthur Schwartz.
Soundtrack (From the 1953 film) .... MGM (M) E 3051 — 15.00 — 22.50 — 30.00
  With the original 1931 star Fred Astaire, Nanette Fabray, India
  Adams, Jack Buchanan.
Studio Cast .... RCA (M) LPM 3155 — 10.00 — 15.00 — 20.00
  Harold Lang, George Britton, Edie Adams.
Studio Cast .... Columbia (M) ML 4751 — 5.00 — 7.50 — 10.00
  Mary Martin and chorus.
Studio Cast .... Monmouth Evergreen (S) MRS 6605 — 2.00 — 3.00 — 4.00
  Nancy Dussault, Clifford David, Karen Morrow.

BARABBAS

Soundtrack .... Colpix (M) CP 510 — 15.00 — 22.00 — 30.00
Soundtrack .... Colpix (S) SCP 510 — 17.00 — 26.00 — 35.00

BARBARA COOK AT CARNEGIE HALL (1975)

Original Cast .... Columbia (S) M 33438 — 2.00 — 3.00 — 4.00
  Barbara Cook.

BARBARELLA (1968)

Soundtrack .... Dynovoice (M) 1908 — 6.00 — 9.00 — 12.00
Soundtrack .... Dynovoice (S) 31908 — 7.50 — 11.25 — 15.00

BARBARIAN AND THE GEISHA, THE (1958)

Soundtrack .... 20th Century Fox (M) 3004 — 18.00 — 27.00 — 36.00

BAREFOOT ADVENTURE

Soundtrack .... Pacific Jazz (M) PJ35 — 7.00 — 11.00 — 15.00
Soundtrack .... Pacific Jazz (S) PJS35 — 10.00 — 15.00 — 20.00

BAREFOOT IN THE PARK (1967)

Soundtrack .... Dot (M) 3803 — 4.00 — 6.00 — 8.00
Soundtrack .... Dot (S) 25803 — 5.00 — 7.50 — 10.00

BARRY MANILOW LIVE (1976)

Original Cast (2 records) .... Arista (S) AL 8500 — 3.00 — 4.50 — 6.00
  Barry Manilow, Debra Byrd, Reparata.

BATMAN (1966)

TV Soundtrack .... 20th Century Fox (M) 3180 — 4.00 — 6.00 — 8.00
TV Soundtrack .... 20th Century Fox (S) S-3180 — 5.00 — 7.50 — 10.00

BAT MASTERSON (1958)
TV Soundtrack (1960) ....Chancellor (M) 7002   6.00   9.00   12.00

BATTLE OF ALGIERS (1967)
Soundtrack....................United Artist (M) UAL-4171   4.00   6.00   8.00
Soundtrack....................United Artist (S) UAS-5171   5.00   7.50   10.00

BATTLE OF BRITAIN
Soundtrack....................United Artists (S) 5201   6.00   9.00   12.00

BATTLE OF THE BULGE (1965)
Soundtrack....................Warner Bros. (M) W-1617   12.00   18.00   24.00
Soundtrack....................Warner Bros. (S) WS-1617   18.00   27.00   36.00

BEACH BLANKET BINGO (1965)
Soundtrack....................Capitol (M) T-2323   6.00   9.00   12.00
Soundtrack....................Capitol (S) ST-2323   7.50   11.25   15.00

BEACH PARTY (1963)
Soundtrack....................Buena Vista (M) BV-3316   6.00   9.00   12.00
Soundtrack....................Buena Vista (S) ST-3316   7.50   11.25   15.00

BEAR COUNTRY (1953)
Soundtrack (1957)....................Disneyland (M) WDL-4011   12.00   18.00   24.00

BEAU JAMES (1957)
Soundtrack....................Imperial (M) 9041   10.00   15.00   20.00

BEAVER VALLEY (1950)
Soundtrack (1957)....................Disneyland (M) WDL-4011   12.00   18.00   24.00

BEBOS GIRL
Soundtrack....................Capitol (M) T-2316   7.00   11.00   15.00
Soundtrack....................Capitol (S) ST-2316   10.00   15.00   20.00

BECAUSE YOU'RE MINE (1952)
Soundtrack (10")....................RCA (M) LM-7015   12.00   18.00   24.00

BECKET (1964)
Soundtrack....................Decca (M) DL-9117   9.00   13.50   18.00
Soundtrack....................Decca (S) DL-79117   12.00   18.00   24.00
Soundtrack (With dialogue)....................RCA (M) LOC-1091   7.50   11.25   15.00
Soundtrack....................RCA (S) LSO 1091   10.00   15.00   20.00

BEDAZZLED (1967)
Soundtrack....................London (S) MS-82009   10.00   15.00   20.00

BEDKNOBS & BROOMSTICKS
Soundtrack....................Vista (S) 5003   3.00   4.00   6.00

BEG BORROW AND STEAL (1960)
Original Cast (Album titled "Clara")....................Commentary (M) CTN 02   20.00   30.00   40.00
Cast star Betty Garrett with Jimmy Komack, Johnny Standley, Sid Tomack.

BEGGER'S OPERA, THE (1751)
Original London Revival Cast....................CBS (S) 70046   5.00   7.50   10.00
Frances Cuka, Hy Hazell, Angela Richards.
Studio Cast (2 records)....................RCA (M) LPM 6048   20.00   30.00   40.00
Old Vic Company, Pro Arte Orchestra.
Studio Cast (2 records)....................RCA (S) LRM 2523   15.00   22.50   30.00
William McAlpine, Ronald Lewis, John Frost.

BEHIND THE GREAT WALL (1959) (Traditional)
Soundtrack....................Monitor (M) MP-525   5.00   7.50   10.00

BEHOLD A PALE HORSE
Soundtrack....................Colpix (M) CP 519   7.00   11.00   15.00
Soundtrack....................Colpix (S) SCP 519   10.00   15.00   20.00

BEI MIR BISTU SCHOEN (1961)
Original Cast....................Decca (M) DL 9115   6.00   9.00   12.00
Leo Fuchs, Jacob Jacobs, Miriam Kressyn.
Original Cast....................Decca (S) DL 79115   10.00   15.00   20.00
Studio Cast (Side 2, "Go Fight City Hall")....................Tikva (M) T 72   10.00   15.00   20.00
Alan Chester and Doris Cohen.

BELIEVERS (1968)
Original Cast....................RCA (M) LOC 1151   4.00   6.00   8.00
Benjamin Carter, Dorothy Dinroe, Jesse DeVore.
Original Cast....................RCA (S) LSO 1151   5.00   7.50   10.00

BELL, BOOK AND CANDLE (1959)
Soundtrack....................Colpix (M) CP-502   20.00   30.00   40.00
Soundtrack....................Colpix (S) SCP-502   24.00   36.00   48.00

BELLE OF NEW YORK, THE (1952)
Soundtrack (10")....................MGM (M) E-108   12.00   18.00   24.00

BELLS ARE RINGING (1956)
Original Cast....................Columbia (M) OL 5170   7.50   11.25   15.00
Judy Holliday, Sidney Chaplin, Jean Stapleton, Eddie Lawrence.
Soundtrack (From the 1960 film)....................Capitol (M) W 1435   6.00   9.00   12.00
Judy Holliday, Dean Martin, Fred Clark, Eddie Foy, Jr., Jean Stapleton.
Soundtrack....................Capitol (S) SW 1435   7.50   11.25   15.00

BELLS OF ST. MARY'S, THE (1945)
Soundtrack (10") (1952)....................Decca (M) DL-5052   12.00   18.00   24.00
Soundtrack (1962)....................Decca (M) DL-4258   5.00   7.50   10.00

BENEATH THE PLANET OF THE APES (1970)
Soundtrack....................Amos (S) AAS-8001   6.00   9.00   12.00

BEN FRANKLIN IN PARIS (1964)
Original Cast....................Capitol (M) VAS 2191   10.00   15.00   20.00
Robert Preston, Ulla Sallert, Franklin Kiser.
Original Cast....................Capitol (S) SVAS 2191   12.00   18.00   24.00

BERLIN TO BROADWAY WITH KURT WEILL (1972)
Original Cast (2 records) (1974)....................Paramount (S) PAS 4000   5.00   7.50   10.00
Margery Cohen, Ken Kercheval, Judy Lander.

BEST FOOT FORWARD (1963)
Original Revival Cast....................Cadence (M) CE 4012   12.00   18.00   24.00
Paula Wayne, Liza Minnelli, Glenn Walken, Karin Wolfe.
Original Revival Cast....................Cadence (S) CLP 24012   20.00   30.00   40.00

BEST OF BURLESQUE (1957)
Original Cast....................MGM (M) E 3644   12.00   18.00   24.00
Sherry Britton, Tom Poston.
Original Cast....................MGM (S) SE 3644   18.00   27.00   36.00

BEST THINGS IN LIFE ARE FREE, THE (1956)
Soundtrack....................Capitol (M) T-765   6.00   9.00   12.00
Soundtrack....................Liberty (M) LRP-3017   5.00   7.50   10.00

BEYOND THE FRINGE (1962)
Original Cast....................Capitol (M) W 1792   4.00   6.00   8.00
Alan Bennett, Peter Cook, Jonathan Miller.

BEYOND THE FRINGE '64 (1964)
Original Cast....................Capitol (M) W 2072   5.00   7.50   10.00
Alan Bennett, Peter Cook, Dudley Moore, Paxton Whitehead.
Original Cast....................Capitol (S) SW 2072   6.00   9.00   12.00

BEYOND THE GREAT WALL
Soundtrack....................Capitol (M) T-10401   12.00   19.00   25.00

BEYOND THE MOON
Soundtrack....................Mainstream (M) 54001   10.00   15.00   20.00
Soundtrack....................Mainstream (S) 4001   12.00   19.00   25.00

BEYOND THE VALLEY OF THE DOLLS (1972)
Soundtrack (Limited release)....................20th Century Fox (S) S-4211   7.50   11.25   15.00

BIBLE, THE
Soundtrack....................20th Century Fox (M) 3184   10.00   15.00   20.00
Soundtrack....................20th Century Fox (S) 4184   15.00   22.50   30.00

BIG BAD WOLF
Soundtrack....................Camden (M) 1087   2.50   3.75   5.00
Soundtrack....................Camden (S) 1087   3.00   4.00   6.00

BIG BOUNCE, THE (1969)
Soundtrack....................Warner Bros. (S) WS-1781   5.00   7.50   10.00

BIG CIRCUS, THE (1959)
Soundtrack....................Todd (M) 5001   10.00   15.00   20.00
Soundtrack....................Todd (S) S-5001   12.00   18.00   24.00

BIG COUNTRY, THE (1958)
Soundtrack....................United Artists (S) UAL 40004   5.00   7.50   10.00

BIGGEST BUNDLE OF THEM ALL
Soundtrack....................MGM (M) 4446   3.00   4.50   6.00
Soundtrack....................MGM (S) 4446   4.00   6.00   8.00

BIG GUNDOWN, THE (1968)
Soundtrack....................United Artist (S) UAS-5190   6.00   9.00   12.00

BIG RED (1962)
Soundtrack (With dialogue)....................(M) ST-1916   5.00   7.50   10.00

BIG VALLEY, THE (1965)
TV Soundtrack....................ABC (M) 527   7.50   11.25   15.00
TV Soundtrack....................ABC (S) S-527   10.00   15.00   20.00

(M) Mono   (S) Stereo   (EP) Extended Play   (Q) Quad   (RI) Re-issued

BIKINI BEACH (1964)
Soundtrack.....................................*Buena Vista (M) BV-3324* 5.00 7.50 10.00
Soundtrack.....................................*Buena Vista (S) ST-3324* 6.00 9.00 12.00

BILLIE
Soundtrack.....................................*United Artists (M) UAL-4131* 3.00 4.00 6.00
Soundtrack.....................................*United Artists (S) UAS-5131* 4.00 6.00 8.00

BILLION DOLLAR BRAIN
Soundtrack.....................................*United Artists (M) 4174* 6.00 9.00 12.00
Soundtrack.....................................*United Artists (S) 5174* 7.00 11.00 15.00

BILLY BARNES L.A. (1962)
Original Los Angeles Cast.....................*Criterion (M) 1001* 10.00 15.00 20.00
Joyce Jameson, Ken Berry, Sylvia Lewis.
Original Los Angeles Cast.....................*Criterion (S) 1001* 12.00 18.00 24.00

BILLY BARNES REVUE (1959)
Original Cast.....................................*Decca (M) DL 9076* 7.50 11.25 15.00
Joyce Jameson, Bert Convy, Patti Regan, Jackie Joseph.
Original Cast.....................................*Decca (S) DL 79076* 12.00 18.00 24.00

BILLY JACK
Soundtrack.....................................*Warner Bros. (S) 1926* 4.00 6.00 8.00

BILLY NONAME (1970)
Original Cast.....................................*Roulette (S) SROC 11* 7.50 11.25 15.00
Donny Burks, Alan Weeks, Hatti Winston.

BILLY ROSE'S JUMBO (1962)
Soundtrack.....................................*Columbia (M) OL-5860* 5.00 7.50 10.00
Soundtrack.....................................*Columbia (S) OS-2260* 7.50 11.25 15.00

BIRDS, THE BEES AND THE ITALIANS
Soundtrack.....................................*United Artists (M) 4157* 7.00 11.00 15.00
Soundtrack.....................................*United Artists (S) 5157* 9.00 13.00 18.00

BIRD WITH THE CRYSTAL PLUMAGE, THE (1970)
Soundtrack.....................................*Capitol (S) SW642* 18.00 27.00 36.00

BIRTH OF THE BLUES, THE (1941)
Soundtrack (1962).....................................*Decca (M) DL-4255* 4.00 6.00 8.00

BITTERSWEET (1929)
Studio Cast (This was the first extended recording. The original cast
production was first held in London, then Boston, then
New York in 1929.).....................*Angel (M) 35814* 10.00 15.00 20.00
Vanesa Lee, Roberto Cardinali, Julie Dawn, John Hauxvell.
Studio Cast.....................................*Angel (S) S 35814* 12.00 18.00 24.00

BLACKBEARD'S GHOST (1968)
Soundtrack (With Dialogue).....................*Disneyland (M) DQ-1305* 5.00 7.50 10.00

BLACKBIRDS OF 1928 (Lew Leslie's) (1928)
Studio Cast (Side 1, "Shuffle Along").....................*RCA (M) LPM 3154* 10.00 15.00 20.00
Studio Cast (With stars of the original cast).....................*Revue (M) 1* 18.00 27.00 36.00
Adelaide Hall, Bill Robinson, Cab Calloway, The Mills Brothers, Duke
Ellington's and Don Redman's Orchestras and members of the
Blackbirds of 1930 cast, Ethel Waters and the Cecil Mack Choir.
Studio Cast (Re-issue).....................*Sutton (M) SU 270* 10.00 15.00 20.00
Studio Cast (Re-channeled stereo).....................*Sutton (S) SSU 270* 12.00 18.00 24.00
Studio Cast (Re-issue, with some
different takes) (1968).....................*Columbia (M) OL 6770* 2.00 3.00 4.00

BLACK CAESAR
Soundtrack.....................................*Polydor (S) 6014* 3.00 4.00 6.00

BLACK NATIVITY (1961)
Original Cast (Traditional gospel songs).....................*Vee Jay (M) LP 5022* 5.00 7.50 10.00
Marion Williams, The Stars of Faith, Princess Stewart.
Original Cast.....................................*Vee Jay (S) SR 5022* 10.00 15.00 20.00
Original Cast.....................................*Vee Jay (S) VJS 8503* 5.00 7.50 10.00

BLACK ORCHID
Soundtrack.....................................*Dot (M) DLP-3178* 15.00 22.00 30.00
Soundtrack.....................................*Dot (S) DLP 25178* 17.00 26.00 35.00

BLACK ORPHEUS (1959)
Soundtrack.....................................*Epic (M) LN-3672* 6.00 9.00 12.00

BLACK TIGHTS (1962)
Soundtrack.....................................*RCA (M) FOC-3* 12.00 18.00 24.00
Soundtrack.....................................*RCA (S) FSO-3* 15.00 22.50 30.00

BLACULA (1972)
Soundtrack.....................................*(S) RCA LSP-4806* 3.00 4.50 6.00

BLESS THE BEASTS AND CHILDREN (1971)
Soundtrack.....................................*A&M (S) 4322* 10.00 15.00 20.00

BLISS OF MRS. BLOSSOM (1968)
Soundtrack.....................................*RCA (S) LSP-4080* 6.00 9.00 12.00

BLOOD AND SAND (1941)
Soundtrack (1952) (10").....................*Decca (M) DL-5380* 15.00 22.50 30.00
Soundtrack (1956).....................*Decca (M) DL-8279* 12.00 18.00 24.00

BLOODY MAMA
Soundtrack.....................................*American Int'l (S) 1041* 4.00 6.00 8.00

BLOOMER GIRL (1944)
Original Cast (1950).....................*Decca (M) DL 8015* 10.00 15.00 20.00
Celeste Holm, David Brooks, Toni Hart.
Original Cast (1966).....................*Decca (M) DL 9126* 5.00 7.50 10.00
Original Cast (Re-channeled stereo).....................*Decca (S) 79126* 6.00 9.00 12.00

BLOOMFIELD (1971) (See: Hero, The)

BLOW UP
Soundtrack.....................................*MGM (M) 4447* 7.00 11.00 15.00
Soundtrack.....................................*MGM (S) 4447* 10.00 15.00 20.00

BLUE (1968)
Soundtrack.....................................*Dot (M) 3855* 10.00 15.00 20.00
Soundtrack.....................................*Dot (S) 25855* 12.00 18.00 24.00

BLUE HAWAII (1961)
Soundtrack.....................................*RCA (M) LPM 2426* 6.00 12.00 18.00
Elvis Presley. First cover came with a red sticker advertising the new hit
single from the album, "Can't Help Falling In Love/Rock-A-Hula Baby."
Soundtrack.....................................*RCA (S) LSP 2426* 6.00 12.00 18.00

BLUE MAX (1966)
Soundtrack.....................................*Mainstream (M) 56081* 12.00 19.00 25.00
Soundtrack.....................................*Mainstream (S) 6081* 20.00 30.00 40.00

BLUE SKIES (1946)
Soundtrack (1950) (10").....................*Decca (M) DL-5042* 7.50 11.25 15.00
Soundtrack (1962).....................*Decca (M) DL-4259* 4.00 6.00 8.00

BOB & CAROL & TED & ALICE
Soundtrack.....................................*Bell (S) 1200* 3.00 4.00 6.00

BOB & RAY - THE TWO & ONLY (1970)
Original Cast.....................................*Columbia (S) S 30412* 2.00 3.00 4.00
Bob Elliott and Ray Goulding.

BOBO, THE (1967)
Soundtrack.....................................*Warner Bros. (M) 1711* 5.00 7.50 10.00
Soundtrack.....................................*Warner Bros. (S) 1711* 6.00 9.00 12.00

BOCCACCIO '70 (1962)
Soundtrack.....................................*RCA (M) FOC-5* 10.00 15.00* 20.00
Soundtrack.....................................*RCA (S) FSO-5* 12.00 18.00 24.00

BOEING, BOEING
Soundtrack.....................................*RCA (M) LOC-1121* 7.50 11.25 15.00
Soundtrack.....................................*RCA (S) LSO-1121* 9.00 13.50 18.00

BOLSHOI BALLET '67 (1966)
Soundtrack (Classical).....................*Command (S) S-11035* 6.00 9.00 12.00

(M) Mono (S) Stereo (EP) Extended Play (Q) Quad (RI) Re-issued

BONANZA (1958)
TV Soundtrack (1961)	MGM (M) E-3960	5.00	7.50	10.00
TV Soundtrack	MGM (S) SE-3960	6.00	9.00	12.00

BONANZA BOUND (1948)
Original Cast	JJA (M) 19764	2.00	3.00	4.00
George Coulouris, Carol Raye, Adolph Green.

BONJOUR TRISTESSE (1958)
Soundtrack	RCA (M) LOC-1040	15.00	22.50	30.00

BONNIE AND CLYDE
Soundtrack	Warner Bros. (S) 1742	5.00	7.00	10.00

BORA, BORA (1971)
Soundtrack (Limited release)	American Int'l (S) A-1029	4.00	6.00	8.00

BORN FREE
Soundtrack	MGM (M) 4368	3.00	4.00	6.00
Soundtrack	MGM (S) 4368	4.00	6.00	8.00

BORN LOSERS (1967)
Soundtrack	Tower (M) T-5082	5.00	7.50	10.00
Soundtrack	Tower (S) ST-5082	6.00	9.00	12.00

BORSALINO (1970)
Soundtrack	Paramount (S) PAS-5019	7.50	11.25	15.00

BOURBON STREET BEAT (1960)
TV Soundtrack	Warner Bros. (M) W-1321	6.00	9.00	12.00
TV Soundtrack	Warner Bros. (S) WS-1321	7.50	11.25	15.00

BOY FRIEND, THE (1954)
Original Cast	RCA (M) LOC 1018	7.50	11.25	15.00
Julie Andrews, Ann Wakefield, John Hewer.
Original London Cast	HMV (M) DLP 1078	25.00	37.50	50.00
Anne Rogers, Anthony Hayes, Denis Hurst.
Original London Revival Cast	Parlphone (S) PCS 7044	12.00	18.00	24.00
Tony Adams, Frances Barlow, Ann Beach.
Original Australian Cast	Ace of Clubs (S) SCL 1263	7.50	11.25	15.00
Deidre Rubenstein, Laurel Veitch, Julia Day.
Original Revival Cast	Decca (S) DL 79177	2.00	3.00	4.00
Sandy Duncan, Ronald Young, Jenne Beauvais, Leon Shaw.
Soundtrack (From the 1972 film)	MGM (S) 1SE 32	5.00	7.50	10.00
Twiggy, Christopher Gable, Max Adrian.

BOY MEETS BOY (1975)
Original Cast	R&P (S) J013	2.00	3.00	4.00
Joe Barrett, Bobby Bower, David Gallegly.

BOY NAMED CHARLIE BROWN
Soundtrack	Columbia (S) DS 3500	3.00	4.00	6.00

BOY ON A DOLPHIN (1957)
Soundtrack	Decca (M) DL-8580	18.00	27.00	36.00

BOYS FROM SYRACUSE (1938)
Original London Cast	Decca (M) 4564	12.00	18.00	24.00
Bob Monkhouse, Denis Quilley, Pat Turner.
Original Revival Cast (1963)	Capitol (M) TAO 1933	7.50	11.25	15.00
Ellen Hanley, Danny Carroll, Cathryn Damon.
Original Revival Cast	Capitol (S) STAO 1933	10.00	15.00	20.00
Studio Cast	Columbia (M) CL 847	7.50	11.25	15.00
Portia Nelson, Jack Cassidy, Bob Shaver.

BRAVE ONE, THE (1956)
Soundtrack	Decca (M) DL-8344	18.00	27.00	36.00

BRAVO GIOVANNI! (1962)
Original Cast	Columbia (M) OL 5800	7.50	11.25	15.00
Cesare Siepi, Michele Lee, Maria Karnilova.
Original Cast	Columbia (S) OS 2200	10.00	15.00	20.00

BREATH OF SCANDAL, A (1960)
Soundtrack	Imperial (M) 9132	7.50	11.25	15.00
Soundtrack	Imperial (S) S-9132	10.00	15.00	20.00

BRECHT ON BRECHT (1962)
Original Cast (2 records)	Columbia (S) O2S 203	2.00	3.00	4.00
Dane Clark, Anne Jackson, Lotte Lenya, Viveca Lindfors.

BREEZY (1973)
Soundtrack	MCA (S) 384	3.00	4.50	6.00

BREWSTER MCCLOUD (1970)
Soundtrack	MGM (S) 1SE 28	3.00	4.50	6.00

BRIDGE ON THE RIVER KWAI (1957)
Soundtrack	Columbia (M) CL-1100	2.00	3.00	4.00

BRIGADOON (1947)
Original Cast (1951) (RCA's first original cast long play album, recorded for 78's in 1947 and first released on LP in 1951)	RCA (M) LOC 1001	10.00	15.00	20.00
David Brooks, Marion Bell, Pamela Britton.
Original Cast (Re-channeled stereo)	RCA (S) LSO 1001	7.50	11.25	15.00
Soundtrack (From the 1954 film)	MGM (M) E 3135	5.00	7.50	10.00
Gene Kelly, Van Johnson, Cyd Charisse.
TV Soundtrack (1967)	CSP (M) CSM 385	12.00	18.00	24.00
Robert Goulet, Sally Ann Howes, Peter Falk, Finlay Currie.
Studio Cast	Columbia (M) CL 1132	5.00	7.50	10.00
Shirley Jones, Jack Cassidy.

BROTHER ON THE RUN (1974)
Soundtrack (Limited release)	Perception (S) PR-45	4.00	6.00	8.00

BUBBLING BROWN SUGAR (1975)
Original Cast	HL (S) 69011	2.00	3.00	4.00
Avon Long, Josephine Premice, Vivian Reed.

BUCCANEER, THE (1959)
Soundtrack	Columbia (M) CL-1278	12.00	18.00	24.00
Soundtrack	Columbia (S) CS-8096	15.00	22.50	30.00

BULLET FOR PRETTY BOY, A (1970)
Soundtrack	American Int'l (S) A-1034	4.00	6.00	8.00

BULLITT (1968)
Soundtrack	Warner Bros. (S) WS-1777	4.00	6.00	8.00

BULLWHIP GRIFFIN (1967)
Soundtrack (With dialogue)	Disneyland (M) DQ-1291	6.00	9.00	12.00

BUNDLE OF JOY (1956)
Soundtrack	RCA (M) LPM-1399	7.50	11.25	15.00

BUNNY LAKE IS MISSING
Soundtrack	RCA (M) LOC 1115	7.00	10.50	14.00
Soundtrack	RCA (S) LOS 1115	8.00	12.00	16.00

(M) Mono (S) Stereo (EP) Extended Play (Q) Quad (RI) Re-issued

BUNNY O'HARE
Soundtrack.............................. *American Int'l (S) 1041* 4.00 6.00 8.00

BUONA SERA, MRS. CAMPBELL (1968)
Soundtrack................ *United Artist (S) UAS-5192* 6.00 9.00 12.00

BURGLARS, THE (1971)
Soundtrack............................... *Bell (S) 1105* 3.00 4.50 6.00

BURKE'S LAW (1964)
TV Soundtrack .... *Liberty (M) LRP-3374* 6.00 9.00 12.00
TV Soundtrack .... *Liberty (S) LST-7374* 7.50 11.25 15.00

BURN
. Soundtrack..................... *United Artists (S) LA303-G* 3.00 4.50 6.00

BUTCH CASSIDY AND THE SUNDANCE KID (1969)
Soundtrack.......................... *A&M (S) SP-4227* 4.00 6.00 8.00

BYE BYE BIRDIE (1960)
Original Cast .... *Columbia (M) OL 5510* 4.00 6.00 8.00
  Chita Rivera, Dick Van Dyke, Paul Lynde.
Original Cast .... *Columbia (S) OS 2025* 5.00 7.50 10.00
Original London Cast .... *Mercury (M) 13000* 7.50 11.25 15.00
  Chita Rivera, Peter Marshall, Angela Baddeley.
Original London Cast .... *Mercury (S) 17000* 10.00 15.00 20.00
Soundtrack (From the 1963 film)............... *RCA (M) LOC 1081* 2.00 3.00 4.00
  Janet Leigh, Dick Van Dyke, Ann Margret, Maureen Stapleton,
  Bobby Rydell, Paul Lynde.
Soundtrack...................... *RCA (S) LSO 1081* 2.00 3.00 4.00

BY JUPITER (1942)
Studio Cast (1 side)..................... *Decca (M) 326* 10.00 15.00 20.00
  Hildegarde.
Original Revival Cast .... *RCA (M) LOC 1137* 7.50 11.25 15.00
  Bob Dishy, Jackie Alloway, Irene Byatt.
Original Revival Cast .... *RCA (S) LSO 1137* 10.00 15.00 20.00

BY THE BEAUTIFUL SEA (1954)
Original Cast .... *Capitol (M) S 531* 50.00 75.00 100.00
  Shirley Booth, Wilbur Evans, Cameron Prud'homme, Richard France,
  Mae Barnes, Libi Staiger, Thomas Gleason.
Original Cast (Re-issue) .... *Capitol (M) T-11652* 2.00 3.00 4.00

BY THE LIGHT OF THE SILVERY MOON (1953)
Soundtrack (10")....................... *Capitol (M) H-422* 10.00 15.00 20.00
Soundtrack (10")..................... *Columbia (M) CL-6248* 10.00 15.00 20.00

C

CABARET (1966)
Original London Cast........................... *CBS (S) 70039* 10.00 15.00 20.00
  Judi Dench, Kevin Colson, Lila Kedrova.
Original Cast................ *Columbia (M) KOL 6640* 2.00 3.00 4.00
  Jill Haworth, Jack Gilford, Bert Convy, Lotte Lenya.
Original Cast................ *Columbia (S) KOS 3040* 2.00 3.00 4.00
Soundtrack (From the 1972 film)............. *ABC (S) D 752* 4.00 6.00 8.00
  Liza Minnelli, Joel Grey, Michael York.

CABIN IN THE SKY (1964)
Original Cast (1968 re-issue of four songs from
  two 78 singles) .... *Columbia (M) CL 2792* 5.00 7.50 10.00
  Ethel Waters.
Original Revival Cast .... *Capitol (M) W 2073* 12.00 18.00 24.00
  Rosetta LeNoire, Ketty Lester, Tony Middleton.
Original Revival Cast .... *Capitol (S) SW 2073* 15.00 22.50 30.00

CACTUS FLOWER
Soundtrack............................... *Bell (S) 1201* 3.00 4.00 6.00

CAINE MUTINY, THE (1954)
Soundtrack (With dialogue) (Limited release)
  (Value is estimated) .... *RCA (M) LOC-1013* 1000.00 1500.00 2000.00

CALAMITY JANE (1953)
Soundtrack (10") .... *Columbia (M) CL-6273* 10.00 15.00 20.00

CALL ME MADAM (1950)
Original Cast (With Dinah Shore singing the
  Ethel Merman role) .... *RCA (M) LOC 1000* 18.00 24.00 36.00
  Paul Lucas, Russell Nype, Galina Talva, Pat Harrington.
Original Cast (10") .... *Decca (M) DL 5304* 10.00 15.00 20.00
Original London Cast........... *Monmouth Evergreen (M) MES7073* 2.00 3.00 4.00
  Billie Worth, Anton Walbrook.
Soundtrack (From the 1953 film) (10") .... *Decca (M) 5465* 10.00 15.00 20.00
  Ethel Merman, George Sanders, Donald O'Conner, Carole Richards.
Soundtrack...................... *Ace of Hearts (M) 137* 7.50 11.25 15.00
Studio Cast (With original cast star) .... *Decca (M) DL 8035* 7.50 11.25 15.00
  Ethel Merman, Dick Haymes, Eileen Wilson.
Studio Cast (1955 re-issue) .... *Decca (M) DL 9022* 5.00 7.50 10.00

CALL ME MISTER (1946)
Original Cast .... *Decca (M) DL 7005* 36.00 54.00 72.00
  Betty Garrett, Lawrence Winters, Paula Bane.
Studio Cast .... *Coral (M) CRL 57082* 10.00 15.00 20.00
  Composer Harold Rome sings five selections.

CAMBRIDGE CIRCUS (1964)
Original London & Original Broadway Cast .....*Odeon (S) PCS 3046* 50.00 75.00 100.00
  (Written by the cast)
  Anthony Buffery, Tim Brooke-Taylor.

CAMELOT (1960)
Original Cast........................ *Columbia (M) OL 5620* 2.00 3.00 4.00
  Julie Andrews, Richard Burton, Robert Goulet, Roddy McDowell.
Original Cast........................ *Columbia (S) OS 2031* 2.00 3.00 4.00
Original London Cast............. *EMI (M) CLP 1756* 12.00 18.00 24.00
  Lawrence Harvey, Elizabeth Larner, Barry Kent.
Soundtrack (From the 1967 film)........... *Warner Bros. (M) B 1712* 2.00 3.00 4.00
  Richard Harris, Vanessa Redgrave.
Soundtrack........................ *Warner Bros. (S) BS 1712* 2.00 3.00 4.00
London Studio Cast........................ *WRC (S) R 851* 7.50 11.25 15.00
  Patrick Macnee, Madge Stephens, Geoffrey Chard.

CAN CAN (1953)
Original Cast........................ *Capitol (M) S 452* 10.00 15.00 20.00
  Lilo, Hans Conreid, Gwen Verdon, Erik Rhodes.
Original London Cast........ *Monmouth Evergreen (M) MES 7073* 2.00 3.00 4.00
  Irene Hilda, Edmund Hockridge, Alfred Marks.
Soundtrack (From the 1960 film)................ *Capitol (M) W1301* 6.00 9.00 12.00
  Frank Sinatra, Shirley MacLaine, Maurice Chevalier, Louis Jourdan.
Soundtrack........................ *Capitol (S) SW 1301* 7.50 11.25 15.00
Studio Cast........................ *Design (S) 1009* 7.50 11.25 15.00
  Mimi Benzell, Felix Knight.
Studio Cast........................ *Halo (M) 50217* 5.00 7.50 10.00
  The National Singers and Orchestra.

CANDIDATE
Soundtrack........................... *Jubilee (M) 5029* 5.00 7.00 10.00
Soundtrack........................... *Jubilee (S) 5029* 6.00 9.00 12.00

(M) Mono (S) Stereo (EP) Extended Play (Q) Quad (RI) Re-issued

TITLE	LABEL & NO.	GOOD	VERY GOOD	NEAR MINT
Original Cast (1955)	Decca (M) DL 9021	7.50	11.25	15.00
Soundtrack (From the 1954 film)	RCA (M) LM 1881	12.00	18.00	24.00
Dorothy Dandridge, Harry Belafonte, Olga James, Pearl Bailey, Diahann Carroll.				

CARMILLA (1972)

Original Cast (Off Broadway)	Vanguard (S) VSD 79322	2.00	3.00	4.00
Margaret Benczak, Donald Harrington, Camille Tibaldeo.				

CARNIVAL (1961)

Original Cast	MGM (M) E 3946	2.00	3.00	4.00
Anna Maria Alberghetti, James Mitchell, Kaye Ballard.				
Original Cast	MGM (S) SE 3946	2.00	3.00	4.00
Original London Cast	Odeon (M) 1476	12.00	18.00	24.00
Sally Logan, Shirley Sands, James Mitchell.				

CAROUSEL (1945)

Original Cast (1949)	Decca (M) DL 8003	10.00	15.00	20.00
John Raitt, Jan Clayton, Jean Darling.				
Original Cast (1955 re-issue)	Decca (M) DL 9020	7.50	11.25	15.00
Original Cast (Re-channeled stereo)	Decca (S) DL 79020	5.00	7.50	10.00
Original Revival Cast (1965)	RCA (S) LSO 1114	2.00	3.00	4.00
John Raitt, Eileen Christy, Susan Watson, Benay Venuta, Edward Everett Horton.				
Soundtrack (From the 1956 film)	Capitol (M) W 694	2.00	3.00	4.00
Gordon MacRae, Shirley Jones, Cameron Mitchell, Robert Rounseville.				
Soundtrack (Re-channeled stereo) (1962)	Capitol (S) SW 694	2.00	3.00	4.00
Soundtrack (2 sides of a 3 record set)	Capitol (M) TCL 1790	3.00	4.50	6.00
Soundtrack	Capitol (S) STCL 1790	3.00	4.50	6.00
TV Soundtrack	CSP Columbia Special Products	10.00	15.00	20.00
Robert Goulet, Mary Grover, Pernell Roberts, Charles Ruggles.				
Studio Cast (With original cast star)	Vista (M) 4029	5.00	7.50	10.00
Jan Clayton and chorus.				

CARPETBAGGERS, THE (1964)

Soundtrack	Ava (M) A-45-ST	4.00	6.00	8.00
Soundtrack	Ava (S) AS-45-ST	5.00	7.50	10.00

CARRY IT ON

Soundtrack	Vanguard (S) 79313	4.00	6.00	8.00

CASANOVA '70 (1965)

Soundtrack	Epic (M) LN-24195	12.00	18.00	24.00
Soundtrack	Epic (S) BN-26195	15.00	22.50	30.00

CASINO ROYALE (1967)

Soundtrack	Colgems (M) 5005	6.00	9.00	12.00
Soundtrack	Colgems (S) 5005	10.00	15.00	20.00

CAST A GIANT SHADOW

Soundtrack	United Artists (M) UAL-4138	4.00	6.00	8.00
Soundtrack	United Artists (S) UAS-5138	5.00	7.50	10.00

CAT & THE FIDDLE, THE (1931)

Original London Cast (1 side exerpts only)	WRC (M) SH 171	2.00	3.00	4.00
With star Peggy Wood.				
Studio Cast	Epic (M) LN 3569	10.00	15.00	20.00
Doreen Hume and Denis Quilley.				
Studio Cast (45 r.p.m. extended play record)	RCA (M) EPA 477	10.00	15.00	20.00
Patricia Neway and Stephen Douglass.				

CATCH MY SOUL

Soundtrack	Metromedia (S) 0176	2.50	3.75	5.00

TITLE	LABEL & NO.	GOOD	VERY GOOD	NEAR MINT

CANDIDE (1956)

Original Cast	Columbia (M) OL 5180	12.00	18.00	24.00
Max Adrian, Robert Rounseville, Barbara Cook.				
Original Cast (Different takes)	Columbia (S) OS 2350	5.00	7.50	10.00
Original Revival Cast (2 records) (1973)	Columbia (S) S2X 32923	3.00	4.50	6.00
Lewis J. Stadlen, Mark Baker, Maureen Brennan.				

CAN HIERONYMOUS MERKIN EVER FORGET MERCY HUMPPE AND FIND TRUE HAPPINESS? (1969)

Soundtrack	Kapp (S) KS-5509	6.00	9.00	12.00

CANTERBURY TALES (1969)

Original Cast	Capitol (S) SW 229	7.50	11.25	15.00
George Rose, Hermione Baddeley, Martyn Green.				
Original Cast (2 sides of a 3 record set)	Capitol (S) SW 292 (3)	10.00	15.00	20.00
Original London Cast	Decca (S) SKL 4956	12.00	18.00	24.00
Wilfrid Brambell, Jessie Evans, Kenneth J. Warren.				

CAPER OF THE GOLDEN BULLS (1967)

Soundtrack	Tower (M) T-5086	5.00	7.50	10.00
Soundtrack	Tower (S) ST-5086	6.00	9.00	12.00

CAPTAIN FROM CASTILE, THE (1947)

Soundtrack (1949)	Mercury (M) MG-20005	7.50	11.25	15.00
Soundtrack (1950) (10")	Mercury (M) MG-25072	10.00	15.00	20.00

CAPTAIN JINKS OF THE HORSE MARINES (1975)

Original Cast (2 records) (World Premiere)	RCA (S) ARL2 1727	3.00	4.50	6.00

CARDINAL, THE

Soundtrack	RCA (M) LOC-1084	10.00	15.00	20.00
Soundtrack	RCA (S) LSO-1084	12.00	15.00	24.00

CARETAKERS, THE (1963)

Soundtrack	Ava (M) A-31	4.00	6.00	8.00
Soundtrack	Ava (S) AS-31	5.00	7.50	10.00

CARMEN JONES (1943)

Original Cast (1950)	Decca (M) DL 8014	10.00	15.00	20.00
Muriel Smith, Luther Saxon, Cozy Cole.				

CELEBRATION (1969)
Original Cast .... Capitol (S) SW 198 — 2.00 — 3.00 — 4.00
Keith Charles, Michael Glenn-Smith.

CERTAIN SMILE, A (1958)
Soundtrack .... Columbia (M) CL-1194 — 12.00 — 18.00 — 24.00
Soundtrack .... Columbia (S) CS-8068 — 18.00 — 27.00 — 36.00

CHAIRMAN
Soundtrack .... Tetragrammaton (S) 5007 — 3.00 — 4.00 — 6.00

CHAPLIN REVUE
Soundtrack .... Decca (M) DL-4040 — 3.00 — 4.00 — 6.00

CHAPLIN'S ART OF COMEDY
Soundtrack .... Mainstream (M) 56089 — 7.00 — 11.00 — 15.00
Soundtrack .... Mainstream (S) 6089 — 10.00 — 15.00 — 20.00

CHAPMAN REPORT, THE
Soundtrack .... Warner Bros. (M) W 1478 — 10.00 — 15.00 — 20.00
Soundtrack .... Warner Bros. (S) WS 1478 — 12.00 — 19.00 — 25.00

CHAPPAQUA
Soundtrack .... Columbia (S) OS-3230 — 5.00 — 7.00 — 10.00

CHARADE (1963)
Soundtrack .... RCA (M) LPM-2755 — 5.00 — 7.50 — 10.00
Soundtrack .... RCA (S) LSP-2755 — 6.00 — 9.00 — 12.00

CHARGE OF THE LIGHT BRIGADE, THE (1968)
Soundtrack .... United Artists (S) UAS 5177 — 7.50 — 11.25 — 15.00

CHARIOTS OF THE GODS (1973)
Soundtrack .... Polydor (S) 6504 — 3.00 — 4.50 — 6.00

CHARLY (1968)
Soundtrack .... World Pacific (S) WS-21454 — 6.00 — 9.00 — 12.00

CHASE, THE (1966)
Soundtrack .... Columbia (M) OL-6560 — 10.00 — 15.00 — 20.00
Soundtrack .... Columbia (S) OS-1960 — 12.00 — 18.00 — 24.00

CHASTITY
Soundtrack .... Atco (S) 302 — 3.00 — 4.00 — 6.00

CHE! (1969)
Soundtrack .... Tetragrammaton (S) T-5006 — 3.00 — 4.50 — 6.00

CHECKMATE (1960)
TV Soundtrack .... Columbia (S) CS-8391 — 5.00 — 7.50 — 10.00

CHEE CHEE (1928)
Studio Cast .... Ava (S) AS 26 — 7.50 — 11.25 — 15.00
Selections by Betty Comden.

CHICAGO (1975)
Original Cast .... Arista (S) 9005 — 2.00 — 3.00 — 4.00
Gwen Verdon, Chita Rivera.

CHITTY CHITTY BANG BANG
Soundtrack .... United Artists (S) 5188 — 3.00 — 4.00 — 6.00

CHOCALONIA (1976)
Original Cast (West Coast) .... Crissy (S) CR 2034 — 5.00 — 7.50 — 10.00
Wade Crookham, Frankie Marshall, Dennis Lybe.

CHOCOLATE SOLDIER (1909)
Soundtrack (1958) (2 records) .... RCA (M) LOP 6005 — 7.50 — 11.25 — 15.00
Soundtrack (1959) .... RCA (M) LOP 1506 — 5.00 — 7.50 — 10.00
Studio Cast (Side 2, "The Student Prince") .... Columbia (M)ML 4060 — 7.50 — 11.25 — 15.00
Rise Stevens, Nelson Eddy.

CHORUS LINE, A (1975)
Original Cast (With 27 members) .... Columbia (S) PS 33581 — 2.00 — 3.00 — 4.00

CHRISTINE (1960)
Original Cast .... Columbia (M) OL 5220 — 10.00 — 15.00 — 20.00
Maureen O'Hare, Morley Meredith, Nancy Andrews.
Original Cast .... Columbia (S) OS 2026 — 15.00 — 22.50 — 30.00

CHRISTMAS THAT ALMOST WASN'T
Soundtrack .... Camden (M) 1086 — 6.00 — 9.00 — 12.00
Soundtrack .... Camden (S) 1086 — 7.00 — 11.00 — 15.00

CHU CHIN CHOW (1917)
London Studio Cast .... HMV (M) CLP 1269 — 12.00 — 18.00 — 24.00
Inia TeWiata, Julie Bryan, Barbara Leigh, Charles Young.

CINCINNATI KID, THE
Soundtrack .... MGM (M) E-4313 — 4.00 — 6.00 — 8.00
Soundtrack .... MGM (S) SE-4313 — 5.00 — 7.00 — 10.00

CINDERELLA (1949)
Soundtrack (1957) .... Disneyland (M) WDL-4007 — 7.50 — 11.25 — 15.00

CINDERELLA (1966)
Soundtrack .... Camden (M) 1085 — 2.50 — 3.75 — 5.00
Soundtrack .... Camden (S) 1085 — 3.00 — 4.00 — 6.00

CINDERELLA LIBERTY
Soundtrack .... 20th Cnetury Fox
Soundtrack .... 20th Century Fox (S) 100 — 3.00 — 4.00 — 6.00

CINDERFELLA (1960)
Soundtrack .... Dot (M) 8001 — 10.00 — 15.00 — 20.00
Soundtrack .... Dot (S) 38001 — 12.00 — 18.00 — 24.00

CINDY (1964)
Original Cast .... ABC (M) OC 2 — 10.00 — 15.00 — 20.00
Sylvia Mann, Johnny Harmon, Lizabeth Pritchett.
Original Cast .... ABC (S) SOC 2 — 12.00 — 18.00 — 24.00

CINERAMA HOLIDAY (1955)
Soundtrack .... Mercury (M) MG-20059 — 7.50 — 11.25 — 15.00

CIRCLE OF LOVE (1965)
Soundtrack .... Monitor (M) MP-602 — 6.00 — 9.00 — 12.00
Soundtrack .... Monitor (S) MPS-602 — 7.50 — 11.25 — 15.00

CIRCUS OF HORRORS (1960)
Soundtrack .... Imperial (M) 9132 — 12.00 — 18.00 — 24.00
Soundtrack .... Imperial (S) S9132 — 15.00 — 22.50 — 30.00

CIRCUS WORLD
Soundtrack .... MGM (M) E 4252 — 4.00 — 6.00 — 8.00
Soundtrack .... MGM (S) SE 4252 — 6.00 — 9.00 — 12.00

CLAMBAKE (1967)
Soundtrack .... RCA (M) LPM 3893 — 20.00 — 40.00 — 60.00
Elvis Presley. Came with a photo loose inside.
Soundtrack .... RCA (S) LSP 3893 — 8.00 — 16.00 — 24.00

CLAMS ON THE HALF SHELL (1975)
Original Cast (Studio recordings from
The revue) .... Atlantic (S) SD 7238 — 2.00 — 3.00 — 4.00
Bette Midler, Lionel Hampton.
Original Cast (On tour, with additional material)
(2 records) .... Atlantic (S) SD 2 9000 — 3.00 — 4.50 — 6.00

CLARA (1960) (See: Beg, Borrow and Steal)

CLAUDINE
Soundtrack .... Up Front (S) UPF 130 — 2.00 — 3.00 — 4.00

CLEOPATRA (1963)
Soundtrack .... 20th Fox (M) FXG-5008 — 5.00 — 7.50 — 10.00
Soundtrack .... 20th Fox (S) SXG-5008 — 6.00 — 9.00 — 12.00

CLOCKWORK ORANGE
Soundtrack .... Warner Bros. (S) B-2573 — 4.00 — 6.00 — 8.00

CLOWN AND THE KIDS, THE (1968)
Soundtrack .... Golden (M) LP-215 — 5.00 — 7.50 — 10.00

CLOWN AROUND (1972)
Original Cast (Not identified) .... RCA (S) LSP 4741 — 75.00 — 112.50 — 150.00

CLOWNS, THE (1970)
Soundtrack .... Columbia (S) S-30772 — 4.00 — 6.00 — 8.00

C'MON LETS LIVE A LITTLE
Soundtrack .... Liberty (M) 3430 — 6.00 — 9.00 — 12.00
Soundtrack .... Liberty (S) 7430 — 7.00 — 11.00 — 15.00

COACH WITH THE SIX INSIDES (1967)
Original Cast .... ESP (M) 1019 — 5.00 — 7.50 — 10.00
Sheila Roy, Van Dexter, Anita Dangler.
Original Cast .... ESP (S) Disc 1019 — 7.50 — 11.25 — 15.00

COBWEB, THE (1955)
Soundtrack (1 Side) .... MGM (M) E-3501 — 25.00 — 37.50 — 50.00

COCO (1969)
Original Cast .... Paramount (S) PMS 1002 — 4.00 — 6.00 — 8.00
Katherine Hepburn, George Rose, Gale Dixon.

(M) Mono   (S) Stereo   (EP) Extended Play   (Q) Quad   (RI) Re-issued

TITLE	LABEL & NO.	GOOD	VERY GOOD	NEAR MINT
COLE (1975)				
Original Cast (2 records)	RCA (S) CRL 2 5054	2.00	3.00	4.00
The music of Cole Porter.				
COLETTE (1970)				
Original Cast	Mio (S) MCS 3001	12.00	18.00	24.00
Zoe Caldwell, Ruth Nelson, Keith Charles.				
COLLECTOR, THE (1965)				
Soundtrack	Mainstream (M) 56053	10.00	15.00	20.00
Soundtrack	Mainstream (S) S-6053	12.00	18.00	24.00
COLLEGE CONFIDENTIAL (1960)				
Soundtrack	Chancellor (M) 6015	5.00	7.50	10.00
Soundtrack	Chancellor (S) S-6015	6.00	9.00	12.00
COMANCHE (1956)				
Soundtrack	Coral (M) 57046	25.00	37.50	50.00
COME BLOW YOUR HORN (1963)				
Soundtrack	Reprise (M) R-6071	7.50	11.25	15.00
Soundtrack	Reprise (S) RS-6071	10.00	15.00	20.00
COMEDIANS, THE (1962)				
Soundtrack	MGM (M) 4494	4.00	6.00	8.00
Soundtrack	MGM (S) 4494	5.00	7.50	10.00
COMEDY IN MUSIC (1953)				
Original Cast	Columbia (M) CL 554	7.50	11.25	15.00
Victor Borge.				
Original Cast	Columbia (M) CL646	7.50	11.25	15.00
Victor Borge.				
Original Cast	MGM (M) E 3995P	7.50	11.25	15.00
Victor Borge.				
COME TOGETHER				
Soundtrack	Capitol-Apple (S) SW-3377	6.00	9.00	12.00
COMING OF CHRIST, THE (1960)				
TV Soundtrack	Decca (M) DL 9093	7.50	11.25	15.00
TV Soundtrack	Decca (S) DL 79093	10.00	15.00	20.00
COMMITTEE (1964)				
Original Cast (Skits written by the cast)	Reprise (M) R 2023	7.50	11.25	15.00
Scott Beach, Hamilton Camp, Garry Goddrow.				
Original Cast	Reprise (S) RS 2023	12.00	18.00	24.00
COMPANY (1970)				
Original Cast	Columbia (S) OS 3550	2.00	3.00	4.00
Dean Jones, Barbara Barrie, George Coe.				
Original Broadway & London Cast	CBS (S) 70108	10.00	15.00	20.00
Larry Kert replaces Jones.				
COMPULSION				
Soundtrack	20th Century Fox (EP) FEP-101	12.00	19.00	25.00

(M) Mono (S) Stereo (EP) Extended Play (Q) Quad (RI) Re-issued

TITLE	LABEL & NO.	GOOD	VERY GOOD	NEAR MINT
CONNECTICUT YANKEE (1927)				
Original Revival Cast (Re-issued from 78's)	JJA (M) 19733	2.00	3.00	4.00
Vivian Segal, Dick Foran, Julie Warren, Vera-Ellen.				
Soundtrack (1962)	Decca (M) DL 4261	5.00	7.50	10.00
Studio Cast (Side 1, "Rio Rita")	RCA (M) LK 1026	10.00	15.00	20.00
Earl Wrightson and Elaine Malbin.				
CONNECTION, THE (1959)				
Original Cast	Blue Note (M) 4027	5.00	7.50	10.00
Original Cast	Blue Note (S) 84027	7.50	11.25	15.00
CONNECTION, THE (1961)				
Original Cast	Parker (M) PLP 806	5.00	7.50	10.00
Score for the off-Broadway "play with music" conducted by composer Cecil Payne.				
Original Cast	Parker (S) PLP 8065	7.50	11.25	15.00
CONSUL, THE (1950)				
Original Cast (2 records)	Decca (M) DX 101	20.00	30.00	40.00
Marie Powers, Patricia Neway, Gloria Lane.				
CONTINENTAL TWIST, THE (1961)				
Soundtrack	Capitol (M) T-1677	4.00	6.00	8.00
Soundtrack	Capitol (S) ST-1677	5.00	7.50	10.00
CONVERSATION PIECE (1934)				
Original London Cast (With original cast star)				
(1 side)	Monmouth Evergreen MES 7062 3	2.00	3.00	4.00
Noel Coward, Yvonne Printempa, George Sanders, Louis Hayward.				
Studio Cast (With original cast star)				
(1951) (2 records)	Columbia (M) L 163	18.00	27.00	36.00
Noel Coward, Lily Pons, Richard Burton.				
COOL BREEZE				
Soundtrack	MGM (S) ISE 35	3.00	4.00	6.00
COOL HAND LUKE (1967)				
Soundtrack	Dot (M) 3833	5.00	7.50	10.00
Soundtrack	Dot (S) 25833	7.50	11.25	15.00
COOL WORLD, THE (1964)				
Soundtrack	Philips (M) 200-138	6.00	9.00	12.00
Soundtrack	Philips (S) 600-138	7.50	11.25	15.00
CORRUPT ONES				
Soundtrack	United Artists (M) 4158	10.00	15.00	20.00
Soundtrack	United Artists (S) 5158	12.00	19.00	25.00
COTTON CLUB REVUE OF 1958 (1958)				
Original Cast Star (Side 2, Cab Calloway standards)	Gone (M) GLP 101	25.00	37.50	50.00
All Cab Calloway.				
COTTON COMES TO HARLEM				
Soundtrack	United Artists (S) 5211	3.00	4.00	6.00
COUNTESS FROM HONG KONG, THE (1967)				
Soundtrack	Decca (M) 1501	4.00	6.00	8.00
Soundtrack	Decca (S) 7-1501	5.00	7.50	10.00
COUNTRY COUSIN (1936)				
Soundtrack (With dialogue) (1959)	Disneyland (M) ST-1903	6.00	9.00	12.00
Soundtrack (With dialogue) (1967)	Disneyland (M) DQ-1306	4.00	6.00	8.00
COURT JESTER, THE (1956)				
Soundtrack	Decca (M) DL-8212	18.00	24.00	36.00
COWARDY (sic) CUSTARD (1973)				
Original London Cast	RCA (S) LSO 6010	2.00	3.00	4.00
The music of Noel Coward.				
COWBOY (1958)				
Soundtrack	Decca (M) DL-8684	15.00	22.50	30.00
CRADLE WILL ROCK (1937)				
Original Cast	American Legion (M) T 1001	12.00	18.00	24.00
Howard daSilva, Edward Fuller, Olive Stanton.				
Original Revival Cast (1965) (2 records)	MGM (M) E 4289 2	6.00	9.00	12.00
Jerry Orbach, Lauri Peters, Nancy Andrews.				
Original Revival Cast	MGM (S) SE 4289 2	7.50	11.25	15.00
CRANKS (1956)				
Original Cast & Original London Cast	HMV (M) CLP 1082	75.00	112.50	150.00
Annie Ross, Anthony Newley, Hugh Bryant, Gilbert Vernon.				
CRICKET ON THE HEARTH, A (1967)				
TV Soundtrack	RCA (M) LOC 1140	7.50	11.25	15.00
TV Soundtrack	RCA (S) LSO 1140	10.00	15.00	20.00

CRIME IN THE STREETS (1956)
Soundtrack (1 Side) . . . . Decca (M) DL-8376 10.00 15.00 20.00

CROMWELL
Soundtrack . . . . Capitol (S) SW 640 6.00 9.00 12.00

CROSS AND THE SWITCHBLADE, THE (1970)
Soundtrack . . . . Light (S) 5550 6.00 9.00 12.00

CRYER AND FORD (1975)
Original Cast (Manhattan Theatre Club) . . . . RCA (S) APL 1 1235 2.00 3.00 4.00
Gretchen Cryer and Nancy Ford.

CRY FOR US ALL (1970)
Original Cast . . . . Project 3 (S) TS 1000 2.00 3.00 4.00
Joan Diener, Robert Weede, Steve Arlen, Tommy Rall.

CUSTER OF THE WEST
Soundtrack . . . . ABC (M) OC-5 6.00 9.00 12.00
Soundtrack . . . . ABC (S) OCS-5 7.00 11.00 15.00

CYCLE SAVAGES (1970)
Soundtrack . . . . American Int'l (S) ST-A-1033 4.00 6.00 8.00

CYRANO (1973)
Original Cast (2 records) . . . . A&M (S) SP 3702 3.00 4.50 6.00
Christopher Plummer, Leigh Berry, Mark Lamos.

D

DAKTARI (1966)
TV Soundtrack (With Dialogue) . . . . Leo (M) CH-1043 5.00 7.50 10.00
TV Soundtrack (1968) . . . . Atlantic (M) 8157 4.00 6.00 8.00
TV Soundtrack . . . . Atlantic (S) SD-8157 5.00 7.50 10.00

DAMES AT SEA (1969)
Original Cast . . . . Columbia (S) OS 3330 2.00 3.00 4.00
David Christmas, Steve Elmore, Tamara Long.
Original London Cast . . . . CBS (S) 70063 10.00 15.00 20.00
Joyce Blair, Blayne Barrington, Rita Burton.

DAMNED, THE
Soundtrack . . . . Warner Bros. (S) 1829 4.00 6.00 8.00

DAMN THE DEFIANT
Soundtrack . . . . Colpix (M) CP 511 7.00 11.00 15.00
Soundtrack . . . . Colpix (S) SCP 511 10.00 15.00 20.00

DAMN YANKEES (1955)
Original Cast (With original green cover) . . . . RCA (M) LOC 1021 15.00 22.50 30.00
Gwen Verdon, Stephen Douglass, Ray Walston, Jean Stapleton.
Original Cast (Re-channeled stereo) . . . . RCA (S) LSO 1021 2.00 3.00 4.00
Soundtrack (From the 1958 film) . . . . RCA (M) LOC 1047 10.00 15.00 20.00
Gwen Verdon, Tab Hunter, Ray Walston.

DANGER (1951)
TV Soundtrack (10") . . . . MGM (M) E-111 12.00 18.00 24.00

DANGEROUS CHRISTMAS OF RED RIDING HOOD (1965)
RIDING HOOD
TV Soundtrack . . . . ABC (M) ABC 536 7.50 11.25 15.00
TV Soundtrack . . . . ABC (S) ABCS 536 10.00 15.00 20.00

DARBY O'GILL AND THE LITTLE PEOPLE (1959)
Soundtrack (With dialogue) . . . . Disneyland (M) ST-1901 6.00 9.00 12.00

DARK OF THE SUN (1968)
Soundtrack . . . . MGM (M) E-4544 12.00 18.00 24.00
Soundtrack . . . . MGM (S) SE-4544 15.00 22.50 30.00

DARK SHADOWS (1969)
TV Soundtrack . . . . Philips (S) 600-314 4.00 6.00 8.00

DARLING (1965)
Soundtrack . . . . Epic (M) LN-24195 6.00 9.00 12.00
Soundtrack . . . . Epic (S) BN-26195 7.50 11.25 15.00

DARLING LILI
Soundtrack . . . . RCA (S) LSPX 1000 3.00 4.00 6.00

(M) Mono (S) Stereo (EP) Extended Play (Q) Quad (RI) Re-issued

---

DARLING OF THE DAY (1968)
Original Cast . . . . RCA (M) LOC 1149 7.50 11.25 15.00
Vincent Price, Patricia Routledge, Brenda Forbes.
Original Cast . . . . RCA (S) LSO 1149 10.00 15.00 20.00

DAVID AND LISA (1963)
Soundtrack . . . . Ava (M) A-21 6.00 9.00 12.00
Soundtrack . . . . Ava (S) AS-21 7.50 11.25 15.00

DAVY CROCKETT (1955)
Soundtrack . . . . Columbia (M) CL-666 10.00 15.00 20.00
Soundtrack (With Dialogue) (1962) . . . . Disneyland (M) WDA-3602 5.00 7.50 10.00

DAYDREAMER, THE
Soundtrack . . . . Columbia (M) OL 6540 6.00 9.00 12.00
Soundtrack . . . . Columbia (S) OS 1940 7.50 11.25 15.00

DAY OF ANGER
Soundtrack . . . . RCA (S) LSO 1165 4.00 6.00 8.00

DAY OF THE DOLPHIN, THE (1973)
Soundtrack . . . . Avco Embassy (S) AV-11014 10.00 15.00 20.00

DAY THE FISH CAME OUT
Soundtrack . . . . 20th Century Fox (M) 4194 6.00 9.00 12.00
Soundtrack . . . . 20th Century Fox (S) 4194 7.50 11.25 15.00

DAYS OF WILFRED OWEN, THE (1966)
Soundtrack (With dialogue) . . . . Warner Bros. (M) B-1635 5.00 7.50 10.00
Soundtrack . . . . Warner Bros. (S) BS-1635 6.00 9.00 12.00

DEADFALL
Soundtrack . . . . 20th Century Fox (S) 4203 12.00 18.00 24.00

DEAD RINGER (1964)
Soundtrack . . . . Warner Bros. (M) W-1536 6.00 9.00 12.00
Soundtrack . . . . Warner Bros. (S) WS-1536 7.50 11.25 15.00

DEADLY AFFAIR, THE (1967)
Soundtrack . . . . Verve (M) 8679-ST 4.00 6.00 8.00
Soundtrack . . . . Verve (S) 6-8679-ST 5.00 7.50 10.00

DEAR JOHN
Soundtrack . . . . Dunhill (M) 55001 5.00 7.00 10.00
Soundtrack . . . . Dunhill (S) 55001 6.00 9.00 12.00

DEAR WORLD (1969)
Original Cast . . . . Columbia (S) BOS 3260 5.00 7.50 10.00
Angela Lansbury, Jane Connell, Carmen Mathews.

DEATH OF A SALESMAN (1949)
Original Cast (Incidental music) (2 records) . . . . Decca (M) DX 102 12.00 18.00 24.00

DEATH WISH
Soundtrack . . . . Columbia (S) PC-33199 3.00 5.00 7.00

DECLINE & FALL OF THE ENTIRE WORLD AS SEEN THROUGH THE EYES OF COLE PORTER, THE (1965)
Original Cast . . . . Columbia (M) OL 6410 6.00 9.00 12.00
Kaye Ballard, Harold Lang, Carmen Alvarez.

TITLE	LABEL & NO.	GOOD	VERY GOOD	NEAR MINT
Original Cast	Columbia (S) OS 2810	7.50	11.25	15.00
Studio Cast (With original cast star)	RIC (S) ST 3002	2.00	3.00	4.00

This album inspired the off Broadway revue and the balance of the show was issued by Columbia. Kaye Ballard, David Allen, Ronny Graham.

DEEP IN MY HEART (1954)
Soundtrack	MGM (M) E-3153	10.00	15.00	20.00

DEEP THROAT, PART II (1974)
Soundtrack	Bryan (S) BRS-101	3.00	4.50	6.00

DELIVERANCE
Soundtrack	Warner Bros. (S) B-2683	3.00	4.00	6.00

DEMI DOZEN (1957)
Original Cast	Offbeat (M) O 4015	10.00	15.00	20.00

Jean Arnold, Ceil Cabot, Jane Connell, Jack Fletcher.

DENNIS THE MENACE
Soundtrack	Colpix (M) CP-204	3.00	4.00	6.00

DE SADE (1969)
Soundtrack	Tower (S) 5170	6.00	9.00	12.00

DESERT SONG (1926)
Original London Cast (Side 2, "The Student Prince")	Monmouth Evergreen (M) MES 7054	2.00	3.00	4.00
Edith Day, Harry Welchman, Dennis Hoey.				
Soundtrack (10") (1952)	RCA (M) LPM 3105	7.50	11.25	15.00
Soundtrack (10") (1953)	Capitol (M) L 351	7.50	11.25	15.00
Soundtrack (1 side) (1953)	Capitol (M) T 354	5.00	7.50	10.00
Soundtrack (1963)	Capitol (M) W 1842	4.00	6.00	8.00
Soundtrack	Capitol (S) SW 1842	5.00	7.50	10.00
Studio Cast	Columbia (M) CL 831	5.00	7.50	10.00

Nelson Eddy, Doretta Morrow, Lee Cass.

DESIRE UNDER THE ELMS (1958)
Soundtrack	Dot (M) 3095	20.00	30.00	40.00

DESTINATION MOON (1950)
Soundtrack (10") (Stevens Conducting)	Columbia (M) CL-6151	15.00	22.50	30.00
Soundtrack (Sandauer Conducting) (1959)	Omega (M) 1003	20.00	30.00	40.00
Soundtrack	Omega (S) OSL-3	30.00	45.00	60.00

DESTRY RIDES AGAIN (1959)
Original Cast	Decca (M) DL 9075	10.00	15.00	20.00
Andy Griffith, Dolores Gray, Scott Brady.				
Original Cast	Decca (S) DL 79075	15.00	22.50	30.00
Studio Cast	RCA (M) CAL 540	4.00	6.00	8.00
Louise O'Brien and Jack Haskell.				

DEVIL & DANIEL WEBSTER, THE (1939)
Studio Cast	Desto (S) 6450	2.00	3.00	4.00
Lawrence Winters, Joel Blankenship, Doris Young.				

DEVIL AT 4 O'CLOCK, THE
Soundtrack	Colpix (M) CP-509	12.00	19.00	25.00
Soundtrack	Colpix (S) SCP-509	15.00	22.00	30.00

DEVILS ANGELS
Soundtrack	Tower (M) T-5074	5.00	7.00	10.00
Soundtrack	Tower (S) DT-5074	6.00	9.00	12.00

DEVIL'S BRIGADE, THE (1968)
Soundtrack (Holmes Conducting)	United Artists (M) UAL-3654	3.00	4.50	6.00
Soundtrack	United Artists (S) UAS-6654	4.00	6.00	8.00

DEVIL'S 8
Soundtrack	Tower (S) 5160	4.00	6.00	8.00

DIAMOND HEAD (1963)
Soundtrack	Colpix (M) CP-440	4.00	6.00	8.00
Soundtrack	Colpix (S) SCP-440	5.00	7.50	10.00

DIAMONDS ARE FOREVER
Soundtrack	United Artists (S) 5220	3.00	4.00	6.00
Soundtrack	United Artists (S) UA-LA301-G	3.00	4.00	6.00

DIAMOND STUDS (1975)
Original & Studio Cast (7" LP)	Pasquotank (S) PS 33 7 003	7.50	11.25	15.00
Composers Jim Wann and Bland Simpson of the original cast and Cass Morgan, not in the show.				

DIARY OF ANNE FRANK, THE (1959)
Soundtrack	20th Century Fox (M) 3012	12.00	18.00	24.00
Soundtrack	20th Century Fox (S) SFX-3012	15.00	22.50	30.00

(M) Mono (S) Stereo (EP) Extended Play (Q) Quad (RI) Re-issued

TITLE	LABEL & NO.	GOOD	VERY GOOD	NEAR MINT

DILLINGER (1973)
Soundtrack	MCA (S) 360	3.00	4.50	6.00

DIME A DOZEN (1962)
Original Cast (2 records)	Cadence (M) 3063 (2)	7.50	11.25	15.00
Gerry Matthews, Jack Fletcher, Mary Louise Wilson.				
Original Cast	Cadence (S) CLP 25063 (2)	12.00	18.00	24.00

DINGAKA (1965)
Soundtrack	Mercury (M) MG-21013	6.00	8.00	12.00
Soundtrack	Mercury (S) SR-61013	7.50	11.25	15.00

DINO (1957)
Soundtrack	Epic (M) LN-3404	15.00	22.50	30.00

DIRTY DINGUS MAGEE
Soundtrack	MGM (S) ISE 24	3.00	4.00	6.00

DIRTY DOZEN, THE
Soundtrack	MGM (M) 4445	7.00	11.00	15.00
Soundtrack	MGM (S) 4445	10.00	15.00	20.00

DIRTY FEET (1965)
Soundtrack	Fink (M) 1007	6.00	9.00	12.00

DIRTY GAME, THE (1966)
Soundtrack	Laurie (M) 2034	5.00	7.50	10.00
Soundtrack	Laurie (S) S-2034	6.00	9.00	12.00

DIVORCE AMERICAN STYLE
Soundtrack	United Artists (M) 4163	5.00	7.00	10.00
Soundtrack	United Artists (S) 5163	6.00	9.00	12.00

DIVORCE ITALIAN STYLE (1962)
Soundtrack	United Artists (M) UAL-4106	5.00	7.50	10.00
Soundtrack	United Artists (S) UAS-5106	6.00	9.00	12.00

DOCTOR DOLITTLE
Soundtrack	20th Century Fox (M) 5101	3.00	4.50	6.00
Soundtrack	20th Century Fox (S) 5101	4.00	6.00	8.00

DR. GOLDFOOT AND THE GIRL BOMBS (1966)
Soundtrack	Tower (M) T-5053	4.00	6.00	8.00
Soundtrack	Tower (S) DT-5053e	5.00	7.50	10.00

191

DR. NO (1963)
Soundtrack.....................United Artists (S) UAS-5108 — 5.00 — 7.50 — 10.00

DOCTOR PHIBES (1971)
Soundtrack (Alternate Title: The Abominable
  Dr. Phibes)......................American Int'l (S) ST-A-1040 — 5.00 — 7.50 — 10.00

DR. SELAVY'S MAGIC THEATRE (1972)
Original Cast (1974)...............United Artists (S) LA 196 G — 5.00 — 7.50 — 10.00
  Denise Delapenha, Mary Delson, Jessica Harper.

DOG OF FLANDERS, A (1959)
Soundtrack.....................20th Century Fox (M) 3026 — 20.00 — 30.00 — 40.00
Soundtrack.....................20th Century Fox (S) S-3026 — 30.00 — 45.00 — 60.00

DO I HEAR A WALTZ? (1965)
Original Cast......................Columbia (M) OL 6370 — 4.00 — 6.00 — 8.00
  Elizabeth Allen, Sergio Franchi, Madeleine Sherwood.
Original Cast......................Columbia (S) OS 2770 — 5.00 — 7.50 — 10.00

DOLCE VITA, LA (Sweet Life, The) (1961)
Soundtrack...........................RCA (M) FOC-1 — 10.00 — 15.00 — 20.00
Soundtrack...........................RCA (S) FSO-1 — 15.00 — 22.50 — 30.00

DOLLARS (1971)
Soundtrack.........................Reprise (S) RS-2051 — 3.00 — 4.50 — 6.00

DONNYBROOK! (1961)
Original Cast.......................Kapp (M) KDL 8500 — 10.00 — 15.00 — 20.00
  Eddie Foy, Art Lund, Joan Fagan, Susan Johnson.
Original Cast.......................Kapp (S) KDS 8500 — 12.00 — 18.00 — 24.00

DON'T BOTHER ME I CAN'T COPE (1972)
Original Cast.......................Polydor (S) PD 6013 — 2.00 — 3.00 — 4.00
  Alex Bradford, Hope Clarke, Bobby Hill.

DON'T KNOCK THE TWIST (1962)
Soundtrack.........................Parkway (M) P-7011 — 7.50 — 11.25 — 15.00

DON'T MAKE WAVES (1967)
Soundtrack............................MGM (M) 4483 — 4.00 — 6.00 — 8.00
Soundtrack............................MGM (S) 4483 — 5.00 — 7.50 — 10.00

DON'T PLAY US CHEAP (1972)
Original Cast & Soundtrack (2 records).........Stax (S) STS 2 3006 — 7.50 — 11.25 — 15.00
  Thomas Anderson, Joshie Jo Armstead, Nate Barnett.

DO RE MI (1960)
Original Cast.......................RCA (M) LOCD 2002 — 10.00 — 15.00 — 20.00
  Phil Silvers, Nancy Walker, John Reardon.
Original Cast.......................RCA (S) LSOD 2002 — 18.00 — 27.00 — 36.00
Original Cast (1965)...............RCA (M) LOC 1105 — 6.00 — 9.00 — 12.00
Original Cast......................RCA (S) LSO 1105 — 10.00 — 15.00 — 20.00
Original London Cast...............Decca (M) LK 4413 — 12.00 — 18.00 — 24.00
  Max Bygraves, Maggie Fitzgibbon, Steve Arlen.

DOUBLE TROUBLE (1967)
Soundtrack..........................RCA (M) LPM 3787 — 11.00 — 22.00 — 33.00
  Elvis Presley. Came with a bonus photo loose inside. Also issued with a
  different cover that replaced the ad for the bonus photo with the LP title.
Soundtrack..........................RCA (S) LSP 3787 — 10.00 — 20.00 — 30.00
  —For more information, see PRESLEY, Elvis in the regular listings.

DOVE, THE (1974)
Soundtrack.........................ABC (S) ABDP-352 — 3.00 — 4.50 — 6.00

DOWN IN THE VALLEY (1948)
Original Cast (1950) (10")...............RCA (M) LM 16 — 12.00 — 18.00 — 24.00
TV Soundtrack (1 side) (Production and star of premiere in 1948 at
  the University of Indiana).............RCA (M) LPV 503 — 10.00 — 15.00 — 20.00
  Marion Bell, William McGraw, Kenneth Smith, Ray Jacquemot.
Studio Cast...........................Decca (M) DL 4239 — 10.00 — 15.00 — 20.00
  Alfred Drake, Jane Wilson, Daniel Slick, Norman Atkins.

DRAGNET (1953)
TV Soundtrack (With Dialogue) (10").........RCA (M) LPM-3199 — 18.00 — 27.00 — 36.00

DRAMATIC SELECTIONS
Soundtrack.............................MGM (M) IE 3 — 6.00 — 9.00 — 12.00
Soundtrack............................MGM (S) SI E 3 — 7.00 — 11.00 — 15.00

DRANGO (1957)
Soundtrack.........................Liberty (M) LRP-3036 — 20.00 — 30.00 — 40.00

DREAM OF KINGS, A (1969)
Soundtrack....................National General (S) MG-1000 — 4.00 — 6.00 — 8.00

(M) Mono (S) Stereo (EP) Extended Play (Q) Quad (RI) Re-issued

DRESSED TO THE NINES (1960)
Original Cast...........................MGM (M) E 3914 — 5.00 — 7.50 — 10.00
  Ceil Cabot, Gordon Connell, Bill Hinnant, Gerry Matthews.
Original Cast...........................MGM (S) SE 3914 — 7.50 — 11.25 — 15.00

DUCK YOU SUCKER (1972)
Soundtrack.....................United Artists (S) UAS-5221 — 4.00 — 6.00 — 8.00

DUDE (1972)
Original Cast (Off Broadway)
  (Limited release)...............Kilmarnock (S) KIL 72007 — 7.50 — 11.25 — 15.00
  Nell Carter, Nat Morris, Jim Farrell.
Original Cast (Volume II)..............Kilmarnock (S) KIL 72003 — 7.50 — 11.25 — 15.00

DUEL AT DIABLO (1966)
Soundtrack.....................United Artists (M) UAL-4139 — 3.00 — 4.50 — 6.00
Soundtrack.....................United Artists (S) UAS-5139 — 4.00 — 6.00 — 8.00

DUMBO (1941)
Soundtrack (1957)..................Disneyland (M) WDL 4013 — 5.00 — 7.50 — 10.00

DUNWICH HORROR, THE (1970)
Soundtrack (Limited release)..............American Int'l (S) A-1028 — 12.00 — 18.00 — 24.00

DUSTY & SWEETS MCGEE
Soundtrack.........................Warner Bros. (S) 1936 — 3.00 — 4.00 — 6.00

DYLAN (1964)
Original Cast (Incidental music) (3 records) . Columbia (M) DOL 301 (3) — 6.00 — 9.00 — 12.00
Original Cast (Incidental music) (3 records) . Columbia (S) DOS 701 (3) — 7.50 — 11.25 — 15.00

DYNAMITE BROTHERS
Soundtrack.........................Prestige (S) 10082 — 3.00 — 4.00 — 6.00

E

EARL OF RUSTON (1971)
Original Cast (Sung by the show's composers and members of the cast
  of the musical, "Salvation").................Capitol (S) ST 465 — 12.00 — 18.00 — 24.00
  Peter Link, C.C. Courtney, Leecy R. Woods, Yolande Bavan, Boni
  Enten, Marta Heflin.

EARTHQUAKE (1973)
Original Los Angeles Cast..............Inner City (S) LRS RT 6075 — 7.50 — 11.25 — 15.00
  Bernie Cowens, Karmello Brooks, Lupe Zuniga, Rod Perry.
Soundtrack...............................MCA (S) 2081 — 3.00 — 5.00 — 7.00

EAST OF EDEN (1955)
Soundtrack.........................Columbia (M) CL-940 — 12.00 — 18.00 — 24.00

EASTER PARADE (1948)
Soundtrack (1950) (10")...............MGM (M) E-502 — 7.50 — 11.25 — 15.00
Soundtrack (1955)....................MGM (M) E-3227 — 5.00 — 7.50 — 10.00

EAST SIDE, WEST SIDE (1963)
TV Soundtrack.......................Columbia (M) CL-2123 — 7.50 — 11.25 — 15.00
TV Soundtrack.......................Columbia (S) CS-8923 — 10.00 — 15.00 — 20.00

EASY COME, EASY GO (1967)
Soundtrack...........................RCA (EP) EPA 4387 — 5.00 — 10.00 — 15.00
  Elvis Presley. RCA dog logo on the side of the label is the first release.
Soundtrack (White label promo. copy).........RCA (EP) EPA 4387 — 3.00 — 6.00 — 9.00
  This is the only Elvis Presley EP that had a specially pressed promo copy.
  —For more information, see PRESLEY, Elvis in the regular listings.

EASY RIDER (1969)
Soundtrack (Traditional Rock).................Dunhill (S) 50063 — 6.00 — 9.00 — 12.00

ECCO (1965)
Soundtrack.........................Warner Bros. (M) W-1600 — 5.00 — 7.50 — 10.00
Soundtrack.........................Warner Bros. (S) WS-1600 — 6.00 — 9.00 — 12.00

EDDIE CANTOR AT CARNEGIE HALL (1950)
Original Cast.......................Audio Fidelity (M) 702 — 2.00 — 3.00 — 4.00
  Eddie Cantor.

EDDIE CANTOR STORY, THE (1954)
Soundtrack (10") (Traditional Pop)...........Capitol (M) L-467 — 15.00 — 22.50 — 30.00

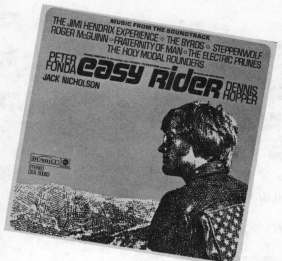

TITLE	LABEL & NO.	GOOD	VERY GOOD	NEAR MINT

EDGE OF THE CITY (1957)
Soundtrack (1 Side) . . . . *MGM (M) E-3501* 25.00 37.50 50.00

EDUCATION OF SONNY CARSON
Soundtrack . . . . *Paramount (S) 1045* 3.00 4.00 6.00

EGYPTIAN, THE (1954)
Soundtrack . . . . *Decca (M) DL-9014* 4.00 6.00 8.00
Soundtrack (Re-channeled stereo) . . . . *Decca (S) DL79014* 3.00 4.50 6.00

8½ (1963)
Soundtrack . . . . *RCA (M) FOC-6* 12.00 18.00 24.00
Soundtrack . . . . *RCA (S) FSO-6* 15.00 22.50 30.00

8 ON THE LAM
Soundtrack . . . . *United Artists (M) 4156* 5.00 7.00 10.00
Soundtrack . . . . *United Artists (S) 5156* 6.00 9.00 12.00

EILEEN (1917)
Studio Cast (Side 1, "Polonaise") . . . . *RCA (M) CAL 210* 12.00 18.00 24.00
Earl Wrightson, Jimmy Carroll, Frances Greer.

EL CID (1961)
Soundtrack . . . . *MGM (M) E-3977* 12.00 18.00 24.00
Soundtrack . . . . *MGM (S) SE-3977* 15.00 22.50 30.00

EL DORADO (1967)
Soundtrack . . . . *Epic (M) 13114* 15.00 22.50 30.00
Soundtrack . . . . *Epic (S) 15114* 20.00 30.00 40.00

ELECTRA GLIDE IN BLUE (1973)
Soundtrack (2 records) . . . . *United Artists (S) LA-062-H* 3.00 4.50 6.00

ELEPHANT CALF, THE (1967)
Original Cast . . . . *Asch (M) FL 9831* 7.50 11.25 15.00
James Antonio, Hilda Brauner, Beeson Carroll, Logan Ramsey.

ELEPHANT CALLED SLOWLY, AN (1971)
Soundtrack . . . . *Bell (S) 1202* 3.00 4.00 6.00

ELEPHANT STEPS (1970)
Original Cast (2 records) . . . . *Columbia (S) M2X 33044* 2.00 3.00 4.00
Karen Altman, Susan Belling, Luther Enstad.

ELEVEN AGAINST THE ICE (1958)
TV Soundtrack . . . . *RCA (M) LPM-1618* 12.00 18.00 24.00

EL GRANDE DE COCA COLA (1973)
Original Cast (7" LP) (Written by the cast) . . . . *Bottle Cap (S) BC 1001* 10.00 15.00 20.00
Ron House, Alan Shearman, John Neville-Andrews.

ELIZABETH TAYLOR IN LONDON (1963)
TV Soundtrack . . . . *Colpix (M) CP-459* 7.50 11.25 15.00
TV Soundtrack . . . . *Colpix (S) SCP-459* 10.00 15.00 20.00

ELMER GANTRY
Soundtrack (1 side) . . . . *United Artists (M) DF-6* 9.00 13.50 18.00
Soundtrack . . . . *United Artists (S) DFS-56* 12.00 18.00 24.00
Soundtrack . . . . *United Artists (M) UAL 4069* 12.00 18.00 24.00
Soundtrack . . . . *United Artists (S) UAS 5069* 15.00 22.50 30.00

(M) Mono (S) Stereo (EP) Extended Play (Q) Quad (RI) Re-issued

TITLE	LABEL & NO.	GOOD	VERY GOOD	NEAR MINT

ELSA LANCHESTER HERSELF (1961)
Original Cast . . . . *Verve (M) 15024* 7.50 11.25 15.00
Elsa Lanchester.
Original Cast . . . . *Tradition (S) 2065* 4.00 6.00 8.00
Elsa Lanchester.
Original Cast . . . . *Tradition (S) 2091* 4.00 6.00 8.00
Elsa Lanchester.

EL TOPO (1972)
Soundtrack . . . . *Capitol-Apple (S) SW-3388* 4.00 6.00 8.00

ELVIS, ALOHA FROM HAWAII VIA SATELLITE (1973)
TV Soundtrack . . . . *RCA (Q) VPSX 6089* 3.00 6.00 9.00
Elvis Presley. Double LP one cover reads stereo, but is in quadrasonic.
The other reads "Quad."
TV Soundtrack . . . . *RCA (S) R 213736* 5.00 10.00 15.00
Stereo two record set available through the RCA Record Club. It has a
slight cover variation from the commercial release. It was also only is-
sued in stereo, not quad.
TV Soundtrack . . . . *RCA (EP) DTFO 2006* 6.00 12.00 18.00
"Stereo Album EP" contains six songs. Designed for jukebox play.
TV Soundtrack . . . . *RCA (Q) UPSX 6089* 450.00 675.00 900.00
Sneak preview LP made in very limited quantity for executives at "Chicken
Of The Sea" Tuna Company, who sponsored the "Aloha From Hawaii" TV
Broadcast April 4, 1973. This LP had a special "Chicken Of The Sea" in-
signia on the front of the album cover, and came with a printed insert
which contained ad schedules for the company for 1973...as well as a
picture of Elvis.

EMIL & THE DETECTIVES
Soundtrack . . . . *Disneyland (M) DO-1262* 6.00 9.00 12.00
Soundtrack . . . . *Disneyland (S) 1262* 7.50 11.25 15.00

ENDLESS SUMMER, THE (1966)
Soundtrack . . . . *World Pacific (M) WP-1832* 5.00 7.50 10.00
Soundtrack . . . . *World Pacific (S) ST-1832* 7.50 11.25 15.00

ENTER LAUGHING (1967)
Soundtrack . . . . *Liberty (M) LOM16004* 4.00 6.00 8.00
Soundtrack . . . . *Liberty (S) LOS17004* 5.00 7.50 10.00

ERIC SOYA'S 17 (1967)
Soundtrack . . . . *Mercury (M) 21115* 2.00 3.00 4.00
Soundtrack . . . . *Mercury (S) 61115* 3.00 4.50 6.00

ERNEST IN LOVE (1960)
Original Cast . . . . *Columbia (M) OL 5530* 15.00 22.50 30.00
Leila Martin, John Irving, Gerrianne Raphael, Louis Admonds.
Original Cast . . . . *Columbia (S) OS 2027* 20.00 30.00 40.00

ESTABLISHMENT (1963)
Original Cast (Skits written by the cast and
Peter Cook) . . . . *Riverside (M) RM 850* 10.00 15.00 20.00
John Bird, Eleanor Bron, John Fortune, Jeremy Geidt.
Original London Cast (Same as above) . . . . *Parlophone (M) 1198* 10.00 15.00 20.00

EVENING WITH BEATRICE LILLIE, AN (1952)
Original Cast . . . . *London (M) LL 1373* 10.00 15.00 20.00
Beatrice Lillie.
Original Cast . . . . *AMR (M) 302* 2.00 3.00 4.00
Beatrice Lillie.

EVENING WITH DIANA ROSS, AN (1976)
Original Cast (2 records) . . . . *Motown (S) M7 877R2* 3.00 4.50 6.00
Diana Ross, Brenda, Shirley and Valorie Jones.

TITLE	LABEL & NO.	GOOD	VERY GOOD	NEAR MINT
EVENING WITH MIKE NICHOLS & ELAINE MAY, AN (1960)				
Original Cast (Excerpts from the Broadway production)	Mercury (S) SR 60865	6.00	9.00	12.00
EVENING WITH RICHARD NIXON, AN (1972)				
Original Cast (A play with music)	Ode (S) SP 77015	5.00	7.50	10.00
The Salvia Sisters, Gene Rupert, Humbert Allen Astredo.				
EVERYTHING I HAVE IS YOURS (1952)				
Soundtrack (10")	MGM (M) E-187	6.00	9.00	12.00
EXODUS				
Soundtrack	RCA (M) LOC 1058	3.00	4.50	6.00
Soundtrack	RCA (S) LSO 1058	3.00	4.50	6.00
EXPERIMENT IN TERROR				
Soundtrack	RCA (M) LPM-2442	7.50	11.25	15.00
Soundtrack	RCA (S) LSP 2442	10.00	15.00	20.00

F

TITLE	LABEL & NO.	GOOD	VERY GOOD	NEAR MINT
FACE IN THE CROWD, A (1957)				
Soundtrack	Capitol (M) W-872	12.00	18.00	24.00
FACES (1968)				
Soundtrack	Columbia (S) OS-3290	3.00	4.50	6.00
FADE OUT FADE IN (1964)				
Original Cast	ABC (M) C 3	7.50	11.25	15.00
Carol Burnett, Jack Cassidy, Dick Patterson, Tina Louise.				
Original Cast	ABC (S) SOC 3	10.00	15.00	20.00
FAMILY AFFAIR, A (1962)				
Original Cast	United Artists (M) UAL 4099	10.00	15.00	20.00
Shelley Berman, Eileen Heckart, Morris Carnovsky, Larry Kert.				
Original Cast	United Artists (S) UAS 5099	15.00	22.50	30.00
FAMILY WAY, THE (1967)				
Soundtrack (Paul McCartney, Composer)	London (M) M-76007	10.00	15.00	20.00
Soundtrack	London (S) MS-82007	12.00	18.00	24.00

TITLE	LABEL & NO.	GOOD	VERY GOOD	NEAR MINT
FALL OF THE ROMAN EMPIRE				
Soundtrack	Columbia (M) OL 6060	15.00	22.00	30.00
Soundtrack	Columbia (S) OS 2460	17.00	26.00	35.00
FANNY (1954)				
Original Cast	RCA (M) LOC 1015	5.00	7.50	10.00
Ezio Pinza, Walter Slezak, Florence Henderson.				
Original Cast (Re-channeled stereo)	RCA (S) LSO 1015	2.00	3.00	4.00
Soundtrack (From the 1961 film)	Warner Bros. (M) W 1416	7.50	11.25	15.00
Soundtrack	Warner Bros. (S) WS 1416	10.00	15.00	20.00
FANTASTIC PLASTIC MACHINE				
Soundtrack	Epic (S) 26469	4.00	6.00	8.00
FANTASTICKS (1960)				
Original Cast	MGM (M) E 3872	2.00	3.00	4.00
Kenneth Nelson, Jerry Orbach, Rita Gardner.				
Original Cast	MGM (S) SE 3872	2.00	3.00	4.00

(M) Mono (S) Stereo (EP) Extended Play (Q) Quad (RI) Re-issued

TITLE	LABEL & NO.	GOOD	VERY GOOD	NEAR MINT
FAR FROM THE MADDING CROWD (1967)				
Soundtrack	MGM (M) 1E-11-ST	5.00	7.50	10.00
Soundtrack	MGM (S) S1E-11ST	6.00	9.00	12.00
FAREWELL TO ARMS, A (1957)				
Soundtrack	Capitol (M) W-918	18.00	27.00	36.00
FASTEST GUITAR ALIVE, THE (1967)				
Soundtrack (Roy Orbison)	MGM (M) E-4475	5.00	7.50	10.00
Soundtrack	MGM (S) SE-4475	6.00	9.00	12.00
FATHOM (1967)				
Soundtrack	20th Century Fox (M) 4195	7.50	11.25	15.00
Soundtrack	20th Century Fox (S) S-4195	10.00	15.00	20.00
FELLINI SATYRICON (1969)				
Soundtrack	United Artists (S) UAS-5203	4.00	6.00	8.00
FELLINI'S ROMA (1972)				
Soundtrack	United Artists (S) LA-052-F	4.00	6.00	8.00
FEMALE PRISONER, THE (1969)				
Soundtrack (Classical)	Columbia (S) OS-3320	5.00	7.50	10.00
FERRY 'CROSS THE MERSEY (1965)				
Soundtrack	United Artists (M) UAL-3387	5.00	7.50	10.00
Soundtrack	United Artists (S) UAS-6387	6.00	9.00	12.00
FIDDLER ON THE ROOF (1964)				
Original Cast	RCA (M) LOC 1093	2.00	3.00	4.00
Zero Mostel, Maria Karnilova, Beatrice Arthur.				
Original Cast	RCA (S) LSO 1093	2.00	3.00	4.00
Original Cast (In Hebrew)	Columbia (M) OL 6490	6.00	9.00	12.00
Original Cast (In Hebrew)	Columbia (S) OS 6490	7.50	11.25	15.00
Original London Cast	CBS (S) 70030	2.00	3.00	4.00
Topol, Miriam Karlin, Paul Whitsun-Jones.				
Original German Cast	London (S) SW 99470	2.00	3.00	4.00
Shmuel Rodensky, Lilly Towska, Eva Berthold.				
Soundtrack (From the 1971 film)	United Artists (S) S 10900	3.00	4.50	6.00
Topol, Norma Crane, Leonard Frey.				
Original German Soundtrack (2 records)	United Artists (S) UAS 29	12.00	18.00	24.00
(The same film soundtrack as the American version, but with dubbed voices in German.)				
55 DAYS AT PEKING (1963)				
Soundtrack	Columbia (M) CL-2028	15.00	22.50	30.00
Soundtrack	Columbia (S) CS-8828	20.00	30.00	40.00
FIGHTER, THE (1952)				
Soundtack (10")	Decca (M) DL-5415	12.00	18.00	24.00
FINAL COMEDOWN, THE (1972)				
Soundtrack	Blue Note (S) 84415	3.00	4.00	6.00
FINEST HOURS, THE (1964)				
Soundtrack (With Dialogue) (2 Record Set)	Mercury (M) MGP-2-104	7.50	11.25	15.00
Soundtrack	Mercury (S) SRP-104	10.00	15.00	20.00
FINIAN'S RAINBOW (1947)				
Original Cast	Columbia (M) OL 4062	7.50	11.25	15.00
Ella Logan, Donald Richards, David Wayne, Dolores Martin.				
Original Cast (Re-channeled stereo)	Columbia (S) OS 2080	2.00	3.00	4.00
Original Cast (Songs by the star)	Capitol (M) H 561	12.00	18.00	24.00
Ella Logan.				
Original Revival Cast	RCA (M) LOC 1057	2.00	3.00	4.00
Jeanie Carson, Howard Morris, Biff McGuire, Jerry Laws.				
Original Revival Cast	RCA (S) LSO 1057	2.00	3.00	4.00
Soundtrack (From the 1968 film)	Warner Bros. (M) G 2550	3.00	4.50	6.00
Fred Astaire, Petula Clark, Tommy Steele, Keenan Wynn.				
Soundtrack	Warner Bros. (S) BS 2550	4.00	6.00	8.00
Studio Cast	Harmony (S) HS 11286	6.00	9.00	12.00
Dean Martin, Frank Sinatra, Debbie Reynolds, Sammy Davis, Jr., Bing Crosby, Rosemary Clooney.				
Studio Cast	RCA (M) LKT 1000	12.00	18.00	24.00
Audrey Marsh, Jimmy Carroll, Jimmy Blair.				
FINNEGAN'S WAKE (1968)				
Soundtrack (With Dialogue)	RCA (S) VDS-118	5.00	7.50	10.00
FIORELLO (1959)				
Original Cast	Capitol (M) WAO 1321	2.00	3.00	4.00
Tom Bosley, Patricia Wilson, Ellen Hanley, Howard DaSilva.				
Original Cast	Capitol (S) SWAO 1321	2.00	3.00	4.00
FIRE DOWN BELOW (1957)				
Soundtrack	Decca (M) DL-8597	12.00	18.00	24.00
FIREFLY (1912)				
Studio Cast	RCA (M) LM 121	12.00	18.00	24.00
Allan Jones, Martha Wright, Elaine Malbin.				

TITLE	LABEL & NO.	GOOD	VERY GOOD	NEAR MINT

FIRST IMPRESSIONS (1959)
Original Cast . . . . *Columbia (M) OL 5400* 6.00 9.00 12.00
  Polly Bergen, Farley Granger, Hermione Gingold.
Original Cast . . . . *Columbia (S) OS 2014* 6.00 9.00 12.00

FISTFUL OF DOLLARS
Soundtrack. . . . . *RCA (M) LOC-1135* 3.00 4.50 6.00
Soundtrack. . . . . *RCA (S) LSO-1135* 3.00 4.50 6.00

FITZWILLY (1967)
Soundtrack. . . . . *United Artists (M) 4173* 5.00 7.50 10.00
Soundtrack. . . . . *United Artists (S) 5173* 6.00 9.00 12.00

FIVE EASY PIECES (1970)
Soundtrack (With dialogue) . . . . *Epic (S) KE-30456* 7.50 11.25 15.00

FIVE PENNIES, THE (1959)
Soundtrack. . . . . *Dot (M) DLP-9500* 6.00 9.00 12.00
Soundtrack. . . . . *Dot (S) DLP-29500* 7.50 11.25 15.00

FLAHOOLEY (1951)
Original Cast . . . . *Capitol (M) S 284* 50.00 75.00 100.00
  Yma Sumac, Barbara Cook, Jerome Courtland, Irwin Corey, Faye
  DeWitt, Marilyn Ross, Lulu Bates.

FLAME IN THE WIND (1970)
Soundtrack (Limited release) . . . . *Unusual (S) 1004* 6.00 9.00 12.00

FLASHER, THE (1972)
Soundtrack (Limited release) . . . . *Green (S) 1008* 5.00 7.50 10.00

FLEA IN HER EAR
Soundtrack. . . . . *20th Century Fox (S) 4200* 7.50 11.25 15.00

FLIGHT OF THE DOVES
Soundtrack. . . . . *London (S) XPS 591* 4.00 6.00 8.00

FLINTSTONES, THE (1961)
TV Soundtrack (With Dialogue) . . . . *Colpix (M) CP-302* 4.00 6.00 8.00

FLORA THE RED MENACE (1965)
Original Cast . . . . *RCA (M) LOC 1111* 10.00 15.00 20.00
  Liza Minnelli, Mary Louise Wilson, Cathryn Damon.
Original Cast . . . . *RCA (S) LSO 1111* 15.00 22.50 30.00

FLOWER DRUM SONG (1958)
Original Cast . . . . *Columbia (M) OL 5350* 2.00 3.00 4.00
  Miyoshi Umeki, Larry Blyden, Juanita Hall.
Original Cast . . . . *Columbia (S) OS 2009* 2.00 3.00 4.00
Original London Cast. . . . . *Angel (M) 35886* 7.50 11.25 15.00
  Kevin Scott, Ida Shepley, Yau Shang Tung.
Original London Cast. . . . . *Angel (S) S 35886* 10.00 15.00 20.00
Soundtrack (From the 1961 film) . . . . *Decca (M) DL 9098* 5.00 7.50 10.00
  Nancy Kwan, James Shigeta, Juanita Hall, Miyoshi Umeki.
Soundtrack. . . . . *Decca (S) DL 79098* 6.00 9.00 12.00

FLOWERING PEACH, A (1954)
Original Cast . . . . *MGM (M) E-3164* 10.00 15.00 20.00

FLY BLACKBIRD (1962)
Original Pre Broadway West Coast Cast. . . *Imaginate (M) LK 1 V13786* 20.00 30.00 40.00
  Ellen Gordon, Jack Crowder, Vera Oliver, George Takei.
Original Cast . . . . *Mercury (M) OCM 2206* 7.50 11.25 15.00
  Avon Long, Leonard Parker, Paul Reid Roman.
Original Cast . . . . *Mercury (S) OCS 6206* 12.00 18.00 24.00

FOLIES BERGERE (1964)
Original Cast (1964) . . . . *Audio Fidelity (M) 2135* 2.00 3.00 4.00
  Patachou and Georges Ulmer.
Original Cast . . . . *Audio Fidelity (S) 6135* 2.00 3.00 4.00

TITLE	LABEL & NO.	GOOD	VERY GOOD	NEAR MINT

FOLIES BERGERE (1957)
Soundtrack. . . . . *Decca (M) DL-8571* 10.00 15.00 20.00

FOLLIES (1971)
Original Cast . . . . *Capitol (S) SO 761* 2.00 3.00 4.00
  Alexis Smith, Gene Nelson, Dorothy Collins.

FOLLOW ME
Soundtrack. . . . . *Uni (S) 73056* 3.00 4.00 6.00

FOLLOW THE BOYS (1962)
Soundtrack. . . . . *MGM (M) E-4123* 2.00 3.00 4.00
Soundtrack. . . . . *MGM (S) SE-4123* 3.00 4.50 6.00

FOLLOW THAT DREAM (1962)
Soundtrack. . . . . *RCA (EP) EPA 4368* 4.00 8.00 12.00
  Elvis Presley. Black label, dog on top.
  —For more information, see PRESLEY, Elvis in the regular listings.

FOOLS
Soundtrack. . . . . *Reprise (S) 6429* 3.00 4.00 6.00

FOR A FEW DOLLARS MORE (1967)
Soundtrack (Holmes Conducting) . . . . *United Artists (M) UAL-3608* 4.00 6.00 8.00
Soundtrack. *United Artists (S) UAS-6608* 5.00 7.50 10.00

FORBIDDEN ISLAND (1959)
Soundtrack. . . . . *Carlton (M) 106* 18.00 24.00 36.00

**FOR COLORED GIRLS WHO HAVE CONSIDERED SUICIDE
  WHEN THE RAINBOW IS ENUF (1976)**
Original Cast (Poetry with background music and one song
  by Diane Wharton) . . . . *Buddah (S) BDS 950070C* 2.00 3.00 4.00
  Trazana Beverley, Laurie Carloe, Rise Collins.

FOR LOVE OF IVY (1968)
Soundtrack. . . . . *ABC (S) SOC-7* 3.00 4.50 6.00

FOR THE FIRST TIME
Soundtrack. . . . . *RCA (M) LM-2338* 5.00 7.50 10.00
Soundtrack. . . . . *RCA (S) LSC-2338* 7.50 11.25 15.00

FORTUNA (1962)
Studio Cast (Composer plays five selections from show)
  (1 side) . . . . *Owl (M) ORLP 4* 10.00 15.00 20.00
  Francis Thorne, piano.

FORTUNE COOKIE, THE (1966)
Soundtrack. . . . . *United Artists (M) 4145* 4.00 6.00 8.00
Soundtrack. . . . . *United Artists (S) 5145* 5.00 7.50 10.00

40 POUNDS OF TROUBLE
Soundtrack. . . . . *Mercury (M) MG-20784* 6.00 9.00 12.00
Soundtrack. . . . . *Mercury (S) SR-60784* 7.00 11.00 15.00

FOR WHOM THE BELL TOLLS (1943)
Soundtrack (Young Conducting) (1950) . . . . *Decca (M) DL-8008* 12.00 18.00 24.00
Soundtrack (1957 Re-issue) . . . . *Decca (M) DL-8481* 12.00 18.00 24.00
Soundtrack (Heindorf Conducting) (1958) . . . . *Warner Bros. (M) B-1201* 10.00 15.00 20.00
Soundtrack. . . . . *Warner Bros. (S) BS-1201* 12.00 18.00 24.00

FOUR BELOW STRIKES BACK (1960)
Original Cast . . . . *Offbeat (M) O 4017* 12.00 18.00 24.00
  Jenny Lou Law, Nancy Dussault, George Furth, Cy Young.

FOUR GIRLS IN TOWN (1956)
Soundtrack (1 Side) . . . . *Decca (M) DL-8424* 15.00 22.50 30.00

FOUR HORSEMEN OF THE APOCALYPSE, THE
Soundtrack. . . . . *MGM (M) E-3993* 7.00 11.00 15.00
Soundtrack. . . . . *MGM (S) SE-3993* 10.00 15.00 20.00

FOUR IN THE MORNING (1966)
Soundtrack (With Dialogue) . . . . *Roulette (M) R-805* 7.50 11.25 15.00
Soundtrack. . . . . *Roulette (S) SR-805* 12.00 18.00 24.00

FOUR SAINTS IN THREE ACTS (1934)
Original Cast (1964) . . . . *RCA (M) LM 2756* 10.00 15.00 20.00
Original Cast (1954) . . . . *RCA (M) LCT 1139* 12.00 18.00 24.00
  Beatrice Robinson-Wayne, Ruby Greene, Inez Matthews.

FOX, THE (1968)
Soundtrack. . . . . *Warner Bros. (S) 1738* 10.00 15.00 20.00

FRANCIS OF ASSISI (1961)
Soundtrack. . . . . *20th Century Fox (M) 3053* 12.00 18.00 24.00
Soundtrack. . . . . *20th Century Fox (S) S-3053* 15.00 22.50 30.00

(M) Mono (S) Stereo (EP) Extended Play (Q) Quad (RI) Re-issued

195

For Whom the Bell Tolls

Ingrid Bergman

TITLE	LABEL & NO.	GOOD	VERY GOOD	NEAR MINT
FRANKIE & JOHNNY (1965)				
Soundtrack	RCA (M) LPM 3553	9.00	18.00	27.00
Elvis Presley. Came with a bonus photo loose inside.				
Soundtrack	RCA (S) LSP 3553	9.00	18.00	27.00
FRANKIE AND JOHNNY (1966)				
Soundtrack	RCA (M) LPM-3553	5.00	7.50	10.00
Soundtrack	RCA (S) LSP-3553	7.50	11.25	15.00
FRANTIC (1961)				
Soundtrack (1 Side)	Columbia (M) CL-1268	5.00	7.50	10.00
Soundtrack (1965)	Fontana (M) MGF-27532	4.00	6.00	8.00
Soundtrack	Fontana (S) SRF-67532	5.00	7.50	10.00
FREE AND EASY (1959)				
Studio Cast (1 side)	Columbia (M) CL 1099	10.00	15.00	20.00
Instrumental suite conducted by Andre Kostelanetz. As "St. Louis Woman" was not a commercial success, it was rewritten first as "Blues-Opera" and then the title was changed to "Free And Easy." It opened in December of 1959 in Holland with the intention of bringing it to Broadway. It never opened in New York.				
FRENCH LINE (1954)				
Soundtrack (10")	Mercury (M) MG25182	15.00	22.50	30.00
FRIENDLY PERSUASION (1956)				
Soundtrack	RCA Unique (M) 110	18.00	24.00	36.00
Soundtrack	Venise (M) 7026	10.00	15.00	20.00
FRIENDS				
Soundtrack	Paramount (S) PAS 6004	5.00	7.50	10.00
FROM ISRAEL WITH LOVE (1972)				
Original Cast	Hed Arzi (S) Ban 14278	10.00	15.00	20.00
Micha Adir, Dani Amihud, Chaya Arad.				
FROM RUSSIA WITH LOVE				
Soundtrack	United Artists (M) UAL 4114	3.00	4.00	6.00
Soundtrack	United Artists (S) UAS 5114	4.00	6.00	8.00
FROM THE SECOND CITY (1961)				
Original Cast (Improvisational skits)	Mercury (M) OCM 6201	5.00	7.50	10.00
Howard Alk, Alan Arkin, Roger Bowen, Severn Darden.				
Original Cast	Mercury (S) OCS 6201	7.50	11.25	15.00
Original Cast	Mercury (M) OCM 6202	5.00	7.50	10.00
Same cast.				
Original Cast	Mercury (S) OCS 6202	7.50	11.25	15.00
Original Cast (1962)	Mercury (M) OCM 6203	5.00	7.50	10.00
Same cast.				
Original Cast (1962)	Mercury (S) OCS 6203	7.50	11.25	15.00
Original Cast (Same cast with added members)	Mercury (S) SR 61224	7.50	11.25	15.00
FROSTY THE SNOWMAN				
Soundtrack	MGM (S) 4733	3.00	4.00	6.00
FUGITIVE KIND, THE (1960)				
Soundtrack	United Artists (M) UAL-4065	12.00	18.00	24.00
Soundtrack	United Artists (S) UAS-5065	18.00	27.00	36.00
FUN AND FANCY FREE (1947)				
Soundtrack (1964)	Disneyland (M) DQ-1248	5.00	7.50	10.00
FUNERAL IN BERLIN				
Soundtrack	RCA (M) LOC-1136	7.50	11.25	15.00
Soundtrack	RCA (S) LSO-1136	10.00	15.00	20.00
FUN IN ACAPULCO (1963)				
Soundtrack	RCA (M) LPM 2756	5.00	10.00	15.00
Elvis Presley.				
SOUNDTRACK	RCA (S) LSP 2756	5.00	10.00	15.00

TITLE	LABEL & NO.	GOOD	VERY GOOD	NEAR MINT
FUNNY FACE (1927)				
Original London Cast (Same stars as original cast)	World Record Club (M) SH 144	2.00	3.00	4.00
Fred Astaire, Adele Astaire, Bernard Clifton, Leslie Henson, Sydney Howard, Gershwin at piano.				
Soundtrack (From the 1957 film) (With the star of the original 1927 cast) (Additional songs by Edens and Gershe)	Verve (M) 15001	12.00	18.00	24.00
Fred Astaire, Audrey Hepburn and Kay Thompson.				
FUNNY GIRL (1964)				
Original Cast	Capitol (M) VAS 2059	2.00	3.00	4.00
Barbra Streisand, Sydney Chaplin, Danny Meehan, Kay Medford, Jean Stapleton, John Lankston.				
Original Cast	Capitol (S) SVAS 2059	2.00	3.00	4.00
Soundtrack (From the 1968 film with the original cast star)	Columbia (S) BOS 3220	2.00	3.00	4.00
Barbra Streisand, Omar Sharif, Kay Medford, Anne Francis, Walter Pidgeon.				
London Studio Cast	M.F.P. (M) 1077	10.00	15.00	20.00
FUNNY THING HAPPENED ON THE WAY TO THE FORUM, A (1962)				
Original Cast	Capitol (M) WAO 1717	2.00	3.00	4.00
Zero Mostel, Jack Gilford, David Burns.				
Original Cast	Capitol (S) SW 1717	2.00	3.00	4.00
Original London Cast	EMI (M) CLP 1685	12.00	18.00	24.00
Frankie Howard, Kenneth Conner, Jon Pertwee.				
Soundtrack (From the 1966 film)	United Artists (M) UAL 4144	5.00	7.50	10.00
Zero Mostel, Phil Sivers, Jack Gilford, Buster Keaton.				
Soundtrack	United Artists (S) UAS 5144	7.50	11.25	15.00
FUZZY PINK NIGHTGOWN, THE (1957)				
Soundtrack	Imperial (M) 9042	7.50	11.25	15.00
Soundtrack	Imperial (S) S-9042	10.00	15.00	20.00

G

TITLE	LABEL & NO.	GOOD	VERY GOOD	NEAR MINT
GAILY, GAILY				
Soundtrack	United Artists (S) 5202	3.00	4.00	6.00
GAME IS OVER, THE				
Soundtrack	Atco (M) 205	5.00	7.00	10.00
Soundtrack	Atco (S) 205	6.00	9.00	12.00
GAMES (1970)				
Soundtrack (Limited Release)	Viking (S) LPS-105	25.00	37.50	50.00
(Includes a cut by Elton John)				
GARDEN OF THE FINZI-CONTINIS				
Soundtrack	RCA (S) LSP 4712	3.00	4.50	6.00
GAS-S-S (1970)				
Soundtrack	American Int'l (S) 1038	3.00	4.00	6.00
GAY DIVORCE, THE (1932)				
Soundtrack (Edited from the 1930's film)	EMI (M) EMTC 101	2.00	3.00	4.00
Fred Astaire, Ginger Rogers, Edward Everett Horton, Betty Grable.				
GAY LIFE (1961)				
Original Cast	Capitol (M) WAO 1560	7.50	11.25	15.00
Walter Chairi, Barbara Cook, Jules Munshin, Loring Smith.				
Original Cast	Capitol (S) SWAO 1560	12.00	18.00	24.00

(M) Mono   (S) Stereo   (EP) Extended Play   (Q) Quad   (RI) Re-issued

GAY PURR-EE
Soundtrack	Warner Bros. (M) B 1479	10.00	15.00	20.00
Soundtrack	Warner Bros. (S) BS 1479	12.00	19.00	25.00

GEISHA BOY, THE (1959)
Soundtrack	Jubilee (M) 1096	10.00	15.00	20.00
Soundtrack	Jubilee (S) S-1096	15.00	22.50	30.00

GENE KRUPA STORY, THE (1959)
Soundtrack	Verve (M) 15010	15.00	22.50	30.00
Soundtrack	Verve (S) 6-15010	18.00	24.00	36.00

GENERAL ELECTRIC THEATER (1959)
TV Soundtrack	Columbia (M) CL-1395	12.00	18.00	24.00
TV Soundtrack	Columbia (S) CS-8190	20.00	30.00	40.00

GENGHIS KHAN (1965)
Soundtrack	Liberty (M) LRP-3412	9.00	13.50	18.00
Soundtrack	Liberty (S) LST-7412	12.00	18.00	24.00

GENTLEMEN MARRY BRUNETTES (1955)
Soundtrack	Coral (M) 57013	15.00	22.50	30.00

GENTLEMEN PREFER BLONDES (1949)
Original Cast	Columbia (M) OL 4290	7.50	11.25	15.00
Carol Channing, Yvonne Adair, Jack McCauley.				
Original Cast (Re-channeled stereo)	Columbia (S) OS 2310	2.00	3.00	4.00
Original London Cast	Odeon (S) 1464	18.00	24.00	36.00
Dora Bryan, Guy Middleton, Donald Stewart, Anne Hart.				
Soundtrack (10") (1 side) (From the 1953 film)	MGM (M) 208	10.00	15.00	20.00
Marilyn Monroe, Jane Russell.				
Soundtrack (1 side) (1955)	MGM (M) E 3231	6.00	9.00	12.00
Studio Cast	Caedmon (M) TC 1148	10.00	15.00	20.00
Original cast star Carol Channing in dialog from the original story by Anita Loos. None of the original score is used but vintage hit tunes of the 20's back Channing.				

GENTLE RAIN (1966)
Soundtrack	Mercury (M) MG-21016	4.00	6.00	8.00
Soundtrack	Mercury (S) SR-61016	5.00	7.50	10.00

GEORGE M! (1968)
Original Cast	Columbia (S) KOS 3200	2.00	3.00	4.00
Joel Grey, Betty Ann Grove, Jill O'Hare, Bernadette Peters.				

GERTRUDE STEIN'S FIRST READER (1970)
Original Cast	Polydor (S) 24 7002	5.00	7.50	10.00
Michael Anthony, Joy Garrett, Frank Giordano, Sandra Thornton and composer Ann Sternberg at the piano.				

GET SMART (1965)
TV Soundtrack (With Dialogue)	United Aritsts (M) UAL-3533	3.00	4.50	6.00
TV Soundtrack	United Artists (S) UAS-6533	4.00	6.00	8.00

GETTING STRAIGHT
Soundtrack	Colgems (S) 5010	4.00	6.00	8.00

GET YOURSELF A COLLEGE GIRL
Soundtrack	MGM (M) E-4273	4.00	6.00	8.00
Soundtrack	MGM (S) SE-4273	5.00	7.00	10.00

GIANT
Soundtrack	Capitol (M) W 773	7.50	11.25	15.00
Soundtrack)re-channeled stereo)	Capitol DW 773	2.00	3.00	4.00

G.I. BLUES (1960)
Soundtrack	RCA (M) LPM 2256	5.00	10.00	15.00
Elvis Presley.				
Soundtrack	RCA (S) LSP 2256	5.00	10.00	15.00

GIFT OF LOVE (1958)
Soundtrack	Columbia (M) CL-1113	15.00	22.50	30.00

GIFT OF THE MAGI (1959)
TV Soundtrack	United Artists (M) UAL-4013	10.00	15.00	20.00
TV Soundtrack	United Artists (S) UAS-5013	20.00	30.00	40.00

GIGI (1953)
Original Cast (1974 release)	RCA (S) ABL 1 0404	2.00	3.00	4.00
Alfred Drake, Agnes Moorehead.				
Soundtrack (From the 1958 film)	MGM (M) E 3641	2.00	3.00	4.00
Leslie Caron, Louis Jourdon, Maurice Chevalier, Hermione Gingold.				
Soundtrack	MGM (S) 3741	2.00	3.00	4.00

GIGOT (1962)
Soundtrack	Capitol (M) W-1754	6.00	9.00	12.00
Soundtrack	Capitol (S) SW-1754	7.50	11.25	15.00

GIRL CRAZY (1930)
Soundtrack (From the 1943 film) (10") (1953)	Decca (M) DL 5412	15.00	22.50	30.00
Soundtrack (From the 1965 film titled "When The Boys Meet The Girls")	MGM (M) E 4334	4.00	6.00	8.00
Connie Francis, Harve Presnell, Liberace, Louis Armstrong, Sam the Sham and The Pharaohs, Herman's Hermits.				
Soundtrack	MGM (S) SE 4334	5.00	7.50	10.00
Studio Cast (1 side) (1962)	Reprise (M) R 6032	3.00	4.50	6.00
Studio Cast	Reprise (S) RS 6032	4.00	6.00	8.00
Studio Cast	Columbia (M) CL 822	5.00	7.50	10.00
Mary Martin, Louise Carlyle, E. Chappell.				

GIRL FRIEND (1926)
Studio Cast (Excerpts) (1 side)	Epic (M) LN 3685	10.00	15.00	20.00
Doreen Hume, Bruce Trent.				

GIRL FROM U.N.C.L.E. (1966)
TV Soundtrack	MGM (M) E-4410	3.00	4.50	6.00
TV Soundtrack	MGM (S) SE-4410	4.00	6.00	8.00

GIRL HAPPY (1965)
Soundtrack	RCA (M) LPM 3338	5.00	10.00	15.00
Elvis Presley.				
Soundtrack	RCA (S) LSP 3338	5.00	10.00	15.00

GIRL IN PINK TIGHTS, THE (1954)
Original Cast (1958)	Columbia (M) ML 4890	20.00	30.00	40.00
Jeanmaire, Charles Goldner, David Atkinson.				

GIRL IN THE BIKINI, THE (1958)
Soundtrack	Poplar (M) 33-1002	24.00	36.00	48.00

GIRL MOST LIKELY, THE (1958)
Soundtrack	Capitol (M) W-930	18.00	27.00	36.00

GIRL ON A MOTORCYCLE (1960)
Soundtrack)1969)	Tetragrammaton (S) T 5000	10.00	15.00	20.00

GIRLS! GIRLS! GIRLS! (1962)
Soundtrack	RCA (M) LPM 2621	5.00	10.00	15.00
Elvis Presley. Came with a large color 1963 calendar.				
Soundtrack	RCA (S) LSP 2621	5.00	10.00	15.00

GIRL WHO CAME TO SUPPER (1963)
Original Cast	Columbia (M) OL 6020	10.00	15.00	20.00
Jose Ferrer, Florence Henderson, Irene Browne, Roderick Cook.				
Original Cast	Columbia (S) KOS 2420	12.00	18.00	24.00
Studio Cast (2 records)	DRG (S) SL 5178	3.00	4.50	6.00
Noel Coward narrates and sings the score including five songs cut from the show.				

GLENN MILLER STORY, THE (1954)
Soundtrack (10") (Traditional pop)	Decca (M) DL-5519	12.00	18.00	24.00
Soundtrack (Traditional pop) (1956)	Decca (M) DL-8226	7.50	11.25	15.00
Soundtrack (Re-channeled stereo)	Decca (S) 78226	5.00	7.50	10.00

GLORY GUYS, THE (1965)
Soundtrack	United Artists (M) UAL-4126	7.50	11.25	15.00
Soundtrack	United Artists (S) UAS-5126	10.00	15.00	20.00

GLORY STOMPERS
Soundtrack	Sidewalk (S) DT-5910	4.00	6.00	8.00

GODFATHER, THE
Soundtrack	Paramount (S) 1003	3.00	4.00	6.00

GOD'S LITTLE ACRE (1958)
Soundtrack	United Artists (M) UAL-40002	20.00	30.00	40.00

TITLE	LABEL & NO.	GOOD	VERY GOOD	NEAR MINT
GODSPELL (1971)				
Original Cast (Off Broadway)	Bell (S) 1102	2.00	3.00	4.00
Lamar Alford, Peggy Gordon, David Haskell.				
Original Australian Cast	SFL (S) 934486	12.00	18.00	24.00
Domenic Luca, Paul Reid Roman, Colette Mann.				
Soundtrack (1973)	Bell (S) 1118	2.00	3.00	4.00
David Haskell, Victor Garber, Robin Lamont, Joanne Jonas.				
GO FIGHT CITY HALL (1961)				
Studio Cast (Side 1, "Bei Mir Bistu Shoen")	Tikva (M) 72	10.00	15.00	20.00
GO, GO, GO, WORLD (1966)				
Soundtrack	Musicor (M) MM-2059	6.00	9.00	12.00
Soundtrack	Musicor (S) MS-3059	7.50	11.25	15.00
GOING MY WAY (1944)				
Soundtrack (10") (1950)	Decca (M) DL 5052	12.00	18.00	24.00
Soundtrack (1 side) (1962)	Decca (M) DL 4257	5.00	7.50	10.00
GOING SURFIN' (1975)				
Soundtrack (Limited Release)	Cowabunga (S) 1001	4.00	6.00	8.00
GOLDEN APPLE, THE (1954)				
Original Cast	RCA (M) LOC 1014	25.00	37.50	50.00
Priscilla Gillette, Stephen Douglass, Kaye Ballard.				
Original Cast (Re-issue) (1960)	Elektra (M) 5000	12.00	18.00	24.00
GOLDEN BOY (1964)				
Original Cast	Capitol (M) VAS 2124	5.00	7.50	10.00
Sammy Davis, Jr., Billy Daniels, Paula Wayne, Kenneth Tobey.				
Original Cast	Capitol (S) SVAS 2124	6.00	9.00	12.00
Original Cast (Re-issue)	Capitol (S) STAO 11655	2.00	3.00	4.00
GOLDEN BREED, THE (1967)				
Soundtrack	Capitol (S) ST-2886	4.00	6.00	8.00
GOLDEN COACH, THE (1954)				
Soundtrack (Traditional)	MGM (M) E-3111	36.00	54.00	72.00
GOLDEN EARRINGS (1947)				
Soundtrack (1950)	Decca (M) DL-8008	12.00	18.00	24.00
Soundtrack (1957)	Decca (M) DL-8481	12.00	18.00	24.00
GOLDEN RAINBOW (1968)				
Original Cast	Kirshner (M) KOM 1001	7.50	11.25	15.00
Steve Lawrence, Eydie Gorme, Scott Jacoby.				
Original Cast	Kirshner (S) KOS 1001	10.00	15.00	20.00
GOLDEN SCREW (1967)				
Original Cast (Composer and partial cast)	Atco (M) 33 208	5.00	7.50	10.00
Tom Sankey, Jack Hopper and The Inner Sanctum.				
Original Cast	Atco (S) SD 33 308	7.50	11.25	15.00
GOLDEN VOYAGE OF SINBAD				
Soundtrack	United Artists (S) UA-LA308-G	3.00	4.00	6.00

TITLE	LABEL & NO.	GOOD	VERY GOOD	NEAR MINT
GOLDFINGER (1964)				
Soundtrack	United Artists (M) UAL-4117	2.00	3.00	4.00
Soundtrack	United Artists (S) UAS-5117	3.00	4.50	6.00
GOLDILOCKS (1958)				
Original Cast	Columbia (M) OL 5340	7.50	11.25	15.00
Don Ameche, Elaine Stritch, Russell Nype, Pat Stanley.				
Original Cast	Columbia (S) OS 2007	10.00	15.00	20.00
GOLIATH AND THE BARBARIANS (1960)				
Soundtrack	American Int'l. (M) 100-M	7.50	11.25	15.00
Soundtrack	American Int'l. (S) 100-S	10.00	15.00	20.00
GONE WITH THE WAVE (1965)				
Soundtrack	Colpix (M) CP-492	4.00	6.00	8.00
Soundtrack	Colpix (S) SCP-492	5.00	7.50	10.00
GONE WITH THE WIND (1973)				
Original London Cast	Columbia (S) SCXA 9252	12.00	18.00	24.00
Harve Presnell, June Ritchie, Patricia Michael.				
Original London Cast	Chappell (S) CHP 101	12.00	18.00	24.00
Composer Harold Rome sings the complete score including songs cut from the show.				
Original Japanese Cast (Sung in Japanese, originally titled "Scarlett") (2 records)	RCA (S) SJET 9210 11	18.00	27.00	36.00
This is the original presentation of this musical.				
Soundtrack (10") (1954)	RCA (M) LPM-3227	15.00	22.50	30.00
Soundtrack (1956)	RCA (M) LPM-1287	10.00	15.00	20.00
Soundtrack (1961)	Camden (M) CAL-625	7.50	11.25	15.00
Soundtrack (1967)	RCA (M) LPM-3859	7.50	11.25	15.00
Soundtrack (Re-channeled stereo)	RCA (S) LSP-3895	6.00	9.00	12.00
GOODBYE AGAIN (1961)				
Soundtrack	United Artists (M) UAL-4091	5.00	7.50	10.00
Soundtrack	United Artists (S) UAS-5091	6.00	9.00	12.00
GOODBYE CHARLIE				
Soundtrack	20th Century Fox (M) TFM-3165	7.50	11.25	15.00
Soundtrack	20th Century Fox (S) TFS-4165	10.00	15.00	20.00
GOODBYE, COLUMBUS (1969)				
Soundtrack	Warner Bros. (S) 1786	3.00	4.00	6.00
GOODBYE GEMINI				
Soundtrack	DJM (S) 9101	3.00	4.00	6.00
GOODBYE MR. CHIPS (1969)				
Soundtrack	MGM (S) ISE 1	4.00	6.00	8.00
GOOD EVENING (1973)				
Original Cast	Island (S) ILPS 9298	2.00	3.00	4.00
Peter Cook and Dudley Moore.				
GOOD NEWS (1927)				
Soundtrack (From the 1947 film) (10") (1950)	MGM (M) E 504	15.00	22.50	30.00
June Allyson, Peter Lawford, Pat Marshall, Joan McCracken.				
Soundtrack (1 side) (1955)	MGM (M) E 3229	10.00	15.00	20.00
Soundtrack (1 side) (1960)	MGM (M) E 3771	5.00	7.50	10.00
Studio Cast (Side 2, "Sally")	World Record Club (M) WRCI 7065	10.00	15.00	20.00
London recording.				
Studio Cast	Signature (S) BSL1 0577	4.00	6.00	8.00
Teresa Brewer sings the songs from this revival score.				
GOOD, THE BAD, AND THE UGLY, THE				
Soundtrack	United Artists (M) 4172	4.00	6.00	8.00
Soundtrack	United Artists (S) 5172	5.00	7.00	10.00
GOODTIME CHARLEY (1975)				
Original Cast	RCA (S) ARL1 1011	2.00	3.00	4.00
Joel Gray, Ann Reinking, Louis Zorich.				
GOOD TIMES				
Soundtrack	Atco (M) 314	4.00	6.00	8.00
Soundtrack	Atco (S) 214	5.00	7.00	10.00
GOSPEL ACCORDING TO ST. MATTHEW, THE (1966)				
Soundtrack (Traditional)	Mainstream (M) 54000	24.00	36.00	48.00
Soundtrack	Mainstream (S) S-4000	30.00	45.00	60.00
GOYA (1959)				
Soundtrack	Decca (M) DL-8236	10.00	15.00	20.00
GRADUATE, THE				
Soundtrack	Columbia (S) OS-3180	3.00	4.00	6.00
GRAND CANYON, THE (1959)				
Soundtrack (Classical)	Disneyland (M) WDL-4019	5.00	7.50	10.00
Soundtrack	Disneyland (S) ST-4019	7.50	11.25	15.00

(M) Mono   (S) Stereo   (EP) Extended Play   (Q) Quad   (RI) Re-issued

TITLE	LABEL & NO.	GOOD	VERY GOOD	NEAR MINT
GRANDMA MOSES (1950)				
Soundtrack (10")	Columbia (M) ML-2185	18.00	27.00	36.00
GRAND PRIX				
Soundtrack	MGM (M) 1E8ST	3.00	4.50	6.00
Soundtrack	MGM (S) 1E8ST	4.00	6.00	8.00
GRASS HARP (1971)				
Original Cast	Painted Smiles (S) PS 1354	2.00	3.00	4.00
Barbara Cook, Carol Brice, Karen Morrow, Ruth Ford.				
GRASSHOPPER				
Soundtrack	National General (S) 1001	3.00	4.00	6.00
GREASE (1972)				
Original Cast (1974)	MGM (S) 1SE 34 OC	2.00	3.00	4.00
Adrienne Barbeau, Don Billett, Walter Bobbie.				
GREAT CARUSO, THE (1951)				
Soundtrack	RCA (M) LM-1127	6.00	9.00	12.00
Soundtrack (Re-channeled stereo)	RCA (S) LSC-1127	3.00	4.50	6.00
GREAT ESCAPE, THE				
Soundtrack	United Artists (M) UAL-4107	4.00	6.00	8.00
Soundtrack	United Artists (S) UAS-5107	5.00	7.00	10.00
GREATEST SHOW ON EARTH (1952)				
Soundtrack (10")	RCA (M) LPM-3018	15.00	22.50	30.00
GREATEST STORY EVER TOLD, THE (1965)				
Soundtrack	United Artists (M) UAL-4120	6.00	9.00	12.00
Soundtrack	United Artists (S) UAS-5120	7.50	11.25	15.00
Soundtrack	United Artists (S) UA-LA277-G	3.00	4.00	6.00
GREAT RACE, THE (1965)				
Soundtrack	RCA (M) LPM-3402	9.00	13.50	18.00
Soundtrack	RCA (S) LSP-3402	12.00	18.00	24.00
GREAT WALTZ (1965)				
Original Revival Cast (Los Angeles)	Capitol (M) VAS 2426	5.00	7.50	10.00
Giorgio Tozzi, Jean Fenn, Frank Porretta.				
Original Revival Cast	Capitol (S) SVAS 2426	7.50	11.50	15.00
Original London Revival Cast	Columbia (S) SCX 6429	10.00	15.00	20.00
Sari Barabas, Walter Cassel, Diane Todd.				
Soundtrack	MGM (S) 1 SE 39 St	4.00	6.00	8.00
Kenneth McKellar, Mary Costa, Ken Barrie.				
GREEK PEARLS, THE (1968)				
Soundtrack	Lyra (M) 1008	5.00	7.50	10.00
Soundtrack	Lyra (S) S-1008	6.00	9.00	12.00
GREEN HORNET, THE (1966)				
TV Soundtrack	20th Century Fox (M) 3186	6.00	9.00	12.00
TV Soundtrack	20th Century Fox (S) S-3186	7.50	11.25	15.00
GREENWICH VILLAGE U. S. A. (1960)				
Original Cast (2 records) (1962)	20th Century Fox (M) TCP 105 2	18.00	27.00	36.00
Jack Betts, Saralou Cooper, Pat Finley, Judy Guyll.				
Original Cast	20th Century Fox (S) TCF 105 2S	25.00	37.50	50.00
Original Cast	20th Century Fox (M) 4005	6.00	9.00	12.00
Original Cast	20th Century Fox (S) S4005	10.00	15.00	20.00
GREENWILLOW (1960)				
Original Cast	RCA (M) LOC 2001	15.00	22.50	30.00
Anthony Perkins, Cecil Kellaway, Pert Kelton, Ellen McCown, William Chapman, Lee Cass.				
Original Cast	RCA (S) LSO 2001	20.00	30.00	40.00
Original Cast (Re-issue)	Columbia (S) P 13974	2.00	3.00	4.00
Studio Cast	RCA (S) LSP 2229	4.00	6.00	8.00
Instrumental album of the score played by the Melachrino Strings.				

TITLE	LABEL & NO.	GOOD	VERY GOOD	NEAR MINT
GREYFRIARS BOBBY (1961)				
Soundtrack (With Dialogue)	Disneyland (M) ST-1914	7.50	11.25	15.00
GROUNDS FOR MARRIAGE (1950)				
Soundtrack (10")	MGM (M) E-536	15.00	22.50	30.00
GUERRE EST FINIE, LA (1967)				
Soundtrack	Bell (M) 6012	5.00	7.50	10.00
Soundtrack	Bell (S) 6012-S	6.00	9.00	12.00
GUESS WHO'S COMING TO DINNER (1967)				
Soundtrack	Colgems (M) COM-108	5.00	7.50	10.00
Soundtrack	Colgems (S) COS-108	6.00	9.00	12.00
GULLIVER'S TRAVELS BEYOND THE MOON (1966)				
Soundtrack	Mainstream (M) 54001	6.00	9.00	12.00
Soundtrack	Mainstream (S) S-4001	7.50	11.25	15.00
GUNN (1967)				
Soundtrack	RCA (M) LPM-3840	4.00	6.00	8.00
Soundtrack	RCA (S) LSP-3840	6.00	9.00	12.00
GUNS FOR SAN SEBASTIAN (1968)				
Soundtrack	MGM (M) E-4565	12.00	18.00	24.00
Soundtrack	MGM (S) SE-4565	18.00	27.00	36.00
GUNS OF NAVARONE				
Soundtrack	Columbia (M) CL-1655	7.00	11.00	15.00
Soundtrack	Columbia (S) CS-8455	10.00	15.00	20.00
GURU, THE (1969)				
Soundtrack	RCA (S) LSO-1158	5.00	7.50	10.00
GUYS & DOLLS (1950)				
Original Cast	Decca (M) DL 8036	12.00	18.00	24.00
Robert Alda, Vivian Blaine, Sam Levene, B.S. Pulley, Stubby Kaye.				
Original Cast (1955)	Decca (M) DL 9023	7.50	11.25	15.00
Original Cast (Re-channeled stereo)	Decca (S) DL 79023	5.00	7.50	10.00
Studio Cast (1 side)	Columbia (M) CL 2567	12.00	18.00	24.00
Rosemary Clooney, Frankie Laine, Jerry Vale, Jo Stafford, Harry James.				
Studio Cast	Harmony (S) HS 11374	5.00	7.50	10.00
Frank Sinatra, Dean Martin, Sammy Davis, Jr., Bing Crosby, Dinah Shore, Allan Sherman, Debbie Reynolds, The McGuire Sisters.				
Soundtrack	JJA (M) 19762	2.00	3.00	4.00
Vivian Blaine, Jean Simmons, Marlon Brando, Frank Sinatra, Stubby Kaye, John Silver.				
Original Revival Cast (1976) (All Black Cast)	Motown (S) M6 876S1	2.00	3.00	4.00
Norma Donaldson, Robert Guillaume, Ernestine Jackson, James Randolph.				
Studio Cast (Disco version)	20th Century Fox (S) ST 514	2.00	3.00	4.00
The Broadway Brass.				
GYPSY (1959)				
Original Cast	Columbia (M) OL 5420	5.00	7.50	10.00
Ethel Merman, Jack Klugman, Sandra Church.				
Original London Cast	RCA (S) SER 5686	2.00	3.00	4.00
Angela Lansbury, Zan Charisse, Barrie Ingham.				
London Studio Cast	M.F.P. (S) 1308	10.00	15.00	20.00
Jimmy Blackburn, Kay Medford, Sonya Petrie.				
Soundtrack (From the 1962 film)	Warner Bros. (M) B 1480	7.50	11.25	15.00
Rosalind Russell, Natalie Wood, Karl Malden.				
Original Revival Cast (1974) (Same recording as RCA 5686, except for some different takes)	RCA (S) LBL1 5004	2.00	3.00	4.00
Angela Lansbury, Zen Charisse, Bonnie Langford.				
GYPSY GIRL				
Soundtrack	Mainstream (M) 56090	7.00	11.00	15.00
Soundtrack	Mainstream (S) 6090	9.00	13.00	18.00

H

TITLE	LABEL & NO.	GOOD	VERY GOOD	NEAR MINT
HAIR (1967)				
Original Cast (Off Broadway)	RCA (M) LOC 1143	2.00	3.00	4.00
Walker Daniels, Gerome Ragni, Steve Dean.				
Original Cast	RCA (S) LSO 1143	2.00	3.00	4.00
Original Cast (1968)	RCA (M) LOC 1150	2.00	3.00	4.00
Ronald Dyson, Gerome Ragni, Steve Curry, Lamont Washington, Diane Keaton.				
Original Cast	RCA (S) LSO 1150	2.00	3.00	4.00
Original Cast (DisinHAIRited. Composers, original cast members, future cast members singing songs originally written for the show and not used, as well as new material)	RCA (M) LOC 1163	6.00	9.00	12.00
Galt MacDermot at the piano and conducting. Jim Rado, Jerry Ragni, Golt MacAermot and cast on vocals.				
Original Cast	RCA (S) LSO 1163	7.50	11.25	15.00

Original London Cast (1969) . . . . *Atco (S) SD 7002* 12.00 18.00 24.00
Vince Edward, Oliver Tobias, Michael Feast.
Original London Cast (Volume 2) (1971) . . . . *Polydor (S) 24 5501* 7.50 11.25 15.00
(Fresh Hair)
Includes some of the material from *"DisinHAIRited."*
Original London Cast (Hair Rave-up) . . . . *Pye (S) NSPL 18314* 7.50 11.25 15.00
Their "after-show" show from midnight till 5 a.m. with the audience
joining the cast on stage.
Original German Cast . . . . *Polydor (S) 249 266* 10.00 15.00 20.00
Original Italian Cast . . . . *RCA (S) PSL 10479* 12.00 18.00 24.00
Original Japanese Cast . . . . *RCA (S) LSO 1170* 7.50 11.25 15.00
Original French Cast . . . . *Phillips (S) 844 977* 10.00 15.00 20.00
Studio Cast (Instrumentals) . . . . *RCA (M) LP 4174* 4.00 6.00 8.00
Music supervision by Don Kirshner.
Studio Cast . . . . *RCA (S) LSP 4174* 5.00 7.50 10.00
Studio Cast (Instrumental jazz concert from
Carleton University) . . . . *Kilmarnock (S) KIL 69001* 10.00 15.00 20.00
Leader and piano, Galt MacDermot; guitar, Charlie Brown; bass, Jimmy
Lewis; percussion, Idris Mohammed.

HALLELUJAH THE HILLS (1964)
Soundtrack . . . . *Fontana (M) 27524* 5.00 7.50 10.00
Soundtrack . . . . *Fontana (S) 67524* 6.00 9.00 12.00

HALLELUJAH TRAIL, THE (1965)
Soundtrack . . . . *United Artists (M) UAL-4127* 7.50 11.25 15.00
Soundtrack . . . . *United Artists (S) UAS-5127* 10.00 15.00 20.00

HALF A SIXPENCE (1965)
Original Cast . . . . *RCA (M) LOC 1110* 5.00 7.50 10.00
Tommy Steele, Ann Shoemaker, Grover Dale, Mercer McLeod, James
Grout.
Original Cast . . . . *RCA (S) LSO 1110* 7.50 11.25 15.00
Original London Cast (Partially from the
original cast) . . . . *Decca (S) SKL 4521* 12.00 18.00 24.00
Tommy Steele, Marti Webb, Anna Barry, James Grout.
Soundtrack (From the 1967 film) . . . . *RCA (M) LOC 1146* 4.00 6.00 8.00
Soundtrack . . . . *RCA (S) LSO 1146* 6.00 9.00 12.00
London Studio Cast . . . . *World Record club)s) T 852* 7.50 11.25 15.00
Barbara Windsor, Marty Wilde and the Mike Sammes Singers.

HALF PAST WEDNESDAY (1962)
Original Cast . . . . *Columbia (M) CL 1917* 7.50 11.25 15.00
Dom DeLuise, Sean Garrison, Audre Johnson.
Original Cast . . . . *Columbia (S) CS 8717* 10.00 15.00 20.00

HALLELUJAH, BABY ! (1967)
Original Cast . . . . *Columbia (M) OL 6690* 7.50 11.25 15.00
Leslie Uggams, Robert Hooks, Allen Case, Clifford Allen.
Original Cast . . . . *Columbia (S) KOS 3090* 10.00 15.00 20.00

HAMLET (1948)
Soundtrack (10") (1951) . . . . *RCA (M) LCT-5* 12.00 18.00 24.00

HAMMERHEAD
Soundtrack . . . . *Colgems (S) 110* 7.00 11.00 15.00

HAMMERSMITH IS OUT! (1972)
Soundtrack . . . . *Capitol (S) SW 861* 6.00 9.00 12.00

HAND IS ON THE GATE, A (1966)
Original Cast (2 records) . . . . *Verve (M) FV 9040 2* 5.00 7.50 10.00
Leon Bibb, Roscoe Lee Browne, Gloria Foster, Moses Gunn,
James Earl Jones.
Original Cast . . . . *Verve (S) FVS 9040 2* 7.50 11.25 15.00

HANG 'EM HIGH
Soundtrack . . . . *United Artists (S) UAS 5179* 5.00 7.50 10.00

(M) Mono (S) Stereo (EP) Extended Play (Q) Quad (RI) Re-issued

---

HANG YOUR HAT ON THE WIND (1969)
Soundtrack . . . . *Disneyland (M) DQ-1332* 3.00 4.50 6.00

HANNIBAL BROOKS
Soundtrack . . . . *United Artists (S) 5196* 4.00 6.00 8.00

HANS BRINKER (1958)
TV Soundtrack . . . . *Dot (M) 9001* 12.00 18.00 24.00

HANS CHRISTIAN ANDERSEN (1952)
Soundtrack (10") . . . . *Decca (M) DL-5433* 10.00 15.00 20.00

HANSEL AND GRETEL (1955)
Soundtrack . . . . *RCA (M) LXA-1013* 7.50 11.25 15.00
Soundtrack (1959) . . . . *RCA (M) LBY-1024* 6.00 9.00 12.00
Soundtrack (1961) . . . . *Camden (M) CAL-1024* 5.00 7.50 10.00
Soundtrack (Re-channeled stereo) . . . . *Camden (S) CA-1024* 4.00 6.00 8.00

HANSEL AND GRETEL (1958)
TV Soundtrack . . . . *MGM (M) E-3690* 6.00 9.00 12.00

HAPPENING, THE
Soundtrack . . . . *Colgems (M) 5006* 6.00 9.00 12.00
Soundtrack . . . . *Colgems (S) 5006* 7.00 11.00 15.00

HAPPIEST GIRL IN THE WORLD (1961)
Original Cast (Traditional) . . . . *Columbia (M) OL 5650* 12.00 18.00 24.00
Cyril Ritchard, Janice Rule, Dran Seitz, Bruce Yarnell.
Original Cast . . . . *Columbia (S) OS 2050* 15.00 22.50 30.00

HAPPIEST MILLIONAIRE, THE
Soundtrack . . . . *Buena Vista (M) BV 5001* 3.00 4.50 6.00
Soundtrack . . . . *Buena Vista (S) ST 5001* 4.00 6.00 8.00

HAPPY END, THE (1929)
Original German Revival Cast (The music of
Kurt Weill) (1960) . . . . *Columbia (M) OL 5630* 5.00 7.50 10.00
Original German Revival Cast . . . . *Columbia (S) OS 2032* 7.50 11.25 15.00

HAPPY ENDING, THE (1969)
Soundtrack . . . . *United Artists (S) 5203* 5.00 7.50 10.00

HAPPY HUNTING (1956)
Original Cast . . . . *RCA (M) LOC 1026* 15.00 22.50 30.00
Ethel Merman, Fernando Lamas, Virginia Gibson.

HAPPY TIME (1968)
Original Cast . . . . *RCA (M) LOC 1144* 5.00 7.50 10.00
Robert Goulet, David Wayne.
Original Cast . . . . *RCA (S) LSO 1144* 7.50 11.25 15.00

HARD DAYS NIGHT, A
Soundtrack . . . . *United Artists (M) UAL 6366* 3.00 4.50 6.00
The Beatles; black United Artist's label.
Soundtrack . . . . *United Artists (S) UAS 6366* 3.00 4.50 6.00
Soundtrack . . . . *United Artists (S) UAS 6366* 3.00 4.50 6.00
The Beatles; pink/orange United Artist label.
Soundtrack . . . . *United Artists (S) UAS 6366* 3.00 4.50 6.00
The Beatles; tan United Artists label.

HARDER THEY COME
Soundtrack . . . . *Mango (S) SMAS-7400* 3.00 4.00 6.00

HARD JOB BEING GOD (1972)
Original Cast . . . . *GWP (S) ST 0236* 4.00 6.00 8.00
Dorothy Lerner, Tom Martel, Susie Welcher, Jim Bieker.

HARD RIDE
Soundtrack . . . . *Paramount (S) 6005* 3.00 4.00 6.00

HARK! (1972)
Original Cast (Touring Company) . . . . *Theatre Archives (S) JGR 300* 12.00 18.00 24.00
Dan Goggin, Marvin Solley, Ron De Salvio.

HARLOW (Neal Hefti) (1965)
Soundtrack . . . . *Columbia (M) OL-6390* 10.00 15.00 20.00
Soundtrack . . . . *Columbia (S) OS-2790* 12.00 18.00 24.00

HARLOW (Nelson Riddle) (1965)
Soundtrack . . . . *Warner Bros. (M) W-1599* 6.00 9.00 12.00
Soundtrack . . . . *Warner Bros. (S) WS-1599* 7.00 11.00 15.00

HARPER
Soundtrack . . . . *Mainstream (M) 56078* 15.00 22.00 30.00
Soundtrack . . . . *Mainstream (S) 6078* 20.00 30.00 40.00

HARRAD SUMMER
Soundtrack . . . . *Capitol (S) ST 11338* 3.00 4.00 6.00

TITLE	LABEL & NO.	GOOD	VERY GOOD	NEAR MINT
HARUM SCARUM (1965)				
Soundtrack	RCA (M) LPM 3468	9.00	18.00	27.00
Elvis Presley.				
Soundtrack	RCA (S) LSP 3468	9.00	18.00	27.00
HARVEY GIRLS, THE (1946)				
Soundtrack (1 Side) (1957)	decca (M) DL-8498	18.00	27.00	36.00
HATARI (1962)				
Soundtrack	RCA (M) LPM-2559	3.00	4.50	6.00
Soundtrack	RCA (S) LSP-2559	4.00	6.00	8.00
HAVING A WILD WEEKEND (1965)				
Soundtrack	Epic (M) LN-24162	3.00	4.50	6.00
Soundtrack	Epic (S) BN-26162	4.00	6.00	8.00
HAWAII				
Soundtrack	United Artists (M) 4143	4.00	6.00	8.00
Soundtrack	United Artists (S) 5143	5.00	7.00	10.00
HAWAIIAN EYE (1959)				
TV Soundtrack	Warner Bros. (M) W-1355	6.00	9.00	12.00
TV Soundtrack	Warner Bros. (S) WS-1355	7.50	11.25	15.00
HAWAIIANS, THE (1970)				
Soundtrack	United Artists (S) 5210	4.00	6.00	8.00
HAZEL FLAGG (1953)				
Original Cast	RCA (M) LOC 1010	75.00	112.50	150.00
Helen Gallagher, Thomas Mitchell, Benny Venuta, John Howard, Jack Whiting, Dean Campbell.				
Original Cast (Re-issue)	RCA (M) CBM 1 2207	2.00	3.00	4.00
HEAD				
Soundtrack	Colgems (S) COSO 5008	10.00	15.00	20.00
HEAR! HEAR! (1955)				
Original Cast	Decca (M) DL 9031	15.00	22.50	30.00
Poley McClintock, Lumpy Brannum, Fred Waring and Pennsylvanians.				
HEART IS A LONELY HUNTER				
Soundtrack	Warner Bros. (S) 1759	6.00	9.00	12.00
HECTOR, THE STOWAWAY PUP (1964)				
TV Soundtrack (With Dialogue)	Disneyland (M) ST-1921	6.00	9.00	12.00
HEIDI (1968)				
TV Soundtrack (With Dialogue)	Capitol (S) SKA02995	7.50	11.25	15.00
HEIMWEH NACH ST. PAULI (1963)				
Original German Cast	MGM (M) E 4195	7.50	11.25	15.00
Original German Cast	MGM (S) SE 4195	9.00	13.50	18.00
HELEN MORGAN STORY, THE (1957)				
TV Soundtrack	Columbia (M) CL-994	7.50	11.25	15.00
Soundtrack (Traditional pop)	RCA (M) LOC-1030	12.00	18.00	24.00
HELL CATS				
Soundtrack	Tower (S) ST-5124	4.00	6.00	8.00
HELLO, DOLLY! (1964)				
Original Cast	RCA (M) LOCD 1087	2.00	3.00	4.00
Carol Channing, David Burns, Eileen Brennan, Sondra Lee.				
Original Cast	RCA (S) LSOD 1087	2.00	3.00	4.00
Original Cast (All Black)	RCA (M) LOC 1147	7.50	11.25	15.00
Pearl Bailey, Cab Calloway, Jack Crowder.				
Original Cast	RCA (S) LSO 1147	10.00	15.00	20.00
Original London Cast	RCA (S) SF 7768	12.00	18.00	24.00
Mary Martin, Loring Smith, Marilynn Lovell, Coco Ramirez.				
Original London Cast	RCA (M) LOCD 2007	10.00	15.00	20.00
Original London Cast	RCA (S) LSOD 2007	12.00	18.00	24.00
Original German Cast	Columbia (S) OS 3110	12.00	18.00	24.00
Tatjana Iwanow, Wolfgang Arps, Ingrid Ernest.				
Soundtrack (From the 1969 film)	20th Century Fox (S) DTCS 5103	2.00	3.00	4.00
Barbra Streisand, Walter Matthau, Michael Crawford, Louis Armstrong.				
London Studio Cast	M.F.P. (M) 1066	10.00	15.00	20.00
Beryl Reid, Arthur Haynes, Patricia Routledge.				
HELLO, GOODBYE (1970)				
Soundtrack	20th Century Fox (S) S-4210	4.00	6.00	8.00
HELLO OUT THERE (1953)				
Studio Cast	Desto (S) DST 6451	2.00	3.00	4.00
John Reardon, Lenya Gabriele, Marvin Worden.				
HELLO, SOLLY! (1967)				
Original Cast	Capitol (M) W 2731	6.00	9.00	12.00
Mickey Katz, Larry Best, Stan Porter, Vivian Lloyd.				
Original Cast	Capitol (S) SW 2731	7.50	11.25	15.00

TITLE	LABEL & NO.	GOOD	VERY GOOD	NEAR MINT
HELL'S ANGELS '69 (1969)				
Soundtrack	Capitol (S) SKAO 303	4.00	6.00	8.00
HELLS ANGELS ON WHEELS				
Soundtrack	Smash (M) 27094	3.00	4.00	6.00
Soundtrack	Smash (S) 67094	4.00	6.00	8.00
HELL'S BELLES				
Soundtrack	Sidewalk (S) 5919	4.00	6.00	8.00
HELL TO ETERNITY (1960)				
Soundtrack	Warwick (M) 2030	12.00	18.00	24.00
Soundtrack	Warwick (S) S-2030	15.00	22.50	30.00
HELP!				
Soundtrack	Capitol (M) MAS 2368	2.00	4.00	6.00
The Beatles; black Capitol label.				
Soundtrack	Capitol (S) SMAS 2368	2.00	4.00	6.00
Soundtrack	Capitol (M) MAS 2368	4.00	8.00	12.00
The Beatles; green Capitol label.				
Soundtrack	Capitol (S) SMAS 2368	4.00	8.00	12.00
Soundtrack	Apple (S) SMAS 2368	1.50	3.00	4.50
The Beatles; value is for label with or without Capitol logo.				
HENNESEY (1959)				
TV Soundtrack	Signature (M) 1049	6.00	9.00	12.00
TV Soundtrack	Signature (S) S-1049	7.50	11.25	15.00
HENRY, SWEET HENRY (1967)				
Original Cast	ABC (M) OC 4	7.50	11.25	15.00
Dom Ameche, Carol Bruce, Neva Small, Louise Lasser.				
Original Cast	ABC (S) SOC 4	10.00	15.00	20.00
HERCULES (1959)				
Soundtrack (With Dialogue)	RCA (M) LBY-1036	20.00	30.00	40.00
HERE'S LOVE (1963)				
Original Cast	Columbia (M) L 6000	7.50	11.25	15.00
Janis Paige, Craig Stevens, Laurence Naismith.				
Original Cast	Columbia (S) OS 2400	10.00	15.00	20.00
HERE WE GO ROUND THE MULBERRY BUSH				
Soundtrack	United Artists (S) UAS 5175	5.00	7.50	10.00
HERO, THE (1971)				
Soundtrack (Alternate Title: Bloomfield)	Capitol (S) SW-11098	3.00	4.50	6.00
HEROES OF TELEMARK, THE (1965)				
Soundtrack	Mainstream (M) 56064	6.00	9.00	12.00
Soundtrack	Mainstream (S) S-6064	10.00	15.00	20.00
HEY BOY, HEY GIRL (1959)				
Soundtrack	Capitol (M) T-1160	7.50	11.25	15.00
HEY, LET'S TWIST				
Soundtrack	Roulette (M) R-25168	5.00	7.00	10.00
Soundtrack	Roulette (S) SR-25168	7.00	11.00	15.00
HEY THERE, IT'S YOGI BEAR				
Soundtrack	Colpix (M) CP 472	4.00	6.00	8.00
Soundtrack	Colpix (S) SCP 472	5.00	7.00	10.00
HIGH BUTTON SHOES (1947)				
Original Cast (1958)	Camden (M) CAL 457	12.00	18.00	24.00
Phil Silvers, Nanette Fabray.				
Original Cast (Re-issue)	RCA (M) LOC 1107	10.00	15.00	20.00
Original Cast (Re-channeled stereo)	RCA (S) LSO 1107	6.00	9.00	12.00
HIGH SOCIETY				
Soundtrack	Capitol (M) W-750	3.00	4.50	6.00
HIGH SPIRITS (1964)				
Original Cast	ABC (M) OC 1	10.00	15.00	20.00
Beatrice Lillie, Tammy Grimes, Edward Woodward.				
Original Cast	ABC (S) SOC 1	12.00	18.00	24.00
Original London Cast	PYE (S) NPL 18100	12.00	18.00	24.00
Cicely Courtneidge, Marti Stevens, Denis Quilley.				
HIGH TIME (1960)				
Soundtrack	RCA (M) LPM-2314	6.00	9.00	12.00
Soundtrack	RCA (S) LSP-2314	7.50	11.25	15.00
HIGH TOR (1956)				
TV Soundtrack	Decca (M) DL-8272	50.00	75.00	100.00
HIS WIFE'S HABIT				
Soundtrack	Capitol (S) SW 641	4.00	6.00	8.00

HIT THE DECK (1927)
Original London Cast (Side 2, "No No Nanette") .... World Record Club (M) SH 176 — 7.50 11.25 15.00
Stanley Holloway, Barry Twins, Ivy Tresmand.
Soundtrack (From the 1955 film) .... MGM (M) E 3163 — 10.00 15.00 20.00
Jane Powell, Tony Martin, Debbie Reynolds, Vic Damone, Ann Miller, Kay Armen.
Studio Cast (Side 2, "The Cat And The Fiddle") ..... Epic (M) LN 3569 — 10.00 15.00 20.00
Doreen Hume and Denis Quilley.

HOLD ON
Soundtrack .... MGM (M) E 4342 — 4.00 6.00 8.00
Soundtrack .... MGM (S) SE 4342 — 5.00 10.00 15.00

HOLIDAY INN (1942)
Soundtrack (1950) (10") .... Decca (M) DL-5092 — 12.00 18.00 24.00
Soundtrack (1962) .... Decca (M) DL-4256 — 6.00 9.00 12.00

HOMER
Soundtrack (Traditional rock) .... Cotillion (S) SD 9037 — 3.00 4.50 6.00

HONEY POT, THE (1967)
Soundtrack .... United Artists (M) UAL-4159 — 4.00 6.00 8.00
Soundtrack .... United Artists (S) UAS-5159 — 6.00 9.00 12.00

HONEY WEST (1965)
TV Soundtrack .... ABC (M) 532 — 5.00 7.50 10.00
TV Soundtrack .... ABC (S) S-532 — 6.00 9.00 12.00

HONG KONG (1961)
TV Soundtrack .... ABC (M) 367 — 6.00 9.00 12.00
TV Soundtrack .... ABC (S) S-367 — 7.50 11.25 15.00

HOOTENANNY HOOT (1963)
Soundtrack .... MGM (M) E-4172 — 2.00 3.00 4.00
Soundtrack .... MGM (S) SE-4172 — 3.00 4.50 6.00

HORSEMEN, THE
Soundtrack .... Sun Flower (S) 5007 — 6.00 9.00 12.00

HORSE SOLDIERS
Soundtrack .... United Artists (M) UAL-4035 — 20.00 30.00 40.00
Soundtrack .... United Artists (S) UAS-5035 — 25.00 37.00 50.00

HOTEL
Soundtrack .... Warner Bros. (M) 1682 — 12.00 19.00 25.00
Soundtrack .... Warner Bros. (S) 1682 — 15.00 22.00 30.00

HOTEL PARIDISO (1966)
Soundtrack .... MGM (M) 4419 — 5.00 7.50 10.00
Soundtrack .... MGM (S) 4419 — 6.00 9.00 12.00

HOT PARTS
Soundtrack .... Kama Sutra (S) 2054 — 3.00 4.00 6.00

HOT ROCK
Soundtrack .... Prophesy (S) 6055 — 3.00 4.00 6.00

HOT ROD RUMBLE (1957)
Soundtrack .... Liberty (M) LRP-3048 — 20.00 30.00 40.00

HOT WHEELS (1969)
TV Soundtrack .... Forward (S) ST-1023 — 4.00 6.00 8.00

HOUR OF THE GUN
Soundtrack .... United Artists (M) UAL 4180 — 6.00 9.00 12.00
Soundtrack .... United Artists (S) UAS 5180 — 7.50 11.25 15.00

HOUSEBOAT (1958)
Soundtrack .... Columbia (M) CL-1222 — 15.00 22.50 30.00

HOUSE IS NOT A HOME, A
Soundtrack .... Ava (M) A-50 — 5.00 7.00 10.00
Soundtrack .... Ava (S) AS-50 — 6.00 9.00 12.00

HOUSE OF FLOWERS (1954)
Original Cast .... Columbia (M) OL 4969 — 5.00 7.50 10.00
Pearl Bailey, Diahann Carroll, Junaita Hall, Ray Walston.
Original Cast (Re-channeled stereo) .... Columbia (S) OS 2320 — 2.00 3.00 4.00
Original Revival Cast (1968) .... United Artists (S) UAS 5180 — 10.00 15.00 20.00
Yolande Bavan, Thelma Oliver, Hope Clare.

HOUSE OF LEATHER (1970)
Original Cast (With composer and studio cast) .... Fontana (S) SRF 67591 — 5.00 7.50 10.00
Dale Menten, Dennis Craswell, Tom Hustlin, Dennis Libby.

(M) Mono   (S) Stereo   (EP) Extended Play   (Q) Quad   (RI) Re-issued

HOW NOW, DOW JONES (1967)
Original Cast .... RCA (M) LOC 1142 — 10.00 15.00 20.00
Anthony Roberts, Marilyn Mason, Brenda Vaccaro.
Original Cast .... RCA (S) LSO 1142 — 12.00 18.00 24.00

HOW SWEET IT IS (1968)
Soundtrack .... RCA (S) LSP-4037 — 6.00 9.00 12.00

HOW TO MURDER YOUR WIFE (1965)
Soundtrack .... United Artists (M) UAL-4119 — 6.00 9.00 12.00
Soundtrack .... United Artists (S) UAS-5119 — 7.50 11.25 15.00

HOW TO SAVE A MARRIAGE, AND RUIN YOUR LIFE (1968)
Soundtrack .... Columbia (S) OS-3140 — 6.00 9.00 12.00

HOW TO STEAL A MILLION (1966)
Soundtrack .... 20th Century Fox (M) 4183 — 5.00 7.50 10.00
Soundtrack .... 20th Century Fox (S) 4183 — 6.00 9.00 12.00

HOW TO STEAL AN ELECTION (1968)
Original Cast .... RCA (S) LSO 1153 — 10.00 15.00 20.00
Dennis Allen, Barbara Anson, Beverly Ballare, Ed Crowley.

HOW TO STUFF A WILD BIKINI (1965)
Soundtrack .... Wand (M) 671 — 6.00 9.00 12.00
Soundtrack .... Wand (S) S-671 — 7.50 11.25 15.00

HOW TO SUCCEED IN BUSINESS WITHOUT REALLY TRYING (1961)
Original Cast .... RCA (S) LSO 1066 — 7.50 11.25 15.00
Soundtrack (From the 1967 film) .... United Artists (M) UAL 4151 — 5.00 7.50 10.00
Robert Morse, Rudy Vallee, Michelle Lee.
Soundtrack .... United Artists (S) UAS 5151 — 7.50 11.25 15.00
Original London Cast .... RCA (M) RD 7564 — 12.00 18.00 24.00
Warren Berlinger, Billy DeWolfe, David Knight.
Original French Cast .... Philips (M) B77988L — 12.00 18.00 24.00

HURRY SUNDOWN
Soundtrack .... RCA (M) LOC-1133 — 10.00 15.00 20.00
Soundtrack .... RCA (S) LSO-1133 — 12.00 18.00 24.00

HUSTLER, THE
Soundtrack .... Kapp (M) KL 1264 — 15.00 22.00 30.00
Soundtrack .... Kapp (S) KS 3264 — 17.00 26.00 35.00

I, A WOMAN, PART 2 (1969)
Soundtrack .... MGM (S) S1E-18ST — 2.00 3.00 4.00

I CAN GET IT FOR YOU WHOLESALE (1962)
Original Cast .... Columbia (M) OL 5780 — 5.00 7.50 10.00
Lillian Roth, Jack Kruschen, Harold Lang, Barbra Streisand, Elliott Gould, Sheree North.
Original Cast .... Columbia (S) OS 2180 — 6.00 9.00 12.00

ICE STATION ZEBRA (1968)
Soundtrack .... MGM (S) S1E 14ST — 7.50 11.25 15.00

ICHABOD AND MR. TOAD (1949)
Soundtrack (10") (1951) .... Decca (M) DL 6001 — 10.00 15.00 20.00
Soundtrack (1 side) (1961) .... Decca (M) DL 9106 — 5.00 7.50 10.00

TITLE	LABEL & NO.	GOOD	VERY GOOD	NEAR MINT

I COULD GO ON SINGING (1963)
Soundtrack	Capitol (M) W-1861	10.00	15.00	20.00
Soundtrack	Capitol (S) SW-1861	15.00	22.50	30.00

I DO! I DO! (1966)
Original Cast	RCA (M) LOC 5780	2.00	3.00	4.00
Mary Martin, Robert Preston.				
Original Cast	RCA (S) LSO 2180	2.00	3.00	4.00
Original London Cast	RCA (S) SF 7938	12.00	18.00	24.00
Anne Rogers, Ian Carmichael.				

IDOL, THE
Soundtrack	Fontana (M) 27559	6.00	9.00	12.00
Soundtrack	Fontana (S) 67559	7.00	11.00	15.00

I HAD A BALL (1964)
Original Cast	Mercury (M) OCM 2210	7.50	11.25	15.00
Buddy Hackett, Richard Kiley, Karen Morrow.				
Original Cast	Mercury (S) OCS 6210	10.00	15.00	20.00

I'LL NEVER FORGET WHAT'S 'IS NAME
Soundtrack	Decca (M) 9163	4.00	6.00	8.00
Soundtrack	Decca (S) 7-9163	5.00	7.50	10.00

ILLYA DARLING (1967)
Original Cast	United Artists (M) UAL 8901	5.00	7.50	10.00
Melina Mercouri, Tito Vandis, Despo Nikos Kourkoulos.				
Original Cast	United Artists (S) UAS 9901	7.50	11.25	15.00

I LOVE MELVIN (1953)
Soundtrack (10")	MGM (M) E-190	7.50	11.25	15.00

IF HE HOLLERS, LET HIM GO (1968)
Soundtrack	Tower (S) ST-5152	7.50	11.25	15.00

IF IT'S TUESDAY, THIS MUST BE BELGIUM (1969)
Soundtrack	United Artists (S) UAS-5197	4.00	6.00	8.00

I'LL SEE YOU IN MY DREAMS (1951)
Soundtrack (10")	Columbia (M) CL-6198	10.00	15.00	20.00

I'LL TAKE SWEDEN (1965)
Soundtrack	United Artists (M) UAL-4121	3.00	4.50	6.00
Soundtrack	United Artists (S) UAS-5121	4.00	6.00	8.00

I MARRIED AN ANGEL (1938)
Soundtrack (From a 1942 radio broadcast)				
(1 side)	Pelican (M) LP 103	5.00	7.50	10.00
Jeanette MacDonald, Nelson Eddy, Binnie Barnes, Edward Everett Horton.				

IMITATION OF LIFE
Soundtrack	Decca (M) DL-8879	7.00	11.00	15.00
Soundtrack	Decca (S) DL-78879	10.00	15.00	20.00

IN CIRCLES (1967)
Original Cast	Avant Garde (M) M 108	5.00	7.50	10.00
Theo Barnes, Al Carmines, Jacque Lynn Colton, David Vaughan.				
Original Cast	Avant Garde (S) AV 108	7.50	11.25	15.00

IN COLD BLOOD (1967)
Soundtrack	Colgems (M) COM-107	7.50	11.25	15.00
Soundtrack	Colgems (S) COS-107	10.00	15.00	20.00

INCREDIBLE JOURNEY (1963)
Soundtrack (With Dialogue)	Disneyland (M) ST-1927	4.00	6.00	8.00

INDISCRETION OF AN AMERICAN WIFE (1954)
Soundtrack (10")	Columbia (M) CL-6277	20.00	30.00	40.00

I NEVER SANG FOR MY FATHER (1970)
Soundtrack	Bell (S) 1204	30.00	45.00	60.00

IN HARMS WAY
Soundtrack	RCA (M) LOC-1100	10.00	15.00	20.00
Soundtrack	RCA (S) LSO-1100	12.00	18.00	24.00

IN LIKE FLINT
Soundtrack	20th Century Fox (M) 4193	10.00	15.00	20.00
Soundtrack	20th Century Fox (S) 4193	12.00	18.00	24.00

INNER CITY (1971)
Original Cast (Off Broadway)	RCA (S) LSO 1171	6.00	9.00	12.00

INN OF THE SIXTH HAPPINESS (1958)
Soundtrack	20th Century Fox (M) 3011	10.00	15.00	20.00
Soundtrack	20th Century Fox (S) S-3011	18.00	27.00	36.00

TITLE	LABEL & NO.	GOOD	VERY GOOD	NEAR MINT

IN SEARCH OF THE CASTAWAYS (1962)
Soundtrack (With Dialogue)	Disneyland (M) ST-3916	4.00	6.00	8.00

INSIDE DAISY CLOVER (1965)
Soundtrack	Warner Bros. (M) W-1616	7.50	11.25	15.00
Soundtrack	Warner Bros. (S) WS-1616	10.00	15.00	20.00

INSIDE U. S. A. (1948)
Original Cast	RCA (M) K 14	7.50	11.25	15.00
Beatrice Lillie, Jack Haley, Billy Williams, Perry Como.				
Studio Cast (With the original cast stars)	Columbia (M) C 162	6.00	9.00	12.00
Original Cast & Studio Cast (Partial re-issue)	JJA (M) 19733	2.00	3.00	4.00

INSPECTOR CLOUSEAU (1969)
Soundtrack	United Artists (S) 5186	6.00	9.00	12.00

INTERLUDE (Skinner (1957)
Soundtrack (1 Side)	Coral (M) 57159	18.00	27.00	36.00

INTERLUDE (Delerue) (1968)
Soundtrack	Colgems (S) 5007	15.00	22.00	30.00

INTERNATIONAL SOIREE (1958)
Original Cast	Audio Fidelity (M) 1881	6.00	9.00	12.00
Patachou and Company.				
Original Cast	Audio Fidelity (S) SD 5881	4.00	6.00	8.00

INTERNS, THE (1962)
Soundtrack	Colpix (M) CP-427	5.00	7.50	10.00
Soundtrack	Colpix (S) SCP-427	7.50	11.25	15.00

INTERRUPTED MELODY (1955)
Soundtrack (Traditional)	MGM (M) E-3185	15.00	22.50	30.00
Soundtrack (Traditional) (1962)	MGM (M) E-3984	6.00	9.00	12.00

IN THE GOOD OLD SUMMERTIME (1949)
Soundtrack (1955)	MGM (M) E-3232	7.50	11.25	15.00

IN THE HEAT OF THE NIGHT (1967)
Soundtrack	United Artists (M) 4160	4.00	6.00	8.00
Soundtrack	United Artists (S) 5160	5.00	7.50	10.00

INVITATION TO THE DANCE (1956)
Soundtrack	MGM (M) E-3207	20.00	30.00	40.00
Soundtrack (5 Bands) (1963)	MGM (M) E-4186	6.00	9.00	12.00
Soundtrack (Re-channeled stereo)	mgm)s) SE-4186	5.00	7.50	10.00

IN WHITE AMERICA (1964)
Original Cast	Columbia (M) OL 2430	2.00	3.00	4.00
Gloria Foster, James Greene, Moses Gunn.				
Original Cast	Columbia (S) OS 2430	2.00	3.00	4.00

IPCRESS FILE (1965)
Soundtrack	Decca (M) DL-9124	5.00	7.50	10.00
Soundtrack	Decca (S) DL-79124	6.00	9.00	12.00

IPI TOMBI (1976)
Original Cast (2 records)	Galaxy (S) GALD 26000	3.00	4.50	6.00

IRENE (1919)
Original London Cast (With original cast star)	Monmouth Evergreen (M) MES 7057	2.00	3.00	4.00
Edith Day, Daisy Hancox, Winnie Collins, Robert Hale.				
Original London Cast	Emi (S) EMC 3139	10.00	15.00	20.00
John Pertwee, Jessie Evans, Eric Flynn, Julie Anthony.				
Original Revival Cast	Columbia (S) KS 32266	2.00	3.00	4.00
Debbie Reynolds, Monte Markham, George S. Irving.				

TITLE	LABEL & NO.	GOOD	VERY GOOD	NEAR MINT

IRMA LA DOUCE (1960)
Original Cast .... Columbia (M) OL 5360		2.00	3.00	4.00
Elisabeth Seal, Keith Mitchell, Clive Revill, George S. Irving.				
Original Cast .... Columbia (S) OS 2029		2.00	3.00	4.00
Original London Cast (With original cast stars) ... Philips (M) BBL 7274		12.00	18.00	24.00
Soundtrack (From the 1963 film)........ United Artists (M) UAL 4109		5.00	7.50	10.00
Shirley MacLaine.				
Soundtrack .... United Artists (S) UAS 5109		6.00	9.00	12.00
Soundtrack (1 side) (1966) .... United Artists (M) UAL 4134		4.00	6.00	8.00
Soundtrack .... United Artists (S) UAS 5134		5.00	7.50	10.00
Studio Cast ....London (M) LL 3197		5.00	7.50	10.00
Joyce Blair, Ian Paterson.				

ISLAND IN THE SKY (1953)
Soundtrack (10") (With Dialogue) .... Decca (M) DL-7029		50.00	75.00	100.00

IS PARIS BURNING
Soundtrack............................ Columbia (M) OL-6630		7.00	11.00	15.00
Soundtrack............................ Columbia (S) OS-3030		10.00	15.00	20.00

I SPY (1965)
TV Soundtrack , Vol. 1 ....Warner Bros. (M) W-1637		7.50	11.25	15.00
TV Soundtrack .... Warner Bros. (S) WS-1637		10.00	15.00	20.00
TV Soundtrack , Vol. 2 (1968) ....Capitol (M) T-2839		6.00	9.00	12.00
TV Soundtrack .... Capitol (S) ST-2839		7.50	11.25	15.00

ITALIAN JOB, THE (1969)
Soundtrack............................ Paramount (S) PAS-5007		6.00	9.00	12.00

IT HAPPENED AT THE WORLD'S FAIR (1963)
Soundtrack............................RCA (M) LPM 2697		9.00	18.00	27.00
Elvis Presley.				
Soundtrack............................ RCA (S) LSP 2697		9.00	18.00	27.00

IT'S A BIRD, IT'S A PLANE, IT'S SUPERMAN (1966)
Original Cast .... Columbia (M) OL 6570		7.50	11.25	15.00
Jack Cassidy, Bob Holliday, Eric Mason, Patricia Marand.				
Original Cast .... Columbia (S) OS 2970		10.00	15.00	20.00

ITS A MAD, MAD, MAD, MAD WORLD
Soundtrack.......................... United Artists (M) UAL-4110		4.00	6.00	8.00
Soundtrack.......................... United Artists (S) UAS-5110		5.00	7.00	10.00

IT STARTED IN NAPLES (1960)
Soundtrack............................... Dot (M) 3324		12.00	18.00	24.00
Soundtrack...............................Dot (S) 25324		18.00	27.00	36.00

IT'S ALWAYS FAIR WEATHER (1955)
Soundtrack............................... MGM (M) E-3241		15.00	22.50	30.00

IVANHOE (1952)
Soundtrack (1952) (10") .... MGM (M) E-179		20.00	30.00	40.00
Soundtrack (1957) .... MGM (M) E-3507		20.00	30.00	40.00

I WALK THE LINE (1970)
Soundtrack............................ Columbia (S) S 30397		3.00	4.50	6.00
Johnny Cash.				

(M) Mono (S) Stereo (EP) Extended Play (Q) Quad (RI) Re-issued

J

TITLE	LABEL & NO.	GOOD	VERY GOOD	NEAR MINT

JACK AND THE BEANSTALK (Livingston) (1956)
TV Soundtrack .... RKO (M) 111		7.50	11.25	15.00

Jack and the beanstalk (Van Heusen) (1967)
TV Soundtrack .... Hanna Barbera (M) HLP-8511		18.00	27.00	36.00

JACK JOHNSON
Soundtrack............................ Columbia (S) S-30455		4.00	6.00	8.00

JACK THE RIPPER (1960)
Soundtrack............................RCA (M) LPM-2199		10.00	15.00	20.00
Soundtrack............................RCA (S) LSP-2199		12.00	18.00	24.00

JACQUES BREL IS ALIVE AND WELL AND LIVING IN PARIS (1968)
Original Cast (2 records) .... Columbia (S) D2S779		3.00	4.50	6.00
Elly Stone, Mort Shuman, Shawn Elliott, Alice Wakefield.				
Original Detroit Cast ....Synchronicity (S) 1306		10.00	15.00	20.00
Barbara Bredius, Charlie Latimer, Mary Ann Paquette.				
Soundtrack (With original cast stars) .... Atlantic (S) SD 2 1000		3.00	4.50	6.00

JAILHOUSE ROCK (1957)
Soundtrack............................ RCA (EP) EPA 4114		5.00	10.00	15.00
Elvis Presley. Black label, dog on top.				
—For more information, see PRESLEY, Elvis in the regular listings.				

JAMAICA (1957)
Original Cast .... RCA (M) LOC 1036		7.50	11.25	15.00
Lena Horne, Ricardo Montalban, Josephine Premice, Adelaide Hall.				
Original Cast .... RCA (S) LSO 1036		12.00	18.00	24.00
Original Cast (Re-issue with 3 additional songs, but				
without the overture) (1965) .... RCA (M) LOC 1103		5.00	7.50	10.00
Original Cast .... RCA (S) LSO 1103		7.50	11.25	15.00
Studio Cast (Demo recording) .... Mark (M) 56 683		2.00	3.00	4.00
Sung by composer Harold Arlen.				

JAMES DEAN STORY, THE (1957)
Soundtrack............................ Capitol (M) W-881		10.00	15.00	20.00

JAUNTY JALOPIES
Soundtrack............................ Paramount (S) 5006		5.00	7.00	10.00

J.B. (1959)
Original Cast (2 records) .... RCA (M) LD 6075		20.00	30.00	40.00
Incidental music.				
Original Cast .... RCA (S) LDS 6075		25.00	37.50	50.00

JEANNE EAGLES
Soundtrack (Album titled "This Is Kim As				
Jeanne Eagles") .... Decca (M) DL 8574		7.50	11.25	15.00
Traditional pop.				

JENNY (1963)
Original Cast .... RCA (M) LOC 1083		12.00	18.00	24.00
Mary Martin, George Wallace, Ethel Shutts.				
Original Cast .... RCA (S) LSO 1083		15.00	22.50	30.00

JERICO JIM CROW (1964)
Original Cast (2 records) .... Folkways (M) FL 9671		3.00	4.50	6.00
Gilbert Price, Micki Grant, Rosalie King, Joseph Attles.				

JESSICA (1962)
Soundtrack........................ United Artists (M) UAL-4096		7.50	11.25	15.00
Soundtrack........................ United Artists (S) UAS-5096		10.00	15.00	20.00

JESUS CHRIST SUPERSTAR (1971)
Original Cast ....Decca (S) DL 71503		2.00	3.00	4.00
Ben Vereen, Jeff Fenholt, Yvonne Elliman.				
Original London Cast..................Decca (S) DXSA 7206		10.00	15.00	20.00
Murray Head, Ian Gillan, Yvonne Elliman, Brian Keith.				
Soundtrack (2 records) .... MCA (S) 2 11000		3.00	4.50	6.00
Ted Neeley, Carl Anderson, Yvonne Elliman.				

JIMMY (1969)
Original Cast .... RCA (S) LSO 1162		5.00	7.50	10.00
Frank Gorshin, Anita Gillette, Julie Wilson.				

JOAN (1971)
Original Cast (2 records) (Limited release) .... Judson (S) JU 1001		30.00	45.00	60.00
Lee Guilliatt, Emily Adams, Jeffrey Apter, David Vaughn.				

JOANNA
Soundtrack........................20th Century Fox (S) 4202		4.00	6.00	8.00

JOE
Soundtrack......................Mercury (S) SRM 1 605 — 3.00 — 4.50 — 6.00
Soundtrack(With dialogue)..............Mercury (S) SRM 1 607 — 3.00 — 4.50 — 6.00

JOE LOUIS STORY, THE (1953)
Soundtrack (10")......................MGM (M) E-221 — 15.00 — 22.50 — 30.00

JOHNNY APPLESEED (1948)
Soundtrack (1 Side) (1964).............Camden (M) CAL-1054 — 6.00 — 9.00 — 12.00
Soundtrack (Re-channeled stereo).......Camden (S) CAL 1054 — 5.00 — 7.50 — 10.00

JOHNNY COOL (1963)
Soundtrack...................United Artists (M) UAL-4111 — 7.50 — 11.25 — 15.00
Soundtrack...................United Artists (S) UAS-5111 — 10.00 — 15.00 — 20.00

JOHNNY JOHNSON (1936)
Studio Cast (1955)..................MGM (M) E 3447 — 12.00 — 18.00 — 24.00
  Burgess Meredith, Hiram Sherman, Evelyn Lear, Lotte Lenya.
Studio Cast (1966)..................Heliodor (M) 25024 — 6.00 — 9.00 — 12.00
Studio Cast (Re-channeled stereo)......Heliodor (S) 25024 — 5.00 — 7.50 — 10.00

JOHNNY STACCATO (1959)
TV Soundtrack......................Capitol (M) T-1287 — 6.00 — 9.00 — 12.00
TV Soundtrack......................Capitol (S) ST-1287 — 7.50 — 11.25 — 15.00

JOHNNY TREMAINE (1957)
Soundtrack......................Disneyland (M) WDL-4014 — 7.50 — 11.25 — 15.00

JOHN PAUL JONES (1959)
Soundtrack......................Warner Bros. (M) W-1293 — 15.00 — 22.50 — 30.00
Soundtrack......................Warner Bros. (S) WS-1293 — 20.00 — 30.00 — 40.00

JONATHAN LIVINGSTON SEAGULL
Soundtrack......................Columbia (S) KS-32550 — 3.00 — 4.00 — 6.00

JOSEPH AND THE AMAZING TECHNICOLOR DREAMCOAT (1977)
Original London Cast (Original recording of the work as first performed
  at the Colet Court School,
  England 1968)..................Scepter (S) SPS 558X — 4.00 — 6.00 — 8.00
  Terry Saunders, David Daltrey, Malcomb Perry.
Original London Revival Cast (1973) (First recording of the revised
  complete work (1973) but not associated with any particular
  theatrical presentation.)..................MCA (S) 399 — 2.00 — 3.00 — 4.00
  Features Gary Gond of the original West End London production
  and Peter Reeves, Maynard Williams, Gordon Waller, Roger Watson.

JOSEPHINE BAKER SHOW (1964)
Original Cast......................RCA (M) LOC 2427 — 7.50 — 11.25 — 15.00
  Josephine Baker.
Original Cast......................RCA (S) LSO 2427 — 10.00 — 15.00 — 20.00

JOY (1970)
Original Cast......................RCA (S) LSO1166 — 5.00 — 7.50 — 10.00
  Oscar Brown, Jr., Jean Pace, Sivuca, Norman Shobey.

JUD
Soundtrack......................Ampex (S) 50101 — 3.00 — 4.00 — 6.00

JUDGEMENT AT NUREMBERG (1961)
Soundtrack...................United Artists (M) UAL-4095 — 12.00 — 19.00 — 25.00
Soundtrack...................United Artists (S) UAS-5095 — 15.00 — 22.00 — 30.00

JUDITH (1966)
Soundtrack......................RCA (M) LOC-1119 — 6.00 — 8.00 — 12.00
Soundtrack......................RCA (S) LSO-1119 — 10.00 — 15.00 — 20.00

JUDY GARLAND AT CARNEGIE HALL (1961)
Original Cast (2 records).............Capitol (M) WAO 1569 — 3.00 — 4.50 — 6.00
  Judy Garland.
Original Cast......................Capitol (S) SWBO 1569 — 3.00 — 4.50 — 6.00

JULIE & CAROL AT CARNEGIE HALL (1962)
Original Cast......................Columbia (S) OS 2240 — 2.00 — 3.00 — 4.00
  Julie Andrews and Carol Burnett.

JULIE & CAROL AT LINCOLN CENTER (1971)
Original Cast......................Columbia (S) S 31153 — 5.00 — 7.50 — 10.00
  Julie Andrews and Carol Burnett.

JULIET OF THE SPIRITS (1965)
Soundtrack......................Mainstream (M) 56062 — 12.00 — 18.00 — 24.00
Soundtrack......................Mainstream (S) 6062 — 18.00 — 27.00 — 36.00

JULIUS CAESAR (1953)
Soundtrack (With Dialogue).............MGM (M) E-3033 — 10.00 — 15.00 — 20.00

(M) Mono (S) Stereo (EP) Extended Play (Q) Quad (RI) Re-issued

---

JUMBO (1935)
Soundtrack (With original cast star in
  the 1950's film)..................Columbia (S) OS 2260 — 7.50 — 11.25 — 15.00
  Jimmy Durante, Doris Day, Stephen Boyd, Martha Raye.
Studio Cast (Side 2, "Babes In Arms")......RCA (M) LPM 3152 — 10.00 — 15.00 — 20.00
  Lisa Kirk, Jack Cassidy, Jordon Bentley.

JUNGLE BOOK, THE
Soundtrack......................Buena Vista (M) 4041 — 2.50 — 3.75 — 5.00
Soundtrack......................Buena Vista (S) 4041 — 3.00 — 4.50 — 6.00

JUNGLE BOOK, THE (Miklos Rozsa) (1942)
Soundtrack (1 Side).................RCA (M) LM-2118 — 20.00 — 30.00 — 40.00

JUNO (1959)
Original Cast......................Columbia (M) OL 5380 — 7.50 — 11.25 — 15.00
  Shirley Booth, Melvyn Douglas, Jack MacGowran, Jean Stapleton.
Original Cast......................Columbia (S) OS 2013 — 10.00 — 15.00 — 20.00

JUST FOR OPENERS (1965)
Original Cast......................Upstairs (M) UD 37W56 — 15.00 — 22.50 — 30.00
  Betty Aberlin, Richard Blair, Madeline Kahn.

JUSTINE (1969)
Soundtrack......................Monument (S) 18123 — 10.00 — 15.00 — 20.00

K

KALEIDOSCOPE
Soundtrack......................Warner Bros. (M) 1663 — 4.00 — 6.00 — 8.00
Soundtrack......................Warner Bros. (S) WS 1663 — 6.00 — 9.00 — 12.00

KARL MARX PLAY (1973)
Original Cast (And European
  Touring Company)...............Kilmarnock (S) KIL 72010 — 12.00 — 18.00 — 24.00
  Phyllis Newman, Ralph Carter, Harold Gould.

KEAN (1961)
Original Cast......................Columbia (M) OL 5720 — 7.50 — 11.25 — 15.00
  Alfred Drake, Lee Venora, Oliver Gray.
Original Cast......................Columbia (S) OS 2120 — 10.00 — 15.00 — 20.00

KELLY'S HEROES
Soundtrack......................MGM (S) 1 SE 23 ST — 3.00 — 4.50 — 6.00

KEY, THE (1958)
Soundtrack......................Columbia (M) CL-1185 — 20.00 — 30.00 — 40.00

KHARTOUM
Soundtrack......................United Artists (M) 4140 — 5.00 — 7.00 — 10.00
Soundtrack......................United Artists (S) 5140 — 7.00 — 11.00 — 15.00

KID GALAHAD (1962)
Soundtrack......................RCA (EP) EPA 4371 — 5.00 — 10.00 — 15.00
  Elvis Presley. Black label, dog on top.
  —For more information, see PRESLEY, Elvis in the regular listings.

KIDNAPPED (1971)
Soundtrack......................American Int'l (S) A-1042 — 5.00 — 7.50 — 10.00

KILLER'S THREE (1968)
Soundtrack......................Tower (S) 5141 — 7.50 — 11.25 — 15.00

KIMBERLEY JIM (1964)
Soundtrack......................RCA (M) LPM-2780 — 5.00 — 7.50 — 10.00
Soundtrack......................RCA (S) LSP-2780 — 7.50 — 11.25 — 15.00

KING & I (1951)
Original Cast......................Decca (M) DL 9008 — 10.00 — 15.00 — 20.00
  Gertrude Lawrence, Yul Brynner.
Original Cast (Re-channeled stereo)......Decca (S) DL 79008 — 5.00 — 7.50 — 10.00
Original London Cast...............Phillips (M) BBL 7002 — 15.00 — 22.50 — 30.00
  Valerie Hobson, Dorean Duke, Herbert Lom, Jan Muzurus.
Soundtrack (From the 1956 film)..........Capitol (M) W 740 — 2.00 — 3.00 — 4.00
  Deborah Kerr, Yul Brynner, Rita Moreno.
Soundtrack......................Capitol (S) SW 740 — 2.00 — 3.00 — 4.00
Soundtrack (2 sides of a 3 record set)
  (1962)......................Capitol (M) TCL 1790 — 5.00 — 7.50 — 10.00
Soundtrack......................Capitol (S) STCL 1790 — 5.00 — 7.50 — 10.00
Studio Cast (With City Center Star).......Columbia (S) OS 2640 — 2.00 — 3.00 — 4.00
  Barbara Cook, Theodore Bikel, Anita Darian.
Original Cast......................RCA (M) LOC 1092 — 2.00 — 3.00 — 4.00
  Rise Stevens, Darren McGavin, Lee Venora.
Original Revival Cast...............RCA (S) LSO 1092 — 2.00 — 3.00 — 4.00

KING CREOLE (1958)
Soundtrack.....................................RCA (M) LPM 1884 — 11.00 — 22.00 — 33.00
Elvis Presley. Came with black and white photo of Elvis.
Soundtrack.....................................RCA (S) LSP 1884 — 5.00 — 10.00 — 15.00
Soundtrack.....................................RCA (EP) EPA 4319 — 5.00 — 10.00 — 15.00
Elvis Presley. This was Volume 1 of an EP set.
Soundtrack.....................................RCA (EP) EPA 4321 — 5.00 — 10.00 — 15.00
Elvis Presley. This was Volume 1 of the EP set.
—For more information, see PRESLEY, Elvis in the regular listings.

KING KONG
Soundtrack.....................................Epic (M) LN-24231 — 6.00 — 9.00 — 12.00
Soundtrack.....................................Epic (S) BN-26231 — 10.00 — 15.00 — 20.00

KING KONG (1960)
Original London Cast (1963)..................London (M) 5762 — 15.00 — 22.50 — 30.00

KING OF HEARTS
Soundtrack.....................................United Artists (M) 4150 — 3.00 — 4.00 — 6.00
Soundtrack.....................................United Artists (S) 5150 — 3.00 — 4.00 — 6.00

KING RAT
Soundtrack.....................................Mainstream (M) 56061 — 7.00 — 11.00 — 15.00
Soundtrack.....................................Mainstream (S) 6061 — 10.00 — 15.00 — 20.00

KINGS GO FORTH (1958)
Soundtrack.....................................Capitol (M) W-1063 — 25.00 — 37.50 — 50.00

KISMET (1953)
Original Cast.................................Columbia (M) 4850 — 10.00 — 15.00 — 20.00
Alfred Drake, Doretta Morrow, Joan Diener, Richard Kiley.
Original Cast (Re-channeled stereo)..........Columbia (S) OS 2060 — 5.00 — 10.00 — 15.00
Soundtrack (From the 1955 film)..............MGM (M) E 3281 — 7.50 — 11.25 — 15.00
Howard Keel, Ann Blyth, Dolores Gray, Vic Damone.
Soundtrack (1965)............................Metro (M) 526 — 6.00 — 9.00 — 12.00
Soundtrack (Re-channeled stereo).............Metro (S) MS 526 — 4.00 — 6.00 — 8.00
Studio Cast..................................London (S) SP 44043 — 2.00 — 3.00 — 4.00
Robert Merrill, Regina Resnik, Kenneth McKeller.
Original Revival Cast (1965)................RCA (M) LOC 1112 — 2.00 — 3.00 — 4.00
Alfred Drake, Anne Jeffreys, Henry Calvin, Don Baddoe.
Original Revival Cast.........................RCA (S) LSO 1112 — 2.00 — 3.00 — 4.00

KISSIN' COUSINS (1964)
Soundtrack.....................................RCA (M) LPM 2894 — 5.00 — 10.00 — 15.00
Elvis Presley. The first issue has a black and white family photo (from the film) in the lower right corner.
Soundtrack.....................................RCA (S) LSP 2894 — 5.00 — 10.00 — 15.00

KISS ME KATE (1948)
Original Cast (The first original cast album ever recorded especially for a long play album).....Columbia (M) OL 4140 — 10.00 — 15.00 — 20.00
Alfred Drake, Patricia Morison, Lisa Kirk.
Original Cast (Re-channeled stereo)..........Columbia (S) OS 2300 — 4.00 — 6.00 — 8.00
Original London Cast.........................World Record Club (M) SHB 26 — 7.50 — 11.25 — 15.00
Patricia Morison, Bill Johnson, Julie Wilson.
Original Cast (Reassembled in 1959)..........Capitol (M) TAO 1267 — 2.00 — 3.00 — 4.00
Original Cast................................Capitol (S) STAO 1267 — 2.00 — 3.00 — 4.00
Soundtrack (From the 1953 film)..............MGM (M) E 3077 — 10.00 — 15.00 — 20.00
Kathryn Grayson, Howard Keel, Ann Miller, Keenan Wynn, James Whitmore.
Soundtrack (1965)............................Metro (M) M 526 — 6.00 — 9.00 — 12.00
Soundtrack (Re-channeled stereo).............Metro (S) MS 526 — 4.00 — 6.00 — 8.00
London Studio Cast...........................MFP (M) 1126 — 10.00 — 15.00 — 20.00
Patricia Routledge, David Holliday, Stella Tanner.
German Studio Cast...........................Ariola (S) S 74343 — 12.00 — 18.00 — 24.00
Olive Moorefield and Peter Alexander.
Studio Cast (Side 2, "Can Can").............Design (S) 1009 — 7.50 — 11.25 — 15.00
Mimi Benzell, Felix Knight.
TV Soundtrack................................Columbia Special Products (S) CSS 645 — 12.00 — 18.00 — 24.00
Robert Goulet, Carol Lawrence, Jessica Walter.

KISS THEM FOR ME (1957)
Soundtrack.....................................Coral (M) 57160 — 18.00 — 27.00 — 36.00

KNICKERBOCKER HOLIDAY (1938)
Original Cast (2 records).....................Joey (M) 7243 — 3.00 — 4.50 — 6.00
Walter Houston, Jeanne Madden.
Original Cast.................................Mark (M) 56-613 — 3.00 — 4.50 — 6.00
Walter Houston, Jeanne Madden.

KNOCK ON WOOD (1954)
Soundtrack (10").............................Decca (M) DL-5527 — 20.00 — 30.00 — 40.00

KOSHER WIDOW (1959)
Original Cast (Off Broadway) (1961)..........Golden Crest (M) 4018 — 10.00 — 15.00 — 20.00
Molly Picon, Irving Jacobson, Mae Schoenfeld.
Original Cast................................Golden Crest (S) 4018 — 15.00 — 22.50 — 30.00

KRAFT TELEVISION THEATRE (1957)
TV Soundtrack................................RKO (M) 127 — 12.00 — 18.00 — 24.00

(M) Mono   (S) Stereo   (EP) Extended Play   (Q) Quad   (RI) Re-issued

KRAKATOA, EAST OF JAVA (1969)
Soundtrack.....................................ABC (S) SOC-8 — 3.00 — 4.50 — 6.00

KURT WEILL CABARET, A (1963)
Original Cast.................................MGM (M) E 4180 — 5.00 — 7.50 — 10.00
Martha Schlamme, Will Holt
Original Cast.................................MGM (S) SE 4180 — 7.50 — 11.25 — 15.00

KWAMINA (1961)
Original Cast.................................Capitol (M) W 1645 — 15.00 — 22.50 — 30.00
Sally Ann Howes, Terry Carter, Brock Peters, Robert Guillaume.
Original Cast.................................Capitol (S) SW 1645 — 20.00 — 30.00 — 40.00

L

LADY AND THE TRAMP, THE (1955)
Soundtrack.....................................Decca (M) DL-5557 — 10.00 — 15.00 — 20.00
Soundtrack (1957)............................Decca (M) DL-8462 — 6.00 — 9.00 — 12.00
Soundtrack.....................................Disneyland (M) DQ-1231 — 3.00 — 4.50 — 5.00

LADY BE GOOD (1924)
Original Revival Cast (With original stars and London Cast).....Smithsonian R 008 (Columbia P 14271) — 2.00 — 3.00 — 4.00
Fred and Adele Astaire, William Kent, George Vollaire.

LADY CAROLINE LAMB
Soundtrack.....................................Angel (S) 36946 — 5.00 — 7.00 — 10.00

LADY IN CEMENT
Soundtrack.....................................20th Century Fox (S) 4204 — 6.00 — 9.00 — 12.00

LADY IN THE DARK (1941)
Original Cast (10") (1 side) (With original star)...Columbia (M) CL6249 — 12.00 — 18.00 — 24.00
Danny Kaye.
Original Cast (1957).........................Columbia (M) HL 7012 — 7.50 — 11.25 — 15.00
Original Cast (1954) (10") (1 side) (With original star).....RCA (M) LRT 7001 — 12.00 — 18.00 — 24.00
Gertrude Lawrence.
Original Cast (1964).........................RCA (M) LPV 503 — 7.50 — 11.25 — 15.00
TV Soundtrack (NBC) (1954)...................RCA (M) LM 1882 — 25.00 — 37.50 — 50.00
Ann Sothern, Carleton Carpenter.
Studio Cast..................................Columbia (S) OS 2390 — 6.00 — 9.00 — 12.00
Rise Stevens, Adolph Green, John Reardon.

LANDLORD
Soundtrack.....................................United Artists (S) 5209 — 3.00 — 4.00 — 6.00

LAND RAIDERS, THE (1969)
Soundtrack.....................................Beverly Hills (S) BHS-21 — 10.00 — 15.00 — 20.00

LAST OF THE AMERICAN HOBOES, THE (1970)
Soundtrack.....................................Beegee (S) BGS-1041 — 3.00 — 4.50 — 6.00

LAST OF THE SECRET AGENTS, THE (1966)
Soundtrack.....................................Dot (M) 3714 — 4.00 — 6.00 — 8.00
Soundtrack.....................................Dot (S) 25714 — 6.00 — 9.00 — 12.00

LAST OF THE SKI BUMS, THE (1969)
Soundtrack.....................................World Pacific (S) WS-21884 — 4.00 — 6.00 — 8.00

LAST PICTURE SHOW
Soundtrack, Vol. 1...........................MGM (S) 1SE 33ST — 4.00 — 6.00 — 8.00
Soundtrack, Vol. 2...........................Columbia (S) S-31143 — 3.00 — 4.50 — 6.00

TITLE	LABEL & NO.	GOOD	VERY GOOD	NEAR MINT
LA STRADA (1969)				
Studio Cast (Instrumental)	United Artists (S) S 6688	7.50	11.25	15.00
Sir Julian plays the score from *"La Strada."*				
LAST REBEL, THE				
Soundtrack	Capitol (S) SW 827	3.00	4.00	6.00
LAST RUN, THE				
Soundtrack	MGM (S) 1SE 33 ST	3.00	4.50	6.00
LAST SUMMER (1969)				
Soundtrack	Warner Bros. (S) WS-1791	6.00	9.00	12.00
LAST SWEET DAYS OF ISAAC (1970)				
Original Cast	RCA (S) LSO 1169	5.00	7.50	10.00
Austin Pendleton, Fredrica Weber, Charles Collins.				
LAST VALLEY				
Soundtrack	Dunhill (S) X 50102	4.00	6.00	8.00
LAWRENCE OF ARABIA (1962)				
Soundtrack	Colpix (M) COMO 5004	3.00	4.50	6.00
Soundtrack	Colpix (S) COSO 5004	4.00	6.00	8.00
Soundtrack (Boxed)	Colpix (M) LE-1000	4.00	6.00	8.00
Soundtrack	Colpix (S) LES-1000	7.50	11.25	15.00
Soundtrack	Colgems (M) 5004	5.00	7.00	10.00
Soundtrack	Colgems (S) 5004	12.00	19.00	15.00
LEARNING TREE, THE (1969)				
Soundtrack	Warner Bros. (S) WS-1812	4.00	6.00	8.00
LEAVE IT TO JANE (1959)				
Original Revival Cast (Off Broadway)	Stand (M) 1002	12.00	18.00	24.00
Kathleen Murray, Dorothy Greener, George Segal.				
Original Revival Cast	Stand (S) SLS 1002	18.00	27.00	36.00
LE MANS				
Soundtrack	Columbia (S) S-30891	3.00	4.00	6.00
LENNY (1971)				
Original Cast (2 Records)	Blue Thumb (S) BTS 9001	5.00	7.50	10.00
Cliff Gorman, Joe Silver, Erica Yohn, Jane House.				
Soundtrack (From the 1974 film)				
(With dialogue)	United Artists (S) UA-LA359-H	5.00	7.50	10.00
LEOPARD, THE				
Soundtrack	20th Century Fox (M) FXG-5015	12.00	18.00	24.00
Soundtrack	20th Century Fox (S) SXG-5015	18.00	27.00	36.00
LES GIRLS (1957)				
Soundtrack (1 Side)	MGM (M) E-3590	10.00	15.00	20.00
LES POUPEES DE PARIS (1964)				
Original Cast (World's Fair)	RCA (M) LOC 1090	7.50	11.25	15.00
Sid and Marty Krofft's Puppets and the voices of Pearl Bailey, Milton Berle, Cyd Charisse, Annie Farga, Gene Kelly, Liberace, Jayne Mansfield, Tony Martin, Phil Silvers, Loretta Young, Edie Adams.				
Original Cast	RCA (S) LSO 1090	10.00	15.00	20.00
LET IT BE				
Soundtrack	Apple (S) AR 34001	1.50	3.00	4.50
The Beatles.				
LET IT RIDE (1961)				
Original Cast	RCA (M) LOC 1064	7.50	11.25	15.00
George Gobel, Sam Levene, Barbara Nichols.				
Original Cast	RCA (S) LSO 1064	10.00	15.00	20.00

TITLE	LABEL & NO.	GOOD	VERY GOOD	NEAR MINT
LET MY PEOPLE COME (1974)				
Original Cast (Off Broadway)	Libra (S) LR 1069	2.00	3.00	4.00
Christine Rubens, Ray Colbert, Tobia Columbus.				
LET NO MAN WRITE MY EPITAPH (1960)				
Soundtrack (Traditional pop)	Verve (M) MG-4043	7.50	11.25	15.00
Soundtrack	Verve (S) 6-4043	10.00	15.00	20.00
LET'S SING YIDDISH (1966)				
Original Cast	Roulette (S) SR 42022	10.00	15.00	20.00
Ben Bonus, Mina Bern, Shmulik Goldstein.				
LIAISONS DANGEREUSES, LES (1961)				
Soundtrack	Epic (M) LA-16022	10.00	15.00	20.00
Soundtrack (1965) (Re-issue)	Fontana (M) M-27539	5.00	7.50	10.00
Soundtrack (Re-channeled stereo)	Fontana (S) S-67539	4.00	6.00	8.00
Soundtrack	Parker (M) PLP-813	7.50	11.25	15.00
Soundtrack	Parker (S) PLPS-813	10.00	15.00	20.00
LIFE & TIMES OF JUDGE ROY BEAN				
Soundtrack	Columbia (S) S-31948	3.00	4.00	6.00
LIGHT FANTASTIC, THE (1963)				
Soundtrack	20th Century Fox (M) FXG-5016	4.00	6.00	8.00
Soundtrack	20th Century Fox (S) SXT-5016	5.00	7.50	10.00
LILAC DOMINO (1914)				
Studio Cast (1 Side)	HMV (S) GES 5778	6.00	9.00	12.00
Aileen Cochrane, Charles Young				
LILAC TIME (1921, Originally Blossom Time)				
London Studio Cast	Angel (m) 35817	10.00	15.00	20.00
(British arrangements, the first extended recording.)				
Heinrich Berte, June Bronhill, Thomas Round.				
London Studio Cast	Angel (S) 35817	12.00	18.00	24.00
LI'L ABNER (1956)				
Original Cast	Columbia (M) OL 5150	6.00	9.00	12.00
Edith Adams, Peter Palmer, Howard St. John, Stubby Kaye, Charlotte Rae, Tina Louise, Julie Newmar.				
Soundtrack (From the 1959 film)	Columbia (M) OL 5460	2.00	3.00	4.00
Peter Palmer, Leslie Parrish, Stubby Kaye, Howard St. John, Julie Newmar, Stella Stevens.				
Soundtrack	Columbia (S) OS 2021	2.00	3.00	4.00
LILIES OF THE FIELD				
Soundtrack	Epic (M) LN 24094	10.00	15.00	20.00
Soundtrack	Epic (S) BN 26094	12.00	18.00	24.00
LILITH				
Soundtrack	Colpix (M) CP 520	7.00	11.00	15.00
Soundtrack	Colpix (S) SCP 520	9.00	13.00	18.00
LION, THE (1962)				
Soundtrack	London (M) M-76001	25.00	37.50	50.00
LION IN WINTER				
Soundtrack	Columbia (S) OS-3250	6.00	9.00	12.00
LIQUIDATOR, THE				
Soundtrack	MGM (M) 4413	6.00	9.00	12.00
Soundtrack	MGM (S) 4413	7.00	11.00	15.00
LITTLE BIG MAN				
Soundtrack	Columbia (S) S-30545	3.00	4.00	6.00
LITTLE FAUSS & BIG HALSY				
Soundtrack	Columbia (S) S 30385	4.00	6.00	8.00

(M) Mono (S) Stereo (EP) Extended Play (Q) Quad (RI) Re-issued

TITLE	LABEL & NO.	GOOD	VERY GOOD	NEAR MINT

LITTLE MARY SUNSHINE   (1959)
Original Cast .... *Capitol (M) WAO 1240*   2.00   3.00   4.00
  Eileen Brennan, William Graham, Elmarie Wendel.
Original Cast .... *Capitol (S) SWAO 1240*   2.00   3.00   4.00
Original London Cast .... *PYE (M) NLP 18071*   25.00   37.50   50.00
  Patricia Routledge, Terrance Cooper, Bernard Cribbins.

LITTLE ME   (1962)
Original Cast .... *RCA (M) LOC 1078*   5.00   7.50   10.00
  Sid Caesar, Virginia Martin, Nancy Andrews.
Original Cast .... *RCA (S) LSO 1078*   7.50   11.25   15.00
Original London Cast .... *World Record Club (S) T789*   12.00   18.00   24.00
  Bruce Forsyth, Eileen Gourlay, Avril Angers.

LITTLE NIGHT MUSIC, A   (1973)
Original Cast .... *Columbia (S) KS 32265*   2.00   3.00   4.00
  Glynis Johns, Len Cariou, Hermione Gingold.
Original London Cast .... *RCA (S) LRL1 5090*   2.00   3.00   4.00
  Jean Simmons, Hermione Gingold, Joss Ackland.

LITTLE PRINCE
Soundtrack .... *ABC (S) DP-854*   3.00   4.00   6.00

LITTLEST ANGEL, THE   (1969)
TV Soundtrack .... *Mercury (S) SRM-1603*   4.00   6.00   8.00

LITTLEST REVUE, THE   (1956)
Original Cast (Off Broadway) .... *Epic (M) LN 3275*   15.00   22.50   30.00
  Beverly Bozeman, Joel Grey, Tammy Grimes, Charlotte Rae.

LITTLE TOOT   (1948)
Soundtrack (1963) .... *Disneyland (M) DQ-1233*   5.00   7.50   10.00

LITTLE WOMEN   (1957)
TV Soundtrack .... *Kapp (M) KL-1104*   18.00   27.00   36.00

LIVE A LITTLE, STEAL ALOT   (1975)
  (See: Murph The Surf)

LIVE FOR LIFE   (1967)
Soundtrack .... *United Artists (M) 4165*   4.00   6.00   8.00
Soundtrack .... *United Artists (S) 5165*   5.00   7.50   10.00

LIVELY SET, THE   (1964)
Soundtrack .... *Decca (M) DL-9119*   5.00   7.50   10.00
Soundtrack .... *Decca (S) DL-79119*   8.00   12.00   16.00

LIVING DESERT, THE   (1953)
Soundtrack (1 side) (1965) .... *Buena Vista (M) BV-3326*   7.50   11.25   15.00

LIVING FREE
Soundtrack .... *RCA (S) LSO-1172*   3.00   4.50   6.00

LIZA AT THE WINTERGARDEN   (1974)
Original Cast .... *Columbia (S) PC 32854*   2.00   3.00   4.00
  Liza Minnelli.

LIZZIE BORDEN   (1965)
Original Cast (3 records) (New York City
  Opera Company) .... *Desto (S) DST 6455 6 7*   4.00   6.00   8.00
  Brenda Lewis, Ellen Faull, Ann Elgar.

LOCK UP YOUR DAUGHTERS   (1959)
Original London Cast .... *Decca (S) SKL 4070*   12.00   18.00   24.00
  Roy Adams, Richard Wordsworth, John Sharpe.
Original London Cast (1963) .... *London (M) 5766*   7.50   11.25   15.00

LOLITA   (1962)
Soundtrack .... *MGM (M) E-4050*   6.00   9.00   12.00
Soundtrack .... *MGM (S) SE-4050*   7.50   11.25   15.00

LOLLIPOP COVER   (1966)
Soundtrack .... *Mainstream (M) 56067*   5.00   7.50   10.00
Soundtrack .... *Mainstream (S) S-6067*   6.00   9.00   12.00

LONG DUEL, THE
Soundtrack .... *Atco (M) 228*   6.00   9.00   12.00
Soundtrack .... *Atco (S) 228*   7.00   11.00   15.00

LONGEST DAY, THE   (1962)
Soundtrack (With dialogue) .... *20th Century Fox (M) FXG-5007*   12.00   18.00   24.00
Soundtrack .... *20th Century Fox (S) SXG-5007*   16.00   22.50   30.00

LONG HOT SUMMER, THE   (1958)
Soundtrack .... *Roulette (M) R-25026*   15.00   22.50   30.00

LONG JOHN SILVER   (1955)
Soundtrack (10″) .... *RCA (M) LPM-3279*   20.00   30.00   40.00

TITLE	LABEL & NO.	GOOD	VERY GOOD	NEAR MINT

LONG SHIPS, THE
Soundtrack .... *Colpix (M) CP-517*   12.00   19.00   25.00
Soundtrack .... *Colpix (S) SCP-517*   15.00   22.00   30.00

LOOK AT MONACO, A   (1963)
TV Soundtrack .... *Columbia (M) CL-2019*   12.00   18.00   24.00
TV Soundtrack .... *Columbia (S) CS-8819*   15.00   22.50   30.00

LOOKING FOR LOVE   (1964)
Soundtrack .... *MGM (M) E-4229*   5.00   7.50   10.00
Soundtrack .... *MGM (S) SE-4229*   6.00   9.00   12.00

LOOK MA I'M DANCIN' !   (1948)
Original Cast (1950) (10″) .... *Decca (M) DL 5231*   75.00   112.50   150.00
  Nancy Walker, Harold Lang, Sandra Deel, Bill Shirley.

LORD JIM   (1965)
Soundtrack .... *Colpix (M) CP-521*   7.50   11.25   15.00
Soundtrack .... *Colpix (S) SCP-521*   10.00   15.00   20.00

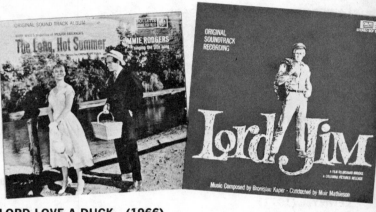

LORD LOVE A DUCK   (1966)
Soundtrack .... *United Artists (M) UAL-4137*   5.00   7.50   10.00
Soundtrack .... *United Artists (S) UAS-5137*   6.00   9.00   12.00

LORDS OF FLATBUSH, THE   (1974)
Soundtrack .... *ABC (S) abcd-828*   7.50   11.25   15.00

LORELEI   (1974)
Original Cast (Pre-Broadway, Detroit) .... *Verve (S) MV 5097 OC*   6.00   9.00   12.00
  Carol Channing, Dody Goodman, Peter Palmer.
Original Cast (Same album as on Verve, but with songs added
  and deleted) .... *MGM (S) M3G 55*   6.00   9.00   12.00
  Same cast as pre-Broadway, except for two supporting parts.

LORETTA YOUNG SHOW, THE   (1960)
TV Soundtrack .... *Decca (M) DL-4124*   10.00   15.00   20.00
TV Soundtrack .... *Decca (S) DL-74124*   12.00   18.00   24.00

LOSS OF INNOCENCE
Soundtrack .... *Colpix (M) CP-508*   12.00   19.00   25.00

LOST CONTINENT, THE   (1957)
Soundtrack .... *MGM (M) E-3635*   36.00   54.00   72.00

LOST HORIZON
Soundtrack .... *Bell (S) 1300*   3.00   4.00   6.00

(M) Mono   (S) Stereo   (EP) Extended Play   (Q) Quad   (RI) Re-issued

LOST IN THE STARS (1949)
Original Cast .... Decca (M) DL 8028 — 7.50 — 11.25 — 15.00
Todd Duncan, Inez Matthews, Sheyla Guyse.
Original Cast (1965) .... Decca (M) DL 9120 — 6.00 — 9.00 — 12.00
Original Cast (Re-channeled stereo) .... Decca (S) 79120 — 4.00 — 6.00 — 8.00

LOST MAN, THE
Soundtrack... Uni (S) 73060 — 3.00 — 4.00 — 6.00

LOVE & LET LOVE (1968)
Original Cast ....Sam Fox (S) X4RS 0371 — 25.00 — 37.50 — 50.00
Marcia Rodd, Tom Lacy, John Cunningham.

LOVE FOR LOVE (1966)
Original London Cast (3 records) .... RCA (M) VDM 112 — 4.00 — 6.00 — 8.00
Incidental music.
Original London Cast................... RCA (S) VDS 112 — 4.00 — 6.00 — 8.00

LOVE GODDESSES, THE (1965)
Soundtrack.................... Columbia (M) CL-2209 — 6.00 — 9.00 — 12.00
Soundtrack.................... Columbia (S) CS-9009 — 10.00 — 15.00 — 20.00

LOVE IN 4 DIMENSIONS (1966)
Soundtrack.................... Request (M) RLP-8090 — 5.00 — 7.50 — 10.00
Soundtrack.................... Request (S) SRLP8090 — 6.00 — 9.00 — 12.00

LOVE IS A BALL
Soundtrack.................... Philips (M) PHM-200082 — 7.00 — 11.00 — 15.00
Soundtrack.................... Philips (S) PHS-600082 — 10.00 — 15.00 — 20.00

LOVE IS A FUNNY THING
Soundtrack.........................United Artists (S) 5207 — 3.00 — 4.00 — 6.00

LOVE IS MY PROFESSION (1959)
Soundtrack (1 Side).................... Everest (M) 5076 — 10.00 — 15.00 — 20.00
Soundtrack.................... Everest (S) 1076 — 12.00 — 18.00 — 24.00

LOVE LIFE (1948)
Studio Cast .... Heritage 0600 — 20.00 — 30.00 — 40.00
Alan J. Lerner, Kaye Ballard, Dorothy Loudon, Roddy McDowell,
Nancy Walker, Jerry Orbach.
Studio Cast .... Painted Smiles 1337 — 2.00 — 3.00 — 4.00

LOVELY TO LOOK AT (1952) See: Roberta

LOVE MACHINE
Soundtrack.......................... Scepter (S) 595 — 3.00 — 4.00 — 6.00

LOVE ME OR LEAVE ME (1955)
Soundtrack (Traditional pop) .... Columbia (M) CL-710 — 7.00 — 11.25 — 15.00
Doris Day sings the songs of Ruth Etting.
Soundtrack (Re-channeled stereo) .... Columbia (S) CS-8773 — 5.00 — 7.50 — 10.00
Soundtrack (3-record EP set) .... Columbia (EP) B-540 — 6.00 — 9.00 — 12.00

LOVE ME TENDER (1956)
Soundtrack.................... RCA (EP) EPA 4006 — 3.00 — 6.00 — 9.00
Elvis Presley. Black label, dog on top.
—For more information, see PRESLEY, Elvis in the regular listings.

LOVERS (1974)
Original Cast (The LP says "stereo",
but it is mono) .... Golden Gloves (M) PG 723 — 7.50 — 11.25 — 15.00
Reathel Bean, Mike Coscone, John Ingle.

LOVES OF ISADORA, THE (1968)
Soundtrack.................................... Kapp (S) 5511 — 6.00 — 9.00 — 12.00

LOVE STORY
Soundtrack.................... Paramount (S) PAS 6002 — 3.00 — 4.50 — 6.00
Soundtrack (2 records) (With dialogue) ..... Paramount (S) PAS 27000 — 7.50 — 11.25 — 15.00

LOVING YOU (1957)
Soundtrack....................RCA (M) LPM 1515 — 11.00 — 22.00 — 33.00
Elvis Presley.
Soundtrack.................... RCA (S) LSP 1515 — 5.00 — 10.00 — 15.00
Soundtrack.................... RCA (EP) EPA 1515 — 5.00 — 10.00 — 15.00
Elvis Presley. Volume one of a two EP set.
Soundtrack.................... RCA (EP) EPA 1515 — 5.00 — 10.00 — 15.00
Volume two of the EP set.
—For more information, see PRESLEY, Elvis in the regular listings.

LUDWIG (1973)
Soundtrack (Classical) .... Philips (S) 1-5401 — 3.00 — 4.50 — 6.00

LULLABY OF BROADWAY (1951)
Soundtrack (10") .... Columbia (M) CL-6168 — 10.00 — 15.00 — 20.00

(M) Mono   (S) Stereo   (EP) Extended Play   (Q) Quad   (RI) Re-issued

LUST FOR LIFE (1956)
Soundtrack.................... Decca (M) DL-10015 — 7.50 — 11.25 — 15.00
Soundtrack.................... Decca (S) 710015 — 10.00 — 15.00 — 20.00

LUTE SONG (1946)
Original Cast (1 side, with lead star) (1950) ...... Decca (M) DL 8030 — 15.00 — 22.50 — 30.00
Mary Martin.

M

MACK & MABEL (1974)
Original Cast .... ABC (S) ABCH 830 — 5.00 — 7.50 — 10.00
Robert Preston, Bernadette Peters, Lisa Kirk, James Mitchell.

MAD ADVENTURES OF RABBI JACOB, THE (1974)
Soundtrack.................................... London (S) 652 — 3.00 — 4.50 — 6.00

MADAME BOVARY (1949)
Soundtrack (1957) .... MGM (M) E-3507 — 20.00 — 30.00 — 40.00

MADAME X
Soundtrack.................... Decca (M) DL-9152 — 10.00 — 15.00 — 20.00
Soundtrack.................... Decca (S) DL7-9152 — 12.00 — 19.00 — 25.00

MADE FOR EACH OTHER
Soundtrack.................................... Buddah (S) 5111 — 3.00 — 4.00 — 6.00

MADEMOISELLE MODISTE (1905)
Studio Cast (Side 2, "Naughty Marietta") ....RCA (M) LPM 3153 — 10.00 — 15.00 — 20.00
Doretta Morrow, Felix Knight.

MADRON
Soundtrack.................................... Quad (S) 5001 — 6.00 — 9.00 — 12.00

MAD SHOW (1965)
Original Cast .... Columbia (M) OL 6530 — 7.50 — 11.25 — 15.00
Jo Anne Worley, Linda Lavin, MacIntyre Dixon.
Original Cast .... Columbia (S) OS 2930 — 10.00 — 15.00 — 20.00

MADWOMAN OF CHAILLOT
Soundtrack....................Warner Bros. (S) WS1805 — 5.00 — 7.50 — 10.00

MAGGIE FLYNN (1968)
Original Cast .... RCA (S) LSOD 2009 — 10.00 — 15.00 — 20.00
Shirley Jones, Jack Cassidy, Robert Kaye.

MAGICAL MYSTERY TOUR
Soundtrack (1 side) .... Capitol (M) MAL 2835 — 4.00 — 8.00 — 12.00
The Beatles; black capitol label.
Soundtrack.................... Capitol (S) SMAL 2835 — 3.00 — 6.00 — 9.00
Soundtrack (1 side) .... Capitol (M) MAL 2835 — 3.00 — 6.00 — 9.00
The Beatles; Green Capitol label.
Soundtrack.................... Capitol (S) SMAL 2835 — 3.00 — 6.00 — 9.00
Soundtrack (1 side) .... Apple (S) SMAL 2835 — 1.50 — 3.00 — 4.50
The Beatles; value is for label with or without Capitol logo.

MAGIC CHRISTIAN
Soundtrack....................Commonwealth United (S) 6004 — 3.00 — 4.00 — 6.00

MAGIC GARDEN OF STANLEY SWEETHEART
Soundtrack.................... MGM (S) 1SE 20 ST — 3.00 — 4.50 — 6.00

MAGIC SHOW (1974)
Original Cast .... Bell (S) 9003 — 2.00 — 3.00 — 4.00
Doug Henning, Dale Soules, David Ogden Stiers.

MAGNIFICENT OBSESSION, THE (1954)
Soundtrack.................... Decca (M) DL-8078 — 12.00 — 18.00 — 24.00

MAGNIFICENT SEVEN, THE (1960)
Soundtrack.................... United Artists (M) UAL-4146 — 6.00 — 9.00 — 12.00
Soundtrack.................... United Artists (S) UAS-5146 — 10.00 — 15.00 — 20.00

MAH-NA MAH-NA
Soundtrack.................................... Ariel (M) 500 — 3.00 — 4.00 — 6.00

MAID OF THE MOUNTAINS (1918)
Original London Cast.............. World Record Club (M) SH 169 — 10.00 — 15.00 — 20.00
Jose Collins, Thorpe Bates, Lauri DeFrece, Mable Sealby.

MAJOR DUNDEE
Soundtrack.................... Columbia (M) OL-6380 — 7.00 — 11.00 — 15.00
Soundtrack.................... Columbia (S) OS-2780 — 9.00 — 13.00 — 18.00

TITLE	LABEL & NO.	GOOD	VERY GOOD	NEAR MINT
MAKE A WISH (1951)				
Original Cast .... RCA (M) LOC 1002		50.00	75.00	100.00
Nanette Fabray, Stephen Douglass, Helen Gallagher.				
Original Cast .... RCA (M) CBM 1 2033		2.00	3.00	4.00
MAKING OF THE PRESIDENT 1960, THE (1960)				
TV Soundtrack (With Dialogue)				
(2 Records) .... United Artists (M) UXL-9		7.50	11.25	15.00
TV Soundtrack .... United Artists (S) UXS-9		10.00	15.00	20.00
MALAMONDO				
Soundtrack................................. Epic (M) LN-24126		6.00	9.00	12.00
Soundtrack................................. Epic (S) BN-26126		7.00	11.00	15.00
MAME (1958)				
Soundtrack (1958, movie titled				
"Auntie Mame") .... Warner Bros. (M) W 1242		12.00	18.00	24.00
Rosalind Russell.				
Soundtrack..................... Warner Bros. (S) WS 1242		18.00	27.00	36.00
Original Cast .... Columbia (M) OL 6600		2.00	3.00	4.00
Angela Lansbury, Beatrice Arthur, Jane Connell.				
Original Cast .... Columbia (S) OS 3000		2.00	3.00	4.00
London Studio Cast .... Musico (S) MOS 1024		10.00	15.00	20.00
Soundtrack (From the 1974 film) .... Warner Bros. (S) WS 2773		4.00	6.00	8.00
Lucille Ball, Beatrice Arthur, Robert Preston.				
MAN AND A WOMAN, A (1966)				
Soundtrack........................... United Artists (M) 4147		5.00	7.50	10.00
Soundtrack............................ United Artists (S) 5147		6.00	9.00	12.00
MAN & BOY				
Soundtrack.................................. Sussex (S) 7011		3.00	4.00	6.00
MAN CALLED ADAM, A (1966)				
Soundtrack............................... Reprise (M) 6180		6.00	9.00	12.00
Soundtrack............................... Reprise (S) 6180		7.50	11.25	15.00
MAN CALLED DAGGER				
Soundtrack................................... MGM (M) 4516		7.00	9.00	12.00
Soundtrack................................... MGM (S) 4516		7.00	11.00	15.00
MAN CALLED FLINTSTONE, THE (1967)				
Soundtrack..................... Hanna Barbera (M) HLP-2055		4.00	6.00	8.00
MAN CALLED HORSE, A (1970)				
Soundtrack............................. Columbia (S) OS 3530		4.00	6.00	8.00

(M) Mono   (S) Stereo   (EP) Extended Play   (Q) Quad   (RI) Re-issued

TITLE	LABEL & NO.	GOOD	VERY GOOD	NEAR MINT
MAN COULD GET KILLED, A (1966)				
Soundtrack........................... Decca (M) DL-4750		5.00	7.50	10.00
Soundtrack........................... Decca (S) DL-74750		6.00	9.00	12.00
MAN FOR ALL SEASONS (1966)				
Soundtrack (With Dialogue)				
(2 Record Set) .... RCA (M) VDM-116		10.00	15.00	20.00
MAN FROM INTERPOL (1962)				
TV Soundtrack .... Top Rank (M) R-627		10.00	15.00	20.00
TV Soundtrack .... Top Rank (S) RS-627		12.00	18.00	24.00
MAN FROM THE EAST (1973)				
Original Cast (Original music from the play) .... Island (S) SMAS 9334		5.00	7.50	10.00
MAN FROM U.N.C.L.E. (1965)				
TV Soundtrack, Vol. 1 .... RCA (M) LPM-3475		5.00	7.50	10.00
TV Soundtrack .... RCA (S) LSP-3475		6.00	9.00	12.00
Soundtrack .... 20th Century Fox (M) 3128		10.00	15.00	20.00
Soundtrack .... 20th Century Fox (S) 4128		12.00	18.00	24.00
TV Soundtrack, Vol. 2 .... RCA (M) LPM-3574		5.00	7.50	10.00
TV Soundtrack .... RCA (S) LSP-3574		6.00	9.00	12.00
MAN IN THE MIDDLE (1964)				
MAN IN THE MOON (1963)				
Original Cast .... Colden (M) LP 104		18.00	27.00	36.00
Bil and Cora Baird, their marionettes, Frank Sullivan, Franz Fazakas.				
MANNIX (1969)				
TV Soundtrack .... Paramount (S) PAS-5004		7.50	11.25	15.00
MAN OF A THOUSAND FACES (1957)				
Soundtrack................................. Decca (M) DL-8623		15.00	22.50	30.00
MAN OF LA MANCHA (1965)				
Original Cast .... Kapp (S) KRS 4505		2.00	3.00	4.00
Richard Kiley, Irving Jacobson, Ray Middleton, Robert Rounseville.				
Original London Cast (2 records) (1968)......... Decca (S) DXS 7203		3.00	4.50	6.00
Keith Mitchell, Joan Diener, Bernard Spear.				
Original Spanish Cast (1963)............ Decca (S) DL 79171		4.00	6.00	8.00
Soundtrack (From the 1972 film)........ United Artists (S) UAS 9906		5.00	7.50	10.00
Peter O'Toole, Sophia Loren.				
MAN WITH A LOAD OF MISCHIEF (1966)				
Original Cast (Off Broadway) .... Kapp (M) KL 4508		10.00	15.00	20.00
Alice Cannon, Lesslie Nicol, Tom Noel.				
Original Cast .... Kapp (S) KS 5508		12.00	18.00	24.00
MARACAIBO (1958)				
Soundtrack................................. Decca (M) DL-8756		25.00	37.50	50.00
MARAT/SADE (1966)				
Original Cast (3 records) (Incidental music) ...... Caedmon (M) 312M		4.00	8.00	12.00
Clifford Rose, Brenda Kempner, Ruth Baker.				
Original Cast .... Caedmon (S) 312S		5.00	7.50	10.00
Soundtrack (From the 1967 film)				
(With dialogue) .... United Artists (M) UAL 4153		2.00	3.00	4.00
Glenda Jackson, John Steiner, Jeanette Landis.				
Soundtrack.......................... United Artists (S) UAS 5153		2.00	3.00	4.00
MARCO THE MAGNIFICENT				
Soundtrack............................ Columbia (M) OL-6470		7.00	11.00	15.00
Soundtrack............................ Columbia (S) OS-2870		10.00	15.00	20.00
MARDI GRAS (1958)				
Soundtrack.................................... Bell (M) 11		7.50	11.25	15.00
Soundtrack.................................... Bell (S) S-11		10.00	15.00	20.00
MARJORIE MORNINGSTAR (1958)				
Soundtrack................................... RCA (M) LOC-1044		20.00	30.00	40.00
MARK TWAIN TONIGHT (1959)				
Original Cast (One man show) .... Columbia (S) OS 2019		5.00	7.50	10.00
Hal Holbrook				
Original Cast (Volume 2) .... Columbia (S) OS 2030		5.00	7.50	10.00
Hal Holbrook				
TV Soundtrack .... Columbia (S) OS 3080		2.00	3.00	4.00
Hal Holbrook				
MARIA GOLOVIN (1958)				
Original Cast (3 records) .... RCA (M) LM 6142		75.00	112.50	150.00
MARRIAGE, ITALIAN STYLE (1964)				
Soundtrack (1966) .... Epic (M) LN-24195		6.00	9.00	12.00
Soundtrack............................. Epic (S) BN-26195		7.50	11.25	15.00
MARRY ME, MARRY ME				
Soundtrack................................. RCA (S) LSO 1160		4.00	6.00	8.00

MARY C. BROWN & THE HOLLYWOOD SIGN (1972)
Original Cast (Score sung by composer) ..... *United Artists (S) S 5657*   5.00   7.50   10.00
   Dory Previn.

MARY JANE
Soundtrack .... *Sidewalk (S) DT-5911*   6.00   9.00   12.00

MARY QUEEN OF SCOTS
Soundtrack .... *Decca (S) 79186*   6.00   9.00   12.00

M*A*S*H (1970)
Soundtrack (With dialogue) .... *Columbia (S) DS 3520*   3.00   4.50   6.00
Soundtrack .... *Columbia (S) S-32753*   3.00   4.50   6.00

MASK & GOWN (1957)
Original Cast .... *GNP (M) 602*   2.00   3.00   4.00
   T.C. Jones.

MASS (1971)
Original Cast (Created for opening of the John F. Kennedy Center for
   the Performing Arts) (2 records) .... *Columbia (S) M2 31008*   3.00   4.50   6.00
   Alan Titus, Norman Scribner Choir, Berkshire Boys Choir.

MASTER OF THE WORLD (1961)
Soundtrack .... *Vee Jay (M) 4000*   9.00   13.50   18.00
Soundtrack .... *Vee Jay (S) 4000*   12.00   19.00   25.00

MATING URGE, THE (1958)
Soundtrack .... *International (M) LP-7777*   12.00   18.00   24.00
Soundtrack (1961) .... *Capitol (M) T-1552*   5.00   7.50   10.00
Soundtrack .... *Capitol (S) ST-1552*   7.50   11.25   15.00

MATTER OF INNOCENCE, A (1969)
Soundtrack .... *Decca (M) 9160*   10.00   15.00   20.00
Soundtrack .... *Decca (S) 7-9160*   12.00   18.00   24.00

MAX MORATH AT THE TURN OF THE CENTURY (1969)
Original Cast (One man show, off Broadway) ...... *RCA (S) LSO 1159*   6.00   9.00   12.00
   Max Morath.

MAYA (Ortolani) (1966)
Soundtrack .... *MGM (M) 4376*   5.00   7.50   10.00
Soundtrack .... *MGM (S) 4376*   6.00   9.00   12.00

MAYA (Salter) (1967)
TV Soundtrack (With Dialogue) .... *MGM (M) CH-1044*   6.00   9.00   12.00

MAYTIME (1917)
Studio Cast (1944 radio broadcast) .... *Pelican (M) LP 121*   5.00   7.50   10.00
   Jeanette MacDonald, Nelson Eddy, Edgar Barrier.

MC KENNA'S GOLD (1969)
Soundtrack .... *RCA (S) LSP-4096*   5.00   7.50   10.00

MC LINTOCK (1963)
Soundtrack .... *United Artists (M) UAL-4112*   15.00   22.50   30.00
Soundtrack .... *United Artists (S) UAS-5112*   18.00   27.00   36.00

ME AND BESSIE (1953)
Original Cast .... *Columbia (S) PC 34032*   2.00   3.00   4.00
   Linda Hopkins.

ME & JULIET (1953)
Original Cast .... *RCA (M) LOC1012*   12.00   18.00   24.00
   Isabel Bigley, Bill Hayes, Joan McCracken, Ray Walston.
Original Cast .... *RCA (M) LOC 1098*   7.50   11.25   15.00
Original Cast (Re-channeled stereo) .... *RCA (S) LSO 1098*   6.00   9.00   12.00

ME AND THE COLONEL (1958)
Soundtrack .... *RCA (M) LOC-1046*   15.00   22.50   30.00
Soundtrack .... *RCA (S) LSO-1046*   18.00   27.00   36.00

MEDITERRANEAN HOLIDAY (1964)
Soundtrack .... *London (M) M-76003*   12.00   18.00   24.00
Soundtrack .... *London (S) MS-82003*   15.00   22.50   30.00

MEDIUM, THE (The Telephone) (1947)
Original Cast (3 sides of 3 records)
   (1949) .... *Columbia (M) OSL 154*   10.00   15.00   20.00
   Maria Powers, Marily Cotlow, Evelyn Keller.
Original Revival Cast
   (Opera Society of Washington .... *Columbia (S) MS 7387*   2.00   3.00   4.00
   Regina Resnik, Judith Blegen, Emily Derr.
Soundtrack (From the 1951 film)
   (2 records) (With Dialogue) .... *Mercury (M) MGL 7*   15.00   22.50   30.00

MEET ME IN ST. LOUIS (1944)
Soundtrack (1 side) (1957) .... *Decca (M) DL-8498*   18.00   27.00   36.00
Judy Garland.

MEGILLA OF ITZIG MANGER (1968)
Original Cast .... *Columbia (S) OS 3270*   10.00   15.00   20.00
   Pesach Burstein, Lillian Lux, Mike Burstein.

MELBA (1953)
Soundtrack (10") .... *RCA (M) LM-7012*   20.00   30.00   40.00

MELODY (1971)
Soundtrack .... *Atco (S) 5 33 363*   3.00   4.50   5.00

ME, NATALIE (1969)
Soundtrack .... *Columbia (S) OS-3350*   4.00   6.00   8.00

MEN IN WAR (1957)
Soundtrack .... *Imperial (M) 9032*   18.00   27.00   36.00

ME NOBODY KNOWS (1970)
Original Cast .... *Atlantic (S) SD 1566*   2.00   3.00   4.00
   Melanie Henderson, Laura Michaels, Jose Fernandez.

MERRY ANDREW (1958)
Soundtrack .... *Capitol (M) T-1016*   15.00   22.50   30.00

MERRY WIDOW (1907)
Original Revival Cast (1949) (Off Broadway) ...... *Decca (M) DL 8004*   12.00   18.00   24.00
   Wilbur Evans, Kitty Carlisle, Felix Knight.
Original 1942 Revival Star
   (With Studio Cast.) .... *Decca (M) DL 8819*   12.00   18.00   24.00
Original Revival Cast (1964) .... *RCA (M) LOC 1094*   6.00   9.00   12.00
   Patrice Munsel, Bob Wright, Sig Arno.
Original Revival Cast .... *RCA (S) LSO 1094*   7.50   11.25   15.00
Soundtrack (From the 1952 film)
   (1 side) (10") .... *MGM (M) E 157*   12.00   18.00   24.00
   Lana Turner, Fernando Lamas, Trudy Erwin.
Soundtrack (1 side) (1955) .... *MGM (M) E 3228*   6.00   9.00   12.00
Studio Cast .... *RCA (M) LK 1020*   7.50   11.25   15.00
   Donald Richards, Elaine Malbin.
Studio Cast (2 records) .... *Melodia (M) 021629*   10.00   15.00   20.00
   In Russian with dialogue.
London Studio Cast .... *Angel (M) 35816*   10.00   15.00   20.00
   Thomas Round, June Bronhill, Howell Glynne, Marion Lowe.
London Studio Cast .... *Angel (S 35816*   12.00   18.00   24.00
Studio Cast .... *Columbia (S) OS 2280*   2.00   3.00   4.00
   Lisa Della Casa, John Reardon, Laurel Hurley.
Studio Cast (Side 1, "The Student Prince") .... *Capitol (M) T 437*   5.00   7.50   10.00
   Gordon MacRae, Lucille Norman.

MEXICAN HAYRIDE (1944)
Original Cast (1950) (10") .... *Decca (M) DL 5232*   75.00   112.50   150.00
   June Havoc, Wilbur Evans, Corinna Mura.

MICKEY ONE (1965)
Soundtrack .... *MGM (M) E-4312*   4.00   6.00   8.00
Soundtrack .... *MGM (S) SE-4312*   5.00   7.50   10.00

MIDNIGHT COWBOY (1969)
Soundtrack .... *United Artists (S) UAS-5198*   4.00   6.00   8.00

MIKADO, THE (1960)
TV Soundtrack .... *Columbia (M) OL-5480*   18.00   27.00   36.00
TV Soundtrack .... *Columbia (S) OS-2022*   25.00   37.50   50.00

MIKE HAMMER (1959)
TV Soundtrack .... *RCA (M) LPM-2140*   7.50   11.25   15.00
TV Soundtrack .... *RCA (S) LSP-2140*   10.00   15.00   20.00

MILANESE STORY, A (1962)
Soundtrack .... *Atlantic (M) 1388*   5.00   7.50   10.00
Soundtrack .... *Atlantic (S) S-1388*   6.00   9.00   12.00

(M) Mono (S) Stereo (EP) Extended Play (Q) Quad (RI) Re-issued

MILANO CALIBRO 9 (1974)
Soundtrack....................PILPS-Cosmos (S) 9001 — 5.00 — 7.50 — 10.00

MILK & HONEY (1961)
Original Cast....................RCA (M) LOC 1065 — 7.50 — 11.25 — 15.00
  Robert Weede, Mimi Benzell, Molly Picon.
Original Cast....................RCA (S) LSO 1065 — 10.00 — 15.00 — 20.00

MINNIE'S BOYS (1970)
Original Cast....................Project 3 (S) TS 60002 SD — 2.00 — 3.00 — 4.00
  Shelley Winters, Arny Freeman, Mort Marshall.

MINX, THE
Soundtrack....................Amsterdam (S) AMS12007 — 5.00 — 7.50 — 10.00

MIRAGE (1965)
Soundtrack....................Mercury (M) MG-21025 — 6.00 — 9.00 — 12.00
Soundtrack....................Mercury (S) SR-61025 — 8.00 — 12.00 — 16.00

MISSION: IMPOSSIBLE (1967)
TV Soundtrack....................Dot (M) 3831 — 4.00 — 6.00 — 8.00
TV Soundtrack....................Dot (S) 25831 — 5.00 — 7.50 — 10.00
TV Soundtrack, Vol. 2 (1969)....................Paramount (S) PAS-5002 — 5.00 — 7.50 — 10.00

MRS. BROWN YOU'VE GOT A LOVELY DAUGHTER
Soundtrack....................MGM (S) 4548 — 3.00 — 4.00 — 6.00

MISSISSIPPI (1935)
Soundtrack (10") (1951)....................Decca (M) DL-6008 — 7.50 — 11.25 — 15.00
Soundtrack (1962)....................Decca (M) DL-4250 — 5.00 — 7.50 — 10.00

MISS LIBERTY (1949)
Original Cast....................Columbia (M) ML 4220 — 5.00 — 7.50 — 10.00
  Eddie Albert, Allyn McLerie, Mary McCarty.

MRS. PATTERSON (1954)
Original Cast....................RCA (M) LOC 1017 — 25.00 — 37.50 — 50.00
  Eartha Kitt, Enid Markey, Ruth Attaway.

MISS SADIE THOMPSON (1953)
Soundtrack (With Dialogue) (10")....................Mercury (M) MG-25181 — 18.00 — 27.00 — 36.00
Soundtrack (With Dialogue) (1 Side) (1957)....................Mercury (M) MG-20123 — 10.00 — 15.00 — 20.00

MISTER BROADWAY (Cohan) (1057)
TV Soundtrack (1 Side)....................RCA (M) LPM-1520 — 15.00 — 22.50 — 30.00

MISTER BROADWAY (Brubeck) (1964)
TV Soundtrack....................Columbia (M) CL-2275 — 5.00 — 7.50 — 10.00
TV Soundtrack....................Columbia (S) CS-9075 — 6.00 — 9.00 — 12.00

MR. BUDDWING (1966)
Soundtrack....................Verve (M) 8638 — 4.00 — 6.00 — 8.00
Soundtrack....................Verve (S) 6-8638 — 5.00 — 7.00 — 10.00

MISTER ED (1962)
TV Soundtrack (With Dialogue)....................Colpix (M) CP-209 — 7.50 — 11.25 — 15.00

MR. IMPERIUM (1951)
Soundtrack (10")....................RCA (M) LM-61 — 15.00 — 22.50 — 30.00

MR. MUSIC (1950)
Soundtrack (10")....................Decca (M) DL-5284 — 10.00 — 15.00 — 20.00
Soundtrack (1962)....................Decca (M) DL-4262 — 5.00 — 7.50 — 10.00

(M) Mono (S) Stereo (EP) Extended Play (Q) Quad (RI) Re-issued

MR. NOVAK (1963)
TV Soundtrack....................MGM (M) E-4222 — 3.00 — 4.50 — 6.00
TV Soundtrack....................MGM (S) SE-4222 — 4.00 — 6.00 — 8.00

MR. PRESIDENT (1962)
Original Cast....................Columbia (M) OL 5870 — 7.50 — 11.25 — 15.00
Original Cast....................Columbia (S) OS 2270 — 10.00 — 15.00 — 20.00
  Robert Ryan Nanette Fabray, Anita Gillette.
Studio Cast....................RCA (M) LPM 2630 — 4.00 — 6.00 — 8.00
  Perry Como, Kaye Ballard, Sandy Steward.
Studio Cast....................RCA (S) LSP 2630 — 5.00 — 7.50 — 10.00

MR. WONDERFUL (1956)
Original Cast....................Decca (M) DL 9032 — 20.00 — 30.00 — 40.00
  Sammy Davis, Jr., The Will Mastin Trio, Jack Carter.

MIXED DOUBLES (Below The Belt) (1966)
Original Cast (Volume 2) (2 records,
  3 sides)....................Upstairs (S) UD 37W56 — 20.00 — 30.00 — 40.00
  Judy Graubart, Madeline Kahn, Larry Moss, Lily Tomlin.

MOBY DICK (1956)
Soundtrack....................RCA (M) LPM-1247 — 15.00 — 22.50 — 30.00

MODERN TIMES (1936)
Soundtrack (1959)....................United Artists (M) UAL-4049 — 6.00 — 9.00 — 12.00
Soundtrack (Re-channeled stereo)....................United Artists (S) UAS-5049 — 4.00 — 6.00 — 8.00
Soundtrack....................United Artists (S) 5222 — 3.00 — 4.50 — 6.00

MODESTY BLAISE
Soundtrack....................20th Century Fox (M) 3182 — 10.00 — 15.00 — 20.00
Soundtrack....................20th Century Fox (S) 4182 — 12.00 — 18.00 — 24.00

MOLLY MAGUIRES (1970)
Soundtrack....................Paramount (S) 6000 — 10.00 — 15.00 — 20.00

MOMENT OF TRUTH, THE (1965)
Soundtrack....................Mainstream (M) 56057 — 5.00 — 7.50 — 10.00
Soundtrack....................Mainstream (S) S-6057 — 6.00 — 9.00 — 12.00

MONDO CANE
Soundtrack....................United Artists (M) UAL-4105 — 3.00 — 4.00 — 6.00
Soundtrack....................United Artists (S) UAS-5105 — 4.00 — 6.00 — 8.00

MONDO CANE NO. 2
Soundtrack....................20th Century Fox (S) TFS-4147 — 5.00 — 7.50 — 10.00
Soundtrack....................20th Century Fox (M) TFM 3147 — 4.00 — 6.00 — 8.00

MONDO HOLLYWOOD
Soundtrack....................Tower (M) T-5083 — 4.00 — 6.00 — 8.00
Soundtrack....................Tower (S) 5083 — 5.00 — 7.00 — 10.00

MONOLOGUES AND SONGS (1958)
Original Cast....................Elektra (M) EKL 184 — 7.50 — 11.25 — 15.00
  Joyce Grenfell with George Bauer at the piano.

MOON IS BLUE, THE (1953)
Soundtrack (1956)....................Crown (M) CLP-5095 — 5.00 — 7.50 — 10.00
Soundtrack....................Crown (S) CST-130 — 6.00 — 9.00 — 12.00

MOON SPINNERS, THE (1964)
Soundtrack....................Buena Vista (M) BV 3323 — 12.00 — 18.00 — 24.00

MORE
Soundtrack....................Tower (S) ST 5163 — 4.00 — 6.00 — 8.00

MORE THAN A MIRACLE
Soundtrack....................MGM (M) 4515 — 6.00 — 9.00 — 12.00
Soundtrack....................MGM (S) 4515 — 7.00 — 11.00 — 15.00

MOST HAPPY FELLA, THE (1956)
Original Cast (Songs, but no dialogue)....................Columbia (M) OL 5118 — 10.00 — 15.00 — 20.00
  Robert Weede, Jo Sullivan, Art Lund, Susan Johnson, Lee Cass.
Original Cast (Re-channeled stereo)....................Columbia (S) OS 2330 — 7.50 — 11.25 — 15.00
Original Cast (Songs and all dialogue)
  (3 records)....................Columbia (M) O3L 240 — 18.00 — 27.00 — 36.00
Original London Cast....................Angel (M) 35887 — 10.00 — 15.00 — 20.00
  Ina Wista, Helena Scott, Art Lund.
Original London Cast....................Angel (S) S 35887 — 12.00 — 18.00 — 24.00

MOTHER EARTH (1972)
Original Cast (Pre Broadway)....................Environmental (S) SP 1001 — 10.00 — 15.00 — 20.00
  Patti Austin, Dee Ervin, Carol Christy.

MOVIE STAR, AMERICAN STYLE
Soundtrack....................Mira (M) 3007 — 4.00 — 6.00 — 8.00
Soundtrack....................Mira (S) 3007 — 5.00 — 7.00 — 10.00

MOUNTAIN, THE (1956)
Soundtrack (1 Side)....................Decca (M) DL-8449 — 15.00 — 22.50 — 30.00

TITLE	LABEL & NO.	GOOD	VERY GOOD	NEAR MINT

M SQUAD (1958)
TV Soundtrack ....RCA (M) LPM-2062 — 6.00 — 9.00 — 12.00
TV Soundtrack ....RCA (S) LSP-2062 — 7.50 — 11.25 — 15.00

MUCH ADO ABOUT NOTHING (1965)
Original London Cast (3 records) ...... RCA (M) VDM 104 — 4.00 — 6.00 — 8.00
  Incidental music.
Original London Cast................ RCA (S) VDS 104 — 4.00 — 6.00 — 8.00

MUNSTERS, THE (1964)
TV Soundtrack (With Dialogue) .... Golden (M) LP-139 — 6.00 — 9.00 — 12.00

MURDERER'S ROW
Soundtrack .... Colgems (M) 5003 — 10.00 — 15.00 — 20.00
Soundtrack .... Colgems (S) 5003 — 12.00 — 19.00 — 25.00

MURDER, INC. (1960)
Soundtrack....Canadian-American (M) CALP-1003 — 12.00 — 18.00 — 24.00
  Sarah Vaughan.

MURDER ON THE ORIENT EXPRESS (1974)
Soundtrack .... Capitol (S) ST-11361 — 4.00 — 6.00 — 8.00

MURMER OF THE HEART (1972)
Soundtrack (Traditional jazz) .... Roulette (S) 3006 — 6.00 — 9.00 — 12.00

MURPH THE SURF (Alternate Title: Live A Little, Steal Alot) (1975)
Soundtrack...................... Motown (S) M6-839-S1 — 3.00 — 4.50 — 6.00

MUSCLE BEACH PARTY (1964)
Soundtrack.................. Buena Vista (M) BV-3314 — 7.50 — 11.25 — 15.00
Soundtrack.................. Buena Vista (S) ST-3314 — 10.00 — 15.00 — 20.00

MUSIC IN THE AIR (1932)
London Studio Cast
  (1 Side) .... World Record Club (M) T 121 — 10.00 — 15.00 — 20.00
  Marion Grimaldi, Andy Cole, Maggie Fitzgibbon,
  Gloria Swanson, John Boles, June Lang.
Soundtrack (From the 1930's film)
  (1 side) .... JJA (M) 1974 — 2.00 — 3.00 — 4.00
Studio Cast (1951) .... RCA (M) LK 1025 — 40.00 — 60.00 — 80.00
  With original revival cast star Jane Pickens.

MUSIC LOVERS
Soundtrack...................... United Artists (S) 5217 — 4.00 — 6.00 — 8.00

MUSIC MAN (1957)
Original Cast .... Capitol (M) WAO 990 — 2.00 — 3.00 — 4.00
  Robert Preston, Barbara Cook, David Burns, The Buffalo Bills.
Original Cast .... Capitol (S) SWAO 990 — 2.00 — 3.00 — 4.00
Original London Cast (1971) .... Stanyan (S) 10039 — 2.00 — 3.00 — 4.00
Soundtrack (From 1962 film) ...... Warner Bros. (M) B 1459 — 2.00 — 3.00 — 4.00
  Robert Preston, Shirley Jones, Buddy Hackett, Hermione Gingold,
  Paul Ford.
Soundtrack .... Warner Bros. (S) 1495 — 2.00 — 3.00 — 4.00

MUTINY ON THE BOUNTY
Soundtrack .... MGM (M) 1E 4 ST — 7.50 — 11.25 — 15.00
Soundtrack .... MGM (S) S1E 4 ST — 10.00 — 15.00 — 20.00

MY COUSIN JOSEFA (1969)
Original Cast (San Diego)............ Harlequin (S) H 3270 — 12.00 — 18.00 — 24.00
  Carla Alberghetti, Jack Ritschel, Leslie Cozzens.

MY FAIRFAX LADY (1957)
Original (San Francisco) Cast
  (Satire on "My Fair Lady") .... Jubilee (M) JGM 2030 — 10.00 — 15.00 — 20.00
  Bert Gordon, Carol Shannon, The Kirby Stone Four and starring
  Billy Gray.

MY FAIR LADY (1956)
Original Cast .... Columbia (M) OL 5090 — 7.50 — 11.25 — 15.00
  Rex Harrison, Julie Andrews, Stanley Holloway, Robert Coote.
Original Cast (Re-recorded in London,
  February 1, 1959 in stereo) .... Columbia (S) OS 2015 — 2.00 — 3.00 — 4.00
Soundtrack (From the 1964 film) ...... Columbia (M) OL 8000 — 2.00 — 3.00 — 4.00
  Same cast stars, some supporting cast changes.
  Audrey Hepburn, Rex Harrison, Stanley Holloway, Wilfrid Hyde-White,
  Theodore Bikel.
Soundtrack...................... Columbia (S) OS 2600 — 2.00 — 3.00 — 4.00
Original Italian Cast .... Columbia (M) OL 8060 — 7.50 — 11.25 — 15.00
  Delia Scala, Gianrico Tedeschi, Mario Carotenuto.
Studio Cast .... Diplomat (M) ND 2214 — 4.00 — 6.00 — 8.00
  (With original cast member Lola Fisher and Richard Torigi, Edgar powell,
  William Reynolds.)
TV Soundtrack (British) .... Avon (M) M 3001 — 7.50 — 11.25 — 15.00
  Hubert Gregg, Elizabeth Larner, John Slater.
Original German Revival Cast .... Philips (S) 840411 (SY) — 12.00 — 18.00 — 24.00
  Paul Hubschmid, Karin Huebner, Alfred Schieske.
Original Revival Cast .... Columbia (S) PS 34197 — 2.00 — 3.00 — 4.00
  (20th Anniversary)
  Ian Richardson, Christine Andreas, George Rose, Robert Coote.

TITLE	LABEL & NO.	GOOD	VERY GOOD	NEAR MINT

MY GEISHA
Soundtrack .... RCA (M) LOC-1070 — 10.00 — 15.00 — 20.00
Soundtrack .... RCA (S) LSO-1070 — 15.00 — 22.50 — 30.00

MY PEOPLE (1963)
Original Chicago Cast .... Contact (S) CS 1 — 10.00 — 15.00 — 20.00
Original Chicago Cast (1966) .... Contact (M) C 1 — 7.50 — 11.25 — 15.00
  Joya Sherrill, Lil Greenwood, Jimmy McPhail, The Irving Burton Singers
  with Duke Ellington.

MYRA BRECKINRIDGE (1970)
Soundtrack (Limited Release) ... 20th Century Fox (S) S-4210 — 15.00 — 22.50 — 30.00

MY SIDE OF THE MOUNTAIN (1969)
Soundtrack .... Capitol (S) ST 245 — 5.00 — 7.50 — 10.00

N

NAGSHEAD (1974)
Original Broadway Recording .... O. Barton (S) OBS 114 — 12.00 — 18.00 — 24.00
  (Due to open 1974 season, but didn't)
Soundtrack (Limited Release) .... JMI (S) 4005 — 5.00 — 7.50 — 10.00
  Phyllis Craig, Donald Lombardi, Lou Toby, Dick Gardner.

NAKED CITY (1958)
TV Soundtrack (With Dialogue) .... Colpix (M) CP-505 — 6.00 — 9.00 — 12.00
TV Soundtrack .... Colpix (S) SCP-505 — 7.50 — 11.25 — 15.00

NAKED MAJA
Soundtrack .... United Artists (M) UA-4031 — 10.00 — 15.00 — 20.00
Soundtrack .... United Artists (S) UAS-5031 — 12.00 — 19.00 — 25.00

NANCY GOES TO RIO (1950)
Soundtrack (10") .... MGM (M) E-508 — 12.00 — 18.00 — 24.00

NASHVILLE COYOTE (1974)

NASHVILLE REBEL (1966)
Soundtrack (Traditional country-western).......... RCA (M) LPM-3736 — 2.00 — 3.00 — 4.00
Soundtrack........................ RCA (S) LSP-3736 — 3.00 — 4.50 — 6.00

NAUGHTY MARIETTA (1910)
Soundtrack (10") (1952) .... RCA (M) LCT 16 — 10.00 — 15.00 — 20.00
Soundtrack (1966) (1 Side) .... RCA (M) LPV 526 — 2.00 — 3.00 — 4.00
Studio Cast .... RCA (M) LK 1005 — 7.50 — 11.25 — 15.00
  Earl Wrightson, Elain Malbin.
Studio Cast (Side 1,
  "Mademoiselle Modiste") .... RCA (M) LPM 3153 — 10.00 — 15.00 — 20.00
  Doretta Morrow, Felix Knight.

NED KELLY
Soundtrack...................... United Artists (S) 5213 — 3.00 — 4.00 — 6.00

NERVOUS SET (1959)
Original Cast .... Columbia (M) OL 5430 — 7.50 — 11.25 — 15.00
  Richard Hayes, Tani Seitz, Larry Hagman, Del Close.
Original Cast .... Columbia (S) OS 2018 — 10.00 — 15.00 — 20.00

NEVADA SMITH (1966)
Soundtrack .... Dot (M) 3718 — 5.00 — 7.50 — 10.00
Soundtrack .... Dot (S) 25718 — 10.00 — 15.00 — 20.00

(M) Mono (S) Stereo (EP) Extended Play (Q) Quad (RI) Re-issued

213

TITLE	LABEL & NO.	GOOD	VERY GOOD	NEAR MINT
NEW FACES OF 1952 (1952)				
Original Cast .... RCA (M) LOC 1008		10.00	15.00	20.00
Robert Clary, Eartha Kitt, Carol Lawrence, Paul Lynde.				
Original Cast (Re-Issue) .... RCA (M) CBM 1 2206		2.00	3.00	4.00
NEW FACES OF 1956 (1956)				
Original Cast .... RCA (M) LOC 1025		15.00	22.50	30.00
T.C. Jones, John Reardon, Maggie Smith.				
NEW FACES OF 1968 (1968)				
Original Cast .... Warner Bros. (S) BS 2551		7.50	11.25	15.00
Madeline Kahn, Leonard Sillman.				
NEW GIRL IN TOWN (1957)				
Original Cast .... RCA (M) LOC 1027		7.50	11.25	15.00
Gwen Verdon, Thelma Ritter, Cameron Prud'Homme.				
Original Cast .... RCA (S) LSO 1027		15.00	22.50	30.00
Original Cast (Re-issue, 1965) .... RCA (M) LOC 1106		4.00	6.00	8.00
Original Cast .... RCA (S) LSO 1106		5.00	7.50	10.00
NEW INTERNS, THE				
Soundtrack .... Colpix (M) CP 473		5.00	7.00	10.00
Soundtrack .... Colpix (S) SCP 473		7.00	11.00	15.00
NEW KIND OF LOVE, A (1963)				
Soundtrack .... Mercury (M) MG-20859		6.00	9.00	12.00
Soundtrack .... Mercury (S) SR-60859		7.50	11.25	15.00
NEW MOON (1928)				
Original London Cast				
(Sigmund Romberg conducting) . Monmouth Evergreen (M) MES 7051		2.00	3.00	4.00
Evelyn Laye, Ben Williams, Howett Worster, Gene Gerrard.				
Soundtrack (Side 2,				
"I Married An Angel") .... Pelican (M) LP 103		5.00	7.50	10.00
Jeanette MacDonald and Nelson Eddy.				
Soundtrack (10") .... Columbia (M) ML 2164		6.00	9.00	12.00
Studio Cast (Side 1,				
"Vagabond King") .... Capitol (M) T 219		7.50	11.25	15.00
Gordon MacRae and Lucille Norman.				
Studio Cast (Side 2, excerpts from				
"The Girl Friend") .... Epic (M) LN 3685		10.00	15.00	20.00
Doreen Hume, Bruce Trent.				
NICHOLAS & ALEXANDRA				
Soundtrack .... Bell (S) 1103		7.00	11.00	15.00

TITLE	LABEL & NO.	GOOD	VERY GOOD	NEAR MINT
NIGHT AT CARNEGIE HALL, A (1947)				
Soundtrack (10") (Traditional) (1950) .... Columbia (M) ML-2113		18.00	27.00	36.00
NIGHT IN VENICE, A (1952)				
Original Revival Cast (1959)				
(Off Broadway) .... Everest (M) 6028		7.50	11.25	15.00
Enzo Stuarti, Thomas Tibbet Hayward, Norwood Smith.				
Original Revival Cast .... Everest (S) 3028		10.00	15.00	20.00
NIGHT OF THE GENERALS				
Soundtrack .... Colgems (M) 5002		10.00	15.00	20.00
Soundtrack .... Colgems (S) 5002		15.00	22.00	30.00
NIGHT OF THE HUNTER (1955)				
Soundtrack (With Dialogue) .... RCA (M) LPM-1136		50.00	75.00	100.00
NIGHT OF THE IGUANA (1964)				
Soundtrack .... MGM (M) E 4247		5.00	7.50	10.00
Soundtrack .... MGM (S) SE 4247		6.00	9.00	12.00
NIGHT THEY RAIDED MINSKY'S				
Soundtrack .... United Artists (S) 5191		6.00	9.00	12.00
Album cover by Frank Frazetta.				
NIKKI, WILD DOG OF THE NORTH (1961)				
Soundtrack (With Dialogue) (1965) .... Disneyland (M) DQ-1281		4.00	6.00	8.00
NINE HOURS TO RAMA (1963)				
Soundtrack .... London (M) M 76002		17.25	37.50	50.00
NO FOR AN ANSWER (1941)				
Original Cast (With the composer, Blitzstein, at				
the piano) .... Theme (M) TALP 103		100.00	150.00	200.00
(1951, off Broadway)				
Carol Channing, Olive Deering, Lloyd Gough.				
Original Cast (Re-issue) .... JJA (M) 19772		2.00	3.00	4.00
NO MAN CAN TAME ME (1959)				
TV Soundtrack (Limited Release) .... Empire (M) EBC-597487		30.00	45.00	60.00
NO, NO, NANETTE (1925)				
Original Revival Cast (1971) .... Columbia (S) S 30563		2.00	3.00	4.00
Ruby Keeler, Jack Gilford, Bobby Van, Helen Gallagher.				
Studio Cast (1971) .... Columbia (S) AS 2 1023		10.00	15.00	20.00
Lee Jordan interviews members of the original cast. This LP also contains selected tracks from Columbia AS 2 1023.				
Original London Cast (1971 Re-issue)				
(Side 2, "Sunny") .... Stanyan (M) 10035		2.00	3.00	4.00
Binnie Hale, Seymour Beard, Gracie Leigh.				
Original London Revival Cast (1971) .... CBS (S) 70126		12.00	18.00	24.00
Anne Neagle, Anne Rogers, Thora Hird, Tony Britton.				
Soundtrack (From the 1950 film re-titled,				
"Tea For Two") '10") .... Columbia (M) CL 6149		12.00	18.00	24.00
Gene Nelson, Doris Day.				
Studio Cast (1 side) .... Epic (M) 3512		10.00	15.00	20.00
Bruce Trent, Doreen Hume.				
London Studio Cast .... Saga (S) 811		10.00	15.00	20.00
Mary Preston, John Parker, John Dane, Barry Monroe.				

(M) Mono (S) Stereo (EP) Extended Play (Q) Quad (RI) Re-issued

NORWOOD
Soundtrack . . . . .Capitol (S) SW 475   3.00   4.00   6.00

NO STRINGS (1962)
Original Cast . . . . .Capitol (M) O 1695   5.00   7.50   10.00
  Richard Kiley, Diahann Carroll, Noelle Adam
Original Cast . . . . Capitol (S) SO 1695   7.50   11.25   15.00
Original London Cast . . . . Decca (S) SKL 4576   12.00   18.00   24.00
  Art Lund, Beverly Todd, Hy Hazell.

NO SUN IN VENICE (1958)
Soundtrack . . . . Atlantic (M) 1284   2.00   3.00   4.00
Soundtrack . . . . .Atlantic (S) S-1284   3.00   4.50   6.00

NOTHING BUT A MAN (1965)
Soundtrack (Traditional rock) . . . . .Motown (M) 630   10.00   15.00   20.00
Soundtrack . . . . .Motown (S) S-630   12.00   18.00   24.00

NOTHING BUT THE BEST
Soundtrack . . . . Colpix (M) CP 477   7.00   11.00   15.00
Soundtrack . . . . .Colpix (S) SCP 477   10.00   15.00   20.00

NOT SO LONG AGO (1960)
TV Soundtrack (With Dialogue) . . . . .RCA (M) LOC-1055   4.00   6.00   8.00
TV Soundtrack . . . . RCA (S) LSO-1055   5.00   7.50   10.00

NOT WITH MY WIFE, YOU DON'T
Soundtrack . . . . .Warner Bros. (M) 1668   5.00   7.00   10.00
Soundtrack . . . . .Warner Bros. (S) 1668   6.00   9.00   12.00

NO WAY TO TREAT A LADY (1968)
Soundtrack . . . . .Dot (M) 3846   5.00   7.50   10.00
Soundtrack . . . . .Dot (S) 25846   6.00   9.00   12.00

NOW IS THE TIME FOR ALL GOOD MEN (1967)
Original Cast (Off Broadway) . . . . .Columbia (M) OL 6730   5.00   7.50   10.00
  Sally Niven, Judy Frank, David Cryer, Donna Curtis.
Original Cast .Columbia (S) OS 3130   7.50   11.25   15.00

NUNS STORY, THE
Soundtrack .Warner Bros. (M) B-1306   20.00   30.00   40.00
Soundtrack .Warner Bros. (S) WB-1306   30.00   40.00   60.00

NYMPH ERRANT
Original Cast (10")
(1 Side) (1954) .RCA (M) LRT 7001   12.00   18.00   24.00
  The music of Cole Porter.

O

OBA KOSA (The King Did Not Hang) (1975)
Original Cast (Recorded while on tour
  in Washington, D.C.) . . . . Kaleidophone (S) KS 2201   3.00   4.50   6.00
  Dance drama with Yoruba Festival Music performed by the Duro Ladipo
  National Theatre (Nigeria).

ODD COUPLE, THE (1968)
Soundtrack (With Dialogue) . . . . .Dot (S) 25862   6.00   9.00   12.00

ODDS AGAINST TOMORROW
Soundtrack . . . . United Artists (M) UAL-4061   12.00   19.00   25.00
Soundtrack . . . . United Artists (S) UAS-5061   15.00   22.00   30.00
Soundtrack (1 side) . . . . United Artists (M) DF-3   7.50   11.25   15.00
Soundtrack . . . . .United Artists (S) DFS-53   10.00   15.00   20.00

ODESSA FILE
Soundtrack . . . . MCA (S) 2084   3.00   4.00   6.00

OF LOVE & DESIRE (1963)
Soundtrack . . . . 20th Century Fox (M) FXG 5014   9.00   13.50   18.00
Soundtrack . . . . .20th Century Fox (M)SXG 5014   12.00   18.00   24.00

OF THEE I SING (1952)
Original Revival Cast . . . . Capitol (M) S 350   75.00   112.50   150.00
  Jack Carson, Paul Hartman, Jack Whiting.
Original Revival Cast (Re-issue) . . . . Capitol (M) T 11651   2.00   3.00   4.00
TV Soundtrack .Columbia (S) S 31763   10.00   15.00   20.00
  Carroll O'Conner, Jack Gilford, Cloris Leachman, Michelle Lee.

OH BOY ! (1917)
Original London Cast . . . . .World Record Club (M) SHB 321   7.50   11.25   15.00
  Dot Temple, Tom Powers, Beatrice Lillie, Billy Leonard.

(M) Mono   (S) Stereo   (EP) Extended Play   (Q) Quad   (RI) Re-issued

OH CALCUTTA! (The Open Window) (1969)
Original Cast . . . . Aidart (S) AID 9903   5.00   7.50   10.00
Original Australian Cast . . . . RCA (S) INTS 1178   7.50   11.25   15.00
  Peter Schickele, Stanley Walden.

OH CAPTAIN ! (1958)
Original Cast . . . . .Columbia (M) OL 5280   7.50   11.25   15.00
  Jacquelyn McKeever, Edward Platt, Susan Johnson, Tony Randall,
  Eileen Rodgers (singing the role of Abbe Lane, who was in the cast,
  but under a conflicting recording contract.)
Original Cast . . . . Columbia (S) AOS 2002   2.00   3.00   4.00
  (Stereo version unreleased until 1977)
Studio Cast . . . . MGM (M) E 3687   6.00   9.00   12.00
  Original cast producer Jose Ferrer and wife, Rosemary Clooney sing
  the score.

OH COWARD ! (1972)
Original Cast (2 records)
  (Off Broadway) . . . . .Bell (S) 9001   7.50   11.25   15.00

OH DAD, POOR DAD, MAMA'S HUNG YOU IN THE CLOSET AND I'M FEELING SO SAD (1967)
Soundtrack . . . . .RCA (M) LPM-3750   5.00   7.50   10.00
Soundtrack . . . . .RCA (S) LSP-3750   7.50   11.25   15.00

OH KAY ! (1926)
Original London Cast (With original cast star)
  (1 side) . . . . Monmouth Evergreen (M) MES 7043   2.00   3.00   4.00
  Excerpts by Gertrude Lawrence, Harold French, Claude Hulbert.
Original Revival Cast (Off Broadway)
  (1960) . . . . 20th Century Fox (M) 4003   10.00   15.00   20.00
  David Daniels, Marti Stevens, Bernie West.
Original Revival Cast . . . . 20th Century Fox (S) SFX 4003   15.00   22.50   30.00
Studio Cast . . . . .Columbia (M) CL 1050   6.00   9.00   12.00
  Barbara Ruick, Jack Cassidy, Allen Case, Roger White.

OH, ROSALINDA! (1957)
Soundtrack (Classical) . . . . .Mercury (M) MG-20145   18.00   27.00   36.00

OH WHAT A LOVELY WAR! (1964)
Original London Cast . . . . London (M) 5906   6.00   9.00   12.00
  Charles Chilton, Avis Bunnage, Fanny Carby.
Original London Cast . . . . .London (S) 25906   7.50   11.25   15.00
  (Traditional pop) . . . . Paramount (S) PAS 5008   5.00   7.50   10.00
  Dirk Bogarde, Phyllis Calvert, Jean Pierre Cassell, John Clements, John
  Gielgud, Jack Hawkins, Kenneth More, Laurence Olivier, Michael Red-
  grave, Vanessa Redgrave, Ralph Richardson, Maggie Smith, Susannah
  York, John Mills.
Studio Cast . . . . World Record Club (M) SH 130   7.50   11.25   15.00
  Original recordings of the World War I songs used in the stage play, taken
  from the original 78's by various recording artists of that period.

OIL TOWN, U.S.A. (1953)
Soundtrack (10") . . . . RCA (M) LFM-3000   12.00   18.00   24.00
Soundtrack (10") (1955) . . . . .ISR (M) 10043   7.50   11.25   15.00

OKLAHOMA (1943)
Original Cast (The first Broadway show to be recorded and released in its
  entirety on 78's. The re-release of the LP's are all excerpts)
  (1949) . . . . .Decca (M) DL 8000   15.00   22.50   30.00
  Alfred Drake, Joan Roberts, Howard daSylva, Celeste Holm, Lee Dixon.
Original Cast (1955) . . . . .Decca (M) DL 9017   10.00   15.00   20.00
Original Cast (Re-channeled stereo) . . . . .Decca (S) DL 79017   7.50   11.25   15.00
Soundtrack (From the 1955 film) . . . . .Capitol (M) WAO 595   2.00   3.00   4.00
  Gordon MacRae, Shirley Jones, Gloria Graham, Gene Nelson, Charlotte
  Greenwood, James Whitmore, Rod Steiger, J.C. Flippen
Soundtrack . . . . .Capitol (S) SWAO 595   2.00   3.00   4.00
Soundtrack (2 sides from a 3 record set)
  (1962) . . . . .Capitol (M) TCL 1790   4.00   6.00   8.00
Soundtrack . . . . .Capitol (S) STCL 1790   4.00   6.00   8.00

Studio Cast .... Columbia (M) CL 223 — 6.00 — 9.00 — 12.00
   Nelson Eddy, Virginia Haskins, Lee Cass, Kaye Ballard.
Original Touring Cast .... Columbia (M) OL 8010 — 2.00 — 3.00 — 4.00
   Stars John Raitt and Florence Henderson with supporting studio cast.
Original Touring Cast .... Columbia (S) OS 2610 — 2.00 — 3.00 — 4.00

OLD MAN AND THE SEA, THE (1958)
Soundtrack .... Columbia (M) CL-1183 — 12.00 — 18.00 — 24.00
Soundtrack .... Columbia (S) CS-8013 — 18.00 — 27.00 — 36.00

OLD YELLER (1957)
Soundtrack (With Dialogue) .... Disneyland (M) WDL-3024 — 7.50 — 11.25 — 15.00
Soundtrack (1960) .... Disneyland (M) WDL-1024 — 5.00 — 7.50 — 10.00
Soundtrack (1 side) (1964) .... Disneyland (M) DQ 1258 — 4.00 — 6.00 — 8.00

OLIVER (1962)
Original Cast .... RCA (M) LOCD 2004 — 2.00 — 3.00 — 4.00
   Clive Revill, Georgia Brown, Bruce Prochnik.
Original Cast .... RCA (S) LSOD 2004 — 2.00 — 3.00 — 4.00
Original London Cast .... Decca (M) SKL 4105 — 12.00 — 18.00 — 24.00
   Ron Moody, Georgia Brown, Paul Whitsum-Jones.
London Studio Cast .... Capitol (S) ST 1784 — 7.50 — 11.25 — 15.00
   Stanley Holloway, Alma Cogan, Violet Carson, Rita Williams.
Soundtrack (From the 1968 film) .... Colgems (S) COSD 5501 — 2.00 — 3.00 — 4.00
   Ron Moody, Oliver Reed, Harry Secombe.

OLYMPUS 7-0000 (1966)
TV Soundtrack .... Command (M) CS-07 — 4.00 — 6.00 — 8.00
TV Soundtrack .... Command (S) SCS-07 — 5.00 — 7.50 — 10.00

OMAR KHAYYAM (1957)
Soundtrack .... Decca (M) DL-8449 — 15.00 — 22.50 — 30.00

ON A CLEAR DAY, YOU CAN SEE FOREVER (1965)
Original Cast .... RCA (M) LOCD 2006 — 2.00 — 3.00 — 4.00
   Barbara Harris, John Cullum, Titos Vandis.
Original Cast .... RCA (S) LSOD 2006 — 2.00 — 3.00 — 4.00
Soundtrack (From the 1970 film) .... Columbia (S) S 30086 — 2.00 — 3.00 — 4.00
   Barbra Streisand, Yves Montand, Bob Newhart, Larry Blyden, Jack Nicholson.

ON ANY SUNDAY (1971)
Soundtrack .... Bell (S) 1206 — 7.50 — 11.25 — 15.00

ONCE A THIEF (1965)
Soundtrack .... Verve (M) MG-8624 — 5.00 — 7.50 — 10.00
Soundtrack .... Verve (S) 6-8624 — 6.00 — 9.00 — 12.00

ONCE UPON A MATTRESS (1959)
Original London Cast .... HMV (M) CLP 1410 — 18.00 — 27.00 — 36.00
   Jane Connell, Peter Grant, Patricia Lambert.
Original Cast .... Kapp (M) KDL 7004 — 6.00 — 9.00 — 12.00
   Carol Burnett, Joe Bova, Allen Case, Jack Gilford.
Original Cast .... Kapp (S) KDS 7004 — 7.50 — 11.25 — 15.00
Original Cast (1966) .... Kapp (M) KL 4507 — 2.00 — 3.00 — 4.00
Original Cast .... Kapp (S) KS 5507 — 2.00 — 3.00 — 4.00

ONE & ONLY, GENUINE, ORIGINAL FAMILY BAND
Soundtrack .... Buena Vista (M) BV 5002 — 4.00 — 6.00 — 8.00
Soundtrack .... Buena Vista (S) ST 5002 — 5.00 — 7.50 — 10.00

ONE-EYED JACKS
Soundtrack .... Liberty (M) LOM 16001 — 12.00 — 19.00 — 25.00
Soundtrack .... Liberty (S) LOS 17001 — 20.00 — 30.00 — 40.00

ONE HUNDRED AND ONE DALMATIANS (1961)
Soundtrack .... Disneyland (M) ST-4903 — 6.00 — 9.00 — 12.00

(M) Mono (S) Stereo (EP) Extended Play (Q) Quad (RI) Re-issued

---

110 IN THE SHADE (1963)
Original Cast .... RCA (M) LOC 1085 — 12.00 — 18.00 — 24.00
   Robert Horton, Inga Swenson, Stephen Douglass.
Original Cast .... RCA (S) LSO 1085 — 15.00 — 22.50 — 30.00

ONE OVER THE EIGHT (1961)
Original London Cast (1963) .... London (M) 5760 — 10.00 — 15.00 — 20.00

ONE STEP BEYOND (1960)
TV Soundtrack .... Decca (M) DL-8970 — 7.50 — 11.25 — 15.00
TV Soundtrack .... Decca (S) DL-78970 — 10.00 — 15.00 — 20.00

1001 ARABIAN NIGHTS (1959)
Soundtrack .... Colpix (M) CP-410 — 12.00 — 18.00 — 24.00
Soundtrack .... Colpix (S) SCP-410 — 15.00 — 22.50 — 30.00

ONE TOUCH OF VENUS (1943)
Original Cast .... Decca (M) DL 9122 — 15.00 — 22.50 — 30.00
   Mary Martin, Kenny Baker.
Original Cast (Re-channeled stereo)
   (1965) .... Decca (S) DL 7-9122 — 10.00 — 15.00 — 20.00

ON HER BED OF ROSES (1969)
Soundtrack .... Mira (M) 3006 — 7.50 — 11.25 — 15.00
Soundtrack .... Mira (S) 3006 — 10.00 — 15.00 — 20.00

ON HER MAJESTY'S SECRET SERVICE
Soundtrack .... United Artists (S) 5204 — 3.00 — 4.00 — 6.00

ON MOONLIGHT BAY (1951)
Soundtrack (10") .... Columbia (M) CL-6186 — 12.00 — 18.00 — 24.00

ON THE BEACH
Soundtrack .... Roulette (M) R-25098 — 12.00 — 18.00 — 24.00
Soundtrack .... Roulette (S) SR-25098 — 15.00 — 22.00 — 30.00

ON THE BRIGHTER SIDE (1963)
Original London Cast .... London (M) 5767 — 12.00 — 18.00 — 24.00

ON THE FLIP SIDE (1966)
TV Soundtrack .... Decca (M) DL-4836 — 4.00 — 6.00 — 8.00
TV Soundtrack .... Decca (S) DL-74836 — 6.00 — 9.00 — 12.00

ON THE TOWN
Original Cast (Side 2,
   "The Lute Song") (1950) .... Decca (M) DL 8030 — 12.00 — 18.00 — 40.00
   Lyn Murray, Betty Comden, Adolph Green, Mary Martin, Nancy Walker.
Original Cast .... Columbia (S) OS 2028 — 12.00 — 18.00 — 24.00
Original London Cast .... CBS (M) Apg 60005 — 12.00 — 18.00 — 24.00
   Elliott Gould, Don McKay, Franklin Kiser, Carol Arthur.
Original Cast Orchestra .... RCA (M) CAL 196 — 15.00 — 22.50 — 30.00
   Ballet music conducted by the composer, Leonard Bernstein.
Original Cast (Re-assembled for this
   recording in 1961) .... Columbia (M) OL 5540 — 2.00 — 3.00 — 4.00
   Nancy Walker, lyricists Betty Comden and Adolph Green, Cris Alexander,
   and conductor-composer Leonard Bernstein.
Original Cast .... Columbia (S) OS 2028 — 2.00 — 3.00 — 4.00
Original Cast .... Columbia (S) 31005 — 2.00 — 3.00 — 4.00
   Re-issue with one additional song, "Carnagie Hall."

ON YOUR TOES (1936)
Original London Cast (1 side) .... Monmouth Evergreen (M) MES 7049 — 2.00 — 3.00 — 4.00
   10 songs from the show by star, Jack Whiting.
Original Revival Cast (1954) .... Decca (M) DL 9015 — 15.00 — 22.50 — 30.00
   Vera Zorina, Bobby Van, Elaine Stritch, Ben Astar.
Studio Cast .... Columbia (M) CL 837 — 7.50 — 11.25 — 15.00
   Portia Nelson, Jack Cassidy, Laurel Shelby.

ORCHESTRA WIVES (1942)
Soundtrack (10") (1954) .... RCA (M) LPT-3065 — 5.00 — 7.50 — 10.00
Soundtrack (2 records) (1959) .... 20th Century Fox (M) TCF-100-2 — 5.00 — 7.50 — 10.00
Soundtrack .... 20th Century Fox (S) TCS-100-2 — 6.00 — 9.00 — 12.00

ORDER IS LOVE, THE (1971)
Original Cast (Mormon musical,
   Provo, Utah) .... Trilogy (S) T 1001 — 2.00 — 3.00 — 4.00
   Gordon Harkness, Rob Nuismer, Janey Luke.

ORIGINAL TV ADVENTURES OF KING KONG, THE (1966)
TV Soundtrack .... Epic (M) LN-24231 — 3.00 — 4.50 — 6.00
TV Soundtrack .... Epic (S) BN-26231 — 4.00 — 6.00 — 8.00

O SAY CAN YOU SEE! (1962)
Original Cast (Revived in 1972 under the title
   "Buy Bonds Buster") .... XTV (M) 87195 — 65.00 — 97.50 — 130.00
   Elmarie Wendel, Paul B. Price, Joyce Kerry, Joel Warfield.

OSCAR, THE
Soundtrack .... Columbia (M) OL-6550 — 7.00 — 11.00 — 15.00
Soundtrack .... Columbia (S) OS-2950 — 10.00 — 15.00 — 20.00

OTHER WORLD OF WINSTON CHURCHILL, THE (1965)
TV Soundtrack (With Dialogue)	Mercury (M) 21033	5.00	7.50	10.00
TV Soundtrack	Mercury (S) 61033	7.50	11.25	15.00

OTLEY (1968)
Soundtrack	Colgems (S) COS-112	7.50	11.25	15.00

OUR MAN FLINT
Soundtrack	20th Century Fox (M) TFM-4179	12.00	18.00	24.00
Soundtrack	20th Century Fox (S) TFS-4170	15.00	22.50	30.00

OUTLAW RIDERS
Soundtrack	MGM (S) 1 SE 26 ST	4.00	6.00	8.00

OUT OF SIGHT (1966)
Soundtrack	Decca (M) 4751	4.00	6.00	8.00
Soundtrack	Decca (S) 7-4751	5.00	7.50	10.00

OUT OF THIS WORLD (1950)
Original Cast	Columbia (M) OL 4390	7.50	11.25	15.00

Charlotte Greenwood, William Eythe, Priscilla Gillette, William Redfield.

OVER HERE ! (1974)
Original Cast	Columbia (S) KS 32961	10.00	15.00	20.00

Patty & Maxene Andrews, Douglass Watson, Mac Intyre Dixon, John Travolta.

OWL & THE PUSSYCAT
Soundtrack (With dialogue)	Columbia (S) S 30410	6.00	9.00	12.00

P

PACIFIC OVERTURES (1976)
Original Cast	RCA (S) ARL1 1367	2.00	3.00	4.00

Miko, Soon-Tech Oh, Yuki Shimoda, Sab Shimono.

PAGAN LOVE SONG (1950)
Soundtrack (10")	MGM (M) E-534	10.00	15.00	20.00

PAINTED SMILES OF COLE PORTER
Studio Cast (Unproduced revue)	Painted Smiles (S) PS 1358	2.00	3.00	4.00

Blossom Dearie, Carmen Alvarez, Karen Morrow.

PAINTING THE CLOUDS WITH SUNSHINE (1951)
Soundtrack (10")	Capitol (M) L-291	20.00	30.00	40.00

PAINT YOUR WAGON (1951)
Original Cast	RCA (M) LOC 1006	10.00	15.00	20.00
	James Barton, Olga San Juan, Tony Bavaar, Rufus Smith.			
Original Cast (Re-channeled stereo)	RCA (S) LSO 1006	6.00	9.00	12.00
Soundtrack (From the 1969 film)	Paramount (S) PMS 1001	5.00	7.50	10.00

Lee Marvin, Clint Eastwood, Jean Seberg, Ray Walston, Tom Ligon.

PAJAMA GAME (1954)
Original Cast	Columbia (M) OL 4840	7.50	11.25	15.00
	John Raitt, Janis Paige, Eddie Foy, Jr., Carol Haney, Reta Shaw.			
Original London Cast	HMV (M) 1062	15.00	22.50	30.00
	Edmund Hockridge, Max Well, Joy Nichols, Elizabeth Seal.			
Soundtrack (From the 1957 film)	Columbia (M) OL 5210	10.00	15.00	20.00

Doris Day, John Raitt, Carol Haney, Eddie Foy, Jr., Reta Shaw, Barbara Nichols.

PAJAMA PARTY (1964)
Soundtrack	Buena Vista (M) BV-3325	5.00	7.50	10.00
Soundtrack	Buena Vista (S) ST-3325	6.00	9.00	12.00

PAL JOEY (1952)
Original Revival Cast	Capitol (M) S 310	36.00	54.00	72.00
	Helen Gallagher, Patricia Northrop, Elaine Strich.			
Original Revival Cast & Studio Cast (1951)	Columbia (M) OL 4364	7.50	11.25	15.00
	Vivienne Segal, Harold Lang.			
Soundtrack (From the 1957 film)	Capitol (M) W 912	7.50	11.25	15.00
	Frank Sinatra, Rita Hayworth, Kim Novak.			
Soundtrack (Re-channeled stereo)	Capitol (S) DW 912	4.00	6.00	8.00

PALM SPRINGS WEEKEND (1963)
Soundtrack	Warner Bros. (M) W-1519	10.00	15.00	20.00
Soundtrack	Warner Bros. (S) WS-1519	12.00	18.00	24.00

PANIC BUTTON (1964)
Soundtrack	Musicor (M) MM-2026	15.00	22.50	30.00
Soundtrack	Musicor (S) MS-3026	20.00	30.00	40.00

PAPILLON
Soundtrack	Capitol (S) ST-11260	4.00	6.00	8.00

PARADE (1960)
Original Cast	Kapp (M) KLD 7005	50.00	75.00	100.00
	Dody Goodman, Richard Tone, Fia Karin, Charles Nelson Reilly.			
Original Cast	Kapp (S) KDS 7005	65.00	97.50	130.00

PARADISE, HAWAIIAN STYLE (1966)
Soundtrack	RCA (M) LPM 3643	5.00	10.00	15.00
	Elvis Presley.			
Soundtrack	RCA (S) LSP 3643	5.00	10.00	15.00

PARENT TRAP, THE
Soundtrack	Buena Vista (M) BV 3309	7.50	11.25	15.00
Soundtrack	Buena Vista (S) ST 3309	10.00	15.00	20.00

PARIS BLUES (1961)
Soundtrack	United Artists (M) UAL-4092	4.00	6.00	8.00
Soundtrack	United Artists (S) UAS-5092	6.00	9.00	12.00
Soundtrack (1964)	Ascot (M) UM 13502	3.00	4.50	6.00
Soundtrack	Ascot (S) US 16502	4.00	6.00	8.00

PARIS HOLIDAY (1958)
Soundtrack	United Artists (M) UAL-40001	15.00	22.50	30.00

PARIS HONEYMOON (1939)
Soundtrack (10") (1951) (1 Side)	Decca (M) DL-6012	6.00	9.00	12.00
Soundtrack (1 Side) (1962)	Decca (M) DL-4253	3.00	4.50	6.00

PARIS '90 (1952)
Original Cast	Columbia (M) ML 4619	45.00	67.50	90.00

Cornelia Otis Skinner.

PARIS WHEN IT SIZZLES (1964)
Soundtrack	Reprise (M) R-6113	5.00	7.50	10.00
Soundtrack	Reprise (S) RS-6113	6.00	9.00	12.00

PARRISH (1961)
Soundtrack	Warner Bros. (M) W 1413	6.00	9.00	12.00
Soundtrack	Warner Bros. (S) WS 1413	7.50	11.25	15.00

PARTY, THE (1968)
Soundtrack	RCA (M) LPM-3997	4.00	6.00	8.00
Soundtrack	RCA (S) LSP-3997	5.00	7.50	10.00

(M) Mono (S) Stereo (EP) Extended Play (Q) Quad (RI) Re-issued

PARTY WITH BETTY COMDEN & ADOLPH GREEN, A (1958)

Original Cast .... *Capitol (M) WAO 1197* 10.00 15.00 20.00
Comden and Green sing selections from their shows (recorded live).
Original Cast .... *Capitol (S) SWAO 1197* 18.00 27.00 36.00

PASSING FAIR (1965)

Original Cast (Intended for Broadway,
but never opened) .... *Proscenium (M) PR 25* 12.00 18.00 24.00
Composer Jim Chapin and Valentine Pringle, Mary Louise, Bill Dillard,
Dolores Perry and Mark Donald.

PATCH OF BLUE, A

Soundtrack .... *Mainstream (M) 56058* 7.00 11.00 15.00
Soundtrack .... *Mainstream (S) 6058* 10.00 15.00 20.00

PATTON

Soundtrack .... *20th Century Fox (S) S-4208* 3.00 4.50 6.00

PAUL SILLS' STORY THEATRE (1970)

Original Cast (Off Broadway)
(2 records) .... *Columbia (S) SG 30415* 3.00 4.50 6.00
Peter Bonerz, Hamid Hamilton Camp, Valerie Harper.

PAWNBROKER, THE

Soundtrack .... *Mercury (M) MG-21011* 6.00 9.00 12.00
Soundtrack .... *Mercury (S) SR-61011* 7.00 11.00 15.00

PEACE (1969)

Original Cast (Off Broadway)
(Limited Release) .... *Metromedia (S) MP 33001* 18.00 27.00 36.00
Cast of 16, billed alphabetically.

PEACH THIEF, THE

Soundtrack (1967) .... *Roulette (M) R 804* 7.50 11.25 15.00
Soundtrack .... *Roulette (S) SR 804* 9.00 13.50 18.00

PECOS BILL (1948)

Soundtrack (1 Side) (1964) .... *Camden (M) CAL-1054* 4.00 6.00 8.00
Soundtrack (Re-channeled stereo) .... *Camden (S) CAS-1054* 3.00 4.50 6.00

PENELOPE (1966)

Soundtrack .... *MGM (M) E-4426* 4.00 6.00 8.00
Soundtrack .... *MGM (S) SE-4426* 5.00 7.50 10.00

PENTHOUSE, THE (1968)

Soundtrack .... *United Artists (M) 4170* 6.00 9.00 12.00
Soundtrack .... *United Artists (S) 5170* 7.50 11.25 15.00

PEPE

Soundtrack .... *Colpix (M) CP 507* 6.00 9.00 12.00
Soundtrack .... *Colpix (S) SCP 507* 10.00 15.00 20.00

PERFORMANCE

Soundtrack .... *Warner Bros. (S) BS 2554* 7.00 11.00 15.00

PERRI (1957)

Soundtrack (With Dialogue) .... *Disneyland (M) ST-3902* 6.00 9.00 12.00
Soundtrack (With Dialogue) (1961) . *Disneyland (M) ST-1909* 5.00 7.50 10.00
Soundtrack (With Dialogue) (1967) . *Disneyland (M) ST-1309* 4.00 6.00 8.00

PETE KELLY'S BLUES (1955)

Soundtrack (Traditional jazz) ...... *Columbia (M) CL-690* 4.00 6.00 8.00
Soundtrack (Traditional jazz) .... *Decca (M) DL-8166* 4.00 6.00 8.00

PETE KELLY'S BLUES (1959)

TV Soundtrack .... *Warner Bros. (M) W-1303* 6.00 9.00 12.00
TV Soundtrack .... *Warner Bros. (S) WS-1303* 7.50 11.25 15.00

PETER AND THE WOLF (1946)

Soundtrack (Classical) (1 Side) (1958) ... *Disneyland (M) WDL-3016* 6.00 9.00 12.00
Soundtrack (Classical) (1 Side) (1960) ... *Disneyland (M) WDL-1016* 5.00 7.50 10.00
Soundtrack (Classical) (1 Side) (1963) ... *Disneyland (M) DQ-1242* 4.00 6.00 8.00

PETER GUNN (1958)

TV Soundtrack, Vol. 2 (1959) .... *RCA (M) LPM-2040* 4.00 6.00 8.00
TV Soundtrack .... *RCA (S) LSP-2040* 6.00 9.00 12.00

PETER PAN (Bernstein) (1950)

Original Cast .... *Columbia (M) OL 4312* 7.50 11.25 15.00
Jean Arthur, Boris Karloff, Marcia Henderson.

PETER PAN (Charlap) (1954)

Original Cast .... *RCA (M) LOC 1019* 2.00 3.00 4.00
Mary Martin, Cyrill Ritchard, Kathy Nolan.
Original Cast (Re-channeled stereo) .... *RCA (S) LSO 1019* 2.00 3.00 4.00

(M) Mono   (S) Stereo   (EP) Extended Play   (Q) Quad   (RI) Re-issued

PETTICOATS & PETTIFOGERS (1969)

Original Cast
(Jackson Hole, Wyoming) .... *Creative Sound (S) CSS 1525* 15.00 22.50 30.00
Neldon Maxfield, Lynne Youngreen, Michael Edwards.

PETULIA (1968)

Soundtrack .... *Warner Bros. (S) 1755* 7.50 11.25 15.00

PEYTON PLACE (1957)

Soundtrack .... *RCA (M) LOC-1042* 12.00 18.00 24.00
Soundtrack .... *RCA (S) LSO-1042* 18.00 27.00 36.00

PHANTOM OF THE PARADISE

Soundtrack .... *A&M (S) 3653* 4.00 6.00 8.00

PHILEMON (1975)

Original Cast .... *Gallery (S) OC 1* 7.50 11.25 15.00
Michael Glenn-Smith, Virginia Gregory, Drew Katzman.

PHOENIX '55 (1955)

Original Cast (Off Broadway)
(1 side) .... *Dolphin (M) 2* 6.00 9.00 12.00

PICKWICK (1965)

Original London Cast .... *Phillips (S) SAL 3431* 12.00 18.00 24.00
Harry Secombe, Jessie Evans, Anton Rodgers.

PICNIC (1955)

Soundtrack .... *Decca (M) DL-8320* 4.00 6.00 8.00
Soundtrack (Re-channeled stereo) ...... *Decca (S) 78320* 3.00 4.50 6.00

PIECES OF EIGHT (1959)

Original Cast .... *Offbeat (M) O 4016* 10.00 15.00 20.00
Ceil Cabot, Del Close, Jane Connell.
Original London Cast (1963) .... *London (M) 5761* 10.00 15.00 20.00

PIED PIPER OF HAMELIN, THE (1957)

TV Soundtrack (Classical) .... *RCA (M) LPM-1563* 18.00 27.00 36.00

PINOCCHIO (1940)

Soundtrack (1956) .... *Disneyland (M) WDL-4002* 7.50 11.25 15.00

PINOCCHIO (1957)

TV Soundtrack (Wilder) .... *Columbia (M) CL-1055* 18.00 27.00 36.00

PINS & NEEDLES (1937)

Studio Cast (With composer) .... *Columbia (S) OS 2210* 2.00 3.00 4.00
Harold Rome, Barbra Streisand, Jack Carroll, Rose Marie Jun.

PIPE DREAM (1955)

Original Cast .... *RCA (M) LOC 1023* 12.00 18.00 24.00
Helen Traubel, William Johnson, Judy Tyler.
Original Cast (Re-issue) .... *RCA (M) LOC 1097* 9.00 13.50 18.00
Original Cast (Re-channeled stereo)
(1965) .... *RCA (S) LSO 1097* 6.00 9.00 12.00

PIPPIN (1972)

Original Cast .... *Motown (S) M 760L* 2.00 3.00 4.00
Eric Berry, Jill Clayburgh, Leland Palmer.

PIRATE, THE (1948)

Soundtrack (10") (1951) .... *MGM (M) E-21* 7.50 11.25 15.00
Soundtrack (1 Side) .... *MGM (M) E-3234* 5.00 7.50 10.00

PLAIN & FANCY (1955)

Original Cast .... *Capitol (M) S 603* 10.00 15.00 20.00
Richard Derr, Barbara Cook, David Daniels.
London Studio Cast .... *Dot (M) DLP 3048* 7.50 11.25 15.00
Virginia Sommers, Jack Drummond, Grace O'Connor.

PLANET OF THE APES

Soundtrack .... *Project 3 (S) 5023* 3.00 4.00 6.00

PLAYGIRLS (1964)

Original Las Vegas Cast .... *Warner Bros. (M) W 1530* 5.00 7.50 10.00
Cara Williams, Kay Stevens, Julie Wilson, Connie Russell.
Original Las Vegas Cast .... *Warner Bros. (S) WS 1530* 7.50 11.25 15.00

PLAYTIME (1968)

Soundtrack .... *United Artists (S) 15554* 4.00 6.00 8.00

PLEASURE SEEKERS, THE

Soundtrack .... *RCA (M) LOC-1101* 7.50 11.25 15.00
Soundtrack .... *RCA (S) LSO-1101* 10.00 15.00 20.00

PLYMOUTH ADVENTURE (1952)

Soundtrack (10") .... *MGM (M) E-179* 20.00 30.00 40.00
Soundtrack (1957) .... *MGM (M) E-3507* 12.00 18.00 24.00

POINT OF ORDER
Soundtrack	Columbia (M) KOL 6070	3.00	4.00	6.00
Soundtrack	Columbia (S) KOS 2470	3.00	4.00	6.00

POLLYANNA (1960)
Soundtrack (With Dialogue)	Disneyland (M) ST-1906	6.00	9.00	12.00
Soundtrack (With Dialogue) (1967)	Disneyland (M) DQ-1307	4.00	6.00	8.00

POLONAISE (1945)
Original Cast and Studio Cast
(Side 2, "Eileen")	RCA (M) CAL 210	12.00	18.00	24.00

Earl Wrightson, Rose Inghram, Mary Martha Briney.

POMEGRANADA (1966)
Original Cast (Off Broadway)
(Limited release)	Patsan (M) PS 1101	20.00	30.00	40.00

Michael Elias, Burton Supree, Margaret Wright, David Vaughn.

POPI
Soundtrack	United Artists (S) 5194	5.00	7.00	10.00

PORGY & BESS (1935)
Original Cast (10") (1950)	Decca (M) DL 7006	20.00	30.00	40.00

Excerpts from the original 1930's cast with Todd
Duncan and Anne Brown, taken from 78's recorded
in 1940.
Original Revival Cast (1952)	Decca (M) DL 8042	15.00	22.50	30.00

From 78's recorded during the 1942 revival with
Todd Duncan, Anne Brown, Eva Jessye Choir, Edward
Matthews, Helen Dowdy, Avon Long.
Original Revival Cast (1955 Re-issue)	Decca (M) DL 9024	10.00	15.00	20.00
Original Revival Cast (Re-channeled stereo)	Decca (S) DL 79024	6.00	9.00	12.00
Soundtrack (From the 1959 film)	Columbia (M) OL 5410	2.00	3.00	4.00

Sidney Poitier, Dorothy Dandridge, Sammy Davis, Jr., Pearl Bailey.
Soundtrack	Columbia (S) OS 2016	2.00	3.00	4.00
Studio Cast	RCA (M) LOC 1507	6.00	9.00	12.00

Lena Horne, Harry Belafonte.
Studio Cast	RCA (S) LOS 1507	7.50	11.25	15.00
Original Cast & Studio Cast (3 records)	Columbia (M) OSL 162	20.00	30.00	40.00

Lawrence Winters, Camilla Williams, Inez Matthews, Avon Long, Helen
Dowdy, Eddie Matthews.
Studio Cast (First complete recording) (3 records)	London (S) OSA 13116	4.00	6.00	8.00

Willard White, Leona Mitchell, McHenry Boatwright, Florence Quivar,
with Lorin Maazel conducting the Cleveland Orchestra and Chorus.
Studio Cast (Jazz version with two full orchestras and three Jazz groups)	Bethlehem (M) EXLP 1	18.00	27.00	36.00

Francis Faye, Mel Torme, and cast.
Studio Cast (2 records)	RCA (S) CPL2 1831	3.00	4.50	6.00

Ray Charles, Cleo Laine.
Original Revival Cast (With the Houston Grand Opera) (1976) (3 records)	RCA (S) ARL3 2109	4.00	6.00	8.00

Donnie Ray Alberts, Clamma Dale.

POSTCARD FROM MOROCCO (1972)
Original Cast (Center Opera of Minnesota)
(2 recrods)	Desto (S) DC 7137 8	3.00	4.50	6.00

Barbara Brandt, Barry Busse, Michael Foreman.

PREMISE, THE (1960)
Original Cast (Skits from the
production)	Vanguard (M) VRS 9092	10.00	15.00	20.00

Theodore J. Flicker, Joan Darling, George Segal, Thomas Aldredge.

PRETTY BOY FLOYD (1960)
Soundtrack	Audio Fidelity (M) 1936	7.50	11.25	15.00
Soundtrack	Audio Fidelity (S 5936	10.00	15.00	20.00

PRIDE AND THE PASSION, THE (1957)
Soundtrack	Capitol (M) W-873	15.00	22.50	30.00

PRIME OF MISS JEAN BRODIE, THE (1969)
Soundtrack	20th Century Fox (S) 4207	4.00	6.00	8.00

PRINCE AND THE PAUPER, THE (1963)
Original Cast	London (M) 28001	7.50	11.25	15.00

Budd Mann, Joe Bousard, Joan Shepard, Robert McHaffey.
Original Cast	London (S) 98001	10.00	15.00	20.00
Soundtrack (With Dialogue)	Disneyland (M) ST-1912	6.00	9.00	12.00
Soundtrack (1967)	Disneyland (M) DQ-1311	4.00	6.00	8.00

PRIVATE HELL 36 (1954)
Soundtrack (10")	Coral (M) 56122	10.00	15.00	20.00
Soundtrack (1958)	Coral (M) 57283	15.00	22.50	30.00

PRIVILEGE (1967)
Soundtrack	Universal (M) 3005	5.00	7.50	10.00
Soundtrack	Universal (S) 73005	6.00	9.00	12.00

(M) Mono   (S) Stereo   (EP) Extended Play   (Q) Quad   (RI) Re-issued

PRIZE, THE (1963)
Soundtrack	MGM (M) E-4192	4.00	6.00	8.00
Soundtrack	MGM (S) SE-4192	5.00	7.50	10.00

PRODUCERS, THE (1968)
Soundtrack (With Dialogue)	RCA (S) LSP-4008	5.00	7.50	10.00

PROFESSIONALS, THE
Soundtrack	Colgems (M) 5001	12.00	19.00	25.00
Soundtrack	Colgems (S) 5001	15.00	22.00	30.00

PROMENADE (1969)
Original Cast
	RCA (S) LSO 1161	7.50	11.25	15.00

Margot Albert, Shannon Bolin, Michael Davis.

PROMISE HER ANYTHING (1966)
Soundtrack	Kapp (M) KL-1476	3.00	4.50	6.00
Soundtrack	Kapp (S) KS-3476	4.00	6.00	8.00

PROMISES, PROMISES (1968)
Original Cast	United Artists (S) S 9902	2.00	3.00	4.00

Jerry Orbach, Jill O'Hara, Edward Winter, Donna McKechnie.
Original London Cast	United Artists (S) S 29075	12.00	18.00	24.00

Anthony Roberts, Betty Buckley, James Congdon, Donna McKechnie
Original Italian Cast	CGD (S) FGS 5063	12.00	18.00	24.00

Catherine Spaak, Johnny Dorelli, Bice Valori.
Studio Cast	Fontana (S) SFL 13192	7.50	11.25	15.00

Aimi MacDonald and Ronnie Carroll.

PRUDENCE & THE PILL
Soundtrack	20th Century Fox (S) 4199	7.50	11.25	15.00

P.S. I LOVE YOU
Soundtrack	Mercury (S) SRMI 610	3.00	4.00	6.00

PSYCH-OUT
Soundtrack	Sidewalk (S) ST-5913	4.00	6.00	8.00

PUFNSTUF (1970)
Soundtrack	Capitol (S) SW 542	4.00	6.00	8.00

PURLIE (1970)
Original Cast
	Ampex (S) A 40101	12.00	18.00	24.00

Cleavon Little, Melba Moore, John Heffernan.

Q

QUICK, BEFORE IT MELTS (1964)
Soundtrack	MGM (M) E-4285	4.00	6.00	8.00
Soundtrack	MGM (S) SE-4285	5.00	7.50	10.00

QUIET CITY, THE (1939)
Original Cast (Incidental music)	Columbia (S) MS 7375	3.00	4.50	6.00

QUIET DAYS IN CLICHY
Soundtrack	Vanguard (S) 79303	6.00	9.00	12.00

QUIET MAN, THE (1952)
Soundtrack (10")	RCA (M) LPM-3089	7.50	11.25	15.00
Soundtrack (10")	Decca (M) DL-5411	6.00	9.00	12.00
Soundtrack (1957)	Decca (M) DL 8566	5.00	7.50	10.00

QUILLER MEMORANDUM, THE (1966)
Soundtrack	Columbia (M) OL-6660	12.00	18.00	24.00
Soundtrack	Columbia (S) OS-3060	18.00	27.00	36.00

QUO VADIS (1951)
Soundtrack (two 10" LP's)	MGM (M) E-103	15.00	22.50	24.00
Soundtrack (With Dialogue) (1957)	MGM (M) E-3524	12.00	18.00	24.00

R

RAGA (1971)
Soundtrack (Ravi Shankar)	Apple (S) SWAO-3384	5.00	7.50	10.00

RAGE TO LIVE, A (1965)
Soundtrack	United Artists (M) UAL-4130	5.00	7.50	10.00
Soundtrack	United Artists (S) UAS-5130	6.00	9.00	12.00

RAILWAY CHILDREN
Soundtrack...................................... Capitol (S) SW-871 6.00 9.00 12.00

RAINBOW BRIDGE
Soundtrack...................................... Reprise (S) 2040 3.00 4.00 6.00

RAINMAKER, THE (1956)
Soundtrack...................................... RCA (M) LPM-1434 18.00 27.00 36.00

RAINTREE COUNTY (1957)
Soundtrack (2 Record Set)................... RCA (M) LOC-6000 50.00 75.00 100.00

Soundtrack...................................... RCA (M) LOC-1038 15.00 22.50 30.00
Soundtrack...................................... RCA (S) LSO-1038 20.00 30.00 40.00

RAISIN (1973)
Original Cast .... Columbia (S) KS 32754 2.00 3.00 4.00
Virginia Capers, Joe Morton, Ernestine Jackson.

RASHOMON (1952)
Original Cast (Incidental music) .... Carlton (M) 5000 15.00 22.50 30.00
Original Cast .... Carlton (S) S 5000 20.00 30.00 40.00

RAT RACE, THE (1960)
Soundtrack (Cover version of Jazz Tracks).......... Dot (M) DLP-3306 10.00 15.00 20.00

REBEL WITHOUT A CAUSE (1955)
Soundtrack (1 Side) .... Columbia (M) CL-940 5.00 7.50 10.00
Soundtrack (1 side) (1957) .... Imperial (M) 9021 4.00 6.00 8.00

RED GARTERS (1954)
Soundtrack (10")................ Columbia (M) CL-6282 10.00 15.00 20.00

REDHEAD
Original Cast .... RCA (M) LOC 1048 5.00 7.50 10.00
Gwen Verdon, Richard Kiley, Leonard Stone.
Original Cast .... RCA (S) LSO 1048 7.50 11.25 15.00
Original Cast (Re-issue) (1965) .... RCA (M) LOC 1104 3.00 4.50 6.00
Original Cast .... RCA (S) LSO 1104 5.00 7.50 10.00

RED, HOT AND BLUE (1936)
Original Cast (1 side) (1956)................... Decca (M) DX 153 7.50 11.25 15.00
Ethel Merman.
Original Cast (1 side) (1965).................... JJC (M) M 3004 5.00 7.50 10.00
Original Cast (Re-channeled stereo) .... JJC (S) ST 3004 4.00 6.00 8.00

RED HOUSE, THE (1947)
Soundtrack (10") (1953) .... Capitol (M) L-453 7.50 11.25 15.00
Soundtrack (1953) .... Capitol (M) T 456 6.00 9.00 12.00

RED MILL (1906)
Studio Cast (Side 1, "Up In Central Park")
(1950) .... Decca (M) DL 8016 7.50 11.25 15.00
Wilbur Evans, Eileen Farrell, Felix Knight.
Studio Cast (Side 1, "Babes In Toyland")
(1957) .... Decca (M) DL 8458 7.50 11.25 15.00
Side 2 is re-issue of Decca DL 8016.

RED SKY AT MORNING
Soundtrack...................................... Decca (S) 79180 3.00 4.00 6.00

RED TENT
Soundtrack...................................... Paramount (S) 6019 5.00 7.00 10.00

REGINA (1958)
Original Revival Cast (Off Broadway)
(3 records).................... Columbia (M) 03L 260 12.00 18.00 24.00
Brenda Lewis, Elisabeth Carron, Carol Brice, Joshua Hecht.
Original Revival Cast.................... Columbia (S) 03S 202 20.00 30.00 40.00

REIVERS, THE
Soundtrack...................................... Columbia (S) OS 3510 5.00 7.50 10.00

REPORTER, THE (1963)
TV Soundtrack .... Columbia (M) CL-2269 6.00 9.00 12.00
TV Soundtrack .... Columbia (S) CS-9069 7.50 11.25 15.00

RESTLESS ONES, THE (1965)
Soundtrack...................................... Supreme (M) M-110 5.00 7.50 10.00
Soundtrack...................................... Supreme (S) MS-210 6.00 9.00 12.00

RETURN OF THE SEVEN
Soundtrack...................................... United Artists (M) 4146 5.00 7.00 10.00
Soundtrack...................................... United Artists (S) 5146 6.00 9.00 12.00

RETURN TO PARADISE (1953)
Soundtrack (With Dialogue) (10") .... Decca (M) DL-5489 25.00 37.50 50.00

REVOLUTION
Soundtrack...................................... United Artists (S) 5185 2.50 3.75 5.00

REVUERS, THE (1938)
Original Cast (With Leonard Bernstein at
the piano) .... JJA (M) 19764 2.00 3.00 4.00
Betty Comden, Adolph Green, Judy Holliday, John Frank, Alvin Hammer.

REX (1976)
Original Cast .... RCA (S) ABL1 1683 2.00 3.00 4.00
Nicol Williamson, Penny Fuller, Tom Aldredge.

RHAPSODY OF STEEL (1958)
Soundtrack...................................... US Steel (M) 502 36.00 54.00 72.00

RHYTHM ON THE RANGE (1936)
Soundtrack (10") (1 Side) (1951) .... Decca (M) DL-6010 5.00 7.50 10.00

RICH, YOUNG AND PRETTY (1951)
Soundtrack (10")........................ MGM (M) E-86 10.00 15.00 20.00
Soundtrack (1955) (1 side) .... MGM (M) E-3236 6.00 9.00 12.00

RICHARD DIAMOND (1959)
TV Soundtrack .... Mercury (M) 36162 6.00 9.00 12.00
TV Soundtrack .... Mercury (S) 80045 7.50 11.25 15.00

RICHARD III (1956)
Soundtrack (With Dialogue)
(3 Record Set) .... RCA (M) LM-6126 12.00 18.00 24.00

RIDER ON THE RAIN (1970)
Soundtrack...................................... Capitol (S) ST 584 5.00 7.50 10.00

RIDE THE WILD SURF (1964)
Soundtrack...................................... Liberty (M) LRP-3368 2.00 3.00 4.00
Soundtrack...................................... Liberty (S) LST-7368 3.00 4.50 6.00

RIO RITA (1927)
Original London Cast
(1 side) .... Monmouth Evergreen (M) MES 7058 2.00 3.00 4.00
Edith Day and Geoffrey Gwyther.
Studio Cast (Side 2, "Connecticut Yankee")
(1952) .... RCA (M) LK 1026 10.00 15.00 20.00
Earl Wrightson and Elaine Malbin.
London Studio Cast (Side 2, "The Great Waltz,"
a 1938 film version)...... World Record Club (S) S 7056 12.00 18.00 24.00
Neil Williams and Rosalind Keene.

RIOT ON THE SUNSET STRIP (1967)
Soundtrack...................................... Tower (M) T-5065 4.00 6.00 8.00
Soundtrack...................................... Tower (S) DT-5065 4.00 6.00 8.00

RISE & FALL OF THE CITY OF MAHOGANNY, THE (1931)
Studio Cast (With original cast star, sung in German)
(3 records) (1958) .... Columbia (M) K3L 243 4.00 6.00 8.00
Lotte Lenya, Gisela Litz, Sigmund Roth, Richard Munch & the North German Radio Chorus.
Studio Cast (1 side) (1955) .... Columbia (M) KL 5056 2.00 3.00 4.00

RISE AND FALL OF THE THIRD REICH (1968)
TV Soundtrack (With Dialogue).................... MGM (M) 1E-12 5.00 7.50 10.00
TV Soundtrack .... MGM (S) 1SE-12 6.00 9.00 12.00

TITLE	LABEL & NO.	GOOD	VERY GOOD	NEAR MINT
RIVER, THE (1951)				
Soundtrack (Traditional)................ Polymusic (M) PR-5003		15.00	22.50	30.00
RIVERWIND (1962)				
Original Cast.................... London (M) 48001		15.00	22.50	30.00
Elizabeth Parrish, Helen Blount, Dawn Nickerson, Brooks Morton.				
Original Cast.................... London (S) AMS 78001		24.00	36.00	48.00
ROAD TO BALI, THE (1952)				
Soundtrack (10")................. Decca (M) DL-5444		15.00	22.50	30.00
Soundtrack (1962)................ Decca (M) DL-4263		12.00	18.00	24.00
ROAD TO HONG KONG				
Soundtrack...................... Liberty (M) LOM 16002		5.00	7.00	10.00
Soundtrack...................... Liberty (S) LOS 17002		7.00	11.00	15.00
ROAD TO MOROCCO, THE (1942)				
Soundtrack (1962) (1 side)........... Decca (M) DL-4257		6.00	9.00	12.00
ROAD TO RIO, THE (1947)				
Soundtrack (1962)................ Decca (M) DL-4260		6.00	9.00	12.00
ROAD TO SINGAPORE (1940)				
Soundtrack (10") (1951)............ Decca (M) DL-6015		12.00	18.00	24.00
Soundtrack (1962)................ Decca (M) DL-4254		6.00	9.00	12.00
ROAD TO UTOPIA, THE (1945)				
Soundtrack (1962)................ Decca (M) DL-4254		6.00	9.00	12.00
ROAD TO ZANZIBAR, THE (1941)				
Soundtrack (1962)................ Decca (M) DL-4255		6.00	9.00	12.00
ROAR OF THE GREASEPAINT, THE SMELL OF THE CROWD, THE (1965)				
Original Cast.................... RCA (M) LOC 1109		2.00	3.00	4.00
Anthony Newley, Cyril Ritchard, Sally Smith				
Original Cast.................... RCA (S) LSO 1109		2.00	3.00	4.00
ROBBER BRIDEGROOM, THE (1975)				
Studio Cast (7" LP)................ THT (S) 761		2.00	3.00	4.00
Virginia Vestoff, Jerry Orbach.				
ROBBERY				
Soundtrack...................... London (M) 76008		7.00	11.00	15.00
Soundtrack...................... London (S) 82008		10.00	15.00	20.00
ROBE, THE (1953)				
Soundtrack...................... Decca (M) DL-9012		6.00	9.00	12.00
Soundtrack...................... Decca (S) 79012		5.00	7.50	10.00
ROBERTA (1933)				
Soundtrack (From the 1935 film)...... JJA (M) 19747		2.00	3.00	4.00
Fred Astaire, Ginger Rogers, Irene Dunn.				
Soundtrack (From a 1935 radio broadcast) (1 side)........... Star Tone (M) ST 204		5.00	7.50	10.00
Fred Astaire, Ginger Rogers, Irene Dunn.				
Studio Cast..................... Columbia (M) CL 841		5.00	10.00	15.00
Joan Roberts, Jack Cassidy, Kaye Ballard, Portia Nelson, Stephen Douglass.				
Studio Cast..................... Decca (M) DLP 8007		12.00	18.00	24.00
Alfred Drake, Kitty Carlisle, Paula Lawrence.				
Soundtrack (From the 1952 film re-titled "Lovely To Look At") (10").......... MGM (M) E 150		12.00	18.00	24.00
Howard Keel, Kathryn Grayson, Red Skelton, Ann Miller, Marge and Gower Champion.				
Soundtrack (1955)................ MGM (M) E 3230		6.00	9.00	12.00
London Studio Cast (1 side)........ World Record Club (M) T 121		10.00	15.00	20.00
Marion Grimaldi, Andy Cole, Maggie Fitzgibbon.				
ROBERT & ELIZABETH (1974)				
Original London Cast.............. HMV (S) CSD 1575		12.00	18.00	24.00
John Clements, June Bronhill, Keith Michell, Alan Dudley.				

TITLE	LABEL & NO.	GOOD	VERY GOOD	NEAR MINT
ROBIN & THE 7 HOODS (1964)				
Soundtrack...................... Reprise (M) R 2021		7.50	11.25	15.00
Soundtrack...................... Reprise (S) RS-2021		10.00	15.00	20.00
ROCCO & HIS BROTHERS				
Soundtrack...................... RCA (M) FOC 2		15.00	22.0	30.00
Soundtrack...................... RCA (S) FSO-2		20.00	30.00	40.00
ROCKABYE HAMLET (1976)				
Original Canadian Cast............ Rising (S) RILP 103		20.00	30.00	40.00
Cal Dodd, Rory Dodd, Cliff Jones.				
ROCK ALL NIGHT (1957)				
Soundtrack...................... Mercury (M) MG-20293		5.00	7.50	10.00
ROCK PRETTY BABY (1956)				
Soundtrack...................... Decca (M) DL-8429		7.50	11.25	15.00
ROCK, ROCK, ROCK (1958)				
Soundtrack (Traditional pop)........ Chess (M) LP-1425		5.00	7.50	10.00
ROCKY HORROR SHOW (1974)				
Original London Cast.............. U.K. (S) UKAL 1006		10.00	15.00	20.00
Tim Curry, Jonathan Adams, Richard O'Brien.				
Original Los Angeles Cast........... Ode (S) SP 77026		2.00	3.00	4.00
Tim Curry, Jamie Donnelly, Boni Enten.				
Soundtrack...................... Ode (S) 78332		7.50	11.25	15.00
Tim Curry, Susan Sarandon, Barry Bostwick, Richard O'Brien.				
ROGUES, THE (1964)				
TV Soundtrack................... RCA (M) LPM-2976		7.50	11.25	15.00
TV Soundtrack................... RCA (S) LSP-2976		10.00	15.00	20.00
ROMANCE OF A HORSE THIEF (1971)				
Soundtrack (Limited release)....... Allied Artists (S) 110-100		12.00	18.00	24.00
ROME ADVENTURE				
Soundtrack...................... Warner Bros. (M) W 1458		6.00	9.00	12.00
Soundtrack...................... Warner Bros. (S) WS 1458		7.00	11.00	15.00
ROMEO AND JULIET (Roman Vlad) (1954)				
Soundtrack (With Dialogue)........ Epic (M) LC-3126		18.00	27.00	36.00
Soundtrack (1966) (With dialogue)..... Epic (M) FLM13104		15.00	22.50	30.00
Soundtrack (Re-channeled stereo)..... Epic (S) S-15104		10.00	15.00	20.00
ROMEO AND JULIET (Nino Rota) (1968)				
Soundtrack (With Dialogue)........ Capitol (S) ST-2993		3.00	4.50	6.00
Soundtrack (With Dialogue) (4 Record Set)............... Capitol (S) SWDR-289		12.00	18.00	24.00
Soundtrack(1969)................ Capitol (S) ST-400		3.00	4.50	6.00
ROOTS OF HEAVEN, THE (1958)				
Soundtrack...................... 20th Century Fox (M) 3005		18.00	27.00	36.00
ROSE MARIE (1924)				
Original London Cast.......... Monmouth Evergreen (M) MES 7050		2.00	3.00	4.00
Edith Day, Derek Oldham, Billy Merson.				
Original London Cast.......... World Record Club (M) SHB 37		2.00	3.00	4.00
Re-issue of Monmouth Evergreen release.				
Soundtrack (3 bands from the 1936 film) (10") (1952)............. RCA (M) LCT 16		12.00	18.00	24.00
Soundtrack (From the 1954 film) (10")...................... MGM (M) E 229		12.00	18.00	24.00
Howard Keel, Fernando Lamas, Ann Blyth, Bert Lahr.				
Soundtrack (1955)................ MGM (M) E 3228		10.00	15.00	20.00
Soundtrack (1960)................ MGM (M) E 3769		6.00	9.00	12.00
Soundtrack (1966)................ RCA (M) LPV 526		2.00	3.00	4.00
Soundtrack (1967)................ Metro (M) M 616		5.00	7.50	10.00
Soundtrack (Re-channeled stereo)..... Metro (S) MS 616		4.00	6.00	8.00
Studio Cast..................... RCA (M) LK 1012		7.50	11.25	15.00
Charles Fredericks, Marion Bell, Christina Lind.				
Studio Cast (2 records)........... Melodia (M) 033551 54		10.00	15.00	20.00
In Russion wih dialogue.				
ROSEMARY'S BABY (1968)				
Soundtrack...................... Dot (S) 25875		4.00	6.00	8.00
ROSENCRANTZ & GUILDENSTERN ARE DEAD (1967)				
Original London Cast (Side 2, "The Royal Hunt Of The Sun") (1968)......... London (S) 88003		7.50	11.25	15.00
Composer Wilkinson conducts a play with music.				
ROSE TATTOO, THE (1955)				
Soundtrack...................... Columbia (M) CL-727		15.00	22.50	30.00
ROTHSCHILDS, THE (1970)				
Original Cast.................... Columbia (S) S 30337		2.00	3.00	4.00
Paul Hecht, Leila Martin, Jill Claburgh, Hal Linden.				

(M) Mono (S) Stereo (EP) Extended Play (Q) Quad (RI) Re-issued

ROUSTABOUT (1964)

Soundtrack.............................RCA (M) LPM 2999		5.00	10.00	15.00
Elvis Presley.				
Soundtrack............................ RCA (S) LSP 2999		5.00	10.00	15.00

ROYAL HUNT OF THE SUN (1965)

Original London Cast (Side 1, "Rosencrantz And Guildenstern Are Dead") (1968) .... London (S) 88003		7.50	11.25	15.00
Composer Wilkinson conducts a play with music.				

ROYAL WEDDING (1951)

Soundtrack (10") .... MGM (M) E-543		10.00	15.00	20.00
Soundtrack (1955) .... MGM (M) E-3235		6.00	9.00	12.00

R.P.M.

Soundtrack .... Bell (S) 1203		3.00	4.00	6.00

R. S. V. P. THE COLE PORTERS (1974)

Original Cast .... Respond (S) PMS 299		15.00	22.50	30.00
Jack and Sally Jenkins.				

RUGANTINO (1964)

Original Cast (The first foreign language musical ever presented in the U.S. with the use of sub-titles)..... Warner Bros. (M) H 1528		7.50	11.25	15.00
Nino Manfredi, Ornella Vanoni, Aldo Fabrizi.				
Original Cast .... Warner Bros. (S) HS 1528		10.00	15.00	20.00

RUGGLES OF RED GAP (1957)

TV Soundtrack .... Verve (M) MG-15000		15.00	22.50	30.00

RULING CLASS, THE (1972)

Soundtrack (With dialogue) .... Avco Embassy (S) AV-11003		7.50	11.25	15.00

RUN, ANGEL, RUN (1969)

Soundtrack.......................... Epic (S) BN-26474		5.00	7.50	10.00

RUN FOR YOUR WIFE

Soundtrack .... London (M) LOC-1129		5.00	7.00	10.00
Soundtrack .... London (S) LSO-1129		6.00	9.00	12.00

RUN OF THE ARROW (1957)

Soundtrack............................Decca (M) DL-8620		20.00	30.00	40.00

RUN WILD, RUN FREE (1969)

Soundtrack........................... SGC (S) 5003		6.00	9.00	12.00

RUSH TO JUDGMENT

Soundtrack........................ Vanguard (M) 9242		3.00	4.00	6.00

RUSSIAN ADVENTURE

Soundtrack (Classical) .... Roulette (M) R 802		5.00	7.00	10.00
Soundtrack .... Roulette (S) 802		6.00	9.00	12.00

RUSSIANS ARE COMING!
THE RUSSIANS ARE COMING!, THE (1966)

Soundtrack .... United Artists (M) UAL-4142		4.00	6.00	8.00
Soundtrack .... United Artists (S) UAS-5142		5.00	7.50	10.00

RYAN'S DAUGHTER (1970)

Soundtrack........................ MGM (S) 1SE-27-ST		5.00	7.50	10.00

(M) Mono   (S) Stereo   (EP) Extended Play   (Q) Quad   (RI) Re-issued

S

SACCO & VANZETTI

Soundtrack............................RCA (S) LSP-4612		5.00	7.50	10.00

SACRED IDOL, THE (1960)

Soundtrack........................... Capitol (M) T-1293		7.50	11.25	15.00
Soundtrack........................... Capitol (S) ST-1293		10.00	15.00	20.00

SAINT, THE (1962)

TV Soundtrack (1965) ....RCA (M) LPM-3467		10.00	15.00	20.00
TV Soundtrack ....RCA (S) LSP-3467		12.00	18.00	24.00
TV Soundtrack (1966) ....RCA (M) LPM-3631		10.00	15.00	20.00
TV Soundtrack ....RCA (S) LSP-3631		12.00	18.00	24.00

SAINT JOAN (1957)

Soundtrack .... Capitol (M) W-865		22.00	33.00	44.00

SAINT LOUIS BLUES (1958)

Soundtrack .... Capitol (M) W-993		12.00	18.00	24.00

ST. LOUIS WOMAN (1946)

Original Cast (This was Capitol's first original cast album which was released on 78's, and re-issued in 1953 on this 10" long play record) .... Capitol (M) 355		18.00	27.00	36.00
Original Cast (1967) .... Capitol (M) DW 2742		7.50	11.25	15.00
Pearl Bailey, Harold Nicholas, Ruby Hill, June Hawkins.				
Original Cast (Re-channeled stereo) .... Capitol (S) DW 2742		6.00	9.00	12.00
Soundtrack (1961) ....Roulette (M) R 25155		4.00	6.00	8.00
Soundtrack .... Roulette (S) RS 25155		5.00	7.50	10.00

SAINT OF BLEEKER STREET, THE (1954)

Original Cast (2 records) ....RCA (M) LM 6032		36.00	54.00	72.00
Maria Di Gerlando, David Aiken, Gabrielle Ruggiero, David Poleri.				

SALAD DAYS (1958)

Original London Cast..................... London (M) 5474		15.00	22.50	30.00
Eleanor Drew, John Warner, James Carincross.				
Original London Cast (1963) .... London (M) 5765		12.00	18.00	24.00

SALLAH

Soundtrack .... Philips (M) PHM-200177		5.00	7.00	10.00
Soundtrack .... Philips (S) PHS-600177		6.00	9.00	12.00

SALLY (1920)

Original London Cast.......... Monmouth Evergreen (M) MES 7053		2.00	3.00	4.00
Dorothy Dickson, Gregory Stroud, Leslie Henson.				
London Studio Cast (Side 1, "Good News")....... World Record Club (M) 7065		10.00	15.00	20.00

SALOME (1953)

Soundtrack (10") .... Decca (M) DL-6026		20.00	30.00	40.00

SALT AND PEPPER

Soundtrack..........................United Artists (S) 5187		4.00	6.00	8.00

SALUDOS AMIGOS (1943)

Soundtrack (1959) .... Disneyland (M) WDL-3030		6.00	9.00	12.00
Soundtrack (1960) .... Disneyland (M) WDL-1039		5.00	7.50	10.00

SALVATION (1969)

Original Cast (Off Broadway) .... Capitol (S) SO 337		5.00	7.50	10.00
Yolande Bavan, Peter Link, C.C. Courtney, Joe Morton.				

SAMSON AND DELILAH (1949)

Soundtrack (10") .... Decca (M) DL-6007		10.00	15.00	20.00
Soundtrack (1 Side) (1957) .... Decca (M) DL-8566		4.00	6.00	8.00

SAND CASTLE, THE (1961)

Soundtrack........................... Columbia (M) CL-1455		7.50	11.25	15.00
Soundtrack........................... Columbia (S) CS-8249		10.00	15.00	20.00

SANDHOG (1954)

Original Cast ....Vanguard (M) VRS 9001		50.00	75.00	100.00
With composers Earl Robinson and Waldo Salt.				

SAND PEBBLES, THE

Soundtrack...................... 20th Century Fox (M) 4139		12.00	18.00	24.00
Soundtrack......................20th Century Fox (S) 4189		15.00	22.50	30.00

SANDPIPER, THE (1965)

Soundtrack......................... Mercury (M) MG-21032		5.00	7.50	10.00
Soundtrack......................... Mercury (S) SR-61032		6.00	9.00	12.00

SAN GENNARO
Soundtrack . . . . Buddah (S) 5011   6.00   9.00   12.00

SARATOGA (1959)
Original Cast . . . . RCA (M) LOC 1051   10.00   15.00   20.00
    Howard Keel, Carol Lawrence, Odette Myrtil, Warde Donovan.
Original Cast . . . . RCA (S) LSO 1051   18.00   27.00   36.00

SATAN IN HIGH HEELS (1962)
Soundtrack . . . . Parker (M) PLP-406   6.00   9.00   12.00
Soundtrack . . . . Parker (S) PLP-406S   7.50   11.25   15.00

SATAN'S SADISTS (1969)
Soundtrack . . . . Smash (S) 67127   4.00   6.00   8.00

SATCHMO THE GREAT (1958)
TV Soundtrack . . . . Columbia (M) CL-1077   10.00   15.00   20.00

SATINS AND SPURS (1954)
TV Soundtrack (10") . . . . Capitol (M) L-547   15.00   22.50   30.00

SATURDAY NIGHT FEVER
Soundtrack (2 records) . . . . RSO (S) RS-2-4001   5.00   7.50   10.00

SAVAGE (1974)
Soundtrack (Limited release) . . . . Money (S) MS-1109   6.00   9.00   12.00

SAVAGE SAM
Soundtrack . . . . Disneyland (M) ST-1925   3.00   4.00   6.00

SAVAGE SEVEN, THE (1968)
Soundtrack . . . . Atco (M) 33-245   5.00   7.50   10.00
Soundtrack . . . . Atco (S) S-33-245   7.50   11.25   15.00

SAVAGE WILD, THE (1970)
Soundtrack . . . . American Int'l (S) A-1032   5.00   7.50   10.00

SAVE THE CHILDREN
Soundtrack (Traditional rock) (2 records) . . . . . . Motown (S) M-800-R2   4.00   6.00   8.00

SAY DARLING (1958)
Original Cast . . . . RCA (M) LOC 1045   12.00   18.00   24.00
    David Wayne, Vivian Blaine, Johnny Desmond.
Original Cast . . . . RCA (S) LSO 1045   20.00   30.00   40.00

SAYONARA (1957)
Soundtrack . . . . RCA (M) LOC-1041   12.00   18.00   24.00
Soundtrack . . . . RCA (S) LSO-1041   18.00   27.00   36.00

SAY ONE FOR ME
Soundtrack . . . . Columbia (M) CL-1337   10.00   15.00   20.00
Soundtrack . . . . Columbia (S) CS-8147   15.00   22.00   30.00

SCALPHUNTERS, THE (1968)
Soundtrack . . . . United Artists (M) UAL-4176   10.00   15.00   20.00
Soundtrack . . . . United Artists (S) UAS-5176   18.00   27.00   36.00

SCANDALOUS JOHN
Soundtrack . . . . Buena Vista (S) BV 5004   3.00   4.50   6.00

SCANDALOUS LIFE OF FRANKIE & JOHNNY, THE (1938)
Original Cast (A ballet by Jerome Moross with some vocal material)
    (1 side) . . . . Desto (M) 6408   2.00   3.00   4.00
    Vienna Symphony Orchestra and vocalists.

SCENT OF MYSTERY (1960)
Soundtrack . . . . Ramrod (M) T-6001   12.00   18.00   24.00
Soundtrack . . . . Ramrod (S) ST-6001   18.00   27.00   36.00

SCROOGE (1970)
Soundtrack . . . . Columbia (S) S-30258   7.50   11.25   15.00

SEARCH FOR PARADISE, THE (1957)
Soundtrack . . . . RCA (M) LOC-1034   12.00   18.00   24.00

SEASIDE SWINGERS (1965)
Soundtrack . . . . Mercury (M) MG-21031   2.00   3.00   4.00
Soundtrack . . . . Mercury (S) SR-61031   3.00   4.50   6.00

SEBASTIAN (1968)
Soundtrack . . . . Dot (M) 3845   4.00   6.00   8.00
Soundtrack . . . . Dot (S) 25845   6.00   9.00   12.00

SECRET AGENT (1966)
TV Soundtrack . . . . RCA (M) LPM-3467   10.00   15.00   20.00
TV Soundtrack . . . . RCA (S) LSP-3467   12.00   18.00   24.00
TV Soundtrack . . . . RCA (M) LPM-3630   10.00   15.00   20.00
TV Soundtrack . . . . RCA (S) LSP-3630   12.00   18.00   24.00

SECRET LIFE OF WALTER MITTY, THE (1964)
Original Cast . . . . Columbia (M) OL 6320   5.00   7.50   10.00
    Marc London, Cathryn Damon, Eugene Roche.
Original Cast . . . . Columbia (S) OS 2720   7.50   11.25   15.00

SECRET OF SANTA VITTORIA, THE (1969)
Soundtrack . . . . United Artists (S) 5200   5.00   7.50   10.00

SECRETS OF LIFE (1956)
Soundtrack . . . . Disneyland (M) WDL-4006   10.00   15.00   20.00

SEDUCED AND ABANDONED (1964)
Soundtrack . . . . CAM (M) 100001   12.00   18.00   24.00

SEE IT NOW (1957)
TV Soundtrack . . . . RCA (M) LM-2212   6.00   9.00   12.00

SEE SAW (1973)
Original Cast . . . . Buddah (S) BDS-950061   2.00   3.00   4.00
    Michele Lee, Ken Howard, Tommy Tune, Cecelia Norfleet.

SELMA (1976)
Original Cast (Live performance)
    (2 records) . . . . Cotillion (S) SD 2 110   3.00   4.50   6.00
    Tommy Butler, Denise Erwin, Janice Barnett, Ernie Banks.

SERENADE (1956)
Soundtrack . . . . RCA (M) LM-1996   7.50   11.25   15.00

SERGEANTS 3
Soundtrack . . . . Reprise (M) R-2013   10.00   15.00   20.00
Soundtrack . . . . Reprise (S) RS-2013   12.00   18.00   24.00

SEVEN BRIDES FOR SEVEN BROTHERS (1954)
Soundtrack (10") . . . . MGM (M) E-224   7.50   11.25   15.00
Soundtrack . . . . MGM (M) E-3235   6.00   9.00   12.00
Soundtrack (1960) . . . . MGM (M) E-3769   4.00   6.00   8.00

SEVEN COME ELEVEN (1961)
Original Cast (Off Broadway) . . . . Columbia (M) XLP 55477   40.00   60.00   80.00
    Philip Bruns, Ceil Cabot, Rex Robbins.

SEVEN DEADLY SINS (1933)
Original German Revival Cast (1956) . . . . Columbia (M) KL 5175   10.00   15.00   20.00

SEVEN GOLDEN MEN (1969)
Soundtrack . . . . United Artists (S) 5193   5.00   7.50   10.00

SEVEN HILLS OF ROME, THE (1958)
Soundtrack . . . . RCA (M) LM-2211   7.50   11.25   15.00

SEVEN LITTLE FOYS, THE (1955)
Soundtrack (10") (Traditional pop) . . . . RCA (M) LPM-3275   15.00   22.50   30.00

SEVENTEEN (1951)
Original Cast . . . . RCA (M) LOC 1003   50.00   75.00   100.00
    Ann Crowley, Kenneth Nelson, Doris Dalton, Frank Albertson.
Original Cast (Re-issue) . . . . RCA (M) CBM 12034   2.00   3.00   4.00

17
Soundtrack . . . . Mercury (M) 21115   4.00   6.00   8.00
Soundtrack . . . . Mercury (S) 61115   5.00   7.00   10.00
Soundtrack . . . . United Artists (M) UAL-4115   4.00   6.00   8.00

"1776" (1969)
Original Cast . . . . Columbia (S) BOS 3310   2.00   3.00   4.00
    William Daniels, Paul Hecht, Clifford David, Roy Poole, David Ford,
    Virginia Vestoff.
Original Cast . . . . Columbia (S) SCX 6424   12.00   18.00   24.00
    Lewis Fiander, Bernard Lloyd, David Kernan.
Soundtrack (From the 1973 film) . . . . Columbia (S) S 31741   4.00   6.00   8.00
    William Daniels, Howard DaSilva, Ken Howard, Roy Poole, David Ford,
    Virginia Vestoff.

SEVENTH DAWN, THE (1964)
Soundtrack . . . . United Artists (M) UAL 4115   4.00   6.00   8.00
Soundtrack . . . . United Artists (S) UAS-5115   5.00   7.50   10.00

SEVENTH HEAVEN (1955)
Original Cast . . . . Decca (M) DL 9001   35.00   52.50   70.00
    Gloria DeHaven, Ricardo Montalban, Kurt Kasznar, Robert Clary, Chita Rivera.

7TH VOYAGE OF SINBAD, THE (1959)
Soundtrack . . . . Colpix (M) CP-504   36.00   54.00   72.00

70 GIRLS, 70 (1971)
Original Cast . . . . Columbia (S) S 30589   12.00   18.00   24.00
    Mildred Natwick, Hans Conried, Lillian Roth, Gil Lamb.

     (M) Mono   (S) Stereo   (EP) Extended Play   (Q) Quad   (RI) Re-issued

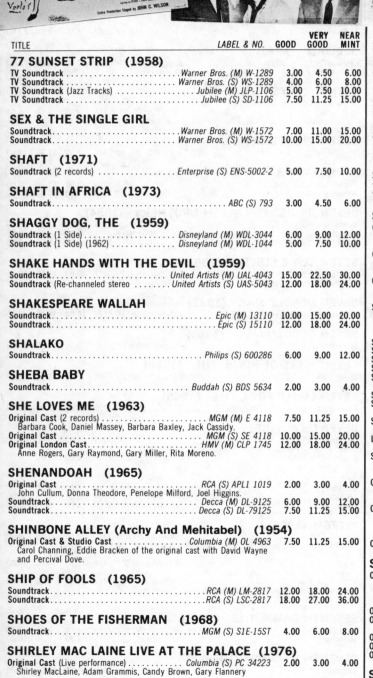

TITLE	LABEL & NO.	GOOD	VERY GOOD	NEAR MINT
77 SUNSET STRIP (1958)				
TV Soundtrack	Warner Bros. (M) W-1289	3.00	4.50	6.00
TV Soundtrack	Warner Bros. (S) WS-1289	4.00	6.00	8.00
TV Soundtrack (Jazz Tracks)	Jubilee (M) JLP-1106	5.00	7.50	10.00
TV Soundtrack	Jubilee (S) SD-1106	7.50	11.25	15.00
SEX & THE SINGLE GIRL				
Soundtrack	Warner Bros. (M) W-1572	7.00	11.00	15.00
Soundtrack	Warner Bros. (S) WS-1572	10.00	15.00	20.00
SHAFT (1971)				
Soundtrack (2 records)	Enterprise (S) ENS-5002-2	5.00	7.50	10.00
SHAFT IN AFRICA (1973)				
Soundtrack	ABC (S) 793	3.00	4.50	6.00
SHAGGY DOG, THE (1959)				
Soundtrack (1 Side)	Disneyland (M) WDL-3044	6.00	9.00	12.00
Soundtrack (1 Side) (1962)	Disneyland (M) WDL-1044	5.00	7.50	10.00
SHAKE HANDS WITH THE DEVIL (1959)				
Soundtrack	United Artists (M) UAL-4043	15.00	22.50	30.00
Soundtrack (Re-channeled stereo)	United Artists (S) UAS-5043	12.00	18.00	24.00
SHAKESPEARE WALLAH				
Soundtrack	Epic (M) 13110	10.00	15.00	20.00
Soundtrack	Epic (S) 15110	12.00	18.00	24.00
SHALAKO				
Soundtrack	Philips (S) 600286	6.00	9.00	12.00
SHEBA BABY				
Soundtrack	Buddah (S) BDS 5634	2.00	3.00	4.00
SHE LOVES ME (1963)				
Original Cast (2 records)	MGM (M) E 4118	7.50	11.25	15.00
Barbara Cook, Daniel Massey, Barbara Baxley, Jack Cassidy.				
Original Cast	MGM (S) SE 4118	10.00	15.00	20.00
Original London Cast	HMV (M) CLP 1745	12.00	18.00	24.00
Anne Rogers, Gary Raymond, Gary Miller, Rita Moreno.				
SHENANDOAH (1965)				
Original Cast	RCA (S) APL1 1019	2.00	3.00	4.00
John Cullum, Donna Theodore, Penelope Milford, Joel Higgins.				
Soundtrack	Decca (M) DL-9125	6.00	9.00	12.00
Soundtrack	Decca (S) DL-79125	7.50	11.25	15.00
SHINBONE ALLEY (Archy And Mehitabel) (1954)				
Original Cast & Studio Cast	Columbia (M) OL 4963	7.50	11.25	15.00
Carol Channing, Eddie Bracken of the original cast with David Wayne and Percival Dove.				
SHIP OF FOOLS (1965)				
Soundtrack	RCA (M) LM-2817	12.00	18.00	24.00
Soundtrack	RCA (S) LSC-2817	18.00	27.00	36.00
SHOES OF THE FISHERMAN (1968)				
Soundtrack	MGM (S) S1E-15ST	4.00	6.00	8.00
SHIRLEY MAC LAINE LIVE AT THE PALACE (1976)				
Original Cast (Live performance)	Columbia (S) PC 34223	2.00	3.00	4.00
Shirley MacLaine, Adam Grammis, Candy Brown, Gary Flannery.				
SHOESTRING '57 (1957)				
Original Cast (Off Broadway) (1960)	Offbeat (M) O 4012	10.00	15.00	20.00
Beatrice Arthur, Fay DeWitt, Dody Goodman, Dorothy Greener.				
Original Cast (Re-issued with added songs)	Painted Smiles (M) PS 1360	2.00	3.00	4.00
Original Cast	Painted Smiles (M) PS 1362	2.00	3.00	4.00

TITLE	LABEL & NO.	GOOD	VERY GOOD	NEAR MINT
SHOESTRING REVUE (1955)				
Original Cast (Off Broadway) (1959)	Offbeat (M) O 4011	10.00	15.00	20.00
Beatrice Arthur, Fay DeWitt, Dody Goodman, Dorothy Greener.				
SHOOT THE PIANO PLAYER				
Soundtrack	Philips (M) 40059	10.00	15.00	20.00
SHOP ON MAIN STREET				
Soundtrack	Mainstream (M) 56082	15.00	22.00	30.00
Soundtrack	Mainstream (S) 6082	17.00	26.00	35.00
SHOTGUN SLADE (1959)				
TV Soundtrack	Mercury (M) 20595	7.50	11.25	15.00
TV Soundtrack	Mercury (S) 60235	10.00	15.00	20.00
SHOWBOAT (1927)				
Original Cast (And 1936 film version cast with studio cast)	Columbia (M) C 55	2.00	3.00	4.00
Helen Morgan, Tess Gardella (Aunt Jemima), James Melton, Paul Robeson.				
Original London Cast (Side 2, "Rio Rita")	Monmouth Evergreen (M) MES 7058	2.00	3.00	4.00
Edith Day and Howett Worster.				
Original Revival Cast (1946, released in 1948)	Columbia (M) OL 4058	10.00	15.00	20.00
Jan Clayton, Carol Bruce, Charles Fredericks, Kenneth Spencer, Helen Dowdy.				
Soundtrack (From the 1951 film) (10")	MGM (M) E 559	10.00	15.00	20.00
Kathryn Grayson, Howard Keel, Marge and Gower Champion, William Warfield.				
Soundtrack (1955)	MGM (M) E 3230	7.50	11.25	15.00
Soundtrack (1959)	MGM (M) E 3767	6.00	9.00	12.00
Soundtrack (1965)	Metro (M) M 527	5.00	7.50	10.00
Soundtrack (Re-channeled stereo)	Metro (S) MS 527	5.00	7.50	10.00
Studio Cast	RCA (M) LOC 1505	4.00	6.00	8.00
Howard Keel, Anne Jeffreys, Gogi Grant.				
Studio Cast	RCA (S) LSO 1505	5.00	7.50	10.00
Studio Cast	RCA (M) LM 2008	10.00	15.00	20.00
Robert Merrill, Patrice Munsel, Rise Stevens, Katherine Graves.				
Studio Cast	Columbia (M) OS 2220	2.00	3.00	4.00
John Raitt, Barbara Cook, William Warfield.				
London Studio Cast	Stanyan (S) 10036	2.00	3.00	4.00
Shirley Bassey, Marlys Watters, Don McKay.				
Studio Cast (Side 1, "No, No, Nanette")	Epic (M) LN 3512	10.00	15.00	20.00
Bruce Trent and Doreen Hume.				
Original London Revival Cast (2 records) (1972)	Stanyan (S) SR 10048	3.00	4.50	6.00
Andre Jobim, Cleo Laine, Thomas Carey, Kenneth Nelson				
Original Revival Cast (Off Broadway) (1966)	RCA (M) LOC 1126	2.00	3.00	4.00
Barbara Cook, Constance Towers, Stephen Douglass, David Wayne, William Warfield, Margaret Hamilton.				
Original Revival Cast	RCA (S) LSO 1126	2.00	3.00	4.00
SHOWGIRL (1961)				
Original Cast (Star Carol Channing's nightclub act recorded in live performance)	Vanguard (M) D 2041	7.50	11.25	15.00
"Showgirl" was based on Channing's nightclub act. No connection with the 1929 Gershwin "Showgirl".				
Original Cast	Vanguard (S) VSD 2041	10.00	15.00	20.00
Original Cast	Roulette (M) R 80001	7.50	11.25	15.00
Carol Channing, Jules Munshin, Les Quat' Jeudis.				
Original Cast	Roulette (S) SR 80001	10.00	15.00	20.00
Original Cast (1963)	Forum (M) F 9054	5.00	7.50	10.00
Original Cast	Forum (S) FS 9054	7.50	11.25	15.00
SHUFFLE ALONG (1921)				
Original Revival Cast (Side 2, "Blackbirds of 1928") (10") (1953)	RCA (M) LMP 3154	10.00	15.00	20.00
Avon Long, Thelma Carpenter, Louise Woods, Laurence Watson.				
Studio Cast (Excerpts by the composers) (2 records)	Columbia (S) C2S 847	3.00	4.50	6.00
Eubie Blake plays and Noble Sissle sings.				

Note: Star and composer excerpts are available on EBM albums 1, 3 and 4.

(M) Mono (S) Stereo (EP) Extended Play (Q) Quad (RI) Re-issued

SICILIAN CLAN
Soundtrack . . . . 20th Century Fox (S) TFS 4209 — 4.00 — 6.00 — 8.00

SIDE BY SIDE BY SONDHEIM (1977)
Original Cast (Broadway & London)
(2 records) . . . . RCA (S) CBL2 1851 — 3.00 — 4.50 — 6.00
   Millicent Martin, Julia McKenzie, David Kernan.

SIDEHACKERS, THE (1969)
Soundtrack . . . . Amaret (S) 5004 — 4.00 — 6.00 — 8.00

SIGN OF AQUARIUS, THE (1969)
Soundtrack . . . . Adell (M) LP-216 — 4.00 — 6.00 — 8.00
Soundtrack . . . . Adell (S) ASLP-216 — 5.00 — 7.50 — 10.00

SILENCERS, THE (1966)
Soundtrack . . . . Reprise (M) R-6211 — 4.00 — 6.00 — 8.00
Soundtrack . . . . Reprise (S) RS-6211 — 5.00 — 7.50 — 10.00
Soundtrack . . . . RCA (M) LOC-1120 — 6.00 — 9.00 — 12.00
Soundtrack . . . . RCA (S) LSO-1120 — 7.50 — 11.25 — 15.00

SILENT RUNNING (1973)
Soundtrack . . . . Decca (S) DL-79188 — 18.00 — 27.00 — 36.00

SILK STOCKINGS (1955)
Original Cast . . . . RCA (M) LOC 1016 — 10.00 — 15.00 — 20.00
   Hildegarde Neff, Don Ameche, Gretchen Wyler, George Tobias.
Original Cast (1965) . . . . RCA (M) LOC 1102 — 7.50 — 11.25 — 15.00
Original Cast (Re-channeled stereo) . . . RCA (S) LSO 1102 — 5.00 — 7.50 — 10.00
Soundtrack (From the 1957 film) . . . . MGM (M) E 3542 — 10.00 — 15.00 — 20.00
   Fred Astaire, Cyd Charisse, Janis Paige, Carol Richards, George Tobias.

SIMPLY HEAVENLY (1957)
Original Cast . . . . Columbia (M) OL 5240 — 10.00 — 15.00 — 20.00
   Claudia McNeil, Melvin Stewart, Anna English.

SINCERELY YOURS (1955)
Soundtrack (Traditional pop) . . . . Columbia (M) CL-800 — 15.00 — 22.50 — 30.00

SING BOY SING (1958)
Soundtrack . . . . Capitol (M) T 929 — 10.00 — 15.00 — 20.00

SING FOR YOUR SUPPER (1939)
Original Cast Recordings . . . . RCA (M) AMVI 1739 — 2.00 — 3.00 — 4.00
   Paul Robeson.
Studio Cast ("Ballad For Americans" was the finale for this revue
and is one side of the LP) . . . . Vanguard (M) VES 9066 — 10.00 — 15.00 — 20.00
   Odetta with the DeCormier Chorale, recording supervised by Karl Robinson.
Studio Cast . . . . United Artists (S) LA 604G — 2.00 — 3.00 — 4.00
   Brock Peters.

SINGING NUN, THE (1966)
Soundtrack . . . . MGM (M) 1E-7-ST — 5.00 — 7.50 — 10.00
Soundtrack . . . . MGM (S) S1E-7-ST — 5.00 — 7.50 — 10.00

SINGIN' IN THE RAIN (1952)
Soundtrack (10") . . . . MGM (M) E-113 — 10.00 — 15.00 — 20.00
Soundtrack (1955) . . . . MGM (M) E-3236 — 7.50 — 11.25 — 15.00
Soudtrack (1960) . . . . MGM (M) E-3770 — 6.00 — 9.00 — 12.00
Soundtrack (1967) . . . . Metro (M) M 599 — 5.00 — 7.50 — 10.00
Soundtrack (Re-channeled stereo) . . . . . . Metro (S) MS 599 — 5.00 — 7.50 — 10.00

SINGLE ROOM-FURNISHED
Soundtrack . . . . Sidewalk (S) ST-5917 — 10.00 — 15.00 — 20.00

SING OUT SWEET LAND (1944)
Original Cast (Traditional folk music)
(1950) . . . . Decca (M) DL 8023 — 10.00 — 15.00 — 20.00
   Alfred Drake, Burl Ives, Alma Kaye, Juanita Hall.
Original Cast (1963) . . . . Decca (M) DL 4304 — 7.50 — 11.25 — 15.00
Original Cast (Re-channeled stereo) . . . . . Decca (S) DL 74304 — 5.00 — 7.50 — 10.00

633 SQUADRON (1964)
Soundtrack . . . . United Artists (S) LA-305-G — 10.00 — 15.00 — 20.00

SKATERDATER
Soundtrack . . . . Mira (M) 3004 — 5.00 — 7.00 — 10.00
Soundtrack . . . . Mira (S) 3004 — 6.00 — 9.00 — 12.00

SKIDOO
Soundtrack . . . . RCA (S) LSO 1152 — 4.00 — 6.00 — 8.00

SKI ON THE WILD SIDE (1967)
Soundtrack . . . . MGM (M) E-4439 — 12.00 — 18.00 — 24.00
Soundtrack . . . . MGM (S) SE-4439 — 15.00 — 22.50 — 30.00

SKYSCRAPER (1965)
Original Cast . . . . Capitol (M) VAS 2422 — 6.00 — 9.00 — 12.00
   Julie Harris, Peter Marshall, Charles Nelson Reilly.
Original Cast . . . . Capitol (S) SVAS 2422 — 7.50 — 11.25 — 15.00

(M) Mono   (S) Stereo   (EP) Extended Play   (Q) Quad   (RI) Re-issued

SLAUGHTER ON 10TH AVENUE (1957)
Soundtrack . . . . Decca (M) DL-8657 — 6.00 — 9.00 — 12.00
Soundtrack . . . . Decca (S) DL-78657 — 10.00 — 15.00 — 20.00

SLAVE TRADE IN THE WORLD TODAY (1964)
Soundtrack . . . . London (M) M-76006 — 15.00 — 22.50 — 30.00

SLEEPING BEAUTY (1959)
Soundtrack . . . . Disneyland (M) WDL-4018 — 5.00 — 7.50 — 10.00
Soundtrack . . . . Disneyland (S) ST-4018 — 7.50 — 11.25 — 15.00

SLENDER THREAD, THE (1965)
Soundtrack . . . . Mercury (M) M6-21070 — 4.00 — 6.00 — 8.00
Soundtrack . . . . Mercury (S) SR-61070 — 5.00 — 7.50 — 10.00

SLIPPERY WHEN WET (1959)
Soundtrack . . . . World Pacific (M) W-1265 — 3.00 — 4.50 — 6.00
Soundtrack . . . . World Pacific (S) WS-1265 — 4.00 — 6.00 — 8.00

SMASHING TIME
Soundtrack . . . . ABC (M) OC-6 — 7.50 — 11.25 — 15.00
Soundtrack . . . . ABC (S) SOC-6 — 10.00 — 15.00 — 20.00

SMILING THE BOY FELL DEAD (1961)
Original Cast . . . . Sunbeam (M) LB 549 — 100.00 — 150.00 — 200.00
   Charles Goff, Danny Meehan, Ted Beniades, Warren Wade.

SNOOPY COME HOME
Soundtrack . . . . Columbia (S) S-31541 — 3.00 — 4.00 — 6.00

SNOW QUEEN, THE (1959)
Soundtrack . . . . Decca (M) DL-8977 — 7.50 — 11.25 — 15.00
Soundtrack . . . . Decca (S) DL7-8977 — 10.00 — 15.00 — 20.00

SNOW WHITE & ROSE RED
Soundtrack . . . . Camden (M) 1084 — 4.00 — 6.00 — 8.00
Soundtrack . . . . Camden (S) 1084 — 5.00 — 7.00 — 10.00

SNOW WHITE AND THE 7 DWARFS (1937)
Soundtrack (10") (1949) . . . . Decca (M) DL-5015 — 15.00 — 22.50 — 30.00
Soundtrack (1957) . . . . Disneyland (M) WDL-4005 — 7.50 — 11.25 — 15.00

SNOW WHITE & THE THREE STOOGES
Soundtrack . . . . Columbia (M) CL 1650 — 12.00 — 19.00 — 25.00
Soundtrack . . . . Columbia (S) CS 8450 — 15.00 — 22.00 — 30.00

SO DEAR TO MY HEART (1949)
Soundtrack (With Dialogue) (1964) . . . . Disneyland (M) DQ-1255 — 5.00 — 7.50 — 10.00

SODOM & GOMORRAH (1963)
Soundtrack . . . . RCA (M) LOC-1076 — 20.00 — 40.00 — 60.00
Soundtrack . . . . RCA (S) LSO-1076 — 36.00 — 54.00 — 72.00

SOL MADRID (1968)
Soundtrack . . . . MGM (M) E-4541 — 4.00 — 6.00 — 8.00
Soundtrack . . . . MGM (S) SE-4541 — 5.00 — 7.50 — 10.00

SOLOMON & SHEBA
Soundtrack . . . . United Artists (M) UAL-4051 — 17.00 — 26.00 — 35.00
Soundtrack . . . . United Artists (S) UAS-4051 — 20.00 — 30.00 — 40.00

SOMEBODY LOVES ME (1952)
Soundtrack (10") . . . . RCA (M) LPM-3097 — 10.00 — 15.00 — 20.00

SOME CAME RUNNING (1959)
Soundtrack . . . . Capitol (M) W-1109 — 15.00 — 22.50 — 30.00
Soundtrack . . . . Capitol (S) SW-1109 — 20.00 — 30.00 — 40.00

SOME LIKE IT HOT (1959)
Soundtrack . . . . United Artists (M) UAL-4030 — 6.00 — 9.00 — 12.00
Soundtrack . . . . United Artists (S) UAS-5030 — 6.00 — 9.00 — 12.00

SOMETHING FOR THE BOYS (1943)
Original Cast & Studio Cast (Armed Forces
Transcription) . . . . Soundstage (M) 2305 — 7.50 — 11.25 — 15.00
   Ethel Merman, Bill Johnson, Betty Garrett, Paula Lawrence.

SOMETIMES A GREAT NOTION
Soundtrack . . . . Decca (S) 79185 — 6.00 — 9.00 — 12.00

SONDHEIM, A MUSICAL TRIBUTE (1973)
Original Cast (2 records) . . . . Warner Bros. (S) 2WS 2705 — 10.00 — 15.00 — 20.00
   Jack Cassidy, Dorothy Collins, Hermione Gingold, Pamela Hall, Glynis
   Johns, Larry Kert, Angela Lansbury, Mary McCarty, Donna McKechnie,
   Anthony Perkins, Chita Rivera, Alexis Smith, Nancy Walker, and many others!

SONG OF BERNADETTE, THE (1943)
Soundtrack (10") (1952) . . . . Decca (M) DL-5358 — 50.00 — 75.00 — 100.00

SONG OF NORWAY (1944)

		GOOD	VERY GOOD	NEAR MINT
Original Cast (1949) .... Decca (M) DL 8002		10.00	15.00	20.00
Robert Shafer, Lawrence Brooks, Helena Bliss, Kitty Carlisle.				
Original Cast (1955) .... Decca (M) DL 9019		7.50	11.25	15.00
Original Cast (Re-channeled stereo) .... Decca (S) DL 79019		5.00	7.50	10.00
Original Revival Cast (Off Broadway)				
(1959) .... Columbia (M) CL 1328		7.50	11.25	15.00
Brenda Lewis, John Reardon, Helena Scott, Sig Arno.				
Original Revival Cast .... Columbia (S) CS 8135		10.00	15.00	20.00
Soundtrack (From the 1973 film) .... ABC (S) SOC 14		7.50	11.25	15.00
Toralv Maurstad, Florence Henderson, Christina Schollin, Frank Porretta, Oscar Homolka, Robert Morley, Edward G. Robinson.				

SONG OF THE SOUTH, THE (1946)

	GOOD	VERY GOOD	NEAR MINT
Soundtrack (1956) .... Disneyland (M) WDL-4001	7.50	11.25	15.00
Soundtrack (1959) .... Disneyland (M) DQ-1205	5.00	7.50	10.00

SONGS OF THE FLINTSTONES

	GOOD	VERY GOOD	NEAR MINT
Soundtrack .... Golden (M) 366	3.00	4.00	6.00

SONG WITHOUT END

	GOOD	VERY GOOD	NEAR MINT
Soundtrack .... Colpix (M) CP 506	7.00	11.00	15.00
Soundtrack .... Colpix (S) SCP 506	10.00	15.00	20.00

SONS OF KATIE ELDER, THE (1965)

	GOOD	VERY GOOD	NEAR MINT
Soundtrack .... Columbia (M) OL-6420	12.00	18.00	24.00
Soundtrack .... Columbia (S) OS-2820	18.00	27.00	36.00

SOPHIA LOREN IN ROME (1964)

	GOOD	VERY GOOD	NEAR MINT
TV Soundtrack .... Columbia (M) OL-6310	15.00	22.50	30.00
TV Soundtrack .... Columbia (S) OS-2710	24.00	36.00	48.00

SO THIS IS LOVE (1953)

	GOOD	VERY GOOD	NEAR MINT
Soundtrack (10") .... RCA (M) LOC-3000	20.00	30.00	40.00

SO THIS IS PARIS (1954)

	GOOD	VERY GOOD	NEAR MINT
Soundtrack (10") .... Decca (M) DL-5553	12.00	18.00	24.00

SOUL HUSTLER

	GOOD	VERY GOOD	NEAR MINT
Soundtrack .... MGM (S) 4943	6.00	9.00	12.00

SOUL TO SOUL

	GOOD	VERY GOOD	NEAR MINT
Soundtrack .... Atlantic (S) 7207	3.00	4.00	6.00

SOUND AND THE FURY, THE (1959)

	GOOD	VERY GOOD	NEAR MINT
Soundtrack .... Decca (M) DL-8885	12.00	18.00	24.00
Soundtrack .... Decca (S) DL-78885	18.00	27.00	36.00

SOUND OF MUSIC (1959)

	GOOD	VERY GOOD	NEAR MINT
Original Cast .... Columbia (M) OL 5450	2.00	3.00	4.00
Mary Martin, Theodore Bikel, Patricia Neway, Kurt Kazner.			
Original Cast .... Columbia (S) OS 2020	2.00	3.00	4.00
Original London Cast .... Stanyan (S) SRS 5003	2.00	3.00	4.00
Jean Bayless, Sylvia Beamish, Olive Gilbert, Constance Shacklock			
Soundtrack (From the 1965 film) .... RCA (M) LOCD 2005	2.00	3.00	4.00
Julie Andrews, Christopher Plummer, Richard Haydn, Eleanor Parker.			
Soundtrack .... RCA (S) LSOD 2005	2.00	3.00	4.00

SOUTHERN STAR, THE (1969)

	GOOD	VERY GOOD	NEAR MINT
Soundtrack .... Colgems (S) COSO-5009	10.00	15.00	20.00

SOUTH PACIFIC (1949)

	GOOD	VERY GOOD	NEAR MINT
Original Cast .... Columbia (M) OL 4180	2.00	3.00	4.00
Mary Martin, Ezio Pinza, Juanita Hall, William Tabbert, Barbara Luna.			

	GOOD	VERY GOOD	NEAR MINT
Original Cast (Re-channeled stereo) .... Columbia (S) OS 2040	2.00	3.00	4.00
Original London Cast .... Columbia (EP)	15.00	22.50	30.00
Mary Martin, Wilbur Evans, Muriel Smith, Peter Grant.			

(M) Mono (S) Stereo (EP) Extended Play (Q) Quad (RI) Re-issued

---

	GOOD	VERY GOOD	NEAR MINT
Original London Cast .... Columbia (EP)	15.00	22.50	30.00
Original Revival Cast (Off Broadway)			
(1967) .... Columbia (M) OL 6700	2.00	3.00	4.00
Florence Henderson, Giorgio Tozzi, Lyle Talbot.			
Original Revival Cast .... Columbia (S) OS 3100	2.00	3.00	4.00
Soundtrack (From the 1958 film) ...... RCA (M) LOCD 2000	10.00	15.00	20.00
Rossano Brazzi, Mitzi Gaynor, John Kerr, Ray Walston, Juanita Hall.			
Soundtrack .... RCA (M) LOC 1032	2.00	3.00	4.00
This soundtrack was re-issued in mono and stereo the same month as the first issue in mono only.			
Soundtrack .... RCA (S) LSO 1032	2.00	3.00	4.00

Note: Two very rare Columbia 45 r.p.m. EP's, containing songs not issued on LP are known to exist, but we do not have their numbers for this edition of the price guide.

SOUTH SEAS ADVENTURE (1958)

	GOOD	VERY GOOD	NEAR MINT
Soundtrack .... Audio Fidelity (M) 1899	7.50	11.25	15.00
Soundtrack .... Audio Fidelity (S) 5899	12.00	18.00	24.00

SPANISH AFFAIR, THE (1958)

	GOOD	VERY GOOD	NEAR MINT
Soundtrack .... Dot (M) 3078	30.00	45.00	60.00

SPARTACUS (1960)

	GOOD	VERY GOOD	NEAR MINT
Soundtrack .... Decca (M) DL-9092	6.00	9.00	12.00
Soundtrack .... Decca (S) DL-79092	7.50	11.25	15.00

SPELLBOUND (1945)

	GOOD	VERY GOOD	NEAR MINT
Soundtrack (10") (1950)			
(Rozsa Conducting) .... REM (M) LP-1	10.00	15.00	20.00
Soundtrack (Heindorf Conducting) (1958) .... Warner Bros. (M) W-1213	5.00	7.50	10.00
Soundtrack .... Warner Bros. (S) WS-1213	6.00	9.00	12.00

SPINOUT

	GOOD	VERY GOOD	NEAR MINT
Soundtrack .... RCA (M) LPM 3702	9.00	18.00	27.00
Elvis Presley. Came with a bonus photo loose inside.			
Soundtrack .... RCA (S) LSP 3702	9.00	18.00	27.00

SPIRIT OF ST. LOUIS, THE (1957)

	GOOD	VERY GOOD	NEAR MINT
Soundtrack .... RCA (M) LPM-1472	15.00	22.50	30.00

SPOON RIVER ANTHOLOGY (1963)

	GOOD	VERY GOOD	NEAR MINT
Original Cast .... Columbia (S) OS 2410	7.50	11.25	15.00
Betty Garrett, Robert Elston, Joyce Van Patten.			

SPORTING CLUB

	GOOD	VERY GOOD	NEAR MINT
Soundtrack .... Buddah (S) 95002	5.00	7.00	10.00

SPY WHO CAME IN FROM THE COLD, THE (1965)

	GOOD	VERY GOOD	NEAR MINT
Soundtrack .... RCA (M) LOC-1118	4.00	6.00	8.00
Soundtrack .... RCA (S) LSO-1118	5.00	7.50	10.00

SPY WITH A COLD NOSE, THE (1966)

	GOOD	VERY GOOD	NEAR MINT
Soundtrack .... Columbia (M) OL-6670	4.00	6.00	8.00
Soundtrack .... Columbia (S) OS-3070	5.00	7.50	10.00

SQUARE ROOT OF ZERO

	GOOD	VERY GOOD	NEAR MINT
Soundtrack .... Mainstream (M) 56070	3.00	4.00	6.00
Soundtrack .... Mainstream (S) 6070	4.00	6.00	8.00

STAGECOACH (1966)

	GOOD	VERY GOOD	NEAR MINT
Soundtrack .... Mainstream (M) 56077	6.00	9.00	12.00
Soundtrack .... Mainstream (S) S-6077	7.50	11.25	15.00

STAR

	GOOD	VERY GOOD	NEAR MINT
Soundtrack .... 20th Century Fox (S) 5102	4.00	6.00	8.00

STAR IS BORN, A (1954)

	GOOD	VERY GOOD	NEAR MINT
Soundtrack (Boxed) .... Columbia (M) BL-1201	18.00	27.00	36.00
Soundtrack (1958) .... Columbia (M) CL-1101	7.50	11.25	15.00
Soundtrack .... Columbia (S) CS-8740	7.50	11.25	15.00

STAR MAKER (1939)

	GOOD	VERY GOOD	NEAR MINT
Soundtrack (10") (1951) .... Decca (M) DL-6013	6.00	9.00	12.00
Soundtrack (1962) .... Decca (M) DL-4254	4.00	6.00	8.00

STARS AND STRIPES FOREVER (1952)

	GOOD	VERY GOOD	NEAR MINT
Soundtrack (Traditional) (10") .... MGM (M) E-176	10.00	15.00	20.00
Soundtrack (1957) .... MGM (M) E-3508	6.00	9.00	12.00

STARS IN YOUR EYES (1939)

	GOOD	VERY GOOD	NEAR MINT
Original Cast (1965) (1 side) .... JJC (M) 3004	5.00	7.50	10.00
Original Cast (Re-channeled stereo) .... JJC (S) ST 3004	4.00	6.00	8.00

STARTING HERE STARTING NOW (1977)

	GOOD	VERY GOOD	NEAR MINT
Original Cast .... RCA (S) ABL 1 2360	5.00	7.50	10.00
Margery Cohen, George Lee Andrews, Loni Ackerman.			

STATE FAIR

	GOOD	VERY GOOD	NEAR MINT
Soundtrack .... Dot (M) DLP 9011	5.00	7.00	10.00
Soundtrack .... Dot (S) DLP 29001	6.00	9.00	12.00

TITLE	LABEL & NO.	GOOD	VERY GOOD	NEAR MINT
STERILE CUCKOO				
Soundtrack	Paramount (S) 5009	4.00	6.00	8.00
STILETTO (1969)				
Soundtrack	Columbia (S) OS-3360	4.00	6.00	8.00
STINGIEST MAN IN TOWN, THE (1956)				
TV Soundtrack	Columbia (M) CL-950	12.00	18.00	24.00
STOOGE, THE (1953)				
Soundtrack (10")	Capitol (M) L-401	10.00	15.00	20.00
Deam Martin.				
STOP THE WORLD I WANT TO GET OFF (1962)				
Original Cast	London (M) 58001	2.00	3.00	4.00
Anthony Newley, Anna Quayle, Jennifer Baker, Susan Baker.				
Original Cast	London (S) AMS 88001	2.00	3.00	4.00
Original London Cast	Decca (M) LK 4408	12.00	18.00	24.00
Anthony Newley, Anna Quayle, Susan Baker, Jennifer Baker.				
Soundtrack (From the 1966 film)	Warner Bros. (M) W 1643	6.00	9.00	12.00
Tony Tanner, Millicent Martin.				
Soundtrack	Warner Bros. (S) WS 1643	7.50	11.25	15.00
STORY OF BIG RED				
Soundtrack	Disneyland (S) ST 1916	3.00	4.00	6.00
STORY OF MOBY DICK, THE (1957)				
Soundtrack (With Dialogue)	Dot (M) 3043	10.00	15.00	20.00
STORY OF POLLYANNA				
Soundtrack	Disneyland (S) ST 1906	4.00	6.00	8.00
STORY OF RUDOLPH THE RED NOSED REINDEER, THE (1964)				
TV Soundtrack (With Dialogue) (1966)	Decca (M) DL-4815	3.00	4.50	6.00
TV Soundtrack	Decca (S) DL-74815	4.00	6.00	8.00
STORY OF STAR WARS, THE				
Soundtrack	20th Century Fox (S) T-550	2.00	3.00	4.00
STRANGE ONE, THE (1957)				
Soundtrack	Coral (M) 57132	18.00	27.00	36.00
STRAWBERRY STATEMENT				
Soundtrack (Traditional rock)				
(2 records)	MGM (S) 2SE 14 ST	4.00	6.00	8.00
STREETCAR NAMED DESIRE, A (1951)				
Soundtrack (10")	Capitol (M) L-289	7.50	11.25	15.00
Soundtrack (1 Side) (1953)	Capitol (M) T-387	5.00	7.50	10.00
STREET SCENE (1947)				
Original Cast (1949)	Columbia (M) ML 4139	9.00	13.50	18.00
Anne Jeffreys, Polyna Stoska, Brian Sullivan.				
STUDENT PRINCE (1924)				
Original London Cast (Side 1,				
"The Desert Song")	Monmouth Evergreen (M) MES 7054	2.00	3.00	4.00
Harry Welchman, Allen Prior, Olaf Olson.				
Studio Cast (Side 1,				
"The Chocolate Soldier")	Columbia (M) ML 4060	5.00	7.50	10.00
Rise Stevens and Nelson Eddy.				
Studio Cast (Side 2, "The Merry Widow")	Capitol (M) T437	5.00	7.50	10.00
Gordon MacRae, Dorothy Warenskjold.				
Studio Cast	Columbia (M) OL 2380	2.00	3.00	4.00
Roberta Peters, Jan Peerce, Giorgio Tozzi.				
Studio Cast	Columbia (S) OS 2380	2.00	3.00	4.00
Soundtrack (Featuring the star from the 1954 film)				
(1 side)	RCA (M) LM 1837	7.50	11.25	15.00
Mario Lanza.				
Soundtrack (1960)	RCA (M) LM 2339	2.00	3.00	4.00
Soundtrack	RCA (S) LSC 2339	2.00	3.00	4.00

TITLE	LABEL & NO.	GOOD	VERY GOOD	NEAR MINT
STUDY IN TERROR, A				
Soundtrack	Roulette (M) 801	7.00	11.00	15.00
Soundtrack	Roulette (S) 801	10.00	15.00	20.00
SUBTERRANEANS				
Soundtrack	MGM (M) E 3812	7.00	11.00	15.00
Soundtrack	MGM (S) SE 3812	10.00	15.00	20.00
SUBWAYS ARE FOR SLEEPING (1961)				
Original Cast	Columbia (M) OL 5730	5.00	7.50	10.00
Sydney Chaplin, Carol Lawrence, Orson Bean, Grayson Hall.				
Original Cast	Columbia (S) OS 2130	7.50	11.25	15.00
SUGAR (1972)				
Original Cast	United Artists (S) UAS 9905	4.00	6.00	8.00
Robert Morse, Tony Roberts, Cyril Ritchard, Elaine Joyce.				
SUMMER & SMOKE				
Soundtrack	RCA (M) LOC-1067	15.00	22.50	30.00
Soundtrack	RCA (S) LSO-1067	18.00	27.00	36.00
SUMMER HOLIDAY				
Soundtrack	Epic (M) LN-24063	5.00	7.00	10.00
Soundtrack	Epic (S) BN-26063	6.00	9.00	12.00
SUMMER LOVE (1958)				
Soundtrack	Decca (M) DL-8714	10.00	15.00	20.00
SUMMER MAGIC (1963)				
Soundtrack	Buena Vista (M) BV-4025	5.00	7.50	10.00
Soundtrack	Buena Vista (S) ST-4025	6.00	9.00	12.00
SUMMER STOCK (1950)				
Soundtrack (10")	MGM (M) E-519	5.00	7.50	10.00
Soundtrack (1955)	MGM (M) E-3234	3.00	4.50	6.00
SUN ALSO RISES, THE (1957)				
Soundtrack	Kapp (M) KDL-7001	25.00	37.50	50.00
SUNDAY IN NEW YORK (1963)				
Soundtrack	RCA (M) LPM-2827	4.00	6.00	8.00
Soundtrack	RCA (S) LSP-2827	5.00	7.50	10.00
SUNFLOWER, THE (1970)				
Soundtrack	Avco Embassy (S) AV-11001	7.50	11.25	15.00
SUNNY (1926)				
Original London Cast (1 side)	Stanyan (M) 10035	2.00	3.00	4.00
Binnie Hale, Dennis Wyndham, Jack Hobbs, Gus Oxley.				
SUNSHINE				
Soundtrack	MCA (S) 387	6.00	9.00	12.00
SUN VALLEY SERENADE (1941)				
Soundtrack (10") (1954)	RCA (M) LPT-3064	6.00	9.00	12.00
Soundtrack (1959)	20th Century Fox (M) TCF-100-2	5.00	7.50	10.00
Soundtrack (Re-channeled stereo)	20th Century Fox (S) TCS100-2	4.00	6.00	8.00
SUPERFLY (1972)				
Soundtrack	Custom (S) 8014	3.00	4.50	6.00
SURF PARTY				
Soundtrack	20th Century Fox (M) TFM 3131	5.00	7.50	10.00
SURVIVAL OF ST. JOAN (1971)				
Original Cast (2 records)	Paramount (S) PAS 9000	10.00	15.00	20.00
F. Murray Abraham, Willie Rook, Lenny Baker, Ronald Bishop.				
SWAN, THE (1956)				
Soundtrack	MGM (M) E-3300	25.00	37.50	50.00

(M) Mono (S) Stereo (EP) Extended Play (Q) Quad (RI) Re-issued

SWEDEN, HEAVEN AND HELL (1969)
Soundtrack...............Ariel (M) LP-216 — 5.00 — 7.50 — 10.00
Soundtrack...............Ariel (S) ASLP-216 — 6.00 — 9.00 — 12.00

SWEET ADELINE (1929)
Soundtrack...............JJA (M) 19747 — 2.00 — 3.00 — 4.00
Irene Dunn, Phil Regan, Joseph Cawthorn, Hugh Herbert.

SWEET BYE AND BYE (1974)
Original Cast (Kansas City Lyric Theatre)
(2 records)...............Desto (S) DC 7179/80 — 3.00 — 4.50 — 6.00
Noel Rogers, Judith Anthony, Carolyn James, Paula Seibel.

SWEET CHARITY (1966)
Original Cast...............Columbia (M) OL 6500 — 2.00 — 3.00 — 4.00
Gwen Verdon, John McMartin, Thelma Oliver.
Original Cast...............Columbia (S) OS 2900 — 2.00 — 3.00 — 4.00
Original London Cast...............CBS (S) 70035 — 10.00 — 15.00 — 20.00
Juliet Prowse, Rod McLennan, John Keston, Sheila O'Neill.
Soundtrack (From the 1969 film)...............Decca (S) DL 71502 — 4.00 — 6.00 — 8.00
Shirley MacLaine, John McMartin, Chita Rivera, Paula Kelly, Stubby Kaye,
Sammy Davis, Jr.

SWEETHEARTS (1913)
Original Revival Cast (From the 1947 show,
a 1951 release)...............RCA (M) CAL 369 — 7.50 — 11.25 — 15.00
Earl Wrightson, Frances Greer, Jimmy Carroll, Christina Lind.

SWEET LOVE, BITTER (1967)
Soundtrack...............Impulse (M) 9142 — 5.00 — 7.50 — 10.00
Soundtrack...............Impulse (S) 9142 — 6.00 — 9.00 — 12.00

SWEET RIDE
Soundtrack...............20th Fox (S) 4198 — 5.00 — 7.00 — 10.00

SWEET SWEETBACK'S BAADASS SONGS (1971)
Soundtrack...............Stax (S) 3001 — 3.00 — 4.50 — 6.00

SWEET SMELL OF SUCCESS, THE (1957)
Soundtrack...............Decca (M) DL-8610 — 10.00 — 15.00 — 20.00
Soundtrack...............Decca (M) DL-8614 — 6.00 — 9.00 — 12.00

SWIMMER, THE
Soundtrack...............Columbia (S) OS-3210 — 17.00 — 26.00 — 35.00

SWINGER, THE (1966)
Soundtrack...............RCA (M) LPM-3710 — 5.00 — 7.50 — 10.00
Soundtrack...............RCA (S) LSP-3710 — 6.00 — 9.00 — 12.00

SWINGER'S PARADISE
Soundtrack...............Epic (M) LN-24145 — 5.00 — 7.00 — 10.00
Soundtrack...............Epic (S) BN-26145 — 6.00 — 9.00 — 12.00

SWINGIN' SUMMER, A (1966)
Soundtrack...............Hanna Barbera (M) HLP-8500 — 5.00 — 7.50 — 10.00

SWITZERLAND (1955)
Soundtrack...............Disneyland (M) WDL-4003 — 4.00 — 6.00 — 8.00

SWORD IN THE STONE (1963)
Soundtrack...............Disneyland (M) DQ-1236 — 6.00 — 9.00 — 12.00
Soundtrack...............Disneyland (M) ST-4901 — 5.00 — 7.50 — 10.00

SYLVIA
Soundtrack...............Mercury (M) MG-21004 — 3.00 — 4.00 — 6.00
Soundtrack...............Mercury (S) SR-61004 — 4.00 — 6.00 — 8.00

SYNANON
Soundtrack...............Liberty (M) LRP-3413 — 3.00 — 4.00 — 6.00
Soundtrack...............Liberty (S) LST-7413 — 4.00 — 6.00 — 8.00

T

TAKE FIVE (1958)
Original Cast (Off Broadway)...............Offbeat (M) 0 4013 — 12.00 — 18.00 — 24.00
Jean Arnold, Ceil Cabot, Ellen Hanley, Ronny Graham.

TAKE ME ALONG (1959)
Original Cast...............RCA (M) LOC 1050 — 5.00 — 7.50 — 10.00
Jackie Gleason, Walter Pidgeon, Eileen Herlie, Robert Morse, Una Merkel.
Original Cast...............RCA (S) LSO 1050 — 10.00 — 15.00 — 20.00

(M) Mono (S) Stereo (EP) Extended Play (Q) Quad (RI) Re-issued

---

TAKING OFF
Soundtrack...............Decca (S) 79181 — 3.00 — 4.00 — 6.00

TAMALPAIS EXCHANGE (1970)
Original Cast (Music and lyrics by
the cast)...............Atlantic (S) SD 8263 — 7.50 — 11.25 — 15.00
Penelope Ann Bodry, Mike Brandt, Susan Kay, Michael Knight.

TAMBOURINES TO GLORY (1958)
Studio Cast (Gospel songs)...............Folkways (M) 3538 — 2.00 — 3.00 — 4.00
novel/play.
The Porter Singers sing the songs of Langston Hughes, written for this

TAMING OF THE SHREW, THE (1967)
Soundtrack (With Dialogue)...............RCA (M) VDM-117 — 6.00 — 9.00 — 12.00

TAMMY AND THE BACHELOR (1957)
Soundtrack (1 Side)...............Coral (M) 57159 — 18.00 — 27.00 — 36.00

TARAS BULBA
Soundtrack...............United Artists (M) UAL 4100 — 17.00 — 26.00 — 35.00
Soundtrack...............United Artists (S) UAS 5100 — 22.00 — 33.00 — 45.00
Soundtrack (1 side) (1964)...............Ascot (M) UM 13504 — 7.50 — 11.25 — 15.00
Soundtrack...............Ascot (S) US 16504 — 10.00 — 15.00 — 20.00

TAROT (1970)
Original Cast (Music from the Mime Production as
played by original "Rubber Duck" Band renamed
Touchstone)...............United Artists (S) S 5563 — 5.00 — 7.50 — 10.00
Tom Constanten, Paul Dresher, Gary Hirsh, Wes Steele, Art Fayer, Jim Byers.

TARZAN (1966)
TV Soundtrack...............MGM (M) LE-902 — 6.00 — 9.00 — 12.00
TV Soundtrack...............MGM (S) LES-902 — 7.50 — 11.25 — 15.00

TARZAN THE APE MAN (1960)
Soundtrack...............MGM (M) E-3798 — 4.00 — 6.00 — 8.00
Soundtrack...............MGM (S) SE-3798 — 5.00 — 7.50 — 10.00

TEENAGE REBELLION
Soundtrack...............Sidewalk (M) T-5903 — 3.00 — 4.00 — 6.00
Soundtrack...............Sidewalk (S) DT-5903 — 4.00 — 6.00 — 8.00

TELEPHONE, THE (1947) (See: The Medium)

TELL ME LIES (1967)
Soundtrack (With Dialogue)...............GRE-GAR (M) 5000 — 7.50 — 11.25 — 15.00
Soundtrack...............GRE-GAR (S) S-5000 — 10.00 — 15.00 — 20.00

TELL ME THAT YOU LOVE ME, JUNIE MOON
Soundtrack...............Columbia (S) DS 3540 — 4.00 — 6.00 — 8.00

TEMPEST, THE (1964)
Original London Cast (3 records)...............Caedmon (M) M 201 — 4.00 — 6.00 — 8.00
Incidental music.
Original London Cast...............Caedmon (S) S 201 — 4.00 — 6.00 — 8.00

TEN COMMANDMENTS, THE (1956)
Soundtrack (2 Record Set)...............Dot (M) DLP-3054 — 7.50 — 11.25 — 15.00
Soundtrack (Stereo Re-recording) (1960)
(2 Record Set)...............Dot (S) 25054 (2) — 10.00 — 15.00 — 20.00

TENDER IS THE NIGHT

TENDERLOIN (1960)
Original Cast...............Capitol (M) WAO 1492 — 10.00 — 15.00 — 20.00
Ron Husmann, Wynne Miller, Eileen Rodgers, Rex Everhard.
Original Cast...............Capitol (S) SWAO 1492 — 12.00 — 18.00 — 24.00

10TH VICTIM, THE (1965)
Soundtrack...............Mainstream (M) 56071 — 10.00 — 15.00 — 20.00
Soundtrack...............Mainstream (S) 6071 — 12.00 — 18.00 — 24.00

TEVYA AND HIS DAUGHTERS (1957)
Original Cast (Off Broadway)...............Columbia (M) OL 5225 — 5.00 — 7.50 — 10.00

TEXAS LI'L DARLIN' (1949)
Original Cast (10")...............Decca (M) DL 5188 — 40.00 — 60.00 — 80.00
Kenny Delmar, Danny Scholl, Mary Hatcher, Fredd Wayne.
Original Cast...............JJA (M) 19752 — 2.00 — 3.00 — 4.00

THAT DARN CAT (1965)
Soundtrack...............Buena Vista (M) BV-3334 — 3.00 — 4.50 — 6.00
Soundtrack...............Buena Vista (S) ST-3334 — 4.00 — 6.00 — 8.00

THAT MAN IN ISTANBUL (1966)
Soundtrack...............Mainstream (M) 56072 — 10.00 — 15.00 — 20.00
Soundtrack...............Mainstream (S) S-6072 — 12.00 — 18.00 — 24.00

TITLE	LABEL & NO.	GOOD	VERY GOOD	NEAR MINT
THAT MIDNIGHT KISS (1949)				
Soundtrack (10") (1951) .... RCA (M) LM-86		10.00	15.00	20.00
Soundtrack (1 Side) (1961) .... RCA (M) LM-2422		4.00	6.00	8.00
THAT'S THE WAY IT IS (1970)				
Soundtrack .... RCA (S) LSP 4445		3.00	6.00	9.00
Elvis Presley.				
THERE'S NO BUSINESS LIKE SHOW BUSINESS (1954)				
Soundtrack .... Decca (M) DL-8091		10.00	15.00	20.00
Ethel Merman.				
THEY CALL ME MR. TIBBS				
Soundtrack .... United Artists (S) 5214		3.00	4.00	6.00
THIEF OF BAGDAD, THE (1940)				
Soundtrack (1 Side) (With Dialogue) (1957) .... RCA (M) LM-2118		20.00	30.00	40.00
THIRD MAN, THE (1950)				
Soundtrack (1956) .... London (M) LL-1560		10.00	15.00	20.00
Featuring the zither of Anton Karas.				
THIRTEEN DAUGHTERS (1961)				
Original Hawaiian Cast (Of the Broadway musical) ...... Mahalo (S) M 3003		2.00	3.00	4.00
Napua Stevens, Kam Fong Chun, Richard Kuga.				
30 IS A DANGEROUS AGE, CYNTHIA (1968)				
Soundtrack .... London (S) MS-82010		7.50	11.25	15.00
36 HOURS (1964)				
Soundtrack .... Vee Jay (M) 1131		6.00	9.00	12.00
Soundtrack .... Vee Jay (S) 1131		7.50	11.25	15.00
THIS COULD BE THE NIGHT (1947)				
Soundtrack (1957) .... MGM (M) E-3530		15.00	22.50	30.00
THIS EARTH IS MINE (1959)				
Soundtrack .... Decca (M) DL-8915		15.00	22.00	30.00
Soundtrack .... Decca (S) DL7-8915		20.00	30.00	40.00
THIS IS THE ARMY (1942)				
Original Cast (All soldier) (10") (1950) .... Decca (M) DL 5108		45.00	67.50	90.00
Earl Oxford, Ezra Stone, Philip Truex, Irving Berlin.				
Original Cast .... JJA (M) 19742		2.00	3.00	4.00
(Decca LP with three added selections, all originally on 78's.)				
THIS PROPERTY IS CONDEMNED				
Soundtrack .... Verve (M) 8664		7.00	11.00	15.00
Soundtrack .... Verve (S) 6-8664		10.00	15.00	20.00
THIS WAS BURLESQUE (1962)				
Original Cast (Off Broadway) .... Roulette (M) R 25185		10.00	15.00	20.00
Ann Corio, Buddy Bryant, Steve Mills, Lisa Carroll.				
Original Cast .... Roulette (S) SR 25185		15.00	22.50	30.00
THOMAS CROWN AFFAIR, THE (1968)				
Soundtrack .... United Artists (S) 5182		5.00	7.50	10.00
THOROUGHLY MODERN MILLIE (1967)				
Soundtrack (Traditional pop) .... Decca (M) DL-1500		6.00	9.00	12.00
Julie Andrews.				
Soundtrack .... Decca (S) DL-71500		7.50	11.25	15.00
THOSE DARING YOUNG MEN IN THEIR JAUNTY JALOPIES (1969)				
Soundtrack .... Paramount (S) PAS-5006		5.00	7.50	10.00
THOSE MAGNIFICENT MEN IN THEIR FLYING MACHINES (1965)				
Soundtrack .... 20th Century Fox (M) 3174		6.00	9.00	12.00
Soundtrack .... 20th Century Fox (S) S-4174		7.50	11.25	15.00
THREE BITES OF THE APPLE (1967)				
Soundtrack .... MGM (M) 4444		4.00	6.00	8.00
Soundtrack .... MGM (S) 4444		5.00	7.50	10.00
THREE FOR THE SHOW (1955)				
Soundtrack (10") .... Mercury (M) MG-25204		20.00	30.00	40.00
THREE FOR TONIGHT (1955)				
Original Cast (Star sings selections) (1 side) ...... RCA (M) LPM 1150		10.00	15.00	20.00
Harry Belafonte.				
Original Cast (Re-channeled stereo) .... RCA (S) LSP 1150		5.00	7.50	10.00

(M) Mono (S) Stereo (EP) Extended Play (Q) Quad (RI) Re-issued

TITLE	LABEL & NO.	GOOD	VERY GOOD	NEAR MINT
THREE IN THE ATTIC (1969)				
Soundtrack .... Sidewalk (S) ST 5918		5.00	7.50	10.00
THREE LITTLE PIGS, THE (1934)				
Soundtrack (With Dialogue) (1961) .... Disneyland (M) ST-1910		5.00	7.50	10.00
THREE LITTLE WORDS (1950)				
Soundtrack (10") .... MGM (M) E-516		12.00	18.00	24.00
Soundtrack (1953) .... MGM (M) E-3229		7.50	11.25	15.00
Soundtrack (1960) .... MGM (M) E-3768		6.00	9.00	12.00
Soundtrack (1967) .... Metro (M) M-615		5.00	7.50	10.00
Soundtrack (Re-channeled stereo) .... Metro (S) MS-615		4.00	6.00	8.00
THREE MUSKETEERS (1928)				
Original London Cast (With original cast star) (1 side) ...... Monmouth Evergreen (M) MES 7050		2.00	3.00	4.00
Dennis King, Adrienne Brune, Raymond Newell, Robert Woollard.				
THREEPENNY OPERA, THE (1933)				
Original German Revival Cast .... Telefunken (M) 97012		10.00	15.00	20.00
Lotte Lenya, Willie Trenk-Trebitsch, Kurt Gerron.				
Original Revival Cast (Off Broadway) (1954) .... MGM (M) E 3121		2.00	3.00	4.00
Lotte Lenya, Scott Merrill, Charlotte Rae, Beatrice Arthur.				
Original Revival Cast (Re-channeled stereo) .... MGM (S) SE 3121		2.00	3.00	4.00
Original German Revival Cast (3 selections) (1955) ...... Columbia (M) KL 5056		6.00	9.00	12.00
Original German Revival Cast (And studio cast, complete recording, sung in German. (1958) (2 records) ...... Columbia (M) O2L 257		12.00	18.00	24.00
Lotte Lenya, Wolfgang Neuss, Willy Trenk-Trebitsch. (Supervised by Lotte Lenya.)				
Original Revival Cast .... Columbia (M) O2S 201		20.00	30.00	40.00
Soundtrack (In German) .... London (M) M 76004		7.50	11.25	15.00
Hildegarde Neff, June Ritchie, Gert Frobe.				
Soundtrack (From the 1964 film) .... RCA (M) LOC 1086		7.50	11.25	15.00
Curt Jurgens, Hildegarde Neff, June Ritchie, Gert Frobe, Sammy Davis, Jr.				
Soundtrack .... RCA (S) LSO 1086		10.00	15.00	20.00
THREE SAILORS AND A GIRL (1953)				
Soundtrack (10") .... Capitol (M) L-485		20.00	30.00	40.00
THREE WISHES FOR JAMIE (1952)				
Original Cast .... Capitol (M) S 317		125.00	187.50	250.00
Bert Wheeler, Anne Jeffreys, John Raitt, Charlotte Rae.				

TITLE	LABEL & NO.	GOOD	VERY GOOD	NEAR MINT
THREE WORLDS OF GULLIVER				
Soundtrack (With dialogue) .... Colpix (M) CP-414		15.00	22.50	30.00
THRILL OF A ROMANCE, THE (1945)				
Soundtrack (1 side) (1958) .... Camden (M) CAL 424		12.00	18.00	24.00
THRILLER (1960)				
TV Soundtrack .... Time (M) 2034		6.00	9.00	12.00
TV Soundtrack .... Time (S) S-2034		7.50	11.25	15.00
THUNDER ALLEY				
Soundtrack .... Sidewalk (S) T-5902		5.00	7.00	10.00
Soundtrack .... Sidewalk (S) ST-5902		6.00	9.00	12.00

TITLE	LABEL & NO.	GOOD	VERY GOOD	NEAR MINT

THUNDERBALL (1965)
Soundtrack................................ United Artists (M) UAL-4132 — 3.00 — 4.50 — 6.00
Soundtrack................................ United Artists (S) UAS-5132 — 4.00 — 6.00 — 8.00

THURBER CARNIVAL (1960)
Original Cast................................ Columbia (M) OL 5500 — 5.00 — 7.50 — 10.00
  Tom Ewell, Peggy Cass, Paul Ford, John McGiver.
Original Cast................................ Columbia (S) KOS 2024 — 7.50 — 11.25 — 15.00

TICKLE ME (1965)
Soundtrack................................ RCA (EP) EPA 4383 — 4.00 — 8.00 — 12.00
  Elvis Presley. RCA dog logo on the side of the label is the first release.
  —For more information, see PRESLEY, Elvis in the regular listings.

TICK...TICK...TICK
Soundtrack................................ MGM (S) 4667 — 3.00 — 4.00 — 6.00

TILL THE CLOUDS ROLL BY (1946)
Soundtrack (10") (1950)................ MGM (M) E-501 — 12.00 — 18.00 — 24.00
Soundtrack (1955)................ MGM (M) E-3231 — 7.50 — 11.25 — 15.00
Soundtrack (1960)................ MGM (M) E-3770 — 6.00 — 9.00 — 12.00
Soundtrack (1966)................ Metro (M) M-578 — 5.00 — 7.50 — 10.00
Soundtrack (Re-channeled stereo)........ Metro (S) MS-578 — 4.00 — 6.00 — 8.00

TIME CHANGES (1969)
Original Cast................................ ABC (S) S 681 — 5.00 — 7.50 — 10.00
  John Mazzarelli, Harry Palmer, Joey Scott.

TIME FOR SINGING, A (1966)
Original Cast................................ Warner Bros. (M) W 1639 — 12.00 — 18.00 — 24.00
  Ivor Emmanuel, Tessie O'Shea, Shani Wallis.
Original Cast................................ Warner Bros. (S) HS 1639 — 15.00 — 22.50 — 30.00

TIME REMEMBERED, A (1957)
Original Cast................................ Mercury (M) MG 20380 — 5.00 — 7.50 — 10.00
  "A Time Remembered" is a play, rather than a musical, but was written with accompanying music and two songs. This is the original score without the dialogue.)
  Vernon Duke, composer, at the piano, songs sung by Tony Travis.
Original Cast................................ Mercury (S) SR 60380 — 10.00 — 15.00 — 20.00

TIME TO LOVE AND A TIME TO DIE, A (1958)
Soundtrack................................ Decca (M) DL-8778 — 15.00 — 22.50 — 30.00

TIME TO SING
Soundtrack................................ MGM (S) 4540 — 4.00 — 6.00 — 8.00

TIP TOES (1925)
Original London Cast (With original cast stars)
  (Side 2, "Wildflower")........ Monmouth Evergreen (M) MES 7052 — 2.00 — 3.00 — 4.00
  Allen Kearns, Dorothy Dickson, Laddie Cliff, John Kirby.

TOAST OF NEW ORLEANS, THE (1950)
Soundtrack (10") (1951)................ RCA (M) LM-75 — 20.00 — 30.00 — 40.00
Soundtrack (1 Side) (1961)................ RCA (M) LM-2422 — 15.00 — 22.50 — 30.00

TO BED OR NOT TO BED (1963)
Soundtrack................................ London (M) M-76005 — 15.00 — 22.50 — 30.00

TO BROADWAY WITH LOVE (1964)
Original Cast (World's Fair)................ Columbia (S) OS 2630 — 10.00 — 15.00 — 20.00
  With 22 alphabetical co-stars.

TOBY TYLER (1960)
Soundtrack (With Dialogue)................ Disneyland (M) ST-1904 — 7.50 — 11.25 — 15.00

TO KILL A MOCKINGBIRD
Soundtrack................................ Ava (M) A-20 — 15.00 — 22.00 — 30.00
Soundtrack................................ Ava (S) AS-20 — 17.00 — 26.00 — 35.00

TOKYO OLYMPIAD (1966)
Soundtrack................................ Monument (M) 8046 — 7.50 — 11.25 — 15.00
Soundtrack................................ Monument (S) 18046 — 10.00 — 15.00 — 20.00

TO LIVE ANOTHER SUMMER, TO PASS ANOTHER WINTER (1971)
Original Cast (2 records)................ Buddah (S) BDS 95004 — 7.50 — 11.25 — 15.00
  Rivka Raz, Aric Lavie, Yona Atari, Ili Gorlizki.

TOM JONES (1968) (Addison)
Soundtrack................................ United Artists (M) UAL-4113 — 5.00 — 7.50 — 10.00
Soundtrack................................ United Artists (S) UAS-5113 — 7.50 — 11.25 — 15.00
Soundtrack (1966) (1 side)................ United Artists (M) UAL-4134 — 4.00 — 6.00 — 8.00
Soundtrack................................ United Artists (S) UAS-5134 — 5.00 — 7.50 — 10.00

TOM JONES (Batchelor/Roberts) (1964)
Original Cast................................ Theatre Productions (M) 59000 — 5.00 — 7.50 — 10.00
  A large alphabetical list of co-stars.
Original Cast................................ Theatre Productions (S) 9000 — 7.50 — 11.25 — 15.00

TOMMY (1969)
Original Cast (2 records)................ Decca (S) DXSW 7205 — 3.00 — 4.50 — 6.00
  The Who.
Soundtrack (2 records)................ Polydor (S) PD 29502 — 3.00 — 4.50 — 6.00
  Ann-Margret, Oliver Reed, Roger Daltrey, Elton John, Eric Clapton, The Who, Jack Nicholson.

TOM SAWYER (1957)
TV Soundtrack................................ Decca (M) DL-8432 — 7.50 — 11.25 — 15.00

TOM THUMB (1958)
Soundtrack (With Dialogue)................ Lion (M) L-70084 — 12.00 — 18.00 — 24.00
Soundtrack (With Dialogue) (1967)................ MGM (M) CH-104 — 7.50 — 11.25 — 15.00

TONIGHT AT 8:30 (1936)
Original Cast (1 side)................ Monmouth Evergreen (M) MES 7042 — 2.00 — 3.00 — 4.00
  Noel Coward and Gertrude Lawrence.

TONIGHT WE SING (1952)
Soundtrack................................ RCA (M) LM-7016 — 12.00 — 18.00 — 24.00

TOO MUCH, TOO SOON (1958)
Soundtrack................................ Mercury (M) MG-20381 — 10.00 — 15.00 — 20.00
Soundtrack................................ Mercury (S) SR-60019 — 15.00 — 22.50 — 30.00

TOP BANANA (1951)
Original Cast................................ Capitol (M) S308 — 50.00 — 75.00 — 100.00
  Phil Silvers, Rose Marie, Judy Lynn, Jack Albertson.
Original Cast................................ Capitol (M) T 11650 — 2.00 — 3.00 — 4.00
  NOTE: In the 1960's a very limited special pressing was issued for the composer with no cover and a rainbow-edged Capitol label. This was not a commercial release, and the value of one would be considerably higher than the $50 - $100 range.

TOPKAPI
Soundtrack................................ United Artists (M) UAL-4118 — 3.00 — 4.00 — 6.00
Soundtrack................................ United Artists (S) UAS-5118 — 4.00 — 6.00 — 8.00

TOP O' THE MORNING (1949)
Soundtrack (10")................ Decca (M) DL-5272 — 6.00 — 9.00 — 12.00
Soundtrack (1962)................ Decca (M) DL-4261 — 4.00 — 6.00 — 8.00

TORCH SONG (1953)
Soundtrack (10")................ MGM (M) E-214 — 20.00 — 30.00 — 40.00

TORN CURTAIN
Soundtrack................................ Decca (M) 9155 — 10.00 — 15.00 — 20.00
Soundtrack................................ Decca (S) 7-9155 — 15.00 — 22.00 — 30.00

TO SIR WITH LOVE (1967)
Soundtrack................................ Fontana (S) 18030 — 7.50 — 11.25 — 15.00
Soundtrack................................ Fontana (S) SRF 67569 — 4.50 — 6.75 — 9.00

TOUCH (1971)
Original Cast (Off Broadway)................ Ampex (S) A 50102 — 5.00 — 7.50 — 10.00
  Norman Jacob, Barbara Ellis, Ken Long, Phyllis Gibbs.

TOUCHABLES, THE (1969)
Soundtrack................................ 20th Century Fox (S) S-4206 — 4.00 — 6.00 — 8.00

TOUCH OF CLASS, A (1973)
Soundtrack................................ Brut (S) 6004 — 5.00 — 7.50 — 10.00

TOUCH OF EVIL (1958)
Soundtrack................................ Challenge (M) CHL-602 — 20.00 — 30.00 — 40.00
Soundtrack (1962)................ Challenge/WB (M) CH-615 — 10.00 — 15.00 — 20.00

(M) Mono (S) Stereo (EP) Extended Play (Q) Quad (RI) Re-issued

TOVARICH (1963)

Original Cast ....Capitol (M) TAO 1940 7.50 11.25 15.00
Viviene Leigh, Jean Pierre Aumont, Alexander Scourby, George S. Irving.
Original Cast .... Capitol (S) STAO 1940 10.00 15.00 20.00
Original Cast .... Capitol (S) STAO 11653 2.00 3.00 4.00

TRAIN, THE (1965)

Soundtrack.................. United Artists (M) UAL-4122 6.00 9.00 12.00
Soundtrack.................. United Artists (S) UAS-5122 7.50 11.25 15.00

TRAP, THE (1966)

Soundtrack........................Atco (M) 33-204 7.50 11.25 15.00
Soundtrack........................Atco (S) S-33-204 10.00 15.00 20.00

TRAPEZE (1956)

Soundtrack.................... Columbia (M) CL-870 10.00 15.00 20.00

TRAPP FAMILY, THE (1961)

Soundtrack (Traditional).......... 20th Century Fox (M) 3044 4.00 6.00 8.00
Soundtrack.................. 20th Century Fox (S) S-3044 5.00 7.50 10.00

T.R. BASKIN

Soundtrack.................... Paramount (S) 6018 3.00 4.00 6.00

TREASURE ISLAND (1950)

Soundtrack (1 Side) .... RCA (M) LY-1 6.00 9.00 12.00
Soundtrack (With Dialogue) (1964) .... Disneyland (M) DQ-1251 5.00 7.50 10.00

TREASURE OF SAN GENNARO, THE (1968)

Soundtrack.................... Buddha (S) BDS-5011 4.00 6.00 8.00

TREE GROWS IN BROOKLYN, A (1951)

Original Cast ....Columbia (M) ML 4405 7.50 11.25 15.00
Shirley Booth, Johnny Johnson, Marcia Van Dyke, Nathaniel Frey.

TREEMONISHA (1975)

Original Revival Cast
(2 records) .... Deutsche Grammophon (S) 2707 083 3.00 4.50 6.00
Carmen Balthrop, Betty Allen, Curtis Rayam.

TRIAL OF BILLY JACK

Soundtrack........................ ABC (S) D-853 3.00 4.00 6.00

TRIP, THE

Soundtrack.................... Sidewalk (M) T-5908 3.00 4.00 6.00
Soundtrack.................... Sidewalk (S) ST-5908 4.00 6.00 8.00

TRIPLE CROSS (1967)

Soundtrack.................. United Artists (M) 4162 7.50 11.25 15.00
Soundtrack..................United Artists (S) 5162 10.00 15.00 20.00

TRIPLE FEATURE

Soundtrack.................... Epic (M) 24195 12.00 19.00 25.00
Soundtrack.................... Epic (S) 26195 15.00 22.00 30.00

TROUBLE IN TAHITI (1952) (See: All In One)

TROUBLEMAKER

Soundtrack.................... Ava (M) A-49 6.00 9.00 12.00

TROUBLE WITH ANGELS, THE

Soundtrack.................... Ava (S) AS-49 7.00 11.00 15.00
Soundtrack.................... Mainstream (M) 56073 7.00 11.00 15.00
Soundtrack.................... Mainstream (S) 6073 10.00 15.00 20.00

TRUE GRIT (1969)

Soundtrack.................... Capitol (S) ST-263 6.00 9.00 12.00

TRUE STORY OF THE CIVIL WAR, THE (1958)

Soundtrack (With Dialogue) .... Coral (M) 59100 12.00 18.00 24.00

TUNES OF GLORY

Soundtrack.................. United Artists (M) UAL-4086 7.00 11.00 15.00
Soundtrack.................. United Artists (S) UAS-5086 10.00 15.00 20.00

TURNABOUT (1956)

Original Cast (This recording was done in 1975 with the original cast members reassembled for the occasion) .... Pelican (S) LP 142 2.00 3.00 4.00
Stars reassembled: Elsa Lanchester, Forman Brown, Bill Buck, Harry Burnett, Dorothy Neumann, Frances Osborne.
The album contains excerpts from a typical revue as performed at the Turnabout Theatre in Hollywood. The Theatre ran 4,535 performances (1941-56).

TURN ON, TUNE IN, DROP OUT (1967)

Soundtrack.................... Mercury (S) 61131 7.50 11.25 15.00
Dr. Timothy Leary.

TUSCALOOSA'S CALLING ME (1975)

Original Cast .... Vanguard (S) VSD 79376 2.00 3.00 4.00
Len Gochman, Patti Perkins, Renny Temple.

25TH HOUR, THE (1967)

Soundtrack........................MGM (M) E-4464 5.00 7.50 10.00
Soundtrack........................MGM (S) SE-4464 6.00 9.00 12.00

TWILIGHT OF HONOR (1963)

Soundtrack........................MGM (M) E-4185 2.00 3.00 4.00
Soundtrack........................MGM (S) SE-4185 3.00 4.50 6.00

TWO A PENNY (1971)

Soundtrack.................... Light (S) LS 5530 4.00 6.00 8.00
Cliff Richard.

TWO BY TWO (1970)

Original Cast .... Columbia (S) S 30338 7.50 11.25 15.00
Danny Kaye, Harry Goz, Madeline Kahn, Michael Karm.

TWO FOR THE ROAD (1967)

Soundtrack........................RCA (M) LPM-3802 7.50 11.25 15.00
Soundtrack........................RCA (S) LSP-3802 10.00 15.00 20.00

TWO FOR THE SEE-SAW (1962)

Soundtrack (1965).................... United Artists (M) UAL 4103 7.50 11.25 15.00
Soundtrack....................United Artists (S) UAS 5103 10.00 15.00 20.00

TWO FOR TONIGHT (1935)

Soundtrack (1951) (10") .... Decca (M) DL-6009 5.00 7.50 10.00
Soundtrack (1962) .... Decca (M) DL-4250 3.00 4.50 6.00

TWO GENTLEMEN OF VERONA (1971)

Original Cast (2 records) .... ABC (S) 1001 3.00 4.50 6.00
Jonelle Allen, Diana Davila, Clifton Davis.
Original Cast (The composer conducts the original orchestra with songs by two lead understudies) .... Kilmarnock (S) KIL 72004 7.50 11.25 15.00
Galt MacDermot, composer. Songs by Sheila Gibbs & Ken Lowny.

TWO MULES FOR SISTER SARA (1970)

Soundtrack........................ Kapp (S) 5512 7.50 11.25 15.00

TWO ON THE AISLE (1951)

Original Cast .... Decca (M) DL 8040 20.00 30.00 40.00
Bert Lahr, Dolores Gray, Colette Marchand, Elliott Reid.

TWO'S COMPANY (1952)

Original Cast .... RCA (M) LOC 1009 50.00 75.00 100.00
Bette Davis, Hiram Sherman, David Burns, George S. Irving.

2001: A SPACE ODYSSEY

Soundtrack, Vol. 1 (Classical) .... MGM (S) S1E-13ST 3.00 4.50 6.00

TWO TICKETS TO BROADWAY (1951)

Soundtrack (10") ....RCA (M) LPM-39 18.00 27.00 36.00

TWO TICKETS TO PARIS (1962)

Soundtrack.................... Roulette (M) R-25182 10.00 15.00 20.00
Soundtrack.................... Roulette (S) SR-25182 12.00 18.00 24.00

TWO WEEKS WITH LOVE (1950)

Soundtrack (10") .... MGM (M) E-530 5.00 7.50 10.00
Soundtrack (1955) (1 side) .... MGM (M) E-3233 3.00 4.50 6.00

(M) Mono (S) Stereo (EP) Extended Play (Q) Quad (RI) Re-issued

U

UGLY DACHSHUND, THE   (1966)
Soundtrack (With Dialogue) (1 Side) .... Disneyland (M) DQ-1290   4.00   6.00   8.00

ULYSSES
Soundtrack .... Columbia (M) OL-6720   5.00   7.00   10.00
Soundtrack .... RCA (M) LOC-1138   5.00   7.50   10.00
Soundtrack .... RCA (S) LSO-1138   6.00   9.00   12.00

UMBRELLAS OF CHERBOURG, THE
  (Parapluies de Cherbourg)   (1964)
Soundtrack .... Philips (M) PCC-216   5.00   7.50   10.00
Soundtrack .... Philips (S) PCC-616   6.00   9.00   12.00

UNCLE MEAT   (1968)
Soundtrack (2 Records)
  (Film Unreleased) .... Reprise (S) RS-2024   6.00   9.00   12.00

UNCLE TOM'S CABIN   (1968)
Soundtrack .... Philips (S) 600272   12.00   18.00   24.00

UNFORGIVEN, THE   (1960)
Soundtrack .... United Artists (M) UAL-4068   12.00   18.00   24.00
Soundtrack .... United Artists (S) UAS-5068   18.00   27.00   36.00
Soundtrack (½ Side) (1964) .... United Artists (M) UM-13502   3.00   4.50   6.00
Soundtrack .... United Artists (S) US-16502   4.00   6.00   8.00

UNSINKABLE MOLLY BROWN   (1960)
Original Cast .... Capitol (M) WAO 1509   6.00   9.00   12.00
  Tammy Grimes, Harve Presnell, Cameron Prud'homme.
Original Cast .... Capitol (S) SWAO 1509   7.50   11.25   15.00
Original Cast .... Capitol (M) W 2152   2.00   3.00   4.00
Original Cast .... Capitol (S) SW 2152   2.00   3.00   4.00
Soundtrack (From the 1964 film) .... MGM (M) E 4232   6.00   9.00   12.00
  Debbie Reynolds, Harve Presnell, Ed Begley, Jack Kruschen, Hermione
  Baddeley.
Soundtrack .... MGM (S) SE 4232   7.50   11.25   15.00

UNTOUCHABLES, THE   (1960)
TV Soundtrack .... Capitol (M) T-1430   7.50   11.25   15.00
TV Soundtrack .... Capitol (S) ST-1430   10.00   15.00   20.00

UP IN CENTRAL PARK   (1945)
Original Cast (Side 2, "The Red Mill")
  (1950) .... Decca (M) DL 8016   20.00   30.00   40.00
  Wilbur Evans, Eileen Farrell, Celeste Holm.

UP THE DOWN STAIRCASE   (1967)
Soundtrack .... United Artists (M) 4169   6.00   9.00   12.00
Soundtrack .... United Artists (S) 5169   7.50   11.25   15.00

UP THE JUNCTION
Soundtrack .... Mercury (S) 61159   6.00   9.00   12.00

V

VAGABOND KING   (1925)
Original Cast (The star and original London cast stars)
  (1 side) .... Monmouth Evergreen (M) MES 7050   2.00   3.00   4.00
  Derek Oldham and Winnie Melville, Dennis King.
Soundtrack (From the 1956 film) .... RCA (M) LM 2004   12.00   18.00   24.00
Studio Cast (Side 2, "New Moon") .... Capitol (M) T 219   7.50   11.25   15.00
  Gordon MacRae and Lucille Norman.

VALIANT YEARS, THE   (1962)
TV Soundtrack .... ABC (M) 387   4.00   6.00   8.00
TV Soundtrack .... ABC (S) S-387   5.00   7.50   10.00

VALLEY OF THE DOLLS
Soundtrack .... 20th Century Fox (M) 4196   5.00   7.50   10.00
Soundtrack .... 20th Century Fox (S) S-4196   6.00   9.00   12.00

VALMOUTH   (1960)
Original London Cast .... PYE (S) NSPL 83004   10.00   15.00   20.00
  Cleo Laine, Barbara Couper, Doris Hare, Fenella Fielding.

VANISHING POINT   (1971)
Soundtrack .... Amos (S) 8002   6.00   9.00   12.00

(M) Mono   (S) Stereo   (EP) Extended Play   (Q) Quad   (RI) Re-issued

---

VANISHING PRAIRIE, THE   (1954)
Soundtrack (10") .... Columbia (M) CL-6332   7.50   11.25   15.00
Soundtrack (1 Side) (1965) .... Buena Vista (M) BV-3326   4.00   6.00   8.00

VERTIGO   (1958)
Soundtrack .... Mercury (M) MG-20384   36.00   54.00   72.00

VERY WARM FOR MAY   (1939)
Studio Cast .... Monmouth Evergreen (S) MES 6808   2.00   3.00   4.00
  Reid Shelton, Susan Watson, D. Carroll.

VIA GALACTICA   (1972)
Studio Cast .... Kilmarnock (S) KIL 72009   7.50   11.25   15.00
  Instrumental; Bill Butler plays with orchestra conducted by the compo-
  ser, Galt MacDermot.

VICTORS, THE   (1963)
Soundtrack .... Colpix (M) CP-516   4.00   6.00   8.00
Soundtrack .... Colpix (S) SCP-516   5.00   7.50   10.00

VICTORY AT SEA   (1952)
TV Soundtrack .... RCA (M) LM-1779   6.00   9.00   12.00

VIKINGS, THE
Soundtrack .... United Artists (M) DF-6   10.00   15.00   20.00
Soundtrack (Re-channeled stereo) .... United Artists (S) DFS-56   6.00   9.00   12.00

VILLA RIDES   (1968)
Soundtrack .... Dot (S) 25870   5.00   7.50   10.00

V.I.P.'S, THE   (1963)
Soundtrack .... MGM (M) E-4152   5.00   7.50   10.00
Soundtrack .... MGM (S) SE-4152   6.00   9.00   12.00

VIRGIN   (1972)
Original Cast (2 records) .... Paramount (S) PAS 8000   10.00   15.00   20.00
  Joe DeVito, Dorothy Lerner, Jim Rast.

VIRGIN AND THE GYPSY, THE (1970)
Soundtrack (Limited release) .... Steady (S) S-122 15.00 22.50 30.00

VISIONS OF 8 (1973)
Soundtrack........................... RCA (S) ABL1-0231 4.00 6.00 8.00

VIVA LAS VEGAS (1964)
Soundtrack........................... RCA (EP) EPA 4382 4.00 8.00 12.00
Elvis Presley. Black label, dog on top.
—For more information, see PRESLEY, Elvis in the regular listings.

VIVA MARIA
Soundtrack........................ United Artists (M) UAL-4135 5.00 7.00 10.00
Soundtrack........................ United Artists (S) UAS-5135 6.00 9.00 12.00

VIVA MAX! (1970)
Soundtrack...........................RCA (S) LSP-4275 4.00 6.00 8.00

VOYAGE EN BALLON, LE (1960)
Soundtrack .... Philips (M) PHM 200029 7.50 11.25 15.00
Soundtrack .... Philips (S) PHS 600029 10.00 15.00 20.00

W

WACKEY WORLD OF MOTHER GOOSE, THE (1967)
Soundtrack........................... Epic (M) LN-24230 7.50 11.25 15.00
Soundtrack........................... Epic (S) BN-26230 10.00 15.00 20.00

WAGON TRAIN (1959)
TV Soundtrack .... Mercury (M) MG-20502 10.00 15.00 20.00
TV Soundtrack .... Mercury (S) SR-60179 12.00 18.00 24.00

WAIKIKI WEDDING (1937)
Soundtrack (10") (1951) .... Decca (M) DL-6011 6.00 9.00 12.00
Soundtrack (1962) .... Decca (M) DL-4252 3.00 4.50 6.00

WAIT A MINUM (1966)
Original London Cast...................... Decca (M) LK 4610 6.00 9.00 12.00
Contains many songs performed on broadway, but not included on the
original cast LP)
Andrew Tracey, Paul Tracey, Jeremy Taylor.
Original London Cast...................... Decca (S) SKL 4610 7.50 11.25 15.00
Original London Cast (Titled, "Always Something New Out Of Africa",
it contains material added to the Original London production of "Wait
A Minum" (For the Broadway production.)...... Decca (M) LK 4731 12.00 18.00 24.00
Jeremy Taylor, Paul Tracey, Andrew Tracey.
Original Cast .... London (M) 58002 2.00 3.00 4.00
Andrew Tracey, Paul Tracey, Kendrew Lascelles.
Original Cast .... London (S) MAS 88002 2.00 3.00 4.00

WAKE UP AND LIVE (1937)
Soundtrack (1964) .... Columbia (M) CL-3068 4.00 6.00 8.00

WALK DON'T RUN
Soundtrack...................... Mainstream (M) 56080 5.00 7.00 10.00
Soundtrack........................ Mainstream (S) 6080 7.00 11.00 15.00

WALKING HAPPY (1966)
Original Cast .... Capitol (M) VAS 2631 6.00 9.00 12.00
Norman Wisdom, Louise Troy, George Rose, Ed Bakey.
Original Cast .... Capitol (S) SVAS 2631 7.50 11.25 15.00

WALK ON THE WILD SIDE (1962)
Soundtrack........................ Choreo (M) A-4-ST 7.50 11.25 15.00
Soundtrack........................ Choreo (S) AS-4-ST 10.00 15.00 20.00
Soundtrack (1966) .... Mainstream (M) 56083 5.00 7.50 10.00
Soundtrack....................... Mainstream (S) S-6083 7.50 11.25 15.00

WALT DISNEY'S MICKEY MOUSE CLUB (1955)
TV Soundtrack (1962) .... Disneyland (M) DQ-1229 4.00 6.00 8.00
TV Soundtrack (1965) .... Disneyland (M) MM-24 3.00 4.50 6.00

WALT DISNEY'S WONDERFUL WORLD OF COLOR (1964)
TV Soundtrack .... Disneyland (M) DQ-1245 4.00 6.00 8.00

WAR AND PEACE (Rota) (1956)
Soundtrack...................... Columbia (M) CL-930 7.50 11.25 15.00

WAR AND PEACE (Ovchinnikov) (1968)
Soundtrack..................... Capitol (S) SWAO-2918 12.00 18.00 24.00

WAR LORD, THE
Soundtrack...................... Decca (M) DL-9149 10.00 15.00 20.00
Soundtrack...................... Decca (S) DL7-9149 12.00 19.00 25.00

WARNING SHOT (1967)
Soundtrack...................... Liberty (M) LRP-3498 7.50 11.25 15.00
Soundtrack...................... Liberty (S) LST-7498 10.00 15.00 20.00

WATER GYPSIES, THE (1955)
Original London Cast (1 side) .... World Record Club (M) SH 228 7.50 11.25 15.00
London Studio Cast (1 side) (1957) .... Dot (M) DPL 3048 6.00 9.00 12.00

WATERHOLE NO. 3 (1967)
Soundtrack (With Dialogue) .... Smash (M) 27096 6.00 9.00 12.00
Soundtrack........................... Smash (S) 67096 7.50 11.25 15.00

WATERLOO (1970)
Soundtrack...................... Paramount (S) PAS-6003 4.00 6.00 8.00

WATERMELON MAN (1970)
Soundtrack...................... Beverly Hills (S) BHS-26 3.00 4.50 6.00

WATTSTAX
Soundtrack, Vol. 1 (2 records) .... Stax (S) STS-3010-2 4.00 6.00 8.00

WAY OF THE WORLD, THE (1968)
Original London Cast (3 records) .... Caedmon (M) TR 339 4.00 6.00 8.00
Incidental music.
Original London Cast...................... Caedmon (S) TRS 339 4.00 6.00 8.00

WAY TO THE FORUM
Soundtrack...................... United Artists (S) UA-LA284-G 3.00 4.00 6.00

WAY WEST, THE
Soundtrack...................... United Artists (M) UAL-4149 7.50 11.25 15.00
Soundtrack......................United Artists (S) UAS 5149 10.00 15.00 20.00

WE'D RATHER SWITCH (1969)
Studio Cast .... Varieties (M) WRS 100 10.00 15.00 20.00
Tricia Sandberg, Yancy Gerber, Martha Wilcox.

WELCOME STRANGER (1947)
Soundtrack (1962)................... Decca (M) DL-4260 4.00 6.00 8.00

WE STILL KILL THE OLD WAY (1968)
Soundtrack...................... United Artists (M) UAL-4183 4.00 6.00 8.00
Soundtrack...................... United Artists (S) UAS-5183 5.00 7.50 10.00

WEST SIDE STORY (1957)
Original Cast .... Columbia (M) OL 5230 2.00 3.00 4.00
Carol Lawrence, Larry Kert, Chita Rivera.
Original Cast .... Columbia (S) OS 2001 2.00 3.00 4.00
Soundtrack (From the 1961 film)............. Columbia (M) OL 5670 2.00 3.00 4.00
Natalie Wood, Richard Beymer, Russ Tamblyn, Rita Moreno, George Chakiris.
Soundtrack........................... Columbia (S) OS 2070 2.00 3.00 4.00
Studio Cast (Composer conducts the symphonic dances)
(1 side) .... Columbia (S) MS 6251 2.00 3.00 4.00
Leonard Bernstein.

WESTWARD HO THE WAGONS! (1956)
Soundtrack...................... Disneyland (M) WDL-4008 10.00 15.00 20.00
Soundtrack (1959)................. Disneyland (M) WDL-3041 6.00 9.00 12.00
Soundtrack (1960)................. Disneyland (M) WDL-1041 5.00 7.50 10.00

WESTWORLD (1973)
Soundtrack........................... MGM (S) 1SE-47-ST 4.00 6.00 8.00

WHAT AM I BID? (1967)
Soundtrack........................... MGM (M) E-4506 2.00 3.00 4.00
Soundtrack...........................MGM (S) SE-4506 3.00 4.50 6.00

WHAT A WAY TO GO! (1964)
Soundtrack.................. 20th Century Fox (M) TFM 3143 5.00 7.50 10.00
Soundtrack.................. 20th Century Fox (S) TFS 4143 7.50 11.25 15.00

(M) Mono (S) Stereo (EP) Extended Play (Q) Quad (RI) Re-issued

WHAT DID YOU DO IN THE WAR, DADDY? (1966)

Soundtrack	RCA (M) LPM-3648	6.00	9.00	12.00
Soundtrack	RCA (S) LSP-3648	7.50	11.25	15.00

WHAT DO YOU SAY TO A NAKED LADY

Soundtrack	United Artists (S) 5206	3.00	4.00	6.00

WHAT IT WAS WAS LOVE (1969)

TV Soundtrack	RCA (S) LSP-4115	4.00	6.00	8.00

WHAT MAKES SAMMY RUN? (1964)

Original Cast	Columbia (M) OL 6040	7.50	11.25	15.00
Steve Lawrence, Sally Ann Howes, Robert Alda.				
Original Cast	Columbia (S) KOS 2440	10.00	15.00	20.00

WHAT'S A NICE COUNTRY LIKE YOU DOING IN A STATE LIKE THIS? (1973)

Original Toronto Canada Cast (Of the Broadway revue) (7" LP)	RMSC (S) 747003	10.00	15.00	20.00
Trudy Desmond, Andrea Martin, Martin Short.				
Original London Cast	Galaxy (S) 6004	12.00	18.00	24.00
Peter Blake, Billy Boyle, Neil McCaul.				

WHAT'S NEW, PUSSYCAT? (1965)

Soundtrack (Album cover art by Frank Frazett)	United Artists (M) UAL-4128	4.00	6.00	8.00
Soundtrack	United Artists (S) UAS-5128	5.00	7.50	10.00

WHAT'S UP, TIGER LILY? (1966)

Soundtrack	Kama Sutra (M) 8053	5.00	7.50	10.00
Soundtrack	Kama Sutra (S) S-8053	6.00	9.00	12.00

WHEN THE BOYS MEET THE GIRLS (See: Girl Crazy)

WHERE'S CHARLIE? (1948)

Original London Cast	Columbia (M) 33SX 1085	25.00	37.50	50.00
Norma Wisdom, Pip Hinton, Marion Grimaldi, Terrance Cooper.				
Original London Cast (Re-issue)	Mountain Evergreen (M) MES 7029	2.00	3.00	4.00
Soundtrack (From the film)	Ecnad (M) 216	7.50	11.25	15.00
Ray Bolger and Allyn McLerie (original cast stars), and Robert Shackleton and Mary Germaine.				

WHERE'S JACK? (1969)

Soundtrack	Paramount (S) 5005	10.00	15.00	20.00

WHERE'S POPPA? (1970)

Soundtrack	United Artists (S) UAS 5216	5.00	7.50	10.00

WHERE THE HOT WIND BLOWS (1960)

Soundtrack	Everest (M) BR-5076	10.00	15.00	20.00
Soundtrack	Everest (S) SDBR-1076	12.00	18.00	24.00

WHISPERERS, THE (1967)

Soundtrack	United Artists (M) 4161	7.50	11.25	15.00
Soundtrack	United Artists (S) 5161	10.00	15.00	20.00

WHITE CHRISTMAS (1954)

Soundtrack (10")	Columbia (M) CL-6338	15.00	22.50	30.00
Soundtrack	Decca (M) DL-8083	12.00	18.00	24.00

WHITE HORSE INN (1936)

Studio Cast (Side 1, "The Girl Friend")	Epic (M) LN 3685	10.00	15.00	20.00
Doreen Hume, Bruce Trent.				
STudio Cast (1961)	Angel (M) 35815	10.00	15.00	20.00
Andy Cole, Mary Thomas, Rita Williams, Charles Young.				
Studio Cast	Angel (S) 35815	12.00	18.00	24.00

(M) Mono (S) Stereo (EP) Extended Play (Q) Quad (RI) Re-issued

WHO IS HARRY KELLERMAN AND WHY IS HE SAYING THOSE TERRIBLE THINGS ABOUT ME? (1971)

Soundtrack	Columbia (S) S-30791	3.00	4.50	6.00

WHOOP-UP (1958)

Susan Johnson, Paul Ford, Ralph Young, Sylvia Syms.

Original Cast	MGM (M) E 3745	12.00	18.00	24.00
Original Cast (Minus the overture on the monaural version)	MGM (S) SE 3745	18.00	27.00	36.00

WHO'S AFRAID OF VIRGINIA WOOLF

Soundtrack	Warner Bros. (M) B 1656	6.00	9.00	12.00
Soundtrack	Warner Bros. (S) BS 1656	7.00	11.00	15.00
Soundtrack	Warner Bros. (M) 2B-1657	20.00	30.00	40.00

WIDE, WIDE WORLD (1956)

TV Soundtrack	RCA (M) LPM-1280	7.50	11.25	15.00

WILD BUNCH (1969)

Soundtrack	Warner Bros. (S) 1814	18.00	27.00	36.00

WILDCAT (1960)

Original Cast	RCA (M) LOC 1060	7.50	11.25	15.00
Lucille Ball, Keith Andes, Edith King, Paula Stewart.				
Original Cast	RCA (S) LSO 1060	10.00	15.00	20.00

WILD EYE (1968)

Soundtrack	RCA (M) LPM-4003	6.00	9.00	12.00
Soundtrack	RCA (S) LSP-4003	7.50	11.25	15.00

WILDFLOWER (1923)

Original London Cast (Side 1, "Tip Toes")	Monmouth Evergreen (M) MES 7052	2.00	3.00	4.00
Kitty Reidy, Howett Worster.				

WILD IN THE STREETS (1968)

Soundtrack	Tower (S) SKAO-5099	7.50	11.25	15.00

WILD IS THE WIND (1957)

Soundtrack	Columbia (M) CL-1090	12.00	18.00	24.00

WILD ONE, THE (1954)

Soundtrack (10")	Decca (M) DL-5515	12.00	18.00	24.00
Soundtrack (1956)	Decca (M) DL-8349	10.00	15.00	20.00

WILD ON THE BEACH (1965)

Soundtrack	RCA (M) LPM-3441	4.00	6.00	8.00
Soundtrack	RCA (S) LSP-3441	5.00	7.50	10.00

WILD RACERS

Soundtrack	Sidewalk (S) 5914	4.00	6.00	8.00

WILD ROVERS (1971)

Soundtrack	MGM (S) 1SE-30ST	3.00	4.50	6.00

WILD WHEELS (1969)

Soundtrack	RCA (S) LSO-1156	3.00	4.50	6.00

WILD, WILD WINTER (1966)

Soundtrack	Decca (M) DL-4699	3.00	4.00	6.00
Soundtrack	Decca (S) DL7-4699	4.00	6.00	8.00

WILL PENNY (1968)

Soundtrack	Dot (M) 3844	7.50	11.25	15.00
Soundtrack	Dot (S) 25844	10.00	15.00	20.00

TITLE	LABEL & NO.	GOOD	VERY GOOD	NEAR MINT

YOUNG LIONS, THE (1958)
Soundtrack . . . . Decca (M) DL-8719 10.00 15.00 20.00
Soundtrack . . . . Decca (S) DL-78719 12.00 18.00 24.00

YOUNG LOVERS
Soundtrack . . . . Columbia (M) OL 7010 7.00 11.00 15.00
Soundtrack . . . . Columbia (S) OS 2510 10.00 15.00 20.00

YOUNG MAN WITH A HORN (1950)
Soundtrack (10") (Traditional pop) . . . . Columbia (M) CL-6106 12.00 18.00 24.00
Soundtrack (1954) . . . . Columbia (M) CL-582 10.00 15.00 20.00

YOUNG PEOPLE (1940)
Soundtrack (1962) . . . . 20th Century Fox (M) 3045 5.00 7.50 10.00
Soundtrack (Re-channeled stereo) . . . . 20th Century Fox (S) S-3045 4.00 6.00 8.00

YOUNG SAVAGES, THE (1961)
Soundtrack . . . . Columbia (M) CL 1672 10.00 15.00 20.00
Soundtrack . . . . Columbia (S) CS 8472 15.00 22.50 30.00

YOUNG WINSTON (1972)
Soundtrack . . . . Angel (S) SFO-36901 4.00 6.00 8.00

YOU ONLY LIVE TWICE (1967)
Soundtrack . . . . United Artists (M) 4155 3.00 4.00 6.00
Soundtrack . . . . United Artists (S) 5155 4.00 6.00 8.00

YOU ONLY LOVE ONCE
Soundtrack . . . . London (S) PS 561 3.00 4.00 6.00

YOUR ARMS TOO SHORT TO BOX WITH GOD (1976)
Original Cast . . . . ABC (S) AB 1004 2.00 3.00 4.00
Salome Bay, Clinton Derricks-Carroll, Sheila Ellis.

YOUR CHEATIN' HEART (1964)
Soundtrack . . . . MGM (M) E-4260 5.00 7.50 10.00
Soundtrack . . . . MGM (S) SE-4260 6.00 9.00 12.00

YOU'RE A BIG BOY NOW (1967)
Soundtrack . . . . Kama Sutra (M) 8058 3.00 4.50 6.00
Soundtrack . . . . Kama Sutra (S) 8058 4.00 6.00 8.00

YOU'RE A GOOD MAN, CHARLIE BROWN (1967)
Studio Cast (This original album musical inspired the
off-Broadway show) . . . . MGM (S) LES 900 10.00 15.00 20.00
Orson Bean, Barbara Minkus, Bill Hinnant, Clark Gesner.
Original Cast (Off Broadway) . . . . MGM (M) 1E 90C 2.00 3.00 4.00
Bill Hinnant, Reva Rose, Karen Johnson.
Original Cast . . . . MGM (S) S1E 90C 2.00 3.00 4.00
TV Soundtrack . . . . Atlantic (S) SD 7252 5.00 7.50 10.00
Wendell Burton, Ruby Persson, Barry Livingston.

YOUR OWN THING (1968)
Original Cast (Off Broadway) . . . . RCA (M) LOC 1148 6.00 9.00 12.00
Rusty Thacker, Leland Palmer, Igors Gavon, Danny Apolinar.
Original Cast . . . . RCA (S) LSO 1148 7.50 11.25 15.00

YOURS, MINE AND OURS (1969)
Soundtrack . . . . United Artists (S) UAS-5181 7.50 11.25 15.00

Z

Z (1969)
Soundtrack . . . . Columbia (S) OS-3370 5.00 7.50 10.00

ZABRISKIE POINT (1971)
Soundtrack . . . . MGM (S) SE-4468 6.00 9.00 12.00

ZACHARIAH (1971)
Soundtrack . . . . ABC (S) OCS-13 5.00 7.50 10.00

ZIEGFELD FOLLIES (1907)
Original Cast (Excerpts) . . . . Veritas (M) VM 107 7.50 11.25 15.00
Original Cast (Excerpts) . . . . Pelican (M) LP 102 5.00 7.50 10.00
Radio Soundtrack (The first program of the series, "The Ziegfeld Follies
Of The Air," 1/27/36) . . . . Nostalgia Special Release (M) 001 5.00 7.50 10.00
Fanny Brice, James Melton, Patty Chafin, and chorus.

(M) Mono (S) Stereo (EP) Extended Play (Q) Quad (RI) Re-issued

---

ZIG ZAG
Soundtrack . . . . MGM (S) 1SE-21 ST 3.00 4.50 6.00

ZITA (1969)
Soundtrack . . . . Philips (S) 600-287 5.00 7.50 10.00

ZIZI (1964)
Original Cast . . . . Philips (S) PHS 600 161 5.00 7.50 10.00
Zizi Jeanmaire.

ZORBA (Kander) (1968)
Original Cast . . . . Capitol (S) SO 118 2.00 3.00 4.00
Herschel Bernardi, Maria Karnilova, John Cunningham.
Original Cast (2 sides of 3 records.) . . . . Capitol (S) SW 292 4.00 6.00 8.00

ZORBA THE GREEK (1964) (Theodorakis)
Soundtrack . . . . 20th Century Fox (M) 3167 4.00 6.00 8.00
Soundtrack . . . . 20th Century Fox (S) S-4167 5.00 7.50 10.00

ZULU (1964)
Soundtrack . . . . United Artists (M) UAL-4116 6.00 9.00 12.00
Soundtrack . . . . United Artists (S) UAS-5116 10.00 15.00 20.00

ZULU & THE ZAYDA, THE (1965)
Original Cast . . . . Columbia (M) OL 6480 7.50 11.25 15.00
Menasha Skulnik, Ossie Davis, Louis Gossett.
Original Cast . . . . Columbia (S) KOS 2880 10.00 15.00 20.00

Various Artists

Collectors will often seek a "various artists" album because of one person or one cut on it, or because it's all rock from a certain period or has a theme that interests them. In other words, they almost always collect it for some reason other than the fact that it falls in this special category of containing "various artists." There are countless reasons for the existence of this type of an album: a group of stars appear together in a live concert; six artists each record two traditional Christmas favorites; the record company releases a sampler of one song each from 12 different albums, and so on. We have chosen to sample only the more valuable records from this category, and all titles, regardless of age or content, appear alphabetically.

TITLE	LABEL & NO.	GOOD	VERY GOOD	NEAR MINT
A				
A & M (Bootleg)	A & M (S) SP 8022	10.00	15.00	20.00
AFTER HOURS	King (M) 528	4.00	10.00	16.00
ALAN FREED MEMORY LANE	End (M) 314	5.00	10.00	15.00
ALAN FREED'S GOLDEN PICS	End (M) 313	5.00	10.00	15.00
ALAN FREED'S TOP 15	End (M) LP 315	5.00	10.00	15.00
ALL GIRL MILLION SELLERS	Ascot (M) AM 13007	3.00	6.00	9.00
ALL STAR 4	Wyncote (M) W-9149	2.00	3.00	4.00
ALL STAR ROCK & ROLL	Atlantic (EP) EP 575	2.00	5.00	8.00
ALL STAR ROCK & ROLL REVUE	King (M) LP 638	4.00	8.00	12.00
ALL THESE THINGS	Instant (M) LP 71000	7.00	10.50	14.00
AMERICAN FOLK BLUES FESTIVAL	Excello (M) 8029	4.00	6.00	8.00
ANTHOLOGY OF BRITISH BLUES	Immediate (M) Z12 52006	4.00	6.00	8.00
ANTHOLOGY OF BRITISH BLUES VOL. 2	Immediate (M) Z12 52014	4.00	6.00	8.00
APOLLO SATURDAY NIGHT	Atco (S) SD 159	4.00	6.00	8.00
APPROVED BY 10,000,000	Teem (M) LP 5004	4.00	8.00	12.00
ART LABOE'S MEMORIES OF EL MONTE	Starla (M) LPM 1960	5.00	7.00	10.00
B				
BANG & SHOUT SUPER HITS	Bang (S) LPS 220	3.00	6.00	9.00
BAREFOOT ROCK & YOU GOT ME	Duke (M) LP 72	4.00	6.00	8.00
BARRELL OF OLDIES	Del Fi (M) DF 1219	4.00	8.00	12.00
BATTLE OF THE BANDS	Star (M) SRM 101	6.00	12.00	18.00
BATTLE OF THE BANDS	Panorama (M) 103	6.00	12.00	18.00
BATTLE OF THE BANDS VOL. 1	Ren Vell (M) LP 317	10.00	15.00	20.00
BATTLE OF THE BANDS VOL. 2	Panorama (M) 108	6.00	12.00	18.00
BATTLE OF THE BLUES	King (M) LP 668	4.00	8.00	12.00
BATTLE OF THE GROUPS	End (M) LP 305	5.00	10.00	15.00
BATTLE OF THE SURFING BANDS	Del Fi (M) DFLP 1235	4.00	8.00	12.00
BATTLE OF THE SURFING BANDS	Del Fi (S) DFST 1235	4.50	9.00	13.50
BEACH PARTY	GSP (M) GSP 6901	4.50	9.00	13.50
BEST IN RHYTHM & BLUES	Dooto (M) LP 204	4.00	10.00	16.00
BEST OF ACAPELLA	Relic (M) 101	4.00	6.00	8.00
BEST OF RHYTHM & BLUES	Jubilee (M) 1014	5.00	12.00	20.00
BEST OF THE BLUES VOL.1	Imperial (M) LP 12257	3.00	6.00	9.00
BEST OF THE BLUES VOL.1	Imperial (S) LP 9257	4.00	8.00	12.00
BEST OF THE BLUES VOL. 2	Imperial (M) LP 9259	4.00	8.00	12.00
BEST OF THE GIRL GROUPS	Pricewise (M) 4004	4.00	8.00	12.00
BEST OF THE OLDIES & GOODIES	Crown (M) CLP 5144	5.00	7.50	10.00
BEST OF THE HIDEOUTS	Hideout (M)	12.00	30.00	48.00
BEST OF TWIST A RAMA USA	Tar (M) 1000	5.00	10.00	15.00
BEST VOCAL GROUPS IN RHYTHM & BLUES	Dooto (M) LP 224	4.00	10.00	16.00
BEST VOCAL GROUPS IN ROCK & ROLL	Authentic (M) AUL 224	5.00	7.50	10.00
BIG BAD BOSS BEAT	Original Sound (M) OSRLP 5008	4.00	6.00	8.00
BIG HITS	Columbia (M) CL 1353	4.00	6.00	8.00
BIG HITS	Columbia (EP) B 2108	1.50	2.25	3.00
BIG HITS	Columbia (M) CL 2574	4.00	6.00	8.00
BIG HITS	Columbia (S) CS 8161	4.00	6.00	8.00
BIG HITS	Columbia (EP) B 13152	4.00	6.00	8.00
BIG HITS FROM ENGLAND & USA	Capitol (M) T 2125	7.50	10.00	15.00
BIG HITS FROM ENGLAND & USA	Capitol (S) ST 2125	7.50	10.00	15.00
BIG HITS OF MID AMERICA	Soma (M) MG 1245	7.00	10.50	14.00
BIG HITS OF MID AMERICA VOL. 2	Soma (M) MG 1246	7.00	10.50	14.00
BIG HOT ROD HITS	Capitol (M) T 2024	3.50	5.25	7.00
BIG HOT ROD HITS	Capitol (S) ST 2024	4.00	6.00	8.00
BIG THREE	FM (M) F 307	3.00	6.00	9.00
BIG THREE	FM (S) FS 307	4.00	8.00	12.00
BLASTS FROM THE PAST	Blast (M) 6803	3.00	6.00	9.00
BLUES	Argo (M) LP 4026	3.00	6.00	9.00
BLUES VOL. 2	Argo (M) LP 4027	3.00	6.00	9.00
BLUES VOL. 4	Argo (M) 4042	4.00	8.00	12.00
BLUES BOX (3 Record Set)	Verve-Folkways (M) 3011	4.00	8.00	12.00
BLUES BOX (3 Record Set)	Verve Folkways (S) 3011	4.00	8.00	12.00
BLUES PIANO CHICAGO PLUS	Atlantic (S) SD 7227	4.50	6.75	9.00
BLUES PROJECT, THE	Elektra (S) EKL 264	6.00	9.00	12.00
BLUES SINGERS	Halo (M) 50180	4.00	8.00	12.00
BLUES THAT GAVE AMERICA SOUL	Duke (M) DLP 82	4.00	6.00	8.00
BOLO BASH	Bolo (M) BLP 8002	5.00	10.00	15.00
BOOGIE WOOGIE RARITIES 1927 - 1932	Milestone (M) MLP 2009	5.00	7.50	10.00
BOPPIN	Jubilee (M) JGM 1118	4.00	10.00	16.00
BORN TO BE COUNTRY BOYS	Share (M) JS6104	4.00	8.00	12.00
BRITISH BEAT A-GO-GO	Majorette (M) M305A	4.00	6.00	8.00
BRUNSWICK'S GREATEST HITS	Brunswick (S) 754186	4.00	8.00	12.00
BUNCH OF GOODIES	Chess (M) LP 1441	4.00	8.00	12.00
C				
CADILLACS MEET THE ORIOLES	Jubilee (M) JGM 1117	4.00	10.00	16.00
CANDY BAR BOOGIE (Bootleg)	Roadhouse (M) LP 5001	4.50	6.75	9.00
CARLOAD OF HITS	Muse (M) 500	3.00	7.50	12.00
CARLOAD OF HITS	Muse (EP) EP 500	2.00	3.00	4.00
CARNIVAL OF SONGS	King (M) LP 819	4.00	8.00	12.00
CHARTBUSTERS	Vernon (S) 251	4.00	8.00	12.00
CHARTBUSTERS VOL IV	Capitol (M) T 2094	6.50	9.75	13.00
CHARTBUSTERS VOL IV	Capitol (S) ST 2094	6.50	9.75	13.00
A CHRISTMAS GIFT FOR YOU (Blue Label)	Philles (M) PHLP 4005	4.00	8.00	12.00
A CHRISTMAS GIFT FOR YOU Red & yellow label	Philles (M) PHLP 4005	2.50	3.75	5.00
CLASSIC BLUES VOL. 1	Blues Way (S) BLS 6061	4.00	6.00	8.00
CLASSICS BLUES VOL. 2	Blues Way (S) BLS 6062	4.00	6.00	8.00
COLLECTORS SHOWCASE VOL. 1	Constellation (M) CS 1	4.00	8.00	12.00
COLLECTORS SHOWCASE VOL. 2 The Moonglows	Constellation (M) CS 2	4.00	8.00	12.00
COLLECTORS SHOWCASE VOL. 3 The Flamingos	Constellation (M) CS 3	4.00	8.00	12.00
COLLECTORS SHOWCASE VOL. V	Constellation (M) CS 5	4.00	8.00	12.00
COLLECTORS SHOWCASE VOL. VI	Constellation (M) CS 6	4.00	8.00	12.00
COLLECTORS SHOWCASE VOL. VII	Constellation (M) CS 7	4.00	8.00	12.00
COME TO A SHINDIG DANCE PARTY	Custom (M) CM 2038	2.50	3.75	5.00
CONNECTICUTS GREATEST HITS	Phase One (M) CP 101	5.00	10.00	15.00
COPULATIN' BLUES	Stash (M) ST 101	4.00	6.00	8.00
CRAB TUNES/NOGGINS	Warner Brothers (S) 1944	3.50	5.25	7.00
CRUISIN SERIES A History of Rock & Roll Radio	Increase (S) CSTM 4451	5.00	7.50	10.00
CURRENT COUNTRY HITS VOL. 1	Columbia (M) HL 9008	3.00	4.50	6.00
CURRENT COUNTRY HITS VOL. 2	Columbia (M) HL 9011	3.00	4.50	6.00
CURRENT COUNTRY HITS VOL. 3	Columbia (M) HL 9016	3.00	4.50	6.00
CURRENT COUNTRY HITS VOL. 4	Columbia (M) HL 9020	3.00	4.50	6.00
CURRENT COUNTRY HITS VOL. 4	Columbia (EP) H4 16	1.50	2.25	3.00
D				
DANCE DISCOTEQUE	Decca (S) 4556	3.00	6.00	9.00
DANCE PARTY	Libra (M) 6001	3.00	6.00	9.00
DANCE THE ROCK & ROLL	Atlantic (M) 8013	4.00	10.00	16.00
DARK MUDDY BOTTOM BLUES	Specialty (S) SPS 2149	4.00	6.00	8.00
DETROIT SOUND, THE	Wyncote (M) W-9208	2.25	3.38	4.50
THE DIMENSION DOLLS VOL. 1	Dimension (M) DLP 6001	10.00	20.00	30.00
DROP DOWN MAMA	Chess (S) 411	4.00	6.00	8.00
DUTCH EXPLOSION	White Whale (S) WW 7130	4.00	6.00	8.00
E				
EARLY CHICAGO	Happy Tiger (M) HT 1017	4.00	6.00	8.00
EARLY L. A.	Together (S) ST T 1014	4.50	5.25	9.00
EARLY R & B (Bootleg)	Chicago 200	4.00	6.00	8.00
EARTH ANGEL	Guest Star (M) 1432	5.00	10.00	15.00
EAST SIDE REVUE	Rampart (M) LP 3303	5.00	10.00	15.00
EAST SIDE REVUE VOL. 2	Rampart (M) 3305	5.00	10.00	15.00
ECHOES OF A ROCK ERA	Roulette (S) RE 115	4.50	6.75	9.00
ECHOES OF A ROCK ERA THE GROUPS (2 Record Set)	Roulette (S) RE 114	4.50	6.75	9.00
ENGLAND'S GREATEST HITMAKERS	London (M) LL 3430	4.00	8.00	12.00
ENGLAND'S GREATEST HITMAKERS	London (S) PS 430	3.00	6.00	9.00
ESP SAMPLER	ESP (S) 1051	4.00	6.00	8.00
EVERYBODY ROCKS	Capitol (M) 1025	6.00	15.00	24.00
EVOLUTION OF THE BLUES SONG	Columbia (M) CL 1583	3.50	5.25	7.00
EVOLUTION OF THE BLUES SONG	Columbia (S) CS 8383	4.00	6.00	8.00
THE EXCELLO STORY	Excello (M) DBL 28025	4.00	6.00	8.00
EXCITING NEW LIVERPOOL SOUND	Columbia (M) CL 2172	5.00	10.00	15.00
EXCERPTS FROM "TOMMY"	Pickwick (S) SPC 3339	4.00	6.00	8.00
F				
FABULOUS OLDIES IN STEREO, Vol. 1	Fabulous Sound (S) 1001	2.50	3.75	5.00
FABULOUS OLDIES IN STEREO, Vol. 2	Fabulous Sound (S) 1002	2.50	3.75	5.00
FABULOUS OLDIES IN STEREO, Vol. 3	Fabulous Sound (S) 1003	2.50	3.75	5.00
FABULOUS OLDIES IN STEREO, Vol. 4	Fabulous Sound (S) 1004	2.50	3.75	5.00
FABULOUS OLDIES IN STEREO, Vol. 5	Fabulous Sound (S) 1005	2.50	3.75	5.00
FANFARE OF HITS	Argo (M) 656	4.00	10.00	16.00
FASCINATORS MEET THE ROB ROYS (Bootleg)	Cap (M) 1008	4.00	6.00	8.00
FILLMORE: The Last Days	Fillmore (S) Z3X 31390	6.00	9.00	12.00

(M) Mono (S) Stereo (EP) Extended Play (Q) Quad (RI) Re-issued

TITLE	LABEL & NO.	GOOD	VERY GOOD	NEAR MINT
FINK ALONG WITH MAD	Big Top (M) 12 1206	4.00	8.00	12.00
FIRST GREAT ROCK FESTIVALS OF THE SEVENTIES: Isle of Wight, Atlanta Pop Festival	Columbia (M) 30805	4.00	6.00	8.00
FOLK FESTIVAL AT NEWPORT VOL. 1	Vanguard (S) VRS 9062	4.00	8.00	12.00
FOLK FESTIVAL OF THE BLUES	Argo (M) LP 4031	3.00	6.00	9.00
FOLK SINGERS AROUND HARVARD SQUARE	Veritas (M) 1	3.00	6.00	9.00
FOOL BRITANNIA	Acapella (M) 1	5.00	7.50	10.00
FORGOTTEN MILLION SELLERS	King (M) LP 792	3.00	6.00	9.00
FOR SEGREGATIONISTS ONLY	Rebel (M) 1000	2.50	6.25	10.00
FOR TWISTERS ONLY	Ace (M) LP 1021	4.00	8.00	12.00
FREAKOUT USA	Sidewalk (M) T 5901	5.00	7.50	10.00
FRIDAY AT THE CAGE A GO GO	Westchester (M) 1005	12.00	24.00	36.00
FROM THE HISTORIC VAULTS OF DUKE/PEACOCK VOL. 2	ABC (S) X-789	3.00	4.50	6.00

G

TITLE	LABEL & NO.	GOOD	VERY GOOD	NEAR MINT
GARDEN OF DELIGHTS	Elktra (S) S3 10	7.00	10.50	14.00
GATHERING AT THE DEPOT	Beta (S) S8047 1414S	9.00	12.00	18.00
GIGANTIC STARS OF ROCK & ROLL	Crown (M) CLP 5013	5.00	12.50	20.00
GOIN TO CHICAGO	Testament (M) T 2218	4.00	8.00	12.00
GOLDEN AGE OF RHYTHM & BLUES (2 Record Set)	Chess (M) 2CH 50030	4.00	6.00	8.00
GOLDEN DOZEN	Columbia (M) CL 1462	4.00	6.00	8.00
GOLDEN ECHOES	Arvee (M) A 433	4.00	8.00	12.00
GOLDEN ENCORES	Cadence (M) CLP 3043	4.00	8.00	12.00
GOLDEN ERA (3 Record Set)	Golden Era Series (M) 123	8.00	16.00	24.00
GOLDEN GASSERS	Capitol (M) T 1561	4.00	6.00	8.00
GOLDEN GROUPS VOL. 1	Relic (M) 5005	4.00	6.00	8.00
GOLDEN GROUPS VOL. 2	Relic (M) 5007	4.00	6.00	8.00
GOLDEN GROUPS VOL. 3	Relic (M) 5012	4.00	6.00	8.00
GOLDEN GROUPS VOL. 4	Relic (M) 5014	4.00	6.00	8.00
GOLDEN GROUPS VOL. 5	Relic (M) 5015	4.00	6.00	8.00
GOLDEN GROUPS VOL. 6	Relic (M) 5016	4.00	6.00	8.00
GOLDEN GROUPS VOL. 7	Relic (M) 5019	4.00	6.00	8.00
GOLDEN GROUPS VOL. 8	Relic (M) 5021	4.00	6.00	8.00
GOLDEN HITS	Mercury (M) MG 20213	4.00	6.00	8.00
GOLDEN HITS FROM THE GANG AT BANG	Bang (M) 215	4.00	8.00	12.00
GOLDEN HITS FROM THE GANG AT BANG	Bang (S) 215	3.00	6.00	9.00
GOLDEN OLDIES	Decca (M) DL 4036	4.00	6.00	8.00
GOLDEN SOUVENIRS	Almor (M) A 103	3.00	6.00	9.00
GOLDEN SOUVENIRS	Almor (S) AS 103	3.00	6.00	9.00
GOLDEN TEEN HITS	Liberty (M) L-5505	3.50	4.25	7.00
GOLD RECORD	Capitol (M) T 830	5.00	7.50	10.00
GONE BUT NOT FORGOTTEN	Class (M) CL 5004	4.00	8.00	12.00
GOSPEL MUSIC VOL. 1	Imperial (M) LM 94007	4.00	6.00	8.00
GREATEST 15 HITS ON ACE	Ace (M) LP 1012	4.50	9.00	13.50
GREATEST GOLDEN GOODIES	Laurie (M) LP 2014	5.00	10.00	15.00
GREATEST HITS FROM THE SOUL OF TEXAS	Wand (M) WDM677	2.50	5.00	7.50
GREATEST HITS FROM THE SOUL OF TEXAS	Wand (S) WDS677	3.00	6.00	9.00
GREATEST ON STAGE	Want (M) 661	2.50	5.00	7.50
GREATEST ON STAGE	Want (S) S 661	3.00	6.00	9.00
GREATEST R & B STARS	Guest Star (M) GS 1906	4.00	8.00	12.00
GREATEST RHYTHM & BLUES HITS VOL. 1	Amazon (M) AM 1007	6.00	12.00	18.00
GREATEST ROCK & ROLL	Atlantic (M) LP 8001	4.00	10.50	16.00
GREATEST ROCK & ROLL VOL. 2	Atlantic (M) 8021	4.00	10.00	16.00
GREATEST SING THEIR SOUL FAVORITES	Wand (M) 660	3.00	6.00	9.00
GREATEST TEENAGE HITS OF ALL TIME	Teem (M) LP 5003	4.00	8.00	12.00
GREATEST TWIST HITS	Atlantic (M) 8058	4.00	8.00	12.00
GREATEST WESTERN HITS	Columbia (M) CL 1257	4.00	6.00	8.00
GREAT GOLDEN GROOVES	Epic (M) LN 24040	4.00	10.00	16.00
GREAT GROUP GOODIES	Atco (M) 33 143	4.00	8.00	12.00
GREAT GROUPS GREAT RECORDS	Laurie (M) LP 2010	5.00	10.00	15.00
GREAT HITS ON DOT	Dot (M) DLP 3049	4.00	6.00	8.00
GREAT SOUL HITS	Brunswick (M) BL 754129	4.00	6.00	8.00
GROUP OF GOLDIES	Group (M) W 33001	4.00	6.00	8.00
GUARANTEED TO PLEASE	Teem (M) LP 5002	4.00	8.00	12.00

H

TITLE	LABEL & NO.	GOOD	VERY GOOD	NEAR MINT
HALL OF FAME	Columbia (M) CL 2600	4.00	6.00	8.00
HALL OF FAME HITS	Columbia (M) CL 1308	4.00	6.00	8.00
HEARTBREAKERS (Bootleg)	Roadhouse (M) LP 5002	4.50	6.75	9.00
HERALD THE BEAT	Herald (M) 0110	5.00	12.50	20.00
HERE ARE THE HITS	Fire (M) FLP 100	6.00	12.00	18.00
HIGHWAY OF BLUES	Audio Lab (M) AL 1520	5.00	15.00	24.00
HILLBILLY HOUSE PARTY	Imperial (M) 9214	3.00	6.00	9.00
HISTORY OF BRITISH BLUES (2 Record Set)	Sire (S) SAS 3701	4.00	6.00	8.00
HISTORY OF RHYTHM & BLUES SERIES VOL. 1 THE ROOTS 1947-52	Atlantic (M) 8161	4.50	5.25	9.00
HISTORY OF RHYTHM & BLUES SERIES VOL. 1 THE ROOTS 1947-52	Atlantic (S) 8161	3.00	4.50	6.00
HISTORY OF RHYTHM & BLUES SERIES VOL. II GOLDEN YEARS 1953-55	Atlantic (M) 8162	4.50	5.25	9.00
HISTORY OF RHYTHM & BLUES SERIES VOL. II GOLDEN YEARS 1953-55	Atlantic (S) 8162	3.00	4.50	6.00
HISTORY OF RHYTHM & BLUES SERIES VOL. III ROCK & ROLL 1956-57	Atlantic (M) 8163	4.50	5.25	9.00
HISTORY OF RHYTHM & BLUES SERIES VOL. III ROCK & ROLL 1956-57	Atlantic (S) 8163	3.00	4.50	6.00
HISTORY OF RHYTHM & BLUES SERIES VOL. IV BIG BEAT 1958-60	Atlantic (M) 8164	4.50	5.25	9.00
HISTORY OF RHYTHM & BLUES SERIES VOL. IV BIG BEAT 1958-60	Atlantic (S) 8164	3.00	4.50	6.00
HISTORY OF SYRACUSE MUSIC Volume 1	ECEIP (M) PSLP 1000	9.00	13.50	18.00
HISTORY OF SYRACUSE MUSIC Volume 2	ECEIP (M) PSLP 1003	6.00	9.00	12.00
THE HISTORY OF SYRACUSE MUSIC Volumes 3 and 4	ECEIP (M) PSLP 1007	6.00	9.00	12.00
HISTORY OF SYRACUSE MUSIC Volume 5	ECEIP (M) PSLP 1011	6.00	9.00	12.00
HISTORY OF SYRACUSE MUSIC VOL. 6	ECEIP (M) PSLP 1001	6.00	9.00	12.00
HITMAKERS	Columbia (M) CL 1485	4.00	6.00	8.00
HITMAKERS	Columbia (S) CS 8276	4.50	6.75	9.00
HITMAKERS	Jerden (M) JRL 7005	7.00	10.50	14.00
HIT MAKERS & THEIR RECORD BREAKERS	King (M) LP 737	4.00	6.00	8.00
HIT PARADE	Mercury (M) MG 25164	4.00	6.00	8.00
HIT PARADE	Mercury (M) MG 25166	4.00	6.00	8.00
HIT PARADE	Mercury (M) MG 25205	4.00	6.00	8.00
HITS I FORGOT TO BUY	Swan (M) LP 512	5.00	10.00	15.00
HITS OF THE HOPS	Warner Brothers (M) W 1448	3.50	5.25	7.00
HITS OF THE HOPS	Warner Brothers (M) WS 1448	4.00	6.00	8.00
HITS THAT JUMPED	Checker (M) 2975	4.50	9.00	13.50
HITSVILLE	Coral (M) CRL 57269	4.00	8.00	12.00
HITSVILLE	Coral (S) CRL 75726	5.00	10.00	15.00
HITTSVILLE, USA	Imperial (M) LP 9084	4.00	10.00	16.00
HITTSVILLE VOL. 2	Imperial (M) LP 9099	4.00	10.00	16.00
HOME OF THE BLUES	Minit (M) LP 0001	4.00	8.00	12.00
HONOR ROLL OF HITS 1926-1927	RCA (M) LPM 3175	4.00	6.00	8.00
HONOR ROLL OF HITS 1926-1927	RCA (EP) EPA 514	1.50	2.25	3.00
HONOR ROLL OF HITS 1926-1927	RCA (EP) EPA 515	1.50	2.25	3.00
HONOR ROLL OF HITS 1927-1928	RCA (M) LPM 3176	4.00	6.00	8.00
HONOR ROLL OF HITS 1928-1929	RCA (EP) EPA 516	1.50	2.25	3.00
HONOR ROLL OF HITS 1928-1929	RCA (EP) EPA 517	1.50	2.25	3.00
HONOR ROLL OF HITS 1928-1929	RCA (M) LPM 3177	4.00	6.00	8.00
HONOR ROLL OF HITS 1930-1931	RCA (EP) EPA 518	1.50	2.25	3.00
HONOR ROLL OF HITS 1930-1931	RCA (EP) EPA 519	1.50	2.25	3.00
HONOR ROLL OF HITS 1930-1931	RCA (M) LPM 3178	4.00	6.00	8.00
HONOR ROLL OF HITS 1932-1933	RCA (EP) EPA 520	1.50	2.25	3.00
HONOR ROLL OF HITS 1932-1933	RCA (EP) EPA 521	1.50	2.25	3.00
HONOR ROLL OF HITS 1932-1933	RCA (M) LPM 3179	4.00	6.00	8.00
HONOR ROLL OF HITS 1934-1935	RCA (EP) EPA 522	1.50	2.25	3.00
HONOR ROLL OF HITS 1934-1935	RCA (EP) EPA 523	1.50	2.25	3.00
HONOR ROLL OF HITS 1936-1937	RCA (M) LPM 3180	4.00	6.00	8.00
HONOR ROLL OF HITS 1936-1937	RCA (EP) EPA 524	1.50	2.25	3.00
HONOR ROLL OF HITS 1936-1937	RCA (EP) EPA 525	1.50	2.25	3.00
HONOR ROLL OF HITS 1938-1939	RCA (M) LPM 3181	4.00	6.00	8.00
HONOR ROLL OF HITS 1938-1939	RCA (EP) EPA 526	1.50	2.25	3.00
HONOR ROLL OF HITS 1938-1939	RCA (EP) EPA 527	1.50	2.25	3.00
HONOR ROLL OF HITS 1940-1941	RCA (M) LPM 3182	4.00	6.00	8.00
HONOR ROLL OF HITS 1940-1941	RCA (EP) EPA 528	1.50	2.25	3.00
HONOR ROLL OF HITS 1940-1941	RCA (EP) EPA 529	1.50	2.25	3.00
HONOR ROLL OF HITS 1942-1943	RCA (M) LPM 3183	4.00	6.00	8.00
HONOR ROLL OF HITS 1942-1943	RCA (EP) EPA 530	1.50	2.25	3.00
HONOR ROLL OF HITS 1942-1943	RCA (EP) EPA 531	1.50	2.25	3.00
HONOR ROLL OF HITS 1944-1945	RCA (M) LPM 3184	4.00	6.00	8.00
HONOR ROLL OF HITS 1944-1945	RCA (EP) EPA 532	1.50	2.25	3.00
HONOR ROLL OF HITS 1944-1945	RCA (EP) EPA 533	1.50	2.25	3.00
HOT CANARIES	Columbia (M) CL 2534	4.00	6.00	8.00
HOT ROD CITY	Vault (M) LP 104	6.00	9.00	12.00
HOT ROD CITY	Vault (S) VS 104	6.50	9.75	13.00
HOT ROD GARY	Capitol (M) 985	6.00	15.00	24.00
HOT ROD RALLY	Capitol (M) T 1997	2.50	5.00	7.50
HOT ROD RALLY	Capitol (S) ST 1997	3.00	6.00	9.00
HOUND DOG'S ORIGINAL ROCK & ROLL MEMORY TIME	Atlantic (M) 8068	4.00	8.00	12.00
HOW TO BLOW YOUR MIND AND HAVE A FREAK OUT PARTY	Audio Fidelity (S) AFSD 6184	6.00	9.00	12.00
HULLABALOO WITH THE STARS	Wyncote (M) W-9080	2.00	3.00	4.00

I

TITLE	LABEL & NO.	GOOD	VERY GOOD	NEAR MINT
I COULDN'T BELIEVE MY EYES	Blues Way (S) BLS 6059	4.00	6.00	8.00
I DIG ROCK & ROLL	Score (M) LP 4002	3.00	6.00	9.00
I DIG ROCK AND ROLL	Score (S) SLP 4002	9.00	22.50	36.00
I ASKED FOR WATER,SHE GAVE ME GASOLINE	Imperial (M) LP 12455	4.00	6.00	8.00

J

TITLE	LABEL & NO.	GOOD	VERY GOOD	NEAR MINT
JACKO'S CHOICE R & B OLDIES	Bonded (M) B 777	3.00	6.00	9.00
JACKPOT OF HITS	Apollo (M) LP 490	5.50	13.75	22.00
JAMES DEAN STORY	Coral (M) CRL 57099	5.00	12.50	20.00
JAMES DEAN STORY	Capitol (M) W 881	4.00	10.00	16.00
JAMES DEAN STORY	Capitol (EP) 881	2.00	4.00	6.00
JAMICA SKA	Atlantic (M) 8098	3.00	6.00	9.00
JUBILEE SURPRISE PARTY	Jubilee (M) J 1107	3.00	4.50	6.00
JUBILEE SURPRISE PARTY	Jubilee (S) SDJ 1107	4.00	6.00	8.00

K

TITLE	LABEL & NO.	GOOD	VERY GOOD	NEAR MINT
KDWD DISC-COVERIES (Minneappolis)	KDWB (M) 63	3.00	6.00	9.00
KEWB DISC-COVERIES (San Francisco)	KEWB (M) 91	3.00	6.00	9.00
KFWB DISC-COVERIES (Los Angeles)	KFWB (M) 98	3.00	6.00	9.00

These LP's contained TOP 40 Hits and 2 Jingles from that radio station. Label number corresponded to station's dial position

TITLE	LABEL & NO.	GOOD	VERY GOOD	NEAR MINT
KINGS SING THE BLUES	Teem (M) LP 5005	4.00	8.00	12.00
KNOWN FACES - NEW FACES - GOING PLACES (Special Product LP)	Columbia (M) 42371	6.00	15.00	20.00
KRLA'S MILLION DOLLAR SOUND	KRLA (M) 1110	4.00	6.00	8.00

(M) Mono   (S) Stereo   (EP) Extended Play   (Q) Quad   (RI) Re-issued

L

TITLE	LABEL & NO.	GOOD	VERY GOOD	NEAR MINT
LA SOUNDTRACK '76	K-West (M) 43446	2.00	3.00	4.00
LET'S HAVE A DANCE PARTY	Ace (M) LP	4.00	8.00	12.00
LET THE GOOD TIMES ROLL	Guest Star (M) GS 1905	4.00	8.00	12.00
LIKE'ER RED HOT	Duke (M) DLP 73	4.00	6.00	8.00
LIVERPOOL TODAY	Capitol (M) T 2544	4.00	8.00	12.00
LIVERPOOL TODAY	Capitol (S) ST 2544	4.50	9.00	13.50
LLOYD THAXTON PRESENTS THE GREATEST DANCE HITS SLAVSON STYLE	Domain (M) 101	4.00	6.00	8.00
LONDON REALLY SWINGS	Columbia Special Products (M) 0301	5.00	10.00	15.00
LOVE THOSE GOODIES	Checker (M) LP 2973	4.50	9.00	13.50

M

TITLE	LABEL & NO.	GOOD	VERY GOOD	NEAR MINT
MAD TWISTS ROCK & ROLL	Big Top (M) 12 1305	4.00	8.00	12.00
MAKING OF 'TOMMY' 1975	Polydor (S) SA010	4.00	6.00	8.00
MARVIN GAYE AND HIS GIRLS TAMMI TERRELL, MARY WELLS AND KIM WESTON	Tamla (S) TS 293	3.50	5.25	7.00
MEMORY LANE	Fire (M) FLP 101	6.00	12.00	18.00
MERRY CHRISTMAS BABY	Hollywood (M) H 501	4.00	8.00	12.00
MICKIE MOST PRESENTS BRITISH GO-GO	MGM (M) E 4306	3.00	6.00	9.00
MICKIE MOST PRESENTS BRITISH GO-GO	MGM (S) SE 4306	3.00	6.00	9.00
MILLION AIRS	Coral (M) CRL 57310	3.00	6.00	9.00
MILLION DOLLAR MUSIC	Dot (M) DLP 3425	3.00	6.00	9.00
A MILLION OR MORE	ABC Paramount (M) ABC 216	5.00	10.00	15.00
MILLION SELLERS DANCE HITS	Parkway (M) 7028	4.00	6.00	8.00
MONEY MUSIC	August (M) LP 100	4.00	8.00	12.00
MONSTER ALBUM	DCP (M) 6805	3.00	6.00	9.00
MONTEREY INTERNATIONAL POP FESTIVAL	Dunhill (S) DSX 50100	3.50	5.25	7.00
MORE OF THE OLDIES AND GOLDIES	Crown (M) CLP 5202	4.00	10.00	16.00
MORE TEENAGE TRIANGLE	Colpix (M) CP 468	3.50	5.25	7.00
MORE TEENAGE TRIANGLE	Colpix (S) SCP 468	4.00	6.00	8.00
MOTORTOWN REVUE No. 2	Motown (M) 615	4.00	8.00	12.00
MOTOWN HITS VOL. 1	Motown (M) 603	4.00	8.00	12.00
MURRAY THE K LIVE FROM THE BROOKLYN FOX IN HIS RECORD BREAKING SHOW	KFM (M) 1001	5.00	10.00	15.00
MURRY THE K PRESENTS	Brooklyn (M) 302	4.00	8.00	12.00
MURRAY THE K PRESENTS	Brooklyn (S) 302	4.00	8.00	12.00
MURRAY THE K'S BLASTS FROM THE PAST	Chess (M) 1461	4.00	8.00	12.00
MURRAY THE K'S GASSERS FOR SUBMARINE RACE WATCHERS	Chess (M) LP 1470	4.00	8.00	12.00
MURRAY THE K'S GOLDEN GASSERSS	Chess (M) LP 1458	4.00	8.00	12.00
MURRAY THE K'S GREATEST HOLIDAY SHOW LIVE FROM THE BROOKLYN FOX	Brooklyn (M) 301	4.00	8.00	12.00
MURRAY THE K'S GREATEST HOLIDAY SHOW LIVE FROM THE BROOKLYN FOX	Brooklyn (S) 301	4.00	8.00	12.00
MURRAY THE K'S 1962 GOLDEN GASSERS	Scepter (M) 510	3.00	6.00	9.00
MURRAY THE K: THE 5TH BEATLE GIVES YOU THEIR FAVORITE GOLDEN GASSERS	Scepter (M) 524	3.00	6.00	9.00
MUSIC FOR HAND-JIVING	London (M) LL 3034	4.00	6.00	8.00
MUSIC JAMES DEAN LIVED BY	Unique (M) LP 109	3.00	6.00	9.00
MY SON THE SURF NUT	Capitol (M) T 1939	3.00	6.00	9.00
MY SON THE SURF NUT	Capitol (S) ST 1939	3.50	7.00	10.50

N

TITLE	LABEL & NO.	GOOD	VERY GOOD	NEAR MINT
NEW HI	Tempo (M) 2	7.00	10.50	14.00
NEW ORLEANS OUR HOME TOWN	Imperial (M) LP 9260	4.00	8.00	12.00
NEWPORT FOLK FESTIVAL 1960 Vol. 1	Vanguard (M) VRS 9083	3.00	6.00	9.00
NEWPORT FOLK FESTIVAL 1960 Vol. 1	Vanguard (S) VSD 2087	3.50	7.00	10.50
NEWPORT FOLK MUSIC FESTIVAL VOL.2	Vanguard (M) VRS 9063	3.00	6.00	9.00
NEWPORT FOLK MUSIC FESTIVAL VOL.2	Vanguard (S) VSD 2054	3.50	7.00	10.50
NIGHT AT THE BOULEVARD	Felsted (M) 7503	5.00	12.50	20.00
NIGHT TRAIN	King (M) 771	4.00	8.00	12.00
A NIGHT TRAIN OF OLDIES	Arrawak (M) 100	5.00	12.50	20.00
1964 IN REVIEW	Gateway (M) 9004	8.00	16.00	24.00
NORTHWEST COLLECTION VOL. 1	Etiquitte (M) ETALB 1028	7.00	10.50	14.00
NUGGETS (2 Record Set)	Elektra (S) 7E 2006	4.00	6.00	8.00

O

TITLE	LABEL & NO.	GOOD	VERY GOOD	NEAR MINT
OFFBEAT GROUPS (Bootleg)	Chicago 203	4.00	6.00	8.00
OFFBEAT GROUPS VOL. 2 (Bootleg)	Chicago 204	4.00	6.00	8.00
OFFBEAT GROUPS VOL. 3 (Bootleg)	Chicago 205	4.00	6.00	8.00
OFFBEAT GROUPS VOL. 4 (Bootleg)	Chicago 206	4.00	6.00	8.00
OFFBEAT GROUPS VOL. 5 (Bootleg)Chicago 207		4.00	6.00	8.00
OLDIES	Dooto (S) 855	4.00	6.00	8.00
OLDIES BUT GOODIES (1959 Issue)	Original Sound (M) LPM 5001	4.00	8.00	12.00
OLDIES BUT GOODIES VOL.2	Original Sound (M) LPM 5003	3.00	6.00	9.00
OLDIES BUT GOODIES VOL.3	Original Sound (M) LPM 5004	3.00	4.50	6.00
OLDIES BUT GOODIES VOL.3	Original Sound (M) LPM 5005	3.00	4.50	6.00
OLDIES BUT GOODIES VOL.5	Original Sound (M) LPM 5007	3.00	4.50	6.00
OLDIES BUT GOODIES VOL.6	Original Sound (M) LPM 5011	3.00	4.50	6.00

The Original Sound series is still easily available and therefore has no value above it's current retail cost. Since the LP's have been re-issued there are collectors who seek the first issue of the earlier volumes, especially Vol. 1. The first issue of any of the volumes would have no volumes advertised on the back cover higher in number (volume) than itself. Vol. 1 would have no LP's advertised on the back. Also the original issues were numbered in the 5000 series. (Vol I was 5001). The 5000 series numbers then became the designated numbers for mono issues.

TITLE	LABEL & NO.	GOOD	VERY GOOD	NEAR MINT
OLDIES AND GOLDIES	Crown (M) CLP 5241	4.00	10.00	16.00
OLDIES GOODIES & WOODIES	Vault (M) LP 103	6.00	9.00	12.00
OLDIES IN HI FI	Chess (M) 1439	4.50	9.00	13.50

(M) Mono (S) Stereo (EP) Extended Play (Q) Quad (RI) Re-issued

TITLE	LABEL & NO.	GOOD	VERY GOOD	NEAR MINT
ONE DOZEN GOLDIES	Carlton (M) 121	4.00	8.00	12.00
ORIGINAL AMATEUR HOUR 25th ANNIVERSARY ALBUM (2 Record Set)	United Artists (M) UXL2	4.00	6.00	8.00
ORIGINAL EARLY TOP 40 HITS	Paramount (S) 1013	2.00	3.00	4.00
ORIGINAL GOLDEN OLDIES	Group (M) W 33002	4.00	6.00	8.00
ORIGINAL GOODIES	Time (M) T 52082	4.00	6.00	8.00
ORIGINAL GOODIES	Time (S) ST 2082	5.00	7.50	10.00
ORIGINAL GREAT NORTHWEST HITS VOL. 1	Jerden (M) JRL 7001	6.50	9.75	13.00
ORIGINAL GREAT NORTHWEST HITS VOL. 2	Jerden (M) JRL 7002	6.50	9.75	13.00
ORIGINAL HIT RECORDS	Roulette (M) R 25106	3.00	4.50	6.00
ORIGINAL HIT RECORDS	Roulette (S) SR 25106	4.00	6.00	8.00
ORIGINAL RECORDING BY THE ARTISTS WHO MADE THESE HITS	Flip (M) 1002	6.00	15.00	24.00
ORIGINAL SURFIN HITS	GNP-Crescendo (M) GNP 84	3.00	6.00	9.00
OUR BEST TO YOU	Everlast (M) 201	6.00	12.00	18.00
OUR SIGNIFICANT HITS	Specialty (M) SP 2112	4.00	6.00	8.00
OUT CAME THE BLUES	Decca (M) DL 4434	5.00	10.00	15.00
OUTTA SIGHT	Capitol (S) SL 6554	4.00	6.00	8.00

P

TITLE	LABEL & NO.	GOOD	VERY GOOD	NEAR MINT
PACKAGE OF 16 BIG HITS	Motown (M) 614	4.00	8.00	12.00
PAJAMA PARTY	Forum (S) SF 9006	3.00	6.00	9.00
PARAGONS MEET THE HARPTONES	Musicnote (M) 8001	5.00	10.00	15.00
PARAGONS MEET THE JESTERS	Jubilee (M) JGM 1098	4.00	10.00	16.00
PARAGONS VS. THE HARP-TONES	Musicnote (M) M-8001	5.00	12.50	20.00
PETAL PUSHERS	Chess (M) LP 1520	4.50	6.75	9.00
PETAL PUSHERS	Chess (S) LPS 1520	5.50	7.75	11.00
PETER COTTONTAIL & OTHER EASTER FAVORITES	Golden 81	3.00	4.50	6.00
PHIL SPECTOR'S CHRISTMAS ALBUM	Apple (S) SW 3400	4.50	6.75	9.00
PICK HITS OF THE RADIO GOOD GUYS VOL. 2	Laurie (M) LLP 2026	4.00	8.00	12.00
PICK OF THE RADIO GOOD GUYS	Laurie (M) 2021	3.00	6.00	9.00
PINS & NEEDLES (25th Anniversary Edition)	Columbia (M) OL 5810	3.50	5.25	7.00
PINS & NEEDLES (25th Anniversary Edition)	Columbia (S) OS 2210	4.00	6.00	8.00
PITCHIN BOOGIE	Milestone (M) MLP 2018	5.00	7.50	10.00
PITTSBURGS GOLDEN OLDIES VOL. 1	Astra (S) ASLP 1002	6.00	12.00	18.00
PITTSBURGH'S GREATEST HITS	Itzy (M) ITZ 4978	6.00	9.00	12.00
PLEASE SAY YOU WANT ME	Epic (M) LN 3702	6.00	12.00	18.00
POP HIT PARTY	Columbia (M) CL 1239	4.00	6.00	8.00
POP HIT PARTY VOL. 1	Columbia (M) CL 1247	4.00	6.00	8.00
POP HIT PARTY VOL. 2	Columbia (M) CL 1269	4.00	6.00	8.00
POP HIT PARTY VOL. 3	Columbia (M) CL 1306	4.00	6.00	8.00
POP PARADE	MGM (M) E 299	4.00	6.00	8.00
POP PARADE	MGM (EP) X 299	1.50	2.25	3.00
POP PARADE	Mercury (M) MGD 25217	4.00	6.00	8.00
POP PARADE	Mercury (M) MGD 25219	4.00	6.00	8.00
POP PARADE	Mercury (EP) EP1-4019	1.50	2.25	3.00
POPULAR FAVORITES	Columbia (EP) B 1864	1.50	2.25	3.00
POPULAR FAVORITES	Columbia (M) CL 1897	4.00	6.00	8.00
POPULAR FAVORITES	Columbia (EP) B 1897	1.50	2.25	3.00
POPULAR FAVORITES	Columbia (M) CL 6294	4.00	6.00	8.00
POPULAR FAVORITES	Columbia (M) CL 6337	4.00	6.00	8.00
POT OF GOLDEN GOODIES	Herald (M) 1015	5.00	12.50	20.00

R

TITLE	LABEL & NO.	GOOD	VERY GOOD	NEAR MINT
R & B HITS	Hollywood (M) H 503	5.00	12.50	20.00
RECORDED LIVE AT THE APOLLO IN NEW YORK Vol. 1	Motown (M) 609	4.00	8.00	12.00
RED BIRD GOLDIES	Red Bird (M) RB 20102	4.00	8.00	12.00
REMEMBER THE OLDIES	Argo (M) LP 649	4.00	10.00	16.00
RHYTHM & BLUES	Guest Star (M) 1900	4.00	8.00	12.00
RHYTHM & BLUES	Savoy (M) MG 15008	4.00	10.00	16.00
RHYTHM AND BLUES, Vol. 1 (10")	Savoy (M) 15008	4.00	10.00	16.00
RHYTHM & BLUES Vol. 1	Savoy (EP) XP 8049	2.00	3.00	4.00
RHYTHM & BLUES Vol. 2	Savoy (EP) XP 8050	2.00	3.00	4.00
RHYTHM & BLUES VOL. 1 THE END OF AN ERA	Imperial (M) LM 94003	4.00	6.00	8.00
RHYTHM & BLUES VOL. 2 SWEET & GREASY	Imperial (M) LN 94005	4.00	6.00	8.00
RHTHM & BLUES IN THE NIGHT	Hollywood (M) 30	4.00	10.00	16.00
RHYTHM N' BLUES GROUPS HIT VOCAL GROUPS	Authentic (M) AULP 501	5.00	7.50	10.00
RISKY BLUES	King (S) KS 1133	5.00	7.50	10.00
ROCK A BALLADS	Cadence (M) CLP 3041	4.00	8.00	12.00
ROCK A HITS	Cadence (M) C 3042	4.00	8.00	12.00
ROCK & ROLL	Grand Ward (M) 33 343	3.00	7.50	12.00
ROCK & ROLL	Regent (M) MG 6015	4.00	10.00	16.00
ROCK & ROLL BANDSTAND	Roulette (M) R 25093	4.00	6.00	8.00
ROCK & ROLL DANCE PARTY	Crown (M) CLP 5001	5.00	12.50	20.00
ROCK & ROLL DANCE PARTY	King (M) LP 536	4.00	10.00	16.00
ROCK & ROLL DANCE PARTY	Modern (M) LMP 1210	5.00	12.50	20.00
ROCK & ROLL DANCE PARTY	RPM (M) LRP 3001	5.00	12.50	20.00
ROCK AND ROLL DANCE PARTY	Somerset (M) P 1300	4.00	8.00	12.00
ROCK & ROLL EVOLUTION OR REVOLUTION?	Laurie (M) LLP 2044	3.00	6.00	9.00
ROCK & ROLL FESTIVAL	United Superior (M) 7761	2.50	3.75	5.00
ROCK & ROLL FOREVER	Atlantic (M) LP 1239	4.00	10.00	16.00
ROCK & ROLL FOREVER	Atlantic (M) 8010	4.00	10.00	16.00
ROCK & ROLL JAMBOREE	End (M) LP 302	5.00	10.00	15.00
ROCK & ROLL ON THE OLD TOWN	Old Town (M) 101	6.00	12.00	18.00
ROCK & ROLL PARTY	Guest Star (M) GS 1406	3.50	7.00	10.50
ROCK & ROLL PARTY No. 2	Regent (M) MG 6042	4.00	10.00	16.00
ROCK & ROLL RECORD HOP	Modern (M) LMP 1211	5.00	12.50	20.00

TITLE	LABEL & NO.	GOOD	VERY GOOD	NEAR MINT
ROCK & ROLL RECORD HOP	Roulette (M) R 25059	4.00	6.00	8.00
ROCK & ROLL REVUE	King (M) LP 513	4.00	10.00	16.00
ROCK & ROLL SOCK HOP	Score (M) LP 4018	3.00	6.00	9.00
ROCK & ROLL VS. RHYTHM & BLUES	Dooto (M) LP 233	4.00	10.00	16.00
ROCK & ROLL With Rhythm & Blues	Aladdin (M) LP 710	5.00	12.50	20.00
ROCKIN AT THE DRIVE-IN	Combo (M) 400	12.00	30.00	48.00
ROCKIN DATE WITH THE SOUTH LOUISIANA STARS	Jin (M) LP 4002	5.00	7.50	10.00
ROCKING 50's	Atlantic (M) 8037	4.00	10.00	16.00
ROCKIN SLUMBER PARTY	Famous (M) F 501	4.00	8.00	12.00
ROCKIN TOGETHER	Atco (M) 103	5.00	10.00	15.00
ROCK ROCK ROCK	Chess (M) LP 1425	6.00	15.00	24.00
ROOF GARDEN 2nd JAMBOREE	IGL (M) LPM 103	9.00	13.50	18.00
ROOTS OF THE BLUES	Atlantic (M) 1348	4.00	8.00	12.00
ROOTS: RHYTHM & BLUES	Roadside (S) RBF 20	5.00	10.00	15.00
ROOTS-THE ROCK AND ROLL SOUND OF LOUISIANA AND MISSISSIPPI	Folkways (M) FJ 2865	5.00	10.00	15.00
RUMBLE	Jubliee (M) JGM 1114	4.00	10.00	16.00
RURAL BLUES VOL. 1 GOIN UP THE COUNTRY	Imperial (M) LM 94000	4.00	6.00	8.00
RURAL BLUES VOL. 2 SATURDAY NIGHT FUNCTION	Imperial (M) LM 94001	4.00	6.00	8.00

S

TITLE	LABEL & NO.	GOOD	VERY GOOD	NEAR MINT
SAN FRANCISCO	San Francisco (S) SD 158	4.00	6.00	8.00
SAN FRANCISCO ROOTS	Vault (M) LP 119	4.00	6.00	8.00
SAN FRANCISCO SOUND VOL. 2	Fifth Pipe Dream (S) 11680	8.00	12.00	16.00
SATURDAY NIGHT AT THE UPTOWN	Atlantic (S) SD 8101	4.00	6.00	8.00
SAVAGE SEVEN (Rock)	Atco (S) 245	5.00	7.50	10.00
SCOOBY DOO	Zephyr (M) ZP 12202G	4.00	10.00	16.00
SCRAPBOOK OF GOLDEN HITS	Wing (M) SRW 16371	2.50	3.75	5.00
SCREAMIN JAY HAWKINS AND LILLIAN BRIGGS	Coronet (M) CX 218	3.00	7.50	12.00
SHAKE A HAND	Guest Star (M) G 1904	4.00	8.00	12.00
SHAKE IT & BREAK IT (2 Record Set)	Capitol TBO 1572	3.00	4.50	6.00
SHAKE SHOUT AND SOUL	Impact (M) LP 2	5.00	10.00	15.00
SHOUTIN SWINGIN & MAKIN LOVE	Chess (M) CHV	4.00	6.00	8.00
SHOW STOPPERS	Wand (M) 652	3.00	6.00	9.00
SHUT DOWN	Capitol (M) T 1918	4.00	8.00	12.00
SHUT DOWN	Capitol (S) ST 1918	4.00	8.00	12.00
SINGER SONGWRITER PROJECT	Elektra (S) 7299	5.00	7.50	10.00
16 GOODIES - BLASTS FROM THE PAST	Blast (M) 6805	4.00	10.00	16.00
16 ORIGINAL GOLDEN OLDIES Vol. 2	Jocko (M) J-LPS 965-2	3.00	4.50	6.00
16 SUCCESSFUL SOUNDS VOL. 1	Flashback (S) 603	4.00	6.00	8.00
61 MORE HITS	Screen Gems-Columbia (M) 1002	10.00	15.00	20.00
SOLID GOLD GROUPS	Atlantic (M) 8065	4.00	8.00	12.00
SOLID GOLD OLD TOWN	Cotillion (S) SD 9032	4.00	6.00	8.00
SOLID GOLD SOUL	Atlantic (M) 8116	4.00	6.00	8.00
SOUL BLUES	Almor (M) A-102	3.00	6.00	9.00
SOUL BLUES	Almor (M) AS-102	2.50	5.00	7.50
STARS ARE SINGING	Columbia (M) CL 1618	4.00	6.00	8.00
SUE STORY	Sue (M) SUE 1021	5.00	10.00	15.00
SUN'S GOLD HITS	Sun (M) LP 1250	6.00	12.00	18.00
SUPER GROUPS FROM HOLLAND	White Whale (S) WW 7129	4.00	6.00	8.00
SURF BATTLE	Crescendo (M) 85	3.00	6.00	9.00
SURF BATTLE	Crescendo (S) 85	4.00	8.00	12.00
SURFINGS GREATEST HITS	Capitol (M) T 1995	4.00	8.00	12.00
SURFINGS GREATEST HITS	Capitol (S) ST 1995	4.50	9.00	13.50
SURF'S UP	Reprise (M) R 6094	3.00	6.00	9.00
SURFS UP AT BANZAI PIPELINE	Northridge (M) NM-101	5.00	10.00	15.00
SURF WAR	Shepard (M) SLP 1300	4.00	8.00	12.00
SWAMP BLUES (2 Record Set)	Excello (M) EXC 8015-8016	5.00	7.50	1.00
SWAMPLAND SOUL FROM THE BAYOUS OF LOUISIANA	Goldband (M) LP 7754	4.50	6.75	9.00

T

TITLE	LABEL & NO.	GOOD	VERY GOOD	NEAR MINT
TEENAGE GOODIES (Maroon Label)	Coral (M) CRL 57431	4.00	8.00	12.00
TEENAGE GOODIES (Maroon Label)	Coral (S) CRL7 57431	4.00	8.00	1200
TEENAGE GOODIES (Yellow Label)	Coral (S) CRL7 57431	3.00	4.50	6.00
TEENAGE PARTY	Gee (M) GLP 702	5.00	10.00	15.00
TEENAGERS DANCE	RCA (M) LPM 1540	4.00	8.00	12.00
TEENAGE TRIANGLE	Colpix (M) CP 444	2.50	5.00	7.50
TEENAGE TRIANGLE	Colpix (S) SCP 444	3.00	6.00	9.00
TELLING YOU KNOW	Tower (M) T 5003	4.50	9.00	13.50
10 SONGS HITS THAT SOLD ONE MILLION RECORDS	Guest Star (M) G 1474	4.00	8.00	12.00
TERRY LEE PRESENTS FOR LOVERS ONLY	Astra (M) 1001	6.00	12.00	18.00
TEXAS GUITAR FROM DALLAS TO L. A.	Atalntic (S) SD 7226	4.50	6.75	9.00
THIS IS BROADWAY'S BEST (2 Record Set)	Columbia (M) B2W 1	3.00	4.50	6.00
THIS IS BROADWAY'S BEST (2 Record Set)	Columbia (S) B2WS 1	4.00	6.00	8.00
THOSE GOOD OLD MEMORIES	Capitol (M) T 1414	5.00	7.50	10.00
THREE AT THE TOP	Tower (M) T 5007	4.00	8.00	12.00
TODAYS HITS	Philles (M) PHLP 4004	7.00	14.00	21.00
TODAY'S TOP HITS VOL. 1	Capitol (M) H 9101	4.00	6.00	8.00
TODAY'S TOP HITS VOL. 2	Capitol (M) H 9102	4.00	6.00	8.00
TODAY'S TOP HITS VOL. 3	Capitol (M) H 9103	4.00	6.00	8.00
TODAY'S TOP HITS VOL. 4	Capitol (M) H 9104	4.00	6.00	8.00
TODAY'S TOP HITS VOL. 5	Capitol (M) H 9105	4.00	6.00	8.00
TODAY'S TOP HITS VOL. 6	Capitol (M) H 9106	4.00	6.00	8.00
TODAY'S TOP HITS VOL. 7	Capitol (M) H 9107	4.00	6.00	8.00
TODAY'S TOP HITS VOL. 8	Capitol (M) H 9108	4.00	6.00	8.00
TODAY'S TOP HITS VOL. 9	Capitol (M) H 9109	4.00	6.00	8.00

TITLE	LABEL & NO.	GOOD	VERY GOOD	NEAR MINT
TODAY'S TOP HITS VOL. 10	Capitol (M) H 91110	4.00	6.00	8.00
TODAY'S TOP HITS VOL. 11	Capitol (M) H9116	4.00	6.00	8.00
TODAY'S TOP HITS VOL. 11	Capitol (EP) EAP 1-9116	2.00	3.00	4.00
TODAY'S TOP HITS VOL. 11	Capitol (EP) EAP 2-9116	2.00	3.00	4.00
TODAY'S TOP HITS VOL. 12	Capitol (M) T 9124	4.00	6.00	8.00
TODAY'S TOP HITS VOL. 13	Capitol (M) T 9127	4.00	6.00	8.00
TODAY'S TOP HITS VOL. 13	Capitol (EP) EAP1-9127	2.00	3.00	4.00
TODAY'S TOP HITS VOL. 13	Capitol (EP) EAP2-9127	2.00	3.00	4.00
TODAY'S TOP HITS VOL. 14	Capitol (M) T 9130	4.00	6.00	8.00
TOMORROW'S HITS	Vee Jay (M) LP 1042	4.00	6.00	8.00
TOP HITS OF '54	Capitol (M) H 9117	4.00	6.00	8.00
TOP HITS OF '54	Capitol (EP) EPA 1-9117	2.00	3.00	4.00
TOP HITS OF '54	Capitol (EP) EPA 2-9117	2.00	3.00	4.00
TOP HITS OF '54 VOL. 2	Capitol (M) L 9119	4.00	6.00	8.00
TOP HITS OF '54 VOL. 2	Capitol (EP) EPA1-9119	2.00	3.00	4.00
TOP HITS OF '54 VOL. 2	Capitol (EP) EPA2-9119	2.00	3.00	4.00
TOP POPS	Decca (M) DL 8860	4.00	6.00	8.00
TOP POPS	RCA (M) LPM 3282	4.00	6.00	8.00
TOP POPS	RCA (EP) EPB 3282	1.50	2.25	3.00
TOP TEEN BANDS VOL. 1	Bud Jet (M) BJ 311	7.00	10.50	14.00
TOP TEEN BANDS VOL. 2	Bud Jet (M) BJ 312	7.00	10.50	14.00
TOP TEEN BANDS VOL. 3	Bud Jet (M) BJ 313	7.00	10.50	14.00
TOP TWELVE	Columbia (M) CL 937	4.00	6.00	8.00
TOP TWELVE VOL. 2	Columbia (M) CL 944	4.00	6.00	8.00
TREASURE CHEST OF HITS	Swan (M) 501	7.00	17.50	28.00
TREASURE CHEST OF MUSTY DUSTIES	Fortune 8011	4.00	8.00	12.00
TREASURE CHEST OF SONG HITS	Columbia (M) CL 613	4.00	6.00	8.00
TREASURE CHEST OF SONG HITS	Columbia (EP) B 1963	2.00	3.00	4.00
TREASURE CHEST OF SONG HITS	Columbia (EP) B 1964	2.00	3.00	4.00
TREASURE CHEST OF SONG HITS	Columbia (EP) B 1965	2.00	3.00	4.00
TREASURED HITS FROM THE SOUTH PRESENTED BY NICK ADAMS	Stax (M) 702	4.50	7.00	9.00
TREASURE TUNES FROM THE VAULT	Chess (M) 1474	4.00	8.00	12.00
A TRIBUTE TO JAMES DEAN	Imperial (M) LP 9021	4.00	8.00	12.00
TUNES FOR TEENS	Decca (M) DL 34441	3.00	6.00	9.00
TUNES TO BE REMEMBERED	Excello (M) 8001	6.00	15.00	24.00
TV RECORD HOP	RCA (M) LPM 1802	4.00	8.00	12.00
TWELVE BIG HITS	Columbia (M) CL 1617	3.50	5.25	7.00
TWELVE BIG HITS	Columbia (S) CS 8417	4.00	6.00	8.00
12 FLIP HITS	Flip (M) 1001	6.00	15.00	24.00
12 GREATEST GOLDEN OLDIES IN THE WHOLE WORLD EVER	Parkway (M) 7031	4.00	8.00	12.00
12 PLUS 3 EQUALS 15 HITS	End (M) LP 310	5.00	10.00	15.00
20 YEARS OF HITS	Acuff-Rose	3.00	6.00	9.00
25 YEARS OF RHYTHM & BLUES HITS	King (M) LP 725	3.00	7.50	12.00
25 YEARS OF RHYTHM & BLUES HITS VOL. 2	King (M) LP 749	3.00	7.50	12.00
21 GUN SALUTE TO '61 PROMO LP (2 Record Set)	MGM (M) DJ 910	3.00	6.00	9.00
TWIST AROUND (Re-Package Of 'Night Train' Album)	King (M) 771	3.00	6.00	9.00
TWISTIN ALL NIGHT LONG	Swan (M) S 506	4.50	9.00	13.50
TWO DOZEN OLDIES	Hammer (M) 5007	3.00	6.00	9.00
TWO TRIPS	Mercury (S) SR 61273	2.25	3.25	4.50

U

TITLE	LABEL & NO.	GOOD	VERY GOOD	NEAR MINT
UNAVAILABLE	Vee Jay (M) 1051	4.00	8.00	12.00
URBAN BLUES VOL. 2 NEW ORLEANS BOUNCE	Imperial (M) LM 94004	4.00	6.00	8.00
URBAN BLUES-BLUES UPTOWN	Imperial (M) LM 94002	4.00	6.00	8.00

V

TITLE	LABEL & NO.	GOOD	VERY GOOD	NEAR MINT
VERY BEST OF THE OLDIES	Del Fi (M) DF 1227	4.00	8.00	12.00

W

TITLE	LABEL & NO.	GOOD	VERY GOOD	NEAR MINT
WE LIKE BOYS	Oldies 33 (M) 8004	4.00	8.00	12.00
WE SING THE BLUES	Minit (M) LP 00003	4.00	8.00	12.00
WE WROTE 'EM & WE SING 'EM	MGM (M) E 3912	3.50	4.25	7.00
WE WROTE 'EM & WE SING 'EM	MGM (S) SE 3912	4.00	6.00	8.00
WHAT'S GOING ON HERE	Trousdale	8.00	12.00	16.00
WHAT'S SHAKIN'	Elektra (S) EKS 74002	5.00	7.50	10.00
WHO, AND THE STRAWBERRY ALARM CLOCK	Philco (S) 734586	7.00	10.50	14.00
WHOPPERS	Jubilee (M) JGM 1119	4.00	10.00	16.00
WHO'S WHO OF COUNTRY MUSIC	Capitol (M) T 2538	4.00	8.00	12.00
WHO'S WHO OF COUNTRY MUSIC	Capitol (S) ST 2538	4.50	9.00	13.50
WILD WILDWOOD	Chancellor (M) CHL 5017	3.00	6.00	9.00
WILD WILDWOOD	Chancellor (S) CHLS 5017	3.50	7.00	10.50
WINNERS OF THE 18 BAND SURF BATTLE	GNP-Crescendo (M) GNP 85	4.00	8.00	12.00
WITH LOVE/A POT OF FLOWERS	Mainstream (M) 56100	6.00	9.00	12.00
WITH LOVE/A POT OF FLOWERS	Mainstream (S) S 6100	7.00	10.50	14.00
WONE - THE DAYTON SCENE	Prism (M) 1966	4.00	8.00	12.00
WORLD OF SURFIN	Almor (M) 108	3.00	6.00	9.00

Y

TITLE	LABEL & NO.	GOOD	VERY GOOD	NEAR MINT
YESTERDAY'S GOODIES	United Artists (M) UAL 3196	3.00	6.00	9.00
YESTERDAY'S GOODIES	United Artists (S) UAS 6196	4.00	8.00	12.00
YOUNG LOVE	Dot (M) DLP 3183	4.00	6.00	8.00
YOUNG RASCALS/THE FOUR SEASONS/JOHNNY RIVERS/ THE BUGGS	Coronet (M) CX 283	3.00	4.50	6.00
YOUNG RASCALS/THE FOUR SEASONS/JOHNNY RIVERS/ THE BUGGS	Coronet (S) CXS 283	2.50	3.75	5.00
YOUNG RASCALS & THE ISLEY BROTHERS	Design (M) DLP 253	3.00	4.50	6.00

(M) Mono   (S) Stereo   (EP) Extended Play   (Q) Quad   (RI) Re-issued

Dealer's and Collector's Directory

ALABAMA

Mike Gill
2426 29th St, Birmingham, 35208 (205) 788-8628
Rock & roll 45's (1955-1964) & Buddy Holly. Records must be VG or better and original labels.

H.A. Hyche
529 Cambridge St., Birmingham, 35224

S.G. Johnson
P.O. Box 63, Decatur, 35602
I collect R&R, C&W of 50's & early 60's; esp. low number releases. Phone: (205) 353-7989.

King Bee Records
1472 Tomahawk Rd., Birmingham, 35214
I am interested in buying wholesale quantities of oldies reissues.

Joe O. Ray
1618 S. Cullom St., Birmingham, 35205 (205) 324-8893
I collect Dylan & other assorted folk & contempt. folk albums & 45's. Also interested in J.F.K. records.

Rhonda Thorn
R #6, Box 174, Russellville, 35653
I collect books, mags, LP's, 45's, photos of the Beatles.

ALASKA

Sam S. Corwin
4218 Checkmate Dr., Anchorage, 99504
I collect soundtrack, original cast, etc. Sell mint-near mint. Want lists researched SASE.

Jerry Hite
1401 Hyder St., Anchorage, 99501
Trying for every Atlantic single & Vee-Jay LP issue. Also have 2,000 LP's from 50's & 2,000 45's from 50's & early 60's to trade.

ARIZONA

Album's of Tucson (David Canterman)
1043 E. Sixth St., Tucson, 85719 (602) 622-0201

Harvey Bond
4728 E. Polk, Phoenix, 85008

Grant Boyd
Box 1988, Phoenix, 85001
I collect folk, rock, jazz; Maxine Sellars, "third stream" type jazz, Abyssinian Baptist Gospel Choir, Joan Baez, Beatles, Dylan. (602) 264-0325.

Duane Eddy Circle, USA (Dave Acker)
4527 E. Riverside, Phoenix, 85040
Fee: $2.00 year; $10.00 life (double for overseas). Write for details.

Vicki Erickson
1645 W. Pampa Ave., Mesa, 85202
I collect advertising & paper records, also 16" & miniature records.

Warren Erickson
1645 W. Pampa Ave., Mesa, 85202
I collect Beatles, Beach Boys, Jan & Dean & Apple records.

Phyllis French
6407 W. Clouse Dr., Phoenix, 85033

N. Grassi
2731 N. Alvernon, Tucson, 85712
I collect 78's, 45's & LP's & 33 1/3 LP's.

Tom Jackson
1617 N. McAllister Ave, Tempe, 85281
I collect favorites & no. one hits. (602) 947-6438.

Paul R. Janesik
6817 W. Palm Ln., Phoenix, 85035 (602) 849-4048
I collect 45's & LP's on Jackie DeShannon, Tommy James, Del Shannon, Jan & Dean & Gene Vincent. Also demos, pic sleeves, concert tapes, etc. Photos wanted.

Jolly Roger Trades
1024 A S. McClintock, Tempe, 85281
We deal in all types of 45's from the 50's to present. Send your wants! (602) 967-2517.

Tom Koehler
Box 27737, Tempe, 85282 (602) 838-2816
I collect Phil Spector, 50's & 60's R&R, Motown sound & disco. I also like compiling artist & label discographies.

J. Lindsay
Rt. 3, Lot 66, Flagstaff, 86001
Bob Dylan, International Submarine Band, Gram Parsons... send your wants. (602) 526-0169.

The 'Mad Daddy"
4213 W. Valencia, Tucson, 85706
I collect R&R, R&B, C&W, rockabilly, top 50 '55-'77, Philles, Gone & End records. (602) 883-6076.

Joseph R. Manzo
3121 W. Greenway Rd., Phoenix, 85023
I collect Jimmie Rodgers, Cylinders, phonographs, discs & all items relating to Cal Stewart (Uncle Josh). (602) 942-4415

Rory Musil
Box 2313, Mesa, 85204
I buy, sell, trade Beatles, British Invasion, tapes, books, records (602) 969-9793

The Nipper Victrola Shop
1520 W. Indian School, Phoenix, 85015
We deal in old phonographs, cylinders, discs & music related items. (602) 274-5200.

William Pagel
P.O. Box 27796, Tempe, 85282
I collect unreleased & rare stuff by Bob Dylan on tape, LP's, 45's, EP's, movies & videotape.

John Rhea
3410 W. Joan De Arc, Phoenix, 85029
I collect LP's: Conway Twitty MGM, Pat Boone Dot, Tommy Sands Cap., Narvel Felts (45's & LP's), Brenda Lee, Bobby Darin, Ventures, Bobby Vee, Billy Vaughn. 942-3176.

William Schuh
P.O. Box 1572, Scottsdale, 85252
I collect 45's 1956-'70. Orig. labels. Want R&R & novelty. Nervous Norvus, Beach Boys, Beatles, Monkees, Standells, etc. Must be VG or near mint cond.

Bill Shaver
5233 N. 67th Dr., Glendale, 85303
I collect Sun records, Johnny Cash; 45's, EP's & 78's. (602) 846-7347

Dwayne Witten
541 W. Holly St, Phoenix, 85003

ARKANSAS

Record World
703 N. West Ave., El Dorado, 71730

Charles R. Womble
8215 2nd St., No. Little Rock, 72117
I collect C/W music & rock & roll of the 50's - but I especially collect anything by Gene Autry that I can find. Phone: 501-835-0839

CALIFORNIA

Alex Aberbom
22364 Cass Ave., Woodland Hills, 91364
50's & 60's Rock & Pop. Sell or trade

Jerry Abraham
375 Drakeley Ave., Atwater, 95301
I collect country/early rock, jazz, Ray Price, Elvis, Gene Krupa, Louis Jordan, Gale Storm. I'm a drummer, and would like to correspond with other drummers.

Robert Abramowitz
18620 Palo Verde, Apt A, Cerritos, 90701
I collect Beatles unreleased recordngs, rare albums, any 45 picture jackets, record oddities, etc. Wish to hear from other Beatle maniacs.

Acorns Records & Tapes
1465 N. Van Ness, Fresno, 93728
Inquiries Welcome! 233-3149

William Anthony
954 Henderson Ave. #63, Sunnyvale, 94086
Wanted: Elvis 45's, 78's LP's & covers. Also Brenda Lee 45's & LP's. In very good to mint condition.

Richard Wesley Ball
934 'A' Alice Lane, Menlo Park, 94025
I collect all Beatle & Apple LP's, 45's; Memorabilia. Buy Trade, sell

Stan Baumruk
436 Alta ista Blvd., L.A., 90036
I collect C/W, rockabilly, 50's & 60's R&R, comedy, novelty. Phone: (213) 935-1606

Carol BERGER
P.O. Box J, Filroy, 95020
I collect everything to do with Bobby Vinton. Write!

L. John Bertelsen
2210 W. 34th St., San Pedro, 90732 (213) 832-6892
I collect vintage R&B, black artists, particularly vocal groups circa '31-'51; obscure labels, early Negro novelty items & sheet music. Send auction lists. I pay top dollar.

Bob Bertram Studios
1069-D Shary Cr., Concord, 94518
I deal in all speeds and all categories of records. Send your wants!

Boogie Boy Records (Jeff Stolper)
P.O. Box 1196, Pacific Palisades, 90272
Collect & deal in R&B vocal groups, rockabilly, blues, all speeds. Send for sale lists; send wants and for sales. Buy, sell & trade.

Frank Brandon
1322 E. Home Ave., Apt B, Fresno, 93728
I collect British Invasion, 60's Punk, Doug Sahm, Pagliano, etc. Send lists!

Bob Brewer
16761 View Point Lane #330, Huntington Beach, 92647

Larry Buck
240 Belle Mill Rd., Sp. 7, Red Bluff, 96080
I collect 45 RPM's late 50's

Everett Caldwell
1135 Oakmont St., Orange, 92667
I buy & seel 45's, LP's & EP's from 50, 60 & 70's. Picture sleeves & photos of artists.

Michael K. Carlton
1095 Davids Rd., Perris, 92370

Century Commercial Corp. (Mark S. Randell
600 S. Commonwealth Ave., #1100, L.A., 90005

Charisma
1110 Burlingame Ave., Burlingame, 94010
We deal in original movie posters magazines, etc.,s'tracks, 50's & 60's rock records. Beatle & Elvis items a specialty. Phone: (415) 344-7555.

Chimaera Records
405 Kipling, Palo Alto, 94301
Specializing in the obscure, O.P., Scarce, rare & strange. Highest cash value paid. Quality guaranteed. All kinds of music & largest spoken word section anywhere

Jim Clarke
15701½ Cornuta, Bellflower, 90706
I collect R&B, novelty, R&B, 45's, LP's, boots of Beatles, insturmentals, pic sleeves, sheet music, photos, etc. Phone: (213) 866-8336

Mike Daniels
44 Creek Rd., Fairfax, 94930

Mr. Warren Debenham
143 Arlington, Berkeley, 94707

The Disc Trip
25 W. 25th Ave. (in the patio), San Mateo, 94403
We buy, sell & trade records, 78's, 45's & LP's. Soundtracks (415) 345-4009

Dino's Oldies
P.O. Box 074, San Diego, 92115
45's of 40's, 50's, and 60's. Buy, sell & trade. I collect "hits" and various artists albums. Send your want list. Free auction lists. (714) 264-1467.

Richard Elliott
2548 Sapra St., Thousand Oaks, 91360
I collect original non-rock pop hits of the 50's & 60's, & recordings of D.J., Martin Block and his 'Make Believe Ball Room) show, also old time radio progrmas.

Elvis Presley Appreciation Club
P.O. Box 291, Sun Valley, 91352
Dedicated to perpetuating Elvis memory. No membership fee Buy, sell, trade Elvis items from '56 to present. Support National Elvis Presley Day - Write for details. (213) 899-1719

Encore Records
4593 El Cajon Blvd., San Diego, 92115
We deal in a large collection of 45's from 50's to present; have a large selection of s'tracks. Phone: (714) 280-6834.

Cheryl & David Evans
18158 Sharon Circle, Yorba Linda, 92686, (714) 966-7299
Blues, country, comedy, novelty, vaudeville, gospel, R&B, R&B, early jazz, party, ethnic. 78's!, 45's, 33's, Cylinders. Buy, sell, trade, auction.

George A. Farris
3814 Hillcrest Dr., El Sobrante, 94803

W.R. Fiedler
P.O. Box 758, Biggs, 95917
I collect all pop records from mid 20's to mid 60's & comedy recordings from this same era. Also collect original radio transcription records.

Steve Fodor
P.O. Box 25884, L.A., 90025
I collect obscure early 50's R&B, Blues, & C/W 45's in small or large quantity. 45's, 78's and LP's for trade-many rarities lists available. (213) 820-2215

Paul Freeman
116 W. 43rd Ave., San Mateo, 94403
I collect anything on Rick Nelson or Ozzie & Harriet; Clint Eastwood, Robert Wagner, Robert Conrad. Phone: (415) 574-0173

Mike Garnese
945 Fremont St., Santa Clara, 95050
I collect 60's & 70's rock. Rare Beatles, Kinks, Apple & Konk artists, British Invasion. Phone: (408) 246-1754.

Lou "Speedy" Gonzales
3101 Delta Ave., Modesto, 95355
I collect oldies-goodies-blues & big bands. Over 30,000 records, 78's-45's-33's. I also deal in sheet music, song books & posters. (209) 527-0642

Carl A. Guido
9215 Guess St., Rosemead 91770
I collect everything to do with the Doors. Also late 60's rock mags.

Jim Harkey
2011 Gisler Ave., Oxnard, 93030
I collect Beatles, world-wide Beatle collection-rare Beatles tracks in "True Stereo", original labels of "Major" hits & oddities.

John Harmer
5001 Reynard, La Crescenta, 91214

Tom Haydon
1083 El Camino Real, Menlo Park, 94025
I collect Blues LP's, books & other literature, Phone: (415) 321-1333.

Eddie Hoover
21142 Aspen Ave., Castro Valley, 94546

Glenn Howard
1606 Lockhart Gulch, Santa Cruz, 95066
All styles of music on 78, LP, 45's. Cylinders, 16mm film, transcriptions, piano rolls, etc. Complete collections bought. 50,000 great records for sale. Send wants. (408) 335-4356

Jack Howard
P.O. Box 1214, Oxnard, 93032
Instrumental jazz & easy-listening, big bands, jazz & dance, guitar or piano w/big band backing. LP's only. Prefer to trade-have all types of albums incl. rock, soul, etc. for trade.

Mrs. James Howard
4260 Ruthelma, Palo Alto, 94306
78's 45's 33's buy large or small collections, every kind of music, US or foreign. 1890's-1970's. Want lists accepted. Send for free auction lists.

John F. Howard
P.O. Box 1214, Palo Alto, 93032
I collect all types LP's, but specialize in pop vocalists & pop vocal groups. Phone: (805) 486-6235.

Conrad & Lorrie Janca
165 W. Elmwood, Apt F, Burbank, 91502
We buy, sell & trade 45's from the 50's to the 70's.

J. Jones
P.O. Box 8472, Stockton, 95208
Disposal of private collection. Mostly jazz, & easy-listening. Some rock. Specify artists.

Mark Kalman
6181 Wooster Ave., L.A., 90056
60's rock & surf, expecially the Beach Boys, Beatles, Bob Dylan & Elvis. Pic sleeves, promos, colored wax & other obscurities.

David Klayman
14534 Clark St., #102, Van Nuys, 91411
I collect rock 45's & LP's, top 40 charts, obscurities, airchecks & radio promo material. Will trade airchecks, jingles, commercials. Phone: (213) 981-2279.

Bernard Klein
2852 Brimhall Dr., Rossmoor, 90720
I collect Beatle bootlegs on CBM and trade Mark of Quality LP's. I also accept private tapes of live concerts. Phone: (213) 431-6414.

David Konjoyan
25 Sarah Ln., Moraga, 94556
I collect any 45's, especially picture covers, promos, & colored vinyl.

David Kraft
5000 Belle Terr. #49, Bakersfield, 93309
I collect 45's & LP's of s'tracks, ep. imported. Phone: (805) 831-5989.

Michael A Lang
6519 Aldea Ave., Van Nuys, 91406
New Orleans R&B (Professor Longhair, Huey "Piano" Smith) R&R (Leon Russell, The Band), Jazz (Charlie Parker, Art Tatum), Classical (20th Century composers). Please send lists.

Don Leite
2049 W. Hedding St., San Jose, 95128
I collect R&B records from the 50's & 60's. 45's & LP's, real to real tapes, 8-track tapes, Buy, sell, trade or made.

Joe A Lewis
4604 Excuela Ct., Richmond, 94804
Many rare country, blues records on 78 rpm for sale or trade. Also have 50's and 60's R&B. Many obscure Black artists/groups. (415) 529-0912

Dennis R. Liff
19439 Lemay St., Reseda, 91335 (213) 345-5380
I collect all rock & rock related LP's from '56 to present, inc: British rock & blues/rock, "Summer of Love" psychedelic era, bootlegs, Bob Dylan, 45's, rock lit., item to trade.

Robert E. Lopez, Jr.
8123 Otis #A, So. Gate, 90280
I collect C/W & 50's rock 45's & LP's. Set sale lsts only.

Karen Lowry
155 Flying Cloud Isle, Foster City, 94404
I collect anything on Donovan, also almost any other type of late 60's acid rock.

Ray Macknic
P.O. Box 7511, Van Nuys, 91406
Sold at auction: Collectors records, LP's; Jazz-soundtracks/personalities/original casts-C/W, Bluegrass/Blues/Folk. Indicate which list.

Jon Manousos
7001 Eastside Rd., Ukiah, 95482
I collect all jazz periods, rural & urban blues; 40-60's R&R, & R&B. Mostly LP's, some 45's. Will buy quality collections. Have selected interests in C/W, gospel & comedy.

Allan Mason
125 Ocean Park Blvd., Santa Monica, 90405
LP's & 45's; ranging from 50's R&R, rockabilly, & rh LP's & 45's; ranging from 50's R&R, rockabilly, & R&B up through, & incl., the new wave of punk rock music (circa '76-'78.)

Tom McMarus
P.O. Box 38, San Jacinto, 92383
I collect R&B and comedy.

Jorge Hernandez Melgar
900 Toyon Dr. #1, Burlingame, 94010
I collect Beatles LP's & 45's.

Dr. E.M. Miholits
P.O. Box 4265, Foster City, 94404
Folk, movie s'tracks, TV themes, easy-listening (instrumental) shows w/o singing.

Jim Norman
307 W. Elm, Lodi, 95240
I collect R&R, R&B & some country. LP's, 45's, 78's, Buy, sell & collect.

Steve Pahnke
24 Sola Ave., San Francisco, 94116
I collect R&B of the 50's & 60's, esp., New Orleans, West Coast & Chicago. Buy, sell & trade. Have many later rock albums for sale/trade. (415) 566-3193

Chris Peake
6526 Homewood, Hollywood, 90028
I collect pop, rockabilly & general rock of the 60's.

John Peters
8 Dale Ct., Orinda, 94563
I collect LP's of black vocal groups & 78's of black vocal groups that are pre-R&B-1940's. Phone: (415) 376-1252.

Lance Phillips
5353 Yosemite Oaks Rd., Mariposa, 95338
I collect postwar blues, 60's British: Sonny Boy Williamson, Little Walter, Walter Horton, Mose Allison, Jr. Wells, Pretty Things, Them, Zombies, Alan Price, Georgie Fame. Send lists

Michael Playtond
5534 W. 78th St., L.A., 90045
I collect jazz, blues & dance bands: Ellington, Wuller, Armstrong, Etc.

Donald H. Prater
1746 Middlefield, Stockton, 95204
I collect Beatles, Presley. Over 30,000 45's C/W R&R, R&B, All kinds to buy, sell & trade. (209) 464-8494

Prelude Enterprises
5730 Park Crest Dr., San Jose, 95118
(408) 269-4209

Norman S. Presley
P.O. Box 59118, L.A. 90059
I collect R&B, pop, C/W 45's from the early 50's to now.

Brad Pueschel
839 Colby St., San Francisco, 94134
I collect rock & pop 45's

William C. Purviance
20149 S. Mapes, Cerritos, 90701 (213) 924-2947
I collect, trade, sell, and buy Elvis 33's-45's-78's-RCA-Sun-and boots. Additional 100's & 100's of R&B-Rockabilly, & comedy & R&R (60's) for unit, sale, etc.

R & T Enterprises
2720 So. Harbor Blvd. Unit A, Santa Ana, 92704

Record Collectors Studio
2240 Main St. Unit 4, Chula Vista, 92011
We buy, sell records, tapes, & collectibles of all categories. Send your wants! (714) 424-7861.

Record Town
1851 W. LaHabra Blvd., LaHabra, 90631
We deal in all areas of recorded entertainment: R&R, R&B, old radio shows, pop, nostalgia, etc. Phone: (213) 691-6216

Remember When Music
760 Market #315, San Francisco, 94102
We search & find wanted records. Also do custom taping.

Repertoire Rendezvous
3032 4th St., Ceres, 95307 (209) 537-9694
R&R from 50's to 70's LP's, 45's (some country-some R&B in LP's & 45's) New cut-outs-new releases-new 12" Disco.

Larry Kevin Roberts
563 La Mirada Ave, Pasadena, 91108
Serious collector of non-rock, 45's only. Show songs, movies, personalities, big bands, obscurities esp. from '48-'52. Buy, sell, trade.

Alice Rogers
10940 Densmore Ave., Granada Hills, 91344
I collect big bands, traditional jazz, blues & boogie woogie. Buy, sell, trade. Phone: (213) 365-1735.

Jesse & Alice Rogers
10940 Densmore Ave., Granada Hills, 91344
Our specialty is out-of-print records, vintage radios & phonographs. Phone: (213) 365-1735.

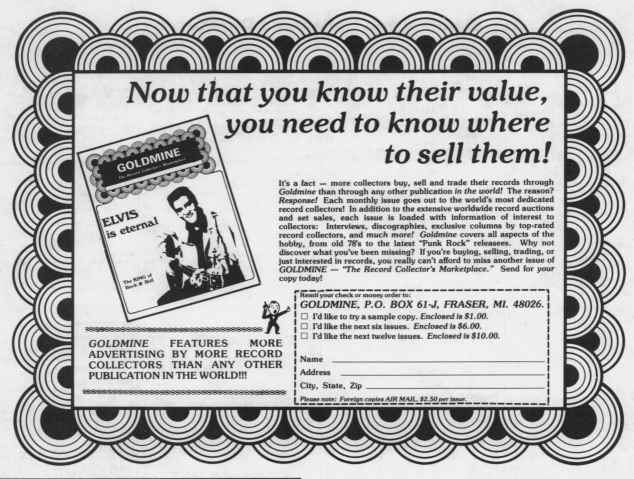

Dan Young
419 Sunnyvale Dr., Healdsburg, 95448
I collect Bob Dylan, Grateful Dead, SF groups, comedy, & a lot more. Phone: (707) 433-4300

COLORADO

Mike Baczuk
709 13th St., Greeley, 80631
I collect 50's R&R, surfing, drag: Elvis, Beatles, Beach Boys, James Dean music.

James E. Beattie
1002 S. Ogden St., Denver, 80209
I collect all pre-'70 records, all speeds. 50's R&R, humor, s'tracks. I buy large collections & have thousands of records for sale.

M.D. Colvin
85 Garland St., Denver, 80226
I am looking for orig. 45 oldies as listed in J. Whitburn's Top Pop Records 1955-1970 Billboard Book.

Duke of Discs
P.O. Box 26544 A, Lakewood, 80226
Ask for our auction catalog of orig. oldie 45's & LP's: Pop rock, C/W. I buy collections. Oversease, please send $11.00 for postage.

Martin Haugen
6288 Union St., Arvada, 80004
I collect rockabilly, bop, R&B.

John Marsh
P.O. Box 9663, Denver, 80209
I collect boots from early Stones & Joe Walsh, R&R, some memorabilia.

Mayo McNeal
Box 6434, Denver, 80206

Ken Mohr
1635 Dover St., Broomfield, 80020
I collect Buddy Holly, Moody Blues, Tornados (English group) & Santo & Johnny. Mint records only. Records for sale in VG to mint condition. Send for list.

Joe Parker
Box 818, Eaton, 80615
I collect 60's R&R: Everything concerning the Beatles.

Record ReUnion
675 S. Union Ave., Pueblo, 81004
Rock, Pop & Soul, C/W. We Buy, sell, trade quality used records & tapes

Recycle Records
2501 Sheridan Blvd. Denver, 80214
Buy, sell, trade records & tapes. Specializing in rare & colored wax LP's & 45's.

Peter Reum
P.O. Box 1523, Greeley, 80631
I collect Beach Boys, surf, (vocal & Instru.) I esp. need Beach Boy promo material & foreign pressing (303) 356-6298.

Mike Stearns
2775 S. Federal #304, Denver, 80236
I collect Beatle LP's, 45's, films, posters, buttons, etc. Dolly Parton 45's & LP's.

Wes World Records
4125 N. Academy, Colo. Springs, 80907

CONNECTICUT

Brad Browne
67 Ledgebrook Dr., Norwalk, 06854
I collect British groups & surf sounds.

Lees Browne
67 Ledgebrook Dr., Norwalk, 06854
I collect bubblegum rock, novelty, Chubby Checker, Raiders, Jan & Dean.

Buddy Holly Memorial Society (Bill Griggs)
75 Belcher Rd., Wethersfield, 06109
All speeds of any records or materials that pertain to Buddy Holly in any way. I buy, sell & trade. I also collect cover records of Buddy Holly Material, as well as tributes. Write for details about joining the Society.

Dave Cook
121 Oak St., Southington, 06489
1940's & 50's country, bluegrass & western. All speeds.

Phillip M. DeVoe
217 Burnside Ave., E. Hartford, 06108
I collect R&R, R&B, s'tracks: Buddy Holly, Gene Vincent, Ritchie Valens, Eddie Cochran, Elvis, Beatles, Rick Nelson, Everly Bros. LP's, 45's & memorabilia of these artists.

David Ford
142 Taft Lane, Windsor Locks, 06096
I collect 50's R&R and rockabilly and pop. (203) 623-0084

Richard Heghinian
76 Wendy Dr., S. Windsor, 06074

Wayne Jones
7 Ellington Rd., E. Hartford, 06108

Halvard Ljongquist
59 Lewis Ave., Wolcott, 06716
Post-war blues, R&B, rockabilly, C/W, jazz. 45's, 78's & LP's Esp. 40's vocal groups & country boogie, records with jive and alcohol lyrics. Trade, buy, sell, send lists.

Robert E. O'Loughlin
P.O. Box 3533, Bridgeport, 06605
I collect R&B, R&R, 45's & LP's of the '58's & early '60's. Mostly New York group harmony, doowop style.

David Ponak
Rt. 2 Box 201, Pomfret Center, 06259
I collect pic sleeves, promos, LP's, EP's, and memorabilia of the Rolling Stones, Beach Boys.

Lisa Ponak
FRD 2 Box 201, Pomfret Center, 06259
I collect LP's & 45's of 60's R&R & C/W. Beatles, Jimi Hendrix, Dylan, Donovan. Esp. promos, pic sleeves, jukebox EP's & interviews. Phone: (203) 974-1086.

Alvin E. Ruda
42 Highview Terr. Apt. 26D, Hamden, 06514

Robert Rymarzick
38 Wrights Lane, Glastonbury, 06033
I collect R&R, R&B, group sounds; buy & sell novelty records Send for lists. 50's 60's, 45's, LP's. Phone: (203) 633-2385

Jimmy Smith
7 Caroline Pl., Greenwich, 06830
I collect acid rock, obscure Rod Stewart & Peter Frampton.

Rock Stamberg
Meadow Ln., Greenwich, 06830
I collect R&B, doowop sounds & Sam the Sham.

L.G. Stefano
232 S. Water St., G7, Warehouse Point, 06088
I collect R&R, blues 45's from 55-65. Billie Holiday, Curtis Lee, Haley Mills, Paul Peterson, Early Paul Anka hits, Xmas pop hits, Del-Vikings, cassettes. (203) 623-5487.

DELAWARE

Bill Cooper
183 S. Main St., Smyrna, 19977
I collect Abba, Bjorn & Benny, Agnetha Fattskog, Anni-Frid Lyngstad.

Disc Collector Publications
P.O. Box, 169, Cheswold, 19936
Deal in new C/W LP's, 45's mainly luegrass & old time country. Collect all country except modern Nashville. 78, 45, tapes, trans. (exchange tapes) Approx. 15,000 discs 500 reel to reel tapes (live shows, etc.) Rather have LP or 45.

Joel Glazier
705 W 38th St, Wilmington, 19802
I collect Beatle & Beatle related-records, articles, books, etc. Interested in trades & foreign items.

Buddy Loveall
100 Kntucky Ave, Wilmington, 19804
I collect Beatles & their related pic sleeves, novelty items, old mags., etc. uy, sell or trade (303) 994-6475.

James L. Norman
P.O. Box 11, Main St., Dagsboro, 19939
Will buy 1950's rock-45's, 45 EP's, VG to mint with pic sleeve, & hard cover, of Elvis, Gene Vincent, Jack Scott, Larry Hall, Timmie Rogers, Virginia Lowe, Bell Notes, Impalas, Eddie Cochran, Nervous Norvous.

DISTRICT OF COLUMBIA (WASHINGTON)

Chip Bishop
901 Sixth St., SW, Apt. 605, 20024
I collect 50's, 60's, 70's pop, R&R & R&B, esp. goups. 45's only. Set Sales only.

Rosser B. Maddox
1101 New Hampshire Ave. NW #1007, 20037
I collect all LP's

Miss Barbara Marvin
4629 Tilden St., N.W., 20016
I collect vocals of swing era (1930-1945), Nina & Fredrick (1935-1950), and country (1930-45).

Mr. Daniel Medina
1418 Hopkin St., NW #1, 20037

Charles Sanders
58 Allison St., NE, 20011
I collect R&R, R&B from the 50's & 60's, 45's & LP's. I buy often, so be sure I'm on your mailing list.

FLORIDA

Sid Arthur
8265 W. Sunrise Blvd., Plantation, 33322
We buy & sell R&B, C/W, jazz, orig. casts, s'tracks, Elvis, swing era, etc. We have over 100,000 45's — LP's, 15,000 78's for mail order sale.

The Book Store
739 E. Silver Springs Blvd., Ocala, 32670
Phone: 622-7812 or 629-0903

Thomas A. Buby
5611 Newberry Rd., Gainesville, 32607
I have a large number of promo. LP's & 45's from 1970's rock & jazz areas as well as selected 1950's & 60's rock.

Dave Bushby
P.O. Box 15883, Orlando, 32808
I collect R&B groups, rockabilly, I buy R&R 45's in any quantity. Ph: (305) 299-5282.

Charlotte's Old Record Gallery
2920 Harborview Rd., Tampa, 33611
10,000 33 1/3 rpm, 12,000, 78 rpm, 6,000, 45 rpm rcds., consisting of jazz, swing, blues, C/W, gospel, collection consists of recordings prior to '50. Filed by artists. Prices are set prices, no auction lists, Want lists desired.

Larry & Lynn Cooper
Rt. 2, Box 580, Thonotosassa, 33592
We buy & sell all catagories. Phone: (813) 936-3698.

Thomas Deuber
1501 E. 142nd Ave. #6, Tampa, 33612
I collect early 50's R&B, R&R, 78's; late 60's early 70's rare LP's (R&R & hard rock), late 40's early 50's R&B, R&R 45's-orig. pressings only.

Bob Grasso
9020 NW 24 Ct., Ft. Lauderdale, 33322
I collect R&B groups, Sun label, blues, Pre-Essex Haley & early 45 rpm issues (1949-50).

Elsie Hine
1147 Delphinium Dr., Orlando, 32807
I sell R&R, C/W, old 78's, LP's.

Hyde & Zeke Record Exchange
919 W. University, Gainsville, 32601
We deal in all types of records in good condition. Buy, sell, trade, mostly LP's. Various artists, hard-to-find labels.

Charles Keebler
19911 Holiday Rd., Miami, 33157
I collect Buddy Holly, Holly tributes & sound-alikes, Jim Croce break-in novelties.

Ron Kircher
P.O. Box 9202, Panama City, 32407
I deal in all recordings from '39 to '65. I send out low-priced 45 & LP sale lists.

Ron LeBow
2128 W. 58th Ave., Ft. Lauderdale, 33313
I collect R&R from the 50's to now: surfing vocals, white group sounds (doowops & ballads). I buy, sell & trade & try to fill want lists. Phone: (305) 733-2485.

Jeff Lemlich
9130 SW 48 St., Miami, 33165
I collect '60's punk & merseybeat 45's. (305) 274-0155.

Loube's Nostalgia Book Store
4802 E. Busch Blvd., Tampa, 33617
We deal in jazz, R&B, R&R, C/W. Out-of-print albums, 45's & 78's. Also R&R movie posters. (813) 985)3743

A.J. Lutsky
P.O. Box 557342, Miami, 33155
I collect film & stage s'tracks, write for extensive free listings. Also have access to 1000's of records in other categories. Also personality LP's. Send your wants.

John Miller
P.O. Box 640116, Wetabr., Miami, 33164
I collect white vocal groups (doowop), surfing, novelty, break-ins. Send for free lists, I also deal in these areas plus s'tracks & personalities.

Richard Minor
9415 S.W. 42nd St., Miami, 33165
50's & 60's R&R, C/W, R&B, blues, rockabilly. Beatles, Elvis, Buddy Holly, Sun, Sam Phillips, etc. Will buy collections. Send lists. Money back guarantee on my stock.

Phoenix Records
1642 W. University, Gainesville, 32603
I deal in used records-buy, sell & trade. Send your lists. Phone: 377-5215

Harry Raymond
2920 Harborview Rd, Tampa, 33611
I collect C/W, jazz, s'tracks on LP, jazz on 78. Phone: (813) 831-2403.

Records
Rt. 2, Box 194, Crystal River, 32629
Buy, sell, trade old R&R, R&B, 60's rock, 78's, 45's & LP's. Any quantity. (904) 795-3809 or (904) 795-7512.

Lou Rallo
Box 47, Orange Park, 32073
I collect R&B, gospel, R&R, blues, 45's, 78's, LP's 1940-'70. Send SASE for list of R&R & R&B T-shirts. Send want lists.

Bobby Salerno
10264 Gulf Blvd., Treasure Island, 33706
I collect Elvis, R&R of the 50's & 60's, Beatles, Surf, doowop, girl groups, Beach Boys. Buy & trade.

Jim Shebly
12240 SW 187 Terr., Miami, 33177
Buy, sell, trade. LP's only. Rockabilly, blues, C&W, folk, R&B, oldtime, R&R, and some pop & jazz. Also have 200 45's from 50's & 60's to sell. free lists. 45's mostly R&B, C&W, R&R, pop, & instrumentals. Send your auction/set price lists.

Bob Sink
1208 Baronwood Place, Brandon, 33511
I collect Beatles (LP's, 45's, EP's, imports, bootlegs, live concerts, outakes), all Apple releases, all late 50's & early/mid 60's rock.

Joseph Weeks/Brian Southard
7200 SW 83 St., Plaza 3-117, Miami, 33143
Interest in early motown, 60's girls groups, female vocals, (Mary Wells, Lesley Gore, Shirelles, Chrystals, Ronettes, Chiffons. Shangri Las, Vandellas, Marvelettes. Also early 60's R&B.

Dan Wells
8730 5th Way N., St. Petersburg, 33702
I collect all 50's R&R & R&B, esp. red wax. (813) 576-4125

Bob Wood
P.O. Box 2394, Pensacola, 32503

William C. Wrigley
1400 NW 10 Ave. 20A, Miami, 33136
CBers: Break ch. 19 for STARBASE whenever you're in Miami.

GEORGIA

Ronald W. Bonds
1948 Glenmar Dr., Decatur, 30032
Always interested in any rare, obscure or unusual items. All type auction & set sale list always wanted!. Records on Bizarre/Straight, ESP, etc., Beefheart, Zappa.

"The Boogie Man"
944 Sharon Cir, Smyrna, 30080
45 rpm R&B, R&R, C&W. Do you like to correspond by tape, join us, "The cassette tape network."

Brian S. Cady
Box 128, Reed Hall, U. of G., Athens, 30602
I collect rock from '64 to now, including the Who, Beatles, & foreign releases (404) 542-4432.

Fantasyland Books & Records
2817 Peachtree Rd., NE, Atlanta 30305
60's & 70's rock, Beatle items, comic books, Buy, sell, trade. Andy Folio, owner. (404) 237-3193

Mike Hall
2 Exchange Pl., Suite 2264, Chamblee, 30338

Mike Jones
R #2, Randal Rd., Cave Spring 30124
I collect records from the 50's & 60's, albums & 45's. Main interest in R&R, pop rock, & C&W. Like some instrumental & movie s'tracks.

Lawrence Long, Jr.
Box 555 B, RT 4, Martinez, 30907
I collect 45's & LP's, Buddy Holly, Elvis Presley, big bands, Beatles, Haley & Comets (Crickets)

A. Raye Smith
2023 Dug Gap Rd., Dalton, 30720
I collect British & U.S. rock. Beatles, records, memorabilia, etc., (404) 278-8980.

Wuxtry
201 College Ave., Athens, 30601 (404) 543-3739
I pay $1.00 and up for used & out-of-print LP's. Now accepting selling & want lists. 1000's of collectors LP's for sale.

HAWAII

Goin' Back Enterprises
P.O. Box 7161, Honolulu, 96821
60's & 70's rock..International distributors & retailers..$1.00 for catalogue-magazine. We sell misc. musical memorabilia.

William A. Kuester
95-019 Waihonu St., Apt. B202, Wahiawa, 96786
I collect LP's, pictures, photos & any items concerning Loretta Lynn & Wanda Jackson, & Teresa Brewer.

Mom N' Pops Records
2915 Kapiolani Blvd., Honolulu, 96826
We deal in R&R, jazz, S'tracks, R&B. We buy LP or 45 collections & specialize in Hawaiian recordings. Send SASE for our lists.

David B. Thompson
1103 A Cornet Ave., Hickam A.F.B., 96553
I collect R&B, R&R LP's, 50's - mid-60's. Ronettes (Philles), Dale Hawkins (Checker/Chess), Freddie Cannon (Swan), Jimmy Clanton (Ace), Link Wray (Swan, Epic), in VG or better.

Richard Young
1056 12th Ave., Honolulu, 96816

IDAHO

Mike Feeney
2136 2nd St., Lewiston, 83501
I collect 50's R&R, R&B & rockabilly - early 60's girl groups & Doowop - Motown & Stax-albums only.

Richard Ochoa
1206 N. 15th St., Coeurd'Alene, 83814
R&R (50-64), R&B, C&W, rockabilly. Elvis, W. Jennings, B. Knox, Chess, Checker, Sun, Atlantic & RCA. Buy, sell or trade have 50,000 45's in stock (40-77) & 2,000 LP's. Send wants.

ILLINOIS

A. Levin Rare Records
454 Central Ave., Highland Park, 60035
45's & LP's of the 50's & early 60's. R&B, R&R, rockabilly. Will buy entire collections. Send for latest set price list.

Chuck Argabrite
10474 Ethel Ct., Rosemont 60018
I collect, Sun, pop, rockabilly & C/W. Will swap tapes R-to-R or 8-tracks with collectors anywhere.

Gary Bernstein
1921 N. Keystone, Chicago, 60639 (312) 276-1380
I collect Elvis rcds. from US (rare) & from foreign. Also, Buddy Holly, Jack Scott, G. Vincent, Janis Martin & Four Lovers, 45's, LP's 78's & EP's. Pic covers & promo material. Jump blues black group sounds from 50's also.

Frank Black
108 Webster Apts., Clinton, 61727

George Bleskin
5935 W. Giddings, Chicago, 60630

Tyler-Travis Bolden
P.O. Box 1164, Effingham, 62401
Beatle records only-33 1/3, 45's, EP's, promo's & bootlegs, I have many Beatle records to trade. (217) 342-3079.

Mr. George Ira Boerema
34W888 N. James Dr., St. Charles, 60174

Gary G. Bowman
611 Cornelia St., Joliet, 60435
I collect R&B, rockabilly 45's or 78's. I buy collections; have 1000's of records in all fields (815) 723-5775.

Buffalo Records
1423 8th St., Rockford, 61104
We sell 50's & 60's rock & pop vocals. Elvis, Beatles, British groups, hit making artists. We have a store location, mail order sales, lists & letters answered if have SASE.

Vern Byrn
124 Main St., Warsaw, 62379
78's, 45's, LP's, Records. Buy & sell Anything on H. Williams L. Frizzell, J. Rodgers, Cowboy Copas, G. Morgan, etc., Old pictures, song folios.

Michael Cain
906 Wilson Ct., Zion, 60099
Buy & trade for rare Beatle records & pic sleeves, U.S. and foreign. (312) 872-2820

William C. Chapman
403 Birchwood Ln., DeKalb, 60115
I collect rock & roll.

Cowboy Carl Records
P.O. Box 116, Park Forest, 60466
We deal in C&W, rockabilly, R&R and soon-punk rock.

Bruce Edelson
8139 Kilpatrick, Skokie, 60076
I collect & sell British rock, punk & 60's rock. Send for my sale & auction list. (312) 674-2203.

Robert Fitzner
1942 S. East Ave., Berwyn, 60402
I collect jazz & big bands; also buy, sell, trade jazz magazines. esp. Down Beat, & Metronome (312) 484-3587.

Devin Ford
4710 W. 83rd St., Chicago, 60652
I collect Kinks, '60's British invasion & rockabilly bought, sold & traded, esp. Kinks!

William J. Kincaid
7406 W. Randolph-Apt. 3A, Forest Park, 60130
I collect 50's rock, Sun, Ace, & all Memphis labels, have a complete Presley collection, bootlegs incl. Extensive rockabilly collection, also complete Jerry Lee Lewis, bootlegs incl.

Paul Koko
724 N. Taylor Ave., Oak Park, 60302
Classical music, esp. conducted by Arturo Toscanini. Want V-discs, transcriptions, 78's, 45's, LP's-Pirates, tapes, memorabilia, (Programs, etc). Please indicate price wanted.

Betty Lacey
14349 Lawndale, Midlothian, 60445
I collect C/W; unusual records of Patsy Cline, transcriptions, also collect & trade C/W song folios, gtars & banjos.

Robert A. Lattin
7813 S. Luna Ave., Burbank, 60459
Am a scavenger for hard-to-get LP;s. Want Nugent, Amboy Dukes, Rory Gallagher, Cactus, & rare recordings. Prefer business by mail.

Don Lego
410 Illinois St., Joliet, 60436

Len Lisiewicz
3550 S. Honore St., Chicago, 60609
Worlds largest or biggest collector of Hawaiian records. Will buy 78's.

Bill Manley
262 Taylor Ave., Glen Ellyn, 60137
Buy, sell, trade 45's, albums. Buy & trade anything on the Monkees. Have many rare 45's.

Ken Miller
727 36th St., Cairo, 62914
I collect 50's & early 60's RRRR£ R&B, C&W; 45's & LP's. Buy, sell & trade. (618) 734-4228.

Larry A. Newlan
615 Railroad St., Lovington, 61937
I collect soundtracks.

Bob Novy
408 S. Phelps, Arlington Hts., 60004
I collect Phil Spector, British Invasion, Punk & surf. Buy, sell, trade.

Robert Pruter
576 Stratford Ave., Elmhurst, 60126
I collect records & record magazines. 1950's doowops. '60's soul, blues, Chicago R&B records especially.

John L. Rinaldo
2510 Bordeaux Dr., Rockford, 61111
I collect 60's R&R; Beach Boys & imports. (815) 877-3337.

Johnny Tracy
1560 Florence Ave., Galesburg, 61401
Buy, sell or trade - 45's, 78's on LP's C/W. Main interest-old W.L.S. on Barn dance material.

Rick Tyler
1138 Lorena Ave., Wood River, 62095

Kim Urban
1309 S. Glenwood, Springfield, 62704
Late 50's to 70's rock & roll.

Ron Vail
706 S. Clayton St. Bloomington, 61701
I collect movie, TV, s'tracks, R&R, LP's, old radio shows, cassettes. (309) 829-4011.

Victrola
202 N. Lafayette, Macomb, 61455
We are a retail store, and we buy & sell all types of records. (309) 837-3720.

V.L. Walsh
619 E. 2nd, Centralia, 62801
I collect novelty, C/W LP's, any & all political related items, Loretta Lynn. Have thousands of 45's for sale. Sen want lists.

Brian Wichmann
576 Dara James, Des Plaines, 60016
I collect Acid/hard rock; British Invasion. Bootlegs & imports of same. VG & better; am principly interest in buying.

Nancy Winters
7 N. Maple Ave., Fox Lake, 60020
Anything by the Stones, bootlegs, LP's, EP's, 45's, tour programs, promo items, magazines, books, posters, etc. Also 60's & 70's rock magazines.

INDIANA

Pete Battistine
5461 Fillmore St., Merrillville, 46410
American top 40 radio programs, '70-'78. Billboard magazines & radio station surveys '67-'78.

John P. Briggs
Briggs Farm, Geneva, 46740
I collect rockabilly, country-rock, surf, genuine punk, Beatles, Stones, Dylan & instrumentals (219) 368-7289.

Fred Calhoun
616 E. North, Kokomo, 46901
I collect blues, R&B, boogie woogie, jazz, 78's, 45's, LP's of the 40's, 50's, 60's, 70's, orig. or otherwise (for listing only).

E.H. Diamond
P.O. Box 29147, Indianapolis, 46226
Want near mint Jimmie Davis, Joni James, Gene Autry. Have approximately 1500 R&B, country, & pop from the 1950's for sale individually.

Golden Memories Records, Inc.
P.O. Box 217, Mooresville, 46158
We issue a catalog of approx. 10,000 different older LP's every two months. Write!

Ffloyd Haas, Jr.
2209 E. Carter Rd., Kokomo, 46901
I collect all speeds of hit tunes, radio records & albums as a whole.

John Hiatt
7801 St. Rd., 227 N., Richmond, 47374
Will buy 45's & LP's of Jack Scott, Buddy Holly, Patience & Prudence, early Fats Domino and most likely a lot of other records of the 50's & 60's.

John E. Parry
1205 Wilson Blvd., Anderson, 46012
I collect jazz & big band, Swing & pop singers, instrumtalists & groups- 78's, 45, 33's - no rock or country.

Tom Petersen
1018 Harrison Ave., Apt. 3A, Dyer, 46311
I collect mainly R&R, 1960 to now. 45's & LP's Also into classical music. Please send any set-sale or auction lists.

Kenneth L. Schilling
1313 W. Ridge Rd., Hobart, 46342

Richard W. Welch
102 Marquette, Ave., South Bend, 46617
I collect Sun, Phillips International, and Flip records. Am interested in records, photos & autographs of the artists, session men, etc., documents, letterheads, etc. of these labels.

IOWA

Doyle D. Haskell
113 S. Washington, Bloomfield, 52537
I buy & sell early 60's-70's. I have a few from the 50's in stock. (515) 664-9512.

Memory Lane
113 S. Washington, Bloomfield, 52537
Send want lists for all types of records. Will try & find for you. Also have walk in store. Closed Saturdays, open Sundays 11 to 3 p.m.

Steve Parrott
525 Terrace Rd., Iowa City, 52240

Sheldon Pinsky
4211 Lincoln Swing, Ames, 50010
I collect ragtime, bannelhouse, honky-tonk, big band swing. I am searching for LP's by ragtime Stan, Johnny Maddox-Dot recording artist. (50-'65).

Danny Sawhill
P.O. Box 2749, Des Moines, 50315
Buy, sell, trade 45's. Specialize in 50's & 60's R&B, C&W, rockabilly, R&R. Thousands of extra's. Want lists welcomed.

KANSAS

Jimmie Applebee
317 E. Washington, Osborne, 67473
I collect all speeds of C/W & 50's-early 60's R&R.

Donald L. Kuhn
1113 Downing Ave., Hays, 67601
I collect 50's & 60's R&R, Annette, Dale Ward, Dickey Lee, old Glen Campbell. (913) 625-5858.

Jerry Lee Letcher
817 Sandusky, Kansas City, 66101
Would like anything on Elvis Presley. Priceless records, like Sun, and original Frankie & Johnnie. (913)281-1719.

Boyd Robeson
2425 W. Maple St., Wichita, 67213
I collect Eddy Arnold radio transcription rcds or will purchase tapes made from these. Gene Autry rcds & tapes, Hank Williams records. (316) 942-3673 or 722-7765.

Larry Waggoner
9030 Suncrest, Wichita, 67212
Primary interest in 50's & 60's popular folk music, also some country & 50's rock, albums & singles. Will correspond with other similar collectors.

KENTUCKY

Tany Berman
1501 Woodluck Ave., Louisville, 50205
I collect anything having to do with Al Jolson. (502) 458-5522

Don C. Copher
Rt. 3, Owingsville, 40360
Am interested in hard-to-find Elvis recordings. Please send free price list.

James Kaysinger
Box 211, Whitesville, 42378
I collect C&W. I buy, sell & trade 78, 45, & LP albums. Also song folios & sheet music. Books wanted-Grand Ole Opry history Vol. I 1957 & stoyr of Grand Ole Opry 1953.

Steve Mallory
3051 Kirklevington Dr., #S, Lexington, 40502
I collect Beatles, Apple, solo Beatles, Beatles compositions by other artists, & their memorabilia. (606) 272-9761.

C. Richard Matthews
Box 589, Pineville, 40977
I collect 50's & 60's. Buy all Johnnie Ray. Send Price list.

Ray Watkins
6810 Sebree Dr. Apt. 4, Florence, 41042
I collect R&R, pop, English rock, will buy, sell or trade 45's & LPs only, including 45 EP's.

LOUISIANNA

Bill Delle
2625 N. Bengal Rd., Metairie, 70002
I collect early to late 50's R&B, & R&R, specializing in New Orleans artists. (504) 729-3129

Hel-lo Record Co., Inc.
710 Aris Ave., Box 9447, Metairie, 70005
We deal in collector 45's & LP's.

Wilson J. Lopez
14730 Florida Blvd., Baton Rouge, 70815
I collect Old Gene Autry records.

Terry Pattison
Box 19702-Mid City, New Orleans, 70179
I collect post-war blues & R&B on 45, 78, & LP's. Orig. only. Main interest in New Orlean R&B of the 50's.

Michael Sallinger Sr.
933 Beechgrove Blvd., Apt. D, Westwego, 70094

MAINE

Dis-Collectors of Maine
P.O. Box 1056, N. Windham, 04062

Nelson Gardner
Box 1082, Portland, 04104
I collect Elvis Presley records, films, memorabilia. C&W, rockabilly, 1950's to present pop & rock.

Larry Gray
12 Cleveland St., Calais, 04619
I collect rock from the 60's & 70's, as well as surf music.

Lee F. Rand
P.O. Box 134, Old Town, 04468

Greg Schulz
Box 37, Lewiston, 04240
I collect 60's rock LP's mostly.

Kenneth Turner
66 Bramhall St., Portland, 04102

Robert W. Vigue
35 Prospect St., Springvale, 04083

Richard Wood
P.O. Box 145, Kennebunk, 04043
I collect Beatles rcds-USA, imports, singles, LP's, EP's, solo Beatles rcds, promos, books, magazines. Anything on Beatles. Am looking for early discs to complete collection.

MARYLAND

Edward Allan
118 Hedgewood Rd., Lutherville, 21093
I sell R&R, R&B, rockabilly, & will trade for rare Elvis material.

Clifford D. Alper
1029 Flagtree Ln., Baltimore, 21208
I buy & sell 33's, 45's, & 78's of pop, C&W, R&R, classical (vocal & instrumental), shows & s'tracks, etc.

Harold E. Bagg, Jr.
2906 Goodwood Rd., Baltimore, 21214

Edward M. Bayes
544 Valleywood Rd., Millersville, 21108
I collect Janis Martin, Del Vikings, Mickey & Sylvia, R&B, R&R, rockabilly. Also foreign pressings, photos, autographs & boots-from 50's artists. (301) 987-5478.

Robert W. Becker, Jr.
50 King Henry Cr., Baltimore, 21237
I collect R&R, R&B, pop, C&W & rockabilly from '50 thru '60.

Larry Black
4808 Guilford Rd., College Park, 20740
I collect groups, R&B, R&R, 50's & 60's. TV shows & 16mm sound films. Phonos, photos, posters & other memorabilia. (301) 277-2555.

Anne Bortner
1416 Catlyn Pl., Annapolis, 21401
I collect anything about, by or related to the Four Seasons.

Ted Goetz
5814 Berkeley Ave., Baltimore, 21215
I collect 45's of 50's: R&B, Whirlin Disc, Onyx, Rama, Aladdin, Federal, Red Robin.

Louis Howard
3821 Ingleside St., Olney, 20832

Harry Jones
11700 Old Columbia Dr., #2017, Silver Springs, 20904
I collect orig. Sun 45's & 78's, R&R, R&B, rockabilly. Send for want list. (301) 622-2344.

James S. King
2313 Mt. Hebron Dr., Ellicott City, 21043
I collect rockabilly, R&B, R&R, 45's, LP's, Elvis soundalikes, Heartbeats, Five Keys, Bobby Rydell, Jimmy Clanton. Phone: (301) 465-7329.

Martin R. Mettee, Jr.
1225 Ten Oaks Rd., Arbutus, 21227
I collect 60's English rock, surf, blues R&B vocal groups, rockabilly. LP's, 45's, & 78's.

Mr. Gary Lynn Morris
425 N. Mulberry St., Hagerstown, 21740
I collect country music. Am looking for albums (old) & 45's by Buck Owens, Roy Price, Mel Tillis, Billy "Crash" Craddock & Elvis, Susan Raye & any other good country singers.

J. Paul Rieger, Jr.
6307 Weidner Ave., Baltimore, 21212
I collect American psychedelic groups, 1966 to 1969.

Charles N. Schemm
7763 Tieknack Rd., Pasadena, 21122
I collect pop, C&W, some R&R. Kay Starr, R. Clooney, Hank Snow, from late 40's to early '50's.

David L. Scott
1278 Riverside Ave., Baltimore, 21230
I collect Elvis, Johnny Crawford, Janis Martin, Bay City Rollers, Kiss.

Mark V. Stein
2202 Milridge Dr., Owings Mills, 21117
I collect James Taylor, Bill Joel, Jesse Colin Young, Youngbloods, Beautiful Day, Little Feat, others. Want rare releases, concert tapes, bootlegs. Have many concert tapes for trade.

Robert H. Tierney
Box 175, Rt. 2, Hanover, 21076
I collect 50's & early 60's R&R, R&B, top 20. Little Eva, Del Shannon, Dimension & Mohawk labels, records pertaining to Kansas City. (301) 799-7871.

Al Tilghman
14 S. Ellamont St., Baltimore, 21229
I collect R&B, jazz, 78's, 45's LP's. Mostly orig. labels. Buy & sell. All records carefully graded & inspected, mostly new & mint. Free finders service provided-send want list.

Brian Weinstein
4225 Roundhill Rd., Wheaton, 20906

MASSACHUSETTS

Mr. Timothy Ahern
6 Ledge Rd., Seekonk, 02771

Sevy Alexander (King Of The Oldies)
408 Pond St., Franklin, 02038

Arthur E Ardolino
25 Porter St., Malden, 02148
I collect R&B, blues, gospel & jazz of the late '40's thru early '60's. LP's & glossy photos only. (617) 321-2227.

Baron Records
11 Dell Ave., Melrose, 02176

Peter Brooks
2 Woburn St., W. Medford, 02155
I collect anything unusual by Felicia Sanders, esp. live concert tapes.

Bill Bruno
161 South St., Foxboro, 02035
I collect R&B, R&R 45's, LP's & EP's from the 50's to now.

Warren R. Carey
3 Marion Dr., Tewksbury, 01876
I deal & collect 45's of R&R, pop, R&B, C&W, from late 40's to now. Also EP's, LP's, pic sleeves, and some 78's. (617) 851-9165.

Roger D. Cofsky
4 Upton St., Millbury, 01527
Rare catalog, $2.00. Records-1955-present. Buy, sell, trade. (617) 755-9343.

Tony Colao
2904 Village Rd., West, Norwood, 02062
I collect LP's of rock & pop from 50's to now. (617) 731-0500.

Robert Cortese
35 Carleton St., Haverhill, 01830
Rockabilly-early to pre-modern electric guitar blues & R&R. Also New York R&B & rare LP's & imports.

Gene Dias
116 Bishop St., Fall River, 02721
I collect 50's R&R, R&B, rockabilly, Elvis, mags of 50's rock, etc.

Mike Flanagan
44 Cedar Ave., Randolph, 02368
I collect 45's & LP's from the 60's to now. (617) 963-4677.

Jack Fitzpatrick
16 Pratt Pl. #23, Revere, 02151
I collect Phil Spector, Ronettes/Ronnie Spector, Diana Ross/Su
mid 60's pure pop.

Glen Gaboury
119 Allen St., E. Longmeadow, 01028
I Collect 50's, early 60's R&R, jazz, classical. Buy, sell, trade. I have some rare recordings.

Chuck Gregory
17 Chavenson St., Fall River, 02723
R&B, R&R, pop, 1948-64, 78, 45, LP's M/St must be in fair to mint condition. Suitable for air play. reissues ok also.

Gene Guzik
1 Upland Rd., Holyoke, 01040
I collect Phil Spector (anything by, about, connected to), Jack Nitzsche, pre-74 Abba, white girl groups: Paris Sisters, Shangri-Las, Roy Orbison, Neil Diamond, classical by Arthur Fiedler & Boston Pops; synthesizer. (413) 533-4510.

Fred A. Johnson
48 W. School, Westfield, 01085
I collect Joni Mitchell live tapes, bootlegs, interviews, etc. Swaps or trades. Collect artists '65-'78, spec. DJ LP's, boots, etc.

Jack Fitzpatrick
16 Pratt Pl. #23, Revere, 02151
I collect Phil Spector, Ronettes/Ronnie Spector, Diana Ross/Supremes, Beach Boys, Orbison, Pitney, Girl-groups & early-mid 60's pure pop.

Roger Kirk
Box 806, Lawrence, 01842
I collect R&B, rock (not punk) from '50 to now. I need promo copies, send for want list. I'm a Philles, Sun, Apple freak!

Ed Lindback
24 Vinton St., Randolph, 02368
45's only, pop chart records from early 50's to present. Top prices paid for records with pic sleeves. Also collect surveys. Buy, sell & trade (617) 963-4508.

Ron Martin
563 King Philip St., Fall River, 02724
I collect R&R, R&B, Elvis 45's EP's, LP's; Elvis mags, souvenirs, etc.

Jon McAuliffe
24 Bowen St., Newton, 02159
I collect Elvis Presley LP's, blues LP's, rockabilly LP's, 50's, 60's, 70's rock & pop LP's.

Gerald M. Mello
114 Barnes St., Fall River, 02723
I collect LP's, 45's, EP's, pic sleeves, live tapes of Buddy Holly. (617) 678-2595

Michael Michel
P.O. Box 505, Kenmore Stn., Boston, 02215
I collect '50's uptemps, R&B vocal groups. I deal in 45's of all types '50-'63.

George A. Moonoogian
197 Broadway, Haverhill, 01830
I collect vintage black vocal group harmony ('20-'57), blues, all aspects of R&B ('40-'57). All speeds. Tapes of black groups on radio & films ('30-'57). Cassette tapes avail. Write!

John H. Moran
121 Stebbins St., Chicopee, 01020
I collect records & movie stills.

The Music Machine
Box 262, Shrewsbury, 01545
Send for our complete oldies catalog; only $1.00!

Keith Joseph O'Conner
70 Vermont St., Holyoke, 01040
I collect all Beatles memorabilia & records; all artists on Apple; Monkees, Herman's Hermits, Dave Clark Five, etc.; Soundtracks.

David Oksanen
220 Bedford St., Bridgewater, 02324
I specialize in Elivs & in 5-'s & 60's R&R. Also, sell & buy Elvis records & misc. related items.

Victor Pearlin
P.O. Box 199A Greendale Stn., Worcester, 01606
I am a dealer specializing in all types of music from the '50's Periodic set-sale lists are free. I collect 50's R&B myself.

Douglas Pederson
11 Emerson Dr., Littleton, 01460

Kip Puiia
8 Westgate Dr., #207, Woburn 01801
I collect 63-66 British Releases; obscure 45's & EP's not released in US; British Invasion memorabilia.

Randolph Music Center, Inc.
340 N. Main St., Randolph, 02368
Interested in buying & selling of LP's & 45's R&R 50's & early 60's. We also fill want lists & mail out auction lists.

The Record Corner
66 Central St., Ipswich, 01938
Specializing in old LP's 45's, R&R, jazz, movie s'track, easy listening, C&W, folk (50's, 60's, & 70's).

Dennis Richard
152 Gilbert St., Lawrence, 01943
I collect Beatles, Stones, Kinks, Who, Its A Beautiful Day, Tom Rush. Buy, sell, trade.

Mike Richard
Box 434 Gardner Rd., Hubbardston, 01452
I collect 50's-60's R&R; Buddy Holly, Ritchie Valens, Big Bopper & info on The Crash, Dr. Demento style music & obituaries of deceased R&R stars. (617) 928-3344.

Jack Shadoian
RFD #3, Amherst, 01002
I collect jazz, pop, classical, LP s'tracks, bop & hard-bop, 40's & 50's, rock, blues. Will buy, sell, trade.

Wesley A. Smith
290 S. Main St., Palmer, 01069
I collect 50's to mid 60's R&R: Early stereo LP's & 45's. Instrumentals like Champs, Ventures, Fireballs, Shadows, etc. Phil Spector records, articles, books. Photos (413) 283-6901 Weekends only.

Watham Record Shop
20 Lexington St., Waltham, 02154

David A. Yeager
67 Parkside St., Longmeadow, 01106
I collect rock, pop, R&B, soul from '64 to '69; and '65 to '68 singles by white male punk rock groups.

MICHIGAN

Black Kettle Records (Fred Reif)
542 Gratiot Ave., Saginaw, 48602
Thousands of 45's, LP's, 78s for sale-Send your want list.

Allen E. Brown
P.O. Box 188, Marne, 49435
I collect 45's of R&B, R&R & C&W from 50's & 60's. Buy, sell or trade.

Mark A. Brown
Rt. 1, Box 382-D, Berrien Springs, 49103
I collect R&R, R&B, country '58-'68. Specialize in 60-63. (616) 471-2146.

Michael Brozovic
6633 Shadowlawn, Dearborn Heights, 48127
Buy, sell & trade everything.

Tom Cederberg
2203 32nd St., Bay City, 48706
I collect 50's R&R, sheet music, anything Elvis. C&W, anything 50's to now. Interested in making foreign contacts. Collection includes 6000 LP's-4500, 45's.

Marianne De Neve
Rt. 1, Box 8, Quinnesec, 49876
I collect records by teenage idols of the late 50's & early 60's such as Bobby Rydell, Rick Nelson, etc., I'm also into western & historical ballads like those by Marty Robbins & Johnny Horten.

Charles J. Domke
41181 Crestwood Dr., Plymouth, 48170
I collect Dixieland jazz, ragtime & coon songs. I'm looking for 78's & cylinders in these categories. (313) 455-1989.

Jeanette Esser
30740 Avondale, Westland, 48185
I collect 45's only. '50-'69 soul groups. Colored discs.

Fantastico Collectors Conventions & Publications (Stu Shapiro), 17106 Richard, Southfield, 48075
Buyer, collector, seller, dealer, promoter. (313) 557-8819.

Craig V. Gordon
Rt. #1, Box 89, Edwardsburg, 49112
Chicago blues artists, Dylan, bootlegs & acid rock.

Jack Harper
2356 Buchanan SW, Grand Rapids, 49507
I collect '22-'50 C&W records, sound folios & paper items. Books or pamphlets or specialty C&W items. (616) 452-4104.

Dennis M. Johns
4013 Moorland Dr., Midland, 48640
I collect top 40, emphasizing '55-'65. Heavy emphasis on Phillies, Motown, Cameo, & Parkway labels.

Dan Kelly
P.O. Box 1454, Grand Rapids, 49501
I collect guitar artist albums', music books. Chet Atkins, Scotty Moore, George VanEps, Johnny Smith, Howard Roberts. Also posters of guitars & artists.

Mrs. V. Kowachek
35420 Hatherly Pl., Sterling Hts., 48077
I collect Soundtracks.

Bill Krohn
Rt. 2, Paw Paw, 49079
I collect non-mainstream, late 60's, early 70's rock; offbeat, little known, unsuccessful & early bands. I'm selling a 12 yr. collection of obscure albums. Send wants for lists.

Looney Tunes
1516 W. Michigan Ave., Kalamazoo, 49007

Jack Micael Meaoff
1691 Vandenbrooks Blvd., Saginaw 48602
I collect Doris Day, Patti Page, Teresa Brewer, old jazz, Calhoun McGuire, Shotglass Noonan, Michigan R&B group from 50's. Dew-Worm Willy & the Spider-Biters.

Diane Otis
5741 Ridgeway Drive, #10, Haslett, 44840
I collect Pre-and Post war blues & rock both 50's & 60's. Any speed, including 78's. Also buy collections.

Jim Pashkot
26769 W. Hills Dr., Inkster, 48141
I collect late 50's, early 60's New Orleans R&B, R&B instrumentals, Bill Doggett, Sil Austin, King Curtis. (313) 563-9350

Ed Pashullewich
11310 Aspen Dr., Plymouth, 48170
I trade, buy & sell 50's & 60's 45's records only.

Warren Peace
316 Stuart #1, Kalamazoo
Buy, sell & trade Les Paul, Beatles, Yardbirds & oddities in rock, blues, fold & old jazz. "The Record Man".

Paul W. Porter
4172 Hi Hill Dr., Lapeer, 48446
All categories of albums & 45's (Want lists accepted) SASE Specializing in: Comedy & instrumental albums, but if it's collectible, I collect it.

M. Radofski
3238 Harris, Ferndale, 48220
Serious collector of Beatles & Bob Dylan material. Orig. pressings. Bootlegs, cassette recordings. Any off the wall material. Hank Williams 78's. trade if I have something you can use or will buy. Have recordings by other artists.

Jerry L. Rathbun
706 Beulah, Lansing, 48910
45's & LP's of the 50's.

Craig Sigworth
146 W. Hickory Grove, Bloomfield Hills, 48013
I collect early 60's punk & British rock; mostly LP's.

Eric J. Stimac
3839 Jennings Dr., Kalamazoo, 49001 (616) 342-5520
Any R&R rarieties. From '60 to 70's Beatles, Lennon, Yardbirds & much more. Imports, boots & promos. Send want lists. Can get just about everything!

Paul D. Welch
36231 Nitchun Dr., Mt. Clemens, 48043
Correspondence with anyone who collects Chet Atkins, Merle Travis or Les Paul. Will buy, sell or trade.

Frank D. Yoworski
505 S. Van Buren, Bay City, 48706

MINNESOTA

Gary D. Bahr
1727 Hodgson Rd., N. Mankato, 56001
I collect R&R 45's, LP's & mini-albums from 60 to now. (507) 387-6926.

Wayne Blessing
573 Laurel Ave. #7, St. Paul, 55102
I collect C&W, 50's R&R, anything on Starday, the Sun family Jack Scott, Carlton. I buy & sell. Want list &/or auction for fee plus SASE plus 25 ¢.

Howie Butler
2343 E. Larpenteur, St. Paul, 55109
I collect pop, blues, jazz, pre-60's R&R: Toni Arden, Otis Rush, Sonny Rollins, Elvis, Fats, Jerry Lee, etc. LP only, buy & sell. Also radio broadcaster cassettes.

Jerry Chamberlain
3704 Auger Ave., White Bear Lake, 55110
I collect R&B & R&R 45's of the 50's & early 60's. (612) 429-7851.

William A. Conrad
P.O. Box 6545, St. Paul, 55106
Buy. sell, trade pop, C&W, R&B, rag, blues, 45's, LP's, 78's.

Gary Lee Schwartz
11014 Co. Rd., 15 Minneapolis, 55441
C&W, blues, rock, s'tracks. LP's, 45's, 78's, 78 rpm jukebox, movie posters. Buy, sell, trade. (612) 545-8727

MISSISSIPPI

Bobby W. Goff, Jr.
P.O. Box 56, Biloxi, 39533
I collect R&B, pop, mostly Southwest & Southeast New Orleans area. Also a little country.

Kate Peart
456 Hanging Moss Cr., Jackson, 39206
I collect Sinatra material: records, tapes, transcriptions, memorabilia.

MISSOURI

Vance De Lozier
Box 541, Warrensburg, 64093
I collect 50's & early 60's pop (mainly 45's)

Gladys Diley
2143 Shimoor Ln., St. Louis, 63141
I collect R&R, rockabilly from the 50's & 60's - 45's only. (314) 434-4121

Encore Records
P.O. Box 12585, St. Louis, 63141
We deal in 50's & 60's 45's, all in excellent condition. We have periodic auctions. Send for our free list. (314) 434-4121.

Harry Hilburn
Box 308, W. Plains, 65775
I collect & deal in R&R 45's, all Elvis, charted records 55-65, any early rock LP's, etc. (417) 256o-797.

Jay Holder
3553 A. S. Spring, St. Louis, 63116
I collect s'tracks, female jazz singers, popular: Doris Day, Anita O'day, June Christy, Peggy Lee, Judy Garland. Prefer Pre-recorded cassettes when available.

Greg Jones
P.O. Box 22413, Sappington, 63126
I collect anything on the Osmonds, Petula Clark, Diana Ross, Supremes, Beach Boys, Bruce Johnston, Also record Co. catalogs, promo material & radio surveys. (314) 842-2815.

Tom Kelly
707 Washington, St. Louis, 63101
R&B, 45's, 78's before '60, '20's records, blues & groups on black dominant labels '45-'60, jazz & blues '20-'40. I have about 50,000 rcds., & will help other collectors with info or taping.

Tom Mix
6 S. Euclid, St. Louis, 63108 (314)361-7353
I collect anything on jazz labels: Riverside, Yazoo, Blue Goose, early Blue Note; also Cap. Beach Boys, Beatles, mid 60's punk, & jazz. Sen want & selling lists w/prices.

Tim Neeley
2519 Lemay Ferry Rd., St. Louis, 63125
I collect anything on Elvis or the Beatles: records, buttons, stills, novelty items, etc. (314) 892-1394.

Richard A. Porter
8004 Brooklyn, Kansas City, 64132
I collect Elvis 45's & LP's, pre-65 DJ copies, Elvis novelties & sound-alikes. (816) 363-2090.

Rockin' Records
P.O. Box 6012, Kansas City, 64110
We deal in R&R, R&B, rockabilly, pop, some C&W, jazz & blues, orig. casts, s'tracks. All speeds. Free catalogue, want lists welcome!

Gary Songer
1702 Westminister, Mexico, 65265
I collect 45's, LP's, & 78's of the 50's: Elvis, Ral Donner, Cochran, Vincent; pic sleeves. (314) 581-6587.

Chuck Turman
4438 Forrest, Kansas City, 64110
I collect 50's & 60's R&R, R&B, doowop, s'tracks; anything on Elvis. Buy, sell trade; will take boots or reissues, too. Have want list; I'd like to hear from you!

Charles M. Vogel
4363 Miami St., St. Louis, 63116
I collect Bealtes, British invasion, boots, Jan & Dean, Beach Boys, early & mid 60's 45's, individual Beatles.

Baron Yama
Box 62, Savannah, 64485
I collect rockabilly, R&R, R&B: 45's & LP's only.

MONTANA

L & C Records
Star Route Box 432, Brady, 59416
I collect pop, rock & C&W from 50's to 70's. 45's & LP's. Please send want lists & request my record list.

Wesley C. Harr
433 W. Iron, Butte, 59701
Collect 78's, primarily R&R, & Country in the 50's. Have many duplicates for trade & many 78's from 30's & 40's to sell or trade. I buy most R&R from 50's on 78's if I can.

Elmer Kerr
Rt. 2, Box 9-11, Stevensville, 59870
I am interested in buying & trading Gene Autry records, photos etc. Also Jimmy Davis, Sam Hill, Hohn Hardy, Jimmy Smith, Tom Long, Bob Clayton.

NEBRASKA

Mike Hall
2601 Winthrop Rd., Lincoln, 68502
Records, rock mags, live tapes, boots, & rock artist posters. Beatles, Jimi Hendrix, Cream, Bubble Puppy, Mountain, West, Bruce I Laing, Ted Nugent, Queen & Wishbone Ash.

Michael J. Majeski
515 S. 31st St., #1, Omaha, 68105
Rock from 64 to now, folk, jazz, San Francisco psychedelic, Jefferson Airplane, Starship, Grateful Dead, Zappa, Mothers, LP's, singles, orig. Ed, posters, display & promo, concert bootlegs (all VG or NM) (Want to buy-nothing to sell now)

Dave "Oz" Osborn
9666 "V" Plaza #18, Omaha, 68127
Am trying to find Abba LP's from Sweden & TV themes on 45's & LP's.

NEVADA

Wm. R. Fellows
5800 Pebble Beach, Las Vegas, 89108
I collect 60's R&R LP's & 45's, personality, posters.

Jim Henry
645-C Denslowe Dr., Reno, 89512
I collect country 78's & 45's, & pre-Beatles R&R 45's.

Les M. Kasten
3805 Haddock Ave., Las Vegas, 89110
I collect Jan & Dean, surf, car, Jan & Arnie, Jan Berry, The Marcels. (702) 452-4365.

Bill Mansfield
2648 Viking Way, Carson City, 89701
I collect 45's, LP's, pic sleeves of C&W, R&R, R&B. Will trade.

Max O. Preeo
5800 Pebble Beach Blvd., Las Vegas, 89108
I collect orig. London or US orig. cast, film s'tracks, personality & related, "theater world" annuals, book about musical comedy, "screen romances," "screen stories," "movie story," mags.

Everett H. Yocam
2725 Kietzke Ln. Sp. 31A, Reno, 89502
I collect 78's, LP's, 10" & 12" big bands, vocalist, C&W, honky tonk, blues, jazz, sell or trade from 1905.

NEW HAMPSHIRE

John C. Banks
Box 697, S. Danville, 03881
I collect R&R; Lou Christie, Johnny Horton, novelty, Coca-Cola records & tapes. I buy only.

Bruce Dumais
1 Memorial Dr., Somersworth, 03878
I collect pop 45's from '54 to '63; R&B groups & one hit artists; greatest hit LP's, (603) 692-5173.

Jack Warner
77 Maryland Ave., Manchester, 03104
I collect obscure rock, Little Richard soundalikes, memorabilia records rockabilly, RIB, blues. I provide massabesic collector records. (603) 625-6779.

NEW JERSEY

Lou Antonicello
95 Stuyvesant Ave., Jersey City, 07306
I collect Elvis, Duane Eddy, Jack Scott, Rockabilly, instrumentals & s'tracks. (201) 451-4717.

Wendy Blume
764 Scotland Rd. #35, South Orange, 07079
I collect anything to do with the Rolling Stones. I edit a Stone fanzine "Let It Rock!"

Joseph Bozza, Jr.
55 Milton Ave., Nutley, 07110
I collect Beach Boys, Jan & Dean-All British rock, early '60's rock to psychedelic era. Magazines & pictures, etc.

Cheap Thrills Ltd.
382 George St., New Brunswick, 08901
Deal in '60's rock, US and U.K. Want Lists welcome. Beatles, Shadows of Knight, Beau Brummels, Nazz, Punk rock, etc.

Duane Christie
637 Seminary Ave., Rahway 07065
I collect Buddy Holly, Elvis, Eddie Cochran, Roy Orbison, Crickets, Jerry Lee Lewis, Carl Perkins, Jape Richardson, & Gene Vincent.

L.J. Chelson
17 Chadowlawn Dr., Livingston, 07039
I collect R&R: 50's rockabilly, instrumentals, 60's surfing vocal & instrumental, British rock, 70's heavy metal.

Frank J. Choloski
16 Fontaine Ave., Bloomfield, 07003
I collect LP's & 45's of the 50's & 60's. Early British rock & roll and surf & hot rod sounds.

Tom Cook
2 Vincent Place, Bridgewater 08807
I collect R&B, R&R vocal groups. from the 50's and early 60's.

John A. Di Rocco
P.O. Box 222, Maple Shade, 08052
I collect R&R, R&B, 45's, 33's, 78's, vocal groups, single artists, Anna, Atlantic, Gee, Linda, Money, Sun, Rama, End, Josie, Winley, & anything by Tommy Edwards on MGM label.

Cathy Dippel
P.O. Box 212, Edgewater, 07020
Anything Beatle-alone or together, past & present. records, pics, mags, Beatle cards. Anything Beatle.

The Doo Wop Shop
P.O. Box 2261, Edison, 08817
We deal & collect R&B & R&R. We put out a bimonthly auction and set sale list. Send us your wants. (201) 738-7666

Tom Dow
137 Julia Avenue, Trenton, 08610

Donald D. Dunn
170 Beech St., Paterson, 07501
I collect Elvis 45's, LP's and collectibles. Buy, sell, trade.

Steve Freedman
Box 2054, East Orange, 07019
Dealer in Beatles, Elvis, Pop star gum card sets, nostalgia, memorabilia.

Andrew J. Foglio
22 Buckingham Dr., Madison, 07940
The Sound of The Past (201) 377-3132. Old records & talking machines 1900-1949.

Robert Geden
830-D Berkley St., New Milford, 07646
I collect rock instrumentals, surf & hot rod music, Dick Dale, Link Wray, Duane Eddy-type twangy guitars. Live tapes wanted (201) 265-9110.

Ed Gofdon
Lot 9-B Karl-Le Mobile Manor, Cardiff, 09232
I collect R&R from 50's & early 60's; rockabilly, instrumental R&R, country. (609) 646-6744. Tape: reel to reel & cass.

James Graczyk
12 Quincy Ln., Bergenfield, 07621
I collect 50's & 60's hard rock rare live recordings by Stones, Yardbirds, Who, Detroit bands, New Wave bands. (201) 384-2306.

J. Ronald Grau
407 S. Union Ave., Cranford, 07016
I collect R&B, pop, & jazz LP's; vocal groups, swing bands. (201) 276-0140.

Tom Kennedy
P.O. Box 347, Absecon, 08201
I collect Elvis--records, albums, memorabilia, bought, sold & collected. Your offers & needs are welcome. Six different Elvis home-movie films available. Send 50¢ for Elvis Memorial Booklet.

Raymond B. Homiski
464 Fourth Ave., Elizabeth, 07206
I collect anything on Elvis & Beatles. Will also trade, have many records from 50's & 60's. Please Write "Elvis R.I.P."

Joe Kivak
P.O. Box 679, Elizabeth, 07207
I collect Dylan & Springsteen, records and concert tapes.

Robert Kordish
Box 496 State Home Rd., Jamesburg, 08831
I collect R&B, R&R, rockabilly of the 50's and early 60's. (201) 521-2760.

Ron Kushner
58 Sherman Pl, Irvington, 07111
I collect Grateful Dead bootlegs.

Michael Lund
60 Lynn Ct., Bogota, 07603
Anything I don't have on Cadence & Carlton. 10" & 12" albums & 45's. Jazz vocals like Mel Torme, Jackie & Roy, Blossom Dearie, Matt Dennis, Irene Kral, Joe Mooney, Frank D'Rone; any labels they are on.

Peter Malloy
8 Woodmont Dr., Chatham TWSP, 07928

James F. McNaboe
235 Prospect Ave., Hackensack, 07601
I collect R&R, R&B, 50's vocal groups.

Mr. Records
P.O. Box 764, Hillside, 07205
78 rpm records, sheet music for sale. All categories, classical, Big bands, vocalists, C&W, early comedy, foreign, polkas, jazz, marches, Send for free catalog.

Never Gone Records
926 Grandview Ave., Union, 07083
45's & LP's for sale. Send 13¢ stamp for complete list of records. Wanted: any Bobby Fuller on Todd, Donna, Exeter, or Del-Fi labels.

Russ Nugent
138-A Tierney Dr., Cedar Grove, 07009 (201) 239-2218
Will buy & sell: (45's) Fontane Sisters, Crew-Cuts, Ella Mae Morse, Pat Boone, McGuire Sisters, Georgia Biggs, Gale Storm, Teresa Brewer, Four Aces, Chordettes, De Castro Sisters, Laurie Sisters, De John Sisters, & Elvis.

The Olde Tyme Music Scene
915 Main St., Boonton, 07005
"Everything from Edison to Elvis" Specialty house in traditional jazz with good stock of out-of-print LP's. Want lists & mail orders handled. Carry old phonos., needles, etc.

Linda Parenti
196 Mill ½t., Apt 3, Belleville, 07109
Specializing in Frankie Valli, Four Seasons, Four Lovers, looking to buy, trade, picture, albums, 45's, etc. Also run Four Seasons Fan Club. (201) 759-5868

R. Joseph Pasco
18 Fulton Rd., Somerset, 08873
I collect modern jazz.

Chester F. Piell
P.O. Box 107, Flemington, 08822
I collect s'tracks, orig. casts, rock & personality: Cliff Richard, Rick Nelson, '57 Go Johnny Go sound-track. (201) 996-4291

Scott Piskin
741 Avenue C, Bayonne, 07002
Looking for Grateful Dead, Hot Tuna, Airplane, & others. Send price list. Bootlegs, 45's, posters, etc.

Platter World
P.O. Box 234, Garfield, 07026
We deal in all records, all speeds. Want lists welcome, send for my list.

Eddie Plungis, Jr.
701 Tuxedo Pl., Linden, 07036
Rock albums from 60's & 70's. All in mint condition. Sell for collectors prices. Will trade, too. Good selection, Yardbirds, Bubble Puppy, etc. (201) 925-6902

Clifford Priga
1300 Edgewood Ave., Westville, 08093
R&B & R&R of 50's - 60's group sounds. Also disco '72-present.

Fred Rathyen Jr.
41 James Ave., Clark, 07066
I collect Frankie Valli & the Four Seasons under any name on EP's 45's, 78's & LP's. Also foreign releases.

The Record Exchange (Les Marella)
113 A Chester Ave., W. Berlin, 08091
I collect records & rock mags., '50's & 60's R&R, esp. psychedelic & San Francisco sounds & Literature. Buy, sell, trade. (609) 627-0841

Edward T. Reilly
501 Washington St., Eatontown, 07730

Mark Restivo
64 Easton Ave., New Brunswick, 08901
I collect 60's; British Rock' Kinks, Beach Boys & obscurities.

Louis Roatche
5419 Gaumer Ave., Pennsauken, 08109
I collect R&B, R&R, acapella, 45's & LP's.

Rick Salierno
P.O. Box 1606, Bloomfield, 07003
I specialize in David Bowie records, also psychedelic, Punk, Bruce Springsteen, 60's & 70's rock, colored vinyl; Buy, sell & trade.

Edward P. Sanseverino
16A Woodmere Apts./W. County Line Rd., Jackson TWP, 08527

John J. Schumitta
409 Brick Blvd. Apt. 26A, Bricktown, 08723
Looking for any & all Elvis 45's, albums, DJ's. Will pay highest prices only Elvis items. (201) 920-1964.

Mark A. Tesoro
6 Lynn Dr., Toms River, 08753
I collect popular on 45's from 50's and reissues of old 78's on 45's from 30's & 40's.

Ken Thompson
2802 Buchanan St., Wall, 07719
I collect oldies 45's & LP's, R&B groups, doowops. Buy, trade. (201) 681-2450.

Joseph P.M. Trapani
253 Andover Dr., Wayne, 07470
Collector of groups of 50's & 60's LP's & oldies but goodies (LP's) type of collections.

Steve Viola
6110 Johnson Pl., W. New York, 07093
I collect Elvis, rockabilly, Beatles, Beach Boys, EP's, boots, mags. (201) 868-1482.

William E. Walker
2009 Wayne Ave., Haddon Heights, 08035
I collect big band, dixieland, early 78's, lesser known bands, & tape & trade air checks, transcriptions & special broadcasts. (609) 547-5779.

Ann M. Walton
4 Wexford Rd., Gibbsboro, 08026
(Dealer)-sheet music, 45's, 33's, 78's, discographys, research done all fields of music. Send want lists.

NEW MEXICO

Roger J. Bernard
3908 Douglas MacArthur NE, Albuquerque, 87110
Buy, sell, trade R&B records, esp. the groups of the 50's.

Louis Holscher
P.O. Box 3019, Las Cruces, 88003
I collect jazz, soul, Northwest Chicago blues, Miles Davis, white blues, 60's R&B, LP's. (505) 646-3821.

Judy Petrungaro
1436 Camino Cerrito SE, Albuquerque, 87123

Mr. Val Wyszynski
NMSU Elec. Music Lab., Box 188, Las Cruces, 88001
Inc.: 1400+ early rock & C&W, 200 LP;s of electronic (synthesizer) music, 78 & 45's of early rock & more. Main interest is era from 50 to 65. Also 130 + tapes (r to r) of early rock, some actual DJ shows of late 50's early 60's of Chicago area.

NEW YORK

Arf Arf
P.O. Box 755, Cooper Stn., New York, 10003
Orig. pressing 45's from 50's to now. All labels, artists & types of music. Catalog $1, deductible from order (212) 243-6484.

Robert Baldwin
79 Oakdale Ave., New Hartford, 13413
I collect R&R 45 & 33's rpm records from late 50's and early sixties.

William D. Baldwin
400 Semloh Dr., Syracuse, 13219
I collect 60's rock.

Scott Barrey
103 S. Ninth St., Olean, 14760
I collect R&B, R&R, & rockabilly 45's. I have over 5,000 78's for trading. Also have C&W & pop 45's for trade. (716) 372-7041.

Burt Belknap
183 Palmdale Dr., #4, Williamsville, 14221
I collect 50's & 60's LP's & 45's of rockabilly, R&B, & pic sleeves. (716) 634-8147.

Charles R. Berger
164 Graham Ave., Staten Island, 10314
I collect pop from '50 to '55: F. Lanie, Hilltoppers, Four Aces, P. Page, K. Starr, etc. (212) 761-4756.

William Cappello
445 Gramatan Ave., EA-1, Mt. Vernon, 10552
Recordings of Vaudevilleans (1890's-1930's). Also British comedians & music hall recordings (Rolf Harris, Charlie Davis, Elsa Lancaster, etc.). Any movie-TV s'tracks.

Chip Chapman
P.O. Box 492, Chadwicks, 13319
Specialize in 60's rock. Interested in Florida groups (Orlando hits) from 60's.

Roy H. Cohen
130-11 60 Ave., Flushing, 11355
I collect s'tracks, Elvis, Sinatra. Films, shows, LP's, 78's. Sell s'tracks, misc. 33 rpm, R&R, R&B, 45's, 78's.

Bill & Jeff Collins
98-25 65th Ave., #5A, Rego Park, 11374
Looking for Neal Diamond recordings: Columbia 42809, Any single recorded by N. Diamond & J. Parker on Shell. LP's open end radio spec. with N. Diamond. UNI 1913. Will pay reasonable prices. No bootlegs.

Frank J. Costanzo
170 Nagle Ave., New York City, 10034
I collect big band era 30's-40's, R&B, jazz, personalities, Dixieland, orig. casts, movies, folk.

Duane F. Coughenour
4168 W. Seneca Tpke., Syracuse, 13215
I collect R&R & R&B, mid 60's to now, & progressive rock. (315) 492-3006.

Bob Couse
113 Lena Terrace, N. Syracuse, 13212
I collect & sell Mersey sound, surf, Gerry & Pacemakers, Bobby Vee, Del Shannon, Doors, Hollies, Searchers, Jan & Dean. Collect & TRADE TAPES. Send SASE (315) 458-5174.

Tony D'Angelo
P.O. Box 432, E. Elmhurst, Queens, 11369
I collect Elvis Presley, stereo 45's of late 50's early 60's & 50's & 60's LP's.

Tony DeLuca
570 Westminster Rd., Brooklyn, 11230

Fred De Poalo
30 S. Cole Ave., Spring Valley, 10977
I collect 50's & early 60's R&R, R&B, rockabilly, doo wops, & Elvis.

Dennis A. Dioguardi
P.O. Box 56-Rosebank, Staten Island, 10305
I want rare items by Beatles, Dion, Valli & 4 Seasons, Holly, J. Maestro, P. Anka, Elegants, Del Satins, British rock. Rcds. or tapes.

Max Diamond
1701 Hertel Ave., Buffalo, 14216

Bruce Proms
1216 Tracy Ave., Schenectady, 12309
R&R, R&B, punk rock from 50's to now. Albums. Will buy, sell, trade. Will sell or trade old 45's for albums.

Ed Engel
45-10 Kissena Blvd., Flushing, 11355
I collect white groups from New York area & surf records. Authority on 4 Seasons, Tokens, Earls, Regents, & the Elligants. Glad to answer any questions.

Flashback Records
412 9th St., (Off 1st Ave.), N.Y.C., 10003
Specializing in 60's-70's collectors rock. LP's, 45's. Good trade in on accepted records. Open Tues-Sat, 2-7. (212) 260-8363.

Dan Friedlander
145 N. Railroad Ave., Babylon, 11702
I collect 45's only of R&B & R&R. Cleftones, Flamingos, Clovers & others. VG to mint only!

Rold Galupo
69-63 Alderton St., Rego Park 11374
I collect records, tapes & glossy photos of doowops & disco. Will buy, trade, sell & will tape music for all occasions for low cost. Have collection from 30's to now, everything but C&W.

R. Getreuer
798 Brookridge Dr., Apt 33, Valley Cottage, 10989
I collect white doo wop group sounds & deal in all types of 45's from 50's to now.

Phillip Grabash
345 E. 80th St., New York, 10021
I collect R&R 45's & LP's from the 50's to now; punk rock & Phil Ochs obscurities are of special interest. (212) 535-7192.

Andre Grabowicz
P.O. Box 1881, Brooklyn, 11202, (212) 499-8598
Original Records: Rare and out of print - rock, jazz, folk, blues, shows, s'tracks, personalities, etc.

John Gray
14 Caddy Pl., Rocky Point, 11778
I collect R&B, R&R, 78's & 45's mostly group harmony, (516) 744-7937.

Benjy Greenberg
9 Richard Pl., Rye, 10580
Worlds No 1 Beatlemaniac

Ray Greenberg
50-35 184th St., Flushing, 11365
I collect shows, s'tracks, documentary, personality, nostalgia; LP's & 78's in all categories except C&W, R&R, folk. Buy, sell, trade, taping service.

Steven L. Gubler
Hyde Park Estates, Apt. 6C, Hyde Park, 12538
I collect still sealed, orig. copy, in mint condition, of the Beatles & Frank Ifield on Vee-Jay records (mono version) Sold to highest bid. Not bootleg.

John Hergula
105-33 Otis Ave., New Yord, 11368
I collect R&B from 50's, & black vocal groups. I buy & sell R&B 45's & LP's. (212) 592-6580

Gary C. Huested
4170 Sluga Dr., Newburgh, 12550
I collect Annette, Dion & Belmonts, Crests, James Darren, Elegants, Buzz Clifford, Johnny Preston, Del Shannon, Phil Spector, Gale Storm, Curtis Lee, Ray Peterson & break-ins.

Robert S. Hyde
229 E. 28th St. 1E, New York, 10016
I collect 60's & 70's punk rock, white vocal & rockabilly of the 50's, punk Colorado-related 60's records, Jan & Dean, fast harmony group records. (212) 532-9115.

The Jimi Hendrix Archives (Tom Richards)
4700 W. Lake Rd., Canandaigua, 14424
Dealer in 60's: Hendrix, Yardbirds, Beatles, British, Texas. All foreign LP;s, EP's, 45's, no 78's.

Martin Karp
2245 Bronxwood Ave., New York, 10469
I collect jazz, big bands, dixieland, Kay Kyser, Four Aces, Toni Arden, Sunny Gale, s'tracks. No opera, classical or C&W. 40's through 60's.

Carl P. Kirschenbaum
27 Pettibone Dr., Albany 12205
I buy, sell, trade 45's; flying saucer, British sound, instrumental surf, Billboard Top 100. Almost anything from 60 to now, 45's only.

Rocky Kreamer
30 Fairway Rd., Corning, 14830
I collect pre-Beatle R&R everything.

John Kurtz
110 Bement Ave., Staten Island, 10310
I collect R&R, C&W, rockabilly & buy & sell LP's in these categories esp. reissues, boots & cut-outs. Check Goldmine or send wants.

Arthur Lane
P.O. Box 1187, New York, 13201
I collect R&B, vocal groups of the 50's & 60s. Will trade, buy & sell. (315) 422-2452

Larry Lapka
11 Wendy Ln., Massapequa, 11762
I collect R&R LP's of the Monkees & Dave Clark Five. Will buy to complete collection. (516) 541-8454.

Howard L. Lent
151-75 22nd Ave., Whitestone, 11357
Wanted: Mint only R&R & R&B, 50-64. Esp. EP's & 45's with pic sleeves. Need a mint Ral Donner "Beyond The Heartbreak" on Reprise.

Gary Levenson
1068 S. Thompson Dr., Bay Shore, 11706
I collect commercials, comedy answer & cut-ins records, jingles, Stan Freburg, Groucho Marx. Send want lists; ask for mine (516) 666-6165

Joseph M. Loglisci
4200 Ave. K #1HH, Brooklyn, 11210
I collect R&R, R&B, early to mid-60s' rock: Phil Spector, surf, Beach Boys, 4 Seasons.

Craig Long
776 Westbrook Dr., N. Tonawanda, 14120
I collect pop, R&R, R&B, jazz, & swing from 20's to 60's. Magazines, catalogs, records.

David Michalak
26 Carhart Ave., Johnson City, 13790

Russ Mason
82 Benson Rd., Freeville, 13068
I collect pop & R&R from '55-'65. 45's & LP's. (607) 257-7765.

Paul L. Michel
9 Woodhall Ln., Clifton Park, 12065
I collect R&B, vocal groups - 50's & early 60's. Black groups & white groups.

Mike Monnat
15 Dickenson Ave., Binghampton, 13901
I collect chart records from 50's & 60's. Early R&B, orig. labels.

James M. Moyer
380 Hartford Rd., Apt. 1-C, Amherst, 14226
I collect anything from 50's & 60's. Specialize in novelty, Annette, Spike Jones, Edd (Kookie) Byrnes, colored plastic, picture sleeves, and radio station playlists.

Robert M. Murray
RR#1 Lake Shore Dr., S. Salem, 10590
I collect 45 rpm (only) R&B, R&R, doowop, Bill Haley, Buddy Holly & Fats Domino.

James E. Plessinger
14 S. Beechwood Rd., Bedford Hills, 10507
I collect s'tracks 45's, Les Paul, Michael Parks; sell or trade all other 45's; Buy or trade s'tracks, O.C.'s, TV. (914) 666-6340

William Price
Box 356, Elbridge, 13060
I collect R&B groups, early blues, & very early pop.

The Record Archive
762 Monroe Ave., Rochester, 14607
We buy & sell out-of-print records of all types. (716) 473-3820.

Mike Redmond
12 Hampton St., Hauppauge, 11787
I collect R&R, R&B 45's & LP's. Pre-'56 R&B vocal groups; girl groups from 50's to mid-60's, photos, magazines. (516) 234-3216

David A. Reiss
3920 Eve Dr., Seaford 11783
Buy & sell 78 rpm records. Popular, Jazz & Classical. Free lists. No Minimums.

Jay Repoley
45 Scarboro Ave., Staten Island, 10305
R&B groups 45's LP's & 78's. Also gospel & R&B from 30's & 40's. Mellow rock LP's & Rock LP's (Moody Blues, early Stones, Beatles, Doors, etc). 981-2550

Martin Rosen
2410 Barker Ave., Bronx, 10467

Richard R. Rosen
Box 42, Homecrest Station, Brooklyn, 11229
I collect & Sell R&B, R&R, doowops from 5-'s & 60's. Send want lists or call (212) 253-1869.

Gary Rosenowitz
902 E. 56th St., Brooklyn, 11234
I collect colored vinyl LP's. Have store Zig Zag Records, 2301 Avenue U, Brooklyn, 11229. Specialize in out-of-print LP's.

Marie E. Sadlo
9 Faye Ave., New Windsor, 12550

Vincent Sansone
47-61 196th St., Flushing, 11358
I collect Beatles, Elvis, Rock, American & British. 60's pop & rock, Left Banke, Shadows of Knight, New Colony Six Spanky & Our Gang, etc., Rock imports.

Peter T. Santacroce
Box 1592, Southampton Coll., Southampton, 11968
I collect LP's of jazz, rock, folk, SF sound, 50's jazz. Sell or trade for LP's. Have 1,000's of 50's-60's 45's, many rare 50's R&B.

Mr. Jack Schnur
41-42 Little Neck Pkwy., Little Neck, 11363
I collect s'tracks. Buy shows, Sinatra (including unreleased cuts), Also Caruso 78's rpm.

Joe Schiavone
181 C Edgewater Park, New York, 10465
I collect groups, will buy or swap all speeds.

Stuart Schneider
208 E. Broadway, New York, 10002
I collect 45's of rockabilly, novelty, comedy LP's. Would consider renting records for taping. (212) 533-3861.

Rick Shaw DWA (Doo-Wops Anonymous)
44 Strawberry Hill Ln., West Nyack, 10994
I collect 50's-60's 45's & LP's: rock, doo-wop, blues & pop folk.

David Shlosh
570 Westminster Rd., Brooklyn, 11230
I collect black vocal groups of 50's; 50's, 60's & 70's rock & pop; big band swing; s'tracks & original casts.

Alan Shutro
140 S. Ash Ave., Flusing, 11355
I deal in LP's from 50's to now; R&R, soul, rock, surf, R&R. Send SASE (large) for free list. (212) 961-4927.

Tedd Sivrais
12 Slauson Ave., Binghamton, 13905
I collect any material of Phil Spector-also hard to find rcds. by Crystals, Ronettes, Chiffons, Darlene Love, & similar girl groups. Buy & sell.

Donna Slating
10 Cochocton St., Naples, 14512

Walter Snyder
224 Jefferson Ave., Mineola, 11501
I collect R&B Black group harmony, from 50's & early 60's.

Mr. Wesley Tillman
474 W. 158th St., Apt. 44, New York, 10032
I collect R&R, R&B, pop & soul of 50's & 60's. LP's & 45's. (212) 690-2582

Stephen J. Tokash
G.P.O. Box 2302, New York, 10001
I collect Elvis & many other artists. Lots to trade & sell. Like to correspond with other collectors (domestic & overseas). All mail will be answered. Send Wants.

Frank Turner
149-36 Delaware Ave., Flusing, 11355
I collect 45's of rockabilly, R&B, R&R, C&W, southern & Chicago blues. Need back auction & sale lists, rock mags, any info on 50's & 60's rcd Co.'s or rockabilly artists.

Antonio Vasquez
1330 Wm. Floyd Pkwy., Shirley, 11967
I collect R&B & early rock from 50's. 78's & 45's. Also trade. (516) 281-2027

Greg F. Wade
297 Olean St., E. Aurora, 14052 (716) 652-4382
I collect movie posters. Rock & blues only 45's, 78's & LP's. Buy single piece or collections.

Marcus Waldman
120-18 Elgar Pl., Bronx, 10475 (212) 320-0261
I collect R&B single artists & groups from '55-65. Specialty is Jackie Wilson, Sam Cooke, Clyde McPhatter, Cadillacs, Flamingoes, etc. Also Elvis. Collect LPS, EP's & 45's. Buy, sell, trade & have recording service avail. Catalog 2.00.

Whirlin' Disc Records
230 Main St., Farmingdale, 11735

Melanie Wilson
15 Woods Rd., Islip Terrace, 11752
I collect Glen Campbell records & Barry Manilow commercials, Groucho Marx on Decca & imported ACE OF Hearts. (AH-103. (516) 277-9750

D. Wiur
41 Locust Ave., Bethpage, 11714
I collect Walker Bros., Yoko Ono, Beefheart, Nico.

Jack Wolak
Star Rt., Depeyster, 13633
I collect T.Rex 45's & EP's-all countries, all lables, Bob Dylan 45's EP's all countries. Prefer discs with pic. sleeves.

Mark Zakarin
P.O. Box 69, Bayside, 11361
I am a collector's show promoter & put out a mial-order promo list.

Edwart Zlotnick
300 W. 55th St., Rm. 16R, New York, 10019
I collect Beatles; 50's to now s'tracks, blues, Buddy Holly, LP's, EP's, 45's, pic sleeves, boots, reel orig. tapes, promo material, displays.

NORTH CAROLINA

Russell Batten
P.O. Box 516, Thomasville, 27360
I collect singles, boots, & rare material on Bob Dylan. (919) 475-9233

Wesley Brooks
680 Brentwood Ct., Winston-Salem, 27104
I collect 50's R&R, R&B; big bands; 40's & 50's C&W. 50's vocal groups, Glen Miller; send all wants. (919) 765-2537.

Robert S. Dean
243 Bedford Dr., Eden, 27288

William H. Melton
469 Rock Creek Rd., Raleigh, 27612
I collect R&R, C&W, rockabilly, R&B 45's.

Rick Scoggins
Box 12274, Charlotte, 28205
I collect Beatles everything. (704) 568-6488.

Thurman Shockley
1437 New Fagge Rd., Eden, 27288
I collect C&W, bluegrass, & R&R of 50's & 60's. (919) 627-4513

John Styers
Rt. 1, Box B-540, Statesville, 28677
I collect Beatles, Beach Boys & surfing music.

John Swain
1220 Banbury Rd., Raleigh, 27607
I collect R&B, rockabilly & pre '56 C&W. I like upbeat music with strong rhythm & lyrics. Buy sell, trade, send all lists.

Mike Valle
P.O. Box 2687, Burlington, 27215
Golden Discs Unlimited has a free catalog. We specialize in early R&R, R&B, group, rockabilly, C&W, blues, instrumentals, novelty & pop from 50's & 60's; all speeds, new & used. (919) 584-0096.

Bill Wall
309 Taft St., Eden, 27288
I collect R&R, R&B, & rockabilly LP's.

THE ELVIS SUN

Volume 1, Number 1   6 Malvern Court, Ruxton, Maryland 21204   (301) 825 6057

$ WORLD RENOWNED COLLECTOR OFFERS BIG REWARD $

DOWLING NEEDS PRESLEY RECORDS

The man responsible for Dowling's obsession.

Presley holding discs Dowling seeks.

Dowling on phone with one of his contacts.

Paul Dowling, 6 Malvern Court, Ruxton, Maryland 21204, noted worldwide Elvis Presley record collector and authority, is desperately seeking more Elvis Presley records for his collection. Anyone who might possess items like United States promotional discs or any foreign records is advised to contact him. Considered the top man in his field, Mr. Dowling has informed us that he will pay top dollar for the following Presley material:

U.S.

—MARCH OF DIMES PRESENTS ELVIS—promotional 45 r.p.m.
—TV GUIDE PRESENTS ELVIS—promotional 45.
—EPB 1035—double Xmas EP (Extended Play with picture cover).
—SPD 23—triple EP (with cover).
—SPD 15—10EP BOXED SET (entire set of 10 records plus box).
—SPD 19—8EP BOXED SET (all records plus box).
—33 R.P.M. singles numbered with a "37" prefix.
—33 R.P.M. singles in STEREO with "68" prefix.
—45 R.P.M. singles in STEREO with "61" prefix.
—SP 76—Don't/Wear My Ring (with picture cover).
—SP 139—Roustabout/One Track Heart (with picture cover).
—HO 0808—Blue Christmas promotional single.
—SUN record label 45's and 78's.
—Any 10-inch LP's (Long Plays, promotional or otherwise).
—LPM 1254—the 10-inch version (with the picture cover).
—Any triple EP's with one or more Elvis songs and picture cover.
—Any one-sided promotional singles.
—Any SP-type promotionals; any "NOT FOR SALE" record labels; dust jackets only; singles, EP's, LP's, etc., with one or more cuts by Elvis (with picture covers).
—Basically, anything unusual or of a promotional nature on Elvis.
—Unreleased songs on SUN or RCA.
—Also, tapes and films of live shows in the 50's; Louisiana Hayride; Grand Ole Opry; Dorsey Shows; Milton Berle Shows; Sinatra Show; Hawaii Benefit Show; etc.

FOREIGN

LONG PLAY'S (LP's) ESPECIALLY WANTED ARE:
—T31-077 JANIS & ELVIS 10" (South Africa).
—31-212 ELVIS PRESLEY ROCKS (South Africa).
—31.673 KING OF THE WHOLE WIDE WORLD (South Africa).
—31.118 CHRISTMAS LP (LPM 1382 picture) (South Africa).
—HEW 7605 GOLDEN HITS OF ELVIS PRESLEY (South Africa).
—LS 5048 LOVING YOU (Japan).
—LS 5086 KING CREOLE (Japan).
—LS 5038 CHRISTMAS LP (Japan).
—SHP 5494 CHRISTMAS LP (Japan).
—Any 10" Long Play's from Japan!!
—WESTERN VOL. 6 (Japan).
—SAP 3001 BEST OF ELVIS (Boxed set) (Japan).
—10" and 12" COCKTAIL LP's (Italy).
—BKL 60 ELVIS PRESLEY (Brazil).
—130.252 GOOD ROCKIN' 10" (Cartoon) (France).
—Any 10" LP's from any country except England!!

PLUS: Singles, EP's, LP's with different covers from Spain, Chile, Peru, India, Egypt, Turkey, Japan, Mexico, Brazil, New Zealand, South Africa, Italy, Germany, Bolivia, Columbia, Greece, Uruguay, etc. Would also appreciate listings of current and deleted Elvis records from these countries. Send details of whatever you have for sale/trade!!

Let me hear from you! Make a friend!

Paul Dowling

NORTH DAKOTA

Dave Baker
1102 E. 4th, W. Fargo, 58078
I collect rock, rockabilly, & R&B from 50's & 60's.

Angeline Kady
2018 University Ave., Grand Forks, 58201
I want to sell my collection of 78's from 30's to 50's; C&W, pop, rock. Also have a Wurlitzer 1015 jukebox, parts & chandelier speaker for sale.

OHIO

Terry Alexander
3361 E. High St., Springfield, 45505
I collect pop from late 50's to early '70's. Annette, Olivia Newton-John, Bee Gees, EP's & Pic. sleeves. (513) 325-8457.

Sandoll Andromeda
5048 Harbor Boulevard, Columbus, 43227
I collect Beatles records & anything assoc. with them. I will buy, sell, or trade Beatle items.

Nick Bazil
7618 Green Valley Dr., Ceveland, 44134
I collect original cast records.

George Belden
613 David Dr., Streetsboro, 44240
I collect live concert recordings.

Gary L. Cowne
840 S. Roys Ave., Columbus, 43204
I collect records, tapes & photos of Abba, Martin Muss & The Hudson Brothers.

Ted Despres
5523 Parkville St., Columbus, 43229
I collect music from mid 50's to date, pop, R&R, hard rock, some C&W mostly to mid 60's. (614) 891-9353

E. Robbie Dumoulin
1580 Ruth Dr., Wooster, 44691

Dusty Disc' Records (Chris Dodge)
P.O. Box 310, Middletown, 45042
Specializing in 45's from the 50's to present. Orig. label R&R, & rockabilly, (513) 422-7090 after 6 pm.

Mike Greenfield
148 S. Whitney St., Youngstown, 44509
I collect 60's pop; Beatles-influended harmonies, mod, punk, psychedelic, local discs. Exchange tapes of obscure rcds., concerts: send for details. (Also country music, '46-'57.

Daniel E. Howe
423 Park Ln., Walbridge, 43465
I collect R&B, R&R, Doowop & group sounds especially with heavy background.

William Johns
554 Kappler Rd., Heath, 43055
I collect 50's R&R & R&B.

J.P. Kehoe
6593 Beverly Dr., Parma Heights, 44130
I collect LP's from Dion, Beatles early-mid 60's, Calif. sounds. 78's from Hank Williams. Any hillbilly 78's from 20's, 30's & 40's.

Robert Kotabish
5667 Meadow Lane, Bedford Heights, 44146
I buy, sell, trade 4 Seasons, Frankie Valli. Also Jay & The Americans, Johnny Rivers.

Jeff Kreiter
Rt. 2, Box 113B Bellaire, 43906
I collect black vocal group sounds from '55-'63. 45's & oddball labels & bass songs.

Jerry Ladd
7255 Jethve Ln., Cincinnati, 45243
I collect Elvis, Annette, Personalities, general R&R from 50's & 60's. 45 sleeves, LP's. Must be VG or better. (513) 271-0570

Lenny Major Records
P.O. Box 706, Ashtabula, 44004
Monthly auction lists, most types of music, we buy, sell 45's/albums. Send us your want lists. "The Maestro of Music."

Dan Liberatore
4266 Noble St., Bellaire, 43906
I collect fast doowops, R&B, & slow ballads with heavy bass. 45's from '55 to '63.

H.G. Loewer
1636 Fruitland, Cleveland, 44124
Wanted: Live bootleg LP's or tapes of any rock concerts; U.S. or foreign. All inquiries answered.

John Marsh
5136 South Ave., Toledo, 43615
All 3 speeds. Buy or trade. Comedy, 50's-70's top 10, country & big bands. Want Freddy Cannon, Flying Saucers & comedy of all types.

John McCarthy
4002 Grove Ave., Cincinnati, 45227
I collect mint 45's & LP's, 78's, R&R, R&B, rockabilly, electronic music, C&W, boogie, classical, modern classic, punk, tapes, mags...& everything else you can imagine, inc. folk music from around the world.

Bob McGuiness
4305-B Cox Dr., Stow, 44224
I collect Beatles everything.

Ken McPeck
2131 Norwood Blvd., Zanesville, 43701
I collect rock, books, mags. Jan & Dean, Duane Eddy, Rick Nelson, Johnny & Hurricanes, Fabian, Frankie Avalon, Bobby Rydell. Collect books, artist & label discographies, fanzines.

Frank Merrill
Box 5693, Toledo, 43613
I collect all types of music '49-'77, esp. novelties, & am trying to get top 20 surveys from every radio station in the world that had them. I pay from $1. to $5. fro those I need, & $10.-$50. for WGN, KPOP, WOV, etc.

Marlene J. Miller
461 Harmony Ln., Campbell, 44405
I collect Frank Sinatra. (216) 755-3451.

Mary Neer
1916 Perkins Dr., Springfield, 45505
I collect all types of music, 45's, LP's & one-sided 78's.

Phillip J. Peachock
435 Lansing Ave., Youngstown, 44506

Steve Petryszyn
4347 Pearl Rd., Cleveland, 44109
My interests are white groups, Sedaka, Manilow, R&B, 5 Satins; photos.

Robert & Company
1910 Lockbourne Rd., Columbus, 43207
We deal in almost everything. Send Your Wants!

Donald Schrock
161 W. 10th Ave., Columbus, 43201
I collect movie theme LP's, 50's jazz, 50's female vocal LP's, & 50's rock instrumental LP's & 45's.

James L. Scott
12716 Speedway Overlook, E. Cleveland, 44112
I collect mostly R&B of 60's & 70's, especially mid '60's. Some rock, disco, & pop.

2nd Time Around, Record & Tape Exchange
1133 Brown St., Dayton, 45409 (513) 228-6399
Over ten thousand LP's - $1.00 or $2.00 per disc. Rock, jazz, blues, country, classical, bi-weekly collector's auction.

Larry Skillman
337 E. Water St., New Lexington, 43764
I collect R&R, Bealtes, 45's & LP's.

Joe Sloat
Box 242 Mid City Station, Dayton, 45402

Dave Sprague
4103 W-58, Cleveland, 44144
Mainly '60's material but send any rock lists. Buy-sell-trade.

Robert Stillwell
574 Abbey Pl., Zanesville, 43701
Want to sell 400 LP;s of big bands & vocalists 30's to 70's. (614) 453-6754.

Jerry Villing
8439 Livington Rd., Cincinnati, 45239
I collect rockabilly & R&B 45's. (513) 385-9733.

Vince Waldron
P.O. Box 426, Yellow Springs, 45387
We carry hard-to-find albums in factory sealed condition. Send us your want lists.

Winfred Wilhoit
6553 Elvin Ln., Hamilton, 45011
I collect R&R, C&W, s'tracks, buy, sell & trade. Send your wants!

Denny Wright
1776 Depot Rd., Salem, 44460
I collect blues, R&R, rockabilly, instrumental & English sounds of 60's. (216) 332-1252

Doug Young
6117 Larchway, Toledo, 43613
I collect rare & common R&B groups, Treat & Chance labels. Also Offbeat labels. Buy Sell & Trade.

OKLAHOMA

Tom Biddle
1150 N. Toledo, Tulsa, 74115
I collect 50's R&B groups & single artists. 45's & 78's. Prefer black groups & single artists. Trade, Buy, & sell any & all R&B & R&R 45's to '65. (918) 835-8782.

Steve Hovis
402 SW 24th St., Lawton, 73505
I collect Elvis, Jack Scott & rockabilly.

Jack L. Jones
2009 N. Osage, Ponca City, 74601
I collect R&R, rockabilly, & C&W of 50's & 60's, doowop, vocal groups LPs, 45's only, foreign labels, promos, cassettes. (405) 762-6134.

Kerry Kudlacek
4909 S. Braden, 13-E, Tulsa, 74135
I collect mostly LP's of folk, blues, rock, comedy & ragtime.

Terry Radcliff
3401 E. 40th Tulsa, 74135
I collect Bing Crosby, Sarah Vaughn, Ella Fitzgarald-LP's & EP's.

Cliff Robnett
7600 NW 25 Terr., Bethany, 73008
I collect early 50's & 60's 45's. Doowop, Beatles, Beach Boys, Elvis, Carl Perkins, & pic sleeves. Will trade mid 60's & earlier for my wants. (405) 787-6703

OREGON

Ken Costello
2840 River Rd., Eugene, 97404
I collect all sound and all speeds of all categories. I deal in records & have more than 50,000 for sale. (503) 688-5590.

Berne Greene
1833 S.E. 7th Ave., Portland, 97214, (503) 232-5964
Rock & soul, pop, 45's LP's, promotional concert movie posters, over 40,000 rcds. in stock. Your wants welcomed. Send for big free rock catalog.

Van Kennell
600 Florence Ave., Astoria, 97103

Butch MacKimmie
206 N. Evans, McMinnville, 97128
I collect rock & jazz, Bealtes, fifties, big band transcriptions.

Craig Moerer
P.O. Box 13247, Portland, 97213
I collect rockabilly, blues, C&W, groups, Quarterly lists sent on request. I buy collections.

Mark K. O'Neil
5518 S.E. 47th Ave., Portland, 97206
I collect ate 60's, early 70's domestic & imported out-of-print LP's, colored vinyl, mellotronic, & esoteric rock is a specialty. Albums only! (503) 774-1411

Keith Pridie
6685 SW Sagert #94, Tualatin, 97062
I collect Beatles.

Richard L. Reese
11403 S.E. Stanley, Milwaukie, 97222
I collect R&R '54-'70: Rick Nelson, Elvis, Beach Boys, Jan & Dean, Beatles.

Shirley Voit
Box 804, 305 E St. Apt. #3, Eugene, 97477
I collect s'tracks, LP only & vocals & instrumentals.

PENNSYLVANIA

Arnold Amber
P.O. Box 153, Lemont Furnace, 15456
I collect '59 thru '63, especially The Lettermen, 4 Seasons & early Beach Boys.

Arboria-Used Books & Records
151 S. Allen St., State College, 16801
LP's only of R&R, jazz, blues, classical. Buy, sell, trade. (814) 237-7624.

Frank Armbruster
306 Grant St., Olyphant, 18447
Sell & trade R&R, R&B, folk, jazz, C&W. Want lists welcomed (717) 489-8991

Rick Balsley
435 N. Walnut St., Wernersville, 19565
Have thousands of 45's (R&B, R&R) willing to sell or trade inc. Beatles. All Elvis collector's & traders please write. Collect C. Stevens, Springsteen, Beatles.

Robert M. brown
P.O. Box 124, Highspire, 17034
I collect LP Albums, easy listening, C&W, big bands, personalities, comedy: Homer & Jethro, Spike Jones, Stan Freberg, Hoosier Hot Shots, Jonathan Winters, etc.

Jim Burleigh
207 Williams St., Towmand, 18848
I collect hits from 50's & 60's. Original labels or reissues.

Bob & Patty Campbell
157 Windsor Ave., Lansdowne, 19050
I collect 40's & 50's New York white group sounds, Beatles & record books.

Dave Chamberlain
R.D. Box 54, Covington, 16917
Anything & everything by Golden Earring, 45's, EP's & LP's by The Sensational Alex Harvey Band & Alex Harvey & His (Big) Soul Band, & tapes by Earwigs, Spiders I Nazz.

Joseph Conti
514 Briarwood Rd., Glenside, 19038
I collect 60's rock: Rolling Stones, Beach Boys, Phil Spector, Garland Jeffries, Denny Laine.

Ken Clee
Stak-O-Wax, P.O. Box 11412, Philadelphia, 19111
I collect 45's from 50's & 60's, R&R, R&B, pic sleeves, doowops; send lists. I deal in all types of music; have discographies of more than 300 artists & labels.

Floyd Copeland
13 Briarwood Rd., Shrewsbury, 17361
I Collect R&B, R&R, rockabilly from 50 to 64. Will buy, trade or sell. Have 1,000's of records after '65-send want list.

Bob Cowan
P.O. Box 8803, Pittsburge, 15221
I collect R&R & R&B from '53-'60; 45's only.

Anne Cramer
223 Elbridge St., Philadelphia, 19111
I deal in 45's & LP's of the 50's & 60's.

Frank Czuri
11403 Althea Rd., Pittsburgh, 15235
I collect male R&B group sounds up to '60's. Gospel groups also.

Edward J. Deem, Jr.
Rd. #1, P.O. Box 73, Industry, 15052
I collect 60's & 70's R&R, R&B, LP's & 45's. Beatles esp. Custom cassettes, buy, sell, trade, early Lennon material wanted.

The Duke
256 Martsolf Ave., Pittsburgh, 15229
FOR SALE: Rare, out-of-print, mint & used LP's. Most categories. $5.00 each plus postage. Catalog $1.00 (Refundable with order). U.S. only.

Lawrence R. Eckert
28 Elmwood St., Pittsburgh, 15205
I collect 50's rock, Buddy Holly, Eddy Cochran, Gene Vincent, etc.

Bob Emery
92 Carol Ln., Richboro, 18954
I collect R&B, R&R, rockabilly 45's from 50's & 60's. Any Guy Mitchell, Marty Robbins 45's. I also collect old radios.

John Evans
2113 Dalton St., McKeesport, 15132
I collect **anything** on Aerosmith, The Runaways, The Chain Reaction. (412) 678-1251

Walt Fisch
712 Picnic Ln., Selinsgrove, 17870
I collect almost anything from 50's & 60's. Specializing in blues, R&B vocal groups & Beatles. Am always willing to trade from my 4000 + collection. (717) 784-2065.

Russel Forsythe
428 Eberhart Rd., Butler, 16001
I collect 60's & 70's rock groups & solo artists 45's & albums. Also am interested in 78's made in different colors plus Teen Mags, 16, Tiger Beat, Flip, etc.

James E. Fries
2206 Evergreen Rd., Pittsburgh, 15209
Elvis & Bealtes, rockabilly & R&R sounds of the 50's. Buy, sell, & trade.

Bob Gallo
P.O. Box 246, Hatfield, 19440
I collect New Orleans R&B, R&R groups, rockers, rockabilly, blues: Smiley Lewis, Prof. Longhair, Charms, Spaniels, Shirley Lee, Willie Eagen; early recds. on Imperial, & Post-colony bayou labels. I buy collections (215) 855-6074

Edward F. Gardner
5 Rodney Rd., Rosemont 19010
I tape 78's 1900-1955. C&W, blues, jazz, pop, vocal, big bands, I pay $$ for tapes of your records. Send for my want list.

Rich Gazak
321 Stevens St., Philadelphia, 19111
I collect Elvis, Beatles, dj copies of any R&R, R&B artist from 50's & 60's, Philly & New York groups, doowop, colored wax. All speeds.

Galen George
709 Napoleon St., Johnstown, 15905
I collect orig. 45's & 78's from 50's & 60's R&R, R&B groups will buy, sell & trade. Want lists invited.

Robert Gibson
6325 Greene St., Philadelphia, 19144
I collect porno covers (Boxer, Blind Faith), movie stars (Jane Marilyn, Gina, etc.), bop, but mainly R&B & R&R of black & white artists. Buy, trade, LP's ONLY.

Larry M. Goldstein
307 Ridgeway St., Philadelphia, 19116

Mark Hennessy
53 E. Chelton Rd., Parkside, 19015
I collect R&R 50's - '62. Buy & swap. 45's only. Many duplicates. Exchange lists. Some country.

Ted Hesbacher
3007 Elliott Ave., Willow Grove, 19090
I collect reocrds, LP's of 50's & 60's, R&R & R&B. I'll trade 45's for LP's or comics.

Wayne Hinsley
226 N. Main St., Butler, 16001 (412) 283-9065
I collect slow R&B, basically 45's & 78's. DJ Stormy Weather, 5 Sharps 45's.

C.E. Hockenbroht
P.O. Box 484, Sunbury, 17801
I collect all music from 30's to 50's. Anything on Spike Jones. I have all speeds & types from 1900 to now-sell or trade for Spike Jones.

Robert E. Hosie
139 Cranbrooke Dr., Coraopolis, 15108
I collect 45's, LP's, 78's all types. Interested in easy listening esp. J. Mathis, Tommy Edwards, Joni James. Will buy, sell or trade. Approx. 10,000 in collection.

Gary Jaffe
Box 18085, Philadelphia, 19148
I collect R&R & R&B from 50's to early 60's & music mags. I also sell records & will accept wants of the Beatles, Elvis & others from '55 to now.

Carl Janusek
1123 Grant Ave., Duquesne, 15110
I collect R&B vocal groups from 50's. Pop groups also: Hilltoppers, 4 Aces, 4 Voices, 4 Lads. (412) 466-7211.

Peter Jensen
Frankford Station, Rt. 14, Philadelphia, 19124
I collect jazz, 50's R&R, bebop inc. Charlie Parker, Dizzy Trombone records, Little Richard, Elvis, Jerry Lee, Sun label, satire mags: 50's-60's Mad, Panic, Help, Playboy, etc.

Michael H. Johnson
15 Grant St., Cokeburg, 15324

Robert Jucknewich
685 Richmond Dr., Sharon, 16146 (412) 981-2794
I collect LP's & 45's of C&W, rock, & instru. oldies. Esp. Ral Donner, Jack Scott, Hank Snow & Johnny Maddox. Send your want lists & ask for mine.

Ted Kacmarik
1523 Oneida Dr., Clairton, 15025
I collect R&R & RIB 45's, EP's, LP's.

Walter M. Keepers, Jr.
6341 Glenlock St., Philadelphia, 19135
I collect bands & singers of 30's & 40's like Boswell Sisters, Annette Hanshaw, etc. Also radio broadcasts on tape of big bands & singers.

David Lee Klees
89 Drinker St., Bloomsburg, 17815
I collect R&R, jazz, blues; esp. pre '64 rock, British Invasion, R&B, pop & 20's & 30's jazz. (717) 784-2004.

Robert G. Kokstein
4905 Quince Dr., Reading, 19606
I collect 45's & LP's of 50's & 60's & Phil Spector, J. Scott, Wanda Jackson, Randy/Rainbows.

Larry's Records
Box 86, Soudersburg, 17577
I collect rcds from 50's & early 60's. R&B & R&R groups, 45's & 78's. I buy, sell & trade rcds. Also collect 8 X 10 glossys of vocal groups.

Sherry McCabe
2 Pierce St., Wellsboro, 16901
Anything & everything by the Bee Gees, & Andy Gibb, inc. tapes & memorabilia.

Archie McCoy
1509 Kinsdale St., Philadelphia, 19126
I collect R&B vocal groups & jazz singers.

Thomas Merkel
R.D. #1 Box 180, New Hope, 18938
I collect R&B, R&R from 50's & 60's - Particularly group sounds.

Mrs. Lesley I. Minnig
695 Cherry Tree Rd., Aston, 19014

Joseph A. Morinelli
901 Fairfax Rd., Drexel Hill, 19026
I collect R&B singles & promotional disco releases 12" & special interest discs.

Mr. & Mrs. William F. Muller
2156 Garfield Ave., West Lawn, 19609
I collect R&B, R&R - '51 to '65. Buy, sell, & trade. I collect Jimmy Reed & novelty (Freeberg, Seville, Goodman, Nervous Norvous, etc.)

Lee Nichols
1714 Nevada St., Pittsburgh, 15218
I collect US, British blues/rock. Clapton, Buchanan, many other lead guitarists, obscure tracks, session work, DJ's, discographies. (412) 243-0882

Paul Nowicki
520 Lancaster Ave., Lancaster, 17603
I collect Elivs & Beatles 45 rpm rcds. 50's-60's pop, R&B, R&R. Pic sleeves. Vogue picture records (78's) Want lists welcome.

John Okolowicz
836 Sunnyside Ave., Audubon, 19407

Tony Pallatto
1013 Larimer Ave., Ext, Turtle Creek, 15145
R&B from 50's, 60's, LP's, ocapello, Memorabilia of early 50's groups, photos, posters, R&R programs, picture sleeves, etc.

J. A. Panarello
442 Blvd. Ave., Dickson City, 18519

John Politis
966 N. Randolph, Philadelphia, 19123
I collect rock & country sheet music & imports. Buy, sell, or trade.

Charles Reinhart
1616 Robert Rd., Lancaster, 17601
I collect rock & soul 45's, LP's: Beatles, Apple records. Buy & sell. (717) 299-4275

Revolver (Max Shenk)
304 Glendale St., Carlisle, 17013, (717) 243-4361
Want to buy Beatles, Beach Boys LP's & 45's, post-'65 Capitol & Reprise singles, Jan & Dean, Jan Berry, Jan & Dean on Dore, I publish "Revolver" a Beatles Fanzine.

Foster J. Ritchie, Jr.
62 Seminary Pl., Forty Fort, 18704
I collect colored vinyl. Either solid or multi-colored. Also old LP's & singles by The Ventures & any 12" Disco 45 singles.

Robert Rooney
435 Bartlett Ave., Ridley Park, 19078
I collect all speeds & tapes of big band & popular music from 30's to '60. Old-time radio shows, too. Will swap tapes with collector.

Craig Satinsky
1029 Fanshawe St., Philadelphia, 19111
I collect what you want. 1,000's of LP's, 50's to 70's. Send wants. (215) 725-1948

Tony Sberna
4057 Cabinet St., Pittsburgh, 15224
Have old 45 rpm records for sale from early 60's & 50's. Flamingos, Hank Ballard, Bo Diddley, Coasters, etc.

Phil Schwartz
6024 N. Warnock St., Philadelphia, 19141
I collect all types of records from '49 to now. Esp. promo copies, 50's R&B, 50's rockabilly.

Max H. Shenk
304 Glendale St., Carlisle, 17013
I collect Beatles, Post-'66 Beach Boys & Beatles/Beach Boys pic sleeves, promo records. Also Elvis EP's in VG or better condition. (717) 243-4361

Harris Sherman
1211 Valley Rd., Lancaster, 17603
I collect anything on Beatles: inc. all emmorabilia, & material on individual Beatles after the breakup. Also anything to do with the Monkees.

Alice & Jesse Simon
P.O. Box 152, Friedens, 15541

Andrew P. Smith
R. D. 3, Box 268, Dillsburg, 17019

Spencer Smith
Box 139, R.D. #4, Mountain Top, 18707
I collect Buddy Holly, Elvis, Johnny Maestro, Ray eterson.

Marilyn Sontheimer
3532 Hazel, Erie, 16508
Wanted: Anything on Elvis Presley.

Joseph Stokes
P.O. Bx 1323, Mechanicsburg, 17055
Buy, sell & trade 45's & LP's. 50's-60's. Low Price cut out LP's for sale or trade. Send your wnat lists.

Henry Sultner
RD #2, Landfill Rd., Felton, 17322
I collect only 45's of R&R & R&B & am a Gone label enthusiast & specialist.

Ken Sweigart
Box 29, Paradise, 17562
I collect all pop music since '20 inc. R&B & C&W; s'tracks, I collect everything *except* Anita Bryant & Charles Manson. (717) 687-6414

Sam Vetovich
1308 W. Willow St., Shamokin, 17872
I collect David Cassidy, Elton John, Tanya Tucker, John Denver, Lesley Duncan, Jim Croce, Olivia Newton-John, Too Morrow & La Costa.

Jerry Wasserman
4712 Holly Circle, Harrisburg, 17110

Tom Welcomer
143 Nissley Str., Middletown, 17057
Buy or trade for Elvis memorabilia; records preferred, but others desirable. Small collection, also must be postpaid. Albums or 45's or 78's. Send Want List.

Robert Wielgus
1233 S. 7th St., Philadelphia, 19147
I collect live tapes, photos & articles on the Beach Boys, 4 Seasons & Annette. Also want sheet music & promo material.

Bill Wolf
P.O. Box 426, Trexlertown, 18087
I collect British 60's & 70's rock. Beatles, (worldwide), London label, Capitol-Canadian label.

Mike Zahorchak
RD #3, Garvin Rd., Evans City, 16033
I collect 45's & 78's of R&R, R&B of the 50's & early 60's. To trade or sell. No list available. Send wants.

RHODE ISLAND

Anthony Andreozzi
34 Whitehall St., Providence, 02909
I deal in R&R, C&W, movies. Prefer personalities such as Marilyn Monroe, Brigitte Bardot, Sophia Loren, Doris Day, etc. Buy, sell, trade all types. Wants welcome.

Dick Chester
15 Centennial St., Warwick, 02886
I collect 45's from 50's & early 60's. R&B & R&R. (401) 738-7253

Gary Monnier
20 Shady Lea Rd., North Kingstown, 02852
V. Pres.; Frankie Valli/Four Seasons International Organization.

Harvey S. Simon
83 Ninth St., Providence 02906
I collect R&R, R&B, rockabilly, motion picture & broadway s'tracks. I buy & sell 50's & 60's RIR, etc.

Frank A. Watson
575 Dyer Ave., Apt M59, Cranston, 02920

SOUTH CAROLINA

Leroy C. Brown, Jr.
518 Audubon Circle, Belvedere, 29841
Interested in folk music, 50's & 60's. War movie s'tracks, historical spoken work & music. Have lots of punk rock & rock music to trade. LP's only.

James C. Davis
110 Lanceway Dr., Mauldin, 29662
I collect R&B & rockabilly 45's, LPs & EPs with covers in VG or better to mint condition. 50's to early 60's. (803) 288-0424.

Larry Jones
48 Appaloosa Dr., Greenville, 29611
I collect 50's oldies, Elvis. Buy, trade. (803) 295-1374.

Ken Neilson
614 Periwinkle Ct., Sumter, 29150
I collect LP's only of Bob Dylan, Frank Zappa & Jimi Hendrix.

Harold J. Newton
7 June Ln., Greenville, 29605

Rich's Record Exhange
4812 Main St., Columbia, 29203

Record Showcase
P.O. Box 146, Goose Creek, 29445
We deal in Elvis records, rockabilly, R&R, R&B from 50's & 60's Send wants. Buy, sell & trade. (803) 553-1991.

Harold L. Swafford
1413 Calhoun, St. Columbia, 29201
I collect R&B LP's. (803) 779-5057 or 754-7903.

Dave Wernick
P.O. Box 28485, Furman University, Greenvi-le, 29613
I collect mainly 45's-looking for 50's R&B, rockabilly, novelty records, etc. & chart singles through '69.

TENNESSEE

Patricia A. Bailey
334 Waterloo St., Lawrenceburg, 38464
Anything concerning Elvis, I'll buy. (615) 762-4423.

Christopher Eckert
241 Cherokee Rd., Nashville, 37205
Beatle Collector-Want 61-62 German Polydor "Tony Sheridan & The Beat Brothers." Love Me Do (version 1) Parlophone R 4949. (615) 297-0721

General S. Gentry
Rt. #1, Norris Freeway, Powell, 37849 (615) 922-8653
I collect C&W: Hank Thompson, anything of him such as books pictures, etc. Jim Reeves, Chet Atkins, Faron Young, Eddy Arnold, Ernest Tubb, Carl Smith, Roy Acuff, etc.

The Great Escape
1919 Division, Nashville, 37203
I collect Beatles, Presley, Orlons, Marcels, all collectables.

Bennie Hess
1106-18th Ave., S., Nashville, 37212
Have for sale a couple of 78 rpm very rare picture rcds. of Jimmie Rodgers; on RCA Victor label. Were purchased in Lubbock, TX 45 yrs. ago & are in mint condition.

Barry Mayer
P.O. Box 23504, Nashville, 37202
I collect 60's British & US rock LP's: Kinks, Beau Brummels, Left Bank, 10CC, Beatles, Beach Boys, Bee Gees, Easybeats, Harpers Bizarre. I deal in 60's rcds. Send for free list, & send wants.

Ed. F. Rupp
Greenwood Dr., Rt. 10, Fairview Hts., Maryville, 37801
I collect mid & late 50's & early 60's top forty. American Bandstand music.

Shiloh Music Center
5001 Lebanon Rd., Old Hickory, 37138
Buy, sell, trade used LP Records. (615) 758-9437.

Ernest Tucker
Box 251, Fayetteville, 37334

TEXAS

Jean Brown
3114 Redfield, Pasadena, 77503 (713) 472-0952
Elvis collector-Anything, everything. All things on Elvis! Records & memorabilia. Buy, sell & trade. Call before 9 C.S.T. Also collect 50's rockabilly, R&B, & R&R.

Billie Buck
4805 Stevens, Ft. Worth, 76114
I collect western, cajun, swing, rockabilly, R&B, Texas R&R, like Milton Brown, Wills, Doug Samm, New Orleans & other Louisiana artists. Will buy, or have s'tracks for trade. (817) 737-5992.

J.J. Cantini, Jr.
7301-Broadway #B-102, Galveston, 77550
I collect chart (45's) & obscure, post 60 LP's. Early black sounds 45 & LP's.

Edy J. Chandler
Box 20664, Houston, 77025
I collect Beatles, Rolling Stones, E.L.P., Nice & Led Zeppelin items. Juke box 33 1/3's, promos, rare discs, mags., store displays, anything unique.

Ralph DeWitt
4423 38th St., Lubbock, 79414, 792-0837
I collect R&R LP's & 45's in 50's & 60's.

L.R. Docks
P.O. Box 13685, San Antonio, 78213
I collect early jazz, blues, C&W, R&R, R&B, rockabilly all speeds. Write for rockabilly list. Will travel to purchase collections. (512) 341-0978

Carl L. Echols, Jr.
5800 Goliad Ave., Dallas, 75206
I collect western swing, bluegrass: Bob Wills, Bill Boyd, Milton Brown, Light Crust Doughboys, Spade Cooley, trad. bluegrass. 78's, LP's, reel & cassette, also radio shows.

Zenda Eby
P.O. Box 6220, Lubbock, 79413
I deal in 78's from 1904-'56 & R&R, Pop & C&W 45's. Send lists. Catalog $1.00

Thomas C. Goodell
6505 Westheimer #357, Houston, 77057
I collect national & regional chart records 50's to now, groups records & all time hit surveys & year end surveys (esp. 55-65), from stations in US. (713) 781-7557.

R.B. Griffith
2633 Brookview, Plano, 75074
I specialize in 50's R&B.

Frank Haecker
423 Woodcrest Dr. (45-2), San Antonio, 78209
Rock record rarities; 13th Floor Elevators, International Artists, punk, Texas music, 50's & 60's & 70's. Bargain prices! Free set sale/auction list!! Write today. Satisfaction guaranteed!

Howell's Nostalgic Antiques (Mr. & Mrs. Arthur Howell)
Box 179-Highway 90, Nome, 77629
Old Time 78's, 10" & 12". New/O,S

Cathy Hudson
P.O. Box 574, Winnsboro, 75494
Country music, early R&R, Waylon Jennings, Johnny Paycheck, Glaser Brothers, Buddy Holly & Crickets, Ray Price. Wish to start a fan club for the Outlaws (Waylon, Willie, etc.) (214) 342-5679

Jerry Knight
Rt. 3, Box 343 K, Ft. Worth, 76140
I collect mostly 45's, 50-65, R&B, pop, some C&W.

Richard A. Lattanzi
P.O. Box 3672, Arlington, 76010

251

I run Connoisseurs Groove Originals & deal in R&R, R&B, rockabilly. 50's-65.

Gilbert Lopez
819 Saldana, San Antonio, 78225

W. Stanton Meals
202 Bellevue Dr., Cleburne, 76031
I collect 30's, 40's, 50's pop; 50's & 60's R&B & R&R. (817) 645-7839.

Scott Moseley
9203 Kristin Dr., Houston, 77031
I collect Elvis & 4- other rockabilly & R&R artists. I trade & sell. I collect 45's, LP's & tapes. (713) 771-6299 or 945-6078.

Jim Morris
322 Recoleta Ave., Apt. 417, San Antonio, 78216
I am interested in R&B, rock, surf, rock s'tracks & posters. LP's, 45's 78's - I buy, sell & trade (512) 826-3464.

New England Records
Drawer 520, Stafford, 77477
"Hank The Drifter" cassettes, "Tribute to Hank Williams" $5.09, 8 songs, album. 45's $1.00.

Roscoe B. Norman
Rt. 1, Box 214, Breckenridge, 76024
I collect & possible trade Roy Acuff, Ernest Tubb, Texas Ruby, Slim Rinehardt, Cousin Ford Lewis, Slim Willet, Wesley Tuttle, 78-or early 45.

Olympic Records
Box 1323, Alvin, 77511
We have auction & set sale lists. Olympic label has Jack Earls, Johnny Powere, Jimmy Carroll, Jack Scott, & others. (713) 331-1326.

Terry A. Parkening
U of T Medical Branch, Box 129, Galveston, 77550
I collect 50's & 60's R&B, R&R, rockabilly, 45's, EP's, LP's of Buddy Holly, Eddie Cochran, D. Hawkins, Vincent, D. Eddy, vocal groups, C. Berry, F. Domino. Buy, sell, trade.

Ram Rocha
4001 Woodcraft, Houston, 77025, (713) 661-4414

Gerry Rosamond
122 S. Westmoreland, Dallas, 75211
I collect all varieties from 50's. I deal in pop, RIR, old cylinders, through '65. 78's, 45's & LP's.

Scott Sayers
7219 Colgate, Dallas, 75225
I collect Sinatra.

Sinatra Society of America
P.O. Box 10512, Dallas, 75207
New Members welcomed. Dues $7.00 US, $8.50 foreign. Bi-monthly newsletter, annual convention. Please write!

Ed Smith
P.O. Box 3380, El Paso, 79923
I got what you need! Send now for a free list of rare & quasi-rare records from 50's & 60's

Joe Specht
Box 237, McMueey Station, Abilene, 79605
I collect C&W 45's & LP's from 40's to now. Some 50's & 60's R&R. (915) 677-5178

John I. Taylor
3317 Reed St., Ft. Worth, 76119
I buy & sell all types & speeds of records. I service want lists from more than a million records.

Robert W. Whitby
421 Celeste St., Everman, 76140
I collect easy listening, C&W, novelty: Ray Anthony, Percy Faith, James Last, Spike Jones, Stan Freberg, Alan Sherman. Please send auctions. (817) 293-4106

Evelyn Wray
925 Beachum St., Arlington, 76011
I deal in rock & country from 50's & 60's. 45's & LP's. Send your want lists. (817) 275-2294.

Wayne Zotopek
P.O. Box 598, Hurst, 76053
I collect R&R, C&W, blues, rockabilly, & Texas labels: Tex-Mex, LP's, R&B.

UTAH

Barbara McGurk
3347 Plaza Way, Salt Lake City, 84109
I collect R&B, doowop, jazz, early jazz pianists, jazz vocalists, and any category of well-performed music, any year.

VERMONT

John Jennings
Box 72, Richford, 05476
I collect big band, jazz & swing music from 30's-40's & 50's & 50's R&R, especially.

VIRGINIA

Lynn Abbott
100 N. Crenshaw Ave., Apt. 1, Richmond, 23221
I collect post-war blues, New Orleans R&B, post-war cajun & Zydeco, & bluegrass, on 78 rpm **only.**

Robert Mike Arbogast
P.O. Box 483, Covington, 24426
I collect R&R, rockabilly, doowop: Buddy Holly, Elvis, Earls, Dion & Belmonts.

David Bernard
5269 Balfor Dr., Virginia Beach, 23462
I collect 40's & 50's vocal group & R&B 78's. Also comedy & novelty singles 1900-1960.

Larry Blevins
8436 Rugby Rd., Manassas, 22110
I collect C&W, 50's, eearly 60's R&R, bluegrass, male solo artists: Jack Scott, Terry Stafford & Johnny Rivers.

Ed Caffey, 3rd
1830 Banning Rd., Norfolk, 23518
I collect late 40's & early 50's pop & some western, boogie-woogie, & rag on orig. labels (45) only. Earlies Mills Bros., Teresa Brewer, Jo Stafford, Fontane Sisters, Piano Red & Sons of Pioneers.

William H. Colhoun
109 49th St., Virginia Beach, 23451
I collect old classical & Dixieland jazz, blues from 30's, 40's, & most of all 20's. Also big bands of 30's, 40s & 50s. Please no R&R or soul. Esp. Tiny Hil Rcds., Cliff Edwards & Wendal Hall.

Jimmy Cole & The Roadmasters
13408 Bristol Rd., Nokesville, 22123 (703) 791-3307

DeLoatch Music Services
P.O. Box 724, Portsmouth, 23705
Specialize in hard-to-find R&B 78's, 45's, LP's, have in stock over 15,000 re-issues-10,000 78's & 45's. 5,000 LP's re-issues C&W, R&B, always specials on 78's.

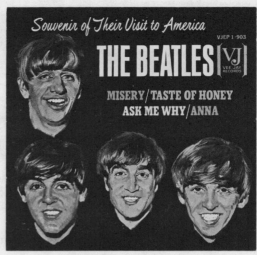
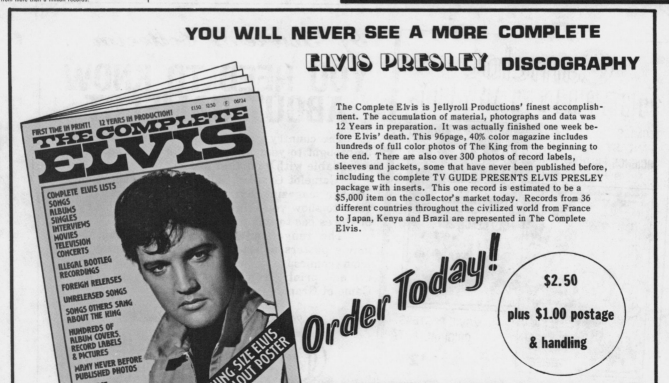

Gay K. Dooley
2604 Hillcrest Ave. NW, Roanoke, 24012

David E. Dzula
Rt. 1, Box 155F, West Point, 23181
Rolling Stones Bootlegs, promos, rare LP's, memorabilia & live/studio tapes. I have a wants list, will trade or buy merchandise from dealers/collectors alike.

Don Gleason
P.O. Box 166, Spotsylvania, 22553
I collect Elvis, Johnny Cash on Sun, any other Suns. Have many misc. records for sale. (703) 972-7620.

Mrs. Francy Glessner
Greenview Farm Rt. 2, Warrenton, 22186
I collect anything & everything on Elvis. (703) 439-8646.

Gina Gustin
9008 Robson Dr., Manassas, 22110
I collect any Jethro Tull bootlegs, photos, articles, etc. (703) 361-4735

Mike Hanlon
13448 Nystrom Ct., Woodbridge, 22193
Rockability: Sun & Phillips & anything related to them. 78's, 45's, boots & originals, LP's & imports. Also records produced by Phil Spector (703) 590-5064.

Mark F. Hoback
937 N. Madison St., Arlington, 22205

Maranatha Memory Lane Records
12592 Warwick Blvd., Newport News 23606
Buy, Sell, Trade. Sent price, Auctions. 200,000 45's, 78's, LP's in stock. All types of music (804) 595-5709.

Henry L. McCorkle
1121 First St., SW #11, Roanoke, 24016
I collect early black groups: Ink Spots, Mills Bros., Deep River Boys, Red Caps, Delta Rhythm Boys, & others.

Lynn McCutcheon
753 Old Waterloo Rd., Warrenton, 22186
I collect R&B, black vocal groups. I want to buy, trade & sell 45's & LP's. (703) 347-7618.

Sandi Lee McFadden
14582D Olde Court House Way, Newport News, 23602

Thomas A. Norris
2624 Memorial St., Alexandria, 22306
50's & 60's R&R and R&R wanted. Some 30's & 40's popular and C&W wanted. Send for my want list.

Austin Pankey
203 Westburg Dr., Lynchburg, 24502
I collect R&R, R&B from late 50's on. Esp. LP's (804) 237-3365.

C.R. Perdue, Sr.
3551 Over Brook Dr., SW, Roanoke, 24018
Sun records for sale. I also have 1,400 old movie posters from 30's to 50's for sale. Westerns, serials, etc.

The Record Box International
P.O. Box 4008, Petersburg, 23803
We buy & sell all types & speeds of records, R&R, R&B, C&W, jazz, classical, orig. casts, s'tracks etc.

Record & Tape Exchange
821 N. Taylor St., Arlington, 22203

Don Riswick
1105-Gaston Ct., Chesapeake, 23323
My collecting interests are Buddy Holly, rock & surf instrumentals & Atlantic label.

Robert Bruce Taylor
2514 N. 12 St., Arlington Co, 22201
I collect early C&W & R&R. Esp. Hank Snow. I also sell 8 track recordings of anything I have. Send want lists. Also Al Jolson.

Don Thore
3200 Jackson Rd., Hopewell, 23860
Wanted: Anything on Sun label. Also C&W 78's.

Dennis W. West
P.O. Box 489, Roanoke, 24153 (703) 389-1982.
Have largest collector record store in southeast US. All types bought & sold. Specialize in '50's blues & rockabilly. Have many rare s'tracks & personalities.

Ernie White
Box 9637, Richmond, 23228

Charles D. Young
185 Colburn Dr., Manassas Park, 22110
I collect R&R LP's & 45's, tapes, related items. Mugwumps, Beefeaters, Hawks, etc. Live Lovin' Spoonful tapes. Promo of Springsteen's "The Fever" (703) 361-7762.

WASHINGTON

Timothy B. Anderson
71 Harbor VW. Pl., Friday Harbor, 98250
Albums from Allman to Zappa.

Kip Ayers
205 A N. 63rd Ave., Yakima, 98908
I collect all Elvis, Beatles & Beach Boys.

Beatles For Sale, U.S.A.
P.O. Box 132, Spokane, 99211
Specializing in Apple records, rare records, 8 & 16mm Beatles films, albums & 45's, etc.

Harry L. Balisure
4634 B. Redwood, Tacoma, 98439
I collect Beatle & Apple records. Main interest in 45's with pic. sleeves. Also sell at reasonable prices using this book as a price guide. (206) 584-6047

Rich Clark
P.O. Box 4722, Vancouver, 98662
Led Zeppelin, Yardbirds, Todd-Nazz memorabilia wanted. Send want lists of any 60's-70's R&R records.

Vicky Colgrove
27822 Pacific Hwy. S., Kent, 98031
Over 1800 45's. buy-sell-trade. Original labels-Original artists, 1949-now.

Les Derby
4546 S. 7th St., Tacoma, 98405
I collect 50's & early 60's-R&R, R&B, rockabilly, all Elvis, and doowop. Buy, sell, or trade. (206) 752-0636.

David Gregg Elford
801 N. Garrison Rd., Bldg. #2, Vancouver, 98664
Any records, Armed Servie or other transcripts, public service spots, or radio shows pertaining to Bob Hope...Also with Dean Martin, Groucho, Jimmy Stewart.

John Fisher
9219 40th Ave., E., Tacoma, 98446

Sue Frederick
#3, 13703 J. St., S., Tacoma, 98444
Buddy Holly, Valens, Bopper, covers of Holly songs, Crickets, Doors, 50's rock & whatever strikes my fancy. Will trade cassettes.

Wes Geesman
4141 University Way, NE, Seattle, 98105
100,000 records, all speeds, tapes, memorabilia, posters for sale. 2nd Time Around Records & Roxy Music. Largest used record operation north of L.A.!

Ed Y. Guanco
15113 122nd Ct., NE, Kirkland, 98033

Bill Hansen
P.O. Box 7113, Tacoma, 98407
I collect Paul McCartney & Wings: Promo material, concert tapes, photos, unusual items; also Beatle pic sleeves, memorabilia, promo material.

Gerald B. Johnson
11416 Rainier Ave., S. Lot 1, Seattle 98178
I collect Beatle rarities like Butcher cover & other early recordings & 60's rock & roll rarities, British Invasion.

Karavan Records
W416 Greta, Spokane, 99208
Buy, sell & trade R&R, R&B, country 45's & LP's, Send want lists. Request to be put on monthly auction list.

Don Kirsch
806 S. Fife, Tacoma, 98405
I collect rockabilly & R&R. Buy, sell, trade. I also deal, & have periodic auctions.

Rich Koch
19302 Auroa Dr., E., Spanaway, 98387
I collect rockabilly, R&R, & pop

Larry J. Long
11504 20th St., NE, Lake Stevens, 98258
Am mostly interested in good R&R from '55 to now; punk or hard rock, Frankie Avalon to Led Zepplin. All except C&W & classical.

Thomas J. Meenach III
E 1721-58th, Spokane, 99205
I am a Beatle collector. Many items for sale & trade. Want: rare interview records/bootlegs. (509) 448-1814.

Mr. Randall C. Nutter
P.O. Box 2130, Spokane, 99210

The Old Curiosity Shop
N 705 Monroe, Spokane, 99201
Specializing in Elvis records & memorabilia. Buy, sell & trade. Also 50's R&R. Wanted: Elvis foreign discs & unusual promo items.

Gary Oswold
10715 24 SW, Seattle, 98146
I collect Elvis, Fats Domino. (206) 246-2916.

Bob Pegg
8420 S. 16th St., Tacoma, 98465
I collect white New York area group rcds. from 57-64. Also Beach Boys & 4 Seasons soundalikes. If you have quantities of these, please get in touch with set-sale list or request my wants. 45's only.

Skip Piacquaeio, Jr.
13826 116th Pl., NE, Kirkland, 98033
I collect R&R, country, R&B: Buddy Holly, Slim Whitman.

Mark Plummer
1666 Larch Dr., Oak Harbor, 98277
I run Ripped Baggies Fan Club (Jan & Dean, Papa Doo Run Run, etc.). Record, tapes, t-shirts for sale; periodic auctions & newsleters. I collect Jan & Dean, Beach Boys, R&R.

R. Robbins
1104 Grant St., Bellingham, 98225
Collect, sell & trade jazz 78's, LP's, EP's, 45's all years. Also 60's & 70's rock LP's only. Send for free list.

Jim Schantz
2037 13th Way, Seattle, 98502
I collect hard rock, rockabilly, blues-rock: Peter Green, Toe Fat, Yardbirds, Johnny Burnette Trio. I specialize in dealing in late 60's, early 70's LP's. (206) 285-4288.

Dick Schmitt
10350 Interlake No., Seattle, 98133
I collect Elvis & R&R 78's & EP's. Send your wants, send for my auction lists.

2nd Time Around Records
4141 University Way NE, Seattle, 98105
We buy, sell & trade records, tapes, posters, songbooks, stereo & musical gear. (206) 632-1698.

Dean Silverstone (Golden Oldies)
1835 McGilvra Blvd. East, Seattle, 98112
Specializing in 45's from 50's, 60's & 70's. Noon - 8 pm. Tuesday thru Saturday. Buy, sell & trade New & Used rcds.

Shirley C. Stearns
22904-86th Pl., West, Edmonds, 98020
I collect 78's & 45's & albums. Early 50's to now. Popular & C&W. Have over 37,000 records. Want 45's. (207) 775-6923.

Chris Trant
421 E. 34th, Tacoma, 98404
I collect Elvis records, memorabilia, & sell beautiful quality concert photos.

WEST VIRGINIA

William Davis
100 22nd St., Dunbar, 25064
I collect rockabilly & doowop.

Jim Fiorilli
103-19th St., Wheeling, 26003
I collect R&R, R&B, 4 Seasons, Tokens, surf music, Jimmy Boyd, Rose Murphy, radio commercials by famous artists.

James Willard Grimmette
MOD 11 CN, Hampden, 25623
I collect C&W, bluegrass, folk, hymns, on 78's, 33 1/3 & 45's rpm. Books, fan club journals, mags on above.

Dick Newman
14 Campbell Ln., Harboursville, 25504
I'm selling all categories. Send your wants & the prices you'll pay & I'll find the item & get back to you. (304) 736-5380.

WISCONSIN

William J. Blumenberg
2845 No. 84th St., Milwaukee, 53222

Roland W. Boeder
710 Division St., La Crosse, 54601
I buy, sell & trade polka records & picture records collection of 15-hundred.

Robert Campagna
302 Ladwig St., Campbellsport, 53010
I collect Gene Autry.

Richard J. Conrardy
2114 N. 23rd St., Sheboygan, 53081
Approx. 3000 45 rpm records. Raning from good to mint condition. mostly R&R from 50's & 60's. Some 70's. I collect & will purchase records.

Buck Hafeman
1603 W. College Ave., Appleton, 54911
I collect old rock 45's, 55-65. Also anything by the King-Elvis. (414) 733-7668.

Steve & Tina Haslehurst
Rt. 9, North Rd., Appleton, 54911
Wanted: Pic sleeves, with or without records. Any amount. Also any early rock albums. Anything on Annette.

Jerry Hildestad
1809 Kropf Ave., Madison, 53704
I collect R&B (vocal groups) & anything on Elvis, also pic of both. (608) 249-3967.

Lee Hylingirl
Room 384C, DHSS, 1 West Wilson, Madison, 53702

Steve Johnson
P.O. Box 843, Milwaukee, 53201
Dealer selling worldwide imported discs of Elvis, Rolling Stones & Beatles. Write for free catalog containing hundreds of the best in imports by these 3.

Paul Juszczak
2413 E. Van Norman, Milwaukee, 53207
Olivia Newton-John items wanted. Promo/foreign records/posters/press kits & any other interesting items. Esp. wanted are foreign 45's with sleeves & Liv's Toomorrow records.

Steve Krupp
Box 7, Princeton, 54968
I collect juke boxes & I'm always interested in a good trade (414) 295-3972.

Ron Lofman
P.O. Box 2242, Madison, 53701
I collect 50's LP's: rock, show, singers, jazz, 10" & 12" LP's Have lsts: specify rock or shows & vocalists for trade.

Carol Mace
P.O. Box 468, 221 Capitol St., Wisconsin Dells, 53965
I collect Elvis records, memorabilia, etc.

Mean Mountain Music
P.O. Box 04352, Milwaukee, 53204
Specialize in rare rockabilly 45's & 78's. Obscure rcds are always on hand. R&R, blues R&B, C&W, vocal groups & instrumentals. 45's & 78's & LP's from 50's, 60's to now. We buy collections & wholesale stocks. Send for list.

Philip Medved
3010 5th Ave., #28, S. Milwaukee, 53172
I collect rockabilly 45's. (414) 764-5141.

Bruce A. Ozanich
1208 S. 29th St., Milwaukee, 53215
50's & 60's R&R, C&W, rockabilly, bluegrass & group R&B. 45's, EP's & LP's. Playable recordings only.

Douglas Ray
309 N. Pelham St., Rhinelander, 54501
D & A Enterprise: mail order for sale & collecting, all speeds and styles. Phone: (715) 362-4734

Richard Rommich
4251 S. 122nd St., Greenfield, 53228
I collect mainly R&R, R&B, pop.

George J. Rubatt
Rt. 1, Box 168, Foxboro, 54836
I collect R&R from 50's. Jack Scott, Elvis, Beatles. Buy & sell 45's, LP's.

Dick Tishken
1441 Oakes Rd. #3, Racine, 53406
I collect R&R, R&B, esp. the Beach Boys, Beatles, Rick Nelson & Ventures. (414) 886-0827.

James Trieb
920 Second St., Hudson, 54016

Donald E. Wettstein
1149 Cherry, Green Bay, 54301
I collect everything that hit the Billboard top 100 from 40-77. CIW, R&B, easy listening 61-77. LP's 45-77, all 78 all EP's, 45 pic sleeves.

FOREIGN

BELGIUM

A.R.S. Records
Hopland 32, 2000 Antwerp
Sell picture sleeve records (60's), handle want-list with prices. Buy: Albums personality's & jazz, 45's RRR, R&B (60's). We come on U.S. buying trips twice a year.

CANADA

Around Again
18 Baldwin St., Toronto, M5T 1L2
We buy, sell & trade LP's from 60's & 70's. We accept want lists.

Leland O. Bales
555 Danbo St., Box 20, Eugene, 97401
I collect old timers such as Hobo Jack Turner on Harmony, 1919.

Robert John Brown
374 GEORGE St., Toronto, Ontario, M5A-2N3
I am interested in chart 45's only from disco, blues, R&B, R&R, rockabilly, country & jazz. Lists of available records from dealers are welcome & appreciated. (416) 964-2346.

R.G. Budd
Suite #310) 110 W 107th Ave., Vancouver, B.C., V5Y-1R8

Wayne B. Cox
480 Lakeshore Rd., E. 707, Missisauga, Ontario
I collect surf, girl group, rockabilly LP's & 45's. Any info on Kathy Young (& Innocents) or Linda cott.

Don's Discs & The Record Hunter
1452 Queen St., West, Toronto, Ontario, M6K 1M2
(416) 531-1288 Linda & Don Keele

Vern Erickson
1790 Lawrence Ave., E., 208, Scarborough Ontario, M1R 2Y2

Diane Gianokos
130 Princess St., St. John, M.B., E2L 1K7
I collect McGuire Sisters records. (506) 693-0973. Frank Sinatra Kitty Wells, Jean Shepard, Gale Storm, Teresa Brewer. Also like tapes of rcds. of these artists.

Golden Music (Mr. R. Cranswick)
544-6th St., Brandon, Manitoba, R7A 3N9
LP's main collection, all varieties of music, 60's R&R - surf, soul, jazz, s'tracks, (disco 45's 12") Classical. Desire to increase collection of disco, surfing rod, Ventures, Buddy Knox.

I.D. Gosling
11 Lane Court, Georgetown, Ontario, L7G 1S4

Ken Hamm
182 S Algoma St., Thunder Bay P, Ontario, P7B 3B9

Robie J. Hartling
2470 Southvale Cr., Ste. 708, Ottawa, Ontario
I'm collecting all Beatles & related materials (promos, pic sleeves, rarities) will buy or trade. (613) 521-0609.

Robert E. Hayes
256 Albert St., Ottawa, Ontario, K1P 5G8
Vintage R&R, R&B, C&W; all speeds & tapes, unusual LP's, colored vinyl, interviews, bootlegs, etc.; absolutely anything regarding Bob Dylan or Jim Reeves.

John L. Hynes
316 St. Clair Ave. E., Toronto, Ontario, M4T 1P4
I collect mint, stereo LP's - 60's rock, U.S. & British. (416) 486-6848

W.B. James
3491 West 7, Vancouver, B.C.
I collect 78's popular.

Johnny Rock N' Roll
68 Indian Rd., Cres., Toronto, Ontario, M6P 2G1
I collect R&R, R&B, rockabilly, doowop, soul acapello, 50's memorabilia, old mags, buttons, Elvis, films, interviews, tapes of old radio shows & TV shows, James Dean, posters (movie), past & present concert tapes. (416) 536-4755.

Mike Kennedy
5317 Manson Ave., Powell River, B.C., V8A 3P5
I collect Beatles, Stones, etc. U.S. & European releases. Also buy or trade reel to reel copies of radio-tv comedy, music, sports.

Doug Kibble
1769 W. 59th Ave., Vancouver, B.C., V6P 1Z3
I collect rockabilly, R&R, C&W, 45's, any EP's with M-covers, 12" LP's with covers, buy or trade.

Lawrence Kirsch
155 Netherwood Cre., Hampstead, Que, H3X 3H3
I trade, buy & sell all sorts of Bob Dylan collectibles, inc. posters, photos, (orig. prefered), EP's, 45's, books, concert programmes, pic sleeves, all rare items! Also trade video tape.

Imants Krumins
121 St. Josephs Dr., Ap 22, Hamilton Ont, L8N 2G1
I collect psychedelic underground, rockaway beach, metal machine music, The Midnight Rider, & R&R animals.

Mario LeGault
30 LeGault St., Ste-Anne De Vellevue, Que, H9X 1Z8
I collect only 45's & LP's of R&R & R&B.

Peter J. MacDonald
2157 Monson Cres., Ottawa Ont, K1J 6A7
I collect 50's R&R, rockabilly, Gene Vincent, Charlie Feathers especially. (613) 746-5310

Bill Mac Ewen
Cornwall RR #2, Prince Edward Island, C0A 1H0
I collect C&W: Hank Williams, Jim Reeves, Hank Snow, Tex Ritter, 10" LP's, EP's, 45's & 78's. C&W sheet music.

David McConnell
Box 424, S0L 1S0, Kindersley, Sask.
I collect 60's & 70's R&R, 45's & LP's also some country.

Alex McNeil
133 S. Windemere Ave., Thunder Bay, Ont.
I collect 50's & 60's R&R, R&B, Bill Haley, Buddy Holly, Also surfing & hot rod music 45 rpm. only. Good to very good condition.

Herb Norenberg
P.O. Box 252, Saskatoon, Sask, S7K 3K4
I collect s'tracks, general film music, & am especially interested in Ennio Morricone, & Bruno Nicolai.

Jack O'Hara
Box 89, Blackie Alta, T0L 0J0

Yvon Olivier
2195 Des-Chenaux, Troi-Rivieres, Quebec
I collect & trade 45's only. Send your lists.

Paperbook & Record Exchange
3402 ½ Younge St., Toronto, Ont, M4N 2M9
We specialize in LP's on jazz, classical, s'tracks, British Bands, male & female vocalists. (only in VG Condition), plus collector's items.

Derwyn Powell
819 13th St., E., Saskatoon, Sask, S7N 0L8
I collect rock, jazz, blues, folk, Stones, Beatles, British groups, other R&R from mid 50's to mid 60's.

Kal Raudoja
121 Donlea Dr., Toronto, Ont
I collect 50's R&R, surveys & hit parade charts, air checks, American Bandstand shows, & tapings from DJ shows. All 50's only.

Mr. Tony C. Rehor
585 Hale St., London, Ont N5W 1H7
I collect rockabilly, R&R, R&B (vocal groups from 50's), originals-LP's, 45's, EP's & 78's.

Hugh W. Reid
P.O. Box 581, M.P.O., Calgary, Alberta, T2P 2J2
I collect R&B & pop '54-'64, mostly insturmental LP's, some 45's. Also reel-to-reel tapes, mags. Have British R&B mags '66-'68 for sale, & other things. Write.

Claude Seary
2863 Glen Lake Rd., Victory, B.C., V9B 4A8
I will buy records, Ragtime to rock for personal collection-78's 45's & LP's.

Dave Smeltzer
550 Jarvis #327, Toronto, Ont, M4Y 1N6
Interested in colored vinyl, will buy, sell or trade, esp. 78 rpm picture records. Would like to near from other collectors & dealers.

Sparrow Photos
P.O. Box 172, Outremount, P.Q., H2V 4M8
Professional color concert photos: Elvis, Beach Boys, Stones, Bowie, Sinatra, Dylan, Kiss, Sparks, McCartney, punk, Elton, Floyd, Fleetwood, Elp, plus 100 others. Send $1.00 for fully illustrated catalog ($1.00 refunded on any purchase).

Jim Stapley
43 Lauber Ave., Cornwall, Ont, K6J 2W1
I am interested in early C&W, especially Gene Autry.

Donna Trecola
433 Brock Ave., Toronto, Ont., M6H 3N7

Dian Jo Wallis
1405 Prince Rupert Blvd., Prince Rupert, B.C. V8J 2Z1
Elvis! Elvis! Elvis! - Records, pictures, etc.

James Wensveen
2807 11th Ave., South, Lethbridge, Alberta T1K 0L2
I collect R&R, R&B, folk & pop. LP's & 45 estended play only. 60's & 70's. Also mags, fanzines, & books.

Neil Winestock
127 Thatcher Dr., Winnipeg, Manitoba R3T 2L7
I collect R&R, folk, R&B, 45's, 78's & LP's of 50's & 60's.

DENMARK

Peter Bendix
Halgreensgade 9, 2300 Copenhagen S.
I collect Phil Spector, Jack Scott, all 50's & 60's pop, soul, C&W, R&B.

N.C. Junker-Poulsen
Regenburgsgade 191 Mf. Th., 8000 Aarhus C.
I collect British Invasion, black music: Beatles, Kinks, N.O. R&B.

ENGLAND

Piers Chalmers
7 Mill Cottages, Bucks Green, W. Sussex
I collect Louisiana R&R, rockabilly, general R&R, Fats Domino, Jerry Lee Lewis, Gene Vincent, Eddie Cochran. Dealer & collector.

Tom Delis
35 Mayflower Ave., Saxmundham, Suffolk
I collect early R&R, Beach Boys, Ricky Nelson, & one-time-hit groups.

Egleton & Chalmers
26 Stanford Ave., Hassocks, Sussex
We buy, sell, trade, wholesale & retail R&R, C&W, blues, 50's pop & early 60's. We put out old R&R masters.

Peter A. Gibbon
30 Oaklea, Welwyn AL6 0QN, Hertfordshire
I collect R&B, blues, vocal groups, soul 45's, LP's, '45-mid 60's. Label discographies, esp. R&B labels. Will exchange discography info. Put me on your lists!

Derek Glenister
28 Nevern Rd., Rayleigh, Essex
I collect R&R, rockabilly, tapes & interviews from 50's R&R radio/TV shows. Photos of Eddie Cochran wanted.

John Harrison
14, The Crescent, Redcar, Cleveland, TS10 3AU
I collect live concerts, air checks, new or old from anywhere in the US, old Billboard/Cashbox mags., any chart details. I'll trade UK 45's/LP's, live UK concert tapes inc. Beatles & Stones, for taped radio air checks from US stations; will also trade air checks of UK radio.

Steve Holloway
28 Groome House, Black Prince Rd., London SE 11
I collect R&R, rockabilly, blues plus any Meteor 45 or 78 buy or trade.

The "Jive Dive"
1 The Parade, Hampton Rd., Hampton Hill, Middlesex UK
Golden Oldies Records Shop (01 977-6715)

Mick Perry
56 Templeton Rd., W7 1AT
West Texas singers: Roy Orbison, Bruce Channel & Johnny Preston, radio KERB radio tapes, Odessa & Midland tv show tapes, Louisianna Hayride tapes all by the Teen Kings. Also all discs on Je-Well & any rare Oribison items.

A. Thomson
30 Elm Grove, Worthing, Sussex BN 11 5LH
If you have any rockabilly orig. to sell, please drop me a line & tell me what you have. Send all auction lists containing rock - rockabilly.

David Treble
24 Longmead Merrow, Guildford, Surrey GU1 2HW
Buy, sell, trade rockabilly.

Vintage Record Center
91 Roman Way, London N78UN
Englands No. 1 oldies specilsts on rock, rockabilly, R&R, instru., R&B, Philles, originals & reissues.

Zephyr Records.
P.O. Box 6, Wallasey, Merseyside L454SJ
We deal in British singles from '67 to present. Send $1.00 for a 100+ page catalog.

FRANCE

Bob Frances
10 Cours Gambetta, Montpellier, 34000
I collect rock, punk, & 60's LP's, Floor Elevator, Jack Scott. I own Sirenes Records (4 Rue Bonnier d'Alco) same city. Send your wants.

Gene Vincent Memorial Society
B.P. 16 - 69 Sathonay
For promotion of Waylon Jennings, Jeny Lee, Elvis, Merle Haggard, Conway Twitty, Hank Williams, Jr.

Mr. & Mrs. Tanquay Le Guyader
21 Avenue Niel, 75017, Paris
Buy, sell, trade R&R, C&W, R&B from 50's. Mostly LP's (10" & 12"), EP's, 78's. Favorite Artist: Hank Williams.

Henri Manierka (Ceresco)
50 Rue Casseneuil, 45300 Villeneuve-sur-Lot
Collection of rock, blues 50's, 60's, 70's. Exchanges against anything European.

Bertrand Patrice
3 Rue Recamier, Evry 91000
I collect R&R, pop, blues from 54-68. All speeds, all Elvis, sell, trade or buy.

GERMANY

Peter Klopsch
1 Berlin 19-Am Postfenn, Schullandheim
All of rockabilly - Gene Vincent.

Voker Kurze
Holunderstr. 47, 2800 Bremen 1
I collect R&R, doowop, highschool, cajn, country-not later than 1965.

Dieter Valpus
6 Frankfurt/M, Diesterwegstrasse 23
I collect C&W LP's, 45's, transcription & hot-jazz (traditional/swing) LP's & 45's, & EP's.

HOLLAND

Menno Smith
Nieuwe Plantage 59, Delft.
I collect records, music mags, & books of rockabilly, hillbilly boogie, white R&R, C&W & rock blues from 50's. I have sales/auction lists periodically.

Paul Vanderkooy
Baambruggester, 49, Den Haag
I collect R&R & early beat, rockabilly-instru., surf, Elvis, Everly Bros., Brasilian imports. Always over 10000 rcds in stock. Specialize in albums & instru. LP's. Ask for free list.

IRELAND

John Dwyer
5 Seminary Pl, Farranree, Cork, Eire
Cliff Richard Records from anywhere. Books, mags, catalogs, & discographical info. on every form of music except classical. Research into British & American charts as well as listing million selling singles from around world.

JAPAN

Kazuo Akimoto
Mena Co-op 1-13-18, Gohtokuji Setagaya-Ku, Tokyo, 154
Soul & R&B needed: Darrel Banks, James Brown, Billy Butler, Jimmy Holiday, Eddie Holman, Jimmy Hughes, Syl Johnson, Little Royal, Manhattans, Freddie Scott, Rufus Thomas.

Forever Records
P.O. Box 16, Hirano, Osaka 547
We need huge amount of oldies LP's & 45's of 50's & 60's. We buy your records at reasonable prices. Send $1.00 for catalog. Esp. the collectors of Elvis, Beatles, Rolling Stones & Elton John can not pass up our catalog. Most of records of single & EP have picture cover.

Yoshiju Kizaki
Villa Gaien 7FD, 38-16, Jingumae 3 Chome, Tokyo/Shibuya-KU 150
I collect 50's & early 60's R&R & top 40. Elvis, Phil Spector, Beach Boys, Jan & Dean, & the Sun label.

Hidefumi Kobayashi
4-5-10 Fujigoaka, Fujiidera, Osaka 583
I collect R&R, rockabilly, louisiana sound, Tex-Mex, southern music. 45's & LP's, all like Sunny & The Sunliners.

Shizuo Miyashita
4-71 Yamasaka-Cho, Osaka/Higashisumiyoshi, 546
I collect 50's R&R & 60's pop. White rockers & Guitar instru. beat groups. Anything about Dick Dale, Del Shannon, Freddy Cannon & Bobby Fuller Four.

Makoto-Nakatani
103, 1-15-4 Shimoigusa, Suginami-Ku, Tokyo 167
Teenage pop singers of the 50's & 60's, Buddy Holly, Bobby Rydel, Fabian, Bobby Vee, Eddie Hodges, Ricky Nelson, Ritchie Valens & many more.

Mr. Norihisa Oguchi
1-2-14, Kyonancho, Musashino City, Tokyo, 180
Anything & everything that has to do with Elvis. Elvis & R&R films in 16 MM sound.

Rhythm & Blues Record Service, Toshiaki Bamba
1-19, Toranomon 4-Chome, Minato-Ku, Tokyo, 105

Hiromichi Wakui
1147 Matsudo, Matsudo City, Chiba-pre.
The Innocence (Kama Sutra KLPS 8059), & Tradewinds (Excursions Kama Sutra KLPS 8057).

WEST GERMANY

Bear Family Records (Richard Weize)
GoethestraBe 9, 2800 Bremen

Dieter Boek
Koelner Landstr. 179, D-4000 Duesseldorf 13
Rockabilly, R&R (50's-62), early pop, instru., guitar, surf, blues, import & export, records producer. World wide dist. of LP: Jim Pewter-The Early Years '59-'73. Important for collectors & dealers anywhere, as this LP inc. also unreleased material.

Helmut Jacob
Wingerstr. 116, 6456 Maintal 1
Singles, LP, cassettes & tapes; rockabilly & R&R; buy, sell, trade. (0618 114 5627)

Diethold Leu
Holzhauserstr. 79, 1000 Berlin-27
Rockabilly, R&R & LP's.

Manfred Luz
AM Graben 5, D-7265 Neubulach 3
I collect rockabilly, rare R&B, hillbilly, western swing, country etc., pictures, stories & so on, buy, sell & trade.

Bernd Marenk
Raiffeisen str. 79, 6000 Frankfurt-60

Wilburts Rec., Wilfried Burtke
Westerstr. 23, D-29 Oldnburg
I collect & sell all kinds of 50's music, esp. R&B, R&R, rockabilly, plus instru 450's, 50's, 60's & boogie woogie, dance-music, easy lstning. For lists send 2 irc's.

Bernd Wolf
Buchsenweg 31, 1000 Berlin 51
I collect R&R, & rockabilly, 45's, EP's & LP's. Please send lists!

Horst Zimmermann
Lindauer Allee 44, 1000 Berlin 51
R&R & rockabilly, 45's EP's & LP's. Send me your lists.

NEW ZEALAND

Kevin Hookway
10 Banbury Pl, Mangere Bridge, Auckland

SWEDEN

Jonas "Mr. R&B" Bernholm
Halsingegatan 14A, 113 23 Stockholm
I collect Jump, New Orleans, doowops, mid-60's soul, etc. I have many european reissues in stock. Will buy boots, 78's, films, reissues, etc. Trades welcome.

The Golden Oldies Shop
Sankt Erixsgatan 96, 113 31 Stockholm
R&R, R&B & pop singles, EP's & Albums on orig. labels 1950-1977. (08/32 2240

Ove Jahannisson
Ribbingsvag 16AI, 191 52 Sollentuna
I collect 50's R&R, rockabilly, early 60's pop & rocking instrumentals. (fast, wild guitars, hammering pianos.) 08/353928

Yngue Magnusson
Storanygatan 16B, 45100 Uddevalla
I collect all types of records. Send your lists.

Goran Tannfelt
Lutzeng 14, Stockholm 115 23
Jan & Dean freak! But also Beach Boys, surf & hot rod, doowop, Byrds, Kinks, Animals, Shangri-Las, Blondie, etc.

Jorn Wounlund
Brusewitzg. 6, Gothenburg 41140
I collect anything & everything on Elvis; Sun records, rockabilly, Buddy Holly, Eddie Cochran, Jerry Lee Lewis, Carl Perkins, Conway Twitty & Wanda Jackson.

SWITZERLAND

Louis Cardinaux
Palud 20, 1630 Bulle
I need Johnny Burnette, Eddie Cochran, Little Richard, Elvis, Ronnie Hawkins & others.

Peter Mohr
Diepoldsauerstr. 21, CH-9443, Widnau
I collect C&W 50-62, R&R, rockabilly. Sales lists welcome. (Set sales preferred)

Peter Sahli
Kappelisackerstr. 19, 3063 Ittigen, Berne
I collect R&R, R&B, rockabilly, doowop, jump, etc. 50-64. All speeds.

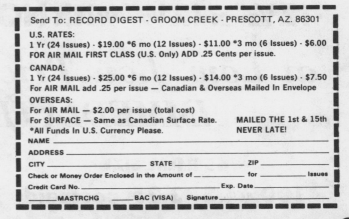
255